Anthony

Textbook of anatomy and physiology

Seventh edition

THERESA GAUTHIER

Seventh edition

Textbook of anatomy and physiology

Catherine Parker Anthony
R.N., B.A., M.S.

Formerly Assistant Professor of Nursing, Science Department,
and Assistant Instructor of Anatomy and Physiology,
Frances Payne Bolton School of Nursing,
Western Reserve University, Cleveland, Ohio;
formerly Instructor of Anatomy and Physiology,
Lutheran Hospital and St. Luke's Hospital,
Cleveland, Ohio

With 336 illustrations, including 210 new (178 by Ernest W. Beck)
and 110 in color
and a
Trans-Vision® insert on human anatomy containing 15 full-color,
full-page color plates (by Ernest W. Beck)

The C. V. Mosby Company

Saint Louis 1967

Seventh edition

Second printing

Previous editions copyrighted 1944, 1946, 1950, 1955, 1959, 1963
Printed in the United States of America
Library of Congress Catalog Card Number 67-20674
Distributed in Great Britain by Henry Kimpton, London

Preface

to seventh edition

Learning or teaching basic facts and principles about the human body is a tremendous undertaking. Thus, the dominating purpose of this seventh edition of *Textbook of anatomy and physiology* is to help both students and teachers with this task. This book differs from others on the same subject in the content selected, in the organization of that content, in the illustrations which were especially designed to elucidate the text, and in literary style.

An earnest effort has been made to include all information necessary for a basic understanding of the body but to omit many details and digressions. Although the latter are necessary to broaden and deepen the understanding of advanced or specialized students of anatomy and physiology, they are not necessary, or even useful, for beginning students of these sciences. Often, too many minutiae and "side excursions" confuse and distract rather than clarify and enrich.

Considerable out-of-date information has been deleted from this edition, and many new findings (about cells and neuroendocrine transducers, the limbic lobe, the hypothalamus, the autonomic nervous system, the thymus gland, the pineal body, to name a few) have been included. Chapters revised most extensively are those on cells, the nervous system, the digestive system, and the endocrine system. Particularly has physiology been emphasized in this edition. Examples of some of the most extensively revised and enlarged discussions are those dealing with temperature regulation, energy balance, and stress responses.

Many new terms appear in the glossary, and two convenient tools for the study of anatomy and physiology, commonly used abbreviations and commonly used prefixes, have been included in this edition. Many new references, valuable for enrichment or for independent study assignments, have been added to the list of suggested supplementary readings, and outdated references have been deleted.

Organization of the content remains essentially the same as that of the sixth edition. Each chapter still opens with an outline survey and closes with an outline summary and review questions. Also, numerous summarizing tables are still interspersed throughout the text.

Of all the many changes in this edition, by far the most striking is the magnificent original artwork created by Ernest W. Beck of Chicago, one of our country's most eminent and creative contemporary medical illustrators.

Style does for written works what seasonings do for food. Both bestow a flavor. But flavor may dull and repel—it does not automatically interest and attract. Empty phrases, for instance, and involved sentence structure often make most of us not want to read any farther. Many writers apparently think that they will be heard for their many words. In my opinion, however, the opposite is more likely to be true. Also, I think that what a student can read rapidly, he enjoys more, understands better, and remembers longer.

Warm appreciation is expressed to those who knowingly or not have helped create this book: Mr. Ernest W. Beck, the medical illustrator; Mrs. Georgeanna Keefe, my secretary; Jack D. Kerth, M.D., my son-in-law; William A. Anthony, M.D., my son; and the hundreds of students I have taught during the past thirty years, all of whom have been teachers of this teacher.

Catherine Parker Anthony

Preface to first edition

"He teacheth ill that teacheth all." (English proverb, 1670.)

Because the course in anatomy and physiology for student nurses must cover such a large body of material in such a short time, and because this material seems difficult both for instructors to teach and for students to learn, one aim has been uppermost in the preparation of this book; namely, so to present the basic facts of body structure and function as to make the teaching of this complex subject less laborious, the learning of it less difficult, and both the teaching and learning more enjoyable.

This is primarily a teaching book, not a reference text. Since an important part of teaching skill lies in knowing what to omit, this book attempts to omit all nonessential, even though interesting, facts and to include all those facts which seem particularly pertinent for a nurse, or any beginning student of the human body, to know. The plan of teaching minimum essentials only and merely suggesting a greater wealth of material, the author believes, stimulates the student's interest and desire to discover more, and, at the same time, makes it possible for the instructor to concentrate on "driving home" the important, basic facts. Numerous devices are included which make it possible for the student to learn these basic facts more easily and quickly.

In short, the main difference between this book and other textbooks on the subject is its plan of presenting the material—a plan which minimizes the amount of time required for the instructor's preparation and which shortens and facilitates the student's learning process.

The essential features of this book are as follows:

1. Brief, topical outlines precede each chapter to help the student in following the arrangement of material and in seeing

the facts in proper relationship. Paragraph headings outline the actual text so that it tallies with the topics in the outline surveys at the beginning of each chapter.

2. Only the main facts of anatomy and physiology are discussed and only the most relevant correlations with nursing and nonprofessional situations are made in the belief that too little is learned when too much is taught. Descriptions and explanations, therefore, are brief and to the point. Facts which the student should remember are emphasized, as are practical applications of those facts. Detailed facts which rightfully belong in a reference book or in a medical textbook, but which are superfluous in a text for a ninety- to one-hundred-hour course, are omitted. Consequently, the book is shorter than most texts on the subject.

3. Only those diagrams and pictures which illustrate points of particular interest or importance are included, but whereever facts are more easily understood from illustrations than from descriptions, illustrations are used. Many of the illustrations are of the simple, diagrammatic type which make such excellent teaching media.

4. The main facts, those which the student should remember, are summarized in outline form at the end of each chapter. These outlines are especially valuable for review purposes as they make it possible for the student to recognize which points are most important and to study them in a form which can be learned easily and quickly. Also, these outline summaries constitute usable lesson plans for lecture or for discussion.

5. A complete list of review questions, some testing memory, some understanding, are included at the close of each chapter. These review questions serve several valuable purposes. They furnish a means by which the student can test herself to make sure that she has learned the facts which the text is designed to teach. They can be used as topics for classroom discussion and for oral drill.

Other features of teaching value in this book include the following:

A list of interest-arousing questions.

A vocabulary at the beginning of each chapter.

Numerous concise, simplified tables.

Study hints.

With this book go three hopes: that the nurse who studies it may gain a clear understanding of the normal body as a basis for understanding variations from the normal; that this understanding may enable her to give more intelligent care to the sick; and that the many correlations of science and nursing situations explained herein may help surround her work with an aura of interest which will make it fascinating instead of merely fatiguing!

Help and encouragement, on the part of several individuals, have made this book possible. I wish, therefore, to acknowledge my indebtedness to these friends: Miss Helen Williams, for her excellent drawings; Dr. Edmund E. Beard, for the use of his photographs of endocrine disorders; Miss Lura B. Eldredge, for her reading of parts of the manuscript and for valuable suggestions; Mr. Harry C. Biddle, for his encouragement and helpful advice; and members of my family, for their patience and faith.

Catherine Parker Anthony

Contents

Contents

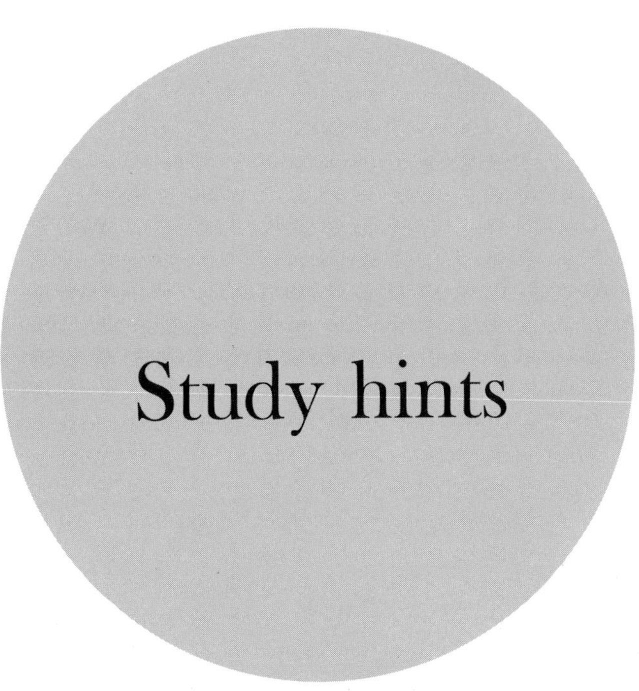

Study hints

If you really want to learn the subject matter in this book, do these things:

1. Start your study period with an active desire to learn the material. Approach with the attitude that what you are about to learn is both interesting and useful for you to know.

2. Have a clear idea in mind what it is you should learn from each chapter. The outline surveys at the beginning of each chapter tell you the main facts to look for and help you follow the arrangement of the material. Consult these outlines frequently while you are studying.

3. Check up on yourself to see whether or not you have learned what the material is trying to teach by answering the review questions at the end of each chapter. Testing knowledge is an important part of learning; do not neglect it.

UNIT
ONE

The body as an integrated whole

I

The body—a structural and functional unit

What a piece of work is man! how noble in reason! how infinite in faculty! in form and moving how express and admirable! in action how like an angel! in apprehension how like a god! the beauty of the world! the paragon of animals!

—Hamlet, in *Hamlet, Prince of Denmark,* Act II, Scene II, by William Shakespeare

Human anatomy and physiology are biological sciences; that is, they are branches of knowledge about living things. *Anatomy* is the science of the structure and *physiology* is the science of the function of the most wondrous of all structures—the human body.

Before attempting to explore details about the body, it seems feasible to examine some of its general characteristics, much as it is prudent to study the map of a strange city before embarking upon an excursion through it. Two general characteristics are these: (1) The body is a structural unit. Literally millions and millions of smaller structural units enter into its formation, and yet the body is itself a single large structural unit. (2) The body is a functional unit. It performs a great number of functions, and yet together all these varied functions achieve a single supreme function—survival.

This chapter explores briefly the two ideas that the body is a structural and a functional unit.

The body—a structural unit composed of many smaller units

The concept of a large unit made up of lesser units is a familiar one. A city, for example, is such a unit. So, also, is a factory, a hospital, an automobile, a sewing machine, or even a molecule. In each instance, the large unit is not a mere collection of the smaller units but is something more than the sum of its parts. The "something more" results from organization of the smaller units, from a relating of each one to the others in a definite way. Disorganize any large unit, break it into its separate parts, no longer arranged in a definite pattern, and you have a lesser thing than before. No longer do you have something that you recognize as one integrated whole, but, instead, several things that are clearly disintegrated, unrelated units. Consider, for example, the difference between an assembled jigsaw puzzle and its disassembled pieces. The assembled jigsaw puzzle, because of the organization or arrangement of the units that compose it, is an integrated whole. Similarly, the body, because of the organization of its component units, is an integrated whole.

Organization underlies integration (unification) of parts. Because organization welds separate parts together to form a whole, it is a foundation stone and a vital characteristic of life. Disorganization produces disintegration and leads to death.

COMPONENT UNITS

Of the many millions of parts making up the body, the smallest and simplest units are those called *cells*. Human cells are microscopic structures; that is, they can be seen only when magnified by a microscope. They are invisible to the naked eye. Cells are not all identical units. There are four main types of human cells: epithelial, muscle, connective, and nerve.

Organizations of large numbers of similar cells are called *tissues*. Unlike cells, tissues are macroscopic structures; that is, they are visible to the naked eye. Because so many cells compose a tissue, it is big enough to be seen without any magnification. Cells are discussed in Chapter II and tissues in Chapter III.

The next step in the integration of the member units of the body is the organization of tissues into *organs*. The stomach, for example, is an organ in which all four primary tissues are organized in a unique pattern. Muscle and connective tissue are so arranged as to form the wall of this hollow organ of specific shape. Epithelial and connective tissues are organized into a lining for the inside of the wall, and nerve tissue is distributed to both wall and lining.

Another step toward integration of the body's many parts occurs with the organization of organs into *systems*. For example, the following organs, plus several accessory ones, make up the digestive system: mouth, pharynx, esophagus, stomach, and intestines. In the human body there are nine major systems of organs: skeletal, muscular, nervous, circulatory, respiratory, digestive, urinary, reproductive, and endocrine. (For names and descriptions of the organs of a system, see chapter on that system.)

In summary, the body is itself a unit, a single large structure, but it is composed of a great many smaller units organized into increasingly larger and more complex units. Cells are organized into tissues, tissues into organs, organs into systems, and systems into the final unit, the body.

ARCHITECTURAL PLAN

The human body has a definite architectural plan, the characteristic features being a backbone, bisymmetry, and two main cavities, one on the anterior (front or ventral) surface and the other on the posterior (back or dorsal) surface. Each of these cavities, in turn, is divided into smaller cavities.

The *ventral cavity* is separated by the diaphragm muscle into (1) a *thoracic* or chest cavity, which has pleural, pericardial, and mediastinal subdivisions, and (2) an *abdominopelvic* cavity, which is subdivided into an upper abdominal and a lower pelvic portion.

The *dorsal cavity* is divided into (1) a *cranial* cavity and (2) a *spinal* cavity.

The body cavities contain the various internal organs or *viscera*. For example, in the thoracic cavity are located the lungs, heart, trachea, esophagus, thymus gland, and certain large blood and lymphatic ves-

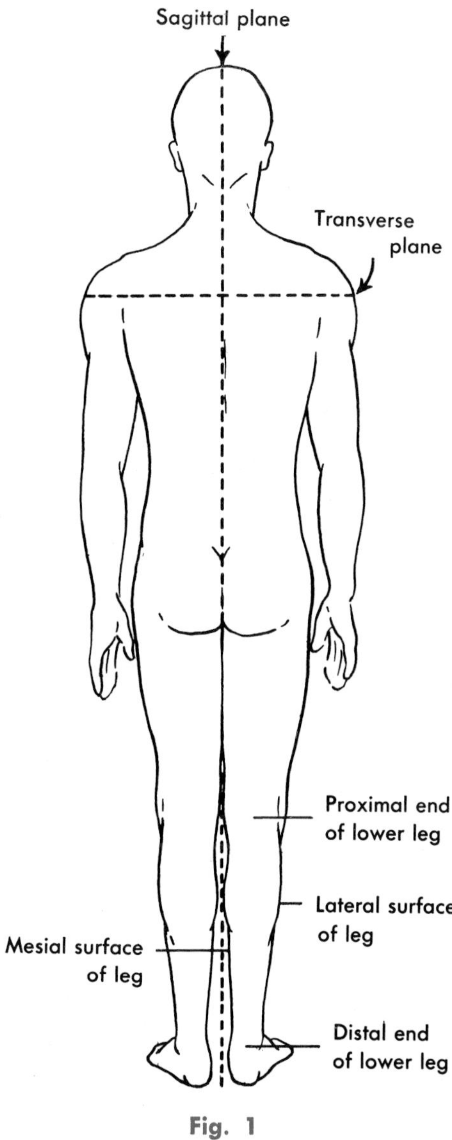

Fig. 1

Posterior view of human figure demonstrating meanings of terms used in describing the body.

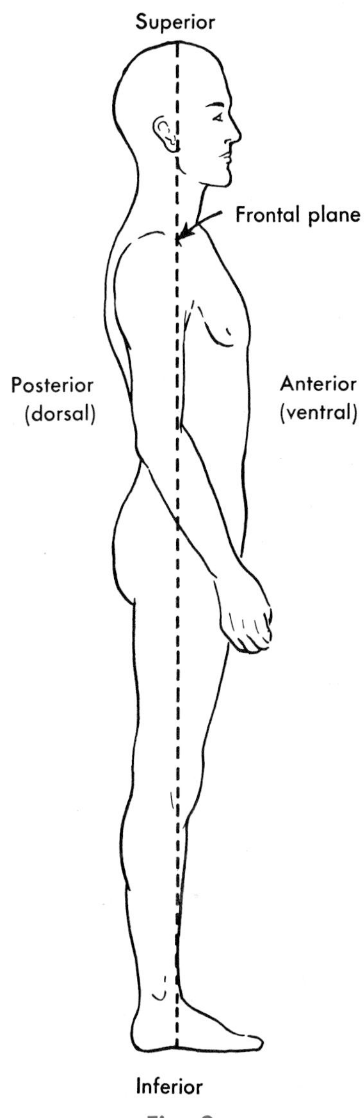

Fig. 2

Lateral view of human figure demonstrating several terms used in describing the body.

sels and nerves, whereas in the abdominal cavity are located the liver, gallbladder, stomach, pancreas, intestines, spleen, kidneys, and ureters. The bladder, certain reproductive organs (uterus, uterine tubes, and ovaries in the female; prostate gland, seminal vesicles, and part of the seminal ducts in the male), and part of the large intestine (namely, the sigmoid colon and rectum) are found in the pelvic cavity.

DESCRIPTIVE TERMS

Directional terms

superior toward the head end of the body; upper. (Example: the hand is part of the superior extremity.)

inferior away from the head; lower. (Example: the foot is part of the inferior extremity.)

anterior or ***ventral*** front. (Example: the kneecap is located on the anterior side of the leg.)

posterior or ***dorsal*** back. (Example: the shoulder blades are located on the posterior side of the body.)

medial or ***mesial*** toward the midline of the body. (Example: the great toe is located at the medial side of the foot.)

lateral away from the midline of the body. (Example: the little toe is located at the lateral side of the foot.)

proximal toward or nearest the trunk or the point of origin of a part. (Example: the elbow is located at the proximal end of the forearm.)

distal away from or farthest from the trunk or the point of origin of a part. (Example: the hand is located at the distal end of the forearm.)

Planes of body

sagittal a lengthwise plane running from front to back, dividing the body or any part of it into right and left sides (Fig. 1).

frontal or ***coronal*** a lengthwise plane running from side to side, dividing the body or any part of it into anterior and posterior portions (Fig. 2).

transverse or ***horizontal*** a crosswise plane dividing the body or any part of it into upper and lower parts (Fig. 1).

Abdominal regions

The abdomen is divided into nine regions by four imaginary lines: a horizontal line at the level of the ninth rib cartilages, a horizontal line at the level of the iliac crest, and two vertical lines through the midpoints of the right and left Poupart's ligaments. (See Fig. 3 for the names of the abdominal regions.)

Anatomical position

The term *anatomical position* refers to an erect standing position with the arms at the side and the palms turned forward (supinated).

The body—a functional unit; one great function made up of many smaller functions

SURVIVAL

Survival is the one great function of the body. Numerous lesser functions—some exceedingly complex and others fairly simple—together achieve survival. Homeostasis, metabolism, and integration, for example, are some of the complex components of survival. Each of these, in turn, consists of many less complex functions. The rest of this chapter relates some general information about homeostasis, metabolism, and integration.

SOME MAJOR COMPONENT FUNCTIONS

Homeostasis

The term *homeostasis* is one of the most important terms in physiology. It comes from two greek words—*homoios,* meaning the same, and *stasis,* meaning standing. "Standing or staying the same," then, is the literal meaning of the word. Walter B. Cannon, a noted physiologist, suggested homeostasis as the special name for the steady states maintained by the body. But he emphasized that although homeostasis means steady states, it does not mean something set and immobile that stays exactly the same all the time. In his words, homeostasis "means a condition which may vary, but which is relatively constant."*

Homeostasis is a condition which changes and yet stays about the same—a condition which stays within the same narrow range.

*From Cannon, W. B.: The wisdom of the body, rev. ed., New York, 1939, W. W. Norton & Co., Inc., p. 24.

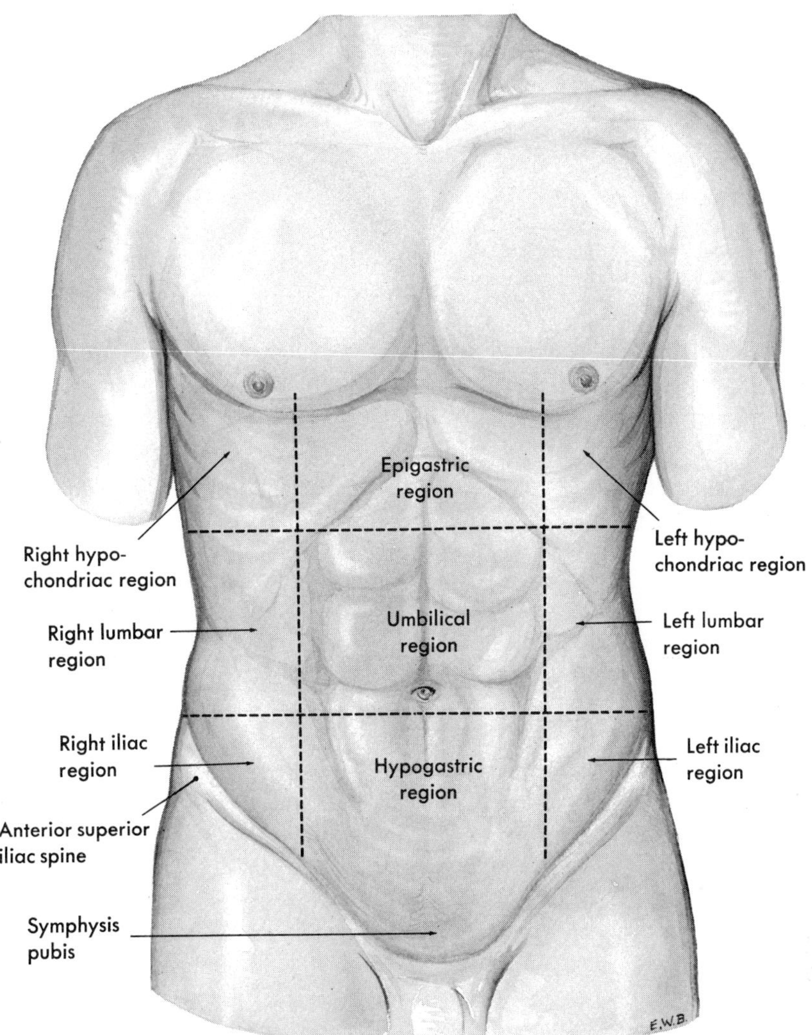

Fig. 3

The nine regions of the abdomen.

We might even use the word to describe a condition other than one in the body. For example, we might refer to homeostasis of the depth of water in a swimming pool (Fig. 4). Imagine that water ran into a pool at one end and out of it at the other. And suppose that the depth of the water changed from time to time, sometimes increasing, sometimes decreasing. But despite these changes, suppose that the depth always stayed within the same narrow range of 58 to 62 inches. When the water increased above 60 inches, something happened automatically to reverse this change and decrease the water so that its level moved back down toward the 60-inch mark. And when the depth of the water decreased below 60 inches, this change away from the

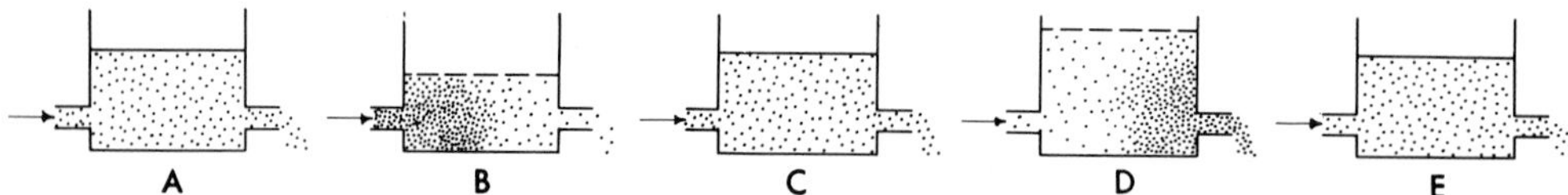

Fig. 4

Homeostasis, a condition that varies but stays within the same narrow range, illustrated by depth of water in a swimming pool. **A,** Balance point ("homeostasis") of water's depth, with input equaling output. **B,** Change away from balance point has occurred; depth has decreased. Compensating change (greater input than output) has started and will increase depth back toward balance point. **C,** Balance restored. **D,** Change away from balance here is increased depth. What compensating change has started? This time it will decrease the depth back toward the balance point. **E,** Balance restored.

balance point also was automatically reversed. The water increased this time and its level again moved backward 60 inches.

Human cells must have a relatively constant environment if they are to survive in a healthy condition. Homeostasis of the environment of cells, in other words, is an essential condition for their healthy survival. This requirement applies to many aspects of the cellular environment—its chemical composition, its osmotic pressure, its hydrogen-ion concentration, its temperature, etc. Even a small shift away from homeostasis of any of these factors makes cells unable to function normally. Because homeostasis is a requirement for healthy survival of cells, it necessarily follows that it is also a requirement for healthy survival of the body. Why? What microscopic living units compose the body?

Cellular environment, it must be remembered, is not synonymous with body environment. The body lives in the atmosphere surrounding it, the gaseous atmosphere of the external world. Body cells likewise live in the atmosphere surrounding them, but this is the liquid atmosphere of an internal world.

The liquid environment around cells is called *extracellular fluid* for the obvious reason that it lies exterior to cells. Extracellular fluid occupies two main locations. It fills in the microscopic spaces between body cells, where it is called appropriately *intercellular fluid* (or *interstitial fluid*), and it flows through blood vessels, where it is called *blood plasma.*

More than one hundred years ago a great French physiologist, Claude Bernard, recognized that the extracellular fluid (or *milieu interne,* as he called it) constituted the internal environment, or, in other words, the cellular environment. He also noted that its physical and chemical composition must be maintained relatively uniform if cells are to maintain their life and health. But it was many years later that Cannon referred to the steady state of the internal environment as *homeostasis.* The term has since become a part of physiological language and is widely used today.

The principle of homeostasis is one of the most fundamental of all physiological principles. It may be stated in this way: the body must maintain relative constancy of its chemicals and processes in order to survive. Or stated even more briefly: health and survival depend upon the body's maintaining or quickly restoring homeostasis.

All body structures play some role in maintaining the various steady states of the body. Homeostasis is virtually the job of every organ. It is, as someone has stated, the "main theme of physiology."

Therefore, homeostatic mechanisms will form the subject matter of a major part of this book. Homeostatic mechanisms consist of many and varied devices by which the body maintains or restores homeostasis.

Metabolism

Metabolism is another part of the great work of the body, survival. Metabolism consists of the myriad chemical reactions forever going on inside living cells. One series of reactions changes more complex compounds into simpler ones and releases energy. This is the process called *catabolism. Anabolism,* the other phase of metabolism, consists of series of chemical reactions which use energy to change simpler compounds into more complex ones.

Catabolism supplies energy for all work done by the body, for every function it performs, whether it be movement of a finger or beating of the heart or growth of a cell or any other function whatever. Anabolism, on the other hand, uses energy instead of supplying it. It is one of the main kinds of physiological work and is done by all living cells.

Anabolism is any process in which a cell builds smaller, simpler molecules up into larger, more complex molecules. In short, anabolism means the synthesis of substances—an imposing variety of them—antibodies, for instance, and enzymes and hormones, and saliva, and sweat, and tears.

Integration

Integration means unification. The body exhibits both structural and functional integration, and both result from organization. Organization, in turn, results from control. As we have already noted, organization creates a single structure (the body) out of many structures (cells, tissues, organs, and systems). Organization also creates a single function (survival) out of many functions (digestion, respiration, circulation, movements, secretion, and all other body functions). To achieve integration of so many functions, nerve impulses and chemicals control the separate processes. They determine whether a given action will occur and, if so, when, how fast, and for how long. Of great importance among the body's control chemicals are three kinds of compounds: enzymes, vitamins, and hormones.

One scientist had this to say about the importance to life of organization: ". . . we should heed the great fact of biological organization, for this, the most important characteristic of life, stands in direct opposition to the behavior of lifeless matter. The latter moves toward ever greater randomness. . . . A living organism, on the contrary, draws out from its chaotic environment particular substances and builds them into a system of ever greater and more organized complexity, thus steadily decreasing the randomness of matter. An organism is not an aggregate, but an integrate. Death releases matter from this unifying control, and the material of the body moves again toward disintegration. . . . Life *is* organization."*

*From Sinnott, Edmund W.: Two roads to truth, New York, 1953, The Viking Press, Inc., p. 131.

Outline summary—The body as an integrated whole

The body—a structural unit composed of many smaller units

COMPONENT UNITS

1. Cells—units of structure
2. Tissues—groups of like cells
3. Organs—composed of several kinds of tissues arranged in orderly manner so as to be able to carry on a special function
4. System—group of organs which work together to accomplish a complex function, such as digestion and absorption of food

ARCHITECTURAL PLAN

1. Backbone
2. Bilateral symmetry
3. Two main cavities

a. ventral cavity
   1. thoracic
      a. pleural portions—contain lungs
      b. pericardial portion—contains heart
      c. mediastinal portion—area between lungs; contains trachea, esophagus, thymus gland, and certain large blood vessels, lymphatic vessels, and nerves
   2. abdominopelvic
      a. Abdominal portion—contains liver, gallbladder, stomach, pancreas, intestines, spleen, kidneys, and ureters
      b. pelvic portion—contains certain reproductive organs, bladder, and part of large intestine
b. dorsal cavity
   1. cranial—contains brain, meninges, pineal and pituitary glands, and blood vessels
   2. spinal—contains spinal cord, meninges, and blood vessels

DESCRIPTIVE TERMS

1. Directional terms
   a. superior—upper
   b. inferior—lower
   c. anterior—front
   d. posterior—back
   e. medial—toward midline
   f. lateral—away from midline
   g. proximal—toward or nearest trunk or point of origin of a part
   h. distal—away from or farthest from trunk or point of origin
2. Planes of body
   a. sagittal—lengthwise, dividing body, or any of its parts, into right and left portions
   b. frontal or coronal—lengthwise, dividing body or any of its parts into anterior and posterior portions
   c. transverse or horizontal—crosswise, dividing body or any of its parts into upper and lower sections
3. Abdominal regions—see Fig. 3
4. Anatomical position—erect, arms at sides, palms forward

The body—a functional unit; one great function made up of many smaller functions

SURVIVAL

The one great function of the body—survival.

SOME MAJOR COMPONENT FUNCTIONS

Homeostasis

1. A state which varies and yet stays about same. Healthy body maintains or quickly restores homeostasis of chemical composition, osmotic pressure, hydrogen-ion concentration, temperature, etc. of extracellular fluid
2. Principle of homeostasis one of most important physiological principles: health and survival depend upon body's maintenance of homeostasis

Metabolism

All chemical reactions occurring in cells
1. Catabolism—series of reactions that change more complex compounds into simpler ones with release of energy
2. Anabolism—series of reactions that use energy to build simpler compounds up into more complex ones

Integration

Control of bodily activities by nerve impulses and chemicals (e.g., enzymes, vitamins, and hormones) so that they function together to achieve survival

Review questions

1. Describe the structural organization of the body, including its general architectural plan and its component units.
2. Name the two cavities on the dorsal surface of the body. What organs do they contain?
3. Identify the divisions of the thoracic cavity and of the abdominopelvic cavity. Name the organs in each.
4. Identify four kinds of structural units of the body in order of increasing complexity.
5. State briefly the principle of homeostasis.
6. Define briefly each of the following terms:

anatomy
anterior
biology
cell
distal
frontal
homeostatic mechanism
hypochondriac region
hypogastric region
iliac region
inferior
integration
lateral
macroscopic
microscopic
organ
physiology
posterior
proximal
sagittal
tissue
transverse plane

Protoplasm

Cell structures
Cell membrane
Cytoplasm
  Endoplasmic reticulum
  Golgi apparatus
  Mitochondria
  Lysosomes
  Ribosomes
  Centrosphere or centrosome
Nucleus
  Chromosomes
  Deoxyribonucleic acid (DNA)
  Nucleoli

Cell physiology
Movement of substances through cell membranes
  Diffusion
  Osmosis
  Filtration
  Active transport mechanisms
  Phagocytosis and pinocytosis
Cell metabolism
  Catabolism
    Glycolysis
    Citric acid cycle
Cell reproduction
  Mitosis

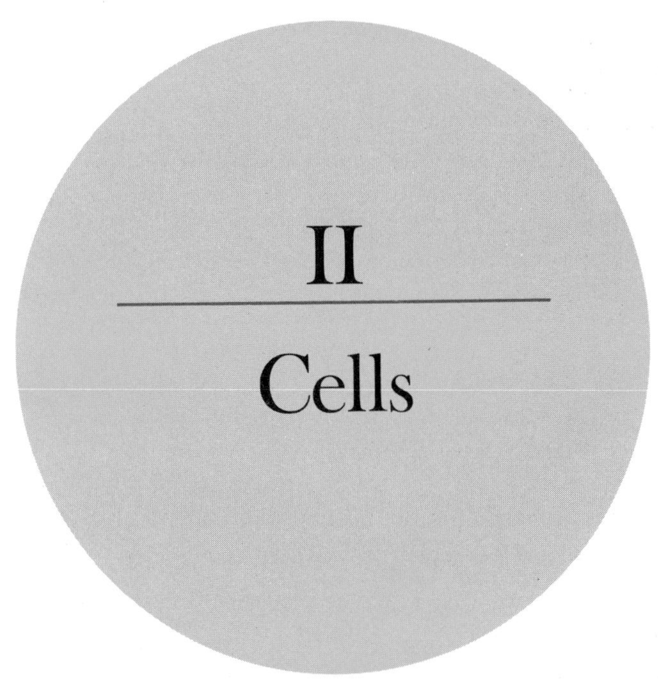

II Cells

Chapter I introduced us to the study of anatomy and physiology with the principle that the body is a structural and functional unit and that the structural unit is made up of many smaller units—cells, tissues, organs, and systems. This chapter presents information about the smallest and simplest of these units—cells. For the past ten years or so, research into the mysteries of these tiny structures has gone on at an almost feverish pace and has produced a veritable "knowledge explosion." Each year has seen the frontiers of this now vast field pushed farther and farther out. Only the main themes of this still unfinished story of the cell will be discussed. Some of the information is old and established, and some is new and tenuous. We shall start with a discussion of the incredible substance called protoplasm.

Protoplasm

Huxley defined protoplasm as the "physical basis of life." It is a general term meaning the material substance composing any cell. In short, protoplasm is living matter.

No unique elements are found in protoplasm. Every element* in it occurs also in nonliving matter. This is not true, however, of the compounds in protoplasm. Certain kinds of compounds—namely, proteins (including enzymes), carbohydrates, lipids, and nucleic acids—occur naturally only in

*"C. HOPKIN'S CaFe is Mighty good" is a statement that should be taken with a grain of NaCl. The capital letters in the preceding statement are symbols for the "baker's dozen" of elements present in human protoplasm: carbon, hydrogen, oxygen, phosphorus, potassium, iodine, nitrogen, sulfur, calcium, iron, magnesium, sodium, and chlorine. Oxygen constitutes 65% of the body; carbon, 18%; hydrogen, 10%; and nitrogen, 3%. In other words, four elements—oxygen, carbon, hydrogen, nitrogen—make up all but 4% of the entire body.

living matter (or matter that once was living).

The chemical composition of protoplasm is not precise and invariable. It differs considerably in different kinds of cells and even in one cell from time to time—a point worth mentioning because a relationship exists between protoplasm's chemical structure and its functions. Structure determines function! You will find this basic principle repeated often in the pages that follow. Here is just one of its many applications: red blood cells contain protein molecules (hemoglobin) whose structure causes them to combine rapidly with oxygen under certain conditions and to dissociate from it rapidly under other conditions. The chemical structure of red cell protoplasm, in other words, determines that these cells will function as oxygen carriers for the body.

You may recall the principle stated in Chapter I that organization is a foundation stone and a vital characteristic of life. This principle applies to the chemicals composing protoplasm. Their particular arrangement or pattern of organization endows protoplasm with the characteristics which distinguish it from nonliving matter. These properties of living matter are irritability (the ability to respond to a stimulus), conductivity (the ability to transmit impulses), contractility (the ability to contract or move), metabolism (use of foods to provide energy and to synthesize complex compounds), and reproduction.

Cell structures

Not so many years ago cells were thought of as very simple structures composed of a membrane, a nucleus, some cytoplasm, and little else. Today their known complexity, both as to structure and function, taxes the imagination. This has come about as a result of the development and use of an imposing array of sophisticated tools and techniques. The electron microscope is an outstanding example of the former and radioautography of the latter. Through its power to make objects appear many thousands of times larger than they are, the electron microscope brings into view teeming numbers of little organs inside cells. Sometimes they can be counted in the thousands. And yet their very existence had not been dreamed of before. Radioautography combines the use of radioactive atoms with a photographic technique and has thereby opened up new vistas in the exploration of cell functions.*

Before going on to the next discussion, study the following outline to learn the names of several kinds of structures that make up a cell.

Cell membrane
Cytoplasm
Membranous organelles
Endoplasmic reticulum
Golgi apparatus
Mitochondria
Lysosomes
Other organelles
Ribosomes
Centrosphere
Inclusions
Food granules
Secretory granules
Pigment granules
Nucleus
Chromosomes
Nucleolus

You already know the names of the three main parts of a cell—cell membrane, cytoplasm, and nucleus. But did you know that cytoplasm contains so many different kinds of organelles? (The term organelle or "little organ" implies that these tiny structures perform special functions for the cell just as organs do for the body as a whole.) Examine Fig. 5 to see what the various cell structures look like under a light microscope. Then notice how different they appear in Fig. 6 under the much greater magnification of the electron microscope.

*See suggested supplementary readings for Chapter II, references 2 and 11, p. 548, if you would like to learn more about radioautography.

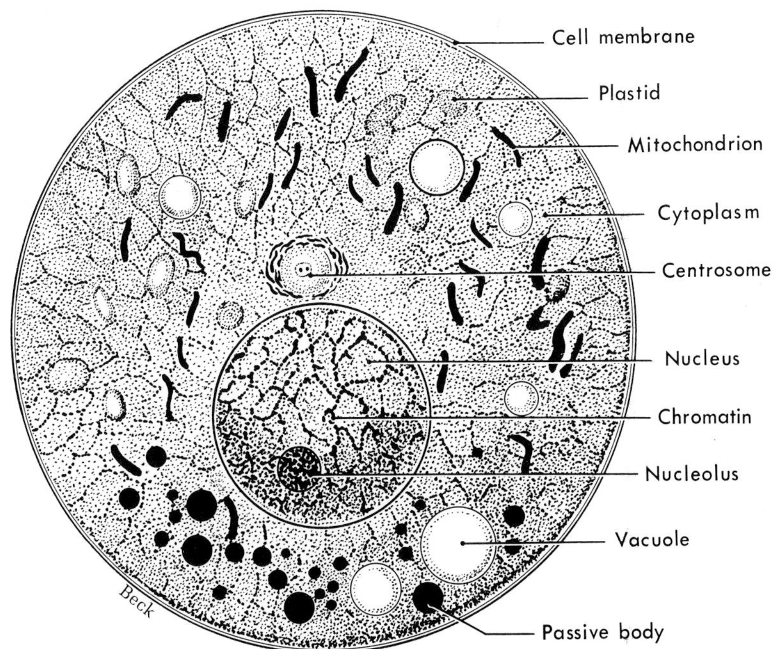

Fig. 5

Diagram of a cell based on what is seen under a light microscope. Compare with Fig. 6. Not all of the structures shown can be demonstrated in all cells.

CELL MEMBRANE

The most gossamer chiffon you can imagine is thick and heavy indeed compared to the membranes that form the boundaries of human cells. Their thinness truly does defy imagination. How can you possibly form a mental picture of a fabric less than 3/10 millionths of an inch thick!* Current opinion generally agrees that protein and lipid molecules compose the cell membrane. Until very recently there was also general agreement that these molecules were arranged in three layers—outer, middle, and inner. The outer and inner layers were thought to consist of protein molecules laid side by side like so many bricks in a pavement. The middle layer was visualized as a double layer, that is, 2 molecules thick, and consisting of lipid molecules. However, the newest research data suggests that protein and lipid molecules may be intertwined to constitute a layer only 1 molecule thick.*

One more feature of cell membrane structure should be mentioned—it has holes in it, extremely tiny ones, called pores. Although no cell membrane pores have been seen, even with the powerful magnification of the electron microscope, those in red blood cells have been measured experimentally and were found to have diameters of about 7 angstroms.† Laboratory findings

---

**Thickness of a cell membrane* is 75 angstrom units. (Since 1 angstrom, as shown below, equals 1/10 of a millimicron or roughly 1/250,000,000 of an inch, 75 angstroms equal about 3/10,000,000 of an inch.) *Diameter of a hydrogen atom* is 1 angstrom unit.

1 meter		About 39.5 inches
1 millimeter	0.001 meter	About 1/25 inch
1 micron	0.001 millimeter	About 1/25,000 inch
1 millimicron	0.001 micron	About 1/25,000,000 inch
1 angstrom unit	0.1 millimicron	About 1/250,000,000 inch

*Membranes of cells only one molecule thick, Sci. Newsletter **90**:78 (July 30), 1966.

†Solomon, Arthur K.: Pores in the cell membrane, Sci. Amer. **203**:146 (Dec.), 1960.

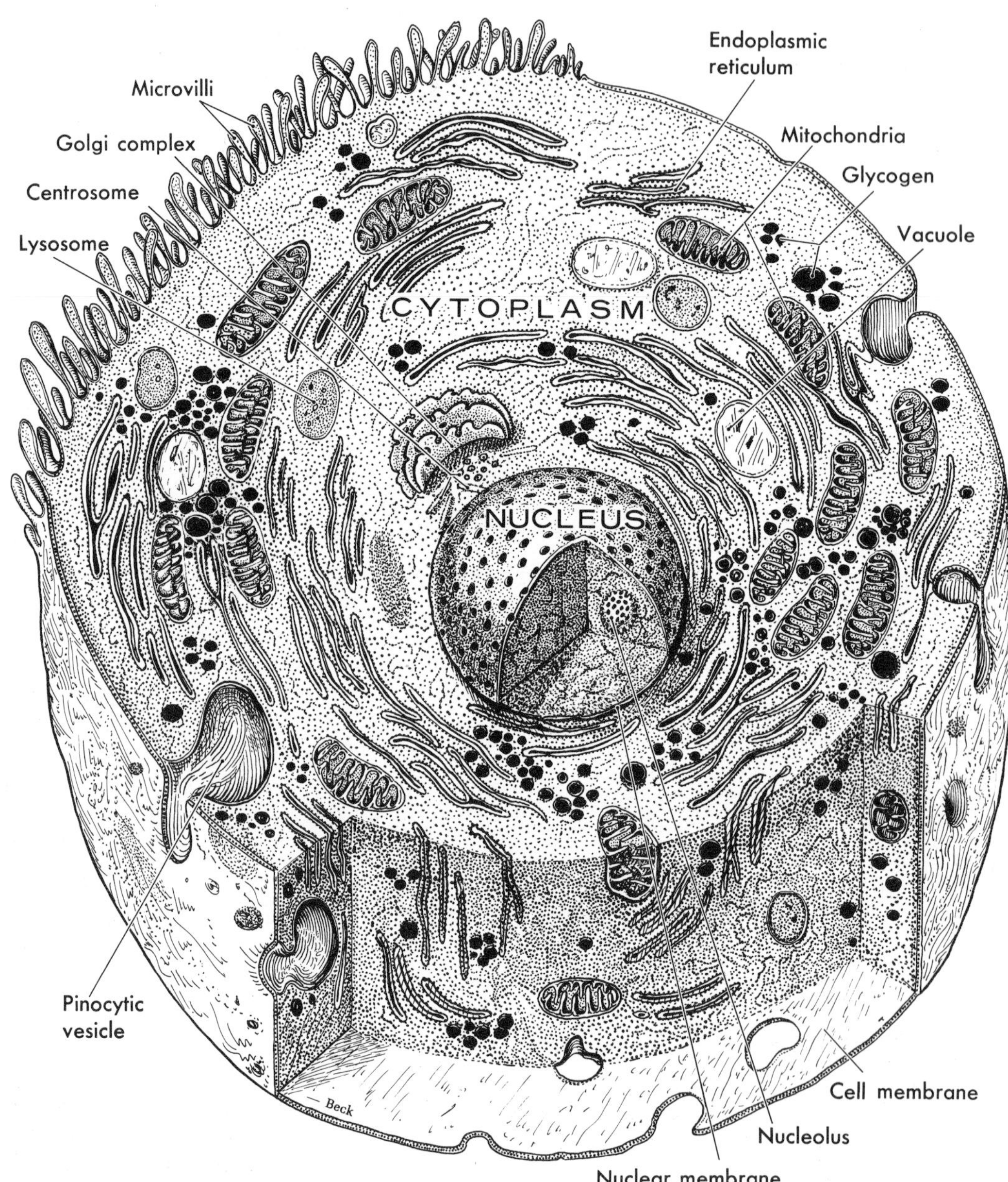

Fig. 6

Modern diagram of a typical cell based on what is seen under an electron microscope. The mitochondria are the sites of the oxidative reactions that provide the cell with energy. The dots that line the endoplasmic reticulum are ribosomes, the sites of protein synthesis.

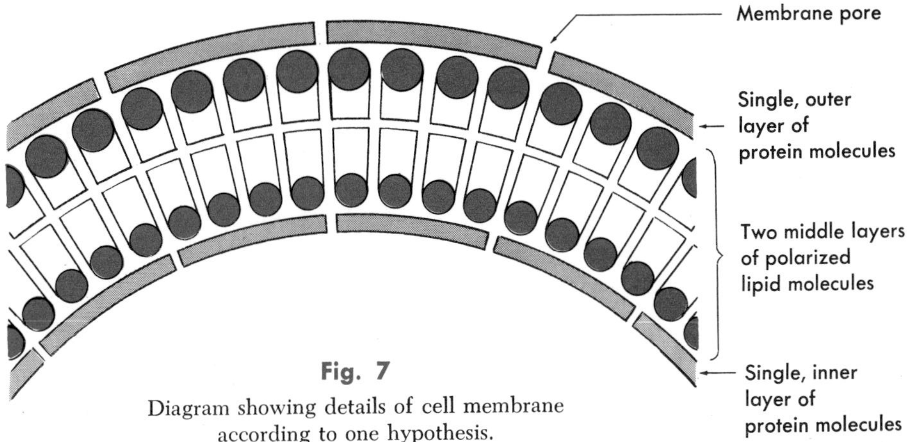

Fig. 7
Diagram showing details of cell membrane according to one hypothesis.

have suggested also that cell pores are few and far apart. In the words of one biochemist, "If one speaks of the membrane as a sieve, it is a sieve with very few holes in it."*

Despite its incredible delicacy, the cell membrane performs lifesaving functions for the cell. First of all, it is the structure which maintains the cell's integrity. It possesses a certain amount of firmness, fantastic as such a claim sounds for a material less than 3/10 millionths of an inch thick. Yet it is true. The membrane is firm enough to keep the many cell structures arranged in the order necessary for their carrying on the activities that maintain cellular life. Perhaps the truth of this is best illustrated when a cell membrane becomes torn open. Then the cell loses its integrity. It becomes disorganized as a result of its substance leaking out and consequently dies.

A second function performed by the cell membrane seems somewhat paradoxical. The membrane serves both as a barrier and at the same time as a gateway. As a barrier, it separates the living substance of the cell from its fluid environment. As a barrier, it keeps some things inside the cell and others outside. But while it is acting as a barrier, it is also serving as a gateway—not an ordinary gateway, however, through which any and all substances may pass, but a highly selective gateway which allows only certain materials to move through it (discussed on pp. 21 to 32).

CYTOPLASM

Cytoplasm is the part of a cell between its membrane and its nucleus. In other words, it is all of a cell's protoplasm except its nucleus. Far from being the homogeneous substance once thought, it consists of hundreds and often thousands of well-organized structures. The main kinds of these cytoplasmic organelles and inclusions are listed on p. 12. (*Inclusions* are cytoplasmic structures which serve no clearly useful function for the cell. *Organelles,* on the other hand, are cytoplasmic structures which do serve a clearly useful function.)

Membranes form the walls of the following four kinds of organelles: the endoplasmic reticulum, the Golgi apparatus, mitochondria, and lysosomes. Although these structures resemble each other in that they all have membranous walls, they differ in shape and size, in their locations in the cytoplasm, and in their functions. The following paragraphs relate basic information about the cytoplasmic organelles.

*From Holter, Heinz: How things get into cells, Sci. Amer. **205**:167 (Sept.), 1961.

Endoplasmic reticulum

Endoplasm means the cytoplasm located toward the center of a cell. Reticulum means network. Therefore the name endoplasmic reticulum means literally a network located deep inside the cytoplasm. And when first seen, it appeared to be just that. Later on, however, electron photomicrographs showed quite clearly that the endoplasmic reticulum actually consists of numerous tubules and vesicles located not only in the endoplasm but also in the ectoplasm (cytoplasm located nearer the periphery of a cell is called ectoplasm). You can observe this in Fig. 6. The endoplasmic reticulum looks like miniature canals winding tortuously through the cytoplasm to open finally to the exterior at the surface of the cell.

There are two types of endoplasmic reticulum, smooth and rough. *Rough endoplasmic reticulum* is so classified because innumerable small granules dot its membranes, giving them a rough appearance. These granules are called ribosomes. *Smooth endoplasmic reticulum,* on the other hand, has no ribosomes attached to it. Hence its membranes appear smooth.

As yet, no one knows for sure what the smooth endoplasmic reticulum does. In contrast, considerable evidence has revealed the functions of the rough endoplasmic reticulum. The ribosomes attached to the membranes of the rough endoplasmic reticulum synthesize proteins. The membranes themselves serve to isolate these proteins, that is, to keep them separated from the cytoplasm of the cell. And, the canals of the rough endoplasmic reticulum provide passageways through which the synthesized proteins move on to the Golgi apparatus. Here, they are thought to be modified—probably condensed. Then they move on again, this time out to the surface of the cell, from which they are secreted.

Golgi apparatus

The Golgi apparatus consists of membranous vesicles of varying shapes located near the nucleus. (In cells which secrete substances, the Golgi apparatus always lies between the nucleus and the part of the cell's surface from which the secretion is extruded.) Many of the Golgi vesicles are flat in shape and are arranged one on top of the other. As suggested in the preceding paragraph, the current concept of the function of the Golgi apparatus is that it condenses substances before they leave the cell as secretions.

Mitochondria

Mitochondria are membranous organelles shaped very much like ultrasmall sausages—if you can imagine sausages that measure perhaps 15,000 angstroms from end to end and a third as much across. (In case inches mean more to you than angstroms, that is a length of only about 3/50,000 of an inch and a width of only 1/50,000 of an inch.) Yet this organelle, tiny as it is, has a highly organized construction. The wall of a mitochondrion, for instance, consists of an outer membrane and an inner membrane barely separated by a thin film of fluid. The inner membrane has several extensions called *cristae* which jut into the interior of the mitochondrion like so many little partitions. And attached to both outer and inner membranes are literally thousands of very small particles. Each miniscule particle, molecular biologists now report, consists of enzymes arranged in the order of their functioning. This is another example, a pretty impressive one, of the principle that organization is a foundation stone and a vital characteristic of life.

Recent studies* have given new insights into the functions of the enzymes which make up the thousands of particles attached to the membranes of each mitochondrion.

*Green, D. E.: The mitochondrion, Sci. Amer. **210**:67 (Jan.), 1964.

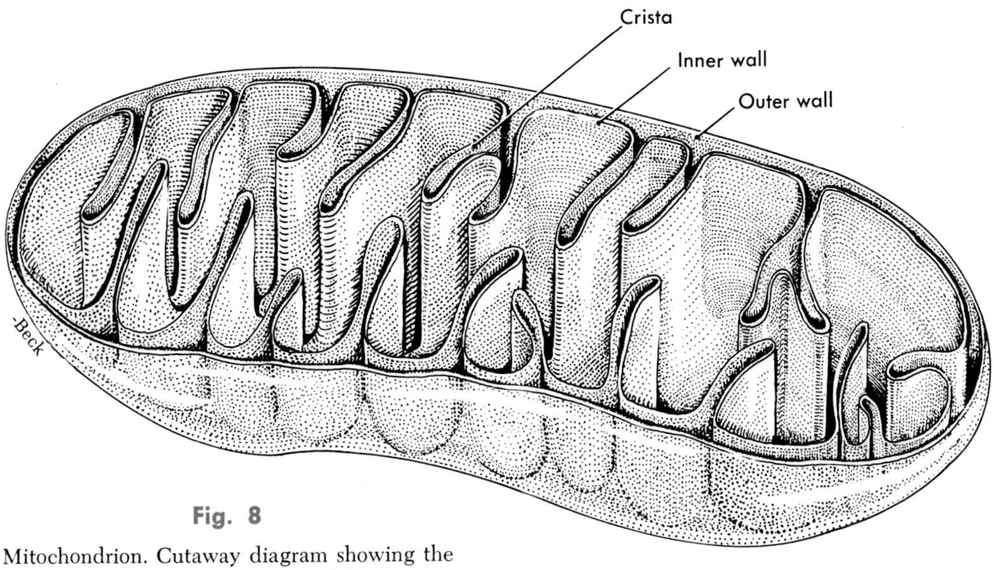

Fig. 8

Mitochondrion. Cutaway diagram showing the two-layered structure of its delicate membranous wall.

Presumably they catalyze the chemical reactions by which cells provide themselves with most of the energy that does their many kinds of work and keeps both them and the body alive. Thus do mitochondria earn their now familiar title, the "power plants" of cells (discussed on pp. 32 to 38).

From the knowledge that mitochondria generate power for cellular work, one might deduce that the number of mitochondria in a cell would be directly related to its amount of activity. And this principle does seem to hold true. In general, the more work the cell does, the more mitochondria its cytoplasm contains. An eminent authority on the molecular structure of mitochondria as related to function had this to say on the subject: "There may be anywhere from 50 to 5,000 mitochondria in a cell, depending on its type and function. A single liver cell of the rat contains about 1,000 mitochondria."*

*From Lehninger, A. L.: How cells transform energy, Sci. Amer. **205**:62 (Sept.), 1961.

Lysosomes

Lysosomes are the newest kind of cytoplasmic organelle to be discovered. They vary considerably in size, shape, and numbers. White blood cells, for instance, contain a particularly large number of lysosomes.

In their earliest, inactive stage, lysosomes look like tiny granules. Later, after they have become active and larger, they show up as the small membranous vesicles or closed sacs which they really are. They contain several kinds of enzymes which can dissolve most of the compounds present in cells. In plain language, they can actually digest the cells themselves. Little wonder, then, that these powerful and dangerous substances are kept sealed up in lysosomes so they cannot mix with the cytoplasm. And little wonder, too, that someone thought to give the nickname "suicide bags" to lysosomes. The term "digestive bags," however, would seem to describe their function more accurately, for lysosomal enzymes usually do not destroy the cells containing them.

Instead, their function is to digest certain large molecules and larger particles (for example, bacteria) that find their way into cells. This probably explains why white blood cells contain so many lysosomes—they serve as scavenger cells for the body, engulfing bacteria and destroying them in their lysosomes.

Ribosomes

Ribosomes are small structures composed of ribonucleic acid (RNA) and protein. Although they are too small to be seen with a light microscope, the electron microscope reveals hundreds of these little spheres. Many are attached to the endoplasmic reticulum, as already mentioned, but many others are scattered through the cytoplasm.

Someone has nicknamed ribosomes "protein factories" in recognition of their function. They synthesize the proteins of a cell, and proteins are one of the most important kinds of biological compounds. Not only are they important quantitatively (every cell contains hundreds of different proteins) but they also are important qualitatively. Just how important you can judge for yourself from these two facts: special catalysts called enzymes make possible the many chemical reactions that have to go on in cells to keep them alive, and all enzymes are proteins. Hence, proteins are vitally important compounds.

A few years ago some biophysicists at the Massachusetts Institute of Technology coined the word *polyribosome* or *polysome* to indicate a group of ribosomes that work together to synthesize proteins. Their research findings and those of other investigators strongly suggest that one ribosome does not fabricate complex protein molecules all by itself but that several ribosomes work together "as if they were machines on an assembly line."* In short, the cell, like present-day industry, seems to prefer assembly lines to individuals working alone.

*From Rich, Alexander: Polyribosomes, Sci. Amer. **209**:44 (Dec.), 1963.

Centrosphere or centrosome

The names of this cytoplasmic organelle suggests its shape and location—a spherical area or body located near the center of the cell. Actually, this means that the centrosphere is located near the nucleus since the nucleus takes up the center space of most cells. With the light microscope and suitably prepared slides, one can see two dots (called *centrioles*) in the centrosphere. The electron microscope, however, reveals that the centrioles are more than just dots. They are tiny cylinders whose walls consist of a definite number of groups of very fine tubules—nine groups of two or three tubules each, to be specific.

Early in the process of cell division, two pairs of centrioles can be seen and, most curiously, one centriole of each pair lies at right angles to the other member of the pair. One pair of centrioles moves to one pole of the cell during cell division and the other pair goes to the other pole.

Centrioles play some part in the formation of the mitotic spindle fibers. They also control polarization of these fibers (see p. 39).

NUCLEUS

The nucleus is a spherical body located in the center of a cell. A double-layered, pore-containing membrane encloses the nucleus and separates it from the cytoplasm. In the nucleus are located tiny structures of gigantic importance—the *chromosomes.*

Chromosomes

The word chromosome is derived from two Greek words—*chroma,* meaning color, and *soma,* meaning bodies. And in a suitably stained cell, chromosomes do appear as "colored bodies" in the nucleus. They look like stubby little rods when a cell has just started the process of dividing to form two cells. But in between successive cell divisions they appear as deeply stained granules and then are called *chromatin granules.* Discovery of the relationship between chromosomes and chromatin granules came not too many years ago (see p. 40).

Deoxyribonucleic acid (DNA)

The preceding paragraph described chromosomes in terms of their microscopic appearance. We can also describe them in terms of their molecular composition and functions. Two kinds of chemical compounds predominate in chromosomes, namely, *deoxyribonucleic acid* and certain types of proteins. Happily, an abbreviation, DNA, is usually used for the tongue-twisting full name, deoxyribonucleic acid. If the title "most important of all compounds in the body" were to be bestowed, it might well go to deoxyribonucleic acid, the main constituent of chromosomes. Why? Because of DNA's functions. It directs the making of each new generation of cells and each new generation of human beings. What the directions or instructions contained in DNA molecules are and how they are carried out have proved mysteries hard to solve. Scientists have not even yet completely untangled their many threads. The following few paragraphs report some of the most significant findings so far concerning the structure of DNA (functions are discussed on p. 40).

DNA is a giant among molecules—a giant in the literal sense since it is an extraordinarily large molecule and a giant in the figurative sense because the importance of its functions equals or outranks that of all other molecules in the body. In 1953, Dr. James D. Watson, Dr. Francis H. C. Crick, and Dr. Maurice H. F. Wilkins discovered the basic structure of the DNA molecule. Nine years later they received the coveted Nobel Prize in medicine in recognition of the brilliance and importance of their discovery. To visualize a DNA molecule, start by picturing a ladder made of a pliable material. Then imagine someone twisting the ladder around and around until it becomes shaped like a steep spiral staircase thousands of turns long. (The Greek word *helix* means spiral, hence the frequent description of DNA as a "helical-shaped molecule.")

A single DNA molecule is made up of thousands of molecules of three different kinds of compounds: a sugar (deoxyribose), an acid (phosphoric), and four nitrogenous bases (adenine, thymine, cytosine, and guanine). Notice that the name deoxyribonucleic acid indicates two facts: that DNA contains a sugar named deoxyribose and that DNA is an acid found in the nuclei of cells. (Deoxyribose is a sugar that is not sweet and whose molecules contain only five carbon atoms instead of six, as do glucose molecules.)

A ladder, as we said earlier, makes a good model to keep in mind when trying to visualize a DNA molecule. Imagine each side of the DNA ladder made up of a long line of sugar (deoxyribose) and phosphate molecules joined alternately one after the other. Now visualize the rungs of the ladder attached to the sugars on each side but not to the phosphates. Then think of every rung as composed of two nitrogenous bases joined to each other by a hydrogen bond. (Study Fig. 9.)

The same two bases always pair off with each other in a DNA molecule—like teenagers "going steady." Adenine always goes with thymine (or, vice versa, thymine with adenine), and guanine always goes with cytosine, or vice versa. Base pairing, as this is called, is one of the structural facts about DNA that has great functional importance (see p. 40). Another one is the fact that although the base pairs are always the same in all DNA molecules, the sequence in which they follow each other is not always the same. For instance, suppose the

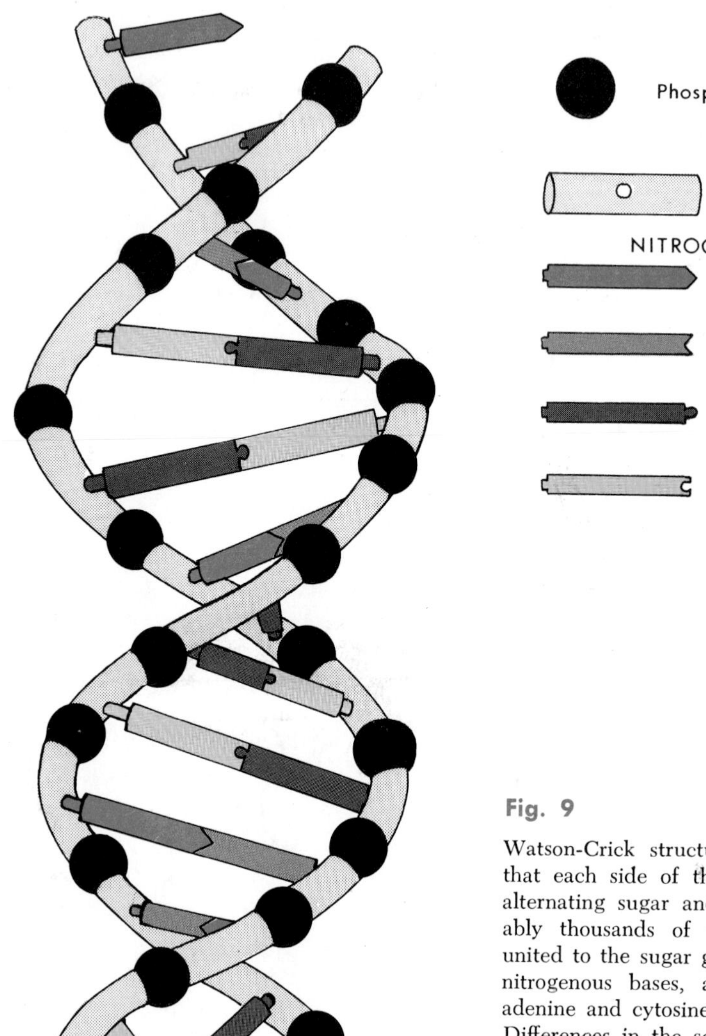

Fig. 9

Watson-Crick structure of DNA molecule. Note that each side of the DNA molecule consists of alternating sugar and phosphate groups, presumably thousands of them. Each sugar group is united to the sugar group opposite it by a pair of nitrogenous bases, adenine-thymine or thymine-adenine and cytosine-guanine or guanine-cytosine. Differences in the sequences of base pairs establish the identity of the many different kinds of DNA.

sequence of base pairs cytosine-guanine, adenine-thymine, thymine-adenine make up the seventh, eighth, and ninth rungs of one chromosome. In another chromosome, the sequence of base pairs for these same rungs might be something entirely different, perhaps cytosine-guanine, guanine-cytosine, cytosine-guanine. These may seem like picayune details, but nothing could be further from the truth, for it is the sequence of the base pairs in DNA molecules that determines all hereditary traits! (More about this appears on p. 40.)

Nucleoli

Nucleoli are minute rounded bodies located in the nucleus. They consist mainly of proteins and ribonucleic acid (RNA). (RNA is similar to DNA but contains the sugar ribose instead of deoxyribose.) The functions served by nucleoli have not yet been established with certainty. Among the hypotheses offered is that they may synthesize and temporarily store RNA (until the time it moves out of the nucleoli into the cytoplasm, where some of it becomes part of ribosomes).

Cell physiology

Every cell carries on certain functions that maintain its own life. For example, all cells move substances through their membranes and metabolize foods. Also, all but a few types of cells reproduce themselves. In addition to these self-serving activities, every cell in the body also performs some special function that helps maintain the life of the body as a whole. Muscle cells provide the function of movement, nerve cells contribute communication services, red blood cells transport oxygen, etc. In return, the body performs vital functions for all of its cells. It brings food and oxygen to them and removes waste from them, to mention only two examples. In short, a relationship of mutual interdependence exists between the body as a whole and its various parts. Optimum health of the body depends upon optimum health of each of its parts, down even to the smallest cell. Conversely, optimum health of each individual part depends upon optimum health of the body as a whole. In equation form, this physiological principle of mutual interdependence might be expressed as follows:

body health ⇌ system health ⇌ organ health ⇌ tissue health ⇌ cellular health

Some parts of the body, of course, are more important for healthy survival than others. Obviously, the heart is far more important than the appendix. And the nerve cells which control respiration are infinitely more important for survival than muscle cells that move the little finger.

Cell physiology deals with all kinds of cell functions, but at this time we shall discuss only the movement of substances through cell membranes, cell metabolism, and cell reproduction.

MOVEMENT OF SUBSTANCES THROUGH CELL MEMBRANES

Heavy traffic moves continuously in both directions through cell membranes. Streaming in and out of all cells, in endless procession, go molecules of water, foods, gases, wastes, and many kinds of ions. Several processes carry on this mass transportation. They are classified under two general headings as physical and physiological processes.

The *physical processes* include diffusion, osmosis, and filtration. The term physical process implies something which occurs in the physical (nonliving) world. But actually substances can move through either living or nonliving membranes by diffusion, osmosis, and filtration. This is because the energy that powers these processes comes from the random, never-ceasing movements of atoms, ions, and molecules and *not* from chemical reactions in cells. Because cells do not take an active part in them, physical processes are also referred to as *passive mechanisms.*

The *physiological processes* include active transport, phagocytosis, and pinocytosis. A physiological process is any type of work done by living cells. The energy that powers any physiological process comes from chemical reactions which take place in living cells. Because this is true, the processes of active transport, phagocytosis, and pinocytosis can move substances through cell membranes only as long as cells are alive and functioning. When they die, these physiological processes cease. In contrast, the physical processes of diffusion, osmosis, and filtration go on even after cellular death.

Physiological processes are also called *active mechanisms* because cells are active during these processes; that is, cellular chemical reactions supply the energy for the physiological processes. Active transport, phagocytosis, and pinocytosis are among the most vital of all kinds of cellular work.

Diffusion

Diffusion means scattering or spreading. It occurs because small particles such as molecules and ions are forever on the go. They move continuously, rapidly, and at random. Here is a convincing way to observe the results of diffusion. Place a cube of sugar on the bottom of each of two cups of water. Immediately skim off a spoonful of liquid from the top of one cup and taste it. About ten minutes later do the same from the other cup. The second sample will taste sweet; the first will not. Sugar molecules in the second cup will have had time to move in all directions—up, out, down, in—to scatter or to diffuse, that is, throughout the water. More of them, however, will have diffused up and away from the cube than down and toward it. In other words, their *net* diffusion will have been away from areas of their greater concentration toward areas of their lesser concentration so that they eventually become evenly distributed throughout the water. Diffusion always results—if enough time elapses—in an even scattering of solute particles among solvent molecules. (Water is the solvent in all body fluids.)

Consider another example—two solutions, 20% and 10% sodium chloride (NaCl), separated by a membrane permeable to both NaCl and water. Sodium chloride particles and water molecules racing in all directions through the solution collide with each other and with the membrane. Some inevitably hit the membrane pores from the 20% side

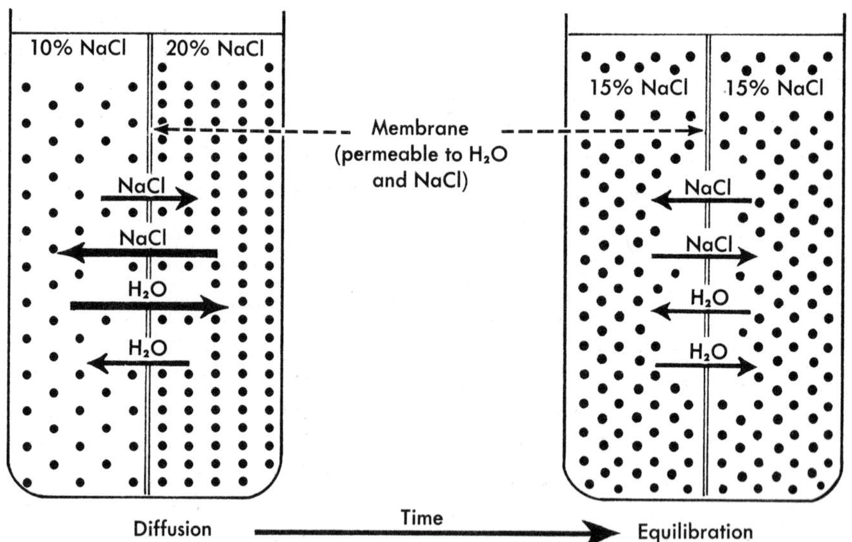

Fig. 10

Diffusion. Because the membrane separating the 10% NaCl from the 20% NaCl is freely permeable to both NaCl and H_2O, both substances diffuse rapidly through the membrane in both directions. But, as the larger arrows indicate, more sodium and chloride ions move out of the 20% solution, where there are more of them, into the 10% solution, where there are fewer of them, than in the opposite direction. Simultaneously, more water molecules move from the 10% solution, where there are more of them, into the 20% solution, where there are fewer of them. Result: equilibration of the concentrations of the two solutions after an elapse of time. From then on, equal numbers of Na ions and Cl ions diffuse in both directions, as do equal numbers of H_2O molecules.

and some from the 10% side. Just as inevitably, some bound through the pores in both directions. For a while, more NaCl particles enter the pores from the 20% side, where they are more numerous or more concentrated. More NaCl particles therefore move through the membrane from the 20% solution into the 10% than diffuse through it in the opposite direction. Using different words for the same thought, *net diffusion* of NaCl takes place from the solution where NaCl concentration is greater into the one where its concentration is lesser. Thus, net diffusion of NaCl occurs "down" the *NaCl concentration gradient*—that is, from the higher NaCl concentration down to the lower NaCl concentration.

During the time that net diffusion of NaCl is taking place between the 20% and 10% solutions, net diffusion of water is also going on. The direction of net diffusion of any substance is always down that substance's concentration gradient. Applying this principle, net NaCl diffusion occurs down the NaCl concentration gradient and net water diffusion occurs down the water concentration gradient. Since the greater concentration of water molecules lies in the more dilute 10% solution (where fewer water molecules have been displaced by NaCl molecules), more water molecules diffuse out of the 10% solution into the 20% solution than diffuse in the opposite direction. This net diffusion of water thus removes water from the more dilute solution and adds it to the more concentrated one, a process that obviously tends to equalize or equilibrate the concentrations of the two solutions. Simultaneously, the net diffusion of NaCl is removing NaCl from the more concentrated solution and adding it to the more dilute one, a process which also tends to equilibrate the two solutions. Note that whereas net diffusion of NaCl and of water both go on at the same time, they go on in opposite directions.

Diffusion of NaCl and water continues even after equilibration has been achieved. But from that moment on, it is equal diffusion in both directions through the membrane and not net diffusion of either substance in either direction.

The following paragraphs summarize some facts and principles worth remembering about diffusion. They have been culled from the diffusion examples just described.

1. *Diffusion* is the movement of solute and solvent particles in all directions through a solution or in both directions through a membrane.
2. *Net diffusion* is the movement of more particles of a substance in one direction than in the opposite direction.
3. Net diffusion of any substance occurs down its own concentration gradient, which means from the higher to the lower concentration of that substance. Following are two applications of this principle: (a) net diffusion of solute particles occurs from the more concentrated to the less concentrated solution. (b) net diffusion of water molecules, in contrast, occurs from the more dilute to the less dilute solution.
4. Net diffusion of the solute in one direction and of water in the opposite direction eventually results in *equilibration*. The concentrations of two solutions soon become equal when the membrane separating the solutions is freely permeable to both solute and water.
5. After two solutions have equilibrated, equal diffusion occurs in both directions through the membrane but net diffusion no longer occurs in either direction. (Equal diffusion means that the number of solute and water particles diffusing in one direction equals the number diffusing in the opposite direction. Net diffusion

means more particles diffusing in one direction than in the other.)

6. Diffusion is a passive transport mechanism because cells are passive, not active and working in this process. Cellular chemical reactions do not supply the energy that moves diffusing particles. The continual random movements characteristic of all molecules and ions (molecular kinetic theory) furnish the energy for diffusion.

Think about these diffusion principles. Make sure that you understand them, for they have many applications in physiology. Our very lives, in fact, depend upon diffusion. Evidence? Oxygen, the "breath of life," enters cells by diffusion through their membranes.

Osmosis

Osmosis is the movement of water through a semipermeable or a selectively permeable membrane,* that is, a membrane which is not freely permeable to all solute particles present. If a membrane is not freely permeable to solute particles, they cannot equilibrate across the membrane. Instead they remain more concentrated on one side than on the other. In other words, a concentration gradient of the not-freely-diffusible solutes is maintained

*A semipermeable membrane is freely permeable to water but impermeable to all solutes present on both sides of the membrane. A selectively permeable membrane is freely permeable to water and some solutes but not freely permeable to all solutes present. All normal living membranes are selectively permeable.

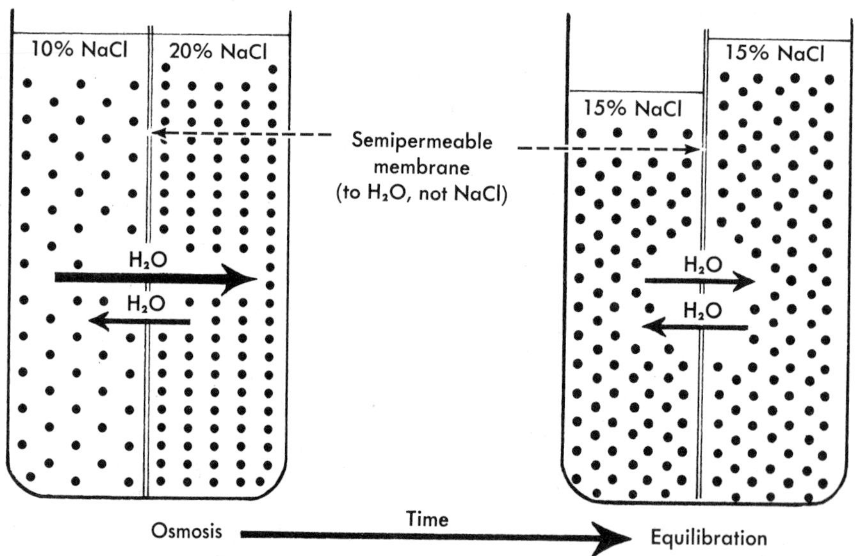

Fig. 11

Osmosis. Osmosis is the diffusion of water through a semipermeable or selectively permeable membrane (one not freely permeable to all solutes present). The membrane shown in this diagram is semipermeable, that is, permeable to water but not to NaCl. Because there are relatively more water molecules in 10% NaCl than in 15% NaCl, more water molecules osmose from the more dilute into the more concentrated solution (as indicated by the larger arrow in the left-hand diagram) than osmose in the opposite direction. The *net* direction of osmosis, in other words, is toward the more concentrated solution. Net osmosis produces three changes: the concentrations of the two solutions equilibrate, the volume of the originally more concentrated solution increases, and so, too, does its pressure.

across the membrane. Hence, another definition for osmosis is that it is the passage of water through a membrane which maintains at least one solute concentration gradient between the two fluids it separates.

Diffusion of water, rather than osmosis, occurs through a membrane which is freely permeable to water and to all solutes present. Such a membrane cannot maintain any concentration gradients between the two solutions it separates. All solutes present diffuse freely through this membrane so they all equilibrate across it. Therefore, water diffuses, not osmoses, through such a membrane. In short, water diffuses through membranes that do not maintain any solute concentration gradients across them and osmoses through membranes that do maintain solute concentration gradients.

Water is said to osmose, rather than diffuse, through normal living membranes because the latter are selectively permeable, are not freely permeable to all solutes present, and therefore maintain certain solute concentration gradients. For example, a normal capillary membrane is not freely permeable to proteins* so maintains a protein concentration gradient between blood and interstitial fluid (fluid surrounding cells). Normal cell membranes are not freely permeable to electrolytes. For example, they maintain sodium and potassium concentration gradients between interstitial and intracellular fluids. Interstitial fluid sodium concentration is many times higher than intracellular fluid sodium concentration. In contrast, intracellular potassium concentration is many times higher than interstitial fluid potassium concentration.

*Proteins are classified as *colloids* (solute particles with diameters from about 1 to 100 millimicrons). The normal capillary membrane is almost impermeable to colloids but freely permeable to *crystalloids* or true solutes (solute particles with diameters less than 1 millimicron) such as ions (electrolytes), glucose, oxygen, etc.

Perhaps the best way to explore the concept of osmosis further is by an example. Imagine that you have a 10% sucrose (cane sugar) solution in a test tube made of cellophane and you suspend this tube in a beaker containing 2% sucrose solution. Cellophane is impermeable to sucrose molecules but freely permeable to water molecules. Therefore, sucrose will not diffuse through the cellophane but water will osmose through it in both directions—not in equal amounts, however.

To deduce the direction in which the greater volume of water will osmose (the direction, that is, of net osmosis), we must first decide which solution contains the greater concentration of water molecules. Pretty clearly, the more dilute of two solutions contains the greater concentration of water molecules. In this case, then, water concentration is greater on the 2% side than on the 10% side of the cellophane membrane. Next, we need to apply the principle already stated that "net diffusion of any substance occurs down the concentration gradient of that substance." Therefore, net osmosis (net water diffusion through the semipermeable cellophane membrane) occurs down the water concentration gradient. In our example, net osmosis takes place from the more dilute 2% sucrose solution into the more concentrated 10% solution. Thus, the solution which at first was more concentrated gains water by net osmosis and becomes more dilute. And the solution which at first was more dilute loses water and becomes more concentrated. Net osmosis, in other words, tends to make the concentrations of the two solutions equal. In briefest form, the principle is this: net osmosis occurs down the water concentration gradient and tends to equilibrate the solutions separated by a membrane.

Net osmosis into the originally more concentrated of our two sucrose solutions increases the volume of this solution. Further, the increase in its volume causes an increase in its pressure, called osmotic pressure—a logical term since it is pressure caused by net osmosis. By definition, then, *osmotic pressure* is the pressure that develops in a solution as a result of net osmosis into that solution. An important principle stems from this definition—osmotic pressure develops in the solution which originally contains the higher concentration of the solute to which the membrane is not freely permeable. For instance, in the example previously given, osmotic pressure would develop in the solution that originally had the 10% sucrose concentration.

Potential osmotic pressure is the maximum osmotic pressure that could develop in a solution if it were separated from distilled water by a semipermeable membrane. (Actual osmotic pressure, on the other hand, is a pressure that already has developed, not just one that could develop.) What determines a solution's potential osmotic pressure? The answer is this: the number of solute particles in a unit volume of solution directly determines its potential osmotic pressure—the more solute particles per unit volume, the greater the potential osmotic pressure. The number of solute particles per unit volume (for example, per liter) of solution, in turn, is determined by the molar concentration of the solution and also, if the solute is an electrolyte, by the number of ions formed by each molecule of solutes. This concept can be expressed by a diagram (Fig. 12) or by formula (see footnote to Fig. 12).

Since it is the number of solute particles per unit volume that directly determines a solution's potential osmotic pressure, one might at first thought jump to the conclusion that all solutions which have the same percent concentration also have the same potential osmotic pressures. Obviously, it is true that all solutions which contain the same percent concentration of the same solute do also have the same potential osmotic pressures. All 5% glucose solutions, for example, have a potential osmotic pressure at body temperature of about 5,300 mm. Hg pressure. But all solutions which contain the same percent concentrations of different solutes do not have the same molar concentrations nor the same potential osmotic pressures. By applying the equation in the footnote, you will discover that 5% NaCl at body temperature has a potential osmotic pressure of more than 33,000 mm. Hg—quite different from 5% glucose's potential osmotic pressure of about 5,300 mm. Hg.

Two solutions which have the same potential osmotic pressures are said to be *isosmotic* to each other. Because they have the same potential osmotic pressures, the same amount of water osmoses in both directions between them when they are separated by a selectively permeable or a semipermeable membrane. No net osmosis, however, occurs in either direction between isosmotic solutions. Hence, no actual osmotic pressure develops in either solution. Their pressures remain the same so isosmotic solutions are also called isotonic (Gr. *isos,* the same; *tonos,* tension or pressure).

By definition, *isotonic solutions* are those whose volumes and pressures will stay the same if the two solutions are separated by a membrane. For example, 0.85% NaCl is referred to as "isotonic saline," meaning that it is isotonic to the fluid inside human cells. Translated more fully, it means that if 0.85% NaCl is injected into human tissues or blood, no net osmosis occurs into or out of cells. Therefore, no change in intracellular volume or pressure takes place. Physicians, of course, understand this. They know that isotonic saline solution, given intramuscularly or intravenously, will not injure or kill cells by causing them either to lose water or to gain it. In more technical terms, they know that isotonic saline solution neither dehydrates nor hydrates human cells.

When two solutions have unequal poten-

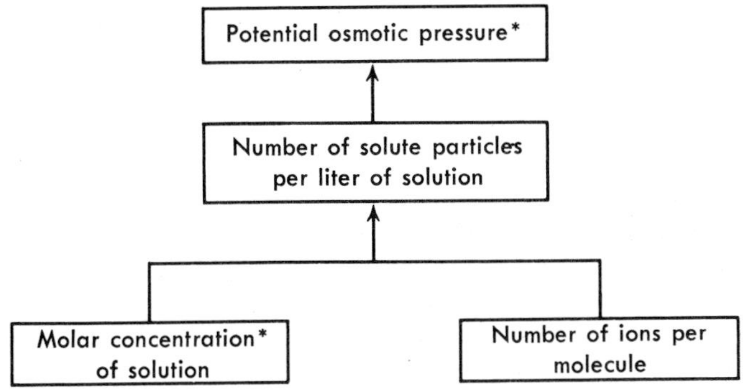

Fig. 12

The number of solute particles (ions and molecules) present in a liter of solution directly determines its potential osmotic pressure. Its molar concentration and the number of ions formed per molecule of electrolyte present determine the number of solute particles and therefore indirectly determine potential osmotic pressure.

**Formula:*

[Potential osmotic pressure of nonelectrolyte (in mm. Hg)] = [Molar concentration of solution] × 19,304†

†Experimentation has shown that a 1.0 molar solution of any nonelectrolyte has a potential osmotic pressure of 19,304 mm. Hg pressure (at body temperature, 37° C.).

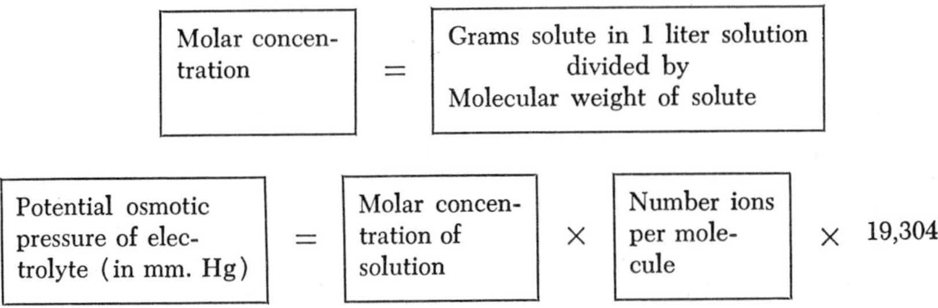

Example: Two solutions commonly used in hospitals are 0.85% NaCl and 5% glucose. What is the potential osmotic pressure of 0.85% NaCl (8.5 grams NaCl per liter) at body temperature?

Molecular weight of NaCl = 58 (NaCl yields 2 ions per molecule in solution)

Using the formula given for computing potential osmotic pressure of an electrolyte:

[Potential osmotic pressure of 0.85% NaCl] $= \frac{8.5}{58} \times 2 \times 19{,}304 =$ *5,657.9 mm. Hg pressure*

Problem: What is potential osmotic pressure of 5% glucose at body temperature? Molecular weight glucose = 180. Glucose does not ionize. It is a nonelectrolyte.

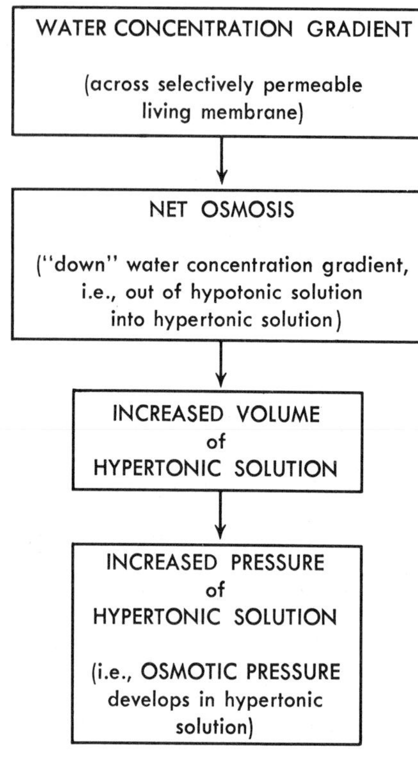

Fig. 13

Effects produced by existence of a water concentration gradient across a selectively permeable membrane.

tial osmotic pressures, their volumes and pressures will change if they are separated by a membrane which is not freely permeable to all the solutes present. Net osmosis will occur into the solution which has the higher potential osmotic pressure. Net osmosis, as we have noted, always occurs down the water concentration gradient. Since the solution which has the lower potential osmotic pressure has the lower concentration of solute particles and therefore the higher concentration of water molecules, net osmosis occurs out of this solution into the solution with the higher potential osmotic pressure. Net osmosis, therefore, increases the volume of the solution with the higher potential osmotic pressure. And the increase in its volume produces an increase in its pressure. This increase in pressure is osmotic pressure—but actual osmotic pressure and not just a potential osmotic pressure.

In summary, when two solutions have unequal potential osmotic pressures and are separated by a selectively permeable or a semipermeable membrane, net osmosis occurs into the solution with the higher potential osmotic pressure, thereby increasing its volume and converting its potential osmotic pressure into an actual osmotic pressure.

When two solutions have unequal potential osmotic pressures, one of them is described as hypertonic and the other as hypotonic.

A *hypertonic solution* may be defined by any of the following statements: (1) a solution which has a higher potential osmotic pressure than another, (2) a solution into which net osmosis occurs when the solution is separated from another by a selectively permeable or semipermeable membrane, (3) a solution whose volume and pressure increase when the solution is separated from another by a selectively permeable or semipermeable membrane, and (4) a solution in which an actual osmotic pressure develops when the solution is separated from another by a selectively permeable or semipermeable membrane.

A *hypotonic solution* has characteristics opposite to those of a hypertonic solution.

Example: The fluid inside human cells is hypertonic to distilled water and, conversely, distilled water is hypotonic to intracellular fluid. If, therefore, distilled water were injected into a vein, net osmosis would occur into blood cells. And eventually, if intracellular volume and pressure increased beyond a certain limit, blood cell membranes would rupture and the cells would die. When this happens to red blood cells, their hemoglobin leaks out and they are said to be hemolyzed. (*Hemolysis* means the destruction of red blood cells with the escape of hemoglobin from them into the surrounding medium.)

Filtration

Filtration is the physical process by which water and solutes pass through a membrane when a hydrostatic pressure gradient exists across that membrane—that is, when the hydrostatic pressure on one side of the membrane is higher than on the other. (*Hydrostatic pressure* is the force or weight of a liquid pushing against some surface.) One principle about filtration has great physiological importance. In capsule form, it is this: filtration always occurs "down" a hydrostatic pressure gradient. Interpreted further, when two fluids have unequal hydrostatic pressures and are separated by a membrane, water and diffusible solutes (those to which the membrane is permeable) filter out of the solution which has the higher hydrostatic pressure into the solution which has the lower hydrostatic pressure.

Note some contrasts between filtration and osmosis. Filtration occurs in only one direction through a membrane—down a hydrostatic pressure gradient. Osmosis goes on in both directions through a membrane. Net osmosis, however, occurs in only one direction—down a water concentration gradient (that is, from a hypotonic into a hypertonic solution). Another difference between filtration and osmosis is that both water and solutes can filter through membranes, whereas only water can osmose through them.

For concrete examples, let us consider the movement of water and solutes through capillary membranes or, in other words, between blood (in capillaries) and interstitial fluid (in microscopic spaces between cells). Blood exerts hydrostatic pressure—commonly called "blood pressure" rather than "blood hydrostatic pressure." For instance, at the arterial ends of capillaries, blood

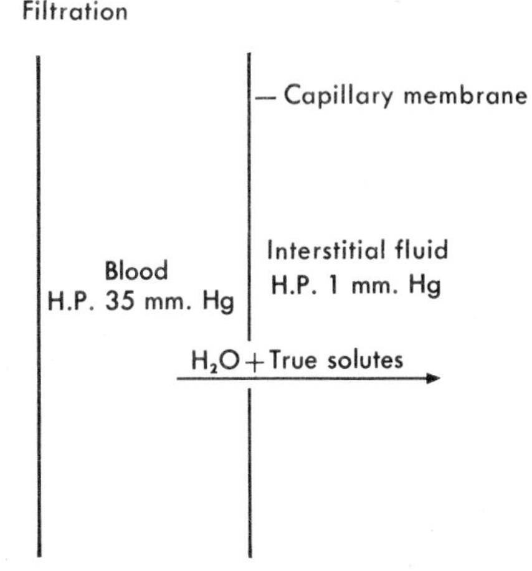

Fig. 14

Filtration occurs down a hydrostatic pressure gradient. Hence, in the capillary illustrated here, water and true solutes filter out of blood into interstitial fluid.

pushes against the inner surface of the capillary membrane with a force of about 35 mm. Hg pressure and interstitial fluid exerts a very slight hydrostatic pressure, perhaps 1 mm. Hg, against the outer surface of the capillary. Therefore, a hydrostatic pressure gradient of about 34 mm. Hg exists across the capillary membrane at the arterial ends of these tiny vessels. The principle that filtration occurs down the hydrostatic pressure gradient operates, causing water and crystalloids (salts, etc.) to filter out of capillary blood into interstitial fluid.

Across capillary membranes or, in other words, between blood and interstitial fluid, two pressure gradients exist—a hydrostatic pressure gradient as described in the preceding paragraph and also an osmotic pressure gradient. Normally, blood has an osmotic pressure of about 25 mm. Hg and interstitial fluid about 2 mm. Hg. Whereas filtration occurs down a hydrostatic pressure gradient (from higher to lower hydrostatic pressure), net osmosis of water occurs up a potential osmotic pressure gradient

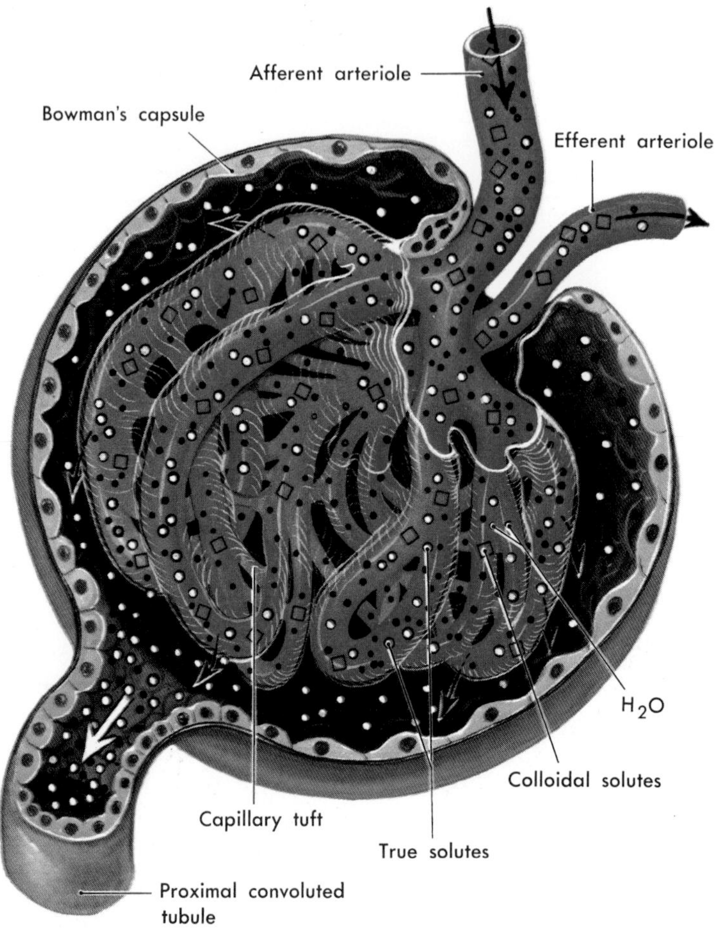

Fig. 15

Diagram to demonstrate filtration. In the kidneys, water (black dots) and true solutes (white dots) filter through the walls of the glomeruli (capillaries) into the Bowman's capsules, but colloidal solutes (squares) remain in the blood because the capillary-capsule membrane is not permeable to them.

(from lower to higher potential osmotic pressure). Perhaps this seems to contradict our earlier statement that net osmosis occurs down a water concentration gradient. But think about it for a moment. Does not a solution which has a higher water concentration (is more dilute) than another necessarily have a lower solute concentration and therefore a lower potential osmotic pressure than the other solution? Hence, when net osmosis occurs from a solution with higher water concentration into one with lower water concentration, it occurs from the solution with lower potential osmotic pressure into the one with higher potential osmotic pressure—in other words, "up" the potential osmotic pressure gradient. Potential osmotic pressure acts as if it were a "water-pulling power"; the higher a solution's potential osmotic pressure, the more water it seems to pull into it or, more accurately, the more water osmoses into it. Hydrostatic pressure, in contrast, acts as a "water-pushing" power; the higher a solution's hydrostatic pressure, the more water it pushes out or, more accurately, causes to filter out of it.

Going back to our example of pressures on capillary membranes (at arterial ends of these tiny vessels), we can summarize the effects of these pressures on water movement between blood and interstitial fluid as follows:

1. The hydrostatic pressure gradient across capillary membranes is a filtration force. It tends to cause filtration (of water and true solutes) out of blood into interstitial fluid.

Blood hydrostatic pressure	35 mm. Hg
Interstitial fluid hydrostatic pressure	1 mm. Hg
Hydrostatic pressure gradient	34 mm. Hg

2. The osmotic pressure gradient across capillary membranes is an osmotic force. It tends to cause net osmosis into blood from interstitial fluid.

Blood osmotic pressure	25 mm. Hg
Interstitial fluid osmotic pressure	2 mm. Hg
Osmotic pressure gradient	23 mm. Hg

3. Because the filtration force (hydrostatic pressure gradient) at the arterial ends of capillaries is stronger than the osmotic force (osmotic pressure gradient), more water filters out of capillary blood into interstitial fluid than osmoses back into it from interstitial fluid.

Filtration force = Hydrostatic pressure gradient =	34 mm. Hg
Osmotic force = Osmotic pressure gradient =	23 mm. Hg
Net filtration force =	11 mm. Hg

Active transport mechanisms

An active transport mechanism is a device that moves molecules or ions through cell membranes in an uphill direction, meaning up their concentration gradients or against their natural tendency. Their natural tendency is to diffuse down their concentration gradient. Net movement of any substance by diffusion is from its high to low concentration (physical law of diffusion). As we know, it is work to make anything move in the opposite direction from that which it naturally tends to go (to make water move uphill, for instance), and work requires energy expenditure. To do the work of active transport, cellular chemical reactions supply the energy. Active transport is one of the most important kinds of cellular work. Some investigators* estimate that about one-fifth of the body's total energy production is expended on active transport mechanisms.

A physical device which moves something against its natural tendency is called a pump. So it seems logical that we should think of active transport mechanisms as physiological or "biological pumps." Active transport mechanisms pump various substances through cell membranes, but probably the most important of these is sodium ions. Sodium ions diffuse down their concentration gradient from interstitial fluid into cells. But about as fast as they diffuse inward through a cell membrane, an active transport mechanism (commonly called the *sodium pump*) pumps them back out again. With energy supplied by cellular chemical reactions, the sodium pump moves sodium ions uphill against the sodium concentration gradient.† Normally, therefore, sodium does not equilibrate across living cell membranes. The sodium pump maintains a steep sodium concentration gradient across cell membranes. Of all the many

---

*Ruch, Theodore C., and Patton, Harry D.: Physiology and biophysics, ed. 19, Philadelphia, 1965, W. B. Saunders Co.

†One way of designating sodium concentration is as milligrams per liter. Expressed this way, interstitial fluid has a sodium concentration of about 3,200 mg. per liter, whereas intracellular fluid has a sodium concentration of only about 345 mg. per liter. Expressed in terms of milliequivalents per liter, interstitial fluid has a sodium concentration of about 139 mEq. per liter and intracellular fluid, about 15 mEq.

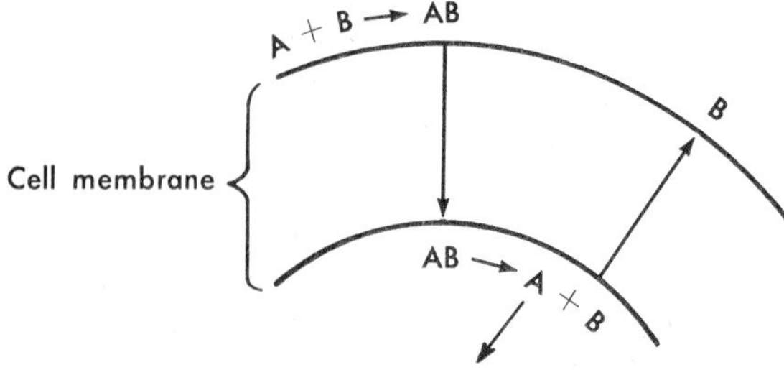

Fig. 16

Scheme to illustrate one hypothesis about active transport mechanisms. **A**, Substance to be transported into the cell. **B**, Carrier compound, which unites with **A** at the outer surface of the cell membrane. **AB** diffuses through the membrane to its inner surface. **AB** dissociates, leaving **A** inside the cell. **B** diffuses back to the outer surface of the membrane, ready to transport another molecule of **A** into the cell.

processes that keep us alive, few are more important than active transport mechanisms. Sodium transport alone plays an essential part in several vital functions—in nerve impulse conduction, in the maintenance of water balance, and in the maintenance of acid-base balance, for example.

Sodium is not the only substance actively transported across cell membranes. Considerable evidence supports the hypothesis of a potassium transport mechanism that pumps potassium into cells and is coupled with sodium transport. Other ions may also be actively transported. And glucose and amino acids, it is generally accepted, are actively transported into cells, although they also probably diffuse through them.

Although very little is known about the chemistry of active transport, several theories have been proposed. Most of them assume the existence of carrier compounds, although none as yet has been identified. In simplest forms, the theories suggest the following steps as the essential parts of an active transport mechanism:

1. On one surface of a cell membrane, a molecule of the substance to be transported (A) combines with a molecule of carrier compound (B) to form a new compound (AB).

$$A + B \longrightarrow AB$$

2. Molecule AB passes through the cell membrane into (or out of) the cell.

3. At the other surface of the cell membrane, AB dissociates, releasing the transported substance.

$$AB \longrightarrow A + B$$

4. Carrier compound molecule B moves back to the surface from which it came, ready to shuttle another molecule of A through the membrane.

Phagocytosis and pinocytosis

Phagocytosis and pinocytosis are also active mechanisms for moving substances through cell membranes but only in one direction—inward. More than sixty years ago Elie Metchnikoff of the Pasteur Institute saw white blood cells engulf bacteria. It reminded him of eating. Therefore, from the Greek words for eating, cell, and action, he coined the word phagocytosis. Some thirty years later, in 1931, W. H. Lewis of Johns Hopkins University saw something similar in time-lapse photographs of some tissue culture cells. These cells, however, were engulfing tiny droplets of fluid instead of solid particles. They seemed to be drinking rather than eating, so he named the process pinocytosis (from the Greek word for drinking).

Both phagocytosis and pinocytosis consist of the same essential steps. A segment of cell membrane forms a small pocket around a bit of solid or liquid material outside the cell, pinches off from the rest of the membrane, and migrates inward as a closed vacuole or vesicle.

CELL METABOLISM

The process of cell metabolism is as intricate as it is vital. It consists of two main processes called catabolism and anabolism.

Each of these, in turn, consists of numerous chemical reactions. *Catabolism* is the process that supplies cells with energy in a form they can use for doing their work. *Anabolism* is the process by which cells synthesize complex compounds of many different kinds—hormones, the proteins called enzymes, structural proteins, and numerous other compounds. Anabolism is one of the several kinds of work which all cells perform. Catabolism supplies the energy that does the work of anabolism and all other kinds of cellular work as well. For a brief account of the chemical and energy changes that make up the process of catabolism, read the following paragraphs. Anabolism is discussed in Chapter XI.

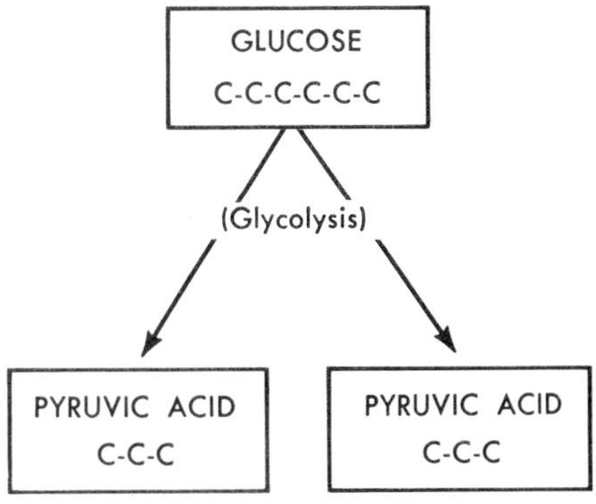

Fig. 17

Glycolysis. Glucose, a molecule containig 6 carbon atoms, is split by a series of chemical reactions into 2 molecules of pyruvic acid, each of which contains only 3 carbon atoms. Fig. 18 shows the series of intermediate reactions in brief form.

Catabolism

Catabolism, one of the two major processes of metabolism, consists of several processes, some of which are different for different kinds of foods. At this time we shall discuss only the catabolism of the carbohydrate glucose and shall try to present only basic facts about this complex process since its detailed study belongs to the science of biochemistry.

Glucose catabolism consists of two successive processes: glycolysis and the citric acid cycle (also called tricarboxylic acid cycle, Krebs cycle, and cellular respiration).

Glycolysis

Glycolysis is the process which changes glucose to pyruvic acid and thereby releases some of the energy stored in glucose molecules. Glycolysis takes place in the cytoplasm of cells. It consists of a series of chemical changes catalyzed by enzymes and accompanied by energy changes. Figs. 17 and 18 show the chemical changes of glycolysis in an abbreviated form. Stated very briefly, the chemical change produced by glycolysis is the breaking apart of 1 molecule of glucose to form 2 molecules of pyruvic acid.

The specific chemical changes, however, are not the most important facts to remember about glycolysis nor about the citric acid cycle. The most important fact is that the chemical changes of catabolism produce energy changes and that these energy changes supply all the energy which does all the work which keeps our cells and bodies alive. In essence, the energy changes produced by the chemical changes of catabolism are these:

1. Energy stored in the chemical bonds of food molecules is released.
2. More than half of the released energy is immediately recaptured, that is, put back into storage in chemical bonds (but in a different kind of bond in a different kind of molecule).
3. Somewhat less than half of the energy released from food molecules is transformed into heat energy. (Incidentally, this is the body's only way of producing heat—by catabolizing food molecules to transform part of their stored energy into heat energy.) In later paragraphs (pp. 34 to 38) more meaning will be given to the idea of energy changes during catabolism.

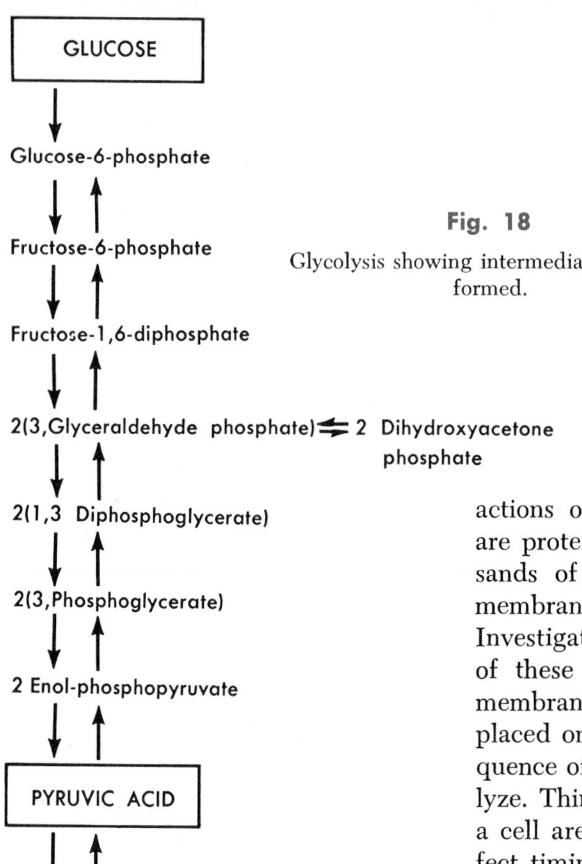

Fig. 18

Glycolysis showing intermediate products formed.

Citric acid cycle

The citric acid cycle (or *Krebs cycle* as it is called in honor of the man who formulated it) is the second and final process in the catabolism of glucose. It consists of a cyclical series of chemical reactions catalyzed by enzymes and accompanied by energy changes. Figs. 19 and 20 show the chemical changes of the citric acid cycle in abbreviated forms. Put in fewest words, the chemical change produced by the citric acid cycle is that pyruvic acid is broken down and oxidized to form carbon dioxide and water. Six molecules of oxygen are used up in the process. In fact, this is the way cells utilize oxygen (to carry on the citric acid cycle) and the reason they must have a continuous supply of oxygen to survive.

Enzymes which catalyze the chemical reactions of the citric acid cycle (Fig. 20) are protein molecules located in the thousands of particles attached to the outer membrane of each mitochondrion (p. 16). Investigators believe that even the placing of these enzyme molecules in the outer membrane particles is precise, that they are placed one after the other in the exact sequence of the chemical reactions they catalyze. Think of that! Even the molecules in a cell are organized so as to produce perfect timing of their functioning—a persuasive illustration, is it not, of the principle, "Organization is a dominant characteristic of life." Now let us examine some of the specific chemical changes of the citric acid cycle to see how they produce energy changes.

Reaction (1) in Fig. 20: This chemical reaction removes 1 carbon dioxide molecule and 2 hydrogen atoms from each pyruvic acid molecule, or a total of 2 carbon dioxide molecules and 4 hydrogen atoms for each glucose molecule catabolized. The 4 hydrogen atoms immediately ionize to form 4 hydrogen ions and 4 electrons.

Molecules of the coenzyme DPN (diphosphopyridine nucleotide) quickly accept these electrons,* shuttle them across the microscopic fluid-filled space between the outer and inner membranes of the mitochondrial wall, and pass them on to enzymes located in particles attached to the inner membrane. There are thousands of

*Green, David E.: The mitochondrion, Sci. Amer. **210**:67 (Jan.), 1964.

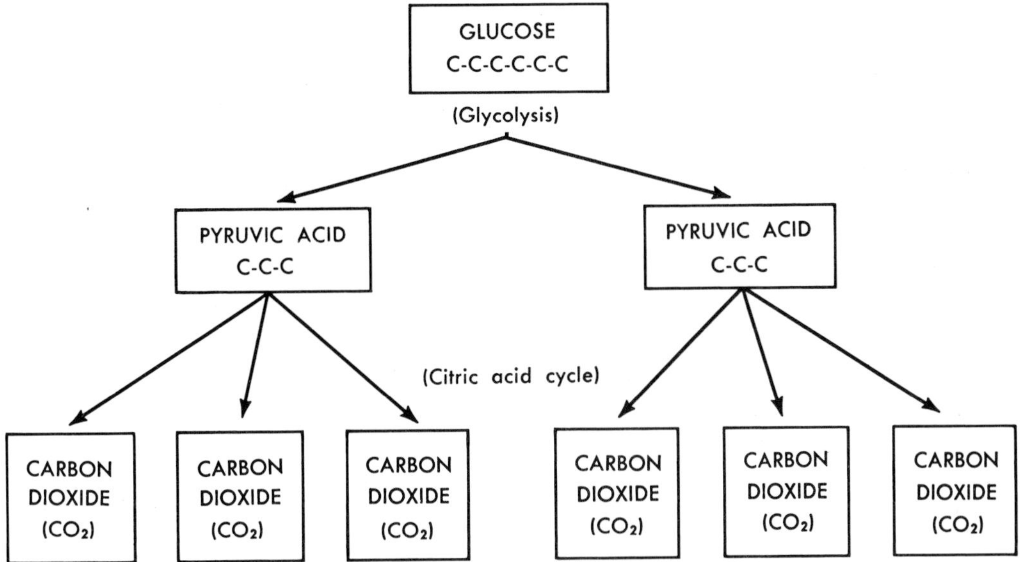

Fig. 19

Scheme to show that catabolism breaks larger molecules down into smaller one. *Glycolysis* splits 1 molecule of glucose (6 carbon atoms) into 2 molecules of pyruvic acid (3 carbon atoms each). The *citric acid cycle* oxidizes 2 molecules of pyruvic acid to 6 molecules of carbon dioxide (1 carbon atom each) and 6 molecules of water.

these tiny particles. Each one consists of a series or chain of several enzymes.

Because electrons are transferred from one enzyme to another in the chain, like so many buckets of water passed along a bucket brigade, these enzymes are referred to as "electron-transfer enzymes," and the inner membrane particles which contain them are known as "*electron-transport particles.*" As the electrons pass down the chain of electron-transfer enzymes, they release energy. Somewhat more than half of this released energy is used to synthesize ATP (adenosine triphosphate) molecules. The rest of it is transformed to heat energy.

Finally, at the end of the electron-transfer chain, the electrons recombine with hydrogen ions to form hydrogen atoms which unite with oxygen to form water.

Briefly then, reaction (1) produces acetyl-CoA + CO_2 + H_2O + ATP + Heat. Acetyl-CoA immediately combines with oxaloacetic acid to form citric acid—reaction (2) in Fig. 20. Citric acid then undergoes a series of changes that eventually convert it to oxaloacetic acid, carbon dioxide, and water. Through the addition of oxygen during several reactions of the citric acid cycle, each pyruvic acid molecule entering the cycle is converted to 3 CO_2 molecules (reactions 1, 6, and 7) and 3 H_2O molecules (reactions 1, 8, and 10). Also, for each pyruvic acid molecule oxidized, 18 ATP molecules are synthesized, using energy released by electron transfer during reactions 1, 8, and 10.

Summarizing the changes of catabolism in equation form:

1. *Glycolysis:*

$$\text{Glucose} \longrightarrow 2 \text{ pyruvic acid} + 2 \text{ ATP} + \text{Heat}$$

2. *Citric acid cycle:*

$$2 \text{ pyruvic acid} + 6O_2 \longrightarrow 6CO_2 + 6H_2O + 36 \text{ ATP} + \text{Heat}$$

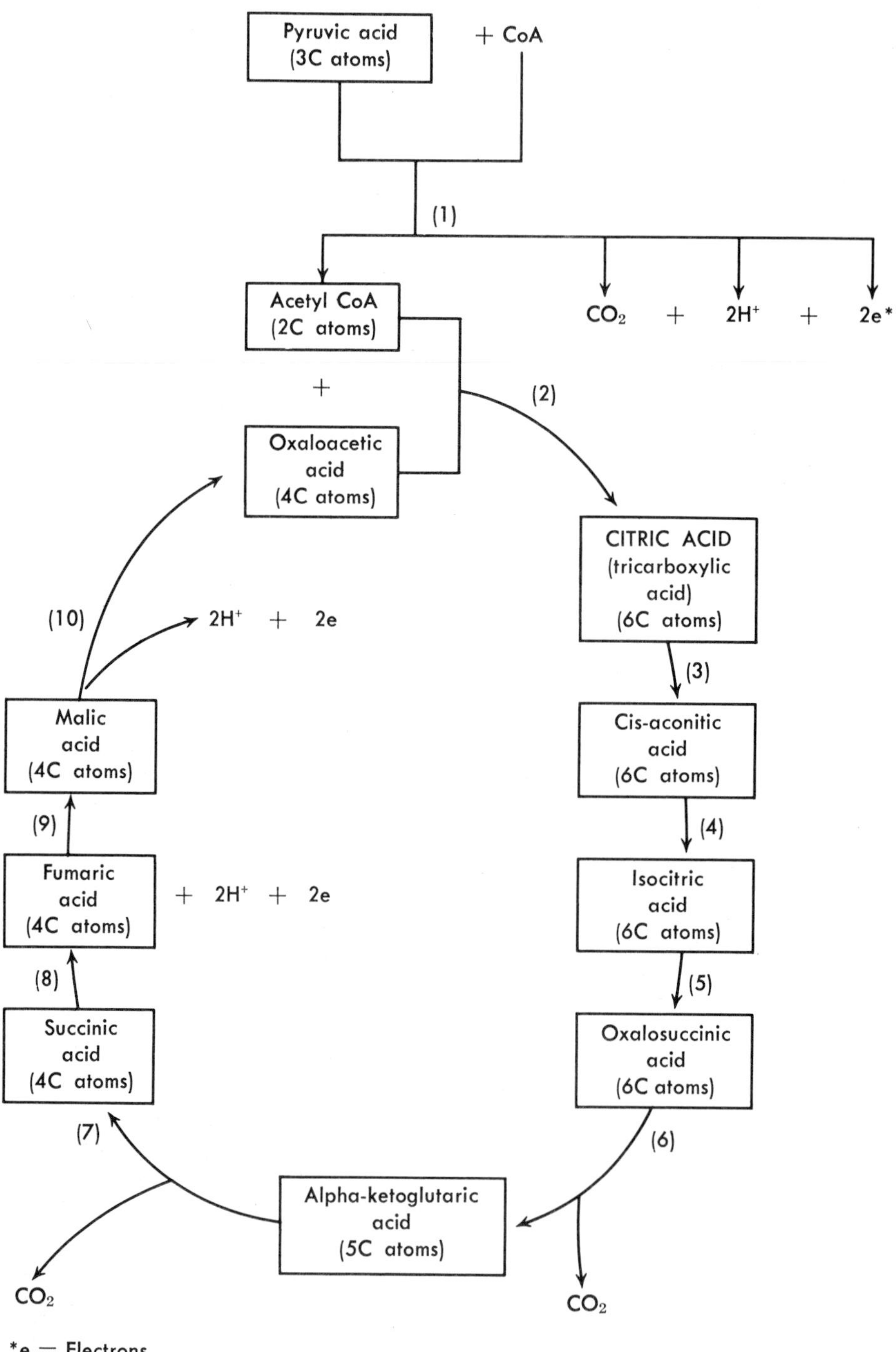

Fig. 20

See text for explanation.

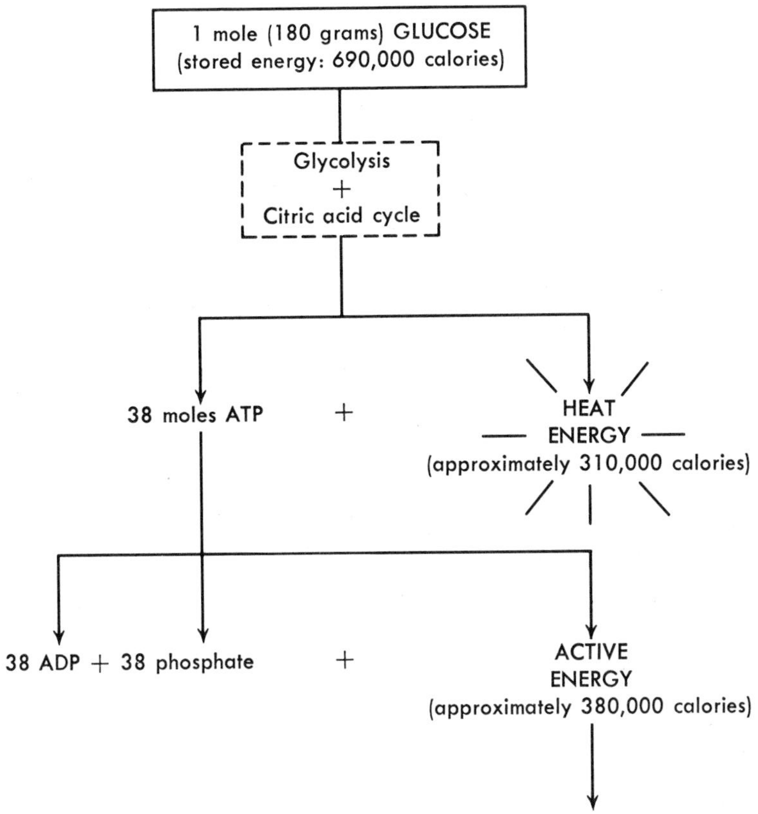

Fig. 21

Catabolism releases energy stored in chemical bonds of glucose molecules. 180 grams or 1 mole of glucose contains 690,000 small calories of stored energy. Catabolism releases about 310,000 calories of this energy as heat and puts about 380,000 calories back in storage in high-energy bonds of 38 moles of ATP. Thus the efficiency of glucose catabolism as a mechanism for supplying cells with usable energy is about 55% (380,000/690,000).

We can even summarize further and indicate the entire complex process of glucose catabolism with one short equation:

$$\underset{\text{(glucose)}}{C_6H_{12}O_6} + 6O_2 \longrightarrow 6CO_2 + 6H_2O + 38\ ATP + Heat$$

Also, see Fig. 21.

The synthesis of ATP is a phosphorylation reaction carried on during the citric acid cycle in the thousands of tiny particles attached to the inner membrane of each mitochondrion (the same structures in which electron-transfer occurs).

$$\underset{\text{(adenosine diphosphate)}}{ADP} + Phosphate + ENERGY \rightarrow \underset{\text{(adenosine triphosphate)}}{ATP}$$

The energy shown in the preceding equation (in other words, the energy used to do the work of synthesizing ATP molecules) is released from the stable chemical bonds in glucose molecules by the passage of electrons down the chains of electron-transfer enzymes. Immediately the process of ATP synthesis puts some of the released energy back in storage in chemical bonds, but in unstable (labile) high-energy bonds of ATP molecules.

As its name suggests, ATP or adenosine triphosphate, contains three phosphate

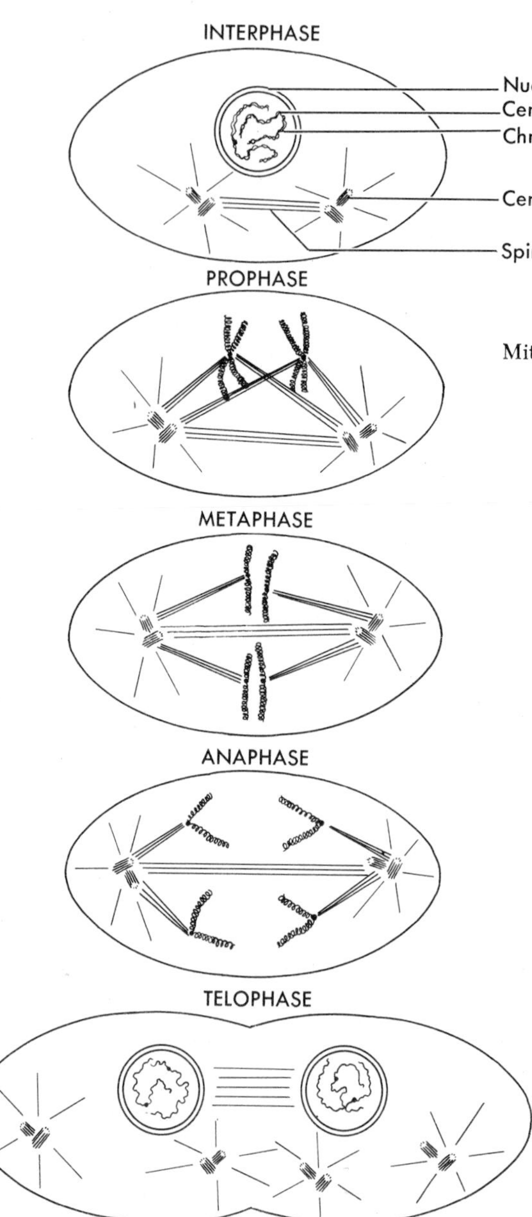

Fig. 22

Mitosis (see Table 1 for explanation).

groups. Only the last two of these are attached by labile, high-energy bonds. A high-energy bond is one which can break apart with explosive rapidity to release active energy which performs some kind of work.

ATP ⟶ ENERGY + ADP + Phosphate

All cellular work, it is now believed, is done by energy set free from high-energy phosphate bonds, mainly those in ATP molecules. Hence, ATP is one of the most important biological compounds known. It supplies energy directly to all kinds of energy-consuming mechanisms in all kinds of living organisms from one-celled plants to billion-celled animals, including man.

Since the citric acid cycle releases most of the energy from food molecules, and since this cycle of chemical reactions takes place inside mitochondria, these tiny structures are aptly described as the power plants of cells.

Albert Lehninger, the biochemist who discovered that citric acid cycle and electron-transfer enzymes are located in mitochondria, writes: "If the classical engineering science of energy transformation is humbled by what is now known about the power plants of the cell, so are the newer and more glamorous branches of engineering. The technology of electronics has achieved amazing success in packaging and miniaturizing the components of a computer. But these advances still fall far short of accomplishing the unbelievable miniaturization of complex energy-transducing components that has been perfected by organic evolution in each living cell."*

CELL REPRODUCTION

Cells reproduce by a process called *cell division.* In other words, cells divide in

*From Lehninger, A.: How cells transform energy, Sci. Amer. **205**:62 (Sept.), 1961.

Table 1. Mitosis—nuclear division (see also Fig. 22)

Prophase	*Metaphase*	*Anaphase*	*Telophase*	*Interphase*
1. Chromosomes shorten and thicken (due to coiling of DNA molecules which compose them); each chromosome consists of two strands (called *chromatids*) attached only at one point (called *centromere*) 2. Nuclear membrane disappears 3. Centrioles move to opposite poles of cell; spindle fibers appear and, under control of centrioles, begin to orient between opposing poles	1. Chromosomes align across equator of spindle fibers; each pair of chromatids attached to spindle fiber at its centromere	1. Two chromatids which compose each chromosome become detached from each other as centromere separates into two centromeres 2. Separated centromeres start moving to opposite poles, each pulling its chromatid along with it; newly separated chromatids now are new chromosomes, and there are twice as many of them as there were before mitosis started	1. New chromosomes start elongating (DNA molecules start uncoiling) 2. Two new nuclear membranes appear enclosing each new set of chromosomes 3. Spindle fibers disappear 4. *Cytokinesis*, or dividing of cytoplasm, usually occurs during telophase; starts as pinching in along equator of old cell and ends with division of old cell into two new cells	1. Period between end of telophase of one cell division and beginning of prophase of next division 2. Two newly formed cells become larger, i.e., grow 3. Chromosomes elongate and become too thin to be visible as such but chromatin granules become visible 4. Each chromosome duplicates, forming two chromatids attached at centromere (DNA duplication)

order to multiply. One cell divides to form two cells. The process of cell division consists of two consecutive processes: mitosis (division of the nucleus) and cytokinesis (division of the cytoplasm).

Mitosis

Mitosis, or nuclear division, consists of a succession of events plainly visible in suitably stained cells viewed with the light microscope. The events of mitosis occur in five phases: prophase, metaphase, anaphase, telophase, and interphase (formerly called resting stage). The events characteristic of each of these phases are summarized in Table 1 (also see Fig. 22).

Chromosome duplication, a process which usually occurs during the interphase, is actually *DNA duplication.* Each DNA molecule within the cell makes a copy of itself—and almost always a perfect copy. Unquestionably, the process of DNA duplication (discussed on p. 40) is one of the most unique and important of all biological phenomena.

Justification for such an extravagant claim lies in the fact that chromosomes consist of genes and genes determine all the potentialities of all new cells. Up until a very few years ago, a gene was defined vaguely as a "factor which determined a hereditary characteristic." Today it is possible to define the term much more specifically. For instance, here is one widely accepted definition. A *gene* is a segment of a DNA molecule which controls the production of one enzyme—the "one gene–one enzyme" hypothesis. Each enzyme, in turn, catalyzes one chemical reaction. Hence, the thousands of genes in a cell together determine its hereditary characteristics by a kind of remote control method as indicated by Fig. 23. The detailed story of how genes control enzyme production, although still unfinished, is too long to be told here.*

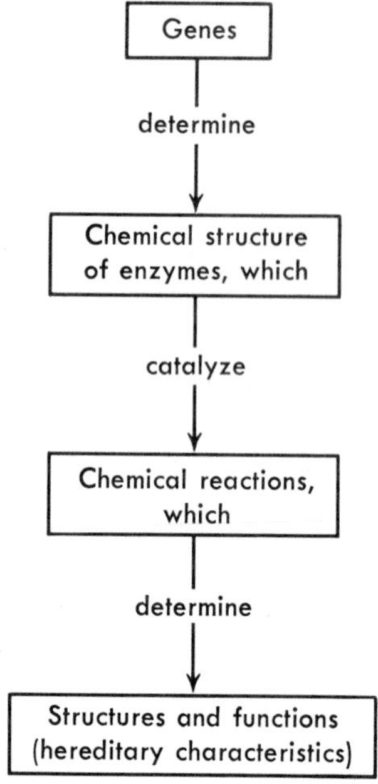

Fig. 23

Brief scheme to show how genes determine hereditary characteristics.

Some arithmetic about genes and DNA may interest you. About 20,000 or more genes, it is estimated, make up the DNA of just one human chromosome! And one gene is believed to consist of a section of the DNA molecule perhaps 500 to 1,000 bases long. (Pairs of nitrogenous bases, you will recall, form the "steps" of the DNA "ladder"—adenine joined to thymine or cytosine joined to guanine.) With 20,000 genes in the DNA of one chromosome and 500 base pairs in one gene, there would be 10,000,000 base pairs in one DNA molecule—as hard to imagine as a microscopic ladder 10,000,000 steps long!

Chromosome or *DNA duplication* occurs during the interphase of mitosis. The tightly coiled DNA molecule uncoils except in small segments. Since the remaining tight little coils are denser than the thin elongated sections, they absorb more stain and show up as *chromatin granules*. The thin sections, in contrast, absorb so little stain that they are invisible. As the DNA molecule uncoils, it comes apart in the midline at the points where the base pairs were joined. Then along each of the two long, separated strands a complimentary strand forms. In other words, each half DNA molecule duplicates itself to create a whole new DNA molecule. The next paragraph tells how.

Intracellular fluid contains many molecules of deoxyribose, phosphate, and nitrogenous bases. By the mechanism of "base-pairing," these substances become attached at their right places along each DNA strand. Interpreted, this means that new thymine (that is, from the intracellular fluid) attaches to "old" adenine in the original DNA strand. And conversely, new adenine attaches to old thymine. Also, new guanine joins old cytosine and, vice versa, new cytosine joins old guanine. Soon each of the two original DNA strands has a complete new complimentary strand attached

*See suggested supplementary readings for Chapter II, references 7, 9, 15, and 17, p. 548.

to it. So the original DNA molecule will have become two molecules. Once again the miracle of DNA duplication will have occurred and each original chromosome will have become two chromosomes. However, they are now called *chromatids,* not chromosomes, and the two chromatids formed from one original chromosome are joined together at one point by a structure called the *centromere.* Two new sets of genes now stand ready to control the destiny of the two new cells which will be formed by the next cell division.

By way of summary, a complete duplicate set of chromosomes (now called chromatids) is formed during the interphase of mitosis. During the anaphase, one set of chromatids moves to one pole of the cell and the other set moves to the opposite pole (and now chromatids become chromosomes). Then, finally, one set of chromosomes enters one new cell and the other set enters the other new cell when the parent cell divides. Hence, each of the two new cells contains a complete set of genes identical to those in the parent cell and hence, too, they have the potentialities to become like their parent cell. In short, heredity is achieved by the mechanism of mitosis.

Outline summary—Cells

Protoplasm

1. Definition—living matter; all cells composed of protoplasm
2. Composition
   a. main elements—carbon, hydrogen, oxygen, and nitrogen
   b. main compounds—water, inorganic salts, and compounds unique to living matter, i.e., proteins (including enzymes), carbohydrates, lipids, and nucleic acids
3. Functional properties—irritability, conductivity, contractility, metabolism, and reproduction

Cell structures

See p. 12

CELL MEMBRANE

1. Structure
   a. about 3/10 millionths inch thick according to present estimates
   b. composed of protein and lipid molecules; according to one theory, double layer of lipid molecules sandwiched between an inner and outer layer of protein molecules
   c. has tiny opening or pores; few in number; spaced far apart
2. Function
   a. maintains cell's integrity, its organization
   b. determines what substances can enter and leave cell

CYTOPLASM

Endoplasmic reticulum

1. Structure—complicated network of tubules or canals in cytoplasm; open at surface of cell; many ribosomes attached to membranes of rough endoplasmic reticulum but not to smooth
2. Functions—ribosomes attached to rough endoplasmic reticulum synthesize proteins; canals of reticulum serve as passageways through which proteins move on way to Golgi apparatus

Golgi apparatus

1. Structure—membranous vesicles near nucleus
2. Function—believed to condense substances before they leave cell as secretions

Mitochondria

1. Structure—microscopic sacs, walls composed of inner and outer membranes separated by fluid; thousands of particles made up of enzyme molecules attach to both membranes
2. Function—"power plants" of cells; mitochondrial enzymes catalyze citric acid cycle, series of reactions that provide about 95% of cell's energy supply

Lysosomes

1. Structure—microscopic membranous sacs
2. Function—"digestive bags"; contain enzymes which digest particles or large molecules which enter cells

Ribosomes

1. Structure—microscopic spheres, large numbers of which attached to endoplasmic reticulum
2. Function—"protein factories"; synthesize many different kinds of proteins, notably enzymes

Centrosphere or centrosome

1. Structure
   a. Centrosphere is spherical body near center of cell, i.e., near nucleus
   b. Centrioles, located in centrosphere, are tiny cylinders, walls of which are composed of fine tubules, nine groups of two or three tubules each
2. Function—centrioles control polarization of spindle fibers and play some part in their formation

NUCLEUS

Spherical body in center of cell; nuclear membrane consists of two layers; has pores in it

Chromosomes

1. Deep-staining bodies in nucleus
2. Composed mainly of DNA but also some protein

Deoxyribonucleic acid (DNA)

1. Structure
   a. very large helical-shaped molecule composed of sugar (deoxyribose), acid (phosphoric), and four nitrogenous bases (adenine, thymine, cytosine, and guanine)
   b. base pairs (adenine-thymine, or vice versa, cytosine-guanine, or vice versa) form "steps" of DNA molecule; attached to deoxyribose at sides; base pairs always same in all DNA molecules but sequence of base pairs differs
2. Function—sequence of base pairs in DNA of different chromosomes is what determines all hereditary traits

Nucleoli

1. Structure—small spherical bodies composed mainly of RNA and also some protein
2. Function—not yet established

Cell physiology

MOVEMENT OF SUBSTANCES THROUGH CELL MEMBRANES

1. By physical (or passive) processes
   a. energy which moves substances comes from random, never-ceasing movements of atoms, ions, and molecules, not from chemical reactions in cell;
   b. diffusion, osmosis, and filtration three types of physical processes which move substances through living or nonliving membrane
2. By physiological (or active) processes
   a. energy which moves substances comes from chemical reactions in the cell
   b. active transport mechanisms, phagocytosis, and pinocytosis types of physiological mechanisms that move substances through living cell membranes

Diffusion

1. Movement of solute and solvent particles in all directions through solution or in both directions through membrane
   a. net diffusion of solute particles—down solute concentration gradient, i.e., from more to less concentrated solution
   b. net diffusion of water—down water concentration gradient, i.e., from less to more concentrated solution
2. Diffusion tends to produce equilibration of solutions on opposite sides of a membrane but many exceptions to this rule when membrane living

Osmosis

1. In living systems, movement of water in both directions through membrane that maintains at least one solute concentration gradient across it
2. Net osmosis—more water osmoses in one direction through membrane than in opposite; net osmosis occurs down water concentration gradient (which is up solute concentration gradient and up potential osmotic pressure gradient); net osmosis tends to equilibrate two solutions separated by selectively permeable membrane
3. Osmotic pressure—pressure that develops in solution as result of net osmosis into it
4. Isotonic solution—one that has same potential osmotic pressure as solution it is isotonic to; no net osmosis between isotonic solutions
5. Hypertonic solution—has greater potential osmotic pressure and higher solute concentration but lower water concentration than solution to which it is hypertonic; net osmosis into hypertonic solution from hypotonic solution
6. Hypotonic solution—has lower potential osmotic pressure and lower solute concen-

tration but higher water concentration than solution to which it is hypotonic; net osmosis out of hypotonic solution into hypertonic solution

Filtration

Movement of water and solutes through a membrane from higher hydrostatic pressure area to lower hydrostatic pressure area

Active transport mechanisms

Devices which move ions or molecules through cell membranes against their concentration gradient, i.e., direction opposite from net diffusion or net osmosis; energy supplied by cellular chemical reactions

Phagocytosis and pinocytosis

1. Phagocytosis—physiological process which moves solid particles into cell; segment of cell membrane forms pocket around particle outside cell, then pinches off from rest of membrane and migrates inward
2. Pinocytosis—physiological process which moves fluid into cell; process similar to phagocytosis

CELL METABOLISM

Catabolism

1. One of two major processes of metabolism
2. Consists of complex series of chemical reactions which take place inside cells and which yield energy, carbon dioxide, and water; about half of energy released from food molecules by catabolism put back in storage in unstable high-energy bonds of ATP molecules and rest transformed to heat; energy in high-energy bonds of ATP can be released as rapidly as needed for doing cellular work
3. Purpose—to continually provide cells with utilizable energy, i.e., energy supplied instantaneously to energy-consuming mechanisms which do cellular work
4. Glycolysis—series of chemical reactions that convert 1 glucose molecule to 2 pyruvic acid molecules and yield small amount of high-energy ATP and of heat
5. Citric acid cycle—series of chemical reactions that oxidize 2 pyruvic acid molecules to 6 carbon dioxide molecules and 6 water molecules and yield about 95% of ATP and heat formed during catabolism
6. Anabolism—synthesis of various compounds from simpler compounds; an important kind of cellular work that uses some of energy made available by catabolism

CELL REPRODUCTION

1. Process of cell division which consists of mitosis (division of nucleus) and cytokinesis (division of cytoplasm)
2. See Table 1 for summary of mitosis

Review questions

1. What are the four main elements in protoplasm?
2. What four kinds of compounds occur naturally only in matter that is or was living?
3. Name several kinds of organelles found in cytoplasm.
4. Define the terms micron and millimicron. About how many millimicrons equal 1 inch?
5. Describe the structure and function of mitochondria.
6. What are ribosomes and what is their presumed function?
7. Describe the structure and postulated function of the endoplasmic reticulum.
8. Describe the structure and postulated function of the Golgi apparatus.
9. Describe the structure and postulated function of the centrioles.
10. Describe DNA structure (Watson-Crick hypothesis). What does the full name of DNA tell us about this substance?
11. Describe a current concept of cell membrane structure.
12. Define the term angstrom. About how many angstroms thick is a cell membrane thought to be? How thick would this be in terms of inches?
13. Define diffusion, osmosis, and filtration.
14. What do the terms net diffusion and net osmosis mean?
15. Explain the terms osmotic pressure and potential osmotic pressure.
16. What factor directly determines the potential osmotic pressure of a solution?
17. Explain the terms isotonic, hypotonic, and hypertonic.
18. Distinguish between physiological and physical processes for moving substances through cell membranes?
19. What are some of the substances believed to be actively transported through membranes?
20. Explain the terms phagocytosis and pinocytosis.
21. Define briefly the following terms:

anabolism	citric acid cycle
ATP	glycolysis
catabolism	metabolism

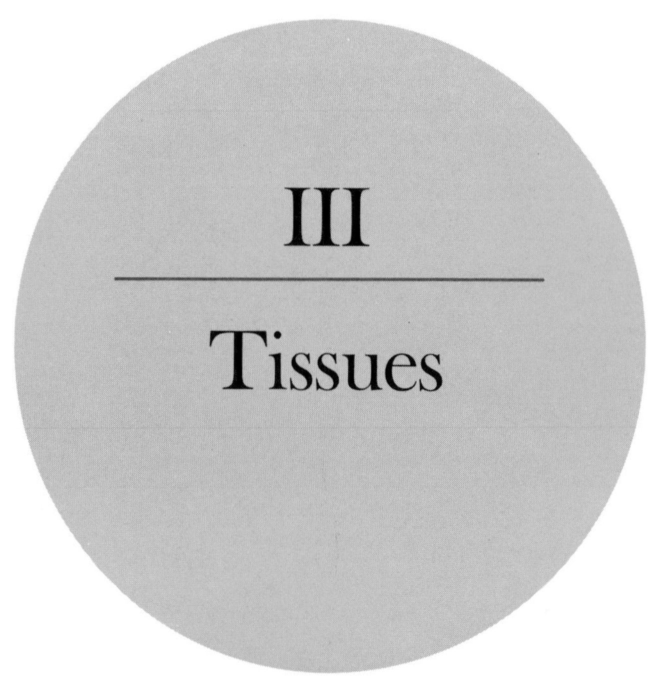

III

Tissues

Epithelial tissue
Simple squamous epithelium
Simple columnar epithelium
Stratified squamous epithelium

Muscle tissue
Connective tissue
Loose, ordinary connective tissue (areolar)
Adipose tissue
Dense fibrous tissue
Bone and cartilage
Hemopoietic tissue
Reticuloendothelial cells

Nerve tissue

Tissues are organizations of cells. Nonliving intercellular substances fill in any spaces between cells. Using appearance and functions as criteria for classification, there are four basic types of tissues—epithelial, muscle, connective, and nerve—and many subtypes. Tissues differ in structure, and because structure determines function, they also differ in function. Not only do cell size, shape, and arrangement vary in different kinds of tissues, but so too does the amount and kind of intercellular substance present. Some tissues contain almost no intercellular material. Others consist predominantly of it. Some intercellular substance has the form of fibers, some is unformed jelly, and some is fluid, the interstitial fluid, that bathes most living human cells.

EPITHELIAL TISSUE

Epithelial tissue performs the functions of protection, secretion, absorption, diffusion, and filtration. Only a fairly sturdy tissue can offer protection so that where this function is needed, epithelial tissue is stratified, that is, it consists of several layers of cells. In contrast, where substances need to move through a tissue, where they need to be absorbed, to filter, or to diffuse, here there is simple epithelial tissue which consists of a single layer of cells. All types of epithelial tissue are composed largely or entirely of cells. In other words, they contain little or no intercellular substance. They also contain no blood vessels. These are located in the connective tissue which epithelial tissue always overlies and adheres to firmly. Another common characteristic of all types of epithelial cells is that they undergo mitosis—a fact of practical importance since it means that old or destroyed epithelial cells can be replaced by new ones. There are several types of epithelial tissue. Three are described in the following paragraphs.

Simple squamous epithelium

Simple squamous epithelium consists of only one layer of flat, scalelike cells. Consequently, substances can readily diffuse or

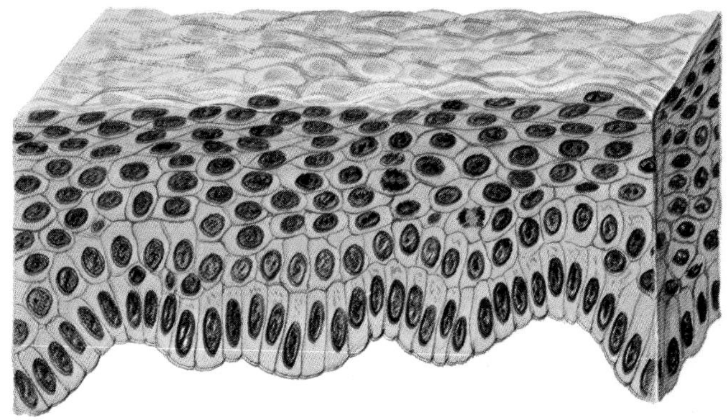

Fig. 24

Stratified squamous epithelium such as lines the mouth.

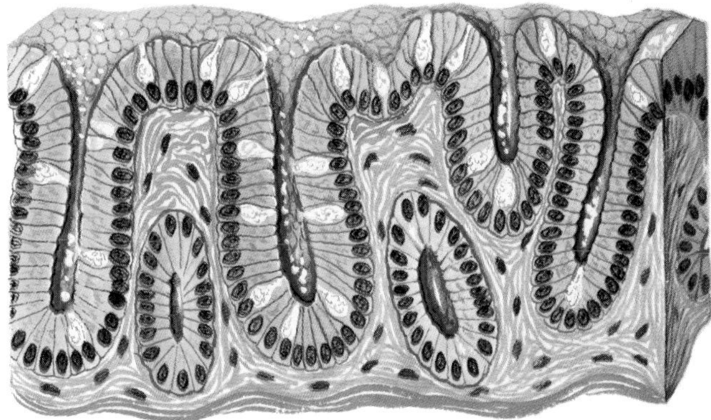

Fig. 25

Simple columnar epithelium with goblet cells such as lines intestines.

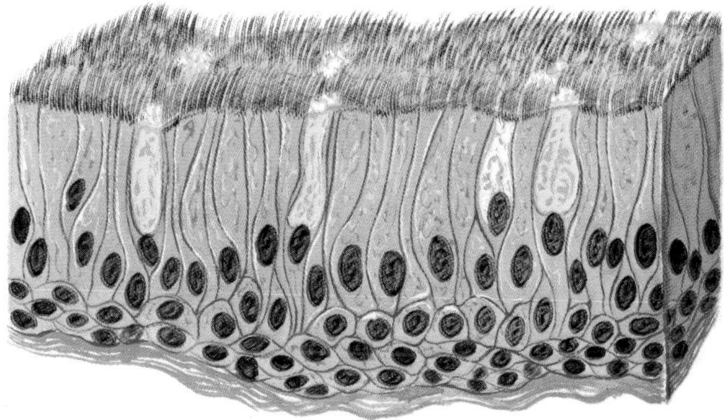

Fig. 26

Pseudostratified ciliated columnar epithelium with goblet cells. Stratified tissue consists of two or more layers of cells. Pseudostratified tissue appears, in certain sections, to meet this requirement but actually does not.

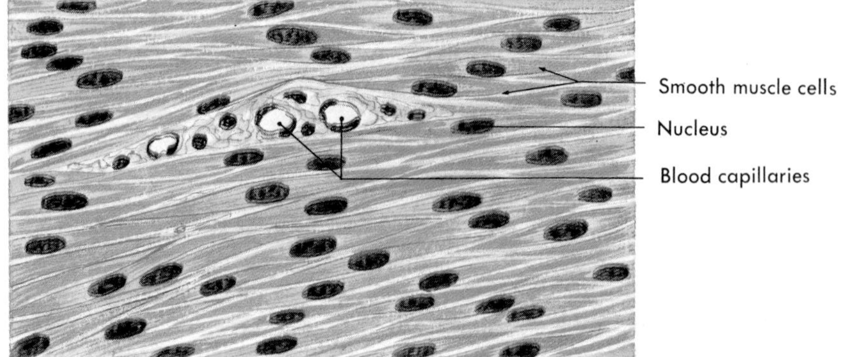

Fig. 27

Smooth or visceral muscle tissue.

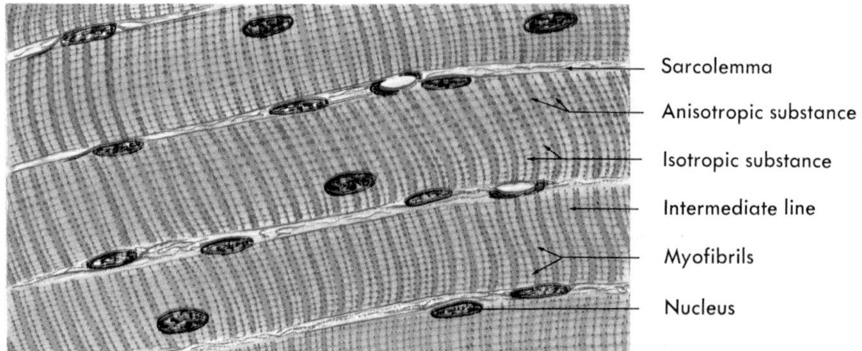

Fig. 28

Skeletal muscle tissue.

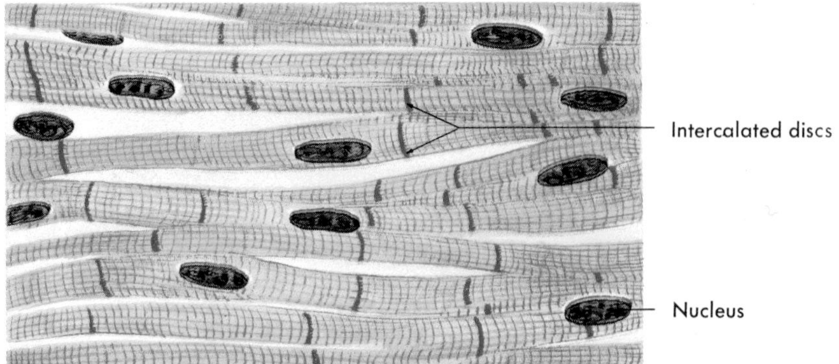

Fig. 29

Cardiac muscle tissue.

filter through this type of tissue. The microscopic air sacs of the lungs, for example, are composed of this kind of tissue, as are the linings of blood and lymphatic vessels and the surfaces of the pleura, pericardium, and peritoneum. (Blood and lymphatic vessel linings are called *endothelium,* and the surfaces of the pleura, pericardium, and peritoneum are called *mesothelium.* Some histologists classify these as connective tissue.)

Stratified squamous epithelium

Stratified squamous epithelium such as shown in Fig. 24 lines the mouth and esophagus. Its several layers of cells serve a protective function. The surface of the skin is composed of a special kind of stratified squamous epithelium (p. 59).

Simple columnar epithelium

Simple columnar epithelium lines the stomach and intestines and parts of the respiratory tract. A single layer of cells composes this tissue, but two types of cells—goblet and columnar—may be present (Fig. 25). Goblet cells are specialized for secreting mucus. Columnar cells are specialized for absorption.

MUSCLE TISSUE

The main specialty of muscle tissue is contraction. Because not all muscle tissue is alike—in location, microscopic appearance, and nervous control—these criteria are used to classify its types. Thus, using location as the criterion, there are three kinds of muscle tissue:

1. *skeletal muscle*—attached to bones
2. *visceral muscle*—in the walls of hollow internal structures such as blood vessels, intestines, uterus, and many others
3. *cardiac muscle*—composes the wall of the heart

With microscopic appearance as the basis of classification, there are only two types of muscle tissue: striated (named for cross striations seen in these cells) and nonstriated or smooth (no cross striations in cells).

On the basis of nervous control, there are also two kinds of muscle tissue: voluntary and involuntary.

Voluntary muscle receives nerve fibers from the cerebrospinal nervous system. Therefore, its contraction can be voluntarily controlled. Involuntary muscle, on the other hand, receives nerve fibers from the autonomic nervous system so that its contraction cannot be voluntarily controlled (except in a few rare individuals). Skeletal muscle is voluntary muscle. Visceral and cardiac muscle are involuntary muscle. Visceral and cardiac muscle are also automatic,* meaning that even without nervous stimulation they continue to contract. Skeletal muscle, in contrast, cannot contract automatically. Anything that cuts off its nerve impulses paralyzes it, that is, puts it immediately out of working order. This is the way poliomyelitis works, for example. It damages nerve cells that conduct impulses to skeletal muscles so that they no longer conduct, and, deprived of stimulation, the muscles are paralyzed.

Finally, combining these classifications, we have the following:

1. *skeletal* or striated voluntary muscle
2. *cardiac* or striated involuntary muscle
3. *visceral* or nonstriated (smooth) involuntary muscle

Because of their elongated narrow shape, muscle cells are often referred to as muscle fibers. Muscle cell cytoplasm is called sarcoplasm, and the cell membrane has the special name sarcolemma. Embedded in the sarcoplasm are many myofibrils and mitochondria. Each myofibril consists of many

*For an account of an interesting experiment that demonstrates cardiac muscle automaticity, see Harary, I.: Heart cells in vitro, Sci. Amer. **206**:141(May), 1962.

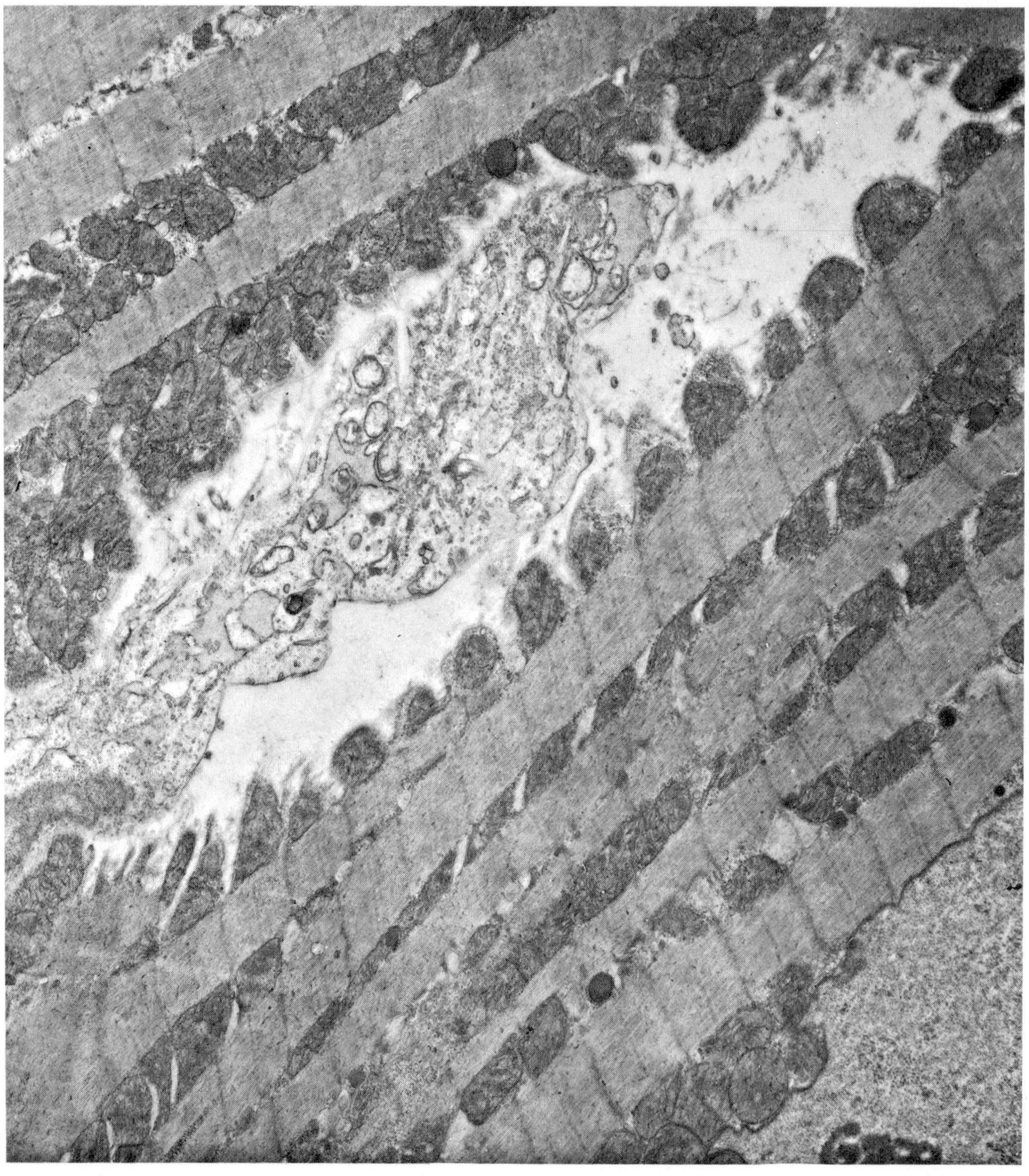

Fig. 30

Electron microphotograph of rabbit heart muscle (×12,500). (Courtesy Department of Pathology, Western Reserve University, Cleveland, Ohio.)

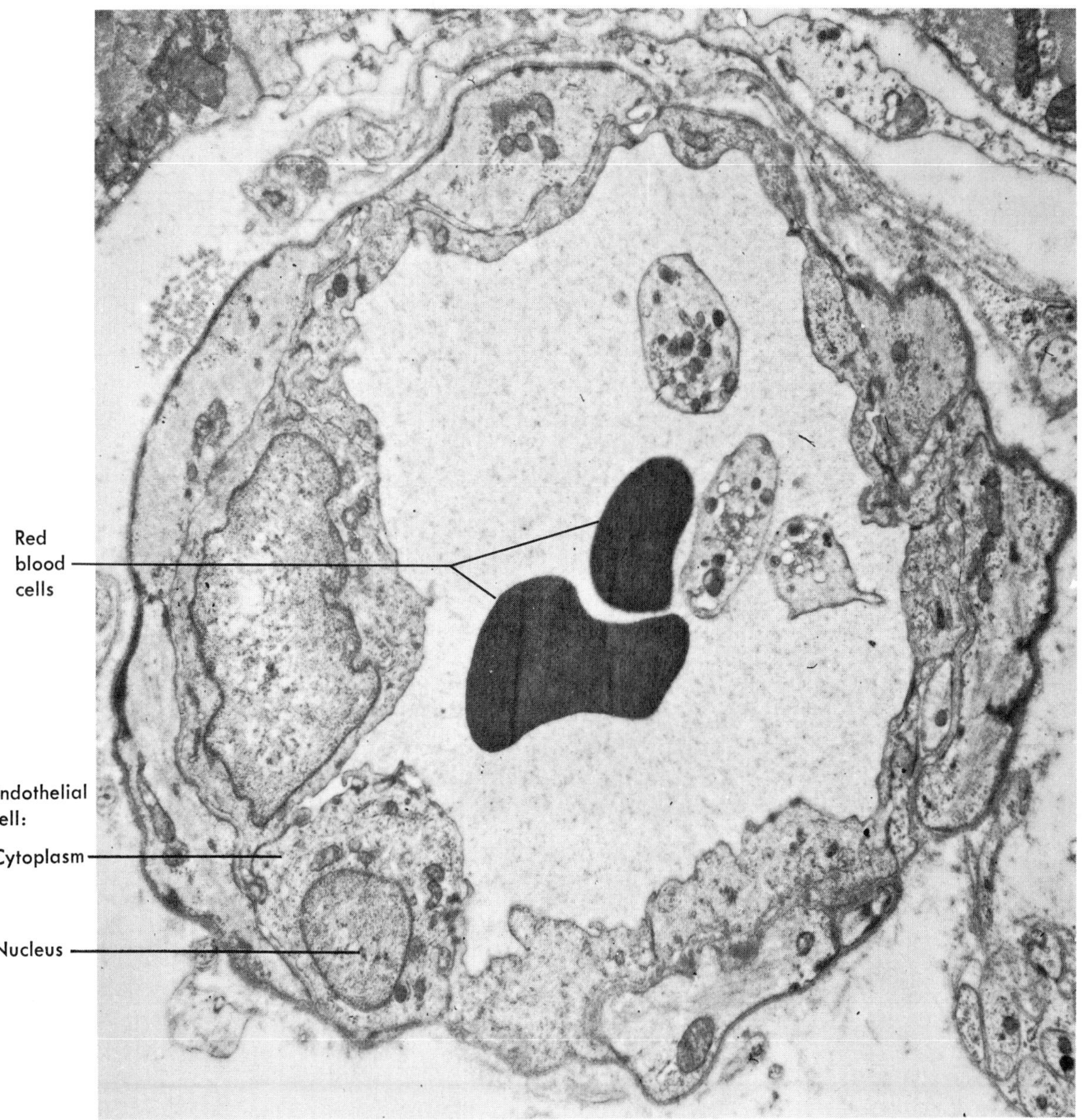

Fig. 31

Electron microphotograph of capillary in rat heart (×12,500). Note the irregularly shaped endothelial cells lining the arteriole and the two black-appearing red blood cells inside the vessel. (Courtesy Department of Pathology, Western Reserve University, Cleveland, Ohio.)

myofilaments, and each myofilament consists of protein molecules. According to Ham,* actin and probably tropomyosin are the proteins composing the finest myofilaments, and myosin is the protein composing the coarser ones. A single striated muscle fiber has many nuclei. It also has many cross striations.

Smooth muscle cells are also long narrow fibers but not nearly so long as striated fibers. For example, one can see the full length of a smooth muscle fiber in a microscopic field but only part of a striated fiber. (According to one estimate, the longest smooth muscle fibers measure about 500 microns and the longest striated fibers about 40,000 microns. Can you translate these measurements into millimeters and inches? If not, and if you are curious, see footnote on p. 13.) Smooth muscle fibers have only one nucleus per fiber and are nonstriated or smooth in appearance.

Under the light microscope cardiac muscle fibers have cross striations and unique dark bands (intercalated disks). They also seem to be incomplete cells that branch into each other to form a big continuous mass of protoplasm known as a syncytium. The electron microscope, however, has revealed that the intercalated disks are actually places where two cell membranes abut at the ends of adjacent cardiac fibers. Cardiac fibers do branch and anastomose but, contrary to previous belief, they do not form a syncytium. A complete cell membrane encloses each cardiac fiber—around its ends (at intercalated disks) as well as its sides.

CONNECTIVE TISSUE

Connective tissue is the most widespread and abundant tissue in the body. It connects and supports—connects tissues to each other, for example, and muscles to bones and bones to other bones. It forms a supporting framework for the body as a whole and for its organs individually. Connective tissue exists in more varied forms than the other three basic tissues. Delicate tissue paper webs, strong, tough cords, rigid bones—all are made of connective tissue.

One scheme of classification lists the following main types of connective tissue: (1) loose, ordinary, including areolar, (2) adipose, (3) dense fibrous, (4) cartilage, (5) bone, (6) hemopoietic,* and (7) reticuloendothelial.

Intercellular material predominates in most connective tissues. And therefore the qualities of the intercellular material largely determine the qualities of the different kinds of connective tissues. Some are soft, others firm or hard; some tough, others delicate; some rigid, others elastic—and in each case it is their intercellular substance that makes them so.

Intercellular substance may consist of either fibers or shapeless jellies or, more commonly, of both. There are three kinds of fibers—collagenous (or collagenic or white), reticular, and elastic. They differ considerably in their properties. Collagenous fibers are tough and strong, reticular fibers are delicate, and elastic fibers are extendable and elastic. Collagenous fibers often occur in bundles—an arrangement that provides great tensile strength. Reticular fibers, in contrast, occur in networks and, although delicate, support small structures such as capillaries and nerve fibers. The protein collagen composes collagenous fibers. You know the hydrated form of this compound as gelatin. Collagenous fibers are also called white fibers because of their white appearance in fresh specimens.

Like intercellular fibers, intercellular jel-

*The fine structure of myofilaments are discussed in Ham, Arthur W., and Leeson, Thomas S.: Histology, ed. 5, Philadelphia, 1965, J. B. Lippincott Co., pp. 486-489.

*Blood is sometimes included as a type of connective tissue, but we shall classify it as a body fluid.

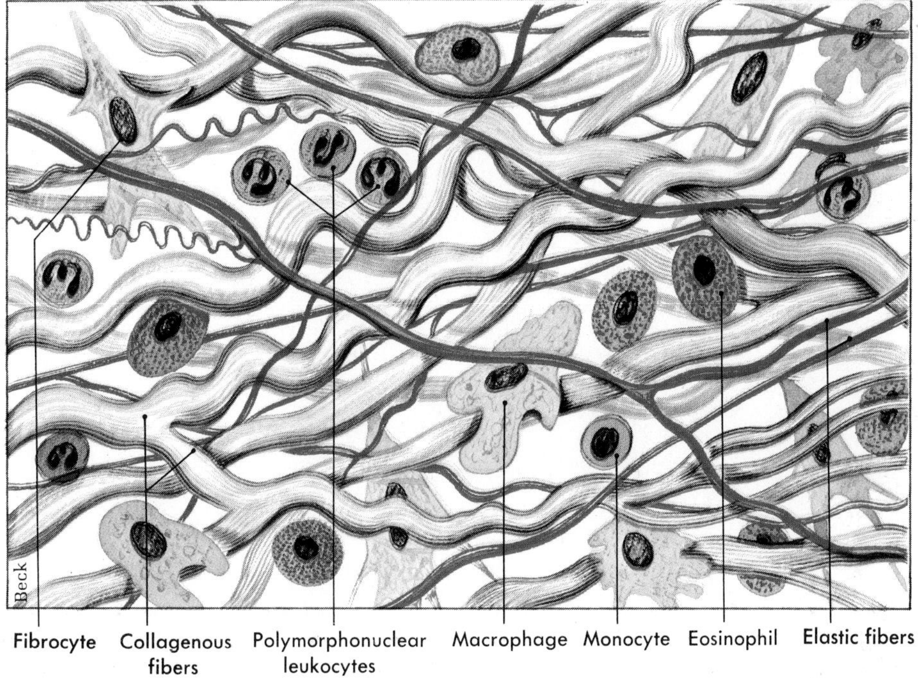

Fig. 32

Areolar connective tissue. The bundles of fibers are collagenous or white fibers. The single (red) strands are elastic fibers. Several fibrocytes are shown between the fibers. Also shown are macrophages and three types of white blood cells: polymorphonuclear leukocytes, eosinophils, and a monocyte.

lies also vary in properties. The ground substance (matrix) in loose, ordinary connective tissue, for example, is a soft, viscous jelly, whereas the matrix of bone is a very hard substance—as "hard as bone," in fact. A compound called hyaluronic acid gives the viscous quality to intercellular jellies, but it can be converted to a watery consistency by the enzyme hyaluronidase. Physicians have made use of this latter fact for some time now. They frequently give a commercial preparation of hyaluronidase intramuscularly or subcutaneously with drugs or fluids. By decreasing the viscosity of intercellular material, the enzyme hastens diffusion and absorption and thereby lessens tissue tension and pain.

Loose, ordinary connective tissue (areolar)

First, a few words of explanation about the names of this kind of tissue. It is called loose because it is stretchable and ordinary because it is one of the most widely distributed of all tissues. It is common and ordinary, not special like some kinds of connective tissue (bone and cartilage, for example) that help form comparatively few structures. Areolar was the early name for the loose, ordinary connective tissue that connects many adjacent structures of the body. It acts like a glue spread between them but an elastic glue that permits movement. The word areolar means like a small space and refers to the bubbles that appear

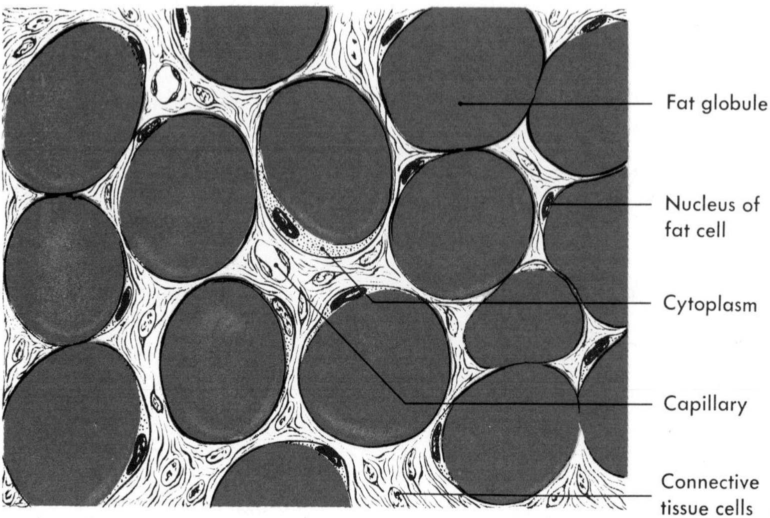

Fig. 33

Adipose tissue. Fat droplet occupies nearly the entire area of the cell. Cytoplasm and nucleus are forced to the periphery of the cell.

as areolar tissue is pulled apart during dissection.

Although intercellular substance is prominent in loose, ordinary connective tissue, cells also are numerous and varied. Collagenous and elastic fibers are interwoven loosely and embedded in a soft viscous ground substance. Of the half dozen or so kinds of cells present, *fibroblasts* are the most common and *macrophages* are second. Fibroblasts synthesize intercellular substances of both types, that is, both fibers and jellies. Macrophages carry on phagocytosis. *Plasma cells, fat cells, mast cells,* and some *white blood cells* (leukocytes) are also found in loose ordinary connective tissue but in smaller numbers than fibroblasts and macrophages. In recent years plasma cells have come into the spotlight as antibody producers.

Adipose tissue

Adipose tissue differs from loose, ordinary connective tissue mainly in that it contains predominantly fat cells and many fewer fibroblasts, macrophages and mast cells. Adipose tissue occurs mainly in certain areas of the body known as fat depots.

Dense fibrous tissue

Dense fibrous tissue consists mainly of fibrous intercellular substance with relatively few fibroblast cells. It composes structures that need great tensile strength, such as tendons and ligaments, and various other structures, including the deeper layer of the skin.

Bone and cartilage

Bone and cartilage are discussed in Chapter V.

Hemopoietic tissue

Hemopoietic tissue is discussed in Chapter IX.

Reticuloendothelial tissue

Various types of connective tissue cells which carry on phagocytosis, although widely scattered throughout the body, are sometimes spoken of as reticuloendothelial tissue or as the *reticuloendothelial system.*

Table 2. **Tissues**

Tissue	*Location*	*Function*
Epithelial		
Simple squamous	Alveoli of lungs	Diffusion of respiratory gases between alveolar air and blood
	Lining blood and lymphatic capillaries (called endothelium; classed as connective tissue by some histologists)	Diffusion; filtration; osmosis
	Surface layer of pleura, pericardium, peritoneum (called mesothelium; classed as connective tissue by some histologists)	Diffusion; osmosis
Stratified squamous	Surface of lining of mouth and esophagus	Protection
	Surface of skin (epidermis)	Protection
Simple columnar	Surface layer of lining of stomach, intestines, and part of respiratory tract	Protection; secretion; absorption; moving of mucus (by ciliated columnar)
Muscle		
Skeletal (striated voluntary)	Muscles which attach to bones	Movement of bones
	Extrinsic eyeball muscles	Eye movements
	Upper one third of esophagus	First part of swallowing
Visceral (nonstriated involuntary or smooth)	In walls of tubular viscera of digestive, respiratory, and genitourinary tracts	Movement of substances along respective tracts
	In walls of blood vessels and large lymphatics	Control of size of blood vessels, thereby aiding in regulation of blood pressure
	In ducts of glands	Movement of substances along ducts
	Intrinsic eye muscles (iris and ciliary body)	Regulation of size of pupils and shape of lens
	Arrector muscles of hairs	Erection of hairs (gooseflesh)
Cardiac (striated involuntary)	Wall of heart	Contraction of heart
Connective (most widely distributed of all tissues)		
Loose, ordinary (areolar)	Between other tissues and organs Superficial fascia	Connection

Continued.

Table 2. Tissues—cont'd

Tissue	*Location*	*Function*
Connective—cont'd		
Adipose (fat)	Under skin Padding at various points	Protection Insulation Support Reserve food
Dense or white fibrous	Tendons Ligaments Aponeuroses Deep fascia Dermis Scars Capsule of kidney, etc.	Furnish flexible but strong connection
Bone	Skeleton	Support Protection
Cartilage		
Hyaline	Part of nasal septum Covering articular surfaces of bones Larynx Rings in trachea and bronchi	Furnish firm but flexible support
Fibrous	Discs between vertebrae Symphysis pubis	
Elastic	External ear Eustachian tube	
Hemopoietic		
Myeloid (bone marrow)	Marrow spaces of bones	Formation of red blood cells, granular leukocytes, platelets; also reticuloendothelial cells and some other connective tissue cells
Lymphatic	Lymph nodes Spleen Tonsils and adenoids Thymus gland	Formation of lymphocytes and monocytes; also plasma cells and some other connective tissue cells
Reticuloendothelial	Widely scattered, e. g., in lining of blood sinusoids of liver, spleen, and bone marrow; also in lining of lymph channels in lymph nodes	Phagocytosis
Nerve	Brain Spinal cord Nerves	Irritability and conduction

They constitute an important part of the body's defense mechanism. Opinions differ somewhat as to which cells belong in the category of reticuloendothelial cells. There does seem to be agreement, however, that the following three types of phagocytic cells belong in this classification:

1. *reticuloendothelial cells*—located in the lining of blood sinusoids* in the liver, spleen, and bone marrow and in the lining of lymph channels in lymph nodes; another name for the reticuloendothelial cells of liver sinusoids is stellate cells of von Kuppfer—stellate because of their starlike shape and von Kuppfer for the man who first described them
2. *macrophages*—one of the commonest type cells in connective tissues; also called tissue histiocytes, resting wandering cells, and clasmatocytes
3. *microglia*—located in the central nervous system

*Sinusoids are tiny blood vessels. They are analogous to capillaries in that they connect the arterial side of circulation to the venous side but differ in minor ways from capillaries.

Reticuloendothelial cells have a mark of distinction interesting to note—they may be either fixed or wandering cells. Many of them, especially macrophages, can come loose from their usual site and wander out into regions where their function of phagocytosis is needed, into inflamed or injured areas. Later, with their defense mission accomplished, they move back to their respective places and remain fixed there until a future need arises. Apropos of this dual nature of reticuloendothelial cells, did you notice one of the names macrophages go by? "Resting wandering cells."

NERVE TISSUE

Nerve tissue is discussed in Chapter VII.

Outline summary—Tissues

1. Definition—organization of cells with nonliving intercellular substances
2. Basic types
   a. epithelial
   b. muscle
   c. connective
   d. nerve

EPITHELIAL TISSUE

1. General functions—protection, secretion, diffusion, filtration, and absorption
2. Main types
   a. simple squamous
   b. simple columnar
   c. stratified squamous

Simple squamous epithelium

1. Single layers of flat cells
2. Functions—diffusion and filtration

Simple columnar epithelium

1. Single layer of columnar and goblet-shaped cells and in some places, ciliated cells
2. Functions—absorption, secretion, and moving mucus

Stratified squamous epithelium

1. Several layers of cells
2. Function—protection

MUSCLE TISSUE

1. General functions—contraction and therefore movement
2. Types
   a. skeletal; also called voluntary
   b. visceral; also called nonstriated or smooth involuntary
   c. cardiac; also called striated involuntary

CONNECTIVE TISSUE

1. General functions—connections, support, and protection
2. Main types
   a. loose, ordinary connective, including areolar
   b. adipose

c. dense fibrous
d. cartilage
e. bone
f. hemopoietic
g. reticuloendothelial cells

3. General characteristics—intercellular material predominates in most connective tissues and determines their physical characteristics; consists of either fibers (collagenous, reticular, and elastic) or jellies or both

Loose, ordinary connective tissue (areolar)

1. One of the most widely distributed of all tissues; intercellular substance is prominent and consists of collagenous and elastic fibers loosely interwoven and embedded in soft viscous ground substance; several kinds of cells present, notably fibroblasts and macrophages, also mast cells, plasma cells, fat cells, and some white blood cells
2. Function—connection

Adipose tissue

1. Similar to loose, ordinary connective tissue but contains mainly fat cells
2. Functions—protection, insulation, support, and reserve food

Dense or white fibrous tissue

1. Fibrous intercellular substance (collagenous fibers) predominate; few fibroblast cells
2. Function—furnish flexible but strong connection

Reticuloendothelial tissue

1. Phagocytic cells that line small lymph and blood channels in lymph nodes, liver, spleen, and bone marrow
2. Macrophages and microglia also classed as reticuloendothelial cells by many authors

Review questions

1. Name the four basic types of tissue.
2. What are the main functions of each basic type of tissue?
3. What are the names of the subtypes of connective tissue?
4. Describe intercellular substance.
5. What is the scientific basis for giving hyaluronidase with fluids or certain drugs that are injected?
6. Name several kinds of connective tissue cells.
7. What kind of cells produce intercellular substances?
8. Name three subtypes of muscle tissue. Give more than one name for each.
9. What special function do reticuloendothelial cells perform?
10. What are the main locations of reticuloendothelial cells?
11. Make a list of terms you have encountered for the first time in this chapter. Define each in your own words.

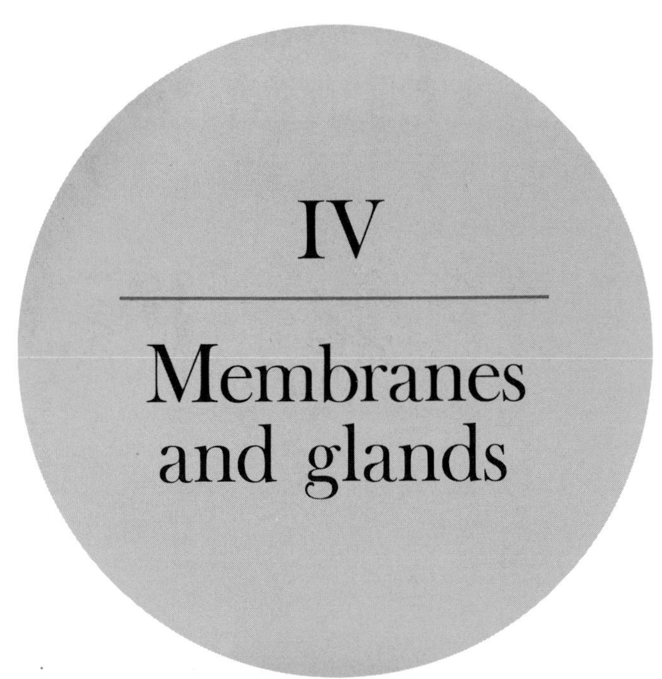

IV Membranes and glands

Membranes

Membranes constitute a special class of organs in that they are merely thin sheets of tissues which cover or line various parts of the body. Of the numerous membranes in the body, four kinds are particularly important: mucous, serous, synovial, and cutaneous (skin). Other miscellaneous membranes (periosteum, fascia, dura mater, sclera, etc.) will be described from time to time.

MUCOUS MEMBRANE

Mucous membrane lines cavities or passageways of the body which open to the exterior, such as the lining of the mouth and entire digestive tract, the respiratory passages, and the genitourinary tract. It consists, as do serous, synovial, and cutaneous membranes, of a surface layer of epithelial tissue over a deeper layer of connective tissue. Mucous membrane performs the functions of protection, secretion, and absorption—protection, for example, against bacterial invasion, secretion of mucus, and absorption of water, salts, and other solutes.

SEROUS AND SYNOVIAL MEMBRANES

Serous and synovial membranes line cavities of the body which do not open to the exterior, otherwise known as closed cavities. Serous membrane that lines the thoracic cavity is called *pleura,* that which lines the abdominal cavity is called *peritoneum,* and that which lines the sac in which the heart lies is called *pericardium.*

Not only does serous membrane line the thoracic and abdominal cavities and the pericardial sac, but it also covers the organs lying in these spaces. The term *visceral layer* is applied to the part of the membrane which covers the organs, while that which lines the cavity is called *parietal layer.* Between the two layers there is a potential space kept moist by a small amount of serous fluid. Think of the thoracic and abdominal cavities as rooms in a

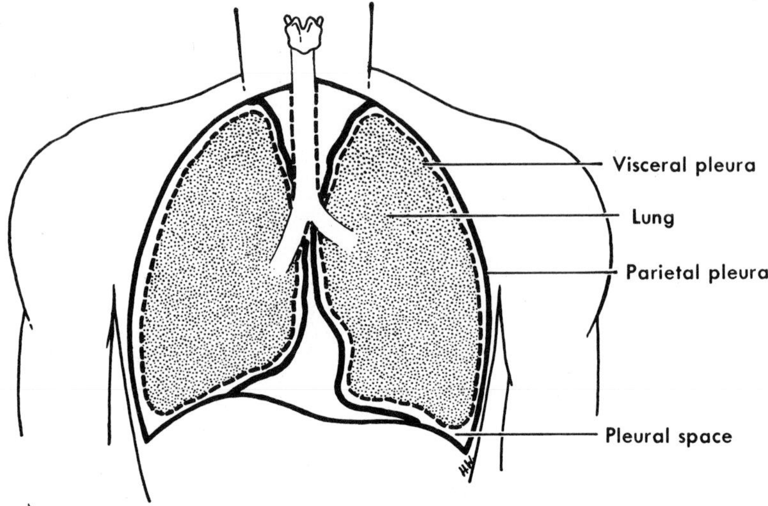

Fig. 34

Diagram showing the relative positions of the visceral and parietal layers of the serous membrane called the pleura.

house. The wallpaper then becomes comparable to the parietal layer of the serous membranes. Imagine the rooms filled with furniture, each piece wrapped tightly in muslin for protection. The muslin wrappings are comparable to the visceral serous membrane which covers each organ in the thoracic and abdominal cavities. Even though the articles of furniture in the rooms be stacked closely against each other and against the walls, still there is air between the pieces and between the pieces and the walls. This air might be likened to the small amount of lubricating serous fluid in the potential space between the visceral and parietal layers of serous membrane. When an organ moves against the body wall, as the lungs do in respiration, or when the heart beats in its serous sac, friction between the moving parts is prevented by the presence of the very smooth moist serous sheets lining the wall surface of the cavity and covering the organ surfaces. The mechanical principle that moving parts must have lubricated surfaces is thereby carried out in the body.

Synovial membrane lines joint cavities, tendon sheaths, and bursae. Its smooth moist surfaces protect against friction.

CUTANEOUS MEMBRANE

Vital, diverse, complex, extensive—these adjectives describe in part the body's largest and one of its most important organs—the skin. In terms of surface area, the skin is as large as the body itself—probably 2,500 to 3,000 square inches in most adults. Skin functions are crucial to survival. They are also diverse, including such different functions as protection, excretion, sensation, and playing a part in maintaining fluid and electrolyte balance and normal body temperature. The skin protects us against entry of unconquerable hordes of microorganisms and minimizes mechanical injury of underlying structures. It bars entry of excess sunlight and of most chemicals. Even water does not penetrate it under most circumstances. The skin protects against too much and too little heat loss. For example, if body temperature increases above certain limits, skin vessels dilate, more blood flows

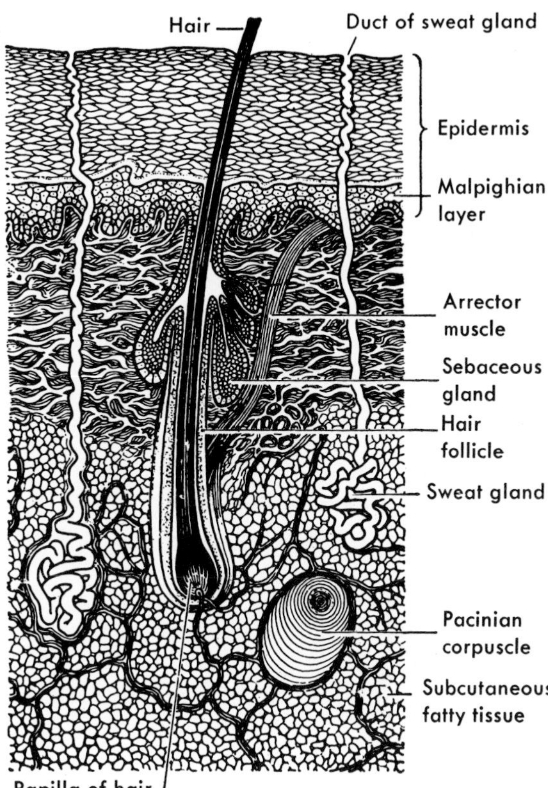

Fig. 35

Highly schematized diagram to show the microscopic structure of the skin in longitudinal section. The wavy lines in the lower part of the figure represent elastic fibers in the derma. (Modified from Cunningham; from Tuttle and Schottelius: Textbook of physiology, St. Louis, The C. V. Mosby Co.)

to the surface, and more heat may be lost by radiation. And at the same time sweat glands secrete more sweat, and more heat may be lost by evaporation.

Millions of microscopic nerve endings are distributed throughout the skin. These serve as antennas or receivers for the body, keeping it informed of changes in its environment—information vital at times to survival.

Epidermis and dermis

Two main layers compose the skin: an outer and thinner layer, the *epidermis,* and an inner, thicker layer, the *dermis.* Epidermis consists of stratified squamous epithelial tissue and dermis of fibrous connective tissue. Underlying the dermis is subcutaneous tissue or superficial fascia made of areolar and in many areas adipose tissue, too. Epidermis, in all parts of the body except the palms of the hands and soles of the feet, has four layers. In the skin of the palms and soles there are five layers of epidermis. From the outside in, they are as follows:

1. *stratum corneum (horny layer)*—dead cells converted to a water-repellent protein called keratin that continually flakes off (desquamates)
2. *stratum lucidum*—so named because of the presence of a translucent compound (eleidin) from which keratin forms; this layer present only in thick skin of palms and soles
3. *stratum granulosum*—so named because of granules visible in cytoplasm of cells (cells die in this layer)
4. *stratum spinosum (prickle cell layer)*—

several layers of irregularly shaped cells

5. *stratum germinativum* (or *basal layer*)—columnar-shaped cells, the only cells in the epidermis that undergo mitosis; new cells produced in this deepest stratum at the rate old keratinized cells lost from the stratum corneum; new cells continually push surfaceward from the stratum germinativum into each successive layer, only to die, become keratinized, and eventually flake off as did their predecessors (Incidentally, this fact illustrates nicely the physiological principle that while life continues the body's work is never done; even at rest it is producing new cells to replace millions of old ones.)

An interesting characteristic of the dermis or deep layer of the skin is its parallel ridges, suggestive on a miniature scale of the ridges of a contour plowed field. Epidermal ridges, the ones made famous by the art of fingerprinting, exist because the epidermis conforms to the underlying dermal ridges.

Have you ever wondered about the array of different skin colors? Two factors are mainly responsible—pigment and blood. Black or brown compounds called melanins are the chief pigments. Special cells (melanoblasts), located mainly in the deepest layer of the epidermis, produce them as inclusions in their cytoplasm. Many factors influence the amount of skin melanins. Prolonged exposure to sunlight comes first to mind, but radiation therapy, adrenal cortex hormone deficiency, and some types of vitamin B deficiency may also cause skin darkening. The pinkish cast characteristic of skin comes from blood in the minute vessels of the dermis. But if blood contains an excess of reduced hemoglobin, then instead of the normal pinkness, the abnormal blueness of cyanosis develops. According to Lundsgaard, cyanosis appears when 100 ml. of blood contains about 5 gm. of reduced hemoglobin.*

Accessory organs of skin

The accessory organs of the skin consist of hair, nails, and microscopic glands.

Hair. Hair is distributed over the entire body except the palms and soles. The structure of a hair has several points of similarity to that of the epidermis. Just as the epidermis is formed by the cells of its deepest layer, reproducing and forcing the daughter cells, which become horny in character, upward, so a hair is formed by a group of cells at its base multiplying and pushing upward and in so doing becoming keratinized. The part of the hair that is visible is the *shaft,* while that which is embedded in the dermis is the *root.* The root, together with its coverings (an outer connective tissue sheath and an inner epithelial coating which is a continuation of the stratum germinativum), forms the hair *follicle.* At the bottom of the follicle is a loop of capillaries enclosed in a connective tissue covering called the hair *papilla.* The cluster of epithelial cells lying over the papilla are the ones that reproduce and eventually form the hair shaft. As long as these cells remain alive, hair will regenerate even though it be cut or plucked or otherwise removed.

Each hair is kept soft and pliable by two or more *sebaceous glands* which secrete varying amounts of oily *sebum* into the follicle near the surface of the skin. Attached to the follicle, too, are small bundles of involuntary muscle known as the *arrector pili muscles.* These muscles are of interest because when they contract, the hair "stands on end," as it does in extreme fright or cold, for example. This mechanism is responsible also for gooseflesh. As the hair is

*Best, Charles H., and Taylor, M. B.: The physiological basis of medical practice, ed. 7, Baltimore, 1961, Williams & Wilkins Co., p. 524.

pulled into an upright position, it raises the skin around it into the familiar little goose pimples.

Hair color is due to different amounts of melanin pigments in the outer layer (cortex) of the hair. White hair contains little or no melanin.

Some hair, notably that around the eyes and in the nose and ears, performs a protective function in that it keeps out some dust and insects. For the hair on the bulk of the skin, however, no function seems apparent.

Nails. The nails are epidermal cells that have been converted to keratin. They grow from epithelial cells lying under the white crescent (lunula) at the proximal end of each nail.

Skin glands. The skin glands include three kinds of microscopic glands, namely, sebaceous, sweat, and ceruminous.

Sebaceous glands secrete oil for the hair. Wherever hairs grow from the skin there are sebaceous glands, at least two for each hair. The oil, or *sebum,* secreted by these tiny glands has value not only because it keeps the hair supple but also because it keeps the skin soft and pliant. Moreover, it prevents excessive water evaporation from the skin and water absorption through the skin. And because fat is a poor conductor of heat, the sebum secreted onto the skin lessens the amount of heat lost from this large surface.

Sweat glands, though very small structures, are very important and very numerous—especially on the palms, soles, forehead, and axillae (armpits). Histologists estimate, for example, that a single square inch of skin on the palms of the hands contains about three thousand sweat glands.

Sweat secretion helps maintain homeostasis of fluid and electrolytes and of body temperature. For example, if too much heat is being produced, as in strenuous exercise, or if the environmental temperature is high, these glands secrete more sweat which, in evaporating, cools the body surface. Inasmuch as sweat contains some nitrogenous wastes, the sweat glands also function as excretory organs.

Ceruminous glands are thought to be modified sweat glands. They are located in the external ear canal. Instead of watery sweat, they secrete a waxy, pigmented substance, the *cerumen.*

Terms used in connection with skin

hypodermic beneath or under the skin.
subcutaneous same as hypodermic.
intracutaneous within the layers of the skin.
diaphoresis profuse perspiration.
pores minute openings of the sweat gland

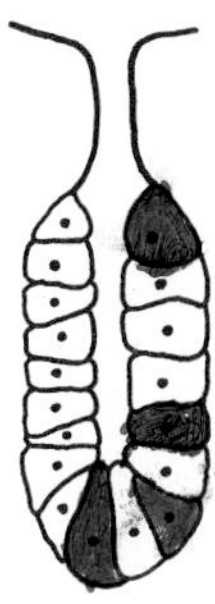

Fig. 36

Simple tubular gland, an exocrine gland with an unbranching duct.

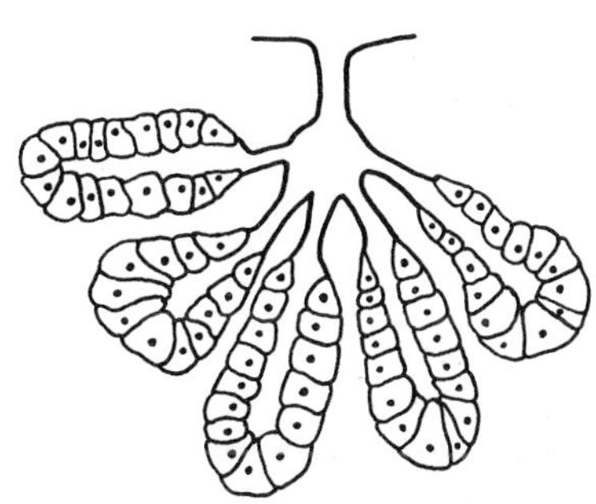

Fig. 37

Compound tubuloalveolar gland, an exocrine gland with a branching duct.

ducts on the surface of the skin; do not "open" or "close" since no muscle tissue enters into their formation; however, any agent which has an astringent action on the skin causes them to become smaller or "closed."

furuncle a boil, an infection of a hair follicle.

Glands

Glands consist of epithelial cells specialized for synthesizing compounds which they secrete either into ducts or blood. *Exocrine glands* secrete into ducts and *endocrine glands* into blood capillaries. Exocrine glands are further classified in several ways. Sweat glands, for example, are *simple tubular exocrine glands* (Fig. 36). Interpreted, simple means that each gland has a single nonbranching duct, and tubular means that its secretory unit is tubular shaped. A salivary gland, in contrast, is a *compound tubuloalveolar gland* (Fig. 37) because it has a branching duct and some tubular and some flask-shaped secretory units.

Outline summary—Membranes and glands

Membranes

1. Definition—thin sheet of tissues that either covers or lines a part of body or divides an organ
2. Types—mucous, serous, synovial, cutaneous, and miscellaneous

MUCOUS MEMBRANE

1. Location—lines cavities and passages that open to exterior
2. Structure—surface layer of epithelial tissue over connective tissue
3. Functions—protection, secretion, and absorption

SEROUS MEMBRANE

1. Location—lines cavities that do not open to exterior
2. Functions—protection and secretion

SYNOVIAL MEMBRANE

1. Location—lines joint cavities, tendon sheaths, and bursae
2. Functions—protection and secretion

CUTANEOUS MEMBRANE

1. Functions
   a. protection against various factors, e.g., microorganisms, sunlight, and chemicals
   b. excretion of sweat
   c. sensations
   d. fluid and electrolyte balance—skin helps maintain this by secreting varying amounts of sweat
   e. normal body temperature—skin helps maintain this by varying amounts of blood flow through it and also by varying amounts of sweat secretion
2. Structure—two main layers: epidermis, outer, thinner layer of stratified squamous epithelium, and dermis, inner, thicker layer of connective tissue

Epidermis

1. Outer layer of stratified squamous epithelial cells
2. Surface cells dead, keratinized, and practically waterproof
3. Only deepest layer of cells undergoes mitosis to replace surface cells that continually desquamate
4. Melanin pigments mainly in deepest layer

Dermis

1. Dense fibrous connective tissue layer underlying epidermis
2. Dermis of palms and soles has numerous parallel ridges
3. Subcutaneous tissue (also called superficial fascia), underlying dermis, composed of areolar tissue or areolar and adipose tissues

Accessory organs of skin

1. Hair
   a. distribution—over entire body except palms and soles
   b. shaft—visible part of hair
   c. root—part of hair embedded in dermis

- d. follicle—root with coverings
- e. papilla—loop of capillaries enclosed in connective tissue covering
- f. germinal matrix—cluster of epithelial cells lying over papilla; these cells undergo mitosis to form hair; must be intact in order for hair to regenerate
- g. sebaceous glands and arrector pili muscles—attach to follicle; contraction of latter produces gooseflesh
- h. color—due to different amounts of melanin pigments in cortex of hair

2. Nails
   - a. are epidermal cells converted to hard keratin
   - b. grow from epithelial cells under lunula ("moons")
3. Skin glands
   - a. sebaceous—secrete oil (sebum) that keeps hair and skin soft; helps prevent excess evaporation and absorption of water and excess heat loss
   - b. sweat—numerous throughout skin, especially on palms, soles, forehead, and axillae; important in heat regulation
   - c. ceruminous—thought to be modified sweat glands; located in external ear canal; secrete ear wax or cerumen

Terms used in connection with skin

See p. 61

Glands

1. Composed of epithelial cells specialized for synthesizing compounds which they secrete either into ducts or blood capillaries
2. Types
   - a. exocrine glands—secrete into ducts
   - b. endocrine glands—secrete into blood
   - c. simple glands—have nonbranching ducts
   - d. tubular glands—secretory unit tubular-shaped
   - e. compound glands—have branching ducts
   - f. alveolar glands—flask-shaped secretory units

Review questions

1. What membranes line closed cavities? Cavities that open to the exterior?
2. What general functions do membranes serve?
3. What functions does the skin perform?
4. Describe the epidermis.
5. Describe the dermis.
6. What is keratin?
7. What is melanin and where is it found?
8. What is superficial fascia?
9. Name and describe the skin glands.
10. Define the following terms:

alveolar gland	exocrine gland
endocrine gland	compound gland

UNIT
TWO

The erect and moving body

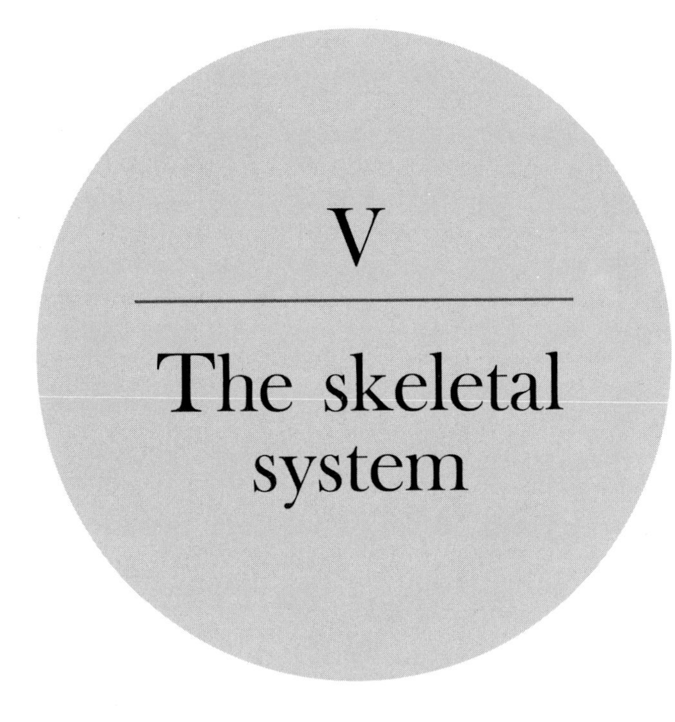

V

The skeletal system

Like all body structures, the skeletal and muscular systems play a part in the body's achievement of its overall goal of survival. These two systems work together to move the body and its parts. This is a function of tremendous importance not only for the enjoyment of life but also for life itself, since without movement a favorable cellular environment cannot possibly be maintained.

The body must adjust to many changes in its external environment in order to maintain homeostasis. Sometimes it adjusts the external environment. Sometimes it adjusts itself. In either case, movements play a part. Suppose, for instance, that environmental temperature drops below the comfort zone. The body then needs to make some kind of adjustment in order to maintain homeostasis of its internal temperature. It may change the environmental temperature back to a comfortable level (by building a fire or setting up the room thermostat, for example), or it may change iself in some way to counteract the environmental change (for instance, shivering and surface blood vessel constriction to produce more heat and lose less, respectively).

Whichever methods the body uses, movements are necessary. Movements require the coordinated activities of nearly all of the body's systems. In order to gain an understanding of how movements are accomplished, we shall start by investigating the two systems whose primary business is movement: the skeletal and muscular systems.

Meaning

The term skeletal system means all the bones of the body plus the joints formed by their attachments to each other. Predominant tissues of the system are two types of connective tissue: bone and cartilage.

Functions

The skeletal system performs five important functions: (1) support, (2) protection, (3) movement and leverage, (4) hemopoiesis, and (5) calcium storage.

Support. Bones support the body much as steel girders support our modern buildings.

Protection. Hard, bony "boxes" protect delicate structures enclosed by them. For example, the skull protects the brain and the rib cage protects the lungs and heart.

Movement and leverage. Bones with their joints constitute levers. Muscles are anchored firmly to bones. As muscles contract, force is applied to the bony levers and movement necessarily results.

Hemopoiesis (blood cell formation). The red bone marrow produces blood cells—normally, all the red cells in the adult, most types of white cells, and the platelets.

Calcium storage. Bones serve as storage depots for calcium.

Bone and cartilage

MICROSCOPIC STRUCTURE

Bone

Bone, like other tissues, consists of living cells and nonliving intercellular substance. And in bone, like other connective tissues, intercellular substance predominates over cells. But in bone the intercellular substance (matrix) is calcified. Calcium salts impregnate the cement substance of the matrix, a fact that explains the rigidity of bones and the familiar expression "as hard as bone." Embedded in the calcified matrix are collagenous fibrils. These serve to reinforce bone much as iron rods reinforce concrete.

Another unique feature of bone structure is the arrangement of its intercellular substance. Concentric cylindrical layers of calcified matrix (usually less than six of them) enclose a central longitudinal canal that contains a blood vessel. Each layer of bone matrix is called a *lamella,* the central canal is an *haversian canal,* and the entire unit of canal and surrounding lamellae is an *haversian system.* According to Ham, most haversian canals contain a single large capillary, but some have a small arteriole and venule, and lymphatics. Bone cells *(osteocytes)* occupy minute spaces called *lacunae* between the lamellae. Microscopic canals (canaliculi), great numbers of them, radiate in all directions from the lacunae to connect them with haversian canals and provide routes for tissue fluid to reach bone cells. Each bone cell is said to lie not farther than 1/10 mm. from an haversian canal. (See Fig. 38.)

There are two types of bone based on the arrangement of lamellae—compact or dense and cancellous or spongy. In *compact bone,* adjacent haversian units fit closely together with the spaces between them filled in with interstitial lamellae. In *cancellous bone,* on the other hand, there are many open spaces between thin processes of bone *(trabeculae)* which are joined together somewhat like the beams of wood in a scaffold. Arrangement of trabeculae in different ways in different bones gives structural strength along the lines of strain on individual bones.

Bones are not the lifeless structures they seem to be. We tend to think of them as lifeless, perhaps because what we see when we look at a bone is its nonliving intercellular substance. But within this hard, lifeless material lie many living bone cells that must continually receive food and oxygen

HUMAN ANATOMY

FULL-COLOR PLATES WITH SIX IN TRANSPARENT

"TRANS-VISION"® SHOWING STRUCTURES OF THE HUMAN TORSO

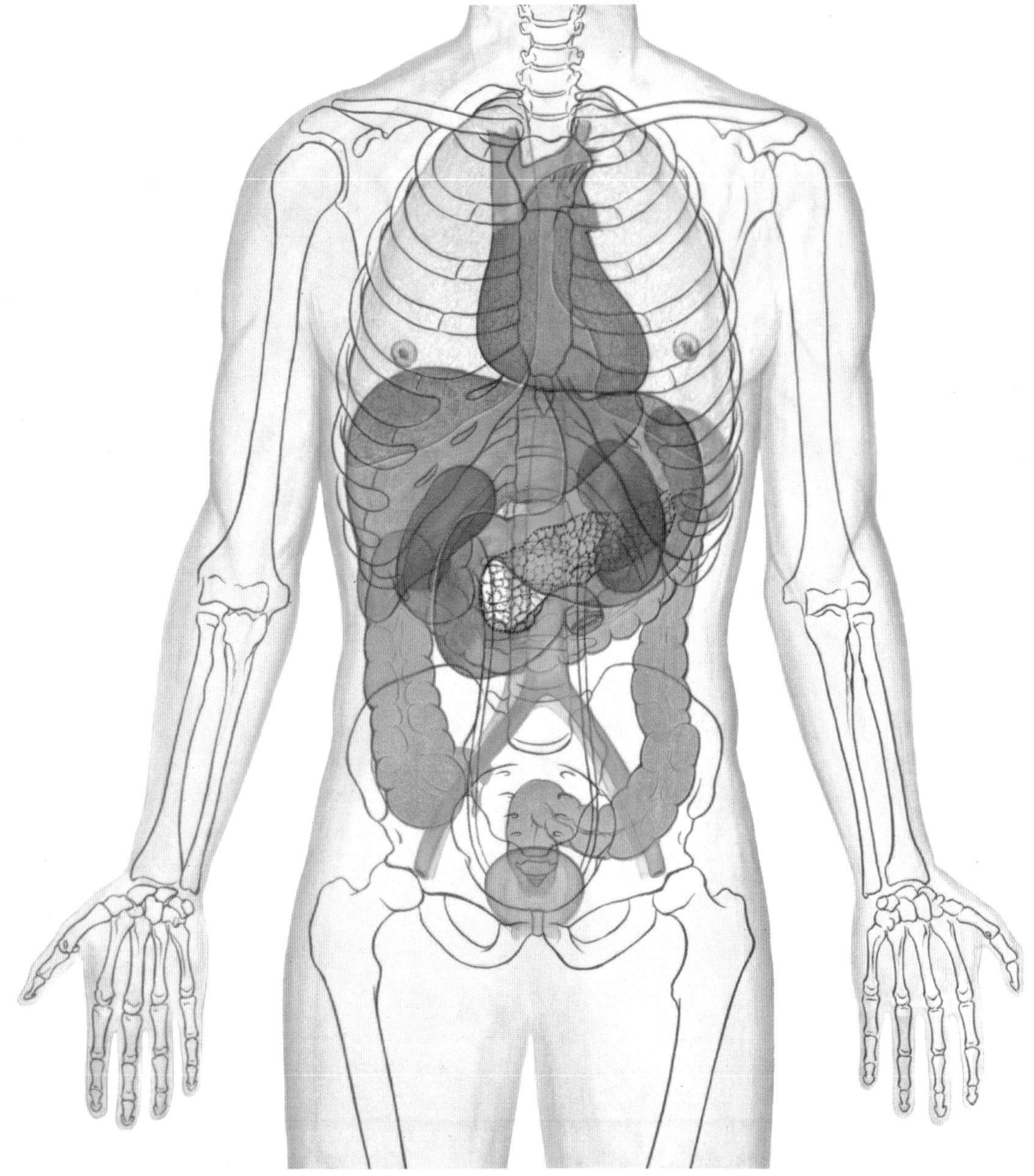

Plate I

ERNEST W. BECK, medical illustrator

in collaboration with

HARRY MONSEN, Ph.D.

Professor of Anatomy, College of Medicine, University of Illinois

Plate VIII

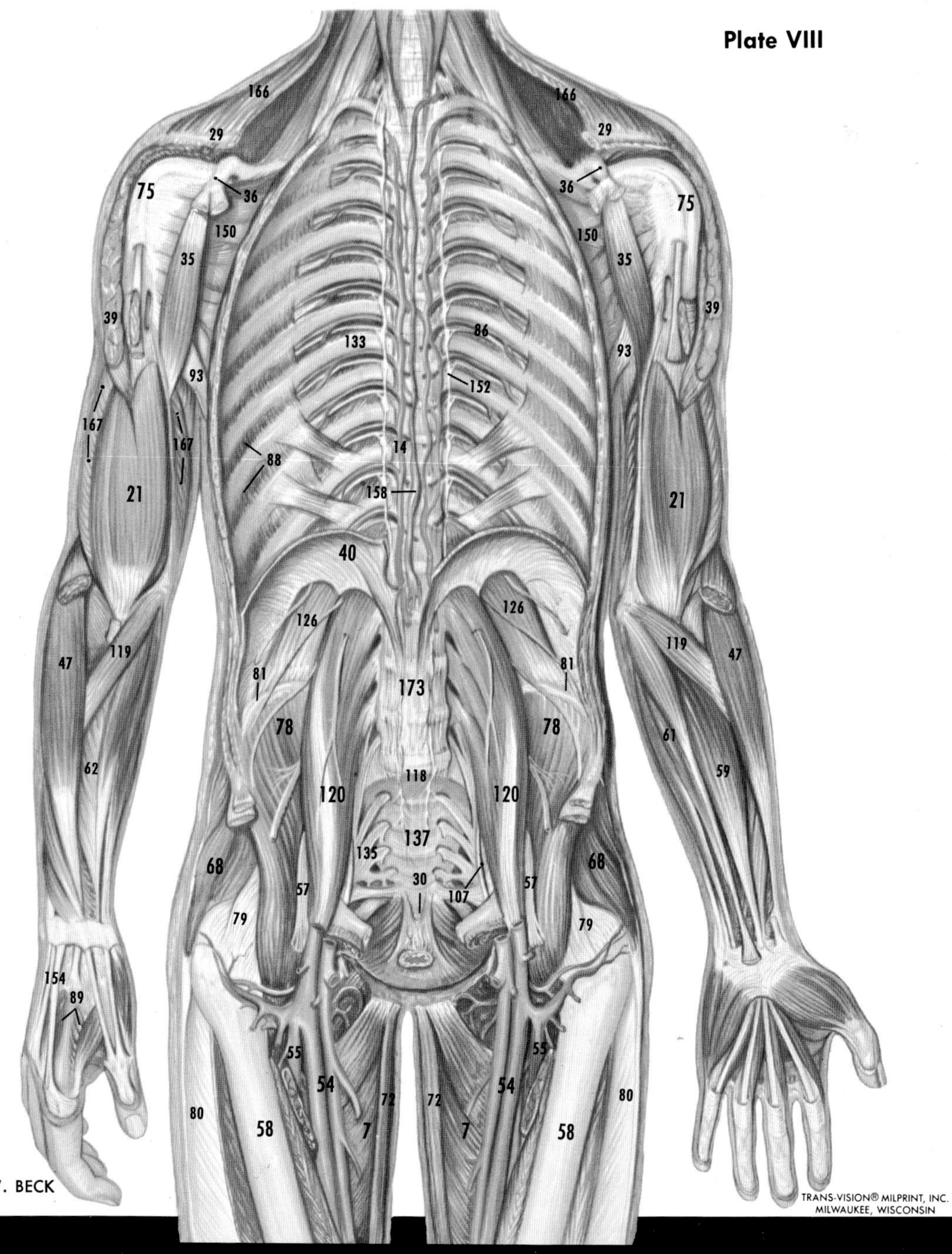

7. Adductor magnus muscle
14. Azygos veins
21. Brachialis muscle
29. Clavicle
30. Coccyx
35. Coracobrachialis muscle
36. Coracoid process of the scapula
39. Deltoid muscle
40. Diaphragm
47. Extensor carpi radialis longus muscle
54. Femoral artery and vein
55. Femoral artery, deep
57. Femoral nerve
58. Femur
59. Flexor carpi radialis muscle
61. Flexor digitorum profundus muscle
62. Flexor digitorum superficialis muscle
68. Gluteus medius muscle
75. Humerus
78. Iliacus muscle
79. Iliofemoral ligament
80. Iliotibial tract
81. Ilium
86. Intercostal artery, vein and nerve
88. Intercostal muscle, internal
89. Interosseous muscles, dorsal
93. Latissimus dorsi muscle
107. Obturator nerve
118. Promontory
119. Pronator teres muscle
120. Psoas muscles (major and minor)
126. Quadratus lumborum muscle
133. Rib
135. Sacral nerves
137. Sacrum
150. Subscapularis muscle
152. Sympathetic (autonomic) nerve chain
154. Tendons of extensor muscles of hand
158. Thoracic duct
166. Trapezius muscle
167. Triceps brachii muscle
173. Vertebral column

Plate IX

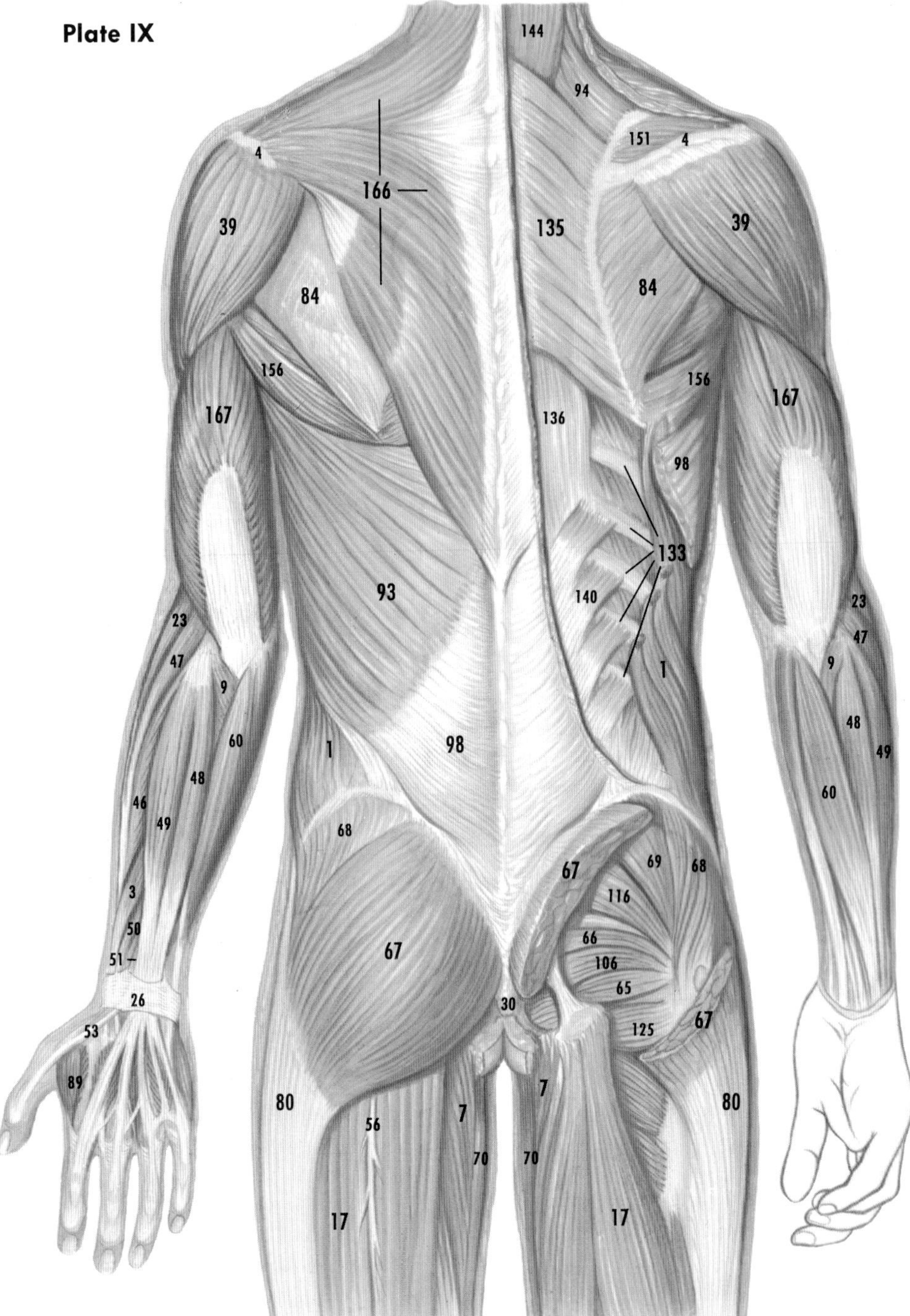

1. Abdominal oblique muscle, external
3. Abductor pollicis longus muscle
4. Acromion process of the scapula
7. Adductor magnus muscle
9. Anconeus muscle
17. Biceps femoris muscle
23. Brachioradialis muscle
26. Carpal ligament, dorsal
30. Coccyx
39. Deltoid muscle
46. Extensor carpi radialis brevis muscle
47. Extensor carpi radialis longus muscle
48. Extensor carpi ulnaris muscle
49. Extensor digitorum communis muscle
50. Extensor pollicis brevis muscle
51. Extensor pollicis longus muscle
56. Femoral cutaneous nerve, posterior
60. Flexor carpi ulnaris muscle
65. Gemellus inferior muscle
66. Gemellus superior muscle
67. Gluteus maximus muscle
68. Gluteus medius muscle
69. Gluteus minimus muscle
70. Gracilis muscle
80. Iliotibial tract
84. Infraspinatus muscle
89. Interosseous muscle, dorsal
93. Latissimus dorsi muscle
94. Levator scapulae muscle
98. Lumbodorsal fascia
106. Obturator internus muscle
116. Piriformis muscle
125. Quadratus femoris muscle
133. Ribs (VII-XII)
135. Rhomboideus muscle
136. Erector spinae muscle
140. Serratus posterior inferior muscle
144. Splenius capitis muscle
151. Supraspinatus muscle
156. Teres major muscle
166. Trapezius muscle
167. Triceps brachii muscle

BONES AND SINUSES OF THE SKULL

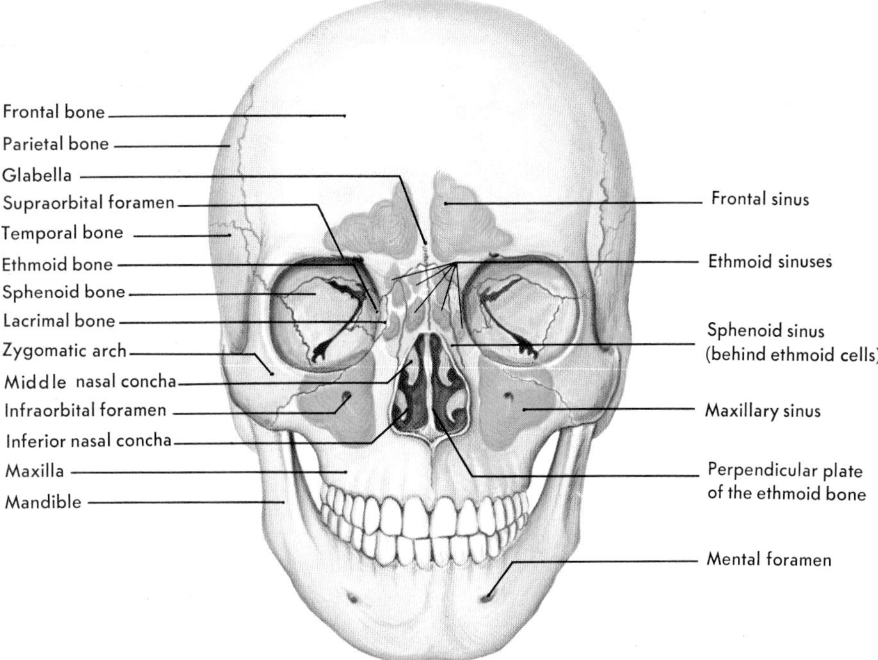

HEMISECTION OF THE HEAD AND NECK

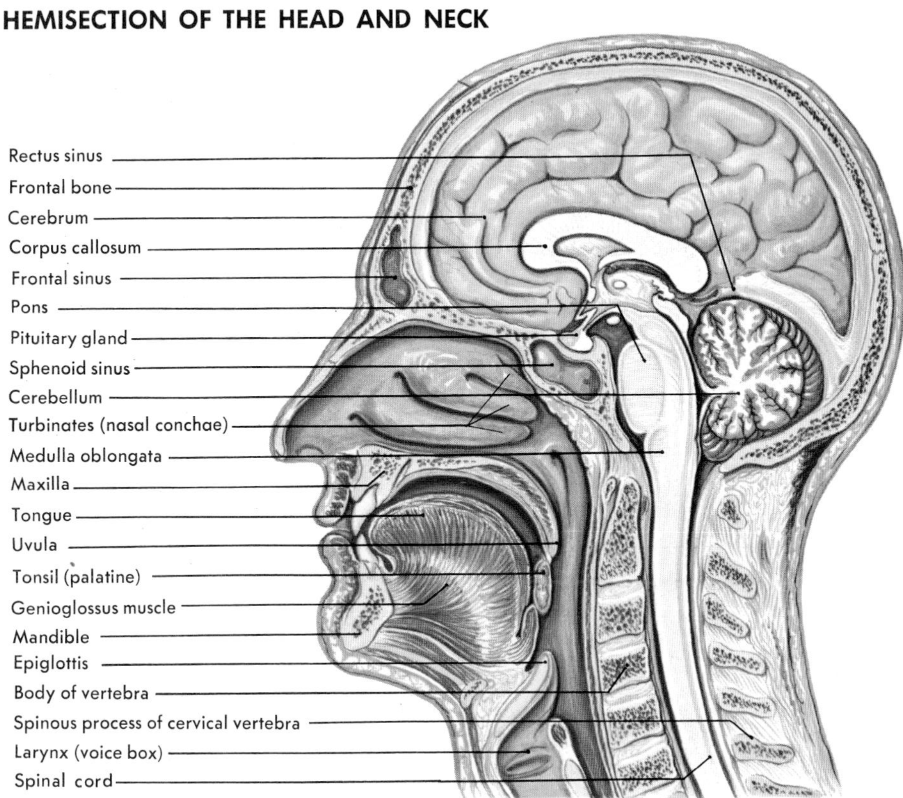

Plate XI

ANATOMY OF THE EAR

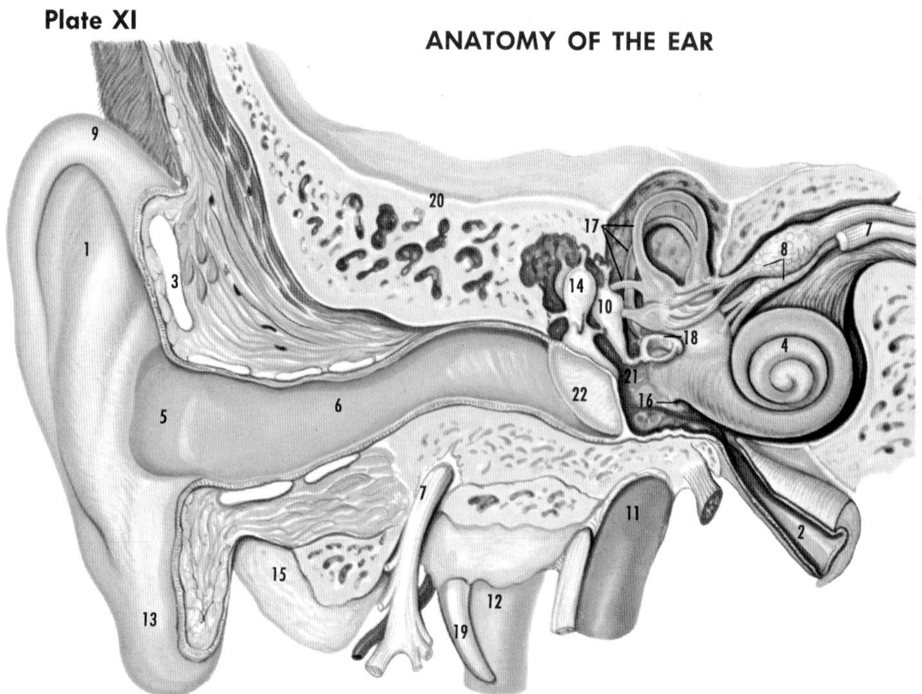

1. Anthelix
2. Auditory tube
3. Cartilage
4. Cochlea
5. Concha (bowl)
6. External acoustic meatus
7. Facial nerve
8. Ganglia of the vestibular nerve
9. Helix
10. Incus (anvil)
11. Internal carotid artery
12. Internal jugular vein
13. Lobe
14. Malleus (hammer)
15. Mastoid process
16. Round window
17. Semicircular canals
18. Stapes (stirrup)
19. Styloid process
20. Temporal bone
21. Tympanic cavity
22. Tympanic membrane (eardrum)

ANATOMY OF THE EYE

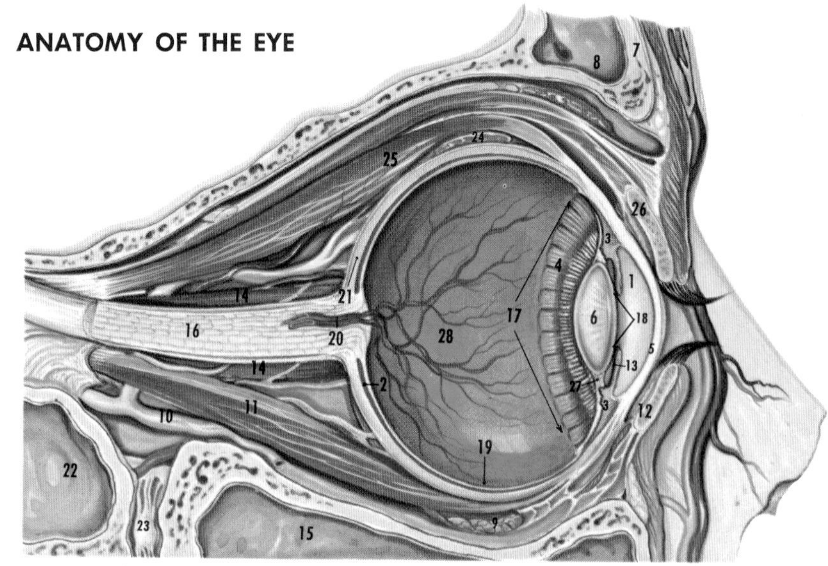

1. Aqueous chamber
2. Choroid
3. Ciliary muscle
4. Ciliary processes
5. Cornea
6. Crystalline lens
7. Frontal bone
8. Frontal sinus
9. Inferior oblique muscle
10. Inferior ophthalmic vein
11. Inferior rectus muscle
12. Inferior tarsus
13. Iris
14. Lateral rectus muscle
15. Maxillary sinus
16. Optic nerve
17. Ora serrata
18. Pupil of the iris
19. Retina
20. Retinal artery and vein
21. Sclera
22. Sphenoid sinus
23. Pterygopalatine ganglion
24. Superior oblique muscle
25. Superior rectus muscle
26. Superior tarsus
27. Suspensory ligament
28. Vitreous chamber

SCHEMATIC BODY CELL

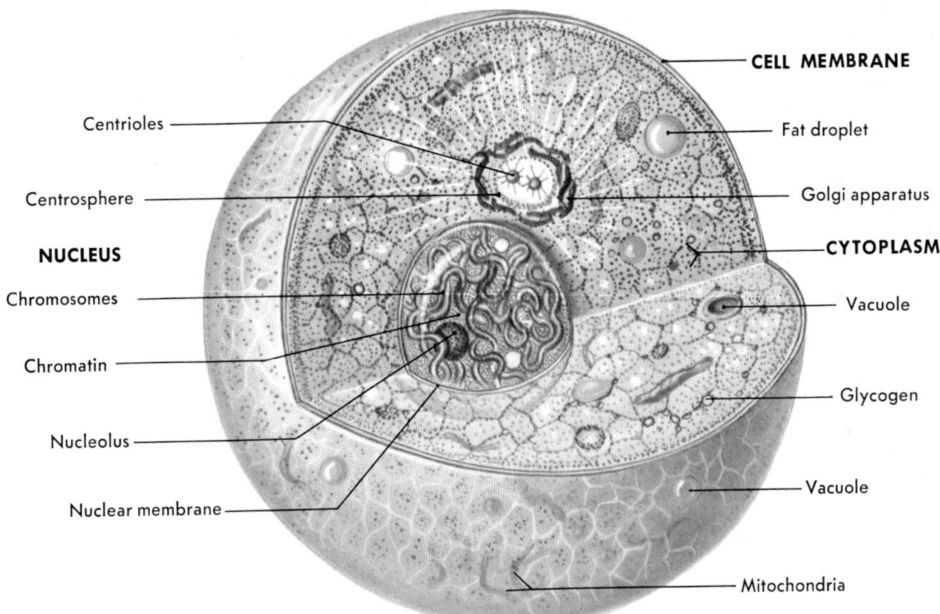

Every living cell, regardless of its shape or size, has three main parts: the cell membrane, cytoplasm, and nucleus. Together they constitute protoplasm. Billions of such cells as shown above make up the tissues of our bodies.

TYPES OF CELLS

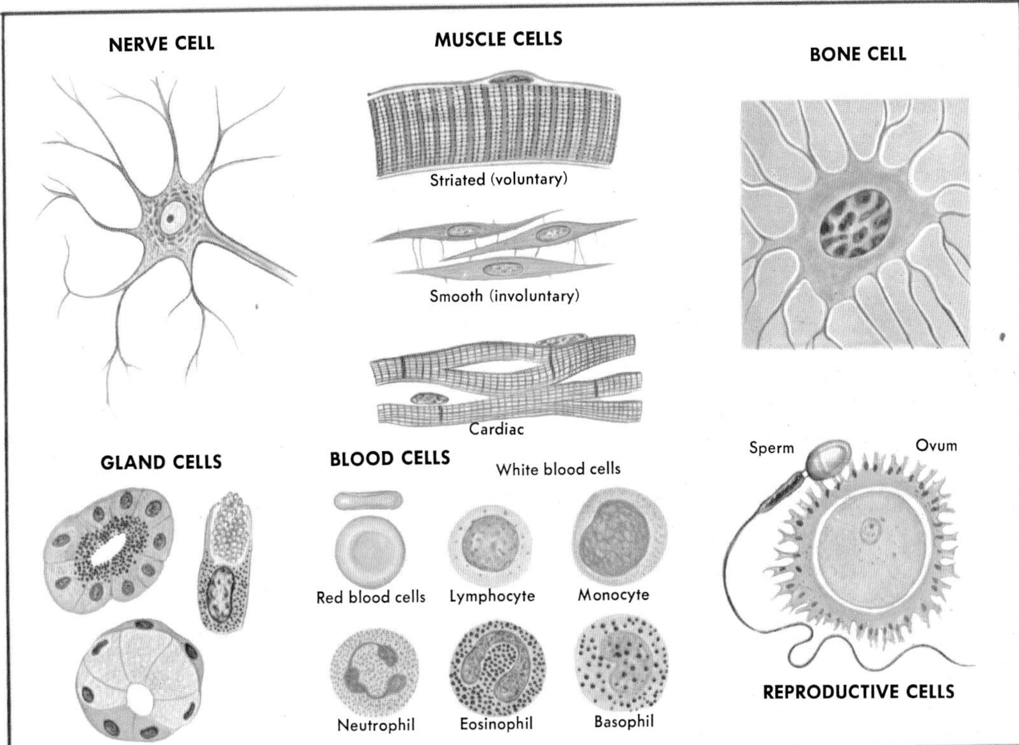

Plate XIII

SKELETON

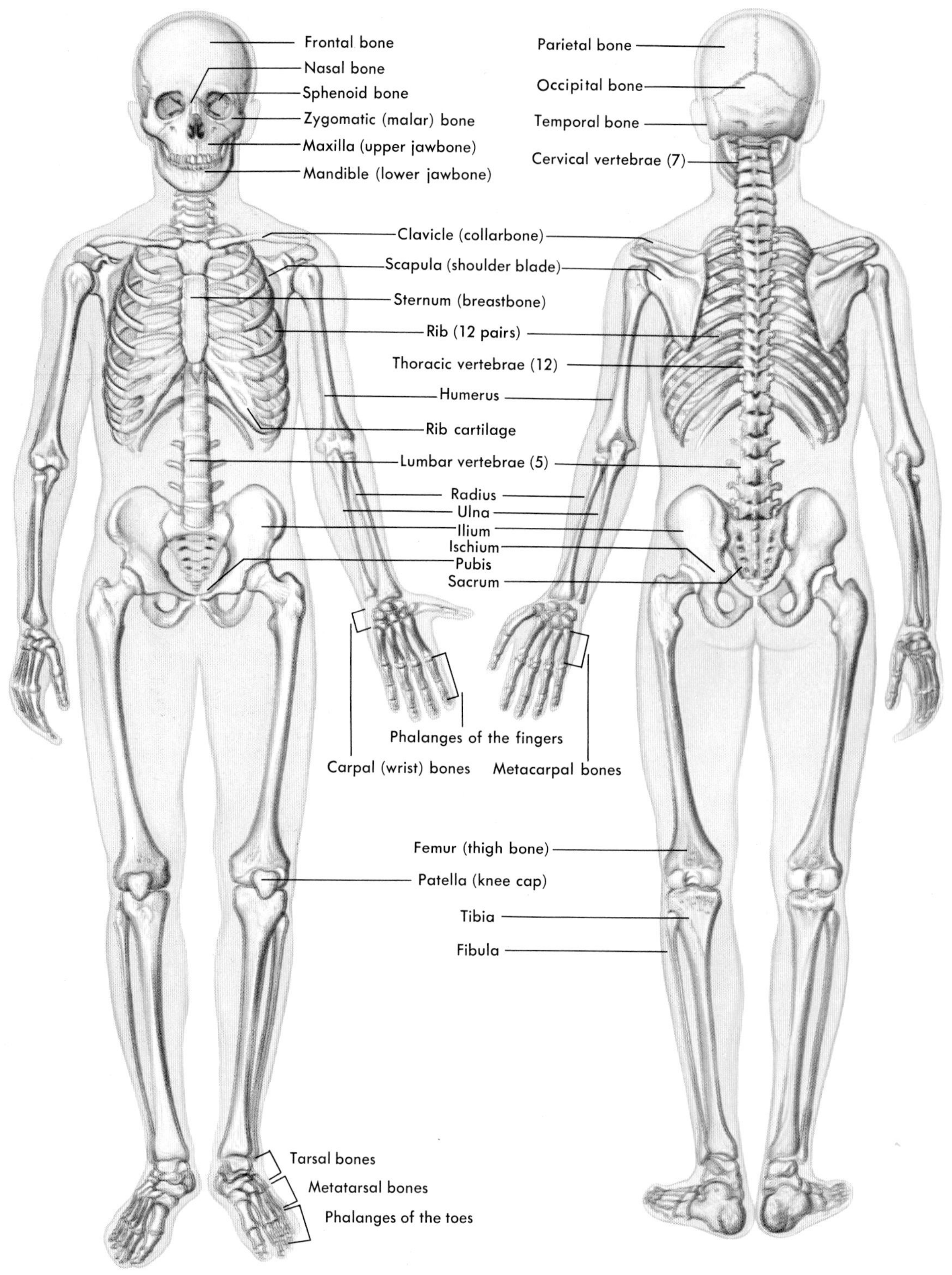

FEMALE PELVIC ORGANS

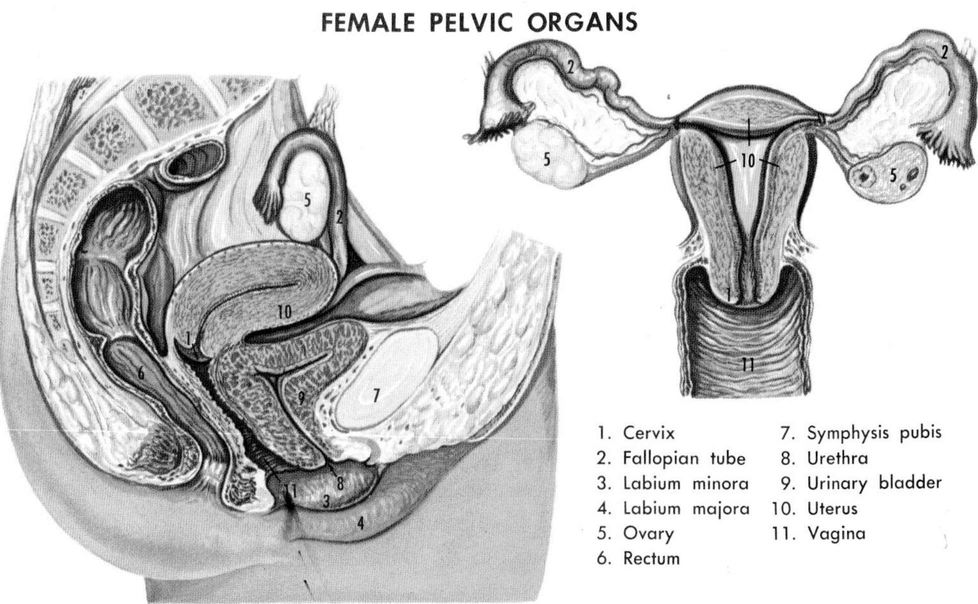

1. Cervix
2. Fallopian tube
3. Labium minora
4. Labium majora
5. Ovary
6. Rectum
7. Symphysis pubis
8. Urethra
9. Urinary bladder
10. Uterus
11. Vagina

MALE PELVIC ORGANS

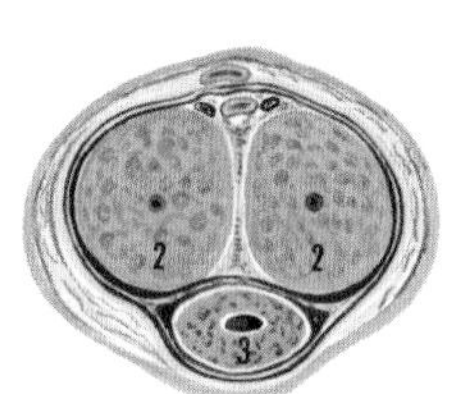

SECTION THROUGH PENIS

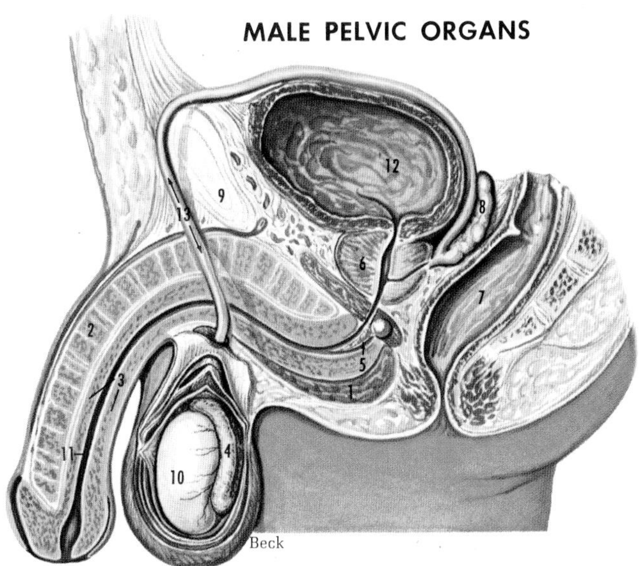

1. Bulb of urethra
2. Corpus cavernosum
3. Corpus spongiosum
4. Epididymis
5. Ejaculatory duct
6. Prostate gland
7. Rectum
8. Seminal vesicle
9. Symphysis pubis
10. Testis
11. Urethra
12. Urinary bladder
13. Vas deferens

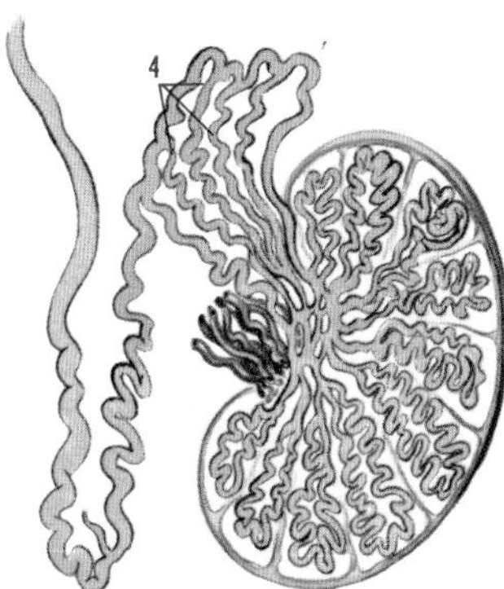

SCHEME OF DUCT ARRANGEMENT IN THE TESTIS AND EPIDIDYMIS

Plate XV

LYMPHATIC ORGANS

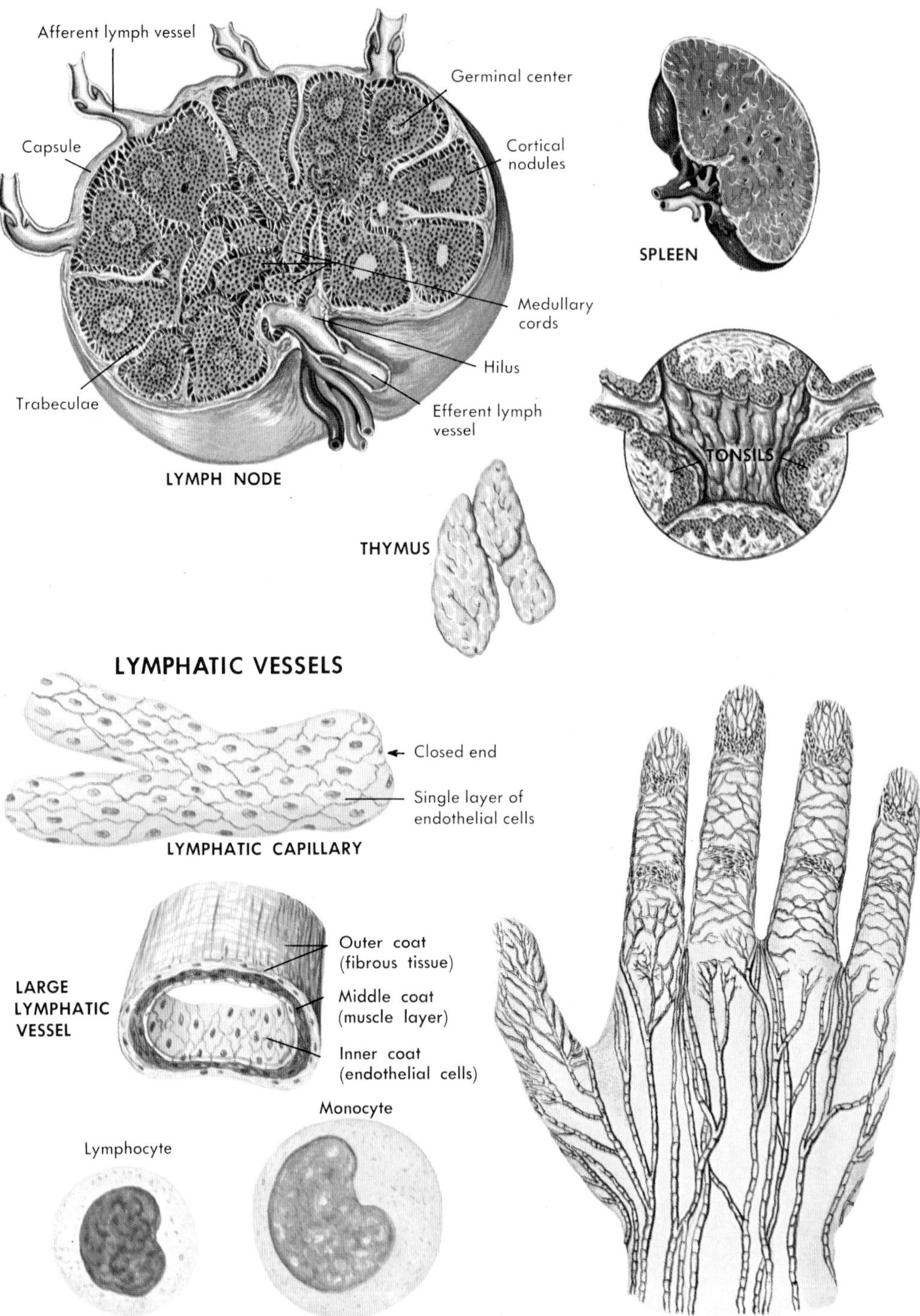

FREE CELLS OF THE LYMPHATIC SYSTEM

LYMPHATICS OF THE HAND

and that must be rid of their wastes. So blood supply to bone is important and abundant. For example, numerous blood vessels from the periosteum (bone covering) penetrate bone by way of *Volkmann's canals* to connect with blood vessels of an haversian canal. Also, one or more arteries supply the bone marrow in the internal medullary cavity of long bones.

Cartilage

Cartilage both resembles and differs from bone. Like bone, cartilage consists more of intercellular substance than of cells. Abundant collagenous fibrils reinforce the matrix of both tissues. But in cartilage the fibrils are embedded in a firm gel instead of in calcified cement substance as they are in bone. Hence cartilage has the flexibility of a firm plastic material rather than the rigidity of bone. Another difference is this—no canal system and no blood vessels penetrate cartilage matrix. Cartilage is avascular and bone is abundantly vascular. Cartilage cells like bone cells lie in lacunae. However, because no canals and blood

Fig. 38

Section of compact bone showing details of an haversian system.

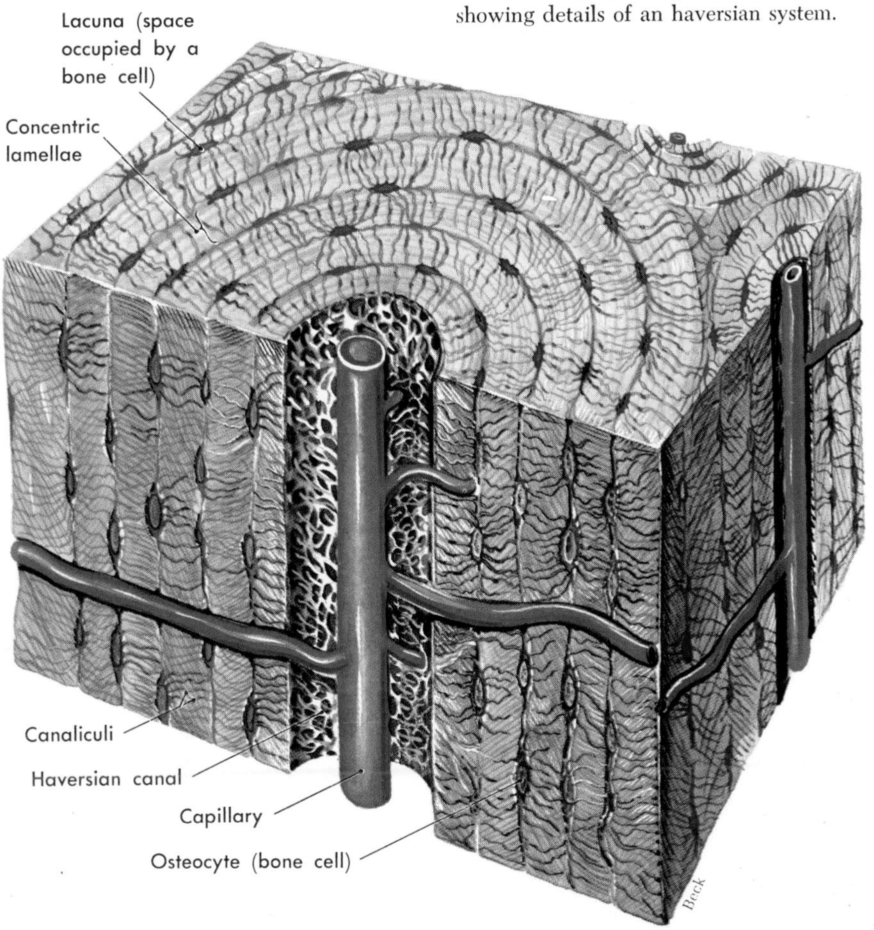

vessels interlace cartilage matrix, nutrients and oxygen can reach the scattered, isolated chondrocytes (cartilage cells) only by diffusion through the matrix gel, from capillaries in the fibrous covering of cartilage (perichondrium) or from synovial fluid in the case of articular cartilage.

Three types of cartilage are hyaline, fibrous, and elastic. They differ structurally mainly as to matrix fibrils. Collagenous fibrils are present in all three types but are most numerous in fibrocartilage. Hence it has the greatest tensile strength. Elastic cartilage matrix contains elastic fibers as well as collagenous fibers so has elasticity as well as firmness. Hyaline is the commonest type of cartilage. It resembles milk glass in appearance. In fact, its name is derived from the Greek word meaning glassy. A thin layer of hyaline cartilage covers articular surfaces of bones where it helps to cushion jolts. Fibrocartilage discs between the vertebrae also serve this purpose. For other locations of cartilage, see Table 2.

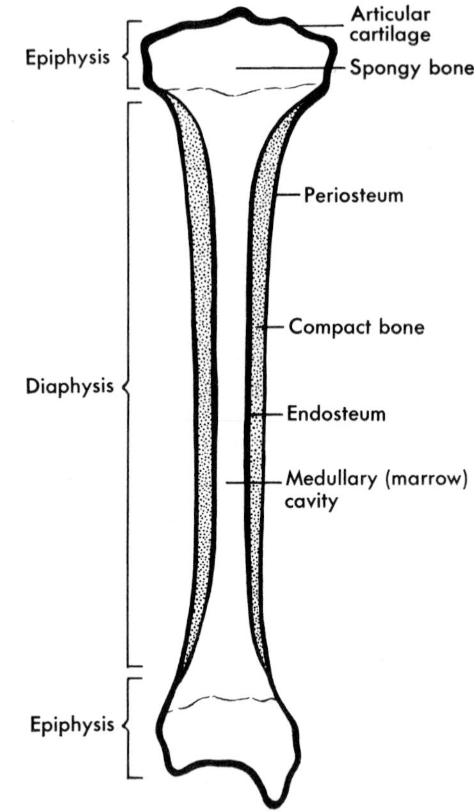

Fig. 39

Diagram to show the structure of a long bone as seen in longitudinal section (also see Fig. 40).

Bones

GROSS STRUCTURE

Types

There are four types of bones, classified according to their shapes, as follows:

1. *long bones*—femur, tibia, fibula, humerus, radius, ulna, and phalanges
2. *short bones*—carpals and tarsals (wrist and ankle bones)
3. *flat bones*—several cranial bones, such as frontal and parietal; also ribs and scapulae
4. *irregular bones*—vertebrae, sphenoid, ethmoid, sacrum, coccyx, and mandible

Structure

Long bones

Each long bone of the body consists of the following parts: (1) diaphysis, (2) epiphyses, (3) articular cartilage, (4) periosteum, (5) medullary (or marrow) cavity, and (6) endosteum (Figs. 39 and 40).

The *diaphysis* is the main shaftlike portion of a long bone. Several structural features accommodate it to its function of providing strong support without cumbersome weight—the thick compact bone used as construction material, for example, and the hollow cylindrical shape which offers the dual advantages of greater strength with less weight compared with a solid cylinder of the same size.

The *epiphyses* are the extremities of long bones. Their somewhat bulbous shape pro-

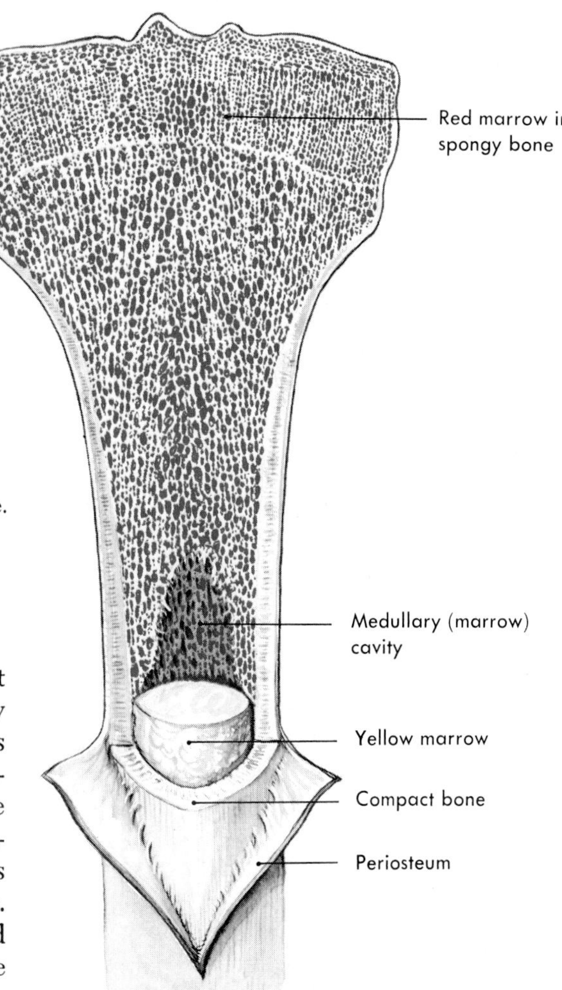

Fig. 40
Cutaway section of a long bone.

vides generous space for muscle attachment near joints and makes for greater stability of the joint. Lightness despite size is achieved by construction of porous cancellous bone with only an outer layer of dense compact bone. Arrangement of the lamellae corresponding to the lines of stress gives added strength to the epiphyses. Marrow fills the cancellous spaces—red marrow in the proximal epiphyses of the humerus and femur and yellow marrow in other epiphyses in the adult.

The *articular cartilage* is the thin layer of hyaline cartilage covering the articular surface of each epiphysis. Resiliency of this material cushions jars and blows.

The *periosteum* is a dense white fibrous membrane that covers bone except at joint surfaces, where articular cartilage forms the covering. Many of the fibers of the periosteum penetrate the underlying bone to weld these two structures to each other (the penetrating fibers are called Sharpey's fibers). Muscle tendon fibers interlace with periosteal fibers to anchor muscles firmly to bone.

The inner layer of the periosteum of growing bones contains osteoblasts (bone-forming cells). Because of its bone-forming cells and blood vessels, the periosteum is necessary for bone growth and repair and for its nutrition and, therefore, for life of its cells. In addition, it serves as the means for attaching muscle tendons and ligaments to bone.

The *medullary* (or *marrow*) *cavity*, running the length of the diaphysis, contains yellow or fatty bone marrow in the adult.

The *endosteum* is the membrane that lines the medullary cavity and haversian canals. It is composed of cells that become active osteoblasts (bone-forming cells) as needed.

Short bones

Short bones consist of a core of cancellous bone encased in a thin layer of compact bone.

Flat bones

A layer of cancellous bone lies between two plates of compact bone. Cancellous bone of the skull bones (diploe), ribs, and sternum contain red marrow.*

Irregular bones

Irregular bones are similar in structure to short bones; that is, a thin layer of compact bone forms a casing over cancellous bone.

NAMES AND NUMBERS

The human skeleton consists of two main parts: the *axial skeleton,* composed of the bones which form the upright part or axis of the body (the skull, hyoid bone, vertebral column, sternum, and ribs) and the *appendicular skeleton,* made up of the bones which are attached to the axial skeleton as appendages (that is, the upper and lower extremities). The names and numbers of the bones in each division of the skeleton, with an identifying remark about each, are given in Table 3. When you are trying to learn these names, locate each bone on your own body. Feel its outline whenever possible. Locate each bone on a skeleton if one is available. Study Figs. 41 to 44.

Axial skeleton

Skull

Twenty-eight irregularly shaped bones form the skull. Eleven of these are paired bones and six are single. All but one of the skull bones are so joined to each other as to be immovable. Only the lower jawbone (mandible) is movable. The skull consists of two major divisions: the cranium or brain case and the face.

Cranium. The frontal, parietal, and occipital bones form the top of the cranium, whereas the temporal bones and the great wings of the sphenoid form its sides. These same bones, plus the small cribriform plate of the ethmoid bone, make up the lower part of the cranium called the *cranial floor* or *base.* Its midportion is formed by the sphenoid bone which serves as a keystone anchoring the frontal, parietal, occipital, and ethmoid bones.

The *frontal bone* constitutes the skeletal framework for the forehead. It contains mucous-lined air-filled spaces, the *frontal sinuses,* and it forms the upper part of the orbits. It unites with the two parietal bones posteriorly in an immovable joint, the *coronal suture.* Several of the more prominent frontal bone markings are described in Table 4.

The two *parietal bones* give shape to the bulging topsides of the cranium. They form immovable joints with several bones: the *lambdoidal suture* with the occipital bone, the *squamous suture* with the temporal bone and part of the sphenoid, and the *coronal suture,* mentioned before, with the frontal bone.

The lower sides of the cranium and part of its floor are fashioned from two *temporal bones.* They house the middle and

*Note that red marrow is found in the adult in only a few locations, mainly in the diploe (spongy bone of the cranial bones), ribs, and sternum, in bodies of the vertebrae, and small amounts in the proximal epiphyses of the femurs and humeri. In newborn infants and children red marrow occurs in many more bones. Because of its hemopoietic function, bone marrow is one of the most important tissues of the body. Its very location, hidden within the bones, suggests its great importance. As the agent which coins millions of vital blood cells daily, it receives maximum protection from the body, the bones acting as a safe-deposit vault for it.

Text continued on p. 76.

Table 3. Bones of skeleton

Part of body	*Name of bone*	*Number*	*Description*
Axial skeleton (80 bones)			Bones that form upright axis of body—skull, hyoid, vertebral column, sternum, and ribs
Skull (28 bones)			
Cranium (8 bones)			Cranium forms floor for brain to rest on and helmetlike covering over it
	Frontal	1	Forehead bone; also forms most of roof of orbits (eye sockets) and anterior part of cranial floor
	Parietal	2	Prominent, bulging bones behind frontal bone; form topsides of cranial cavity
	Temporal	2	Form lower sides of cranium and part of cranial floor; contain middle and inner ear structures
	Occipital	1	Forms posterior part of cranial floor and walls
	Sphenoid	1	Keystone of cranial floor; forms its midportion; resembles bat with wings outstretched and legs extended downward posteriorly; lies behind and slightly above nose and throat; forms part of floor and side walls of orbit
	Ethmoid	1	Complicated irregular bone that helps make up anterior portion of cranial floor, medial wall of orbits, upper parts of nasal septum, and side walls and part of nasal roof; lies anterior to sphenoid and posterior to nasal bones
Face (14 bones)	Nasal	2	Small bones forming upper part of bridge of nose
	Maxillary	2	Upper jaw bones; form part of floor of orbit, anterior part of roof of mouth, and floor of nose and part of sidewalls of nose
	Zygomatic (malar)	2	Cheekbones; form part of floor and sidewall of orbit
	Mandible	1	Lower jaw bone; largest, strongest bone of face
	Lacrimal	2	Thin bones about size and shape of fingernail; posterior and lateral to nasal bones in medial wall of orbit; help form sidewall of nasal cavity; often missing in dry skull
	Palatine	2	Form posterior part of hard palate, floor, and part of sidewalls of nasal cavity and floor of orbit
	Inferior conchae (turbinates)	2	Thin scroll of bone forming kind of shell along inner surface of sidewall of nasal cavity; lies above roof of mouth
	Vomer	1	Forms lower and posterior part of nasal septum; shaped like ploughshare

Continued.

Table 3. Bones of skeleton—cont'd

Part of body	*Name of bone*	*Number*	*Description*
Axial skeleton —cont'd *Skull—cont'd*			
Ear bones (6 bones)	Malleus (hammer) Incus (anvil) Stapes (stirrup)	2 2 2	Tiny bones referred to as auditory ossicles in middle ear cavity in temporal bones; resemble, respectively, miniature hammer, anvil, and stirrup
Hyoid bone		1	U-shaped bone in neck between mandible and upper part of larynx; claims distinction as only bone in body not forming a joint with any other bone; is suspended by ligaments from styloid processes of temporal bones
Vertebral column (26 bones)			Not actually a column but a flexible segmented rod shaped like an elongated letter S; forms axis of body; head balanced above, ribs and viscera suspended in front, and lower extremities attached below; encloses spinal cord
	Cervical vertebrae	7	First or upper seven vertebrae
	Thoracic vertebrae	12	Next twelve vertebrae; twelve pairs of ribs attached to these
	Lumbar vertebrae	5	Next five vertebrae
	Sacrum	1	Five separate vertebrae until about 25 years of age; then fused to form one wedge-shaped bone
	Coccyx	1	Four or five separate vertebrae in child but fused into one in adult
Sternum and ribs (25 bones)			Sternum, ribs, and thoracic vertebrae together form bony cage known as *thorax;* ribs attach posteriorly to vertebrae, slant downward anteriorly to attach to sternum (see description of false ribs below)
	Sternum	1	Breast bone; flat dagger-shaped bone
	True ribs	7 pairs	Upper seven pairs; fasten to sternum by costal cartilages
	False ribs	5 pairs	False ribs do not attach to sternum directly; upper three pairs of false ribs attach by means of costal cartilage of seventh ribs; last two pairs do not attach to sternum at all; therefore, are called "*floating*"
Appendicular skeleton (126 bones)			Bones that are appended to axial skeleton: upper and lower extremities, including shoulder and hip girdles
Upper extremities (including shoulder girdle) (64 bones)	Clavicle	2	Collar bones; shoulder girdle joined to axial skeleton by articulation of clavicles with sternum; scapula does not form joint with axial skeleton

Table 3. Bones of skeleton—cont'd

Part of body	*Name of bone*	*Number*	*Description*
Appendicular skeleton—cont'd			
Upper extremities—cont'd	Scapula	2	Shoulder blades; scapulae and clavicles together comprise shoulder girdle
	Humerus	2	Long bone of upper arm
	Radius	2	Bone of thumb side of forearm
	Ulna	2	Bone of little finger side of forearm; longer than radius
	Carpals (navicular, lunate, triquetrum, pisiform, greater and lesser multangular, capitate, and hamate)	16	Arranged in two rows at proximal end of hand (Figs. 69 and 70)
	Metacarpals	10	Long bones forming framework of palm of hand
	Phalanges	28	Miniature long bones of fingers, three in each finger, two in each thumb
Lower extremities (62 bones)	Ossa coxae or pelvic bones	2	The large hip bones; with sacrum and coccyx these three bones form basinlike pelvic cavity; lower extremities attached to axial skeleton by pelvic bones
	Femur	2	Thigh bone; longest, strongest bone of body
	Patella	2	Kneecap; largest sesamoid bone of body*; is embedded in tendon of quadriceps femoris muscle
	Tibia	2	Shin bone
	Fibula	2	Long, slender bone of lateral side of lower leg
	Tarsals (calcaneus, talus, navicular, first, second, and third cuneiforms, cuboid)	14	Bones that form heel and proximal or posterior half of foot (Fig. 74)
	Metatarsals	10	Long bones of feet
	Phalanges	28	Miniature long bones of toes; two in each great toe, three in other toes
Total		206*	

*An inconstant number of small, flat, round bones known as *sesamoid bones* (because of their resemblance to sesame seeds) is found in various tendons in which considerable pressure develops. Because the number of these bones varies greatly between individuals, only two of them, the patellae, have been counted among the 206 bones of the body. Generally two of them can be found in each thumb (in flexor tendon near metacarpophalangeal and interphalangeal joints) and great toe plus several others in the upper and lower extremities. *Wormian bones,* the small islets of bone frequently found in some of the cranial sutures, have not been counted in this list of 206 bones either because of their variable occurrence.

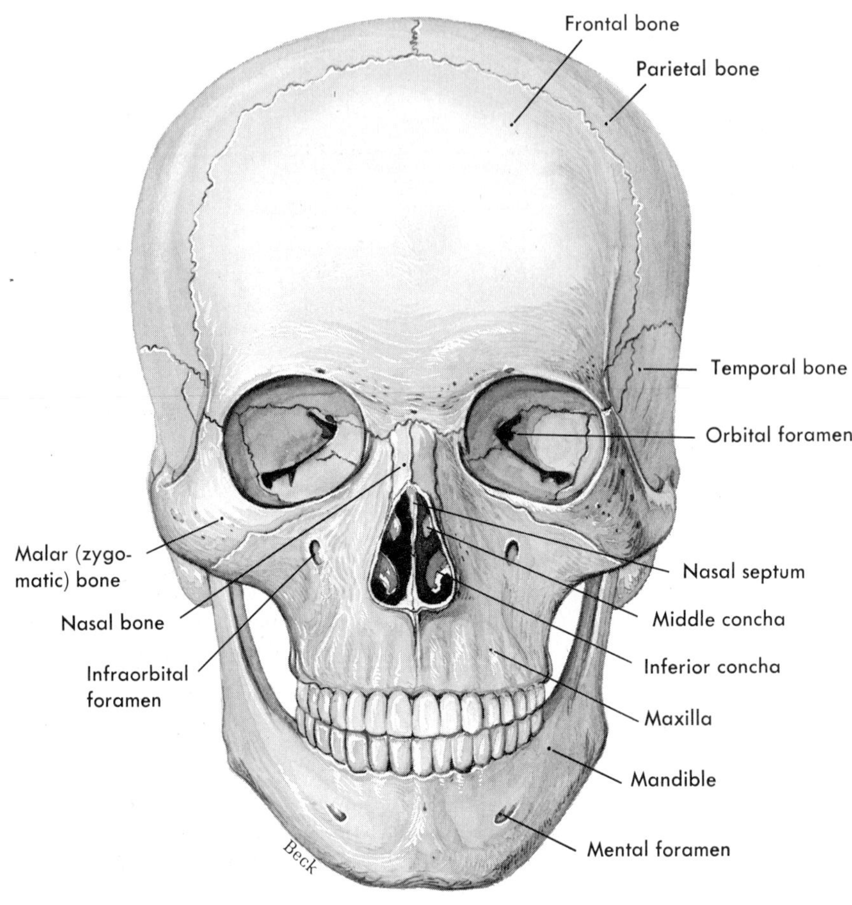

Fig. 41
Skull viewed from the front.

inner ear structures and contain the *mastoid air cells,* notable because of the occurrence of mastoiditis, an inflammation of the mucous lining of these spaces. A description of several other temporal bone markings is included in Table 4.

The *occipital bone* makes the framework of the lower, posterior part of the skull. It forms immovable joints with three other cranial bones—the parietal, temporal, and sphenoid—and a movable joint with the first cervical vertebra. Consult Table 4 for a description of some of its markings.

The *sphenoid bone* resembles a bat with its wings outstretched and legs extended downward posteriorly. It constitutes the center portion of the cranial floor and forms part of floor and sidewalls of the orbit. It contains fairly large mucosa-lined air-filled spaces, the *sphenoid sinuses.* Several prominent sphenoid markings are described in Table 4 (also see Figs. 45 to 47).

The *ethmoid,* a complicated, irregular bone, lies anterior to the sphenoid but posterior to the nasal bones. It helps fashion the anterior part of the cranial floor, the medial walls of the orbits, the upper parts of the nasal septum and of the sidewalls

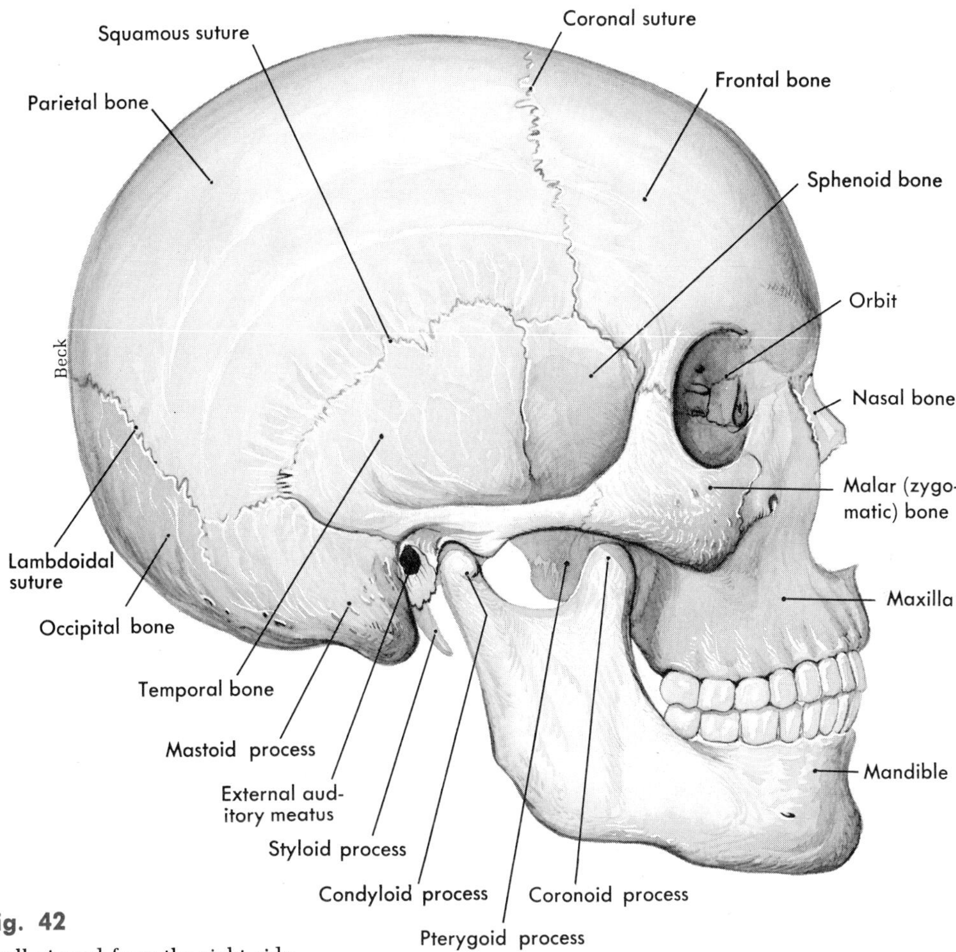

Fig. 42
Skull viewed from the right side.

of the nasal cavity, and the part of the nasal roof perforated by small foramina through which olfactory nerve branches reach the brain. The lateral masses of the ethmoid are honeycombed with sinus spaces. More ethmoid markings are described in Table 4 (also see Figs. 45, 47, and 51 to 53).

Face bones. Fourteen bones are commonly said to form the framework of the face, but actually more are involved since some of the cranial bones, particularly the frontal and ethmoid, also help shape the face.

Just as the sphenoid acts as the keystone in the architecture of the cranium, so the *maxillae* serve in this capacity for the face. With the exception of the mandible, all the face bones articulate with the maxillae, which also articulate with each other, in the midline. The maxillae form part of the floor of the orbits, part of the roof of the mouth, and part of the floor and sidewalls of the nose. Each maxilla contains a mucosa-lined space, the maxillary sinus or *antrum of Highmore*. This sinus is the largest of the paranasal sinuses. For other markings of the maxillae see Table 4.

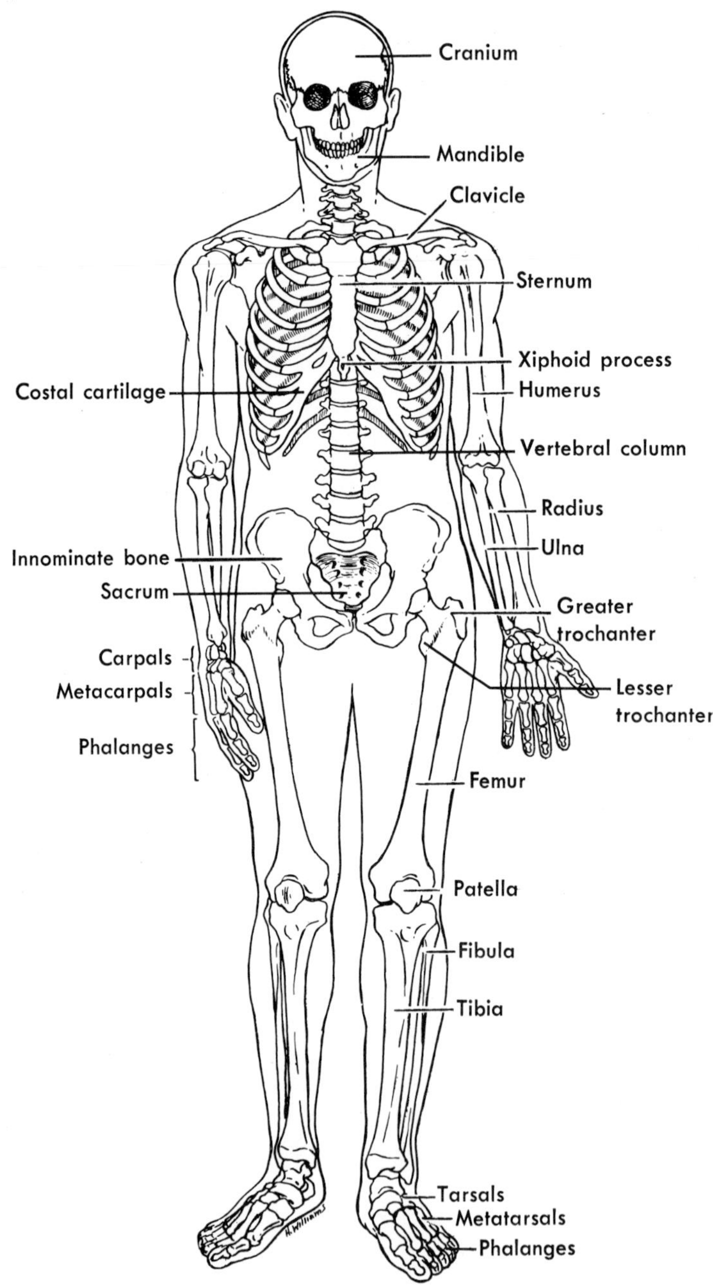

Fig. 43

Skeleton, anterior view.

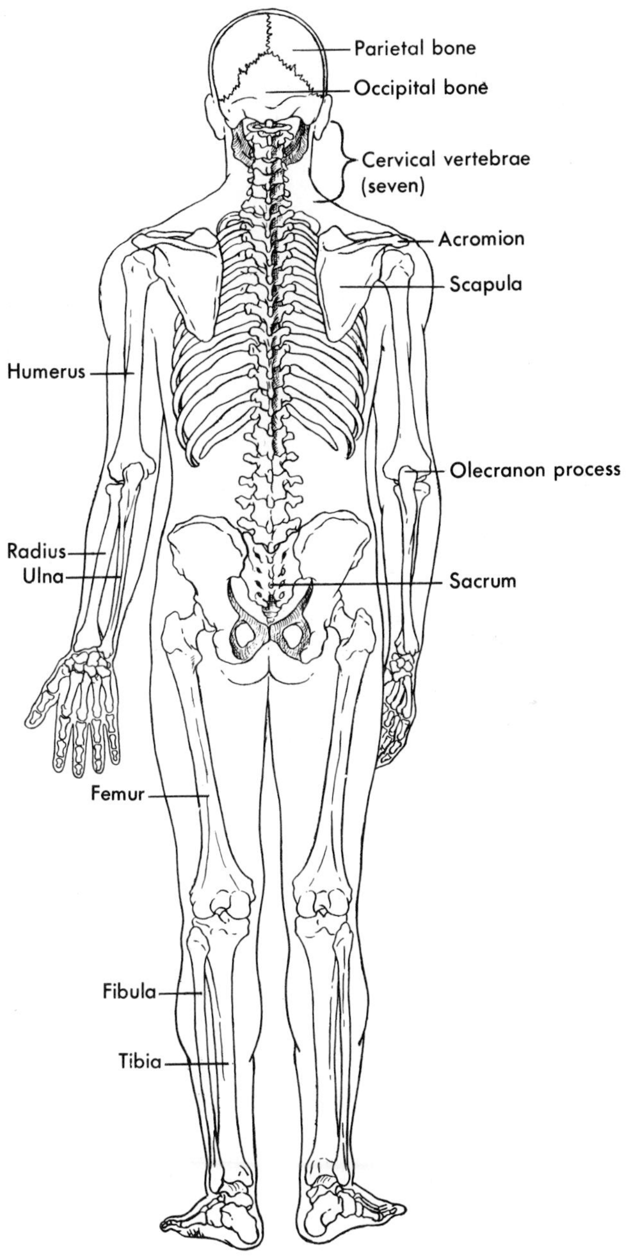

Fig. 44
Skeleton, posterior view.

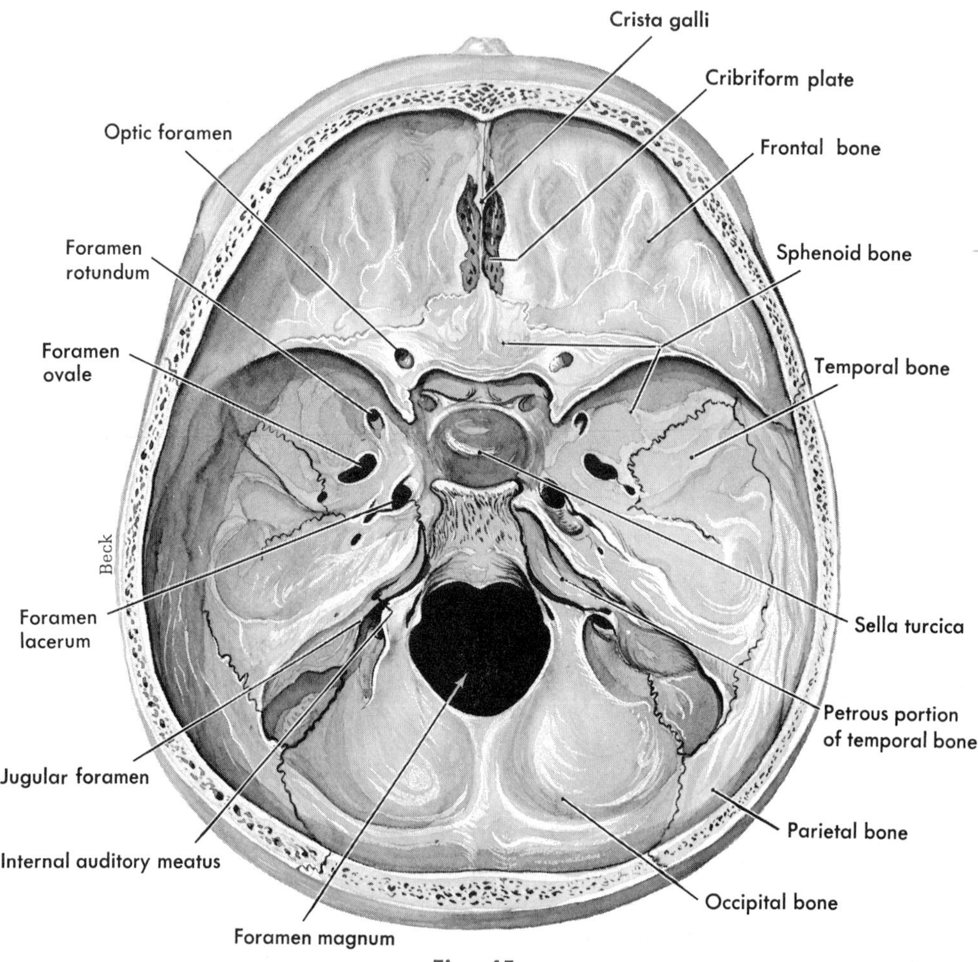

Fig. 45

Floor of the cranial cavity.

Unlike the upper jaw, which is formed by a pair of bones, the lower jaw consists of a single bone, the *mandible,* due to fusion of its halves during infancy. It is the largest, strongest bone of the face. It articulates with the temporal bone in the only movable joint of the skull. Its major markings are identified in Table 4.

The cheek is shaped by the underlying *zygomatic* or malar bone. This bone also forms the outer margin of the orbit and, with the zygomatic process of the temporal bone, makes the zygomatic arch. It articulates with four other face bones: the maxillae and the temporal, frontal, and sphenoid bones.

Shape is given to the nose by the two *nasal bones,* which form the upper part of the bridge of the nose, and *cartilage,* the lower part. Though small bones, the nasal bones enter into five articulations: with the perpendicular plate of the ethmoid, the cartilaginous part of the nasal septum, the frontal bone, maxillae, and with each other.

An almost paper-thin bone, shaped and sized about like a fingernail, lies just posterior and lateral to each nasal bone. It

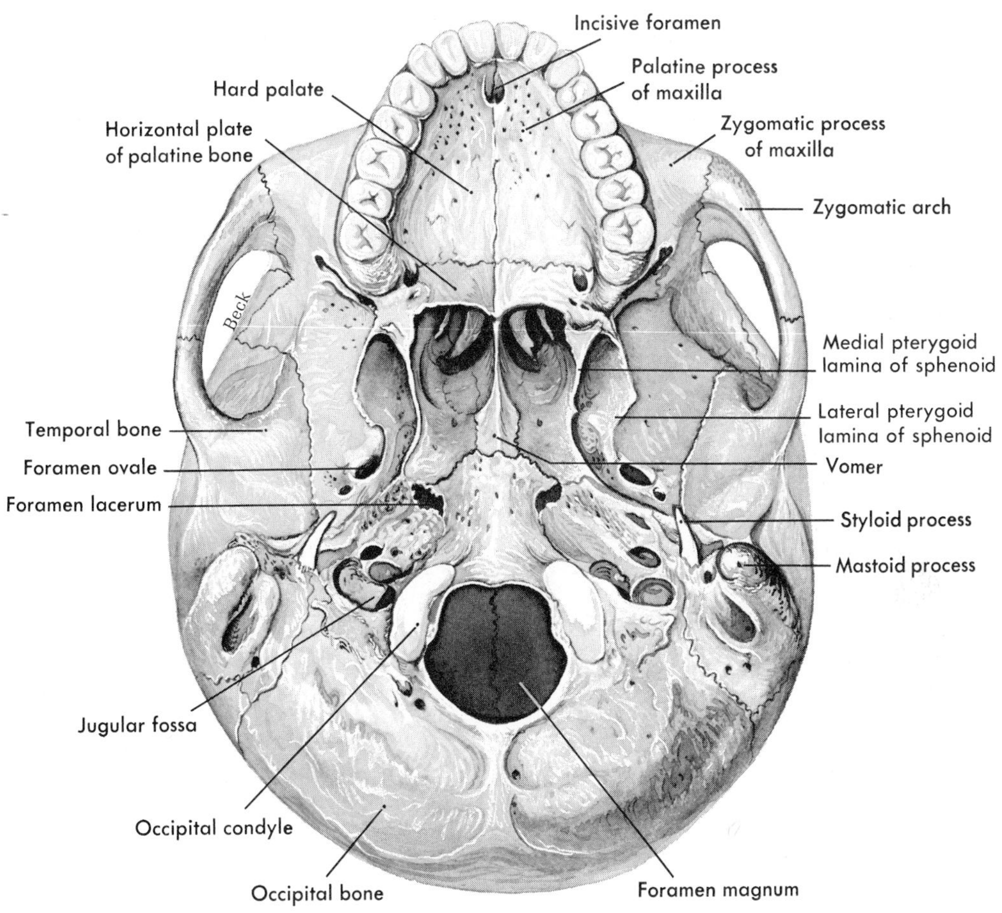

Fig. 46

Skull viewed from below.

helps form the sidewall of the nasal cavity and the medial wall of the orbit. Because it contains a groove for the nasolacrimal duct, this bone is called the *lacrimal bone.* It joins the maxilla, frontal bone, and ethmoid.

An irregular bone whose horizontal and vertical portions are joined in such a way as to make the bone roughly L shaped and which forms the framework for the inferior and lateral walls of the posterior part of the nasal cavity is known as the *palatine bone* because it also forms the posterior part of the hard palate. In addition, it has a small upper projection which helps form the floor of the orbit. The two palatine bones are united in the midline like two L's facing each other. They articulate also with the maxillae and the sphenoid.

The *inferior nasal concha* is a scroll-like bone which forms a kind of ledge projecting into the nasal cavity from its lateral wall. In each nasal cavity there are three of these ledges, formed respectively by the superior and middle conchae (which are projections of the ethmoid) and the inferior concha (which is a separate bone). They are mucosa covered and divide each nasal

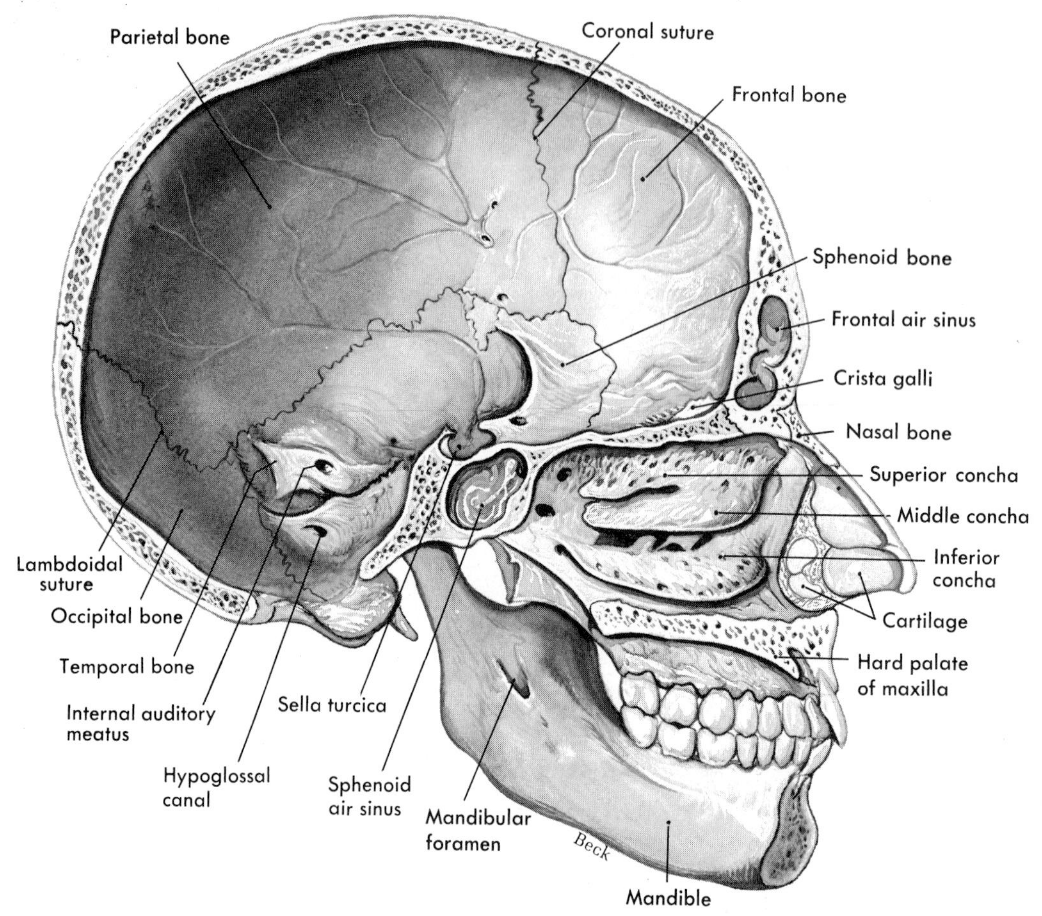

Fig. 47

Left half of skull viewed from within. The perpendicular plate of the ethmoid is removed to reveal the nasal concha.

cavity into three narrow, irregular channels, the *nasal meati.* The inferior nasal conchae form immovable joints with the ethmoid, lacrimal, maxillary, and palatine bones.

Two structures which enter into the formation of the nasal septum have already been mentioned, the perpendicular plate of the ethmoid bone and the septal cartilage. One other structure, the *vomer bone,* completes the septum posteriorly. It is usually described as being shaped like a ploughshare. It forms immovable joints with four bones: the sphenoid, ethmoid, palatine, and maxillae.

Ear bones. See Table 3.

Special features. Sutures, fontanels, sinuses, orbits, nasal septum, and wormian bones are described in Table 4.

Hyoid bone

The hyoid bone is a single bone in the neck—a part of the axial skeleton. Its U shape may be felt just above the larynx and below the mandible where it is suspended

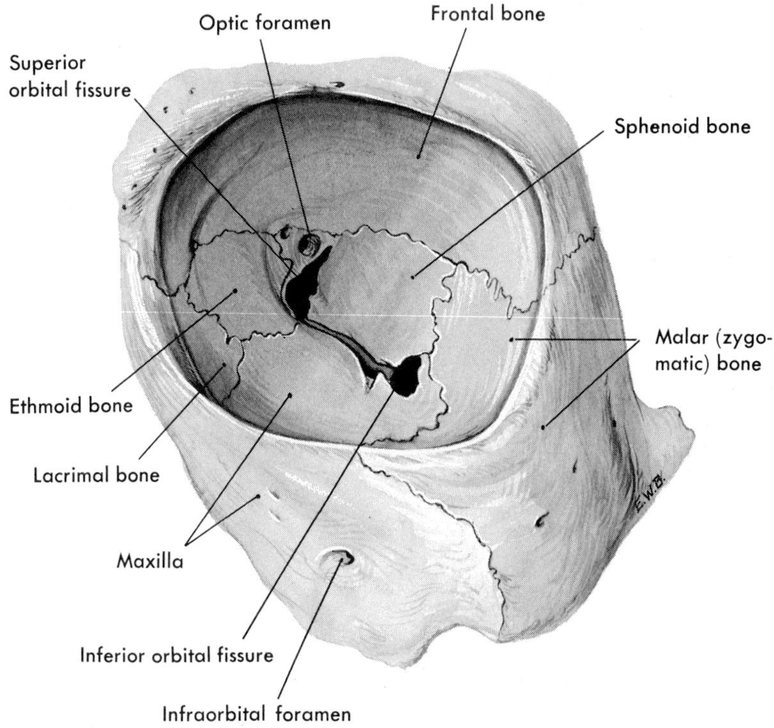

Fig. 48
Bones that form the left orbit.

from the styloid processes of the temporal bones. One of the pairs of extrinsic tongue muscles (hyoglossus) originates on the hyoid bone, and certain muscles of the floor of the mouth (mylohyoid, geniohyoid) insert on it (Fig. 54). The hyoid claims the distinction of being the only bone in the body which does not articulate with any other bone.

Vertebral column

The vertebral column constitutes the longitudinal axis of the skeleton. It is a flexible rather than a rigid column because it is segmented—that is, made up of twenty-six (typical in adult) separate bones called vertebrae, so joined to each other as to permit forward, backward, and sideways movement of the column. The head is balanced on top of this column, the ribs and viscera are suspended in front, the lower extremities are attached below, and the spinal cord is enclosed within. It is, indeed, the "backbone" of the body.

The seven *cervical vertebrae* constitute the skeletal framework of the neck. The next twelve vertebrae are called *thoracic vertebrae* for the obvious reason that they lie behind the thoracic cavity. The next five spinal bones, the *lumbar vertebrae,* support the small of the back. Below the lumbar vertebrae lie the *sacrum* and *coccyx.* In the adult the sacrum is a single bone which has resulted from the fusion of five separate vertebrae, and the coccyx is a single bone that has resulted from the fusion of four or five vertebrae.

All the vertebrae resemble each other

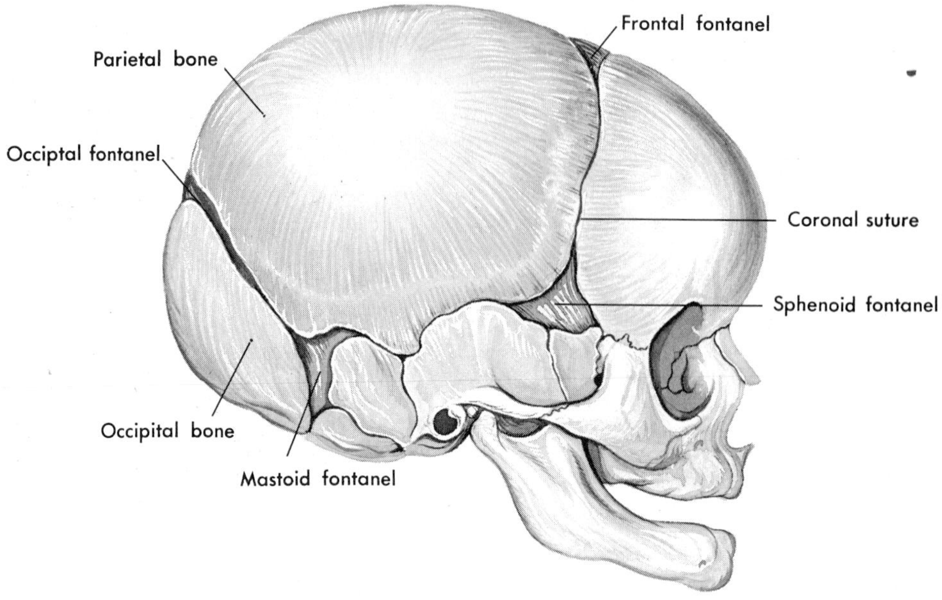

Fig. 49
Skull at birth viewed from side.

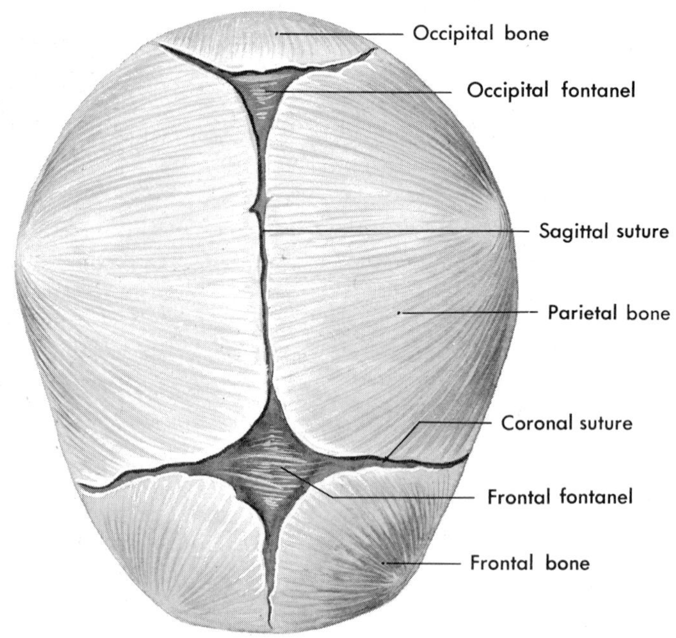

Fig. 50
Skull at birth viewed from above.

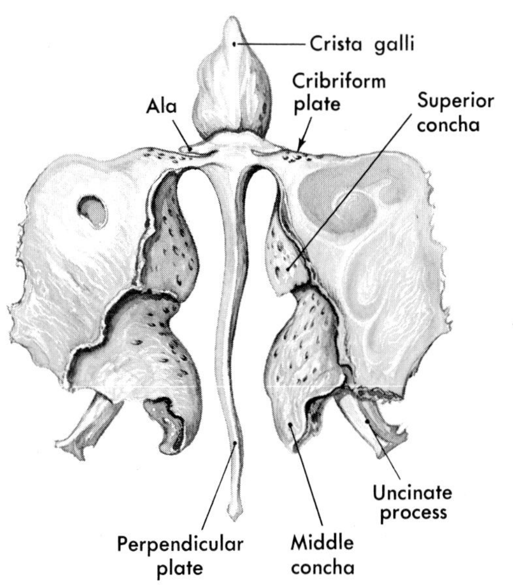

Fig. 51
Ethmoid bone viewed from behind.

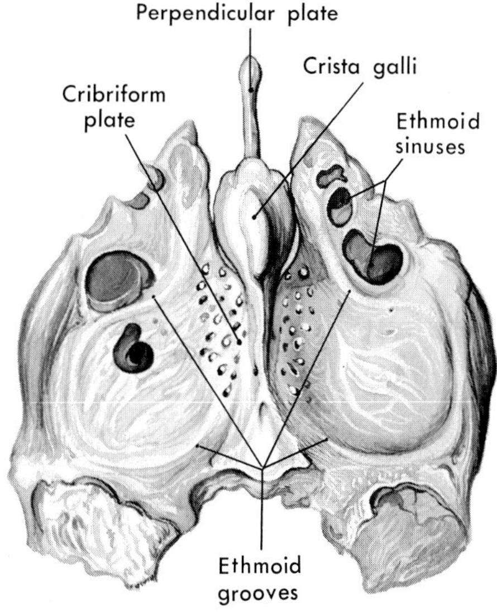

Fig. 52
Ethmoid bone viewed from above.

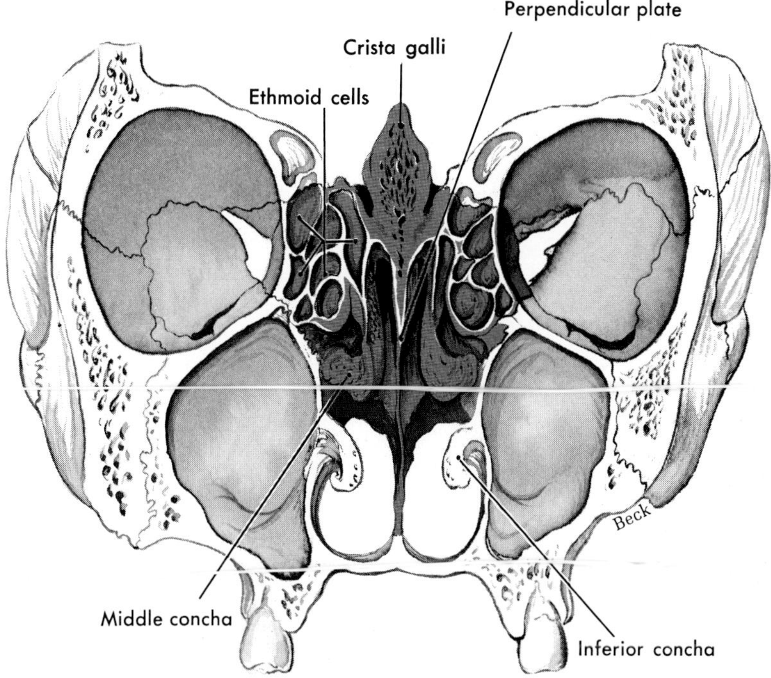

Fig. 53
Skull in coronal section to reveal the ethmoid bone (shown in red) as seen from behind.

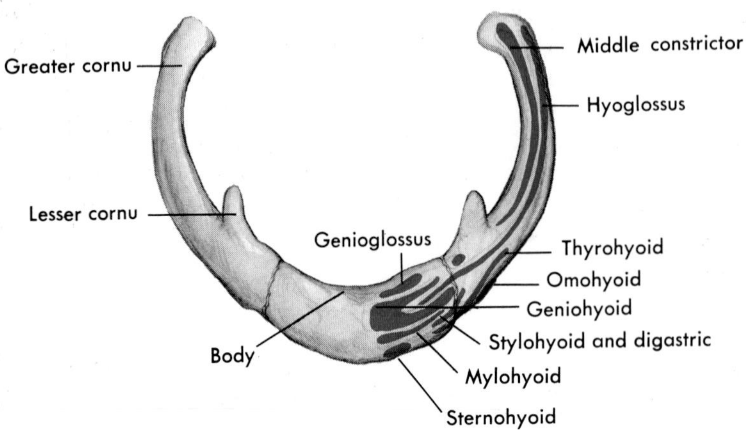

Fig. 54

Hyoid bone with muscle attachments.

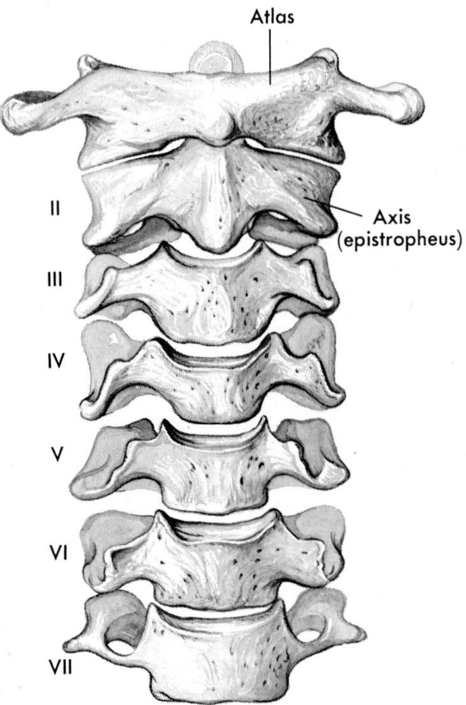

Fig. 55

The seven cervical vertebrae viewed from in front.

in certain features and differ in others. For example, all except the first cervical vertebra have a flat, rounded mass placed anteriorly and centrally, known as the *body,* plus a sharp or blunt *spinous process* projecting inferiorly in the posterior midline and two transverse processes projecting laterally. All but the sacrum and coccyx have a central opening, the *vertebral foramen.* An upward projection (the *dens*) from the body of the second cervical vertebra furnishes an axis for rotating the head. A long, blunt spinous process which can be felt at the back of the base of the neck characterizes the seventh cervical vertebra. Each thoracic vertebra has articular facets for the ribs. More detailed descriptions of separate vertebrae are given in Table 4. The vertebral column as a whole articulates with the head, ribs, and hip bones, whereas the individual vertebrae articulate with each other in joints between their bodies and between their articular processes. For a description of intervertebral joints, see Table 6.

In order to increase the carrying strength of the vertebral column and to make balance possible in the upright position, the vertebral column is curved. At birth there is a continuous posterior convexity from head to coccyx. Later, as the child learns to sit and stand, secondary posterior concavities necessary for balance develop in the cervical and lumbar regions. Not uncommonly, spinal curves deviate from the normal. For example, the lumbar curve frequently shows an exaggerated concavity *(lordosis)*, whereas any of the regions may have a lateral curvature *(scoliosis)*. The so-called hunchback is an exaggerated convexity in the thoracic region *(kyphosis)*.

Sternum

The *medial part* of the anterior chest wall is supported by the *sternum*, a somewhat dagger-shaped bone consisting of three parts: the upper handle part or *manubrium*, the middle blade part or *body*, and a blunt cartilaginous lower tip, the *xiphoid process*. The latter ossifies during adult life. The manubrium articulates with the clavicle and first rib, whereas the next nine ribs join the body of the sternum, either directly or indirectly, by means of the *costal cartilages*.

Ribs

Twelve pairs of ribs, together with the vertebral column and sternum, form the

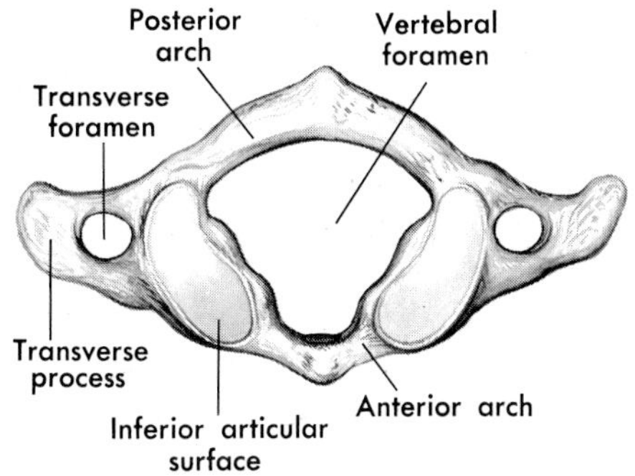

Fig. 56

First cervical vertebra (atlas) viewed from below.

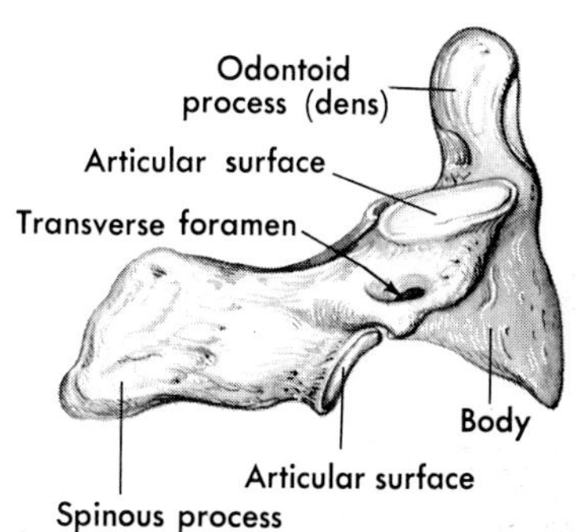

Fig. 57

Second cervical vertebra (the axis or epistropheus) viewed from the side.

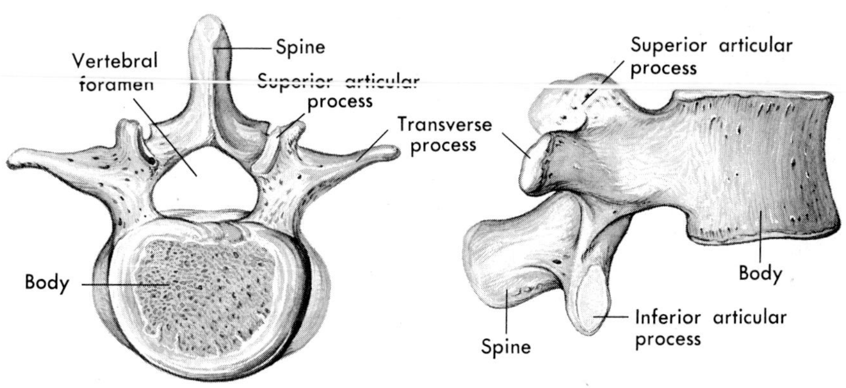

Fig. 58

Third lumbar vertebra viewed from above.

Fig. 59

Third lumbar vertebra viewed from side.

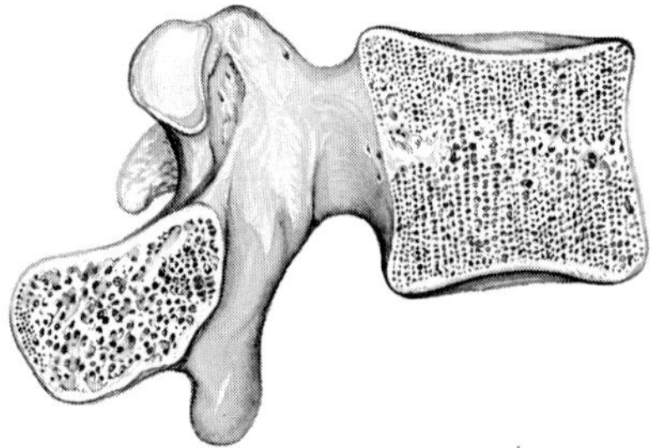

Fig. 60
Third lumbar vertebra sectioned.

bony cage known as the *thorax*. Each rib articulates with both the body and transverse process of its corresponding thoracic vertebra. In addition, the second through the ninth ribs articulate with the body of the vertebra above. From its vertebral attachment each rib curves outward, then forward and downward, a mechanical fact important for breathing. Anteriorly each of the first seven ribs joins a costal cartilage which attaches it to the sternum. Each of the costal cartilages of the next three ribs, however, joins the cartilage of the rib above to be thus indirectly attached to the sternum. Because the two costal cartilages of the eleventh and twelfth ribs do not attach even indirectly to the sternum, they are designated floating ribs.

Appendicular skeleton

Upper extremity

The upper extremity consists of the bones of the shoulder girdle, upper arm, lower arm, wrist, and hand. Two bones, the *clavicle* and *scapula,* compose the *shoulder girdle.* Contrary to appearances, this girdle forms only one bony joint with the trunk: the sternoclavicular joint between the sternum and clavicle. At its outer end the clavi-

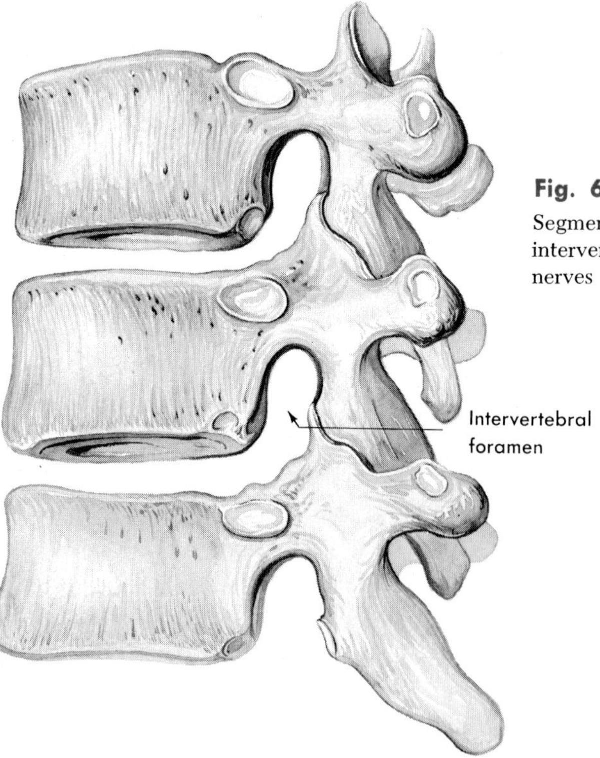

Fig. 61
Segment of the vertebral column showing the intervertebral foramina through which spinal nerves emerge from the spinal cavity.

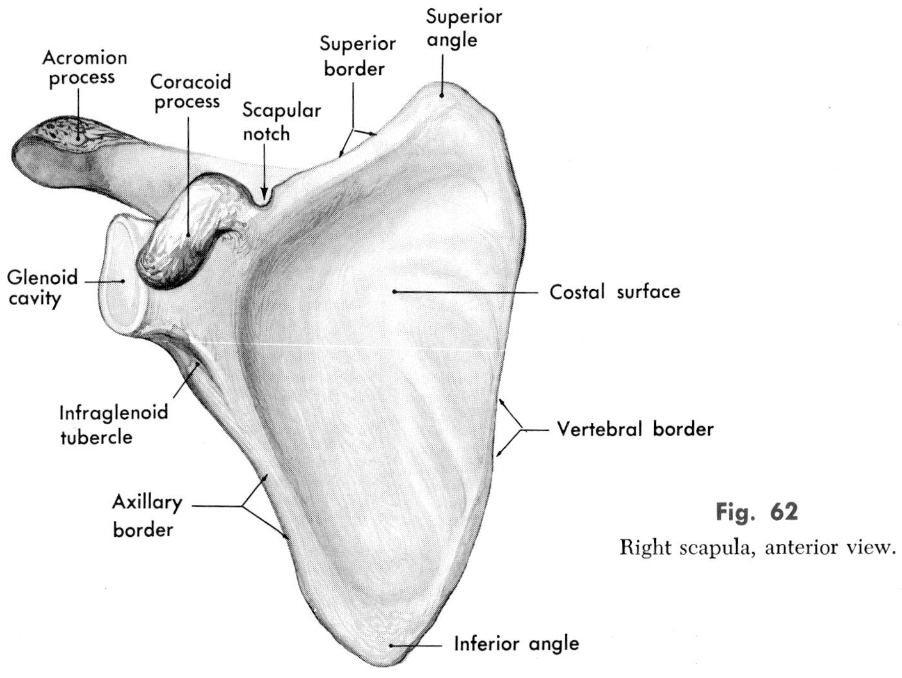

Fig. 62
Right scapula, anterior view.

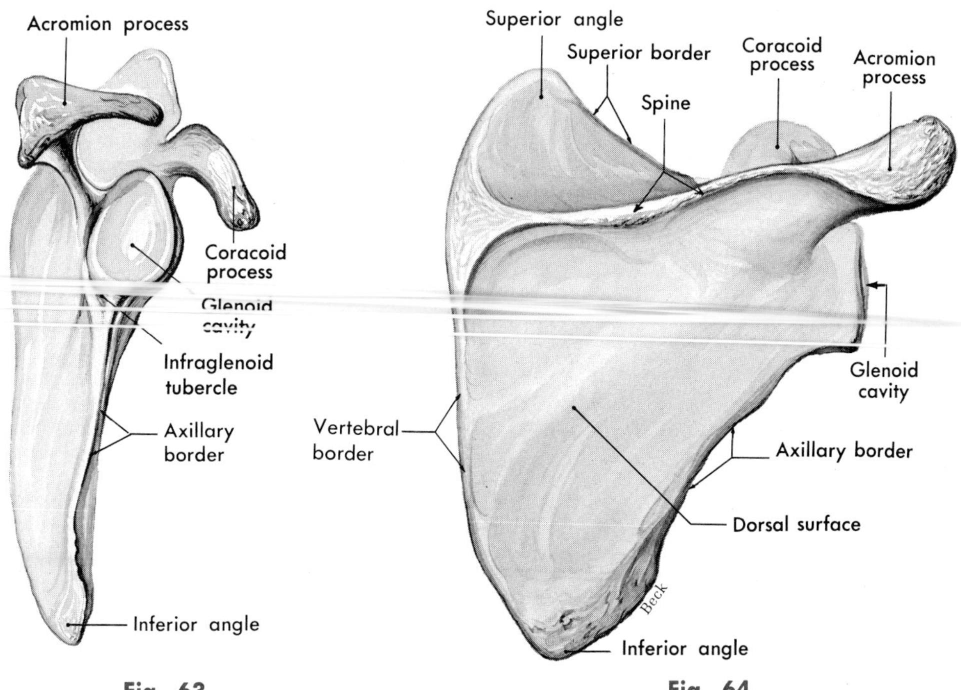

Fig. 63
Right scapula, lateral view.

Fig. 64
Right scapula, posterior view.

cle articulates with the scapula which attaches to the ribs by muscles and tendons, not by a joint. All shoulder movements, therefore, involve the sternoclavicular joint. Various markings of the scapula are described in Table 4.

The *humerus* or upper arm bone, like other long bones, consists of a shaft or diaphysis and two ends or epiphyses. The upper epiphysis bears several identifying structures: the head, anatomical neck, greater and lesser tubercles, intertubercular groove, and surgical neck. On the diaphysis are found the deltoid tuberosity and the radial groove. The distal epiphysis has four projections—the medial and lateral epicondyles, the capitulum, and the trochlea—and two depressions, the olecranon and coronoid fossae. For descriptions of all of these markings, see Table 4. The humerus articulates proximally with the scapula and distally with both the radius and ulna.

Two bones form the framework for the lower arm: the *radius* on the thumb side and the *ulna* on the little finger side. At the proximal end of the ulna, the olecranon process projects posteriorly and the coronoid process anteriorly. There are also two depressions: the semilunar notch on the anterior surface and the radial notch on the lateral surface. The distal end has two projections: a rounded head and a sharper styloid process. For more detailed identification of these markings, see Table 4. The ulna articulates proximally with the humerus and radius and distally with a fibrocartilaginous disc but not with any of the carpal bones.

The radius has three projections: two at its proximal end, the head and deltoid tuberosity, and one at its distal end, the styloid process (Figs. 67 and 68). There are two proximal articulations: one with the capitulum of the humerus and the other with the radial notch of the ulna. The three distal articulations are with the navicular and lunate carpal bones and with the head of the ulna.

The eight *carpal bones* (Figs. 69 and 70) form what most people think of as the upper part of the hand but what, anatomically speaking, is the wrist. Only one of these bones is evident from the outside, the *pisiform bone,* which projects anteriorly on the little finger side as a small, rounded elevation. Ligaments bind the carpals closely and firmly together in two rows of four each: proximal row (from little finger toward thumb)—pisiform, triquetrum, lunate, and navicular bones; distal row—hamate, capitate, lesser multangular, and greater multangular bones. The joints between the carpals and the joint between the carpals and radius permit wrist and hand movements.

Of the five *metacarpal bones* which form the framework of the hand, that of the thumb forms the most freely movable joint with the carpals. This fact has great significance. Because of the wide range of movement possible between the thumb metacarpal and the greater multangular bone, particularly the ability to oppose the thumb to the fingers, the human hand has much greater dexterity than the forepaw of any animal and has enabled man to manipulate his environment effectively. The heads of the metacarpals, prominent as the proximal knuckles of the hand, articulate with the phalanges.

Lower extremity

Bones of the hip, thigh, lower leg, ankle, and foot constitute the lower extremity. Strong ligaments bind the two hip bones (*os coxae* or *os innominatum*) to the sacrum posteriorly and to each other anteriorly to form the *pelvic girdle,* a stable, circular base which supports the trunk and attaches the lower extremities to it. In early life each innominate bone is made up of three separate bones. Later on they fuse into a single, massive, irregular bone which is

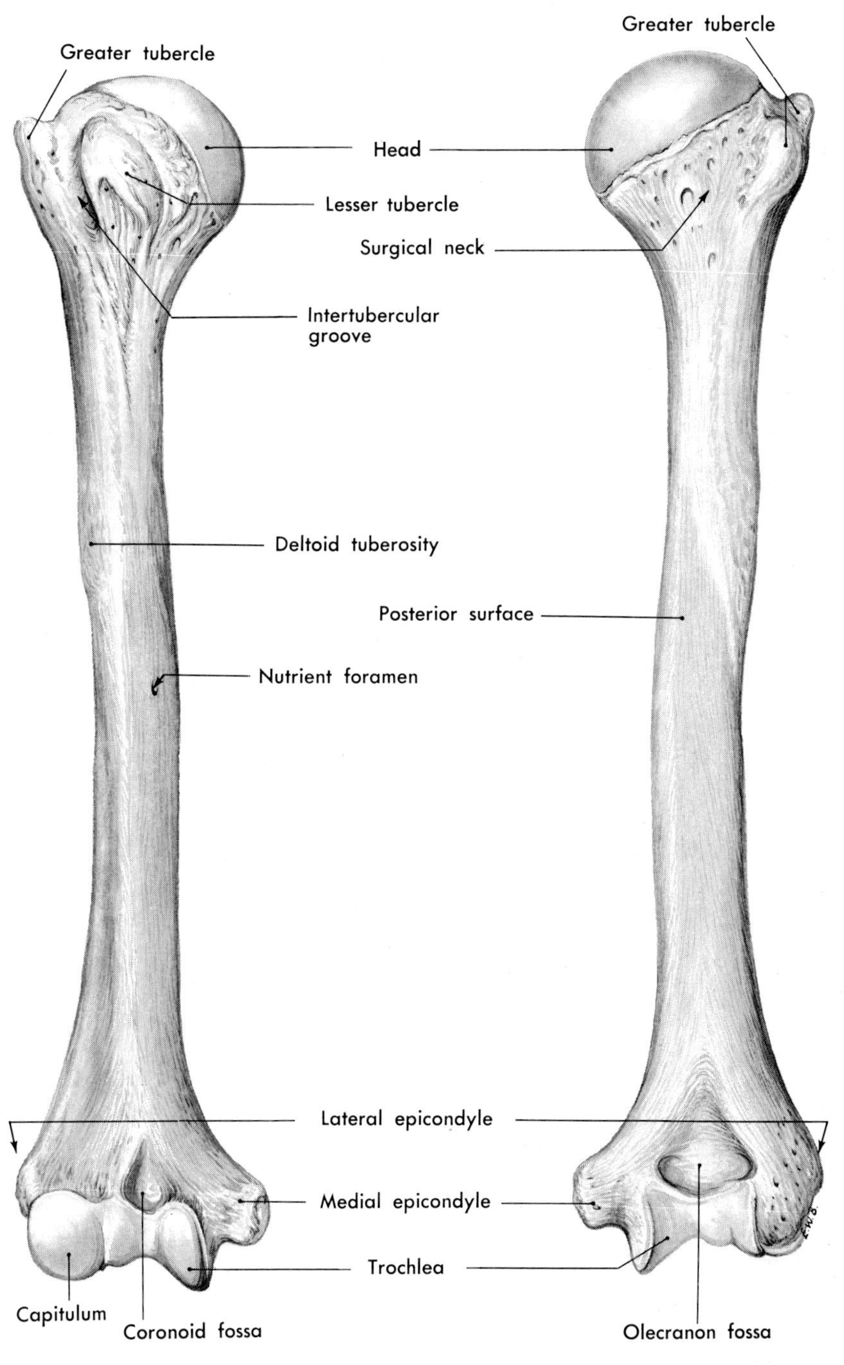

Fig. 65
Right humerus, anterior view.

Fig. 66
Right humerus, posterior view.

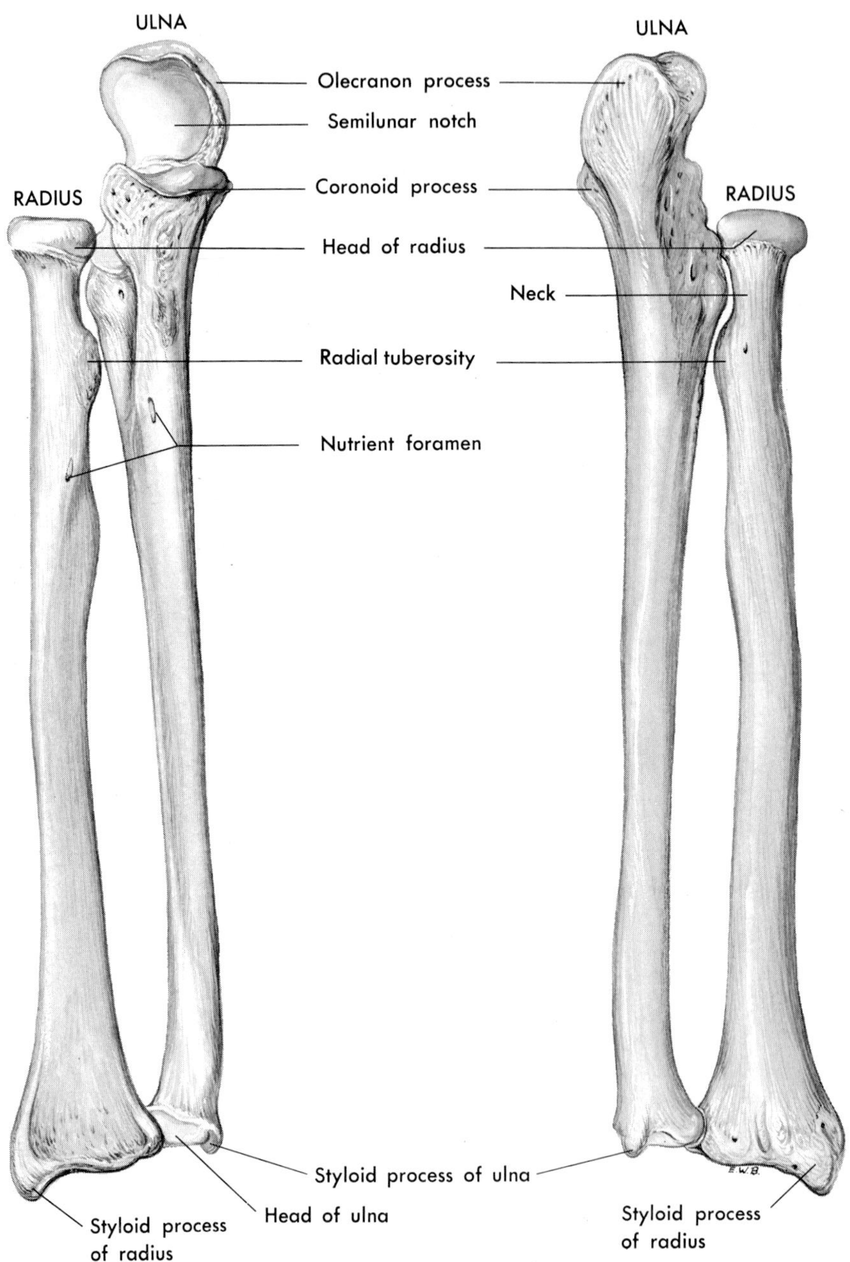

Fig. 67
Right radius and ulna, anterior surfaces.

Fig. 68
Right radius and ulna, posterior surfaces.

broader than any other bone in the body. The largest and uppermost of the three bones is the *ilium;* the strongest, lowermost, the *ischium;* and the anteriormost, the *pubis.* Numerous markings are present on the three bones. These are identified in Table 4 (also see Fig. 71).

The two thigh bones or *femurs* have the distinction of being the longest and heaviest bones in the body. Several prominent markings characterize them. For example, three projections are conspicuous at each epiphysis: the head and greater and lesser trochanters proximally and the medial and lateral condyles and adductor tubercle distally (Fig. 72). Both condyles and the greater trochanter may be felt externally. For a description of the various femur markings, see Table 4.

The largest sesamoid bones in the body,

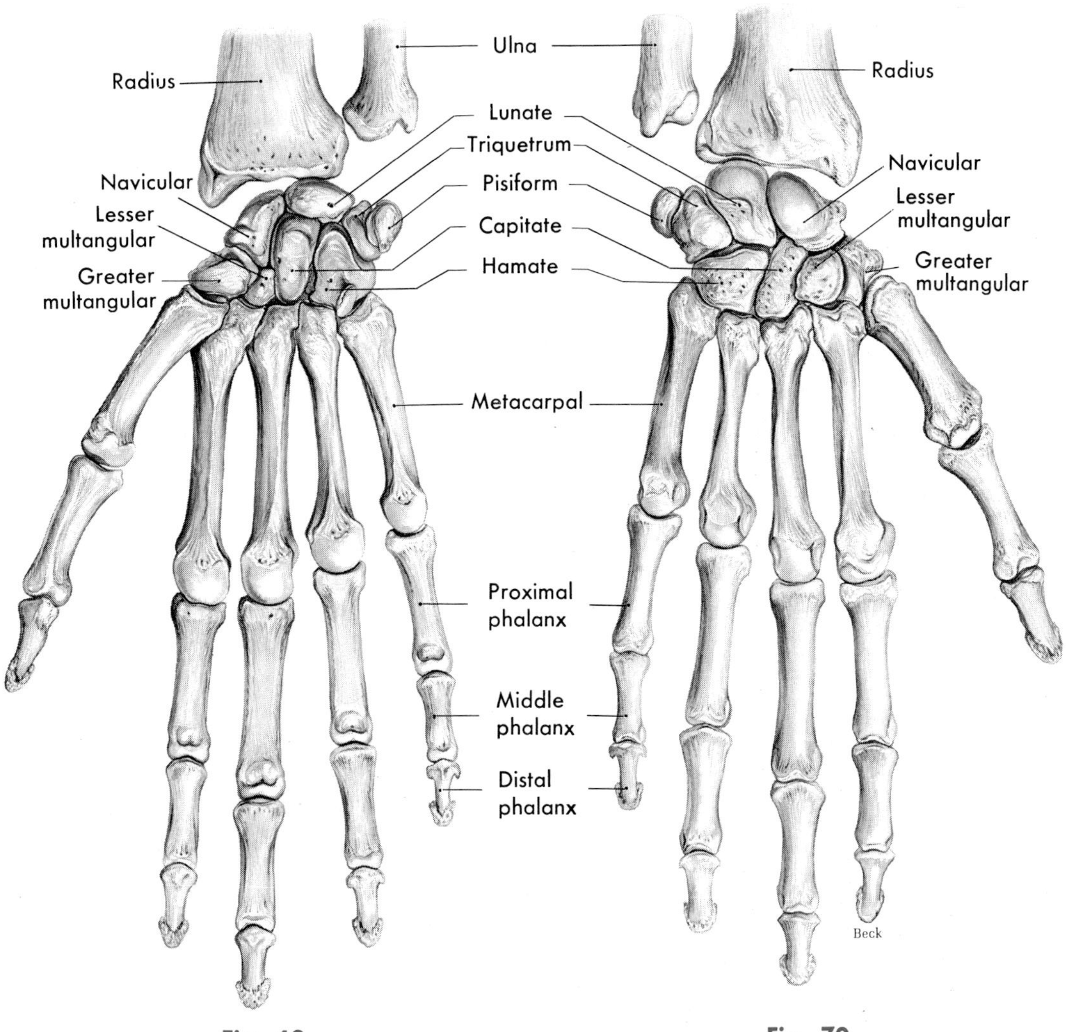

Fig. 69
Bones of the right hand and wrist, palmar surface.

Fig. 70
Bones of the right hand and wrist, dorsal surface.

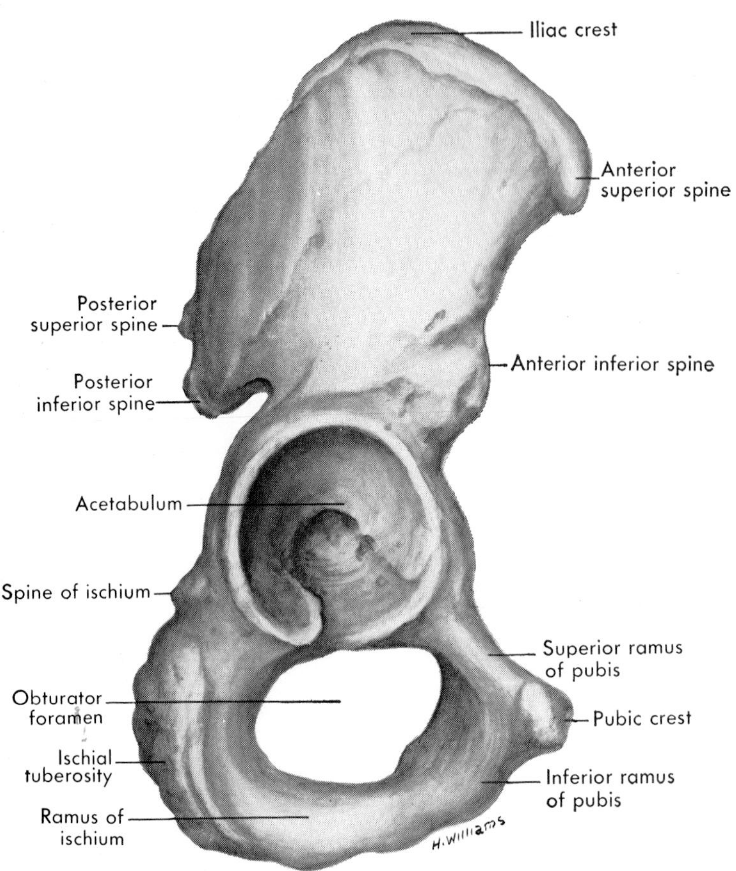

Fig. 71

Right hip bone viewed from the side with the bone turned so as to look directly into the acetabulum. (From Francis and Farrell: Integrated anatomy and physiology, St. Louis, The C. V. Mosby Co.)

and the one which is almost universally present, is the *patella* or kneecap, located in the tendon of the quadriceps femoris muscle as a protection to the underlying knee joint. When the joint is extended, the patellar outline may be distinguished through the skin, but as the knee flexes it sinks into the intercondylar notch of the femur and can no longer be delineated.

The *tibia* is the larger and stronger and the more medially and superficially located of the two lower leg bones, whereas the *fibula* is smaller and more laterally and deeply placed. The fibula articulates with the lateral condyle of the tibia. The tibia in turn articulates with the femur in the largest and one of the most stable joints of the body. Distally the tibia articulates again with the fibula and also with the talus. The latter fits into a boxlike socket (ankle joint) formed by the medial and lateral malleoli, projections of the tibia and fibula, respectively. For other tibial markings, see Table 4 and Fig. 73.

Structure of the *foot* is similar to that of the hand with certain differences which adapt it for supporting weight. One ex-

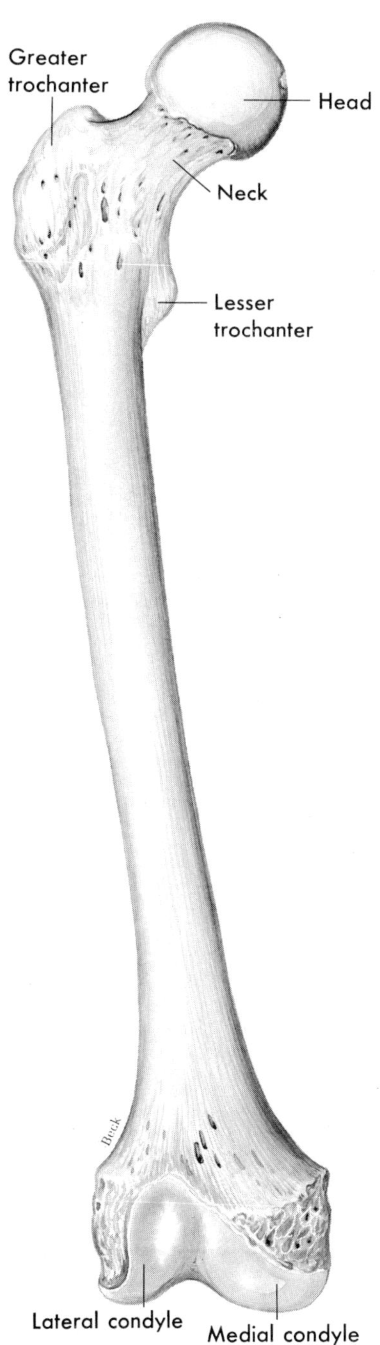

Fig. 72

Right femur, anterior surface.

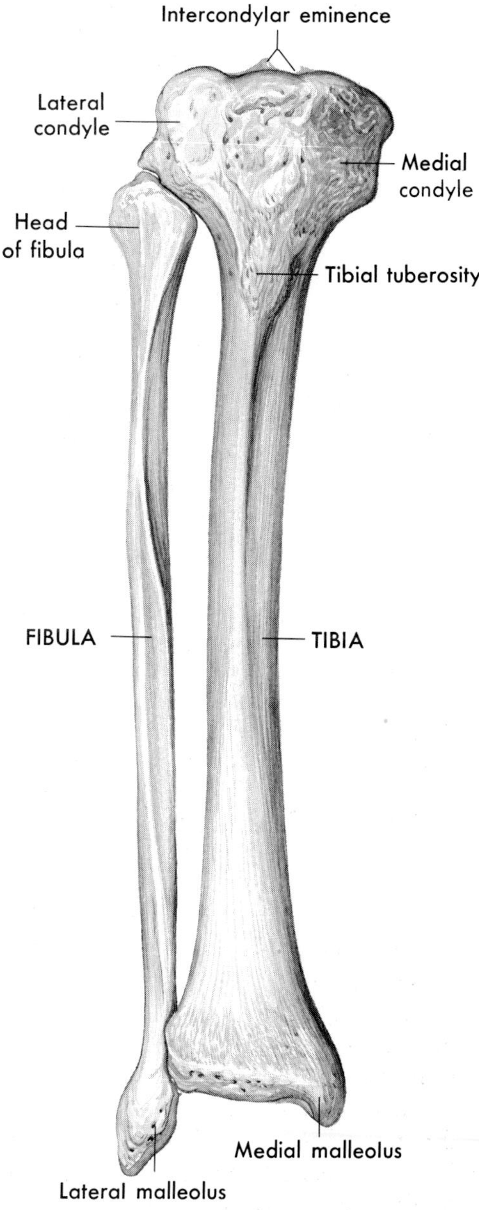

Fig. 73

Right tibia and fibula, anterior surface.

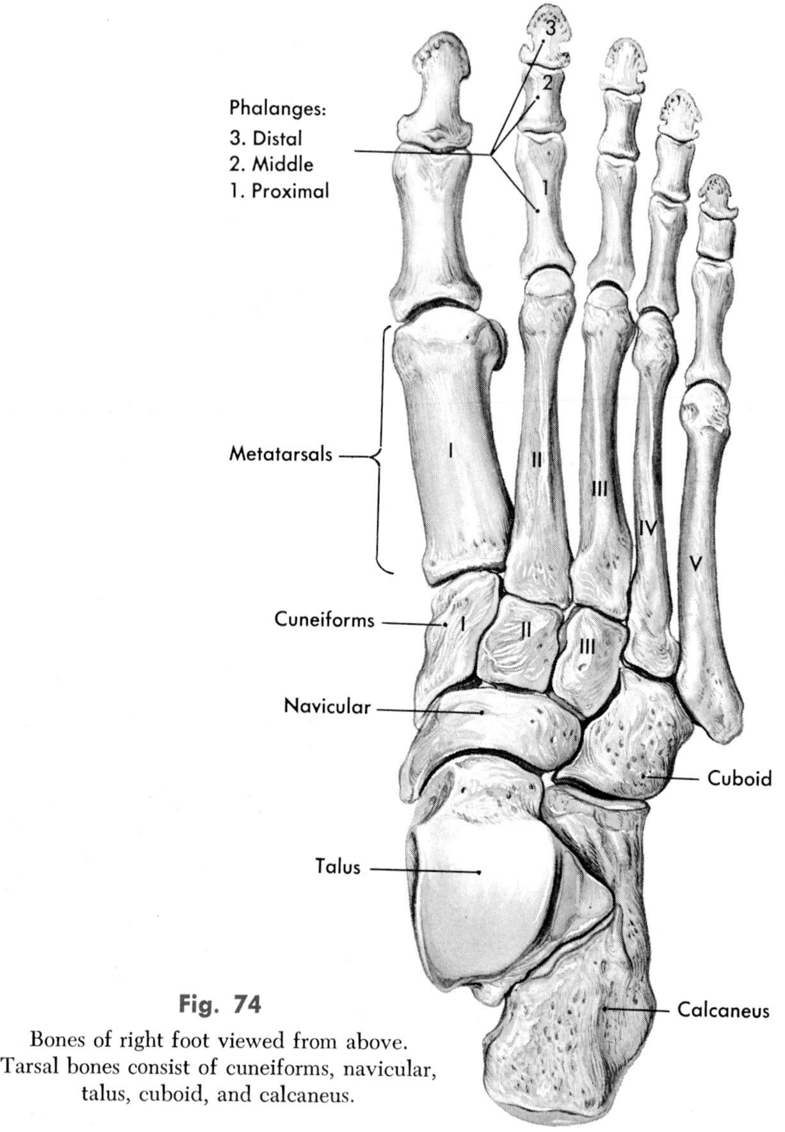

Fig. 74

Bones of right foot viewed from above. Tarsal bones consist of cuneiforms, navicular, talus, cuboid, and calcaneus.

ample of this is the much greater solidity and the more limited mobility of the great toes compared to the thumb. Then, too, the foot bones are held together in such a way as to form springy lengthwise and crosswise arches. This is architecturally sound since arches are known to furnish more supporting strength per given amount of structural material than any other type of construction. Hence, the two-way arch construction makes a highly stable base. The longitudinal arch has an inner or medial portion and an outer or lateral portion, both of which are formed by the placement of tarsals and metatarsals. Specifically some of the tarsals (calcaneus, talus, navicular, and cuneiforms) and the first three metatarsals form the medial longitudinal

Fig. 75
Arches of the foot (see p. 96 and Table 41).

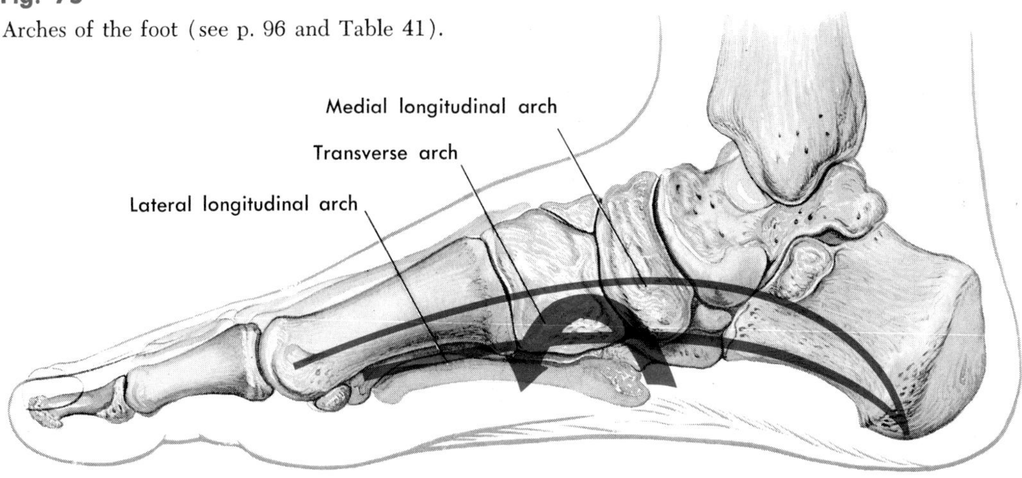

Fig. 76
Flatfoot results when there is a weakening of tendons and ligaments attaching to the tarsal bones. Downward pressure by the weight of the body gradually flattens out the normal arch of bones.

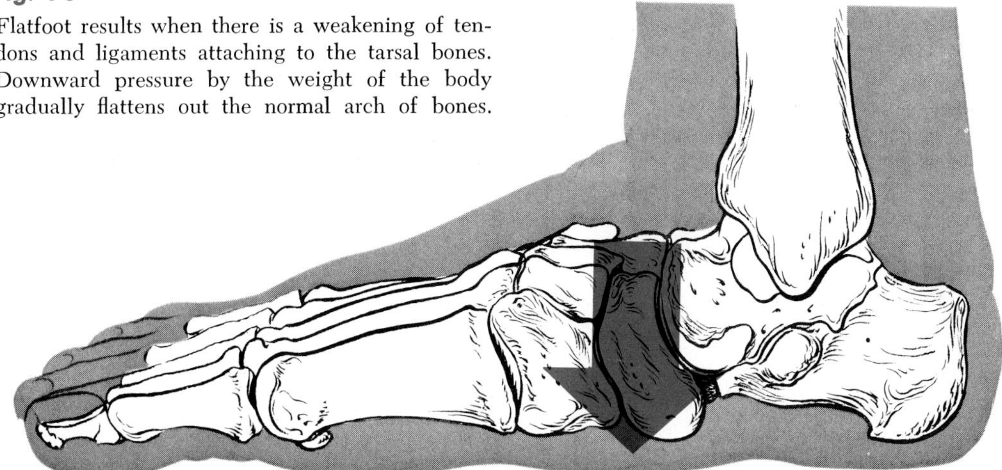

arch, and the calcaneus and cuboid tarsals plus the fourth and fifth metatarsals shape the lateral longitudinal arch (Figs. 74 to 76). The transverse arch results from the relative placement of the distal row of tarsals and the five metatarsals. (See Table 4 for specific bones of different arches.) Strong ligaments and leg muscle tendons normally hold the foot bones firmly in their arched positions, but not infrequently these weaken, causing the arches to flatten, a condition aptly called fallen arches or flatfeet. Note that the tarsals and metatarsals play the major role in the functioning of the foot as a supporting structure, with the phalanges relatively unimportant. The reverse is true for the hand. Here, manipulation is the main function rather than sup-

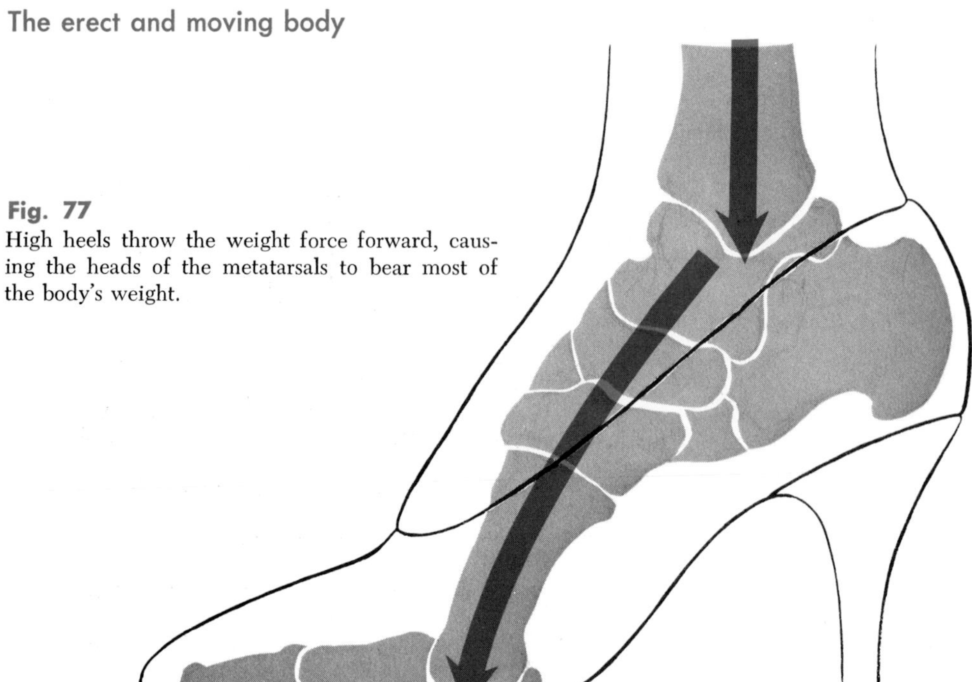

Fig. 77
High heels throw the weight force forward, causing the heads of the metatarsals to bear most of the body's weight.

port. Consequently, the phalanges are all important and the carpals and metacarpals are subsidiary.

MARKINGS

Various points on bones are labeled according to the nature of their structure. This method of identifying definite parts of different bones proves helpful when locating other structures such as muscles, blood vessels, and nerves. Definitions of some of the common terms applied to bone markings follow.

Depressions and openings

1. *fossa*—a hollow or depression (example, mandibular fossa of the temporal bone)
2. *sinus*—a cavity or spongelike space in a bone (example, the frontal sinus)
3. *foramen*—a hole (example, foramen magnum of the occipital bone)
4. *meatus*—a tube-shaped opening (example, the external auditory meatus)

Projections or processes

Those projections or processes which fit into joints are as follows:

1. *condyle*—a rounded projection that enters into the formation of a joint (example, condyles of the femur)
2. *head*—a rounded projection beyond a narrow necklike portion (example, head of the femur)

Those projections to which muscles attach include the following:

1. *trochanter*—a very large projection; greater trochanter of femur
2. *crest*—a ridge (example, the iliac crest); a less prominent ridge is called a *line* (example, ileopectineal line)
3. *spinous process* or *spine*—a sharp projection (example, anterior superior iliac spine)
4. *tuberosity*—a large, rounded projection (example, ischial tuberosity)
5. *tubercle*—a small, rounded projection (example, rib tubercles)

Text continued on p. 109.

Table 4. Bone markings*

Bone	*Marking*	*Description*
Frontal	*Supraorbital margin*	Arched ridge just below eyebrows
	Frontal sinuses	Cavities inside bone just above supraorbital margin; lined with mucosa; contain air
	Frontal tuberosities	Bulge above each orbit; most prominent part of forehead
	Superciliary arches	Ridges caused by projection of frontal sinuses; eyebrows lie over these ridges
	Supraorbital notch (sometimes foramen)	Notch or foramen in supraorbital margin slightly mesial to its midpoint; transmits supraorbital nerve and blood vessels
	Glabella	Smooth area between superciliary ridges and above nose
Temporal	*Mastoid process*	Protuberance just behind ear
	Mastoid air cells	Air-filled mucosa-lined spaces within mastoid process
	External auditory meatus (or *canal*)	Opening into ear and tube extending into temporal bone
	Zygomatic process	Projection which articulates with malar (or zygomatic) bone
	Internal auditory meatus	Fairly large opening on posterior surface of petrous portion of bone; transmits eighth cranial nerve to inner ear and seventh cranial nerve on its way to facial structures
	Squamous portion	Thin, flaring upper part of bone
	Mastoid portion	Rough-surfaced lower part of bone posterior to external auditory meatus
	Petrous portion	Wedge-shaped process that forms part of center section of cranial floor between sphenoid and occipital bones; name derived from Greek word for stone because of extreme hardness of this process; houses middle and inner ear structures
	Mandibular fossa	Oval-shaped depression anterior to external auditory meatus; forms socket for condyle of mandible
	Styloid process	Slender spike of bone extending downward and forward from undersurface of bone anterior to mastoid process; often broken off in dry skull; several neck muscles and ligaments attach to styloid process
	Stylomastoid foramen	Opening between styloid and mastoid processes where facial nerve emerges from cranial cavity
	Jugular fossa	Depression on undersurface of petrous portion; dilated beginning of internal jugular vein lodged here
	Jugular foramen	Opening in suture between petrous portion and occipital bone; transmits lateral sinus and ninth, tenth, and eleventh cranial nerves

*Those that seem particularly important because they are places of muscle attachment are set in italics.

Continued.

Table 4. Bone markings*—cont'd

Bone	*Marking*	*Description*
Temporal—cont'd	Carotid canal (or foramen)	Channel in petrous portion; best seen from undersurface of skull; transmits internal carotid artery
Occipital	*Foramen magnum*	Hole through which spinal cord enters cranial cavity
	Condyles	Convex, oval processes on either side of foramen magnum; articulate with depressions on first cervical vertebra
	External occipital protuberance	Prominent projection on posterior surface in midline short distance above foramen magnum; can be felt as definite bump
	Superior nuchal line	Curved ridge extending laterally from external occipital protuberance
	Inferior nuchal line	Less well-defined ridge paralleling superior nuchal line short distance below it
	Internal occipital protuberance	Projection in midline on inner surface of bone; grooves for lateral sinuses extend laterally from this process and one for sagittal sinus extends upward from it
Sphenoid	*Body*	Hollow, cubelike central portion
	Great wings	Lateral projections from body; form part of outer wall of orbit
	Lesser wings	Thin, triangular projections from upper part of sphenoid body; form posterior part of roof of orbit
	Sella turcica (or *Turk's saddle*)	Saddle-shaped depression on upper surface of sphenoid body; contains pituitary gland (Fig. 45)
	Sphenoid sinuses	Irregular air-filled mucosa-lined spaces within central part of sphenoid (Fig. 47)
	Pterygoid processes	Downward projections on either side where body and greater wing unite; comparable to extended legs of bat if entire bone is likened to this animal; form part of lateral nasal wall
	Optic foramen	Opening into orbit at root of lesser wing; transmits second cranial nerve
	Superior orbital fissure	Slitlike opening into orbit; lateral to optic foramen; transmits third, fourth, and part of fifth cranial nerves
	Foramen rotundum	Opening in greater wing that transmits maxillary division of fifth cranial nerve
	Foramen ovale	Opening in greater wing that transmits mandibular division of fifth cranial nerve
Ethmoid	*Horizontal (cribriform) plate*	Olfactory nerves pass through numerous holes in this plate

*Those that seem particularly important because they are places of muscle attachment are set in italics.

Table 4. Bone markings*—cont'd

Bone	*Marking*	*Description*
Ethmoid—cont'd	*Crista galli*	See Figs. 51 and 53; meninges attach to this process
	Perpendicular plate	Forms upper part of nasal septum (Figs. 51 and 53)
	Ethmoid sinuses	Honeycombed, mucosa-lined air spaces within lateral masses of bone
	Superior and middle turbinates (conchae)	Help to form lateral walls of nose (Figs. 51 and 53)
	Lateral masses	Compose sides of bone; contain many air spaces (ethmoid cells or sinuses); inner surface forms superior and middle conchae
Mandible	Body	Main part of bone; forms chin
	Ramus	Process, one on either side, that projects upward from posterior part of body
	Condyle (or *head*)	Part of each ramus that articulates with mandibular fossa of temporal bone
	Neck	Constricted part just below condyles
	Alveolar process	Teeth set into this arch
	Mandibular foramen	Opening on inner surface of ramus; transmits nerves and vessels to lower teeth
	Mental foramen	Opening on outer surface below space between two bicuspids; transmits terminal branches of nerves and vessels which enter bone through mandibular foramen; dentists inject anesthetics through these foramina
	Coronoid process	Projection upward from anterior part of each ramus; temporal muscle inserts here
	Angle	Juncture of posterior and inferior margins of ramus
Maxilla	*Alveolar process*	Arch containing teeth
	Maxillary sinus or antrum of Highmore	Large air-filled mucosa-lined cavity within body of each maxilla; largest of sinuses
	Palatine process	Horizontal inward projection from alveolar process; forms anterior and larger part of hard palate
	Infraorbital foramen	Hole on external surface just below orbit; transmits vessels and nerves (Fig. 48)
	Lacrimal groove	Groove on inner surface; joined by similar groove on lacrimal bone to form canal which houses nasolacrimal duct
Palatine	Horizontal plate	Joined to palatine processes of maxillae to complete posterior part of hard palate
Special features of skull	*Sutures*	Immovable joints between skull bones
	1. *Sagittal*	1. Line of articulation between two parietal bones

*Those that seem particularly important because they are places of muscle attachment are set in italics.

Continued.

Table 4. Bone markings*—cont'd

Bone	*Marking*	*Description*
Special features of skull—cont'd	*Sutures*—cont'd	
	2. *Coronal*	2. Joint between parietal bones and frontal bone
	3. *Lambdoidal*	3. Joint between parietal bones and occipital bone
	Fontanels	"Soft spots" where ossification incomplete at birth; allow some compression of skull during birth; also important in determining position of head before delivery; six such areas located at angles of parietal bones
	1. *Anterior* (or *frontal*)	1. At intersection of sagittal and coronal sutures (juncture of parietal bones and frontal bone); diamond shaped; largest of fontanels; usually closed by 1½ years of age
	2. *Posterior* (or *occipital*)	2. An intersection of sagittal and lambdoidal sutures (juncture of parietal bones and occipital bone); triangular in shape; usually closed by second month
	3. Anterolateral (or *sphenoid*)	3. At juncture of frontal, parietal, temporal, and sphenoid bones
	4. Posterolateral (or *mastoid*)	4. At juncture of parietal, occipital, and temporal bones; usually closed by second year
	Sinuses	
	1. *Air* (or *bony*)	1. Spaces or cavities within bones; those which communicate with nose called *paranasal sinuses* (frontal, sphenoidal, ethmoidal, and maxillary); mastoid cells communicate with middle ear rather than nose, therefore not included among paranasal sinuses
	2. *Blood*	2. Veins within cranial cavity (Figs. 198 and 199)
	Orbits formed by	
	1. Frontal	1. Roof of orbit (Fig. 48)
	2. Ethmoid	2. Medial wall
	3. Sphenoid	3. Lateral wall
	4. Lacrimal	4. Medial wall
	5. Maxillary	5. Floor
	6. Zygomatic	6. Lateral wall
	7. Palatine	7. Floor
	Nasal septum formed by	Partition in midline of nasal cavity; separates cavity into right and left halves
	1. Perpendicular plate of ethmoid	1. Forms upper part of septum
	2. Vomer bone	2. Forms lower, posterior part
	3. Cartilage	3. Forms anterior part
	Wormian bones	Small islands of bones within suture

*Those that seem particularly important because they are places of muscle attachment are set in italics.

Table 4. Bone markings*—cont'd

Bone	*Marking*	*Description*
Vertebral column	General features	Anterior part of vertebrae (except first two cervical) consists of body; posterior part, of neural arch which, in turn, consists of two pedicles, two laminae, and seven processes projecting from laminae
	Thoracic vertebrae	
	1. *Body*	1. Main part; flat, round mass located anteriorly; supporting or weight-bearing part of vertebra
	2. *Pedicles*	2. Short projections extending posteriorly from body
	3. *Laminae*	3. Posterior part of vertebra to which pedicles join and from which processes project
	4. *Neural arch*	4. Formed by pedicles and laminae; protects spinal cord posteriorly; together, neural arches form spinal cavity; congenital absence of one or more neural arches known as *spina bifida* (cord may protrude right through skin)
	5. *Spinous process*	5. Sharp process projecting inferiorly from laminae in midline
	6. *Transverse processes*	6. Right and left lateral projections from laminae
	7. *Superior articulating processes*	7. Project upward from laminae
	8. *Inferior articulating processes*	8. Project downward from laminae; articulate with superior articulating processes of vertebrae below
	9. *Spinal foramen*	9. Hole in center of vertebra formed by union of body, pedicles, and laminae; spinal foramina, when vertebrae superimposed one upon other, form spinal cavity which houses spinal cord
	Cervical vertebrae	
	1. General features	1. Foramen in each transverse process for transmission of vertebral artery, vein, and plexus of nerves; short bifurcated spinous processes except on seventh vertebrae where it is extra long and may be felt as protrusion when head bent forward; bodies of these vertebrae small, while spinal foramina large and triangular
	2. *Atlas*	2. First cervical vertebra; lacks body and spinous process; superior articulating processes concave ovals which act as rockerlike cradles for condyles of occipital bone; named atlas because supports head as Atlas was thought to have supported world (Fig. 56)

*Those that seem particularly important because they are places of muscle attachment are set in italics.

Continued.

Table 4. Bone markings*—cont'd

Bone	*Marking*	*Description*
Vertebral column—cont'd	*Cervical vertebrae*—cont'd 3. *Axis* (epistropheus)	3. Second cervical vertebra; so named because atlas rotates about this bone in rotating movements of head; *dens*, or odontoid process, peglike projection upward from body of axis, forming pivot for rotation of atlas (Fig. 57)
	Lumbar vertebrae	Strong, massive; superior articulating processes directed inward instead of upward; inferior articulating processes, outward instead of downward; short, blunt spinous process (Figs. 58 to 60)
	Sacral promontory	Protuberance from anterior, upper border of sacrum into pelvis; of obstetrical importance because its size limits anteroposterior diameter of pelvic inlet
	Intervertebral foramina	Opening between vertebrae through which spinal nerves emerge (Fig. 61)
	Curves	Curves have great structural importance because increase carrying strength of vertebral column, make balance possible in upright position (if column were straight, weight of viscera would pull body forward), absorb jars from walking (straight column would transmit jars straight to head), and protect column from fracture
	1. *Primary*	1. Column curves at birth from head to sacrum with convexity posteriorly; after child stands, convexity persists only in *thoracic* and *sacral* regions which, therefore, are called primary curves
	2. *Secondary*	2. Concavities in *cervical* and *lumbar* regions; cervical concavity results from infant's attempts to hold head erect (3 to 4 months); lumbar concavity, from balancing efforts in learning to walk (10 to 18 months)
	3. *Abnormal*	3. *Kyphosis*, exaggerated convexity in thoracic region (hunchback); *lordosis*, exaggerated concavity in lumbar region, a very common condition; *scoliosis*, lateral curvature in any region
Sternum	*Body* *Manubrium* *Xiphoid process*	Main central part of bone Flaring, upper part Projection of cartilage at lower border of bone
Ribs	*Head*	Projection at posterior end of rib; articulates with corresponding thoracic vertebra and one above, except last three pairs, which join corresponding vertebra only

*Those that seem particularly important because they are places of muscle attachment are set in italics.

Table 4. Bone markings*—cont'd

Bone	*Marking*	*Description*
Ribs—cont'd	Neck	Constricted portion just below head
	Tubercle	Small knob just below neck; articulates with transverse process of corresponding thoracic vertebra; missing in lowest three ribs
	Body or shaft	Main part of rib
	Costal cartilage	Cartilage at sternal end of true ribs; attaches ribs (except floating ribs) to sternum
Scapula (Figs. 62 to 64)	*Borders*	
	1. Superior	1. Upper margin
	2. Vertebral	2. Margin toward vertebral column
	3. Axillary	3. Lateral margin
	Spine	Sharp ridge running diagonally across posterior surface of shoulder blade
	Acromion process	Slightly flaring projection at lateral end of scapular spine; may be felt as tip of shoulder; articulates with clavicle
	Coracoid process	Projection on anterior surface from upper border of bone; may be felt in groove between deltoid and pectoralis major muscles, about 1 inch below clavicle
	Glenoid cavity	Arm socket
Humerus (Figs. 65 and 66)	*Head*	Smooth, hemispherical enlargement at proximal end of humerus
	Anatomical neck	Oblique groove just below head
	Greater tubercle	Rounded projection lateral to head on anterior surface
	Lesser tubercle	Prominent projection on anterior surface just below anatomical neck
	Intertubercular (bicipital) groove	Deep groove between greater and lesser tubercles; long tendon of biceps muscle lodges here
	Surgical neck	Region just below tubercles; so named because of its liability to fracture
	Deltoid tuberosity	V-shaped, rough area about midway down shaft where deltoid muscle inserts
	Radial groove	Groove running obliquely downward from deltoid tuberosity; lodges radial nerve
	Epicondyles (medial and lateral)	Rough projections at both sides of distal end
	Capitulum	Rounded knob below lateral epicondyle; articulates with radius; sometimes called radial head of humerus
	Trochlea	Projection with deep depression through center similar to shape of pulley; articulates with ulna
	Olecranon fossa	Depression on posterior surface just above trochlea; receives olecranon process of ulna when lower arm extends

*Those that seem particularly important because they are places of muscle attachment are set in italics.

Continued.

Table 4. Bone markings*—cont'd

Bone	*Marking*	*Description*
Humerus—cont'd	*Coronoid fossa*	Depression on anterior surface above trochlea; receives coronoid process of ulna in flexion of lower arm
Ulna (Figs. 67 and 68)	*Olecranon process*	Elbow
	Coronoid process	Projection on anterior surface of proximal end of ulna; trochlea of humerus fits snugly between olecranon and coronoid processes
	Semilunar notch	Curved notch between olecranon and coronoid, into which trochlea fits
	Radial notch	Curved notch lateral and inferior to semilunar notch; head of radius fits into this concavity
	Head	Rounded process at distal end; does not articulate with wrist bones but with fibrocartilaginous disc
	Styloid process	Sharp protuberance at distal end; can be seen from outside on posterior surface
Radius (Figs. 67 and 68)	*Head*	Disc-shaped process forming proximal end of radius; articulates with capitulum of humerus and with radial notch of ulna
	Radial tuberosity	Roughened projection on ulnar side, short distance below head; biceps muscle inserts here
	Styloid process	Protuberance at distal end on lateral surface (with forearm supinated as in anatomical position)
Os coxa (Fig. 71)	*Ilium*	Upper, flaring portion
	Ischium	Lower, posterior portion
	Pubic bone or pubis	Mesial, anterior section
	Acetabulum	Hip socket; formed by union of ilium, ischium, and pubis
	Iliac crests	Upper, curving boundary of ilium
	Iliac spines	
	1. *Anterior superior*	1. Prominent projection at anterior end of iliac crest; can be felt externally as "point" of hip
	2. Anterior inferior	2. Less prominent projection short distance below anterior superior spine
	3. Posterior superior	3. At posterior end of iliac crest
	4. Posterior inferior	4. Just below posterior superior spine
	Greater sciatic notch	Large notch on posterior surface of ilium just below posterior inferior spine
	Gluteal lines	Three curved lines across outer surface of ilium —posterior, anterior, inferior, respectively
	Iliopectineal line	Rounded ridge extending from pubic tubercle upward and backward toward sacrum
	Iliac fossa	Large, smooth, concave inner surface of ilium above iliopectineal line

*Those that seem particularly important because they are places of muscle attachment are set in italics.

Table 4. Bone markings*—cont'd

Bone	*Marking*	*Description*
Os coxa—cont'd	*Ischial tuberosity*	Large rough, quadrilateral process forming inferior part of ischium; in erect sitting position body rests on these tuberosities
	Ischial spine	Pointed projection just above tuberosity
	Symphysis pubis	Cartilaginous, amphiarthrotic joint between pubic bones
	Superior pubic ramus	Part of pubis lying between symphysis and acetabulum; forms upper part of obturator foramen
	Inferior pubic ramus	Part extending down from symphysis; unites with ischium
	Pubic arch	Angle formed by two inferior rami
	Pubic crest	Upper margin of superior ramus
	Pubic tubercle	Rounded process at end of crest
	Obturator foramen	Large hole in anterior surface of os coxa; formed by pubis and ischium; largest foramen in body
	Pelvic brim (or *inlet*)	Boundary of aperture leading into true pelvis; formed by pubic crests, iliopectineal lines, and sacral promontory; size and shape of this inlet has great obstetrical importance since if any of its diameters too small, infant skull cannot enter true pelvis for natural birth
	True (or lesser) *pelvis*	Space below pelvic brim; true "basin" with bone and muscle walls and muscle floor; pelvic organs located in this space
	False (or greater) *pelvis*	Broad, shallow space above pelvic brim, misnamed because really part of abdominal cavity, but is false "basin" in that instead of "floor," it has only an aperture, pelvic inlet, and its bony walls, being present only at sides and back, are less complete than those of true pelvis
	Pelvic outlet	Irregular circumference marking lower limits of true pelvis; bounded by tip of coccyx and two ischial tuberosities
	Pelvic girdle (or bony pelvis)	Complete bony ring; composed of two hip bones (ossa coxae), sacrum, and coccyx; forms firm base by which trunk rests upon thighs and for attachment of lower extremities to axial skeleton
Femur (Fig. 72)	*Head*	Rounded, upper end of bone; fits into acetabulum
	Neck	Constricted portion just below head
	Greater trochanter	Protuberance located inferiorly and laterally to head
	Lesser trochanter	Small protuberance located inferiorly and mesially to greater trochanter
	Linea aspera	Prominent ridge extending lengthwise along concave posterior surface

*Those that seem particularly important because they are places of muscle attachment are set in italics.

Continued.

Table 4. Bone markings*—cont'd

Bone	*Marking*	*Description*
Femur—cont'd	Gluteal tubercle	Rounded projection just below greater trochanter; rudimentary third trochanter
	Supracondylar ridges	Two ridges formed by division of linea aspera at its lower end; medial supracondylar ridge extends inward to inner condyle, lateral ridge to outer condyle
	Condyles	Large, rounded bulges at distal end of femur; one on mesial and one on lateral surface
	Adductor tubercle	Small projection just above inner condyle; marks termination of medial supracondylar ridge
	Trochlea	Smooth depression between condyles on anterior surface; articulates with patella
	Intercondyloid notch	Deep depression between condyles on posterior surface; cruciate ligaments which help bind femur to tibia lodge in this notch
Tibia (Fig. 73)	*Condyles*	Bulging prominences at proximal end of tibia; upper surfaces concave for articulation with femur
	Intercondylar eminence	Upward projection on articular surface between condyles
	Crest	Sharp ridge on anterior surface
	Tibial tuberosity	Projection in midline on anterior surface
	Popliteal line	Ridge that spirals downward and inward on posterior surface of upper third of tibial shaft
	Medial malleolus	Rounded downward projection at distal end of tibia; forms prominence on inner surface of ankle
Fibula (Fig. 73)	*Lateral malleolus*	Rounded prominence at distal end of fibula; forms prominence on outer surface of ankle
Tarsals (Figs. 74 to 76)	*Calcaneus*	Heel bone
	Talus	Uppermost of tarsals; articulates with tibia and fibula; boxed in by medial and lateral malleoli
	Longitudinal arches	Tarsals and metatarsals so arranged as to form arch from front to back of foot
	1. *Inner*	1. Formed by calcaneus, navicular, cuneiforms, and three medial metatarsals
	2. *Outer*	2. Formed by calcaneus, cuboid, and two lateral metatarsals
	Transverse (or *metatarsal*) *arch*	Metatarsals and distal row of tarsals (cuneiforms and cuboid) so articulated as to form arch across foot; bones kept in two arched positions by means of powerful ligaments in sole of foot and by muscles and tendons

*Those that seem particularly important because they are places of muscle attachment are set in italics.

Identification

Many of the markings found on bones are described in Table 4. Those that seem particularly important because they are places of muscle attachment are set in italics.

DIFFERENCES BETWEEN MALE AND FEMALE SKELETONS

Both general and specific differences exist between male and female skeletons. The general difference is one of size and weight, the male skeleton being larger and heavier. The specific differences concern the shape of the pelvic bones and cavity. Whereas the male pelvis is deep and funnel shaped, with a narrow pubic arch (usually less than 90 degrees), the female pelvis is shallow, broad, and flaring, with a wider pubic arch (usually greater than 90 degrees). The childbearing function obviously explains the necessity for these and certain other modifications of the female pelvis.

AGE CHANGES IN SKELETON

Skeletal changes from infancy to adulthood are mainly changes in the size of the bones and in the proportionate sizes between different bones, whereas changes in the bones from young adulthood to old age are mainly a matter of changes in the texture and in the contour of the margins and bone markings. Some of the major modifications which occur from infancy to young adulthood are as follows:

1. The head becomes proportionately smaller. Whereas the infant head is approximately one-fourth the total height of the body, the adult head is only about one-eighth the total height.
2. The thorax changes shape, roughly speaking, from round to elliptical.
3. The pelvis becomes relatively larger and in the female relatively wider.
4. The legs become proportionately longer and the trunk proportionately shorter.
5. The vertebral column develops two curves not present at birth—the cervical curve when the infant starts lifting up his head (at about 3 months of age) and the lumbar curve when the child begins standing (toward the end of the first year). Both of these secondary curves are concave posteriorly, whereas the primary thoracic and sacral curves are convex posteriorly.
6. The cranium shows several modifications. It grows rapidly during early childhood, enlarging its capacity from approximately 350 ml. at birth to approximately 1,500 ml. (about adult size) by 6 years of age. The fontanels close by about 1½ or 2 years of age, and the sutures begin to fuse in the 20's.
7. The facial bones also show several changes between infancy and adulthood. Unlike the cranial bones, their growth is slow during early childhood but rapid during the teens. Whereas the infant face compared with the entire skull bears the relationship of 1:8, the adult face bears the relationship of 1:2 to the adult skull. The sinuses are much larger in the adult. For example, at birth, only rudimentary maxillary and mastoid sinuses exist. The ethmoid and sphenoid sinuses start to appear at about 6 years of age and the frontal at about 7 years. All of the bony sinuses, but especially the frontal, grow rapidly during adolescence.
8. The epiphyses of the long bones are composed of cartilage at birth but become completely ossified (except for the thin layer of articular cartilage) by adulthood. Demonstration of epiphyseal cartilage on x-ray films indicates that skeletal growth has not ceased.

Changes in the skeleton continue to occur from adulthood to old age. Both bone margins and projections, for example, look different in old bones than in young. Instead of clean-cut, distinct margins, old bones characteristically have indistinct, shaggy-appearing margins (marginal lipping and spurs)—a regrettable change because the restricted movements of old age stem partly from this piling up of bone around joint margins. Also, an increase in bone along various projections develops in old age, making ridges and processes more pronounced.

Joints between bones (articulations)

Bones are joined to one another in several ingenious ways which permit a great variety of movement. Where free movement is essential, the articulating ends of the bones are so shaped and the joint so constructed as to permit and even facilitate unhampered motion. Where only slight movement is desirable, bone shape and joint structure make only slight movement possible. Where no movement between the bones is preferable, this, too, is accomplished by bone shape and joint structure. How important normal joint structure and function are for the productiveness and enjoyment of life, probably most of us seldom consider. But disease often makes this tragically clear. Joint structure in all too many cases becomes so altered that crippling immobility results—sometimes only limitation of a single movement and sometimes almost complete immobilization. To inquire into joint structure and action is, therefore, an essential part of the study of anatomy and physiology. Basic information includes understanding what structural kinds of joints exist between bones and what kinds of movements each type permits.

KINDS

A confusing array of terms has grown up around the subject of joint classification. Different anatomists have used different criteria for identifying joint types and have muddled matters even more by using various names for the same kind of joint.

One of the simpler ways of classifying joints is to divide them into two main structural types: diarthroses and synarthroses.

Diarthroses are joints in which a small space, the joint cavity, exists between the articulating surfaces of the two bones that form the joint. Because there is this cavity with no tissue growing between the articulating surfaces, the surfaces are free to move against one another. And therefore functionally, diarthrotic joints are classified as freely movable joints. By far the majority of our joints belong to this category.

Diarthroses share several characteristics besides that of having a joint cavity. A thin layer of hyaline cartilage covers the joint surfaces of the articulating bones, a sleevelike, fibrous capsule lined with smooth, slippery synovial membrane encases the joint, and additional ligaments grow between the bones, lashing them firmly together. Crescent-shaped pieces of cartilage are found in some diarthrotic joints interposed between the articulating ends of the two bones. Examples are the semilunar cartilages of the knee joint and the glenoid cartilages of the shoulder joint.

Synarthroses are joints that do not have a joint cavity but instead have tissue (fibrous, cartilage, or bone) growing between their articulating surfaces and making them unable to move freely against one another.

Diarthroses and synarthroses are divided into subtypes according to such characteristics as the shape of the joint surfaces of the united bones and the type of connective tissue between them. See Table 5 for a summary of the main kinds of joints with examples of each. A description of individual joints is given in Table 6.

MOVEMENTS

Joints permit the following kinds of movements: (1) flexion, (2) extension, (3) abduction, (4) adduction, (5) rotation, (6) circumduction, and (7) special movements such as supination, pronation, inversion, eversion, protraction, and retraction.

Flexion. Flexion decreases the size of the angle between the anterior surfaces of articulated bones (exception, flexion of the knee and toe joints decreases the angle between the posterior surfaces of the articulated bones). Flexing movements are *bending* or *folding* movements. For example, bending the head forward is flexion of the joint between the occipital bone and the atlas, and bending the elbow is flexion of the elbow joint or of the lower arm. Flexing movements of the arms and legs may be thought of as "withdrawing" movements.

Extension. Extension is the return from flexion. Whereas bending movements are flexions, *straightening* movements are extensions. Extension restores a part to its anatomical position from the flexed position. Continuation of extension beyond the anatomical position is called *hyperextension*. Examples include flexion of the head, bending it forward as in prayer, extension of the head, returning it to the upright anatomical position from the flexed position, and hyperextension of the head, stretching it backward from the upright position. Extension of the foot at the ankle joint is commonly referred to as *plantar flexion*, while flexion of the ankle joint is called *dorsal flexion.*

Abduction. Abduction moves the bone away from the median plane of the body. An example is moving the arms straight out to the sides.

Adduction. Adduction is the opposite of abduction. It moves the part toward the median plane of the body. Examples: bringing the arms back to the sides; adduction of the fingers means moving them toward the third finger; adduction of the toes is movement toward the second toe.

Rotation. Rotation is the pivoting or moving of a bone upon its own axis somewhat as a top turns on its axis. An ex-

Text continued on p. 116.

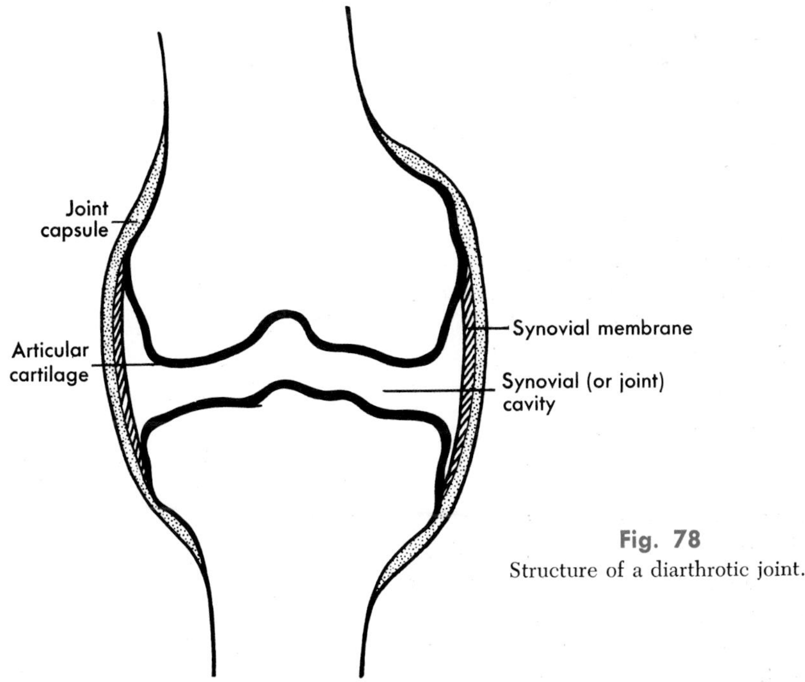

Fig. 78
Structure of a diarthrotic joint.

Table 5. Joints

Diarthroses	*Synarthroses*
1. **Ball and socket** *Other names:* spheroidal; endarthroses *Description:* ball-shaped head fits into concave socket *Movement:* widest range of all joints; triaxial *Examples:* shoulder joint and hip joint	1. **Cartilaginous** *Other name:* synchondrosis *Description:* cartilage grows between two articulating surfaces, usually reinforced by ligaments *Movements:* bending and twisting or slight compression *Examples:* between bodies of vertebrae; between diaphysis and epiphysis of growing bones; replaced by bone in full-grown bones
2. **Hinge** *Other name:* ginglymus *Description:* spool-shaped surface fits into concave surface *Movement:* in one plane about single axis (uniaxial); like hinged-door movement *Examples:* elbow, knee, ankle, and interphalangeal joints	2. **Fibrous** *Description:* thin layer of fibrous tissue; continuous with periosteum; connects articulating bones *Movement:* none *Example:* sutures of skull; in older adults fibrous connection replaced by bone
3. **Pivot** *Other name:* trochoid *Description:* arch-shaped surface rotates about rounded or peglike pivot *Movement:* rotation; uniaxial *Example:* between axis and atlas; between radius and ulna	
4. **Ellipsoidal** *Other names:* condyloid, ovoid *Description:* oval-shaped condyle fits into elliptical cavity *Movements:* in two planes at right angles to each other; back and forth and side to side; biaxial *Example:* wrist joint (between radius and carpals)	
5. **Saddle** *Description:* saddle-shaped bone into socket that is concave-convex in opposite direction; modification of condyloid joint *Movement:* same kinds of movement as condyloid joint but freer; like rider in saddle; biaxial *Example:* thumb, between metacarpal and carpal bones	
6. **Gliding** *Other name:* arthrodia *Description:* articulating surfaces; usually flat *Movement:* gliding, a nonaxial movement *Example:* between carpal bones	

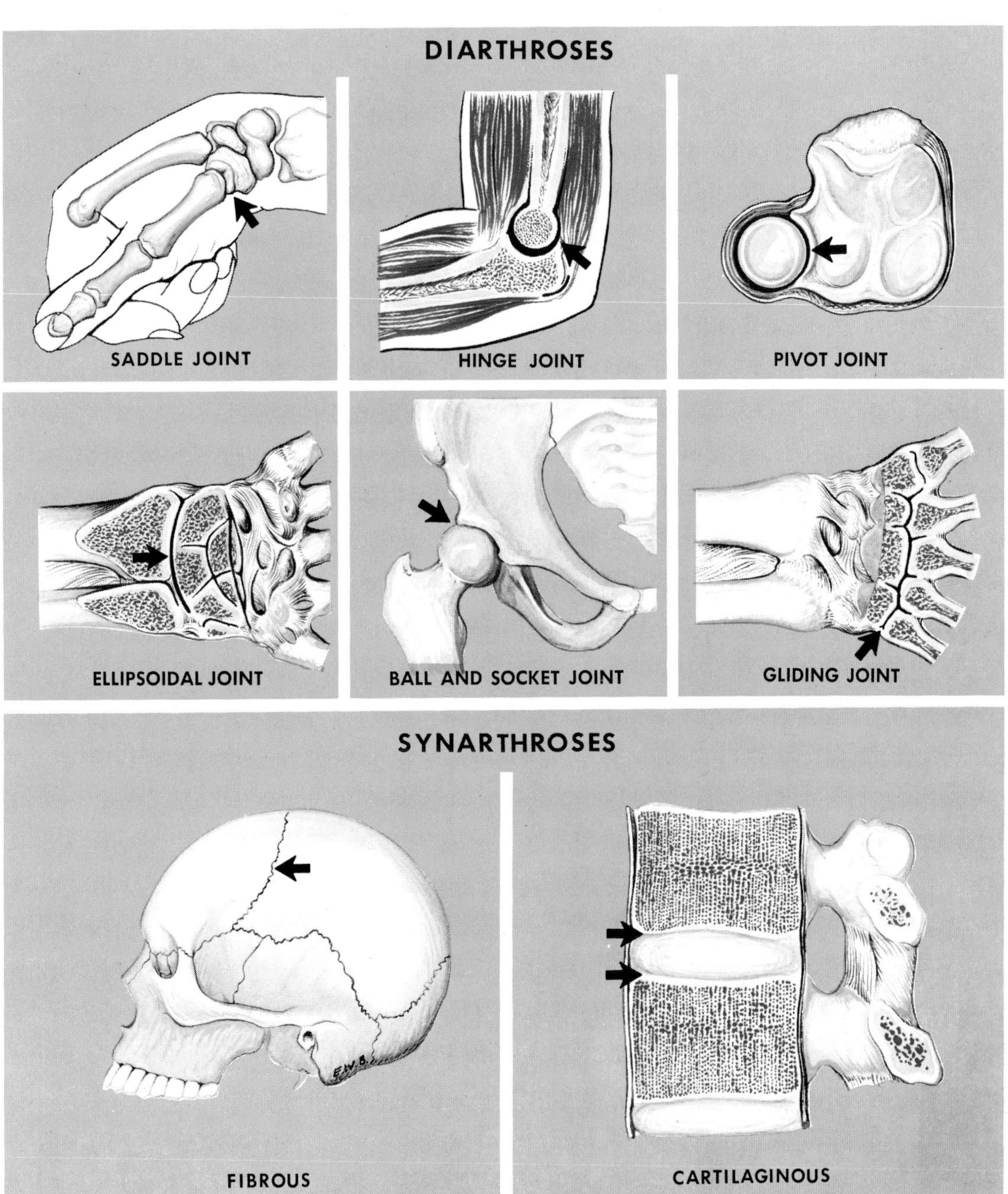

Fig. 79

Examples of diarthroses (movable joints with a joint cavity) and synarthroses (joints without a joint cavity). Refer to Tables 5 and 6 for complete description and other examples.

Table 6. Description of individual joints

Name	*Articulating bones*	*Type*	*Movements*
Atlantoepistropheal	Anterior arch of atlas rotates about dens of axis (epistropheus)	Diarthrotic (pivot type)	Pivoting or partial rotation of head
Vertebral*	Between bodies of vertebrae	Synarthrotic, cartilaginous; amphiarthrotic by other system of classifying	Slight movement between any two vertebrae but considerable motility for column as whole
	Between articular processes	Diarthrotic (gliding)	
Clavicular			
Sternoclavicular	Medial end of clavicle with manubrium of sternum; only joint between upper extremity and trunk	Diarthrotic (gliding)	Gliding; weak joint that may be injured comparatively easily
Acromioclavicular	Distal end of clavicle with acromion of scapula	Diarthrotic (gliding)	Gliding; elevation, depression, protraction, retraction
Thoracic	Heads of ribs with bodies of vertebrae	Diarthrotic (gliding)	Gliding
	Tubercles of ribs with transverse processes of vertebrae	Diarthrotic (gliding)	Gliding
Shoulder	Head of humerus in glenoid cavity of scapula	Diarthrotic (ball and socket type)	Flexion, extension, abduction, adduction, rotation, and circumduction of upper arm; one of most freely movable of joints
Elbow	Trochlea of humerus with semilunar notch of ulna; head of radius with capitulum of humerus	Diarthrotic (hinge type)	Flexion and extension
	Head of radius in radial notch of ulna	Diarthrotic (pivot type)	Supination and pronation of lower arm and hand; rotation of lower arm on upper as in using screwdriver

*Joints of the vertebral column are securely maintained by a series of strong ligaments which bind the vertebrae firmly to each other in such a way that they cannot easily be moved out of position (dislocated). Two long ligaments hold the bodies of the vertebrae together. One grows out of the posterior surface of the bodies (posterior common ligament) and the other arises from the anterior surfaces (anterior common ligament). In addition, short ligaments connect the tops of each two spinous processes (supraspinous ligaments), each two laminae (subflava ligaments), and each two spinous processes (interspinous ligaments). In the cervical region the supraspinous ligaments are known as the ligamentum nuchae.

Table 6. Description of individual joints—cont'd

Name	*Articulating bones*	*Type*	*Movements*
Wrist	Navicular, lunate, and triquetral bones articulate with radius and articular disc	Diarthrotic (condyloid)	Flexion, extension, abduction, and adduction of hand
Carpal	Between various carpals	Diarthrotic (gliding)	Gliding
Hand	Proximal end of first metacarpal with greater multangular	Diarthrotic (saddle)	Flexion, extension, abduction, adduction, and circumduction of thumb and opposition to fingers; motility of this joint accounts for dexterity of human hand compared with animal forepaw
	Distal end of metacarpals with proximal end of phalanges	Diarthrotic (hinge)	Flexion, extension, limited abduction, and adduction of fingers
	Between phalanges	Diarthrotic (hinge)	Flexion and extension of finger sections
Sacroiliac	Between sacrum and two ilia	Diarthrotic; joint cavity mostly obliterated after middle life	None or slight; e.g., during late months of pregnancy and during delivery
Symphysis pubis	Between two pubic bones	Synarthrotic (or amphiarthrotic), cartilaginous	Slight, particularly during pregnancy and delivery
Hip	Head of femur in acetabulum of os coxa	Diarthrotic (ball and socket)	Flexion, extension, abduction, adduction, rotation, and circumduction
Knee	Between distal end of femur and proximal end of tibia; largest joint in body	Diarthrotic (hinge type)	Flexion and extension; slight rotation of tibia
Tibiofibular	Head of fibula with lateral condyle of tibia	Diarthrotic (gliding type)	Gliding
Ankle	Distal ends of tibia and fibula with talus	Diarthrotic (hinge type)	Flexion (dorsiflexion) and extension (plantar flexion)

Continued.

Table 6. Description of individual joints—cont'd

Name	*Articulating bones*	*Type*	*Movements*
Foot	Between tarsals	Diarthrotic (gliding)	Gliding; inversion and eversion
	Between metatarsals and phalanges	Diarthrotic (hinge type)	Flexion, extension, slight abduction, and adduction
	Between phalanges	Diarthrotic (hinge type)	Flexion and extension

ample is holding the head in an upright position and turning it from one side to the other.

Circumduction. Circumduction causes the bone to describe the surface of a cone as it moves. The distal end of the bone describes a circle. It combines flexion, abduction, extension, and adduction in succession. Examples are dropping the head to one shoulder, then to the chest, to the other shoulder, and backward and describing a circle with the arms outstretched.

Special movements. *Supination* is a movement of the forearm which turns the palm forward as it is in the anatomical position. *Pronation* is turning the forearm so as to bring the back of the hand forward. *Inversion* is a special movement of the ankle which turns the sole of the foot inward, while *eversion* turns it outward. *Protraction* moves a part forward, such as sticking out the jaw. *Retraction* is a reverse of protraction.

Bone formation and growth

The embryo skeleton when first formed consists of "bones" which are not really bones at all but hyaline cartilage or fibrous membrane structures shaped like bones.

Complicated processes (the details of which belong to the study of embryology) slowly replace these structures with bone. The process called *intramembranous ossification* replaces with bone the membranous predecessors of bones. *Endochondral ossification,* on the other hand, replaces cartilaginous structures with bone. The flat skull bones, some of the face bones, and part of the clavicle are formed by intramembranous ossification. By birth most of the skeleton has been ossified but not completely so until about 25 years of age.

The mechanism of ossification is still not definitely known. Basic steps in the process, however, seem to be these: groups of *osteoblasts* (bone-forming cells) appear in the membranous or cartilaginous structures undergoing ossification and synthesize the collagenous fibrils and cement that constitute the organic substance of the new bone matrix. More or less simultaneously, the deposition of complex calcium salts (presumably tricalcium phosphate, calcium carbonate, and others) occurs. The mechanism of calcification, however, has not yet been established. But at any rate, ossification, according to the present concept, consists of two main processes: synthesis of the organic bone matrix by osteoblasts, fol-

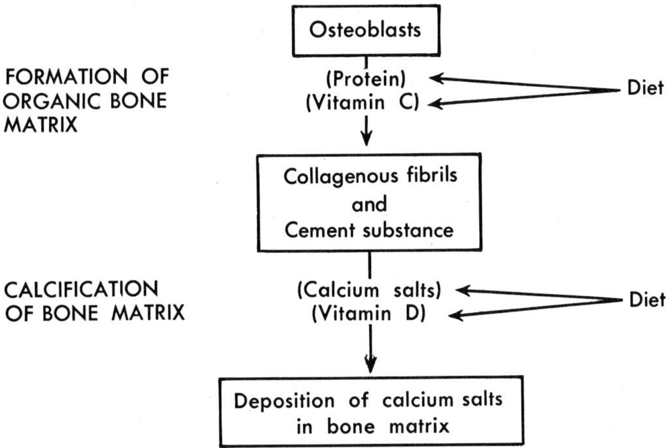

Fig. 80

Scheme to show two basic steps in ossification: formation of organic bone matrix (collagenous fibrils and cement) and calcification of bone matrix. Osteoblasts using proteins and vitamin C supplied by the diet synthesize organic bone matrix. Vitamin D promotes calcification of the bone matrix.

lowed quickly by calcification of the matrix (Fig. 80).

In long bones, endochondral ossification starts in the diaphysis and in both epiphyses and proceeds toward each other. A layer of cartilage known as *epiphyseal cartilage* remains between the diaphyseal and epiphyseal centers of ossification. As long as bone growth continues, proliferation of epiphyseal cartilage cells brings about a thickening of the layer of cartilage from time to time. Ossification of this additional cartilage then follows; that is, osteoblasts synthesize organic bone matrix and the matrix undergoes calcification. As a result, the bone becomes longer. When epiphyseal cartilage cells stop multiplying and the cartilage has become completely ossified, bone growth has ended. This is the scientific fact that underlies the clinical practice of x-raying a child's wrist to determine whether he "will grow anymore." If the x-ray film reveals a layer of epiphyseal cartilage, the answer is "yes"; if not, it is "no." He will have attained his full height.

Bones grow in diameter by the combined action of two special kinds of cells: osteoclasts and osteoblasts. Osteoclasts enlarge the diameter of the medullary cavity by eating away the bone of its walls. At the same time osteoblasts from the periosteum build new bone around the outside of the bone. By this dual process a bone with a larger diameter and larger medullary cavity has been produced from a smaller bone with a smaller medullary cavity.

Surprising though it seems at first thought, bones may become diseased. An example familiar to most of us is *rickets,* a condition more common to childhood than later years. *Osteoporosis,* in contrast, is a bone disease occurring commonly in the older years. The defect in this malady lies in the first step of ossification, in the synthesis of the organic bone matrix by osteoblasts. But, you may be asking, why do osteoblasts still need to synthesize bone matrix in old age? Is not ossification completed long before this, in young adulthood? This seems logical, but it is not so. Bone is not formed once and for all to last a lifetime. It is not just an inert structural material. Bone is a living tissue and as such is subject to the vicissitudes of any living tissue. It continually breaks down and is resorbed. But also it is continually being repaired and formed anew. Normally the two opposing processes balance each other. But under some circumstances they become unbalanced, and one or the other process dominates. This happens in osteoporosis, for example. Bone formation lags behind bone breakdown. Consequently bones become thin and their density decreases, making them less strong. With this increased fragility, fractures occur more easily. You yourself undoubtedly know some old person who has "fallen and broken his hip." But actually the sequence is often the reverse: the bone breaks first (frequently in a femur weakened by osteoporosis) and causes the fall.

Inadequate amounts of sex hormones in the blood and inadequate activity are believed to be the major factors responsible for senile osteoporosis. Estrogens (female hormones) stimulate osteoblasts to synthesize organic bone matrix.

With postmenopausal estrogen deficiency, therefore, osteoblasts lack this stimulus so fail to form matrix fast enough to keep up with the normal pace of matrix destruction. Insufficient activity operates similarly. Muscular activity puts strains on the skeleton, and these skeletal strains are natural stimulants of osteoblasts, so decreased activity means decreased osteoblasts stimulation and often the gradual development of osteoporosis.

Suggestion: Study Fig. 80 carefully and then try to explain why a diet deficient in vitamin C or proteins might lead to osteoporosis. On the basis of the information in this diagram, do you think vitamin D deficiency might produce osteoporosis? What kind of defect in bone do you think it would produce?

Outline summary— The skeletal system

Meaning

All bones and their joints

Functions

1. Furnishes supporting framework
2. Affords protection
3. Provides levers for muscle action
4. Hemopoiesis by red bone marrow
5. Calcium storage

Bone and cartilage

MICROSCOPIC STRUCTURE

Bone

1. Mainly calcified matrix—cement substance impregnated with calcium salts and reinforced by collagenous fibrils
2. Lamellae—concentric cylindrical layers of calcified matrix enclosing haversian canal that contains blood vessel
3. Haversian system—canal and surrounding lamellae
4. Lacunae—microscopic spaces containing osteocytes (bone cells); lie between lamellae
5. Canaliculi—microscopic canals radiating in all directions from lacunae, connecting them with haversian canals; routes by which tissue fluid reaches osteocytes
6. Compact bone (or solid bone)—no empty spaces; lamellae fit closely together
7. Cancellous bone (or spongy bone)—many spaces in matrix which is arranged mainly in trabeculae rather than lamellae

Cartilage

1. Similar to that of bone with following exceptions:
   a. cartilage matrix—firm gel; bone matrix—calcified cement substance
   b. cartilage matrix—no canal system, no blood vessels; bone matrix—extensive canal network

Bones

GROSS STRUCTURE

Types

1. Long (femur)
2. Short (carpals)
3. Flat (parietal)
4. Irregular (vertebrae)

Structure

1. Long bones—see Figs. 38 to 40
2. Short bones—thin layer of compact bone encasing "core" of cancellous bone
3. Flat bones—layer of cancellous bone between two plates of compact bone
4. Irregular bones—thin layer of compact bone encasing cancellous bone

NAMES AND NUMBERS

Total, 206 bones—Table 3, pp. 73 to 75

Axial skeleton (80 bones)

1. Skull (28 bones)
   a. cranium (8 bones)—frontal, parietal (2), temporal (2), occipital, sphenoid, and ethmoid
   b. face (14 bones)—nasal (2), maxillary (2), malar (2), mandible, lacrimal (2), palatine (2), inferior turbinates (2), and vomer
   c. ear ossicles (6 bones)—malleus (2), incus (2), and stapes (2)
2. Hyoid (1 bone)
3. Vertebral column (26 vertebrae)
   a. cervical (7)
   b. thoracic (12)
   c. lumbar (5)
   d. sacrum
   e. coccyx
4. Sternum and ribs (25 bones)—sternum, true ribs (7 pairs), false ribs (5 pairs, 2 pairs of which are floating)

Appendicular skeleton (126 bones)

1. Upper extremities (64 bones)—clavicle (2), scapula (2), humerus (2), ulna (2), radius (2), carpals (16), metacarpals (10), and phalanges (28)
2. Lower extremities (62 bones)—os coxa (2), femur (2), patella (2), tibia (2), fibula (2), tarsal (14), metatarsal (10), and phalanges (28)

MARKINGS

Depressions and openings

1. Fossa—hollow or depression
2. Sinus—cavity of spongelike air space within bone
3. Foramen—hole
4. Meatus—tube-shaped opening

Projections or processes

1. Those which fit into joints
   a. condyle—rounded projection entering into formation of joint
   b. head—rounded projection beyond narrow neck
2. Those to which muscles attach
   a. trochanter—very large process
   b. crest—ridge
   c. spinous process or spine—sharp projection
   d. tuberosity—large, rounded projection
   e. tubercle—small rounded projection

Identification

See Table 4, pp. 99 to 108

DIFFERENCES BETWEEN MALE AND FEMALE SKELETONS

1. Male skeleton larger and heavier
2. Male pelvis deep and funnel shaped with narrow pubic arch; female pelvis shallow, broad, and flaring with wider pubic arch and larger iliosacral notch

AGE CHANGES IN SKELETON

1. Changes in absolute and proportionate sizes of bones from infancy to adulthood
2. Changes in texture and in contour of margins and bone markings from youth to old age

Joints between bones (articulations)

KINDS

1. Diarthroses
   a. characteristics
      1. thin layer of hyaline cartilage covers articular surfaces
      2. fibrous, synovial-lined capsule forms true joint cavity; no tissue grows between articular surfaces of bones
      3. ligaments hold articulating bones firmly connected
   b. subtypes—see Table 5, p. 112
2. Synarthroses
   a. characteristics
      1. no joint cavity
      2. cartilage, fibrous tissue, or bone grows between articulating surfaces of bones
   b. subtypes—see Table 5, p. 112

MOVEMENTS

1. Flexion—angle at joint decreases

2. Extension—angle at joint increases; return from flexion
3. Abduction—moving bone away from body's median plane
4. Adduction—moving bone back toward body's median plane
5. Rotation—pivoting bone upon its axis
6. Circumduction—describing surface of cone with moving parts
7. Special movements
   - a. supination—movement of forearm which turns palm forward
   - b. pronation—movement of forearm which turns back of hand forward
   - c. inversion—ankle movement turning sole of foot inward
   - d. eversion—ankle movement turning sole of foot outward
   - e. protraction—moving part forward
   - f. retraction—pulling part back; opposite of protraction

Bone formation and growth

1. Formation
   - a. skeleton preformed in hyaline cartilage and fibrous membranes; most cartilaginous or membranous structures changed into bone before birth but not complete until about 25 years of age
   - b. endochondral ossification—incompletely understood process which replaces hyaline cartilage "bones" with true bones; see Fig. 80 for summary of postulated basic steps of this mechanism
   - c. intramembranous ossification – process which replaces fibrous membrane "bones" with true bones
2. Growth
   - a. in length—by continual thickening of epiphyseal cartilage followed by ossification
   - b. in diameter—medullary cavity enlarged by osteoclasts destroying bone around it while new bone added around circumference by osteoblasts
3. Correlation with bone disease; osteoporosis—deficient synthesis of organic bone matrix by osteoblasts lacking stimulation of normal amounts of sex hormones in blood and of adequate muscular activity

Review questions

1. What general functions does the skeletal system perform?
2. Describe the microscopic structure of bone and cartilage.
3. What functions does a long bone perform? Describe the structure of a long bone, indicating how various structural characteristics contribute to its function.
4. Describe the general plan of the skeleton.
5. Name the bones of the adult skeleton.
6. Describe the structural features of diarthrotic joints that facilitate movement.
7. Give examples of several types of diarthrotic joints.
8. Explain the functions of the periosteum.
9. What joint(s) unites the shoulder girdle with the trunk? The pelvic girdle with the trunk?
10. Name the several kinds of movements possible at joints. Define each movement named.
11. Describe the intervertebral joints.
12. Name the primary and secondary curves of the spine. Describe each.
13. Name the five pairs of bony sinuses in the skull.
14. Name the bones which fuse to form the coccyx.
15. What is the true pelvis? The false pelvis? Name the boundary line between the true and false pelves.
16. Through what opening does the spinal cord enter the cranial cavity?
17. Explain the basic steps in the process of ossification according to the concept described in the text.
18. Deficiency of what vitamin causes inadequate calcification of bone?
19. Deficiency of what vitamin causes inadequate synthesis of bone matrix (osteoporosis)?
20. Explain why osteoporosis often develops after the menopause.
21. Define or make an identifying statement about each of the following terms:

condyle	medullary cavity
crest	osteoblast
diaphysis	osteoclast
diarthroses	periosteum
endosteum	rotation
epiphysis	scoliosis
foramen	sinus
fossa	spinous process
haversian system	synarthroses
kyphosis	trochanter
lordosis	trabeculae

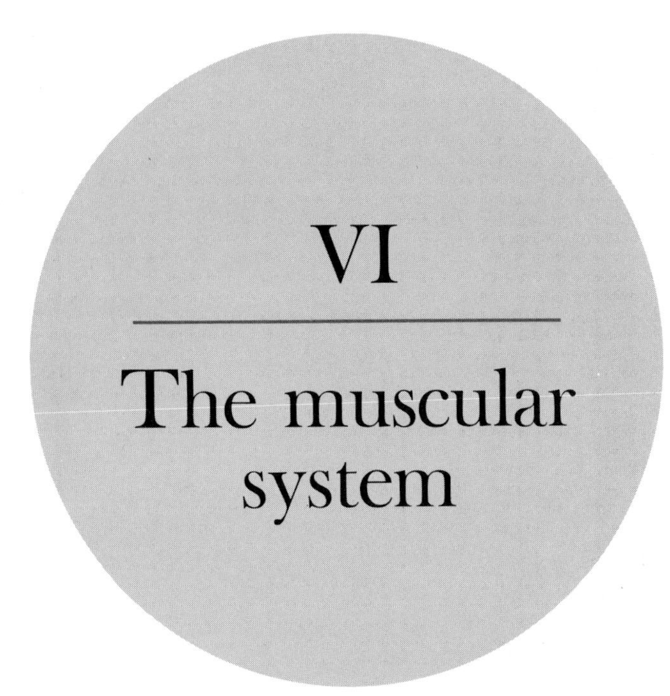

VI

The muscular system

Man's survival depends in large part upon his ability to adjust to the changing conditions of his environment. Movements constitute the major part of this adjustment. Whereas most of the systems of the body play some role in accomplishing movement, it is the skeletal and muscular systems acting together which actually produce movements. We have investigated the architectural plan of the skeleton and have seen how its joint structures and firm supports make movement possible. However, bones and joints cannot move themselves. They must be moved by something. Muscle tissue, because of its contractility, extensibility, and elasticity, is admirably suited to this function. In this chapter we shall try to discover how muscles move bones and to do this we shall try to answer many other questions—how the structure of muscles adapts them to their function, how energy is made available for their work, how muscle activity contributes to the health and survival of the whole body—to mention only a few.

Meaning

Properly speaking, the term muscular system means all the muscles of the body—those attached to the bones, those helping to make up the walls of numerous internal structures, and the muscle which composes the wall of the heart. More commonly, however, the term refers to skeletal muscles only—those muscle masses which attach to bones and move them about, the masses of "red meat" of the body.

General functions

If you have any doubts about the importance of muscle function to normal life, you have only to observe a person with extensive paralysis—a victim of severe poliomyelitis, for example. Any of us possessed of normal powers of movement can little imagine life with this matchless power lost. But cardinal as it is, movement is not the only contribution muscles make to healthy survival. They also perform two other essential functions: maintenance of posture and production of a large portion of body heat.

Movement. Movement consists sometimes of locomotion, sometimes of movements of parts of the body, sometimes of changes in the size of openings, and sometimes of propulsion of substances through tubes, for example. Propulsion of blood through arteries by heart movements is one example of the latter. Passage of food through the digestive tract by contractions of the stomach and intestines is another. By means of locomotion, adjustments are made to the external environment. Desirable objects are approached, and undesirable or dangerous ones are repelled. By means of internal movements, vital adjustments and processes are accomplished. Consider the following examples: contraction and relaxation of the iris muscles which allow just the right amount of light to enter the eyes, contractions of the digestive tract muscles which promote digestion and elimination, and contractions of the heart which keep the blood circulating.

Posture. The continued partial contraction of many skeletal muscles makes possible standing, sitting, and other maintained positions of the body.

Heat production. Chemical changes that occur in muscle cells to make mechanical energy available for movement also release heat energy. In fact, they produce such a major share of total body heat that they constitute one of the most important parts of the mechanism for maintaining homeostasis of temperature. Do you recall the term that means the series of chemical changes referred to here? If not, see p. 9.

Functional characteristics of muscle tissue

As noted in Chapter III, there are three types of muscle tissue, and they differ as to microscopic structure, nervous control, and location. They are similar, however, as to certain functional characteristics. All three types possess a high degree of irritability, conductivity, extensibility, elasticity, and contractility.

Irritability or the ability to respond to a stimulus and *conductivity* or the ability to transmit impulses are discussed at some length in the chapter on the nervous system (pp. 178 to 180). Physiotherapists make practical use of the fact that muscle tissue is itself irritable,* independently of the nerve tissue supplying it. They cause paralyzed muscles to contract by stimulating them directly with an electrical current—a treatment aimed at preventing muscle withering from disuse.

Extensibility means the ability to be stretched. *Elasticity* means the ability to resume an original length after a stretching force is removed.

Contractility is the ability to contract, to shorten, and to thicken—a property more highly developed in muscle than in any other tissue. Contractility is the functional specialty of muscle tissue—its big contribution.

*The independent excitability of muscle was first demonstrated in 1850 by the classic curare experiment of Claude Bernard. (Curare is a drug long used by South American Indians as an arrow poison. It is now known to block the passage of impulses from nerve to muscle by paralyzing the myoneural junctions.) Bernard injected curare into the dorsal lymph sac of a frog and then electrically stimulated the motor nerve to its leg. No contraction resulted, an indication that nerve impulses were not reaching the leg muscle. Next he stimulated the muscle directly and contraction occurred. Thus he demonstrated that muscle cells are themselves irritable, that is, able to respond to stimulation independently of their nerve supply.

Muscle contraction

TYPES

Much of our information about muscle contraction has come from studies made on muscle-nerve preparations, usually the gastrocnemius muscle of a frog with its motor nerve. Electrical or sometimes other kinds of stimuli are applied to cause contraction and a graphic record is made. A common method of doing this is to attach the muscle to one end of a lever and place the writing point end of the lever against a smoked drum (kymograph). From such studies and others, several kinds of muscle contraction have been described. Some of them are described in the following paragraphs.

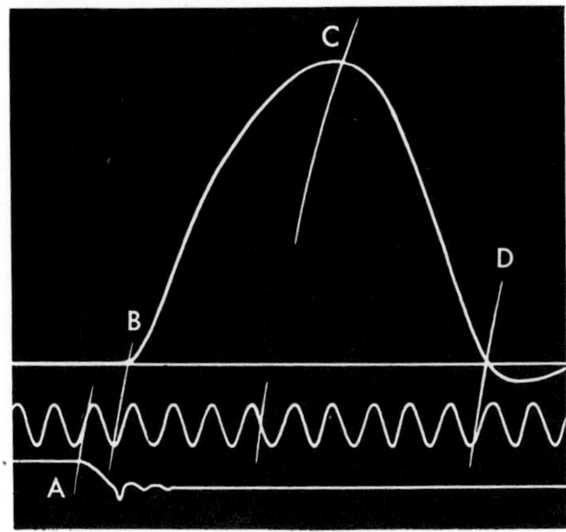

Fig. 81

Kymographic record of a muscle twitch. **A,** Stimulus applied. **B,** Beginning of contraction. **C** to **D,** Relaxation. Each wave of line below the kymographic record represents 1/100 second of time. (From Tuttle and Schottelius: Textbook of physiology, St. Louis, The C. V. Mosby Co.)

Twitch contraction. A twitch is a quick, jerky contraction in response to a single stimulus. Fig. 81 shows a kymographic record of such a contraction. It reveals that the muscle does not shorten at the instant of stimulation, but a fraction of a second later, and that it reaches a peak of shortening and then gradually resumes its former length. These three phases of contraction are spoken of, respectively, as the *latent period,* the *contraction phase,* and the *relaxation phase.* The entire twitch usually lasts less than 1/10 second. Twitch contractions do not produce our normal movements (with the exception of the involuntary winking movement).

Tetanic contraction (tetanus). A tetanic contraction is a more sustained contraction

Fig. 82

Kymographic records. Tracings **A** to **D,** Incomplete tetanus tracing. **E,** Complete tetanus. Faradic shocks of same intensity used throughout. (From Tuttle and Schottelius: Textbook of physiology, St. Louis, The C. V. Mosby Co.)

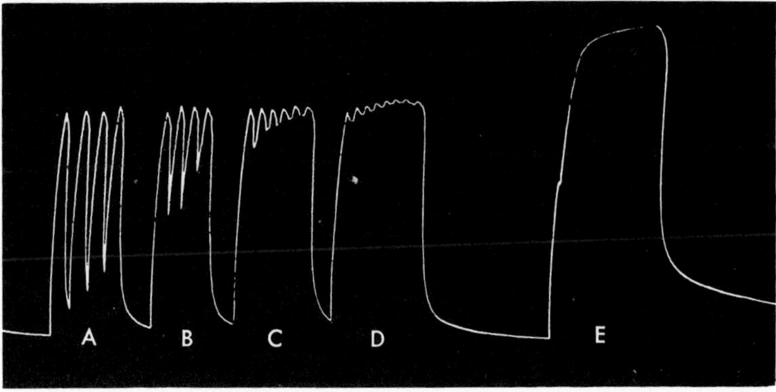

than a twitch. It is produced by a series of stimuli bombarding the muscle in rapid succession. About 30 stimuli per second, for example, evoke a tetanic contraction by a frog gastrocnemius muscle, but the rate varies for different muscles and different conditions. Fig. 82 shows kymographic records of incomplete and complete tetanus. Our normal smooth movements are produced by complete tetanic contractions. Incomplete tetanic contractions, on the other hand, produce coarse, fine tremors. The disease tetanus or lockjaw produces complete tetanus of the jaw muscles, making it impossible for the patient to terminate the contraction at will—in other words, his jaws are "locked."

Tonic contraction (tone; tonus). A tonic contraction is a continual, partial contraction. At any one moment a small number of the total fibers in a muscle contract, producing a tautness of the muscle rather than a recognizable contraction and movement. Different groups of fibers scattered throughout the muscle contract in relays. Tone is particularly important for maintaining posture. A striking illustration of this fact is the following: when a person loses consciousness, his muscles lose their tone and he collapses in a heap, unable to maintain a sitting or standing posture. Muscles with less tone than normal are described as flaccid muscles and those with more than normal tone as spastic. Impulses over stretch reflex arcs (pp. 228 to 230) maintain tone.

Treppe (staircase phenomenon). Treppe is a phenomenon in which increasingly stronger twitch contractions occur in response to constant strength stimuli repeated at the rate of about once or twice a second. In other words, a muscle contracts more forcefully after it has contracted a few times than when it first contracts—a principle made practical use of by athletes when they warm up but one not yet satisfactorily explained. Presumably it relates partly to the rise in temperature of active muscles and partly to their accumulation of metabolic products. After the first few stimuli, muscle responds to a considerable number of successive stimuli with maximal contractions and after these it responds with less and less strong contractions. The relaxation phase becomes shorter and finally disappears entirely (Fig. 83). In other

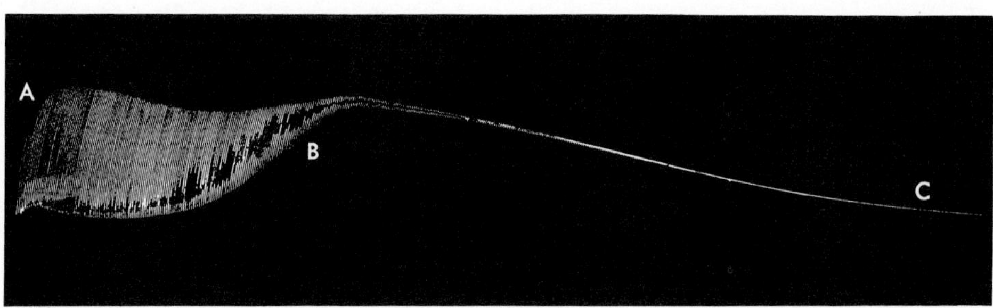

Fig. 83

Diagram showing changes in character of contraction when a muscle is stimulated repeatedly by constant strength stimuli. Curve **A**, Treppe or staircase phenomenon. Each of first several contractions is stronger than the preceding one. Curve **B**, Contracture. Incomplete relaxation phase in each of the next series of contractions, producing a prolonged contraction. Curve **C**, Fatigue. No contraction in response to stimulation after a great many repetitions of the stimulus. (From Francis and Knowlton: Textbook of anatomy and physiology, St. Louis, The C. V. Mosby Co.)

words, the muscle stays partially contracted —an abnormal state of prolonged contraction called *contracture.*

Repeated stimulation of a muscle eventually lessens its irritability and contractility and may result in *muscle fatigue,* a condition in which the muscle does not respond to the strongest stimuli. Complete muscle fatigue, however, very seldom occurs in the body, although it can be readily induced in an excised muscle.

Isotonic contraction. *Iso* means same and *tonic* means pressure or tension. Therefore, an isotonic contraction is one in which the pressure or tension within a muscle remains the same but in which the length of the muscle changes. It shortens, producing movement.

Isometric contraction. An isometric contraction is a contraction in which muscle length remains the same but in which muscle tension increases. You can observe isometric contraction by pushing your arms against a wall and feeling the tension increase in your arm muscles. Isometric contractions do not produce movements or do work. Isotonic contractions, on the other hand, both produce movements and do work.

Fibrillation. Fibrillation is an abnormal type of contraction in which individual fibers contract asynchronously, producing a flutter of the muscle but no effective movement. Fibrillation of the heart, for example, occurs fairly often.

Convulsions. Convulsions are abnormal uncoordinated tetanic contractions of varying groups of muscles.

MECHANISM

A few years ago, Huxley proposed a hypothesis to explain muscle contraction. It it now known as the sliding-filament hypothesis for reasons which will become apparent as you read on. Huxley and associates discovered amazing detail about the fine structure of muscle cells. They showed that a single muscle cell or fiber consists of many smaller fibrils and that, incredibly, each tiny fibril is itself composed of even smaller filaments. Molecules of the protein myosin were found to make up the coarser-appearing filaments, and molecules of the protein actin were discovered to compose the finer ones. Huxley's sliding-filament hypothesis proposes that a muscle fiber shortens or contracts as a result of its fine actin filaments sliding toward each other

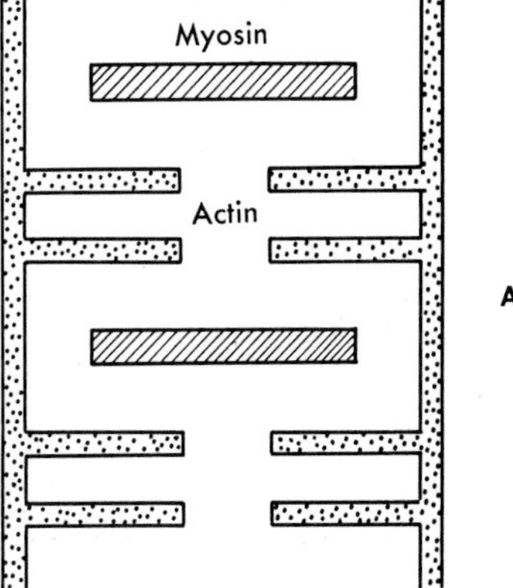

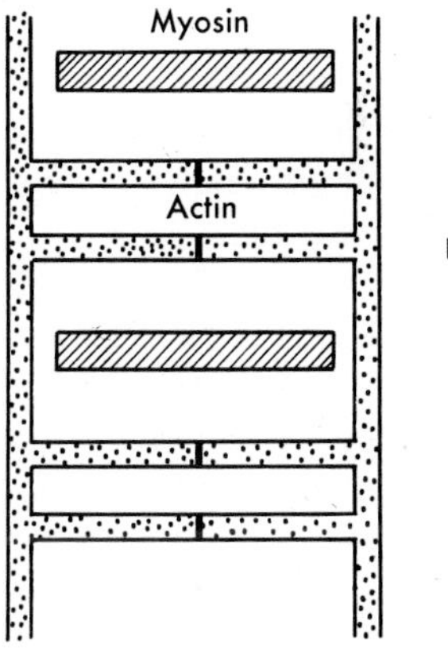

Fig. 84

Scheme to show arrangement of actin and myosin molecules in a myofibril. **A,** Muscle relaxed. **B,** Muscle contracted by actin filaments moving together. (Modified from Huxley.)

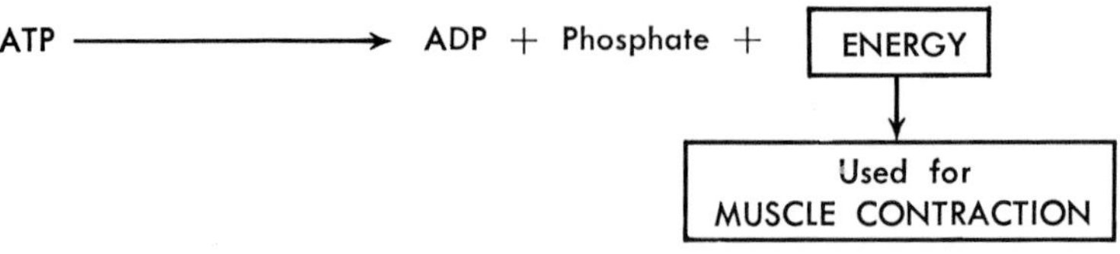

ADP + CP ⟶ ATP + Creatine

Fig. 85

Predominant chemical reactions occurring in muscle cells during contraction. Energy for muscle contraction comes from the breakdown of adenosine triphosphate (ATP) to adenosine diphosphate (ADP) and phosphate (first equation). Then ADP combines with creatine phosphate (CP, a high-energy compound formed as shown in Fig. 86) and thereby replaces ATP (second equation) about as rapidly as it is being used for a while. But to provide themselves with enough ATP to carry on prolonged work, muscle cells must carry on the slower process of catabolism.

along the coarser myosin filaments.* If you examine Fig. 84, you may find it easier to visualize this action.

Presumably the hydrolysis of adenosine triphosphate (ATP) releases the energy which does the work of sliding actin filaments toward each other. In other words, ATP breakdown is thought to furnish the energy for muscle contraction as well as for other kinds of cellular work. Nerve impulses arriving at a muscle cell apparently trigger ATP breakdown. How they do this is not well understood. But in one way or another stimulation acts to break ATP's terminal high-energy bonds. Result? ATP molecules split apart into adenosine diphosphate (ADP) and phosphate, and as ATP's terminal bonds are broken, energy is released from them and does the work of contracting the muscle fiber (see first equation in Fig. 85).

As you already know from the discussion on pp. 34 to 38, ATP is produced in all cells by catabolism. But muscle cells also have another and more rapid way of producing ATP—specifically, by combining ADP with creatine phosphate (CP; phosphocreatine) as shown in the second equation in Fig. 85. CP is a high-energy phosphate compound synthesized in muscle cells when they are not contracting. At such times, muscle cells are synthesizing more ATP than they are hydrolizing to supply their low-energy needs of the moment. Thus, during these periods they convert some of the excess ATP to high-energy creatine phosphate, which they also store (see second equation in Fig. 86). Then later, during periods of strenuous contraction, when the cell needs more ATP quickly, this reaction reverses itself and almost instantaneously provides more ATP, as indicated by the second equation in Fig. 85.

Other chemical changes also occur in muscle during strenuous exercise. Soon after vigorous activity begins, pyruvic acid starts to accumulate in muscle cells and is reduced to lactic acid. The reason is this: respiration and circulation cannot accelerate enough to supply the cells with as much oxygen as they need to oxidize the pyruvic acid via the citric acid cycle as rapidly as it forms by glycolysis. Most of the lactic acid (about four-fifths according

*For a more complete discussion of this hypothesis, see Ham, Arthur W., and Leeson, Thomas S.: Histology, ed. 5, Philadelphia, 1965, J. B. Lippincott Co., pp. 486-493.

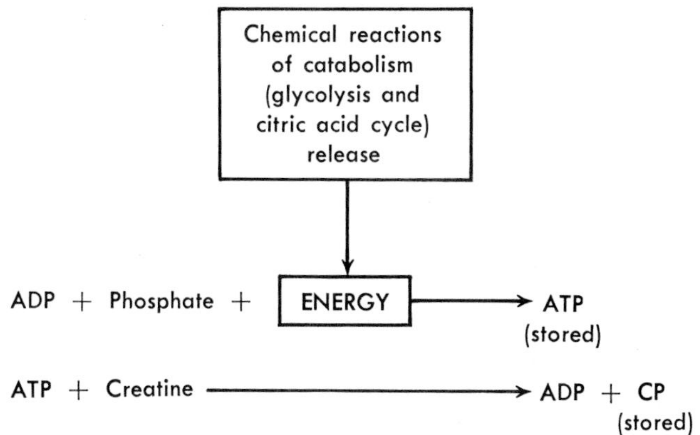

Fig. 86

Scheme to show the predominant chemical reactions occurring in muscle cells when they are not contracting. An excess of adenosine triphosphate (ATP) is being synthesized. Some of it is stored as such, and some is converted to high-energy creatine phosphate for storage.

to some investigators) diffuses out of the cells and is carried by the blood to the liver, there to be gradually resynthesized to glycogen or glucose. A smaller amount remains behind in the muscle cells. Here, after the strenuous bout of exercise ends and oxygen again becomes available, the lactic acid is oxidized back to pyruvic acid and on through the citric acid cycle to carbon dioxide and water.

The amount of oxygen required for oxidation of the lactic acid accumulated during strenuous exercise is referred to as the *oxygen debt.* It is a debt that has to be repaid before exercise can continue—a fact all of us have observed when we have stopped to catch our breath during some strenuous exertion. For example, if you were to run the 100-yard dash, according to one authoritative source,* you might need more than 6 liters of oxygen to oxidize all the pyruvic acid formed by glycolysis during that short sprint. But the maximum oxygen you could consume in that same brief time would fall short of this—probably less than 1 liter. You would, therefore, have incurred an oxygen debt of several liters which would be repaid by your breathing rapidly and deeply for some time after your strenuous exertion. (See Figs. 87 and 88.)

Muscle cells obey the all-or-none law when they contract. This means that they either contract with all the force possible under existing conditions or they contract not at all. A strong stimulus, in other words, produces no stronger contraction of a single muscle cell than a weak one provided that conditions are the same. But if conditions at the time of stimulation change, then the force of the cell's contraction changes. If, for example, at one time a muscle fiber is receiving sufficient oxygen and at another time too little oxygen, it will contract more forcefully under the adequate oxygen condition than under the deficient oxygen condition.

Skeletal muscles

GROSS STRUCTURE

Size, shape, and fiber arrangement

Skeletal muscles are organs composed mainly of skeletal muscle tissue. They vary considerably in size, shape, and arrangement of fibers. They range from extremely

*Best, Charles H., and Taylor, M. B.: The physiological basis of medical practice, ed. 7, Baltimore, 1961, Williams & Wilkins Co., p. 879.

Strenuous exertion
O_2 used faster than can be supplied
CELLULAR HYPOXIA
Slowing of citric acid cycle
Decreasing ATP synthesis
Accumulating pyruvic acid
$(+H_2)$
Accumulating lactic acid
"Oxygen debt"

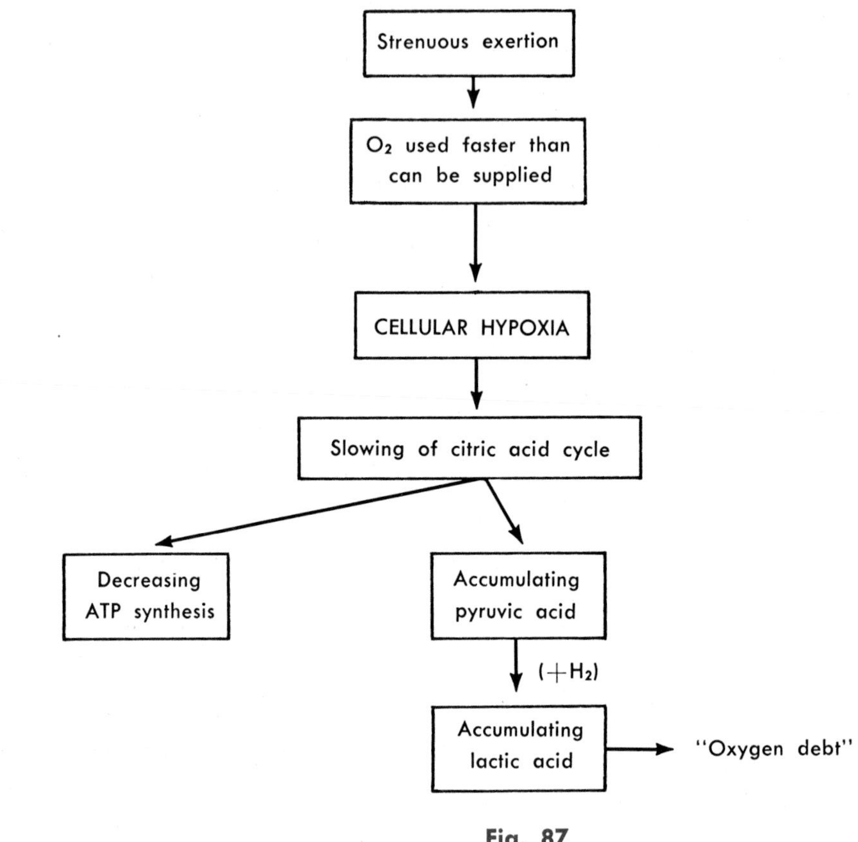

Fig. 87

Creation of oxygen debt during strenuous exertion.

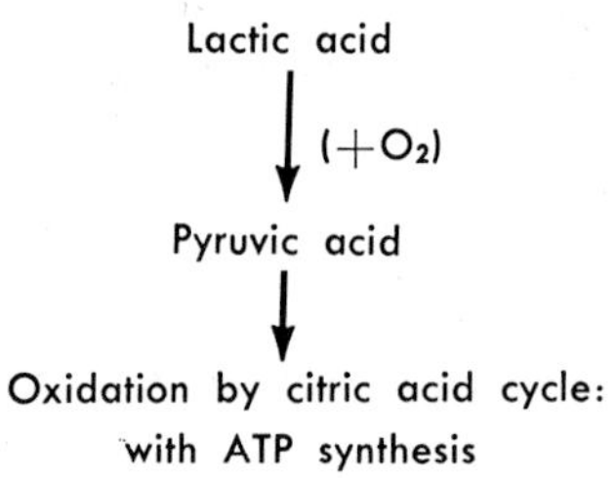

Lactic acid
$(+O_2)$
Pyruvic acid
Oxidation by citric acid cycle: with ATP synthesis

Fig. 88

Repayment of oxygen debt after strenuous exertion.

tiny strands, as for example, the stapedius muscle of the middle ear, to large masses such as the muscles of the thigh. Some skeletal muscles are broad in shape and some narrow. Some are long and tapering and some short and blunt. Some are triangular, some quadrilateral, and some irregular. Some form flat sheets and others, bulky masses.

Arrangement of fibers varies in different muscles. In some muscles the fibers are parallel to the long axis of the muscle, in some they converge to a narrow attachment, and in some they are oblique and either pennate (like the feathers in an old-fashioned plume pen) or bipennate (double-feathered as in the rectus femoris). Fibers may even be curved, as in the sphincters of the face, for example. The direction of the fibers composing a muscle is significant because of its relationship to function. For instance, a muscle with the bipennate fiber arrangement can produce the strongest contraction.

Connective tissue components

A fibrous connective tissue sheath *(epimysium)* envelops each muscle and extends into it as partitions between bundles of its fibers *(perimysium)* and between individual fibers *(endomysium)*. Because all three of these structures are continuous with the fibrous structures that attach muscles to bones or other structures, muscles are most firmly harnessed to the structures they pull against during contraction. The epimysium, perimysium, and endomysium of a muscle, for example, may be continuous with fibrous tissue that extends from the muscle as a *tendon,* a strong tough cord continuous at its other end with the fibrous covering of bone (periosteum). Or the fibrous wrapping of a muscle may extend as a broad, flat sheet of connective tissue *(aponeurosis)* to attach it to adjacent structures, usually the fibrous wrappings of another muscle. So tough and strong are tendons and aponeuroses that they are not often torn, even by injuries forceful enough to break bones or tear muscles. They are, however, occasionally pulled away from bones.

You may recall that a continuous sheet of loose connective tissue known as the superficial fascia lies directly under the skin. Under this lies a layer of dense fibrous connective tissue, the *deep fascia.* Extensions of the deep fascia form the epimysium, perimysium, and endomysium of muscles and their attachments to bones and other structures and also enclose viscera, glands, blood vessels, and nerves.

Fig. 89

A motor unit. Here, a single nerve fiber branches to supply many muscle fibers. Note the motor end plates (myoneural junctions). (Modified from Bremer: A textbook of histology, New York, Blakiston Division, McGraw-Hill Book Co.)

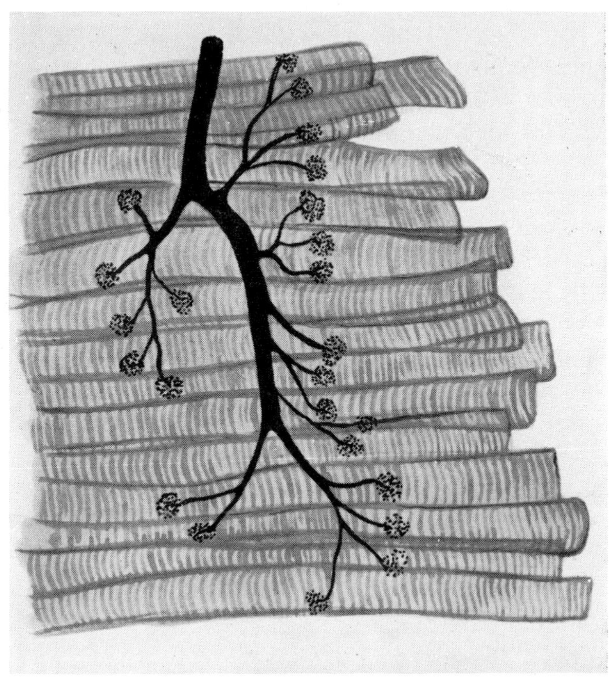

Nerve supply

A nerve cell that transmits impulses to a skeletal muscle is called a *somatic motor neuron.* One such neuron plus the muscle cells in which its axon terminates constitutes a *motor unit* (Fig. 89). A motor unit may consist of one motor neuron and just one muscle cell, or it may consist of one motor neuron and a hundred or more muscle cells. This means that one motor neuron may cause a single muscle fiber to contract, or it may cause more than a hundred fibers to contract simultaneously. The functional principle seems to be this: the fewer the number of muscle fibers supplied by a single motor neuron (in other words, the fewer the muscle fibers in a muscle's motor units), the more precise the movements produced by that muscle. For example, in certain small muscles of the hand each motor unit includes only a few muscle fibers, and these muscles produce precise finger movements. In contrast, motor units in large abdominal muscles that do not produce precise movements include more than a hundred muscle fibers each.

At the place where a motor nerve fiber contacts a muscle fiber, the sarcoplasm of the muscle fiber projects outward like a tiny mound. This area of contact between a nerve and muscle fiber is known as the *motor end plate* or *myoneural junction.* Here is a curiosity-provoking detail about motor end plates—numerous mitochondria occur in both the muscle and nerve fibers in this contact area. In addition to the many motor nerve endings, there are also many sensory nerve endings in skeletal muscles. These will be described in the chapter on the nervous system.

ACTIONS

Several methods of study have been used to amass the present-day store of knowledge about muscle actions. They vary from the traditional and relatively simple procedures, such as observing and palpating muscles in action, manipulating dissected muscles to observe movements, or deducing movements from knowledge of muscle anatomy, to the newer more complicated method of electromyography (recording action potentials from contracting muscles). As a result, there is now a somewhat overwhelming amount of knowledge about muscle actions. So perhaps we will find it easier to thread our way through this maze of detail if we start with general principles and then go on to details that seem to us most useful.

Basic principles

1. *Skeletal muscles contract only if stimulated.* They do not have the quality of automaticity inherent in cardiac and visceral muscle. Although nerve impulses are the natural stimuli for skeletal muscles, electrical and some other artificial stimuli can also activate them. A skeletal muscle deprived of nerve impulses by whatever cause is a functionless mass. One should, therefore, think of a skeletal muscle and its motor nerve as a physiological unit, always functioning together, either useless without the other.

2. *Skeletal muscles produce movements by pulling on bones.* Most of our muscles span at least one joint and attach to both articulating bones. When they contract, therefore, their shortening puts a pull on both bones, and this pull moves one of the bones at the joint—draws it toward the other bone, much as a pull on marionette strings moves a puppet's parts. (In case you are wondering why both bones do not move since both are pulled on by the contracting muscle, the reason is that one of them is normally stabilized by contraction of other muscles or by its own less mobile structure.)

3. *Bones serve as levers, and joints serve as fulcrums of these levers.* (By definition, a *lever* is any rigid bar free to turn about a

fixed point called its *fulcrum.*) A contracting muscle applies a pulling force on a bone lever at the point of the muscle's attachment to the bone. This causes the bone (referred to as the insertion bone) to move about its joint fulcrum. We have already noted that a skeletal muscle and its motor nerve act as a functional unit. Now we can add bones and joints to this unit and can describe the physiological unit for movement as a neuromusculoskeletal unit. Disease of any one of these parts of the unit—of nerve or muscle or joint—can, as you might infer, cause abnormal movements or complete loss of movement. Poliomyelitis, for example, and multiple sclerosis and hemiplegia all involve the neural part of the unit. In contrast, muscular dystrophy affects the muscular part and arthritis the skeletal part.

4. *Muscles that move a part usually do not lie over that part.* In most cases the body of a muscle lies proximal to the part moved. Thus muscles that move the lower arm lie proximal to it, that is, in the upper arm. Applying the same principle, where would you expect muscles that move the hand to be located? Those that move the lower leg? Those that move the upper arm?

5. *Skeletal muscles almost always act in groups rather than singly.* In other words, most movements are produced by the coordinated action of several muscles. Some of the muscles in the group contract while others relax. To identify each muscle's special function in the group, the following classification is used:

(a) *prime movers*—muscle or muscles whose contraction actually produces the movement

(b) *antagonists*—muscles which relax while the prime mover is contracting to produce movement (exception: contraction of the antagonist at the same time as the prime mover when some part of the body needs to be held rigid, such as the knee joint when standing*)

(c) *synergists*—muscles which contract at the same time as the prime mover

Synergists may help the prime mover produce its movement, or they may stabilize a part, hold it steady, so the prime mover produces a more effective movement.

6. *Skeletal muscles contract according to the graded strength principle*—not according to the all-or-none principle, as do the individual muscle cells composing them. In other words, skeletal muscles contract with varying degrees of strength at different times—a fact of practical importance. (How else, for example, could we match the force of a movement to the demands of a task?)

Several generalizations may help explain the fact of graded strength contractions. The strength of the contraction of a skeletal muscle bears a direct relationship to the initial length of its fibers, to their metabolic condition, and to the number of them contracting. If a muscle is moderately stretched at the moment when contraction begins, the force of its contraction is increased. This principle, established years ago, applies experimentally to heart muscle also (Starling's law of the heart, discussed in Chapter 9). Outstanding among metabolic conditions that influence contraction are oxygen and food supply.

With adequate amounts of these essentials, a muscle can contract with greater force than possible with deficient amounts. The greater the number of muscle fibers

*Antagonistic muscles have opposite actions and opposite locations. If the flexor lies anterior to the part, the extensor will be found posterior to it. For example, the pectoralis major, the flexor of the upper arm, is located on the anterior aspect of the chest, while the latissimus dorsi, the extensor of the upper arm, is located on the posterior aspect of the chest. The antagonist of a flexor muscle is obviously an extensor muscle; that of an abductor muscle, an adductor muscle. Some frequently used antagonists are listed in Table 8.

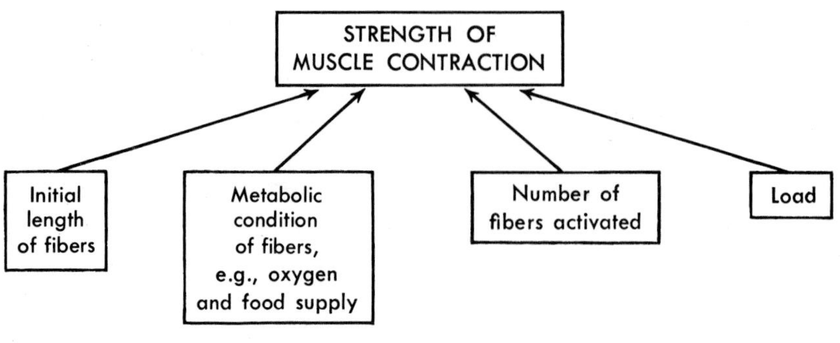

Fig. 90
Strength of muscle contraction.

contracting simultaneously, the stronger is the contraction of a muscle. How large this number is depends upon how many motor units are activated, and this, in turn, depends upon the intensity and frequency of stimulation. In general, the more intense and the more frequent a stimulus, the more motor units and therefore fibers are activated and the stronger is the contraction. Contraction strength also relates to previous contraction, the warm-up principle discussed on p. 124.

Another factor that influences the force of contraction is the size of the load imposed on the muscle. Within certain limits the heavier the load, the stronger is the contraction. Lift a pencil, for example, and then a heavy book and you can feel your arm muscles contract more strongly with the book.

The factors that influence muscle contraction are summarized in Fig. 90.

Hints on how to deduce actions

To understand muscle actions, you need first to know certain anatomical facts such as which bones muscles attach to and which joints they pull across. Then if you relate these structural facts to functional principles (for instance, those discussed in the preceding paragraphs), you may find your study of muscles more interesting and less difficult than you anticipate. Some specific suggestions for deducing muscle actions are as follows.

1. Start by making yourself familiar with the names, shapes, and general locations of the larger muscles, using Table 7 (p. 135) as a guide.

2. Try to deduce which bones the two ends of a muscle attach to from your knowledge of the shape and general location of the muscle. For example, look carefully at the deltoid muscle as illustrated in Figs. 93 to 95. To what bones does it seem to attach? Check your deductions with Table 10 (p. 138).

3. Next, make a guess as to which bone moves when the muscle shortens. (The bone moved by a muscle's contraction is its *insertion* bone; the bone that remains relatively stationary is its *origin* bone.) In many cases you can tell by trying to move one bone and then another which one is the insertion bone. In some cases either bone may function as the insertion. Although not all muscle attachments can be deduced as readily as those of the deltoid, they can all be learned more easily by using this deduction method than by relying on rote memory alone.

4. Deduce a muscle's actions by applying the principle that its insertion moves toward its origin. Check your conclusions with the text. Here, as in steps 2 and 3, the method of deduction is intended merely as

a guide and is not adequate by itself for determining muscle actions.

5. To deduce which muscle produces a given action (instead of which action a given muscle produces as in step 4), start by inferring the insertion bone (bone that moves during the action). The body and origin of the muscle will lie on one or more of the bones toward which the insertion moves—often a bone or bones proximal to the insertion bone. Couple these conclusions about origin and insertion with your knowledge of muscle names and locations to deduce the muscle that produces the action.

For example, if you wish to determine the prime mover for the action of raising the upper arms straight out to the sides, you infer that the muscle inserts on the humerus since this is the bone that moves. It moves toward the shoulder, that is, the clavicle and scapula, so that probably the muscle has its origin on these bones. Because you know that the deltoid muscle fulfills these conditions, you conclude, and rightly so, that it is the muscle that raises the upper arms sidewise.

6. Do not try to learn too many details about muscle origins, insertions, and actions. Remember, it is better to start by learning a few important facts thoroughly than to half learn a mass of relatively unimportant details. Remember, too, that trying to learn too many minute facts usually results in not retaining even the main facts.

NAMES

Reasons for names

Muscle names seem more logical and therefore easier to learn when one understands the reasons for the names. Each name describes one or more of the following features about the muscle.

1. *its action*—as flexor, extensor, adductor, etc.
2. *direction of its fibers*—as rectus or transversus
3. *its location*—as tibialis or femoris
4. *number of divisions composing a muscle*—as biceps, triceps, or quadriceps
5. *its shape*—as deltoid (triangular), trapezius, or quadratus
6. *its points of attachment*—as sternocleidomastoid

A good way to start the study of a muscle is by trying to find out what its name means.

Muscles grouped according to location

Just as names of people are learned by associating them with their physical appearance, so the names of muscles should be learned by associating them with their appearance. As you learn each muscle name, study the illustrations to familiarize yourself with the muscle's size, shape, and general location. To help you in this task, the names of some of the major muscles are grouped according to their location in Table 7.

Muscles grouped according to function

The following terms are used to designate muscles according to their main actions (Table 8, p. 136, gives examples).

1. *flexors*—decrease the angle of a joint (between the anterior surfaces of the bones except in the knee and toe joints)
2. *extensors*—return the part from flexion to normal anatomical position; increase the angle of a joint
3. *abductors*—move the bone away from the midline
4. *adductors*—move the part toward the midline
5. *rotators*—cause a part to pivot upon its axis
6. *levators*—raise a part
7. *depressors*—lower a part
8. *sphincters*—reduce the size of an opening
9. *tensors*—tense a part, that is, make it more rigid

10. *supinators*—turn the hand palm upward
11. *pronators*—turn the hand palm downward

ORIGINS, INSERTIONS, FUNCTIONS, AND INNERVATIONS OF REPRESENTATIVE MUSCLES

Basic information about many muscles is given in Tables 7 through 21. Each table has a description of a group of muscles that move one part of the body. Muscles that the author judges to be most important for beginning students of anatomy to know are set in boldface type and the origins and insertions so judged are set in italics. Remember that the actions listed for each muscle are those for which it is a prime mover. Actually, a single muscle contracting alone rarely accomplishes a given action. Instead, muscles act in groups as prime movers, synergists, and antagonists (p. 131) to bring about movements. As you study the muscles described in Tables 7 through 21, try to follow the hints for studying muscle actions given on pp. 132 and 133.

Weak places in abdominal wall

There are several places in the abdominal wall in which rupture (hernia) with protrusion of part of the intestine may occur. At these points the wall is weakened due to the presence of an interval or space in the abdominal aponeuroses. Any undue pressure on the abdominal viscera, therefore, can force a portion of the parietal peritoneum and often a part of the intestine as well through these nonreinforced places. The weak places are (1) the *inguinal canals,* (2) the *femoral rings,* and (3) the *umbilicus.* Hernia also occurs occasionally in the diaphragm and some other areas.

Piercing the aponeuroses of the abdominal muscles are two canals, the *inguinal canals,* one on the right and the other on the left. They lie above, but parallel to, the inguinal ligaments and are about 1½ inches long. In the male the spermatic cords extend through the canals into the scrotum, whereas in the female the round ligaments of the uterus are in this location. The internal opening of each canal is a space in the aponeurosis of the transverse muscle known as the internal inguinal ring. The external openings or *external inguinal rings* are spaces in the aponeuroses of the external oblique muscles. They are located inferiorly and mesially to the internal rings. The fact that they are larger in the male than in the female probably explains why external inguinal hernia occurs more often in men than in women.

The *femoral rings* are openings in the groin just below the inguinal ligaments, slightly lateral to the external inguinal ring and medial to the femoral veins. They have a diameter of about ½ inch and are usually somewhat larger in females, a fact which accounts for the greater prevalence of femoral hernia in women than in men.

Bursae

Definition. Bursae are small connective tissue sacs lined with synovial membrane and containing synovial fluid.

Locations. Bursae are located wherever pressure is exerted over moving parts, for example, between skin and bone, between tendons and bone, or between muscles, or ligaments, and bone. Some bursae which fairly frequently become inflamed (bursitis) are as follows: the subacromial bursa, between the head of the humerus and the acromion process and the deltoid muscle; the olecranon bursa, between the olecranon process and the skin; the prepatellar bursa, between the patella and the skin. Inflammation of the prepatellar bursa is known as housemaid's knee, whereas olecranon bursitis is called student's elbow.

Function. Bursae act as cushions, relieving pressure between moving parts.

Text continued on p. 164.

Table 7. Muscles grouped according to location

Location	*Muscles*	*Figures illustrating*
Neck	Sternocleidomastoid	92
Back	Trapezius	92–95
	Latissimus dorsi	93
Chest	Pectoralis major	92
	Serratus anterior	92
Abdominal wall	External oblique	92, 93
Shoulder	Deltoid	92–95
Upper arm	Biceps brachii	94, 96
	Triceps brachii	94, 95, 97
	Brachialis	99
Forearm	Brachioradialis	95, 100
	Pronator teres	94, 100
Buttocks	Gluteus maximus	93, 102, 105
	Gluteus medius	93, 106
	Tensor fasciae latae	101
Thigh		
Anterior surface	Quadriceps femoris group	101, 103
	Rectus femoris	101, 103
	Vastus lateralis	101, 103
	Vastus medialis	101, 103
	Vastus intermedius	103
Medial surface	Gracilis	101, 104
	Adductor group (longus, brevis, magnus)	101, 104
Posterior surface	Hamstrings	102
	Biceps femoris	102, 108
	Semitendinosus	102, 109
	Semimembranosus	102, 110
Leg		
Anterior surface	Tibialis anterior	101
Posterior surface	Gastrocnemius	102
	Soleus	102
Pelvic floor	Levator ani	117
	Levator coccygeus	117
	Rectococcygeus	117

Table 8. Muscles grouped according to function

Part moved	*Example of flexor*	*Example of extensor*	*Example of abductor*	*Example of adductor*
Head	Sternocleidomastoid	Semispinalis capitis		
Upper arm	Pectoralis major	Trapezius Latissimus dorsi	Deltoid	Pectoralis major with latissimus dorsi
Forearm	With forearm supinated: biceps brachii With forearm pronated: brachialis With semisupination or semipronation: brachioradialis	Triceps brachii		
Hand	Flexor carpi radialis and ulnaris Palmaris longus	Extensor carpi radialis, longus, and brevis Extensor carpi ulnaris	Flexor carpi radialis	Flexor carpi ulnaris
Thigh	Iliopsoas Rectus femoris (of quadriceps femoris group)	Gluteus maximus	Gluteus medius and gluteus minimus	Adductor group
Leg	Hamstrings	Quadriceps femoris group		
Foot	Tibialis anterior	Gastrocnemius Soleus	Evertors Peroneus longus Peroneus brevis	Invertor Tibialis anterior
Trunk	Iliopsoas Rectus abdominis	Sacrospinalis		

Table 9. Muscles that move shoulder*†

Muscle	*Origin*	*Insertion*	*Function*	*Innervation*
Trapezius	*Occipital bone* (protuberance)	*Scapula* (spine and acromion)	Raises or lowers shoulders and shrug them	Spinal accessory, second, third, and fourth cervical nerves
	Vertebrae (cervical and thoracic)	*Clavicle*	Extend head when occiput acts as insertion	
Pectoralis minor	*Ribs* (second to fifth)	*Scapula* (coracoid)	Pulls shoulder down and forward	Medial and lateral anterior thoracic nerves
Serratus anterior	*Ribs* (upper eight or nine)	*Scapula* (anterior surface, vertebral border)	Pulls shoulder forward; abducts and rotates it upward	Long thoracic nerve

*When trying to learn the origins and insertion of the muscles listed in this table, refer frequently to illustrations of each muscle and to the skeleton. Also, when possible, feel each muscle on your own body.

†Muscles judged by the author to be most important for beginning students of anatomy to know are set in boldface type and the origins and insertions so judged are set in italics.

Table 10. Muscles that move upper arm*†

Muscle	*Origin*	*Insertion*	*Function*	*Innervation*
Pectoralis major	*Clavicle* (medial half) *Sternum* *Costal cartilages of true ribs*	*Humerus* (greater tubercle)	Flexes upper arm Adducts upper arm anteriorly; draws it across chest	Medial and lateral anterior thoracic nerves
Latissimus dorsi	*Vertebrae* (spines of lower thoracic, lumbar and sacral) *Ilium* (crest) Lumbodorsal fascia‡	*Humerus* (intertubercular groove)	Extends upper arm Adducts upper arm posteriorly	Thoracodorsal nerve
Deltoid	*Clavicle* *Scapula* (spine and acromion)	*Humerus* (lateral side about halfway down—deltoid tubercle)	Abducts upper arm Assists in flexion and extension of upper arm	Axillary nerve
Coracobrachialis	Scapula (coracoid process)	Humerus (middle third, medial surface)	Adduction; assists in flexion and medial rotation of arm	Musculocutaneous nerve
Supraspinatus	Scapula (supraspinous fossa)	Humerus (greater tubercle)	Assists in abducting arm	Suprascapular nerve
Teres major	Scapula (lower part, axillary border)	Humerus (upper part, anterior surface)	Assists in extension, adduction, and medial rotation of arm	Lower subscapular nerve
Teres minor	Scapula (axillary border)	Humerus (greater tubercle)	Rotates arm outward	Axillary nerve
Infraspinatus	Scapula (infraspinatus border)	Humerus (greater tubercle)	Rotates arm outward	Suprascapular nerve

*When trying to learn the origins and insertion of the muscles listed in this table, refer frequently to illustrations of each muscle and to the skeleton. Also, when possible, feel each muscle on your own body.
†Muscles judged by the author to be most important for beginning students of anatomy to know are set in boldface type, and the origins and insertions so judged are set in italics.
‡Lumbodorsal fascia—extension of aponeurosis of latissimus dorsi; fills in space between last rib and iliac crest.

Table 11. Muscles that move lower arm*†

Muscle	*Origin*	*Insertion*	*Function*	*Innervation*
Biceps brachii	*Scapula* (supraglenoid tuberosity) *Scapula* (coracoid)	*Radius* (tubercle at proximal end)	Flexes supinated forearm Supinates forearm and hand	Musculocutaneous nerve
Brachialis	*Humerus* (distal half, anterior surface)	*Ulna* (front of coronoid process)	Flexes pronated forearm	Musculocutaneous nerve
Brachioradialis	Humerus (above lateral epicondyle)	Radius (styloid process)	Flexes semipronated or semisupinated forearm; supinates forearm and hand	Radial nerve
Triceps brachii	*Scapula* (infraglenoid tuberosity) *Humerus* (posterior surface—lateral head above radial groove; medial head, below)	*Ulna* (olecranon process)	Extends lower arm	Radial nerve
Pronator teres	Humerus (medial epicondyle) Ulna (coronoid process)	Radius (middle third of lateral surface)	Pronates and flexes forearm	Median nerve
Pronator quadratus	Ulna (distal fourth, anterior surface)	Radius (distal fourth, anterior surface)	Pronates forearm	Median nerve
Supinator	Humerus (lateral epicondyle) Ulna (proximal fifth)	Radius (proximal third)	Supinates forearm	Radial nerve

*When trying to learn the origins and insertion of the muscles listed in this table, refer frequently to illustrations of each muscle and to the skeleton. Also, when possible, feel each muscle on your own body.

†Muscles judged by the author to be most important for beginning students of anatomy to know are set in boldface type, and the origins and insertions so judged are set in italics.

Table 12. Muscles that move hand*

Muscle	*Origin*	*Insertion*	*Function*	*Innervation*
Flexor carpi radialis	Humerus (medial epicondyle)	Second metacarpal (base of)	Flexes hand Flexes forearm	Median nerve
Palmaris longus	Humerus (medial epicondyle)	Fascia of palm	Flexes hand	Median nerve
Flexor carpi ulnaris	Humerus (medial epicondyle) Ulna (proximal two-thirds)	Pisiform bone Third, fourth, and fifth metacarpals	Flexes hand Adducts hand	Ulnar nerve
Extensor carpi radialis longus	Humerus (ridge above lateral epicondyle)	Second metacarpal (base of)	Extends hand Abducts hand (moves toward thumb side when hand supinated)	Radial nerve
Extensor carpi radialis brevis	Humerus (lateral epicondyle)	Second, third metacarpals (bases of)	Extends hand	Radial nerve
Extensor carpi ulnaris	Humerus (lateral epicondyle) Ulna (proximal three-fourths)	Fifth metacarpal (base of)	Extends hand Adducts hand (move toward little finger side when hand supinated)	Radial nerve

*When trying to learn the origins and insertion of the muscles listed in this table, refer frequently to illustrations of each muscle and to the skeleton. Also, when possible, feel each muscle on your own body.

Table 13. Muscles that move thigh*†

Muscle	*Origin*	*Insertion*	*Function*	*Innervation*
Iliopsoas (iliacus and psoas major)	*Ilium* (iliac fossa)	*Femur* (small trochanter)	Flexes thigh	
	Vertebrae (bodies of twelfth thoracic to fifth lumbar)		Flexes trunk (when femur acts as origin)	Femoral and second to fourth lumbar nerves
Rectus femoris	*Ilium* (anterior, inferior spine)	*Tibia* (by way of patellar tendon)	Flexes thigh Extends lower leg	Femoral nerve
Gluteal group				
1. **Maximus**	*Ilium* (crest and posterior surface) Sacrum and coccyx (posterior surface) Sacrotuberous ligament	*Femur* (gluteal tuberosity) *Iliotibial tract*‡	Extends thigh—rotates outward	Inferior gluteal nerve
2. **Medius**	*Ilium* (lateral surface)	*Femur* (greater trochanter)	Abducts thigh—rotates outward; stabilizes pelvis on femur	Superior gluteal nerve
3. **Minimus**	*Ilium* (lateral surface)	*Femur* (greater trochanter)	Abducts thigh; stabilizes pelvis on femur Rotates thigh medially	Superior gluteal nerve
Tensor fasciae latae	*Ilium* (anterior part of crest)	*Tibia* (by way of *iliotibial tract*)	Abducts thigh Tightens iliotibial tract‡	Superior gluteal nerve
Piriformis	Vertebrae (front of sacrum)	Femur (medial aspect of greater trochanter)	Rotates thigh outward Abducts thigh Extends thigh	First or second sacral nerves
Adductor group				
1. **Brevis**	*Pubic bone*	*Femur* (linea aspera)	Adducts thigh	Obturator nerve
2. **Longus**				
3. **Magnus**				
Gracilis	Pubic bone (just below symphysis)	*Tibia* (medial surface behind sartorius)	Adducts thigh and flexes and adducts leg	Obturator nerve

*When trying to learn the origins and insertion of the muscles listed in this table, refer frequently to illustrations of each muscle and to the skeleton. Also, when possible, feel each muscle on your own body.

†Muscles judged by the author to be most important for beginning students of anatomy to know are set in boldface type, and the origins and insertions so judged are set in italics.

‡The iliotibial tract is part of the fascia enveloping all the thigh muscles. It consists of a wide band of white fibrous tissue attached to the iliac crest above and the lateral condyle of the tibia below. The upper part of the tract encloses the tensor fasciae latae muscle.

Table 14. Muscles that move lower leg*†

Muscle	*Origin*	*Insertion*	*Function*	*Innervation*
Quadriceps femoris group				
1. **Rectus femoris**	*Ilium* (anterior, inferior spine)	*Tibia* (by way of patellar tendon)	Flexes thigh Extends leg	Femoral nerve
2. **Vastus lateralis**	*Femur* (linea aspera)	*Same*	Extends leg	Femoral nerve
3. **Vastus medialis**	*Femur*	*Same*	Same	Femoral nerve
4. **Vastus intermedius**	*Femur* (anterior surface)	*Same*	Same	Femoral nerve
Sartorius	*Os innominatum* (anterior, superior iliac spines)	*Tibia* (medial surface of upper end of shaft)	Adducts and flexes leg Permits crossing of legs tailor fashion	Femoral nerve
Hamstring group				
1. **Biceps femoris**	*Ischium* (tuberosity)	*Fibula* (head of)	Flexes leg	Hamstring nerve (branch of sciatic nerve)
	Femur (linea aspera)	*Tibia* (lateral condyle)	Extends thigh	Hamstring nerve
2. **Semitendinosus**	*Ischium* (tuberosity)	*Tibia* (proximal end, medial surface)	Same	Hamstring nerve
3. **Semimembranosus**	*Same*	*Tibia* (medial condyle)	Same	Hamstring nerve

*When trying to learn the origins and insertion of the muscles listed in this table, refer frequently to illustrations of each muscle and to the skeleton. Also, when possible, feel each muscle on your own body.
†Muscles judged by the author to be most important for beginning students of anatomy to know are set in boldface type, and the origins and insertions so judged are set in italics.

Table 15. Muscles that move foot*†

Muscle	*Origin*	*Insertion*	*Function*	*Innervation*
Tibialis anterior	*Tibia* (lateral condyle of upper body)	*Tarsal* (first cuneiform) Metatarsal (base of first)	Flexes foot Inverts foot	Common and deep peroneal nerves
Gastrocnemius	*Femur* (condyles)	*Tarsal* (calcaneus by way of Achilles tendon)	Extends foot Flexes lower leg	Tibial nerve (branch of sciatic nerve)
Soleus	*Tibia* (underneath gastrocnemius) *Fibula*	*Same as gastrocnemius*	Extends foot (plantar flexion)	Tibial nerve
Peroneus longus	Tibia (lateral condyle) Fibula (head and shaft)	First cuneiform Base of first metatarsal	Extends foot (plantar flexion) Everts foot	Common peroneal nerve
Peroneus brevis	Fibula (lower two-thirds of lateral surface of shaft)	Fifth metatarsal (tubercle, dorsal surface)	Everts foot Flexes foot	Superficial peroneal nerve
Tibialis posterior	Tibia (posterior surface) Fibula (posterior surface)	Navicular bone Cuboid bone All three cuneiforms Second and fourth metatarsals	Extends foot (plantar flexion) Inverts foot	Tibial nerve
Peroneus tertius	Fibula (distal third)	Fourth and fifth metatarsals (bases of)	Flexes foot Everts foot	Deep peroneal nerve

*When trying to learn the origins and insertion of the muscles listed in this table, refer frequently to illustrations of each muscle and to the skeleton. Also, when possible, feel each muscle on your own body.

†Muscles judged by the author to be most important for beginning students of anatomy to know are set in boldface type, and the origins and insertions so judged are set in italics.

Table 16. Muscles that move head*†

Muscle	*Origin*	*Insertion*	*Function*	*Innervation*
Sternocleido-mastoid	*Sternum* *Clavicle*	*Temporal bone* (mastoid process)	Flexes head (prayer muscle) One muscle, alone, rotates head toward opposite side; spasm of this muscle alone or associated with trapezius called torticollis or wryneck	Accessory nerve
Semispinalis capitis	Vertebrae (transverse processes of upper six thoracic, articular processes of lower four cervical)	Occipital bone (between superior and inferior nuchal lines)	Extends head; bends it laterally	First five cervical nerves
Splenius capitis	Ligamentum nuchae Vertebrae (spinous processes of upper three or four thoracic vertebrae)	Temporal bone (mastoid process) Occipital bone	Extends head Bends and rotates head toward same side as contracting muscle	Second, third, and fourth cervical nerves
Longissimus capitis	Vertebrae (transverse processes of upper six thoracic, articular processes of lower four cervical)	Temporal bone (mastoid process)	Extends head Bends and rotates head toward contracting side	

*When trying to learn the origins and insertion of the muscles listed in this table, refer frequently to illustrations of each muscle and to the skeleton. Also, when possible, feel each muscle on your own body.
†Muscles judged by the author to be most important for beginning students of anatomy to know are set in boldface type, and the origins and insertions so judged are set in italics.

Table 17. Muscles that move abdominal wall*†

Muscle	*Origin*	*Insertion*	*Function*	*Innervation*
External oblique	*Ribs* (lower eight)	*Ossa coxae* (iliac crest and pubis by way of inguinal ligament)‡ *Linea alba*§ by way of an aponeurosis‖	Compresses abdomen Important postural function of all abdominal muscles is to pull front of pelvis upward, thereby flattening lumbar curve of spine; when these muscles lose their tone, common figure faults of protruding abdomen and lordosis develop	Lower seven intercostal nerves and iliohypogastric nerves
Internal oblique	*Ossa coxae* (iliac crest and inguinal ligament) *Lumbodorsal fascia*	*Ribs* (lower three) *Pubic bone* *Linea alba*	Same as external oblique	Last three intercostals; iliohypogastric and ilioinguinal nerves

*When trying to learn the origins and insertion of the muscles listed in this table, refer frequently to illustrations of each muscle and to the skeleton. Also, when possible, feel each muscle on your own body.

†Muscles judged by the author to be most important for beginning students of anatomy to know are set in boldface type, and the origins and insertions so judged are set in italics.

‡*Inguinal ligament* (or Poupart's)—lower edge of aponeurosis of external oblique muscle, extending between the anterior superior iliac spine and the pubic tubercle of the pubic bone. This edge is doubled under similarly to a hem on material. The inguinal ligament forms the upper boundary of the *femoral triangle*, a large triangular area in the thigh; its other boundaries are the adductor longus muscle mesially and the sartorious laterally.

§*Linea alba*—literally, a white line; extends from xiphoid process to symphysis pubis. Formed by fibers of aponeurosis of right abdominal muscles interlacing with fibers of aponeuroses of the left abdominal muscles; comparable to a seam up the midline of the abdominal wall, anchoring its various layers. During pregnancy the linea alba becomes pigmented and is known as the *linea nigra*.

‖*Aponeurosis*—sheet of white fibrous tissue which attaches one muscle to another or attaches it to bone or other movable structures; for example, the right external oblique muscle attaches to the left external oblique muscle by means of an aponeurosis.

Continued.

Table 17. Muscles that move abdominal wall*†—cont'd

Muscle	*Origin*	*Insertion*	*Function*	*Innervation*
Transversalis	*Ribs* (lower six) *Ossa coxae* (iliac crest, inguinal ligament) *Lumbodorsal fascia*	*Pubic bone* *Linea alba*	Same as external oblique	Last five intercostals; iliohypogastric and ilioinguinal nerves
Rectus abdominis	*Ossa coxae* (pubic bone and symphysis pubis)	*Ribs* (costal cartilage of fifth, sixth, and seventh ribs) Sternum (xiphoid process)	Same as external oblique; because abdominal muscles compress abdominal cavity, they aid in straining, defecation, forced expiration, childbirth, etc.; abdominal muscles are antagonists of diaphragm, relaxing as it contracts and vice versa Flex trunk	Last six intercostal nerves

*When trying to learn the origins and insertion of the muscles listed in this table, refer frequently to illustrations of each muscle and to the skeleton. Also, when possible, feel each muscle on your own body.

†Muscles judged by the author to be most important for beginning students of anatomy to know are set in boldface type, and the origins and insertions so judged are set in italics.

Table 18. Muscles that move chest wall*†

Muscle	*Origin*	*Insertion*	*Function*	*Innervation*
External intercostals	Rib (lower border; forward fibers)	Rip (upper border of rib below origin)	Elevate ribs	Intercostal nerves
Internal intercostals	Rib (inner surface, lower border; backward fibers)	Rib (upper border of rib below origin)	Probably depress ribs	Intercostal nerves
Diaphragm	*Lower circumference of thorax* (of rib cage)	*Central tendon of diaphragm*	Enlarges thorax, causing inspiration	Phrenic nerves

*When trying to learn the origins and insertion of the muscles listed in this table, refer frequently to illustrations of each muscle and to the skeleton. Also, when possible, feel each muscle on your own body.
†Muscles judged by the author to be most important for beginning students of anatomy to know are set in boldface type, and the origins and insertions so judged are set in italics.

Table 19. Muscles of pelvic floor*

Muscle	*Origin*	*Insertion*	*Function*	*Innervation*
Levator ani	Pubis—posterior surface Ischium (spine)	Coccyx	Together form floor of pelvic cavity; support pelvic organs; if these muscles are badly torn at childbirth, or become too relaxed, uterus or bladder may prolapse, i.e., drop out	Pudendal nerve
Coccygeus (posterior continuation of levator ani)	Ischium (spine)	Coccyx Sacrum	Same as levator ani	Pudendal nerve

*When trying to learn the origins and insertion of the muscles listed in this table, refer frequently to illustrations of each muscle and to the skeleton. Also, when possible, feel each muscle on your own body.

Table 20. Muscles that move trunk*†

Muscle	*Origin*	*Insertion*	*Function*	*Innervation*
Sacrospinalis (erector spinae)			Extend spine; maintain erect posture of trunk Acting singly, abduct and rotate trunk	Posterior rami of first cervical to fifth lumbar spinal nerves
Lateral portion consists of				
1. Iliocostalis lumborum	Iliac crest, sacrum (posterior surface), and lumbar vertebrae (spinous processes)	Ribs, lower six		
2. Iliocostalis dorsi	Ribs, lower six	Ribs, upper six		
3. Iliocostalis cervicis	Ribs, upper six	Vertebrae, fourth to sixth cervical		
Medial portion consists of				
1. Longissimus dorsi	Same as iliocostalis lumborum	Vertebrae, thoracic ribs		
2. Longissimus cervicis	Vertebrae, upper six thoracic	Vertebrae, second to sixth cervical		
3. Longissimus capitis	Vertebrae, upper six thoracic and last four cervical	Temporal bone, mastoid process		
Quadratus lumborum (forms part of posterior abdominal wall)	Ilium (posterior part of crest) Vertebrae (lower three lumbar)	Ribs (twelfth) Vertebrae (transverse processes of first four lumbar)	Both muscles together extend spine One muscle alone abducts trunk toward side of contracting muscle	First three or four lumbar nerves
Iliopsoas	See muscles that move thigh, p. 141		Flexes trunk	

*When trying to learn the origins and insertion of the muscles listed in this table, refer frequently to illustrations of each muscle and to the skeleton. Also, when possible, feel each muscle on your own body.

†Muscles judged by the author to be most important for beginning students of anatomy to know are set in boldface type.

Table 21. Muscles of facial expression and of mastication*

Muscle	*Origin*	*Insertion*	*Function*	*Innervation*
Epicranius (occipitofrontalis)	Occipital bone	Tissues of eyebrows	Raises eyebrows, wrinkling forehead, horizontally	Cranial nerve VII
Corrugator supercilii	Frontal bone (superciliary ridge)	Skin of eyebrow	Wrinkles forehead vertically	Cranial nerve VII
Orbicularis oculi	Encircles eyelid		Closes eye	Cranial nerve VII
Orbicularis oris	Encircles mouth		Draws lips together	Cranial nerve VII
Platysma	Fascia of upper part of deltoid and pectoralis major	Mandible—lower border Skin around corners of mouth	Draws corners of mouth down—pouting	Cranial nerve VII
Buccinator	Maxillae	Skin of sides of mouth	Permits smiling Blowing (e.g., as in playing a trumpet)	Cranial nerve VII
Muscles of mastication				
Masseter	Zygomatic arch	Mandible (external surface)	Closes jaw	Cranial nerve V
Temporal	Temporal bone	Mandible	Closes jaw	Cranial nerve V
Pterygoids (internal and external)	Under surface of skull	Mandible (mesial surface)	Grate teeth	Cranial nerve V

*When trying to learn the origins and insertion of the muscles listed in this table, refer frequently to illustrations of each muscle and to the skeleton. Also, when possible, feel each muscle on your own body.

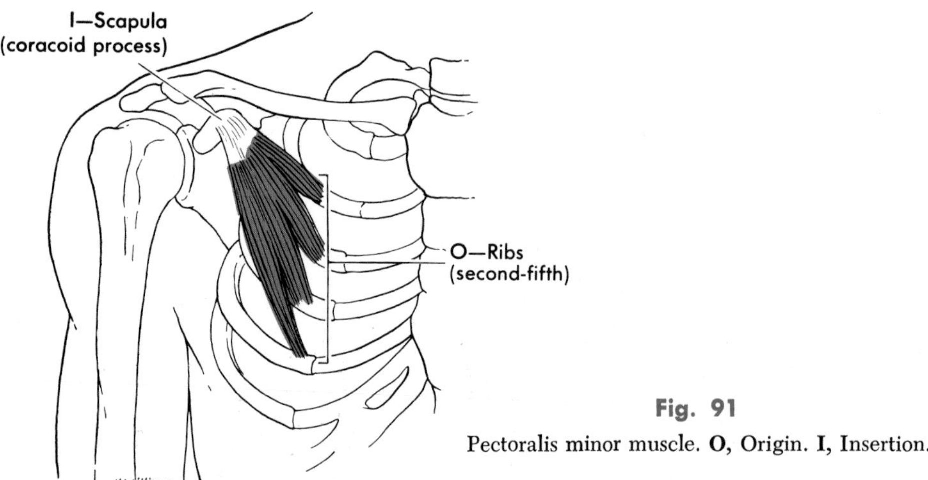

Fig. 91
Pectoralis minor muscle. **O**, Origin. **I**, Insertion.

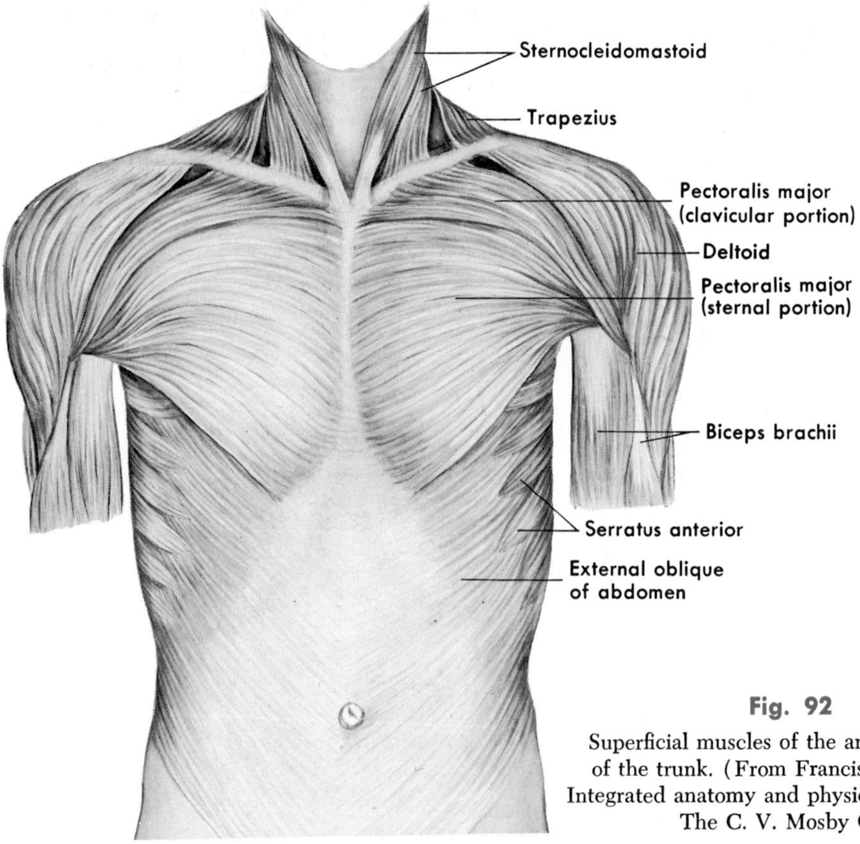

Fig. 92
Superficial muscles of the anterior surface of the trunk. (From Francis and Farrell: Integrated anatomy and physiology, St. Louis, The C. V. Mosby Co.)

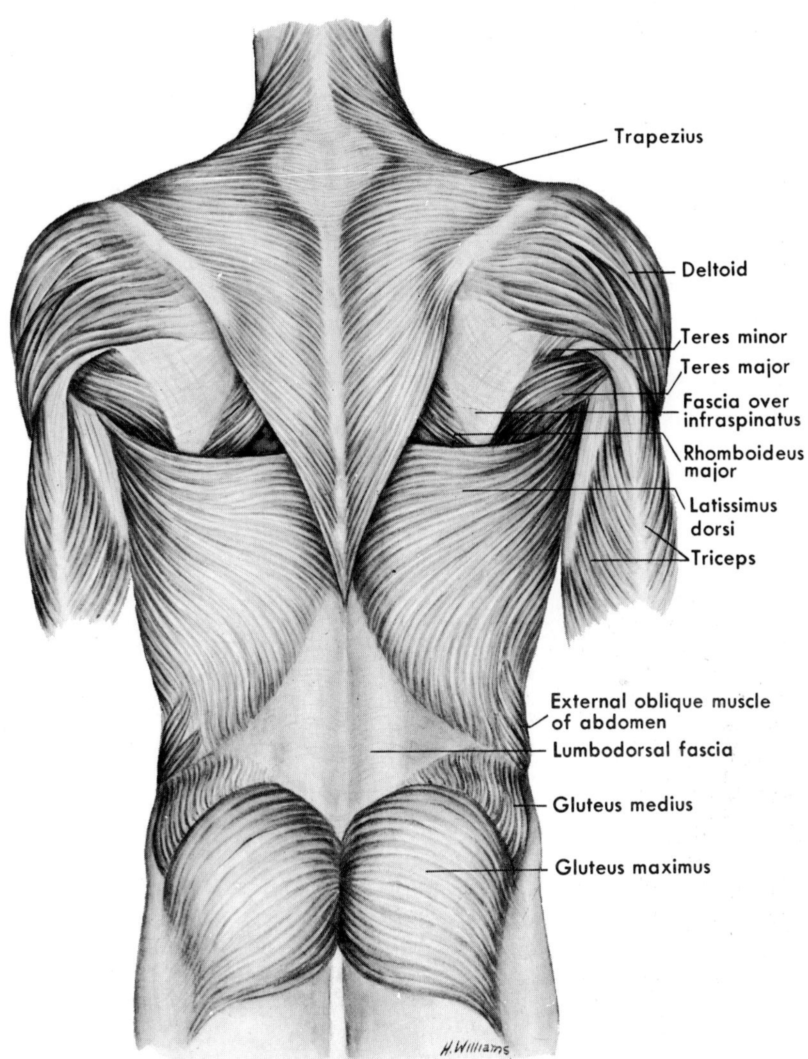

Fig. 93

Superficial muscles of the posterior surface of the trunk. (From Francis and Farrell: Integrated anatomy and physiology, St. Louis, The C. V. Mosby Co.)

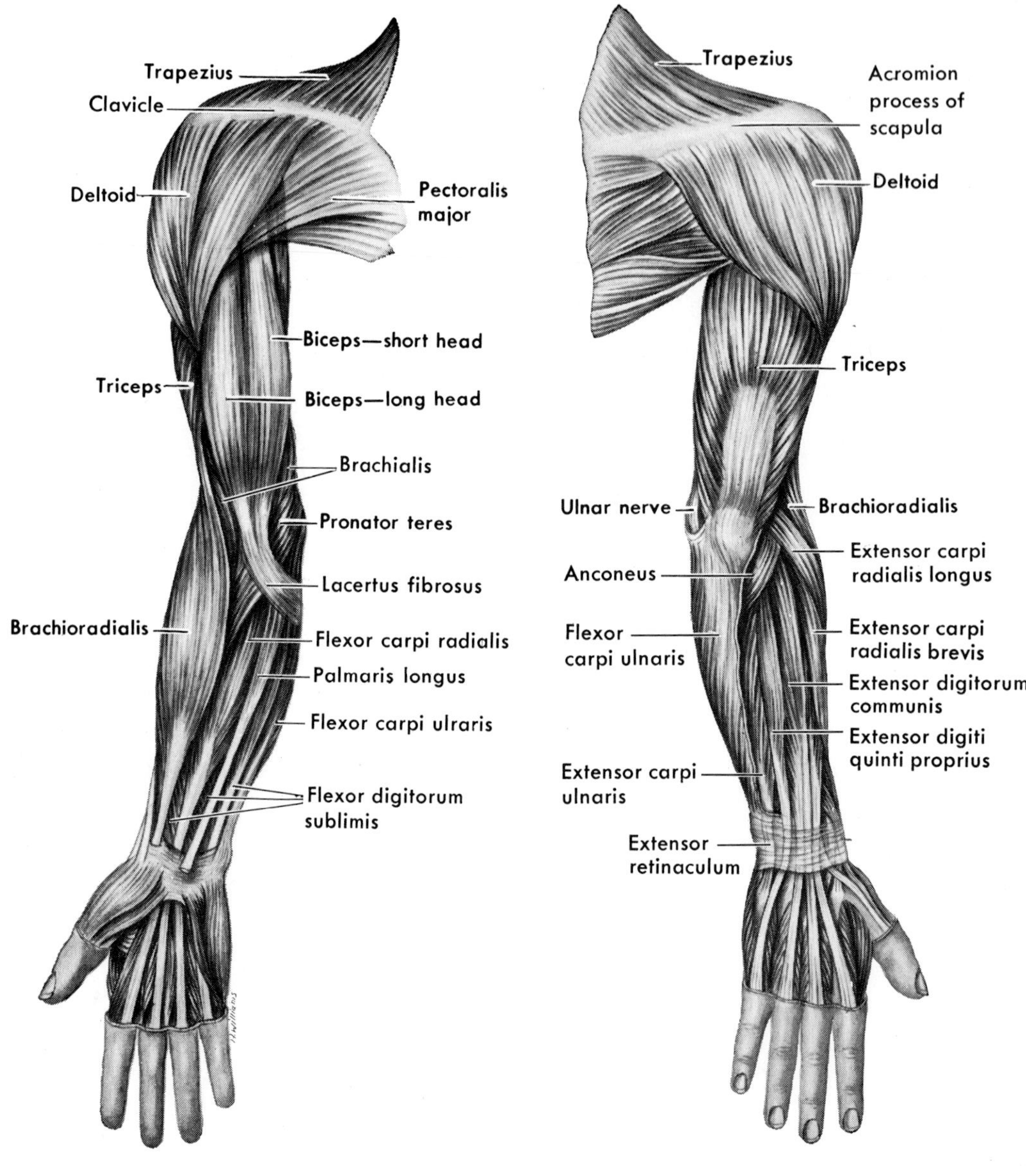

Fig. 94

Muscles of the flexor surface of the upper extremity.

Fig. 95

Muscles of the extensor surface of the upper extremity.

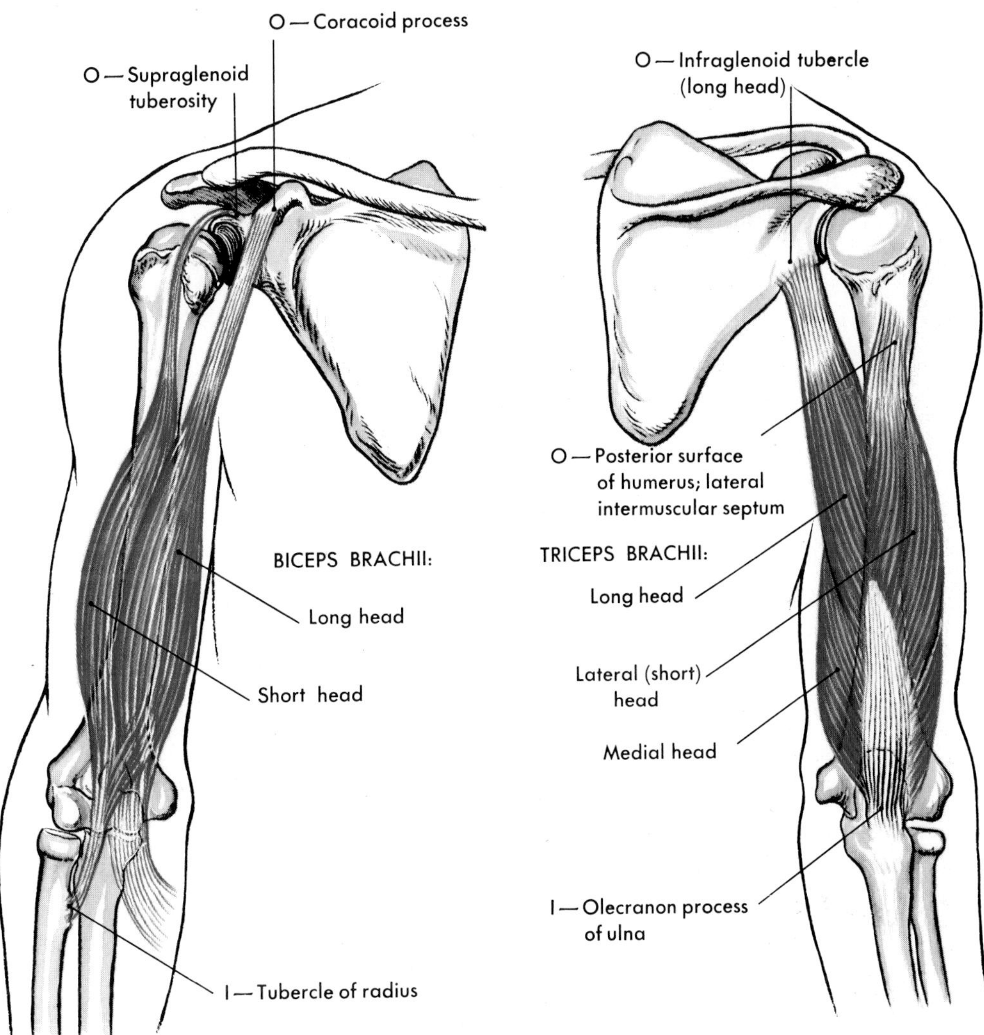

Fig. 96
Biceps brachii muscle. **O,** Origin. **I,** Insertion.

Fig. 97
Triceps brachii muscle. **O,** Origin. **I,** Insertion.

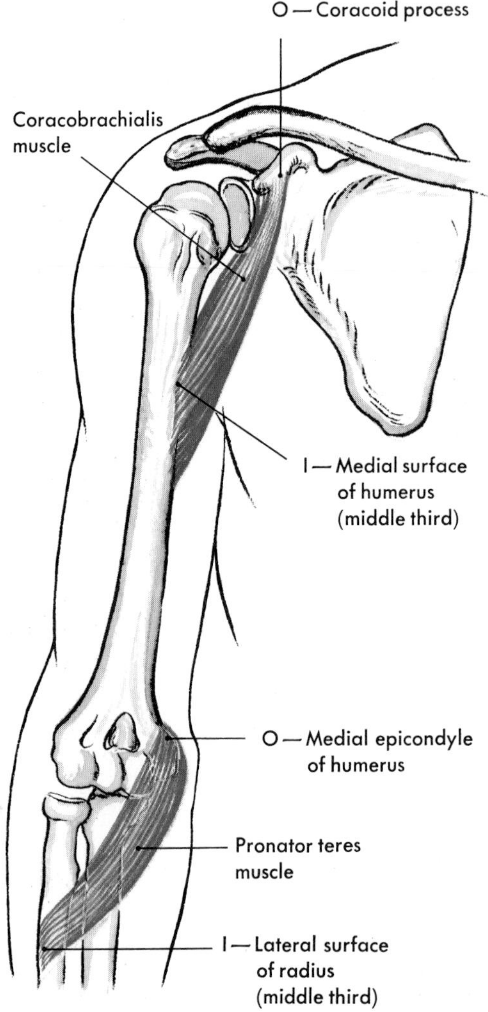

Fig. 98
Coracobrachialis and pronator teres muscles. **O**, Origin. **I**, Insertion.

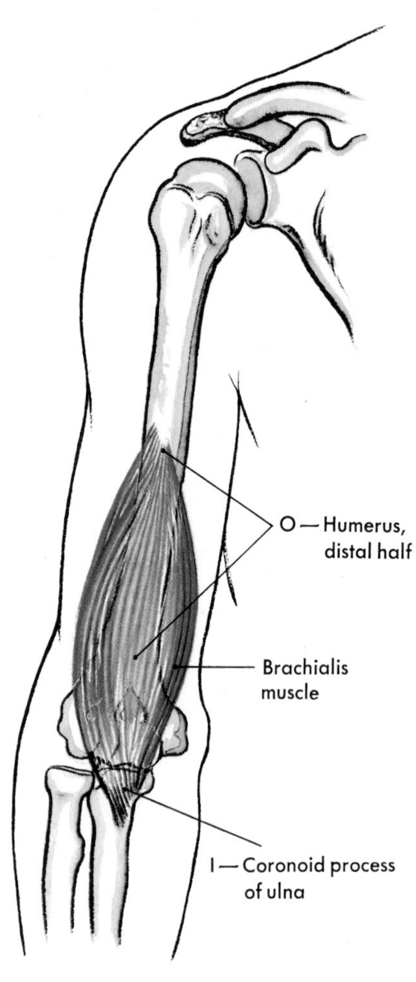

Fig. 99
Brachialis muscle. **O**, Origin. **I**, Insertion.

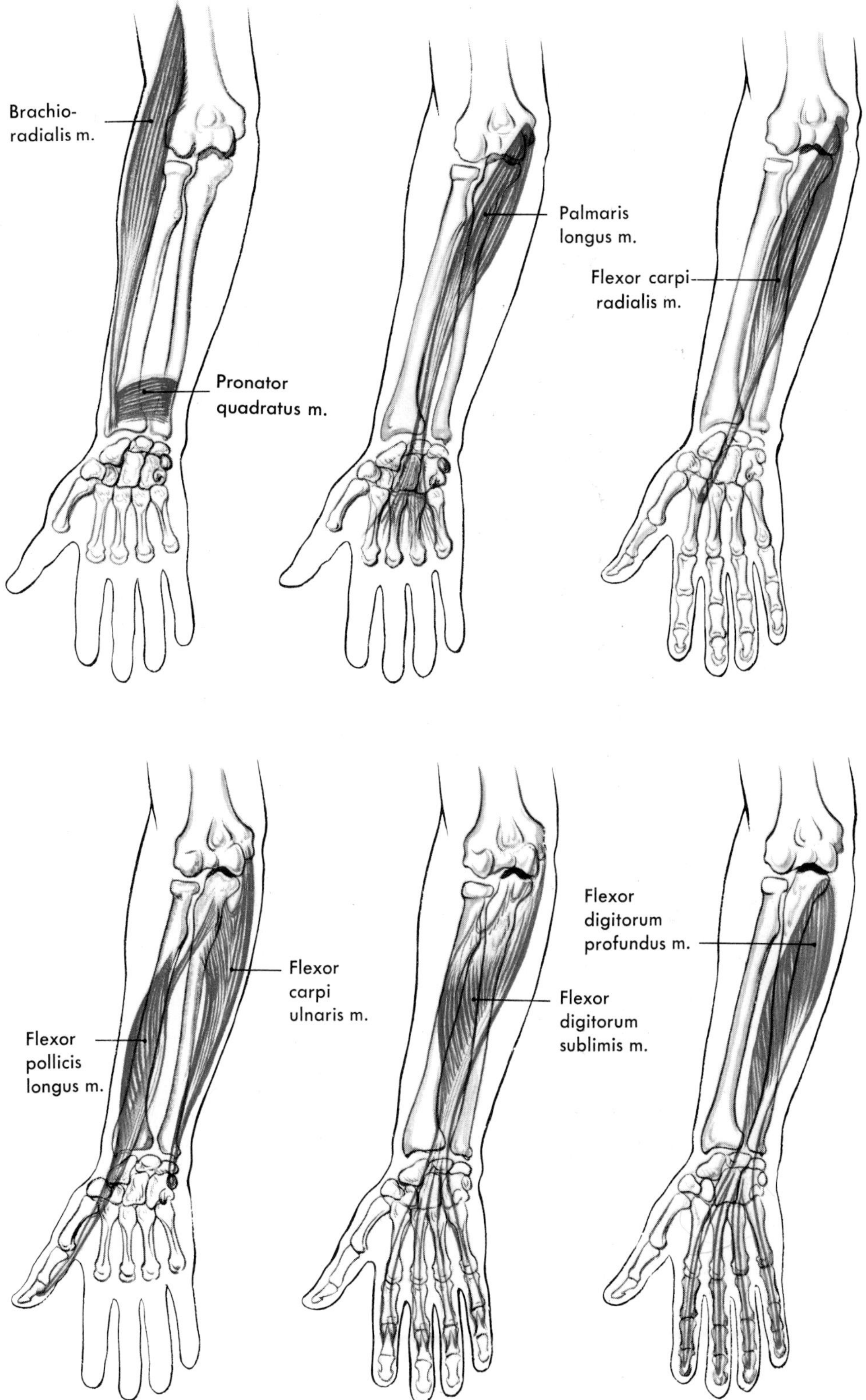

Fig. 100

Some muscles of the anterior (volar) aspect of the right forearm.

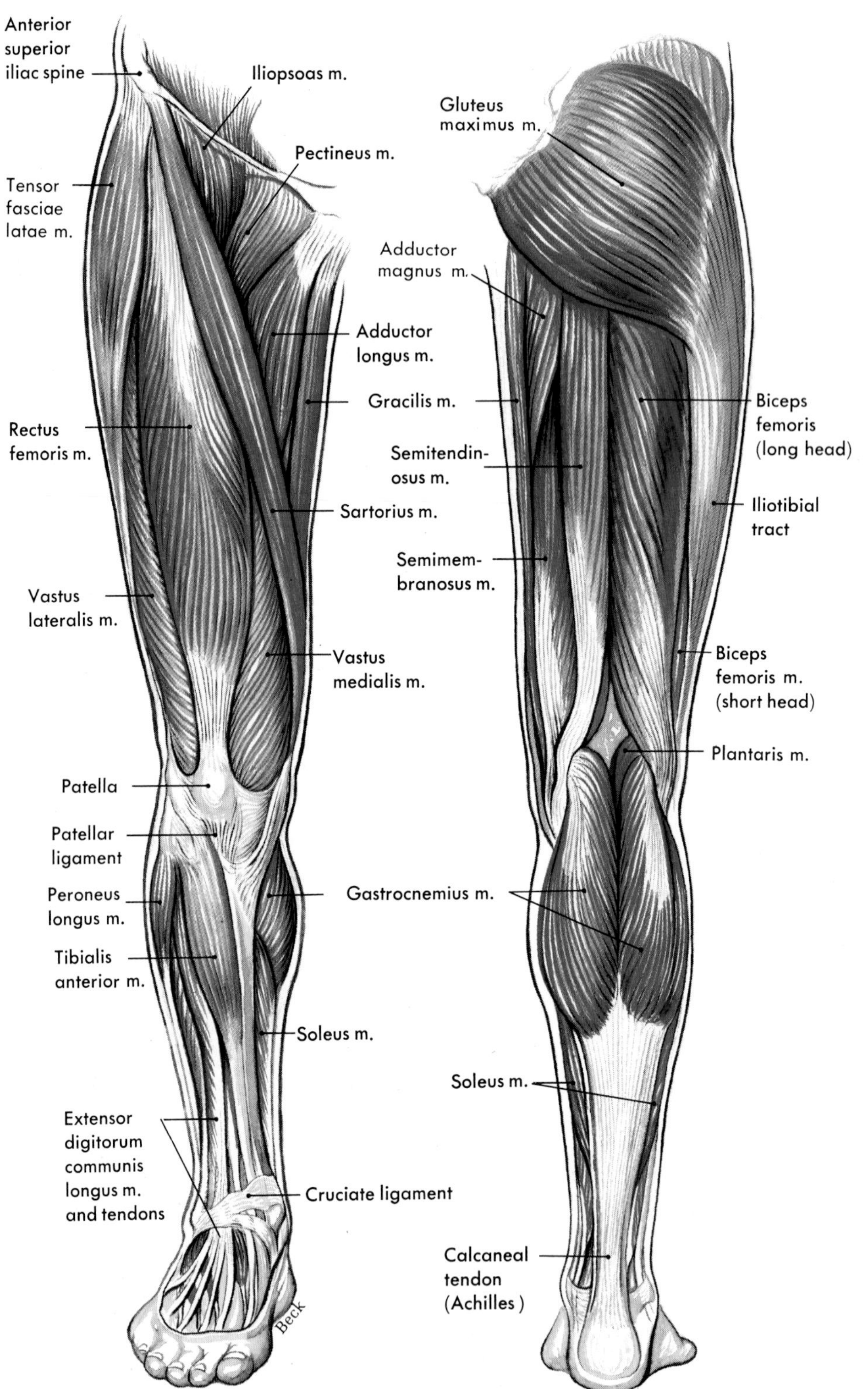

Fig. 101
Superficial muscles of the right thigh and leg, anterior view.

Fig. 102
Superficial muscles of the right thigh and leg, posterior view.

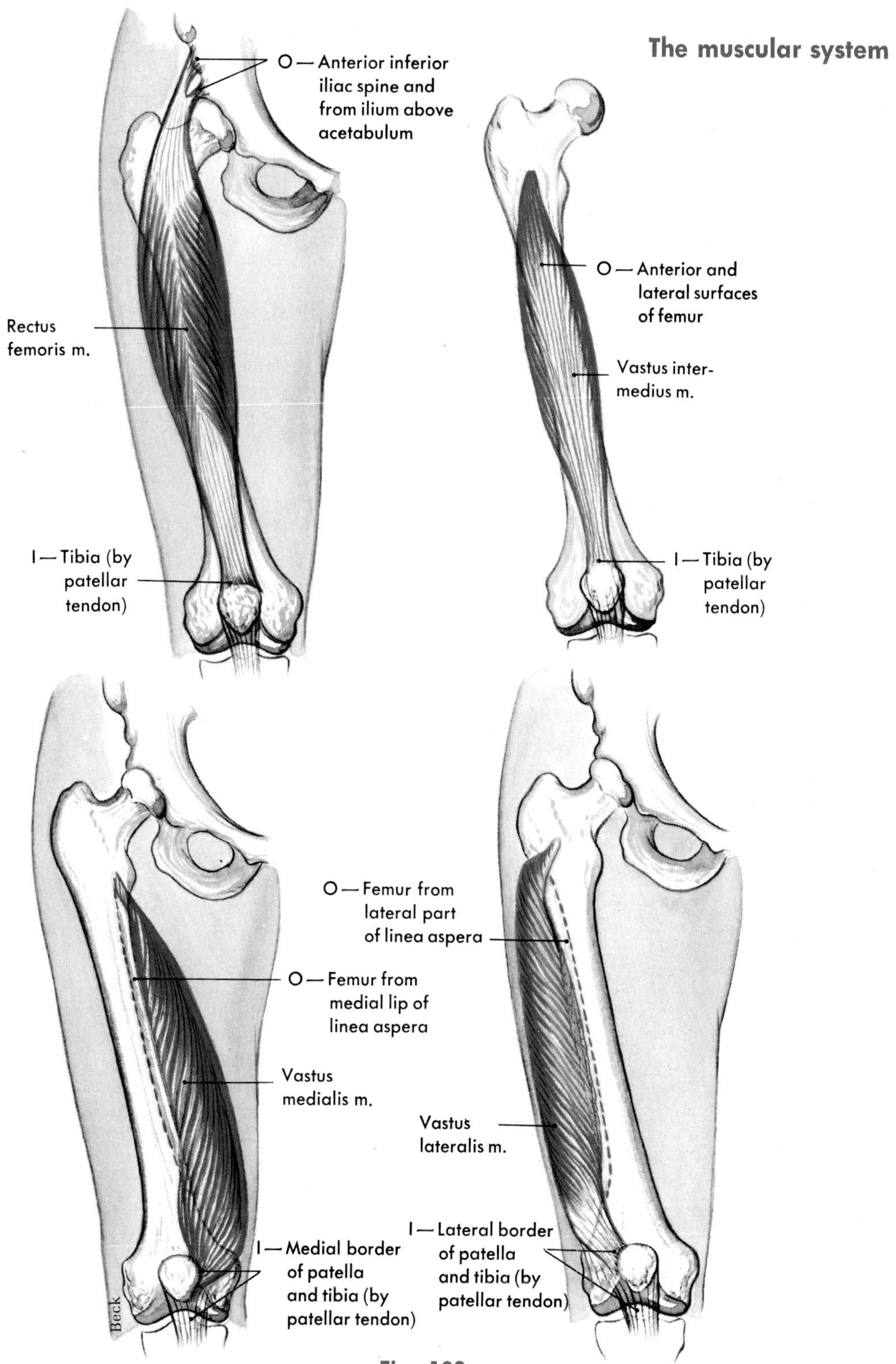

Fig. 103

Quadriceps femoris group of thigh muscles: rectus femoris, vastus intermedius, vastus medialis, and vastus lateralis.

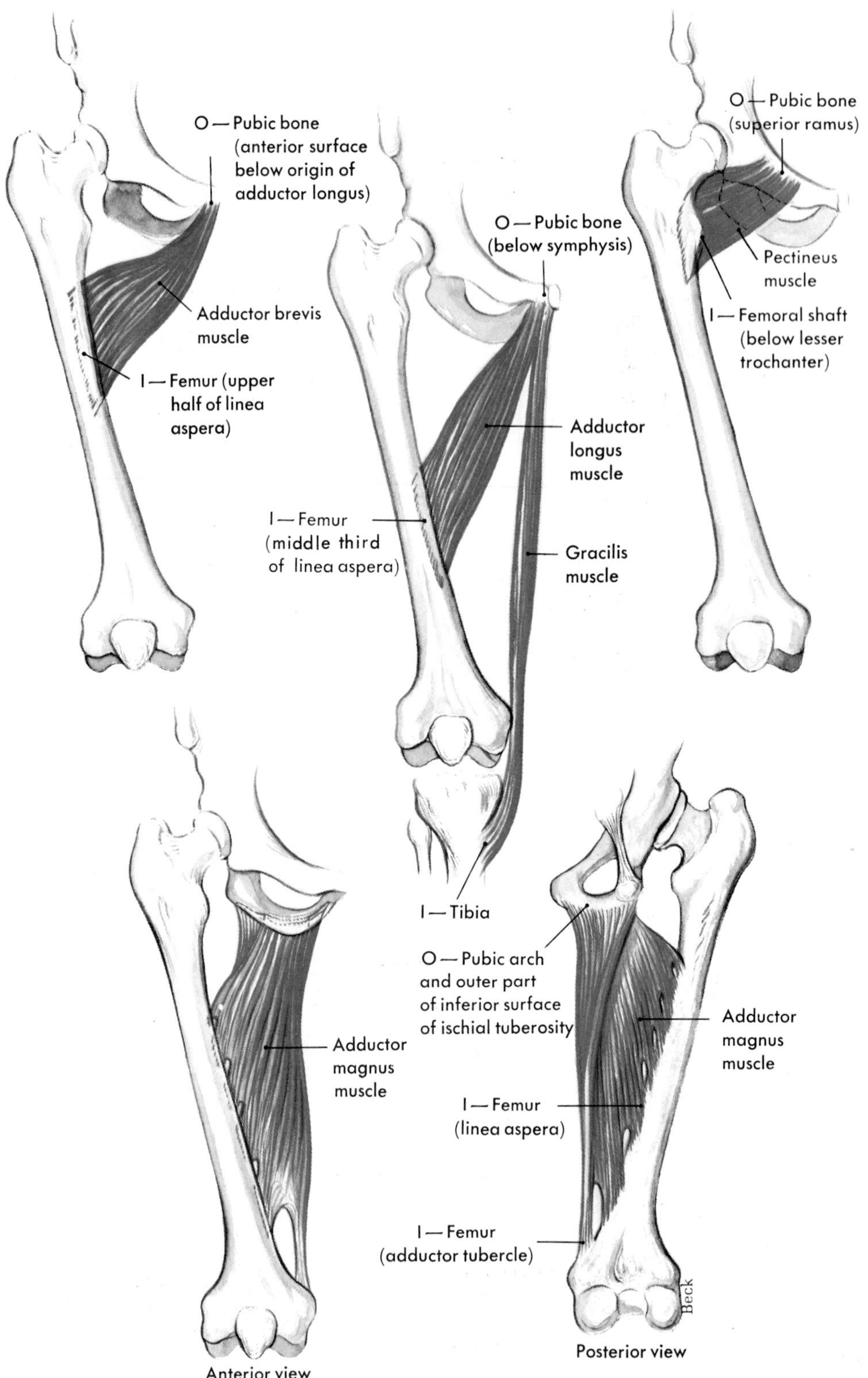

Fig. 104

Muscles which adduct the thigh.

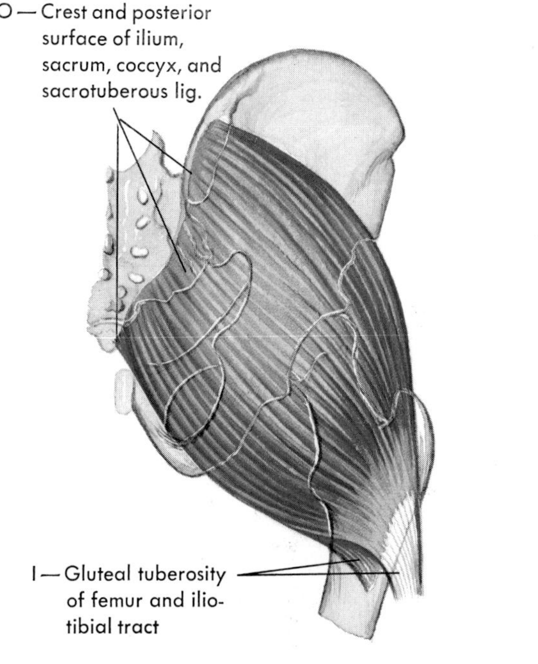

Fig. 105

Gluteus maximus muscle. **O**, Origin. **I**, Insertion.

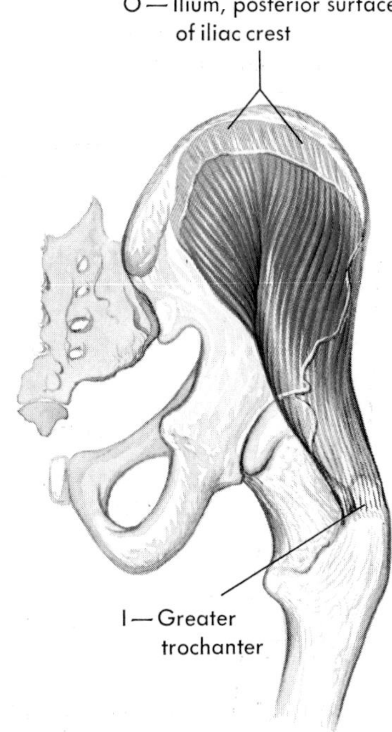

Fig. 107

Gluteus medius muscle. **O**, Origin. **I**, Insertion.

Fig. 106

Gluteus minimus muscle. **O**, Origin. **I**, Insertion.

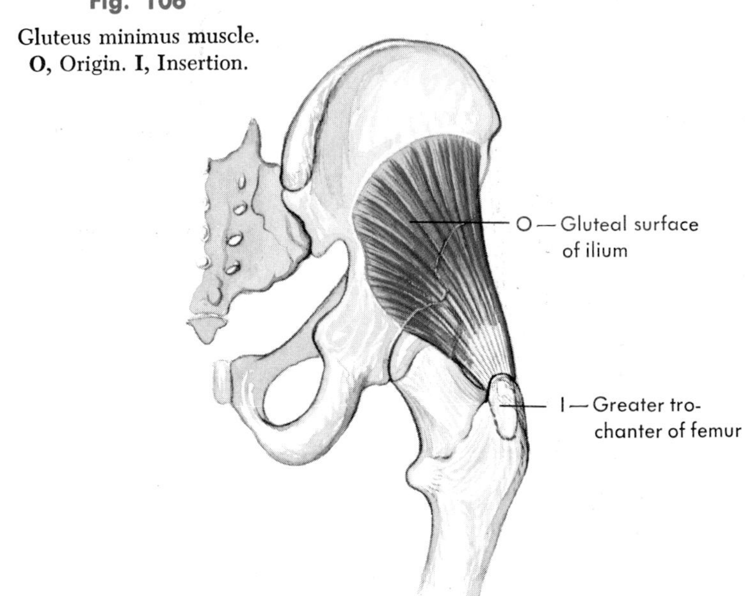

Fig. 108
Biceps femoris muscle, short and long heads.

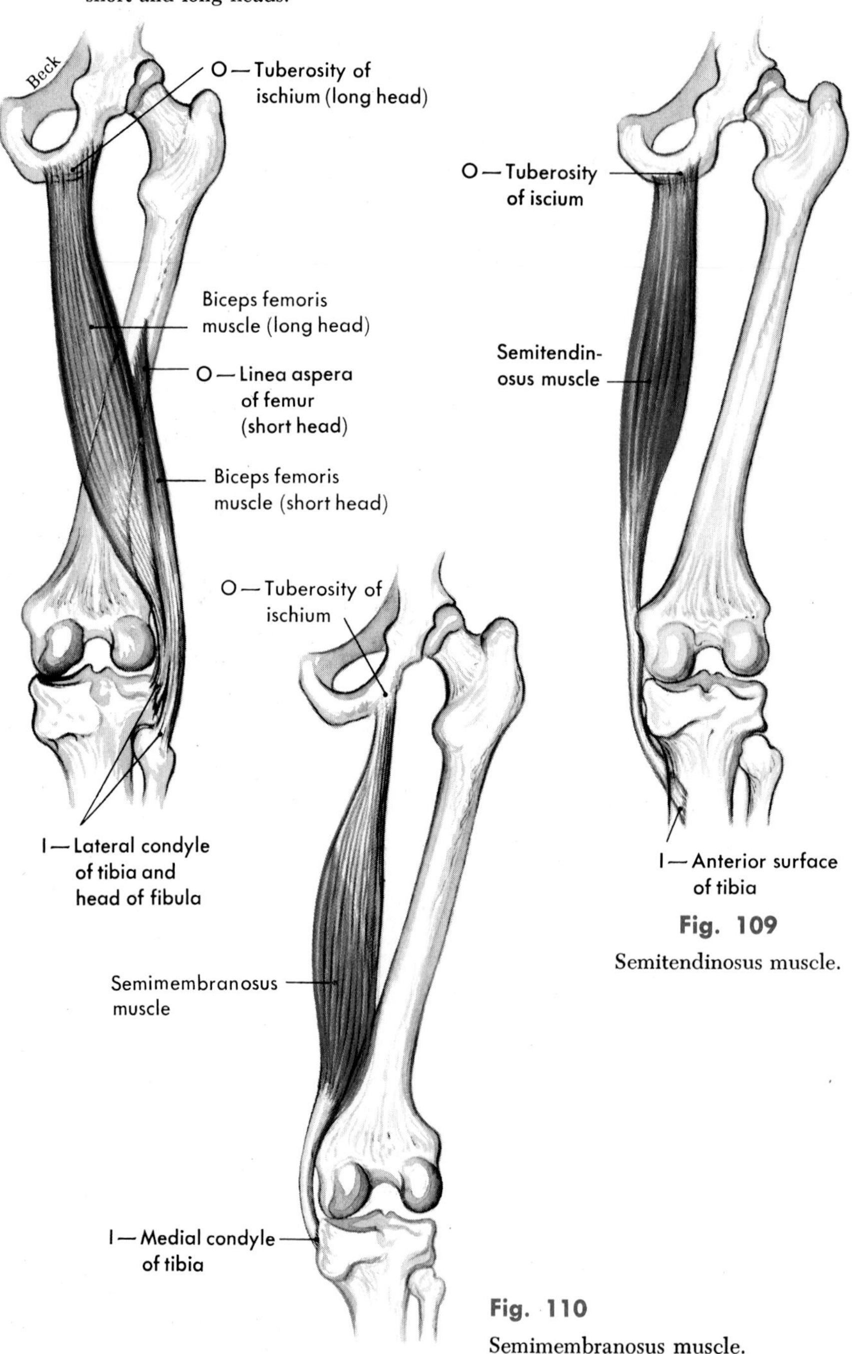

Fig. 109
Semitendinosus muscle.

Fig. 110
Semimembranosus muscle.

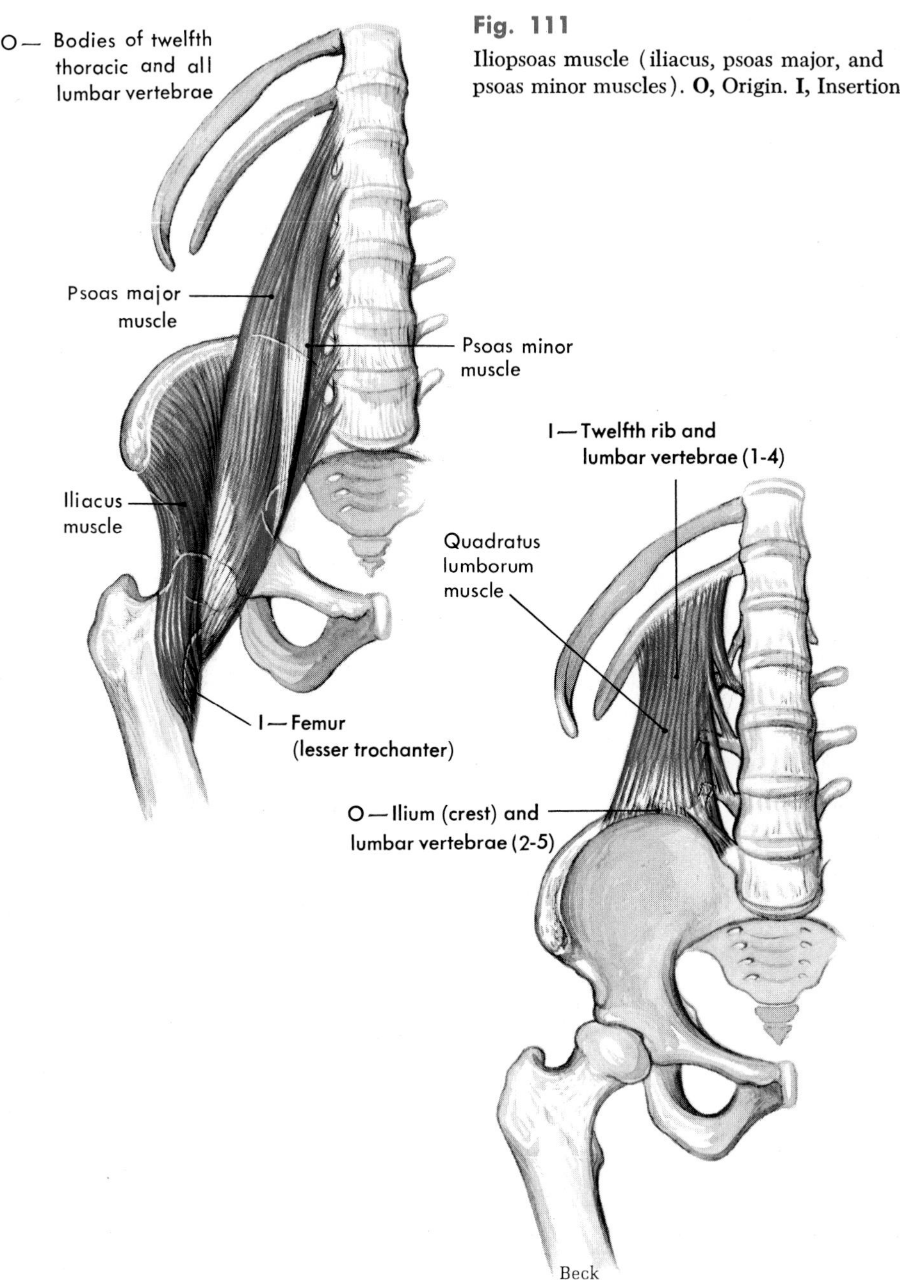

Fig. 111
Iliopsoas muscle (iliacus, psoas major, and psoas minor muscles). **O**, Origin. **I**, Insertion.

Fig. 112
Quadratus lumborum muscle.
O, Origin. **I**, Insertion.

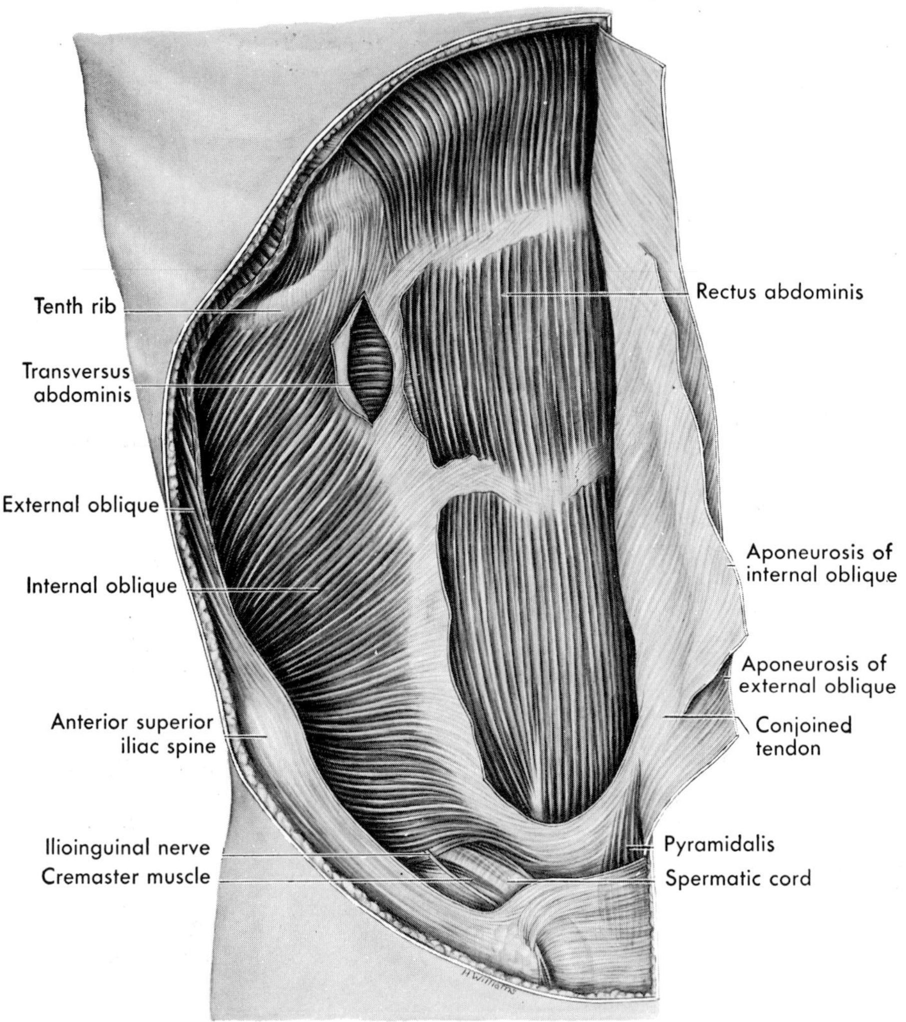

Fig. 113

Deep muscles of the abdominal wall.
(From Francis and Farrell: Integrated anatomy and physiology, St. Louis, The C. V. Mosby Co.)

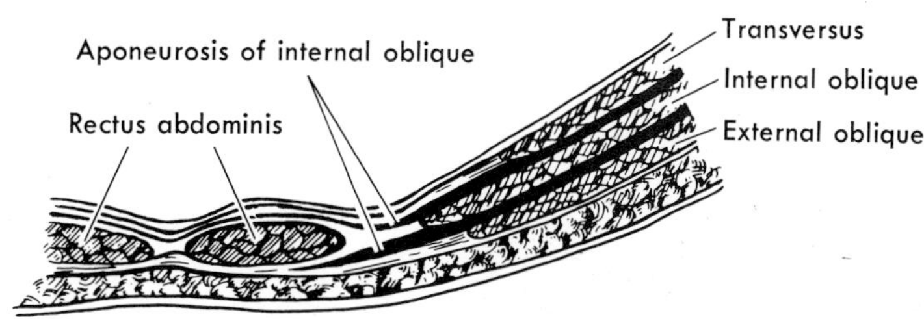

Fig. 114

Horizontal section of the anterolateral abdominal wall. The aponeurosis of the internal oblique muscle splits into two sections, one lying anterior and the other posterior to the rectus abdominis muscle, thereby forming an encasing sheath around this muscle.

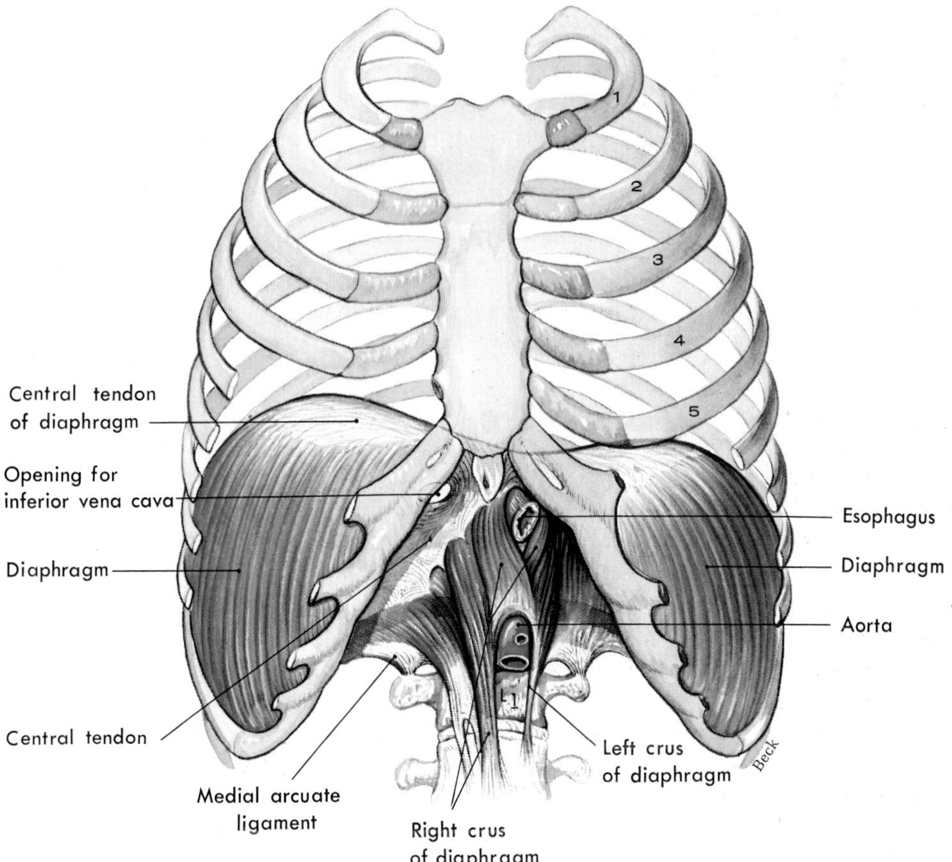

Fig. 115

The diaphragm as seen from the front. Note the openings in the vertebral portion for the inferior vena cava, esophagus, and aorta.

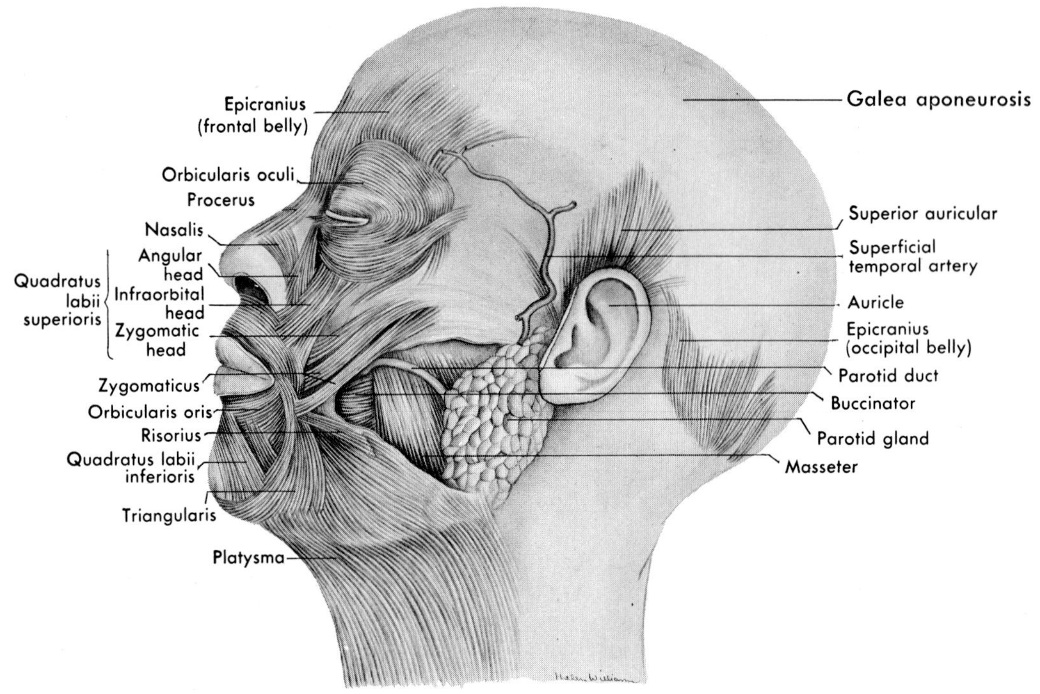

Fig. 116

Muscles of the head. These muscles make possible various facial expressions. (From Francis and Farrell: Integrated anatomy and physiology, St. Louis, The C. V. Mosby Co.)

Tendon sheaths

Definition and location. Tendon sheaths are tube-shaped structures which enclose certain tendons, notably those of the wrist and ankle. In structure they resemble the bursae in that they are made of connective tissue lined with synovial membrane. An inner layer of synovial membrane covers the tendon surface.

Function. The moist smooth surface of the synovial membrane lining the sheath and covering the tendon facilitates the gliding movements of the tendon.

Posture

We have already discussed the major role muscles play in movement and heat production. We shall now turn our attention to a third way in which muscles serve the body as a whole—that of maintaining the posture of the body. Let us consider a few aspects of this important function.

Meaning. The term posture means simply position or alignment of body parts. "Good posture" means many things. It means body alignment which most favors function; it means position which requires the least muscular work to maintain, which puts the least strain on muscles, ligaments, and bones; it means keeping the body's center of gravity over its base. Good posture in the standing position, for example, means head and chest held high, chin, abdomen, and buttocks pulled in, knees bent slightly, and feet placed firmly on the ground about 6 inches apart.

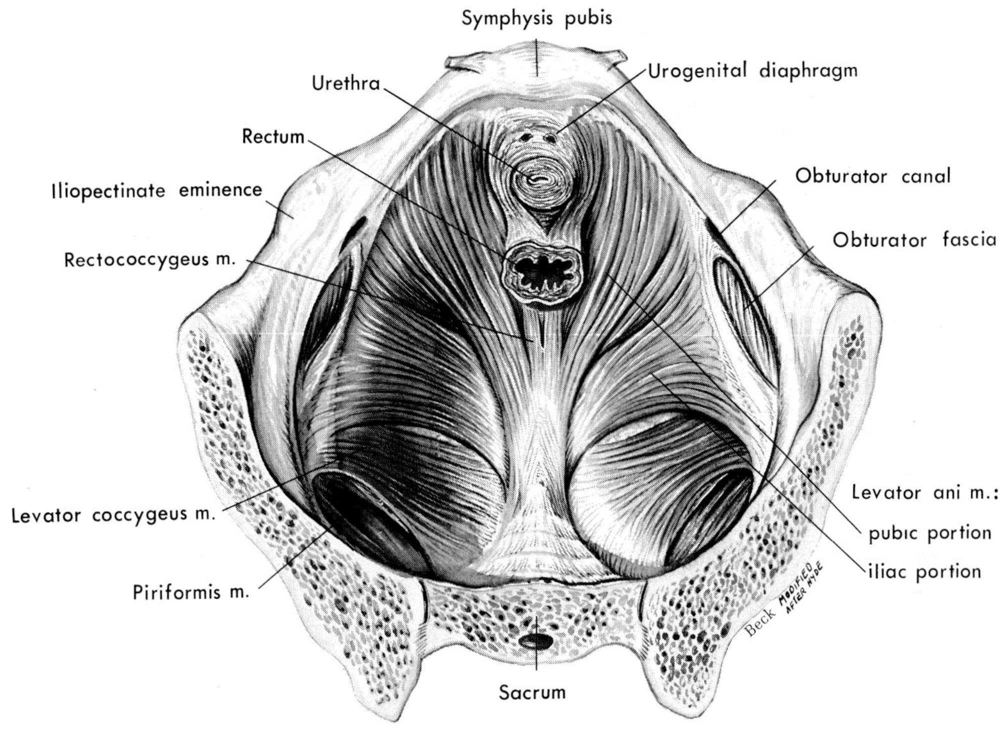

Fig. 117
Pelvic floor viewed from above.

How maintained. Since gravity pulls on the various parts of the body at all times, and since bones are too irregularly shaped to balance themselves upon each other, the only way the body can be held upright is for muscles to exert a continual pull on bones in the opposite direction from gravity. Gravity tends to pull the head and trunk forward and downward; muscles (head and trunk extensors) must therefore pull backward and upward on them. Gravity pulls the lower jaw downward; muscles must pull upward on it, etc. Muscles exert this pull against gravity by virtue of their property of tonicity. Because tonicity is absent during sleep, muscle pull does not then counteract the pull of gravity. Hence, for example, we cannot sleep standing up.

Many structures other than muscles and bones play a part in the maintenance of posture. The nervous system is responsible for the existence of muscle tone and also regulates and coordinates the amount of pull exerted by the individual muscles. The respiratory, digestive, circulatory, excretory, and endocrine systems all contribute something toward the ability of muscle to maintain posture. This is one of many examples of the important principle that all body functions are interdependent.

Importance to body as whole. The importance of posture can perhaps be best evaluated by considering some of the effects of poor posture. Poor posture throws more work on muscles to counteract the pull of gravity and therefore leads to fatigue more quickly than good posture. Poor posture puts more strain on ligaments. It puts abnormal strains on bones and may eventually produce deformities. It interferes with various functions such as respirations, heart action, and digestion. It probably is not going too far to say that it even detracts from one's feeling of self-confidence and joy. In support of this last claim may be cited our use of such expressions as "shoulders squared, head erect" to denote confidence and joy and "down-in-the-mouth," "long-faced," and "bowed down" to signify dejection and anxiety. The importance of posture to the body as a whole might be summed up in a single sentence: maximal health and good posture are reciprocally related; that is, each one depends upon the other.

Outline summary— The muscular system

Meaning

All muscles of body but especially skeletal muscles

General functions

1. Movement—sometimes locomotion, sometimes movement within given area
2. Posture
3. Heat production

Functional characteristics of muscle tissue

1. Irritability—ability to respond to stimulus
2. Conductivity—ability to transmit impulses
3. Extensibility—ability to be stretched
4. Elasticity—ability to resume former length when stretching force removed
5. Contractility—ability to contract or shorten

Muscle contraction

TYPES

1. Twitch contraction
   a. definition—quick, jerky contraction in response to single stimulus
   b. kymographic record—reveals three successive phases in twitch contraction: *latent period,* fraction of second following stimulation in which no change apparent; *contraction period,* in which muscle fibers shorten; *relaxation period,* in which fibers return to original length
2. Tetanic contraction
   a. definition—sustained, smooth contraction
   b. kymographic record—wavy line plateau for incomplete tetanus; straight line plateau for complete tetanus; normal smooth movements produced by tetanic contractions
3. Tonic contraction
   a. continual, partial contractions
   b. produced by activation of small groups of motor units at one time; act in relays, i.e., as one group of fibers relaxes, another group of motor units becomes active; characteristic of all healthy muscles
4. Treppe
   a. series of increasingly stronger contractions in response to constant strength stimuli applied at rate of 1 or 2 per second
   b. kymographic record—staircase phenomenon
   c. contracture—incomplete relaxation after repeated stimulation or certain kinds of injury
   d. fatigue—failure of muscle to contract in response to stimulation
5. Isotonic contraction—muscle shortens and performs work but tension within muscle remains unchanged
6. Isometric contraction—muscle length remains unchanged so it does no work but tension within muscle increases
7. Fibrillation—abnormal contraction in which individual fibers contract asynchronously, producing no effective movement
8. Convulsions—uncoordinated tetanic contractions of varying groups of muscles

MECHANISM

1. Stimulation of muscle triggers breakdown of ATP within muscle cells to ADP and inorganic phosphate with release of energy
2. Energy released from ATP breakdown used to do work of muscle contraction
3. All-or-none law—applies to muscle cells but not to muscle organs; if muscle cell

contracts at all, contracts with maximal force for existing conditions

4. Sources of ATP
   a. catabolism
      1. less than 10% of ATP produced during catabolism is produced during glycolysis, anaerobic first phase of catabolism (anaerobic means chemical reactions that do not utilize oxygen); over 90% of ATP produced during citric acid cycle, aerobic second phase of catabolism (aerobic means chemical reactions that do utilize oxygen); hence, without adequate oxygen supply, only small amount of ATP produced by cell—not enough for cell to carry on its normal activities; see **5,d** below
   b. creatine phosphate breakdown
      1. when creatine phosphate breaks down to creatine and inorganic phosphate, energy released and utilized for synthesizing ATP from ADP and inorganic phosphate
5. Results of strenuous muscular activity
   a. cells' rate of catabolism increased to meet increased need for ATP to supply more energy
   b. respiration and circulation unable to increase oxygen delivery to cells enough to equal their increased oxygen need (accelerated citric acid cycle uses more oxygen); in other words, oxygen supply inadequate in relation to oxygen needed
   c. citric acid cycle slows or stops
   d. ATP production decreased markedly (because of slow citric acid cycle); pyruvic acid starts accumulating and is reduced to lactic acid, thereby creating oxygen debt; part of lactic acid diffuses out of cells, carried to liver, and synthesized back to glycogen or glucose
6. Recovery after cessation of strenuous muscular activity—oxygen debt gradually repaid; lactic acid remaining in muscle cells oxidized back to pyruvic acid which is then oxidized via citric acid cycle to carbon dioxide and water with ATP formation

Skeletal muscles

GROSS STRUCTURE

Size, shape, and fiber arrangement

Wide variation in different muscles

Connective tissue components

1. Epimysium—fibrous connective tissue sheath that envelops each muscle
2. Perimysium—extensions of epimysium, partitioning each muscle into bundles of fibers
3. Endomysium—extensions of perimysium between individual muscle fibers
4. Tendon—strong, tough cord continuous at one end with fibrous wrappings (epimysium, etc.) of muscle and at other end with fibrous covering of bone (periosteum)
5. Aponeurosis—broad flat sheet of fibrous connective tissue continuous on one border with fibrous wrappings of muscle and at other border with fibrous coverings of some adjacent structure, usually another muscle
6. Deep fascia—layer of dense fibrous connective tissue underlying superficial fascia under skin; extensions of deep fascia form epimysium, etc. and also enclose viscera, glands, blood vessels, and nerves

Nerve supply

One motor neuron, together with skeletal muscle fibers it supplies, constitutes *motor unit;* number of muscle fibers per motor unit varies; in general, more precise movements produced by muscle in which motor units include fewer muscle fibers

ACTIONS

Basic principles

1. Skeletal muscles contract only if stimulated
2. Skeletal muscles produce movements by pulling on insertion bones across joints
3. Bones serve as levers and joints as fulcrums of these levers
4. Muscles that move part usually do not lie over that part but proximal to it
5. Skeletal muscles almost always act in groups rather than singly; most movements, i.e., produced by coordinated action of several muscles
6. Skeletal muscles contract according to graded strength principle in contrast to individual muscle cells that compose them which contract according to all-or-none law

Hints on how to deduce actions

1. Deduce bones that muscle attaches to from illustrations of muscle
2. Make guess as to which bone moves (insertion)
3. Deduce movement muscle produces by applying principle that its insertion moves toward its origin

NAMES

Reasons for names

1. Muscle names describe one or more of following features about muscle
   - a. its action
   - b. direction of fibers
   - c. its location
   - d. number of divisions composing it
   - e. its shape
   - f. its points of attachment

Muscles grouped according to location

See p. 135

Muscles grouped according to function

- a. flexors—decrease angle of joint
- b. extensors—return part from flexion to normal anatomical position
- c. abductors—move bone away from midline of body
- d. adductors—move bone toward midline of body
- e. rotators—cause part to pivot upon its axis
- f. levators—raise part
- g. depressors—lower part
- h. sphincters—reduce size of opening
- i. tensors—tense part or make it more rigid
- j. supinators—turn hand palm upward
- k. pronators—turn hand palm downward

ORIGINS, INSERTIONS, FUNCTIONS, AND INNERVATIONS OF REPRESENTATIVE MUSCLES

See Tables 9 through 21, pp. 137 to 149

Weak places in abdominal wall

1. Inguinal rings—right and left internal; right and left external
2. Femoral rings—right and left
3. Umbilicus

Bursae

1. Definition—small connective tissue sacs lined with synovial membrane and containing synovial fluid
2. Locations—wherever pressure exerted over moving parts
   - a. between skin and bone
   - b. between tendons and bone
   - c. between muscles or ligaments and bone
   - d. names of bursae that frequently become inflamed (bursitis)
     1. subacrominal—between deltoid muscle and head of humerus and acromion process
     2. olecranon—between olecranon process and skin; inflammation called student's elbow
     3. prepatellar—between patella and skin; inflammation called housemaid's knee
3. Function—act as cushion, relieving pressure between moving parts

Tendon sheaths

1. Definition and location—tube-shaped structures which enclose certain tendons, notably those of wrist and ankle; made of connective tissue lined with synovial membrane
2. Function—facilitate gliding movements of tendon

Posture

1. Meaning—position or alignment of body parts
2. How maintained—by continual pull of muscles on bones in opposite direction from pull of gravity; i.e., posture maintained by continued partial contraction of muscles, or muscle tone; therefore, indirectly dependent on many other factors; e.g., normal nervous, respiratory, and circulatory systems, health in general
3. Importance to body as whole—essential for optimal functioning of most of body; e.g., respiration, circulation, digestion, joint action, etc.; briefly, maximal health dependent upon good posture, good posture dependent upon health

Review questions

1. Differentiate between the three kinds of muscle tissue as to structure, location, and innervation.
2. Describe several physiological properties of muscle tissue.
3. What property is more highly developed in muscle than in any other tissue?
4. State a principle describing the usual relationship between a part moved and the location of muscles (insertion, body, and origin) moving the part.
5. Applying the principle stated in question 4, where would you expect muscles that move the head to be located? Name two or three muscles that fulfill these conditions.
6. Applying the principle stated in question 4, what part of the body do thigh muscles move? Name several muscles that fulfill these conditions.

7. What bone or bones serve as a lever in movements of the forearm? What structure constitutes the fulcrum for this lever?
8. Explain the meaning of the term neuromusculoskeletal unit.
9. Name the main muscles of the back, chest, abdomen, neck, shoulder, upper arm, lower arm, thigh, buttocks, leg, and pelvic floor.
10. Name the main muscles that flex, extend, abduct, and adduct the upper arm; that raise and lower the shoulder; that flex and extend the lower arm; that flex, extend, abduct, and adduct the thigh; that flex and extend the lower leg and thigh; that flex and extend the foot; that flex, extend, abduct, and adduct the head; that move the abdominal wall; that move the chest wall.
11. Discuss the chemical reactions thought to make available energy for muscle contraction.
12. What physiological reason can you give for athletes using a warming-up period before starting a game?
13. Why does an individual pant after strenuous exercise?
14. Curare preparations are often given during surgery. Would you expect this to make the patient's muscles more relaxed or more rigid? Why?
15. In general, where are bursae located? Give several specific locations.
16. Name several weak places in the abdominal wall where hernia may occur.
17. What and where are the inguinal canals? Of what clinical importance are they?
18. Good posture depends upon tonicity of the antigravity muscles, particularly of those which hold the head and trunk erect and the abdominal wall pulled in. Name several muscles that perform these functions.
19. Define the following terms:

aponeurosis	motor unit
bursa	origin
contraction	oxygen debt
contracture	tetanus
elasticity	tone
extensibility	treppe
fibrillation	twitch
insertion	

UNIT
THREE

Integration and control of the body

Cells
Neuroglia
- Types
- Structure
- Functions

Neurons
- Classification
- Structure
- Function

Nerve impulse
- Nature
- Conduction

Brain and cord coverings

Brain and cord fluid spaces

Formation and circulation of cerebrospinal fluid

Organs
Brain
- Cerebrum
  - Hemispheres, fissures, and lobes
  - Cerebral cortex
  - Cerebral tracts
  - Basal ganglia
  - Functions
- Diencephalon—thalamus, epithalamus, subthalamus, and hypothalamus
  - Thalamus
    - Structure and location
    - Functions
  - Hypothalamus
    - Structure and location
    - Functions
- Cerebellum
  - Structure and location
  - Functions
- Medulla oblongata
  - Structure and location
  - Functions
- Pons varolii
  - Structure and location
  - Functions
- Midbrain
  - Structure and location
  - Functions of pons and midbrain

Spinal cord
- Location
- Structure
- Functions

Cranial nerves
- First (olfactory)
- Second (optic)
- Third (oculomotor)
- Fourth (trochlear)
- Fifth (trifacial or trigeminal)
- Sixth (abducens)
- Seventh (facial)

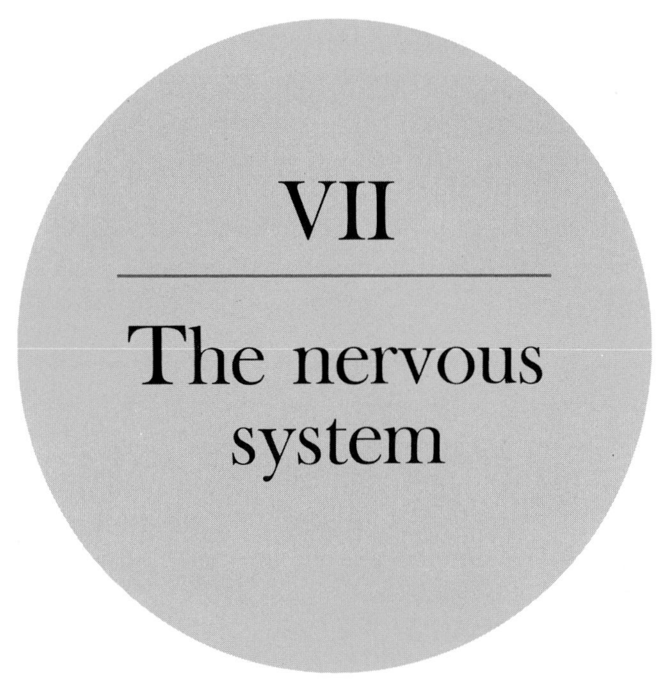

VII

The nervous system

If you want to understand the body, you need to remind yourself frequently of some principles stated in the first chapter of this book—briefly, that the body is made up of millions of smaller structures that carry on a host of different activities. But, and this is the important point, together all of these diverse activities accomplish the one big, all-encompassing function of the body—survival. If you think about this for a moment, you realize that the only way many units can be made to function as a single unit (whether the units are cells, or people, or parts of a machine) is by organization—that is, controlling their numerous activities so as to coordinate and integrate them. And this necessitates communication or, in other words, some means of getting information to and from the component units. The body has two kinds of communication devices: nerve impulses and chemicals.

The foregoing principles about a large unit composed of smaller units have many familiar applications. A hospital, to name just one example, is such a unit. Quite obviously, the activities of the hundreds of individuals who make up a modern hospital must be organized, coordinated, and integrated, and communication must take place between the individuals. Complete chaos would prevail otherwise. A disorganized hospital could not survive functionally. In no time at all it would be utterly unable to carry on its one great function of giving care to sick people.

The nervous system, one of the body's two vital communication and integration facilities, is discussed in this chapter and the next chapter. Chemical control devices are considered in Chapter XIV.

Facts, theories, and questions about the nervous system are as abundant and complex as they are fascinating. We shall approach this large body of material by considering cells of the nervous system, the nerve impulse, brain and cord coverings, brain and cord fluid spaces, formation and circulation of cerebrospinal fluid, organs of the nervous system, sensory neural pathways, the arousal or alerting mechanism, motor neural pathways to skeletal muscles, reflexes, and the autonomic nervous system in this chapter and the sense organs in Chapter VIII.

Cells

Structures of the nervous system are composed of two main kinds of cells: neuroglia and neurons (nerve cells). Neuroglia will be discussed first and then neurons. Several subtypes of each will be mentioned.

NEUROGLIA

Types

Neuroglia are interesting cells. Their special functions still remain somewhat of a mystery, and mysteries usually win our interest. Then, too, most tumors of the nervous system arise from neuroglia, a fact which makes them clinically important as well as interesting. Histologists identify the following three types (Fig. 118): (1) astrocytes, (2) microglia, and (3) oligodendroglia.

Structure

Astrocytes are star-shaped cells with numerous processes. Some of their processes form a thick network that twines around nerve cells and their processes. Other astrocyte processes attach by little "sucker feet" to adjacent blood vessels, thereby holding nerve cells close to their blood vessels.

Microglia are small cells that move about in inflamed or degenerating brain tissue, in which they become larger and carry on phagocytosis; that is, they engulf and destroy microorganisms or cellular debris in nervous tissue.

Oligodendroglia have fewer processes than astrocytes and microglia but are also interposed between neurons and their blood vessels.

Functions

Neuroglia support nerve cells and connect them to blood vessels. They also serve a defense or protective function. Astrocytes and oligodendroglia furnish support and connection. Microglia, through their phagocytic activity, protect against infection. And astrocytes may function similarly. At any rate, they greatly increase in numbers during infections of the nervous system. But whether support and protection are the sole functions of neuroglia is now being questioned. For example, recent evidence indicates that they also play a part in forming the myelin sheath of neurons in the brain and spinal cord.

NEURONS

Classification

Classification according to function. Based on function, neurons may be classified as (1) sensory (afferent) neurons, (2) motoneurons (motor or efferent neurons), and (3) interneurons (internuncial or intercalated neurons).

Sensory (afferent) neurons transmit nerve impulses to spinal cord or brain.

Motoneurons (motor or efferent neurons) transmit nerve impulses away from brain or spinal cord to or toward muscle or glandular tissue.

Interneurons (internuncial or intercalated neurons) conduct impulses from sensory to motor neurons. They lie entirely within the central nervous system (brain and spinal cord).

Classification according to structure. Structurally, neurons fall into three classifications, (1) multipolar, (2) bipolar, and (3) unipolar, depending upon the number of processes extending from the cell body.

Multipolar neurons have several dendrites but only one axon. Most of the neurons in the brain and spinal cord are multipolar.

Bipolar neurons have only one dendrite

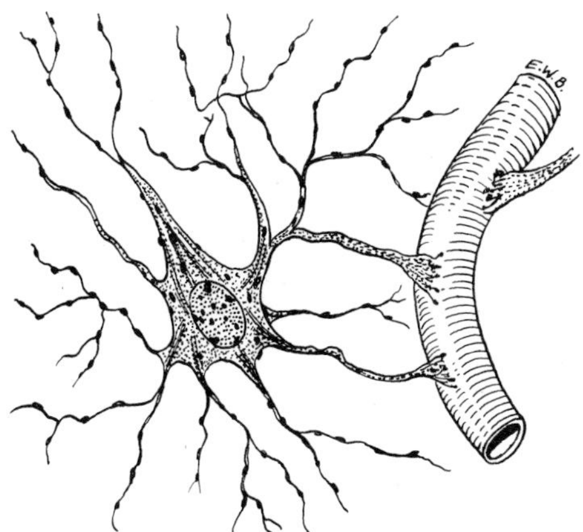

Fibrous astrocyte of white matter with footplates against blood vessel

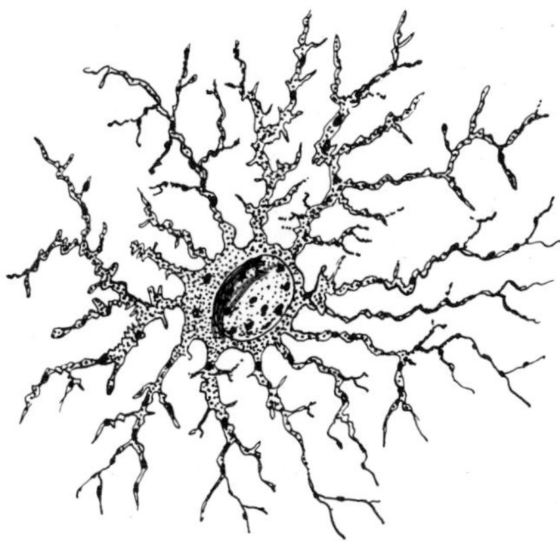

Protoplasmic (nonfibrous) astrocyte of gray matter

Microglial cell with processes extending to two nerve cell bodies

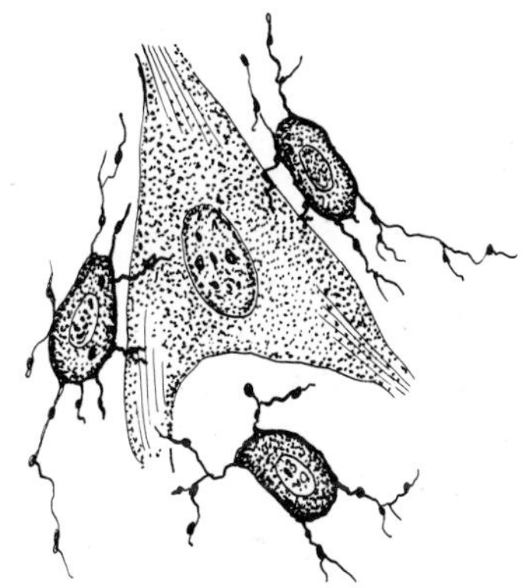

Oligodendroglial cells near a nerve cell body

Fig. 118

Neuroglial cells of the central nervous system. Astrocytes and oligodendroglia support neurons and connect them to blood vessels within the nerve tissue. Microglia show phagocytic activity when nerve tissue is injured or diseased so serve as a protective function.

and one axon. They are found in the retina and spiral ganglion of the inner ear, for example.

Unipolar neurons have only one process coming off from the cell body. Most sensory neurons are bipolar at first but later become unipolar. The two processes which originally emerge from the cell body become fused for a short distance to form one process. However, it divides almost immediately into two branches—a peripheral branch that functions as a dendrite and a central branch that functions as an axon (see Fig. 119).

Structure

Structure of neurons, like that of other cells, illustrates the principle that structure determines function. The basic function of neurons is to respond to stimuli by trans-

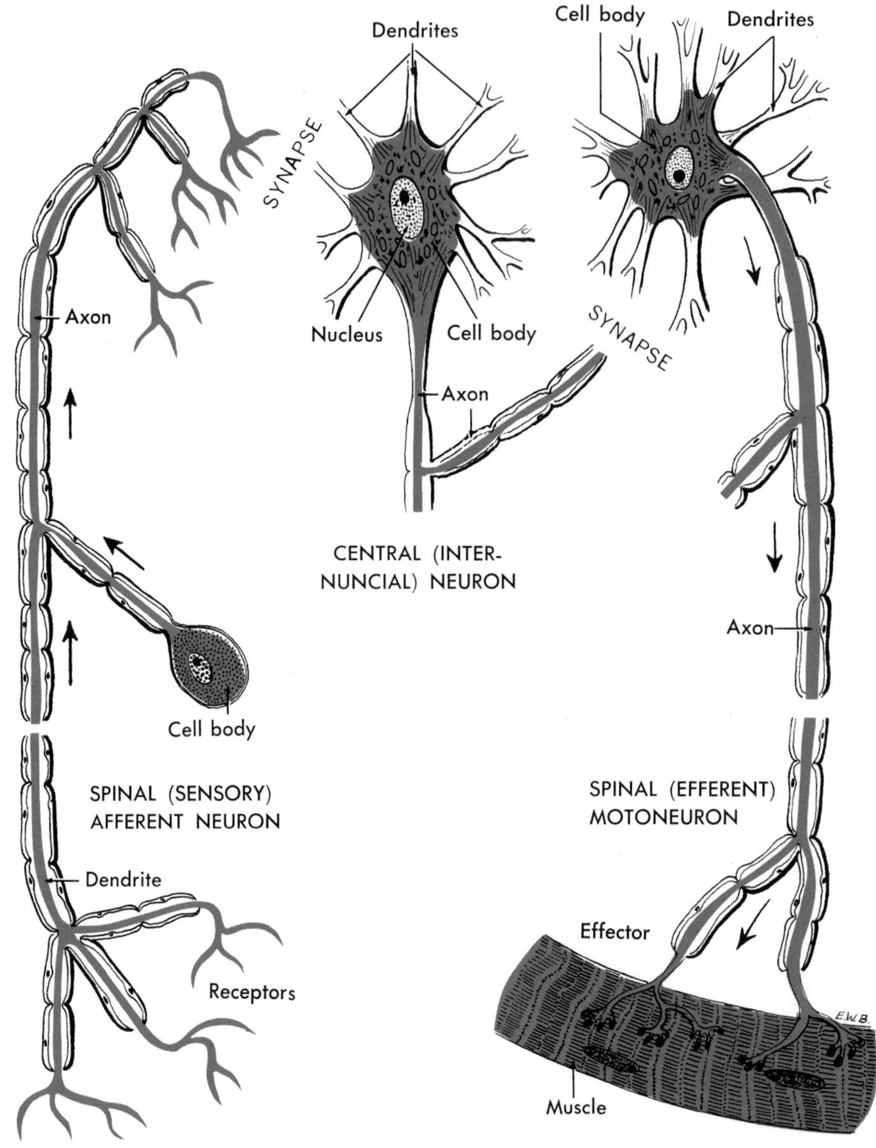

Fig. 119

Diagrammatic representation of a three-neuron reflex arc. Note that each neuron has three parts: a cell body and two extensions, dendrite(s) and an axon. (See Fig. 120 for more details about axon coverings.)

mitting nerve impulses. In other words, neurons are specialists in irritability and conductivity. An example of a structural feature that adapts neurons to their function of conducting impulses is a long process extending out from the cell body of many neurons. This structure is what makes possible the function of conducting impulses over long distances.

The following paragraphs describe briefly the structures characteristic of neurons: (1) dendrites, (2) axon, (3) myelin sheath,

(4) neurilemma, (5) neurofibrils, and (6) Nissl bodies.

Dendrites are one of two types of processes that extend out from the main part of a neuron, its *cell body*. Dendrites conduct impulses to the cell body of the neuron. It is because they branch extensively like tiny trees that they are called dendrites or dendrons (from Greek word for tree). The distal ends of dendrites of sensory neurons are called *receptors* because they receive the initial stimulus (Fig. 119).

Axons are single processes that extend out from the neuron cell body and conduct impulses away from it. A neuron has only one axon, but often this has one or more side branches *(axon collaterals)*. Moreover, axons terminate in many branched filaments. Axons vary considerably in length. Some are 3 feet or more long. Others measure only a fraction of an inch. Axons vary also in diameter—a point of interest because it relates to velocity of impulse conduction. In general, axons with a large diameter conduct more rapidly than those with a small diameter. Later, we shall apply this principle to specific nerves.

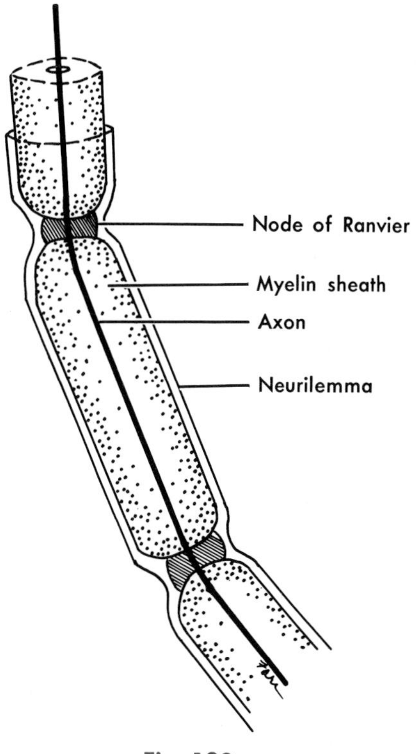

Fig. 120

Diagram of an axon and its coverings.

The *myelin sheath* is a segmented wrapping surrounding a nerve fiber. The small gaps between segments of the sheath are called *nodes of Ranvier*. Widely accepted today is the "jelly roll hypothesis" of myelin formation, which states that myelin consists of a double layer of cell membranes of *Schwann cells*. These are satellite cells of nerve fibers located along fibers of peripheral nerves. One Schwann cell winds itself in "jelly roll" fashion around each segment of the fiber. (A segment is the section of fiber between two successive nodes of Ranvier.)

The *neurilemma* is a continuous sheath around the segmented myelin sheath. Like the latter, it is also thought to derive from Schwann cells. It plays an essential part in peripheral nerve fiber regeneration. Unfortunately, however, brain and spinal cord fibers do not have a neurilemma and are not known to regenerate. This means, of course, that if disease or injury causes them to degenerate, the destruction is permanent, a fact with serious clinical implications.

Neurofibrils are fine fibrils present in dendrites, cell bodies, and axons. Various studies made with the electron microscope have shown that bundles of neurofibrils interlace to form a network in neuron cytoplasm.

Nissl bodies, as revealed by studies under the electron microscope, consist of groups of flat, membranous sacs and numerous RNA granules scattered between them. In other words, they constitute the rough-surfaced vesicles of the endoplasmic reticulum of a neuron (p. 16), and they occupy the minute spaces between the neurofibril bundles. Cells with numerous rough-surfaced vesicles usually specialize in protein synthesis (for example, exocrine cells of the pancreas). Reasoning from this fact, you would expect Nissl bodies to perform the same function. But why should neurons, whose specialty is conduction, also specialize in protein synthesis? No one can answer this positively as yet. However, radioautographic studies* have indicated that proteins are synthesized in the cell bodies of neurons and then quickly migrate down to their axons. Other evidence also suggests this sequence of events. For instance, after an axon is severed, the disconnected segment soon degenerates *(axon reaction)* and Nissl substance in the cell body decreases and eventually disappears *(chromatolysis)*.

In addition to the special structures just described, neurons have many organelles not unique to them. For instance, they have *mitochondria* and, of course, a *cell membrane*. They also have a *Golgi apparatus*. Incidentally, Golgi first saw this structure in neurons.

Function

Neurons perform the specific function of conducting impulses and thereby perform the general functions of communication and integration. Because impulses travel at almost lightning speed, they provide a means for both rapid control of individual structures and for integration of many activities of many different structures.

Nerve impulse

Nature

According to widely accepted present-day theory, a nerve impulse is a self-propagating wave of negativity that travels along the surface of the neuron membrane. Some of the major tenets of this membrane theory (first proposed in 1902 by Bernstein and modified in recent years by Hodgkin and co-workers) are the following (refer to Fig. 121).

1. When a neuron is resting, that is, when it is not conducting impulses, the outer surface of its membrane is from 70 to 90 mv. positive to the inner surface of the membrane. This fact—that the outside of a resting neuron's membrane is positive to the inside—is expressed by several different terms. For example, the resting neuron's membrane is said to be *polarized*, or a potential difference is said to exist across the membrane. *Potential difference* means a difference in the electrical charges on the outer and inner surfaces of the membrane. The term *resting potential* means the potential difference across a nonconducting neuron's membrane.

The direct cause of the resting potential, briefly stated, is the separation of oppositely charged ions by the cell membrane. The membrane comes between a few positive ions that it keeps outside the cell and an equal number of negative ions that it keeps inside the cell. This, in turn, makes the outer surface of the membrane positive to the inner surface. The normal resting potential usually ranges between 70 and 90 mv.*

2. When an adequate stimulus is applied to a neuron, it greatly increases the membrane's permeability to sodium ions at the point of stimulation.

3. Sodium ions rush into the cell at the stimulated point. Therefore, at this point, the excess of positive ions outside rapidly dwindles to zero. Therefore, also, the mem-

*Droz, B., and Leblond, C. P.: Axonal migration of proteins in the central nervous system and peripheral nerves as shown by radioautography, J. Comp. Neurol. **121**:325, 1963.

*If you would like to delve further into the complex physiology of membrane polarization, see suggested supplementary readings for Chapter 7, reference 7, p. 549.

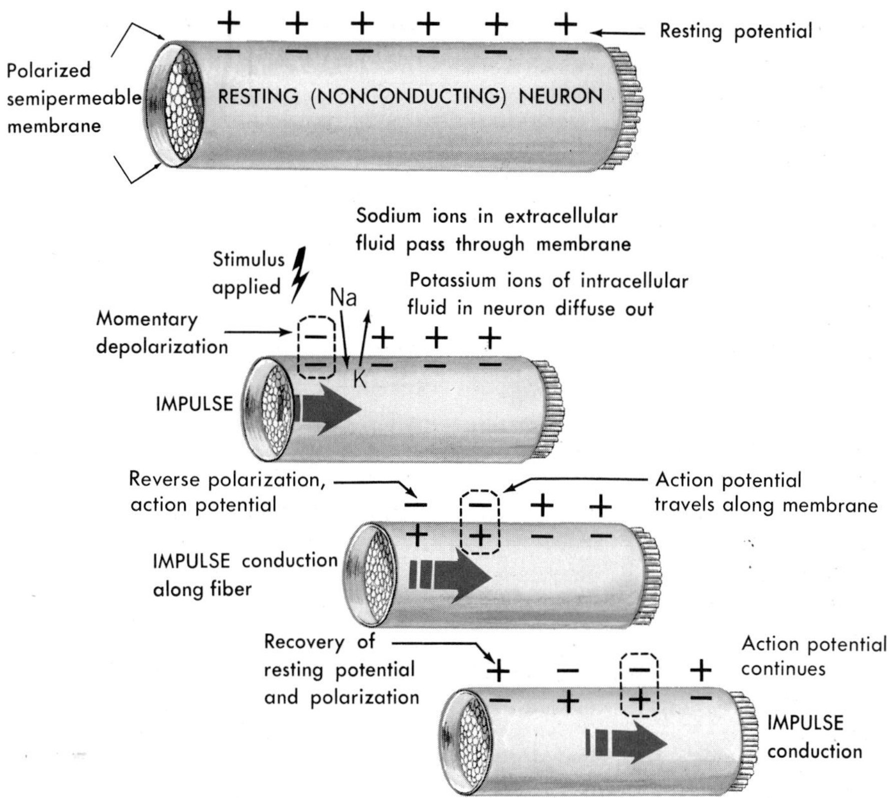

Fig. 121

Upper diagram represents polarized state of the membrane of a nerve fiber when it is not conducting impulses. Lower diagrams represent nerve impulse conduction—a self-propogating wave of negativity or action potential travels along membrane.

brane potential decreases to zero at this point, because now positive and negative ions are no longer kept apart at this point on the membrane. In other words, the stimulated point of the membrane is no longer polarized. It is *depolarized.* But only for an instant—for more sodium ions continue to stream into the cell. Almost instantaneously, therefore, an excess of positive ions develops inside the cell and leaves an excess of negative ions outside. The resting potential has thereby become reversed. And it is no longer a resting potential. It is now an action potential. Whereas a typical resting potential is 70 mv. with the outside of the membrane positive to the inside, the *action potential* is about 30 mv. with the outside negative to the inside.

4. The negative, stimulated point of the membrane sets up a local current with the positive point adjacent to it, and this local current acts as a stimulus. Consequently, within a fraction of a second, the next point on the membrane becomes depolarized and its potential reverses from positive to negative. In other words, the action potential moves from the point originally stimulated to the next point on the membrane. This cycle goes on repeating itself over and over again in rapid succession, and thereby

the action potential travels point by point out the full length of the nerve fiber, much as a wave moves in crest by crest from sea to shore—hence the definition of *action potential* (or its synonym, *nerve impulse*) as a "self-propagating wave of negativity which travels along the surface of a neuron's membrane."

5. By the time the action potential has moved from one point on the membrane to the next (a matter of thousandths of a second), the first point has repolarized—its resting potential has been restored. *Repolarization* results from the fact that the increased permeability to sodium induced by stimulation lasts only momentarily. It is quickly replaced by increased permeability to potassium which, therefore, diffuses outward (because potassium concentration inside the cell is much greater than that outside the cell). In much less time than it takes to tell, there are again a few excess positive ions on the outer surface of the membrane separated from an equal number of negative ions on the inner surface of the membrane, and this restores the resting potential (outside positive, inside negative).

Conduction

Initiation of conduction. Normally, impulse conduction begins when a stimulus acts on receptors. (A *stimulus* is a change in the environment; for example, a change in pressure or temperature. *Receptors* are the distal ends of dendrites of sensory neurons.) When a stimulus acts on a receptor, the receptor membrane potential decreases below its resting level (explained in paragraphs 2 and 3 of the preceding discussion). If it decreases down to a certain critical level, known as the *threshold of stimulation,* it triggers off impulse conduction. In short, it initiates an action potential that rapidly propagates itself the full length of the sensory dendrite, cell body, and axon.

Whether or not a stimulus initiates conduction depends upon the intensity or "strength" of the stimulus. A stimulus just strong enough to decrease the receptor potential to its threshold is just strong enough to initiate impulse conduction and is called a *threshold stimulus* (or liminal stimulus). Any stimulus weaker than this is a *subthreshold stimulus* (or subliminal stimulus). It decreases the membrane potential but not down as low as the threshold level so does not trigger off impulse conduction.

Course of conduction. Impulse conduction generally begins with stimulation of receptors and ends with a response by effectors. (*Effectors* are muscles and glands.) In traveling from receptors to effectors, impulses are conducted over routes called "neural pathways" or *reflex arcs.* And, of course, the cells that make up these pathways are neurons, the "conduction specialists" of the body. The simplest reflex arcs are the so-called two-neuron (Fig. 122) and three-neuron arcs (Figs. 119 and 123). Theoretically, a *two-neuron or monosynaptic arc* consists of one sensory neuron, one motoneuron, and a synapse between them. Actually, however, more than one of each kind of neuron probably always functions in these arcs.

A *three-neuron arc* consists of at least one sensory neuron, one interneuron, one motoneuron, and two synapses—that is, a synapse between the sensory neuron and interneuron and another between the interneuron and motoneuron. A *synapse* is a contact point between the end of an axon filament of one neuron and the dendrite or cell body of another neuron. Figs. 123 to 125 show different types of three-neuron arcs.

Besides simple two- and three-neuron arcs, extremely complex neural pathways also exist. But let us now turn our attention to the rate of conduction and then conduction across synapses.

Rate of conduction. The general principle is that the rate of impulse conduction

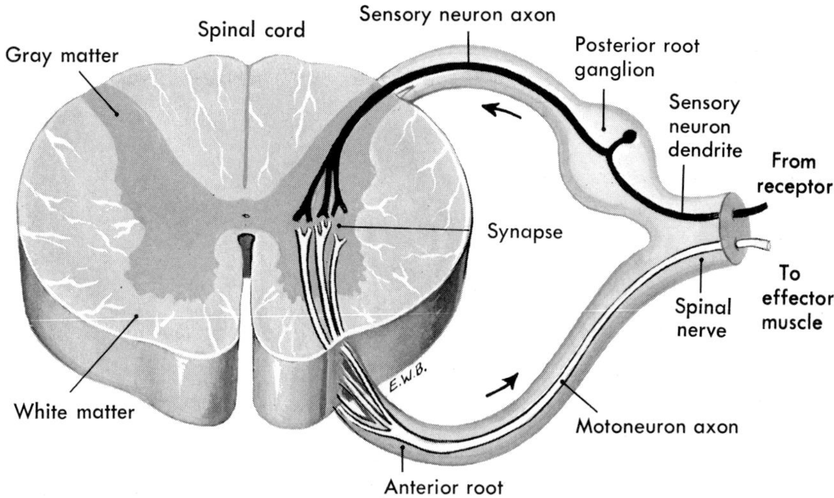

Fig. 122

A two-neuron reflex arc; also called a monosynaptic arc because impulses cross only one synapse in traversing it. Conduction over such arcs produces stretch reflexes such as the knee jerk.

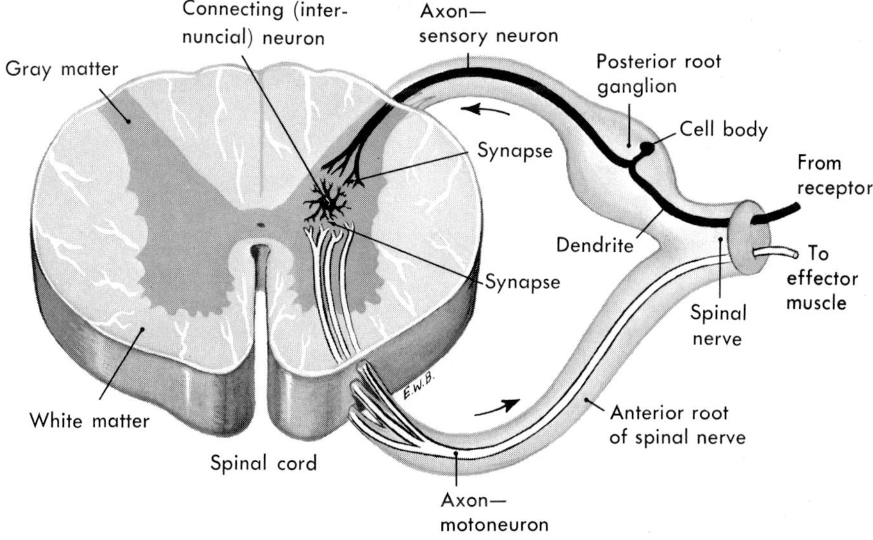

Fig. 123

Three-neuron reflex arc, consisting of a sensory neuron, a connecting (internuncial) neuron, and a motoneuron. Note the presence of two synapses in this arc—between (1) sensory neuron axon terminals and internuncial neuron dendrites and (2) between internuncial axon terminals and motoneuron dendrites and cell bodies (located in anterior gray matter). Nerve impulses traversing such arcs produce many spinal reflexes. Example: withdrawing the hand from a hot object.

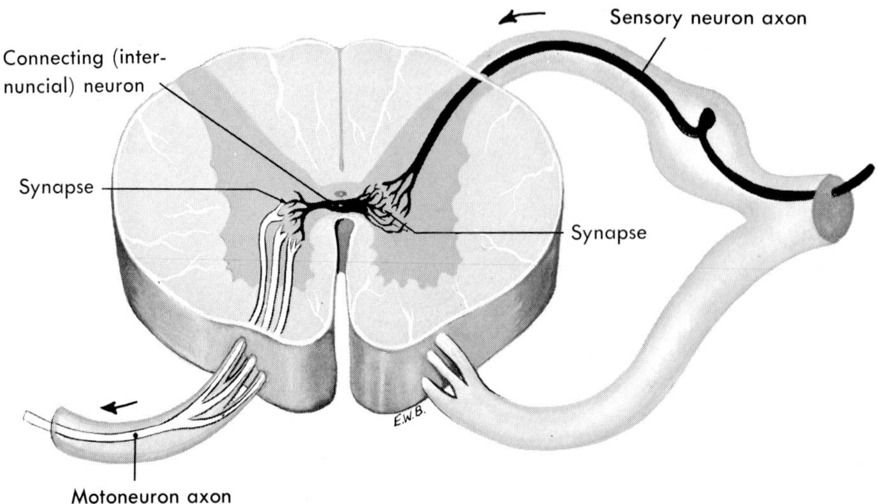

Fig. 124

Contralateral reflex arc. Afferent impulses enter the cord on one side and efferent impulses leave it on the other side. Figs. 122 and 123 show ipsilateral arcs (impulses enter and leave the cord on the same side).

Table 22. Functions served by fibers classified according to diameter of axons

Classification	*Functions of sensory fibers*	*Functions and locations of motor fibers*
A fibers Fibers with large diameter; fastest conducting; about 100 meters per second or more than 3 miles per minute	Proprioception, touch, pressure, some heat, cold, some pain	Skeletal muscle contractions
B fibers Fibers with diameter of intermediate size	Some pain	Preganglionic autonomic
C fibers Fibers with small diameter; slowest conducting; about ½ meter per second or 1 mile per hour	Some pain, perhaps some touch, pressure, heat, cold	Postganglionic autonomic

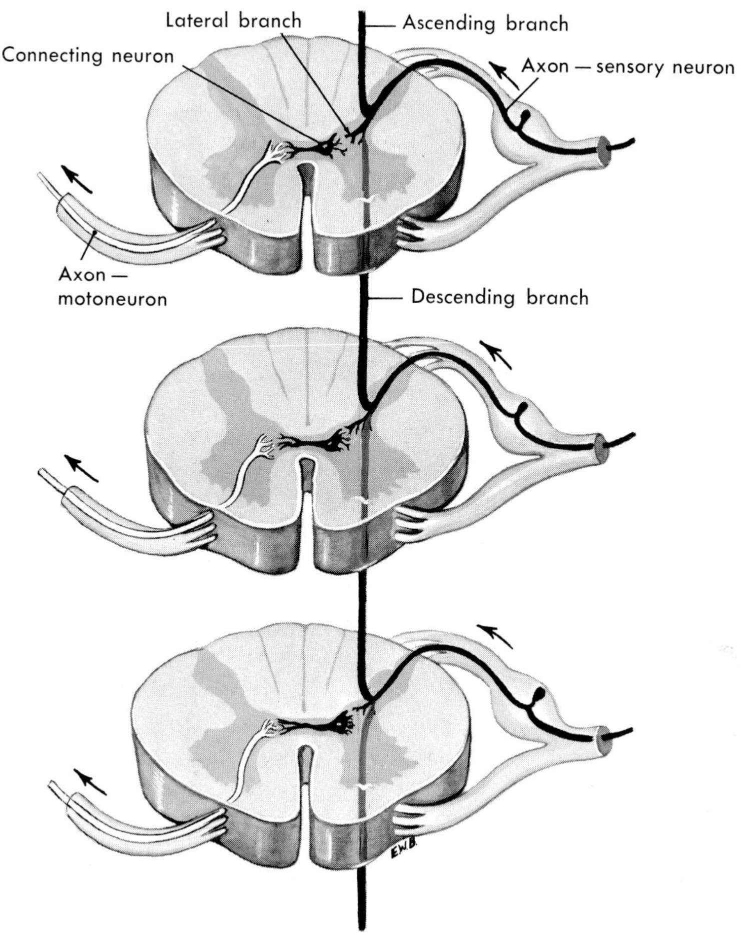

Fig. 125

Intersegmental reflex arcs, showing a sensory fiber splitting into ascending and descending branches that give rise to lateral branches that synapse with their respective connecting neurons. Such arrangements make possible the activation of more than one effector by impulses over a single sensory fiber and account for the phenomenon of divergence.

varies directly with the diameter of an axon—the larger the diameter, the faster the conduction. Fibers with a large diameter are classed as A fibers, those with a small diameter are classed as C fibers, and those with a diameter of intermediate size are classed as B fibers. Read Table 22, in which the functions served by each class of fibers are summarized, and then try to answer this question: What "survival value" do you see in the fastest conducting fibers serving the functions they do?

Conduction across synapses. Many axon filaments terminate in little knobs called *synaptic knobs,* or *end feet,* or *end buttons* (Fig. 126). Each synaptic knob contacts either a dendrite or a cell body of another neuron, and the point of contact constitutes a *synapse.* (Actually there is a space about a millionth of an inch wide, called the *synaptic cleft,* between the synaptic knob and the dendrite or cell body.)

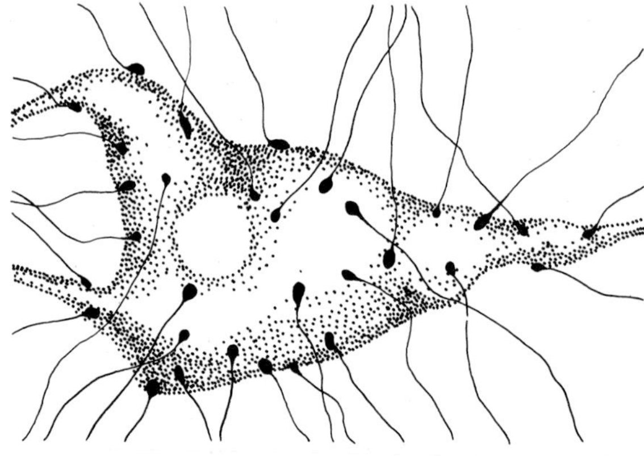

Fig. 126

Synaptic knobs (end feet or end buttons) on motoneuron cell body.

Numerous mitochondria and hundreds of tiny neurovesicles lie crowded together inside each synaptic knob. A *neurovesicle* contains a "transmitter substance," only a few thousand molecules per vesicle.

Once an action potential is initiated, it travels all the way down to the neuron's axon terminals, but there it ends. It does not cross over a synapse to another neuron. Instead, the action potential is generated anew in the next neuron, in the postsynaptic neuron, that is.

How is a nerve impulse generated anew in a postsynaptic neuron? Today's most widely held concept of synaptic conduction states that when the action potential reaches an axon's synaptic knobs, it causes them to eject their transmitter substance into the synaptic cleft. In a flash, the chemical diffuses across this infinitesimal space and contacts the membrane of the postsynaptic neuron. Here it serves as a stimulus and lowers that neuron's membrane potential. The transmitter substance constitutes a threshold stimulus and triggers impulse conduction by the postsynaptic neuron, provided there is enough of it to lower the neuron's membrane potential to its threshold of stimulation level. The latter generally lies somewhere between 10 and 18 mv.* (outside of membrane, positive to inside). The instant the potential reaches this critical level, it then decreases further with explosive rapidity all the way down through 0 to −30 mv. Briefly, then, a threshold amount of transmitter substance causes a postsynaptic neuron's potential to decrease from its resting level of, say, +70 to a threshold level of +18 and then instantaneously to −30 (the action potential or nerve impulse).

A subthreshold amount of transmitter substance also decreases a postsynaptic neuron's resting potential, but not down as far as the critical threshold level. A subthreshold amount of transmitter produces what is called an *excitatory postsynaptic potential* (EPSP), that is, a lowered resting potential in the dendrite and cell body of the postsynaptic neuron. It does not initiate an action potential in this neuron. For example, a subthreshold amount of transmitter substance might decrease a neuron's resting potential from +70 to +60 mv. But this is above the threshold level that triggers off impulse conduction and, therefore, this neuron would be said to be *facilitated,* not stimulated. Its resting potential would have become an excitatory potential but not an action potential. *Acetylcholine* is known to be the excitatory transmitter substance ejected at some synapses, but what it is at others is not known. Within seconds, an enzyme, *cholinesterase,* inactivates acetylcholine, thereby stopping synaptic conduction.

The synaptic knobs of some axons release a transmitter substance that inhibits rather than excites or stimulates postsynaptic neurons. This substance increases the neuron's membrane potential, that is, produces an *inhibitory postsynaptic potential* (IPSP)—about 80 mv., for example. The chemical

*Eccles, Sir John: The synapse, Sci. Amer. **212:** 56 (Jan.), 1965.

identity of the inhibitory transmitter is still not known.

Dozens of synaptic knobs from dozens of different axons synapse with any one postsynaptic neuron. Some of these knobs release excitatory transmitter. Some release inhibitory transmitter. And the algebraic sum of the two opposing chemicals determines their effect on the postsynaptic neuron. Together, they may merely facilitate it, or actually stimulate it, or, just the opposite, inhibit it. (Inhibition and facilitation are discussed further on p. 226.)

Conduction across neuromuscular junctions. Neuromuscular junctions are contact places between a motoneuron's axon terminals and a muscle cell's membrane. Axons of motoneurons release acetylcholine at their junctions with skeletal muscle cells. This initiates impulse conduction along the muscle cell membrane, and contraction follows almost immediately.

Brain and cord coverings

Because the brain and spinal cord are both delicate and vital, nature has provided them with two protective coverings. The outer covering consists of bone: cranial bones encase the brain and vertebrae encase the cord. The inner covering consists of membranes, known as *meninges,* which, in turn, are composed of three distinct layers of tissues (Figs. 127 and 145): the *dura mater,* made of strong white fibrous tissue and serving both as the outer layer of the meninges and also as the inner periosteum of the cranial bones; the *arachnoid membrane,* a delicate, cobwebby layer between the dura mater and the innermost layer of the meninges; and the *pia mater,* which is a transparent layer adherent to the outer surface of the brain and cord and contains blood vessels.

Fig. 127

Meninges of the brain as seen in coronal section through the skull.

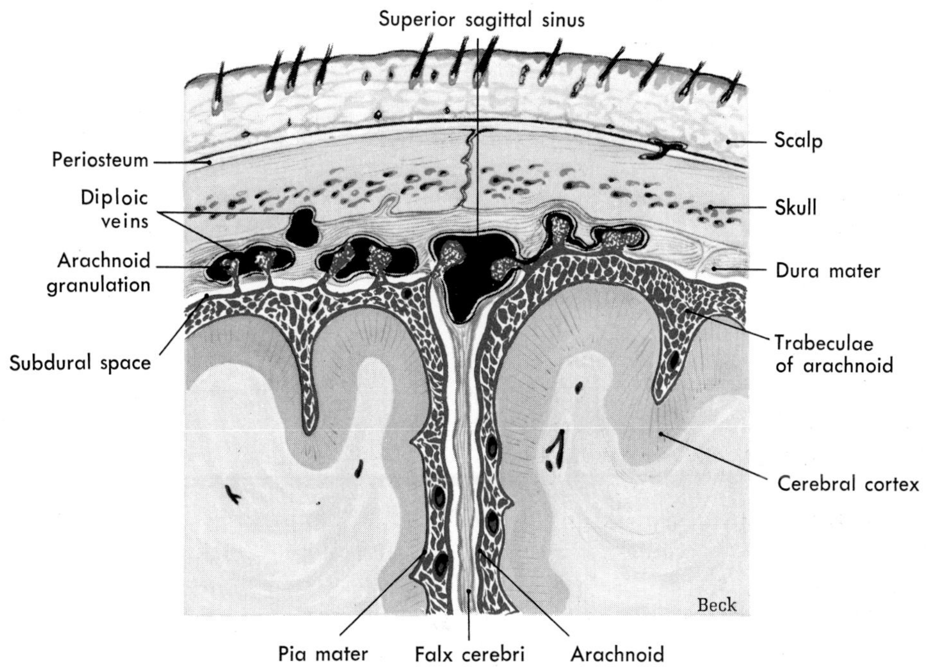

Three extensions of the dura mater should be mentioned: the falx cerebri, falx cerebelli, and tentorium cerebelli. The *falx cerebri* projects downward into the longitudinal fissure to form a kind of partition between the two cerebral hemispheres. The *falx cerebelli* separates the two cerebellar hemispheres. The *tentorium cerebelli* separates the cerebellum from the occipital lobe of the cerebrum. It takes its name from the fact that it forms a tentlike covering over the cerebellum.

Between the dura mater and the arachnoid membrane there is a small space called the *subdural space,* and between the arachnoid and the pia mater is another space, the *subarachnoid space.* Inflammation of the meninges is called *meningitis.* It most often involves the arachnoid and pia mater or the *leptomeninges,* as they are sometimes called.

Brain and cord fluid spaces

In addition to the bony and membranous coverings, nature has further fortified the brain and spinal cord against injury by providing a cushion of fluid both around them and within them. The fluid is called *cerebrospinal fluid,* and the spaces containing it are (1) the subarachnoid space around the brain, (2) the subarachnoid space around the cord, (3) the ventricles and aqueduct inside the brain, and (4) the central or spinal canal inside the cord.

The *ventricles* are cavities or spaces inside the brain. They are four in number. Two of them, the lateral (or first and second) ventricles, are located one in each cerebral hemisphere and are shaped roughly like the hemispheres themselves. The third ventricle is little more than a lengthwise slit in the cerebrum beneath the corpus callosum and longitudinal fissure at about its midpoint. The fourth ventricle is a diamond-shaped space between the cerebellum posteriorly and the medulla and pons anteriorly. Actually it is an expansion of the central canal of the cord after the cord enters the cranial cavity and becomes enlarged to form the medulla. (See Fig. 128.)

Formation and circulation of cerebrospinal fluid

Cerebrospinal fluid is found in each ventricle. It is a clear fluid formed primarily by filtration out of the blood in networks of capillaries known as choroid plexuses. From each lateral ventricle the fluid seeps through an opening, the interventricular foramen (of Munro), into the third ventricle, thence through a narrow channel, the cerebral aqueduct (or aqueduct of Sylvius), into the fourth ventricle, from which it circulates into the central canal of the cord. Openings in the roof of the fourth ventricle (the foramen of Magendie and foramina of Luschka) permit the flow of fluid into the subarachnoid space around the cord and thence into the subarachnoid space around the brain. From the latter space it is gradually absorbed into the venous blood of the brain. Thus cerebrospinal fluid "circulates" from blood in the choroid plexuses, through ventricles, central canal, and subarachnoid spaces, and back into the blood. Occasionally some condition interferes with this circuit. For example, a brain tumor may press against the cerebral aqueduct, shutting off the flow of fluid from the third to the fourth ventricle. In such an event, the fluid accumulates within the lateral and third ventricles because it continues to form even though its drainage is blocked. This condition is known as *internal hydrocephalus.* If the fluid accumulates in the subarachnoid space around the brain, *external hydrocephalus* results. Subarachnoid hemorrhage, for example, may lead to formation of blood clots which block drainage of the cerebrospinal fluid from the subarachnoid space. With de-

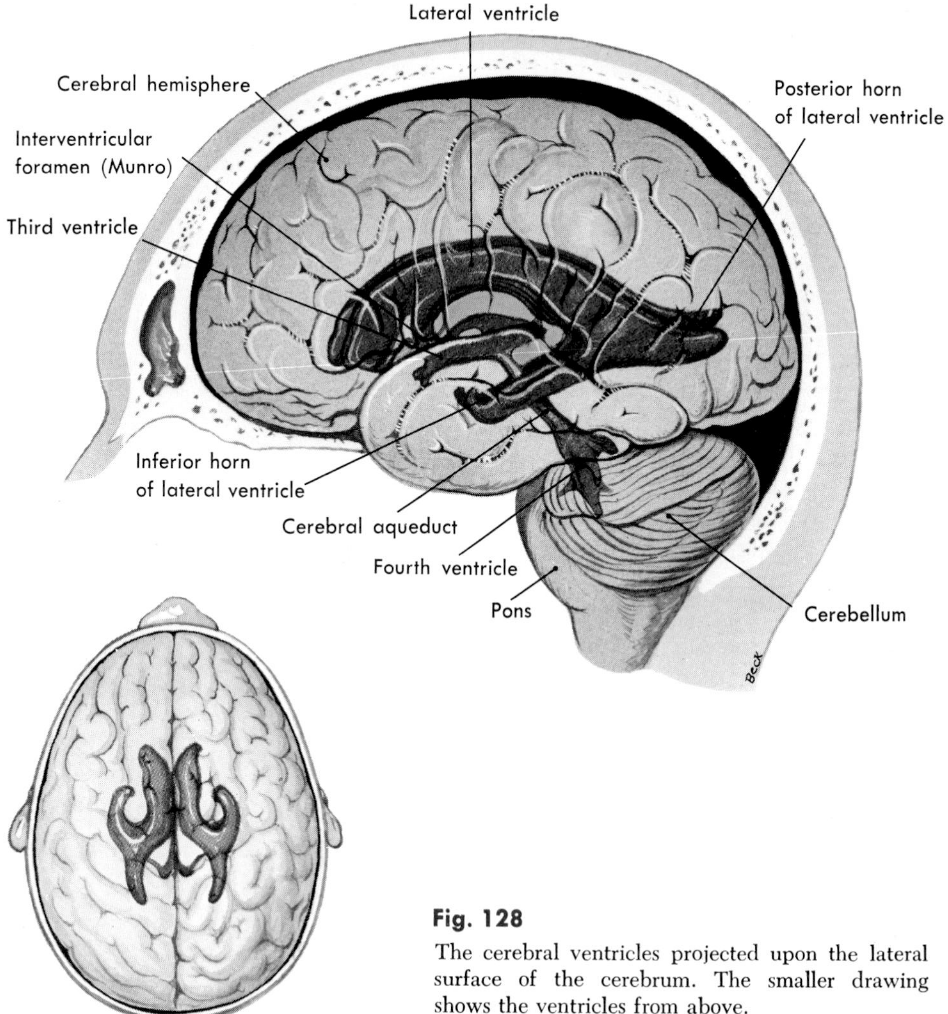

Fig. 128
The cerebral ventricles projected upon the lateral surface of the cerebrum. The smaller drawing shows the ventricles from above.

creased drainage, of course, an increased amount of fluid remains in the space.

Withdrawal of some of the cerebrospinal fluid from the subarachnoid space in the lumbar region of the cord is known as a *lumbar puncture.*

The amount of cerebrospinal fluid in the average man is about 135 ml.* Since approximately 550 ml.* is secreted daily, the fluid must continually circulate and be reabsorbed or excessive amounts will soon accumulate.

*Hamilton, W. J. (editor): Textbook of human anatomy, New York, 1957, The Macmillan Co., p. 805.

Organs

Organs of the nervous system are few in number: the brain, spinal cord, nerves, and ganglia. (By definition, a *nerve* is a cordlike structure composed of bundles of nerve fibers enclosed in a connective tissue sheath, and a *ganglion* is a cluster of neuron cell bodies.) The brain and spinal cord together constitute the central nervous system (CNS). Nerves and ganglia make up the peripheral nervous system (PNS).

BRAIN

The brain is one of the largest of adult organs. In most adults it weighs about 3 pounds but generally is smaller in women than in men and in older persons than in younger persons. It attains full size by about the eighteenth year but grows rapidly only during the first nine years or so.

The three divisions of the embryological neural tube and the major parts of the brain that develop from them are shown schematically in Fig. 129.

Cerebrum

Hemispheres, fissures, and lobes

A deep groove, the *longitudinal fissure,* divides the cerebrum into two halves called hemispheres, which are, however, not completely separated from each other but are joined on their inferior surface by a structure composed of white matter and known as the *corpus callosum.* Prominent fissures, in addition to the longitudinal fissure already named, include the fissure of Rolando and the fissure of Sylvius. The *central sulcus* (the currently preferred name for the fissure of Rolando) forms the boundary line between the frontal and parietal lobes. The fissure of Sylvius separates the temporal lobe below from the frontal and parietal lobes above.

Each cerebral hemisphere is subdivided into five *lobes,* each of which, with one exception, bears the name of the bone lying over it: frontal lobe, parietal lobe, temporal lobe, occipital lobe, and island of Reil (or insula). The latter is located in the fissure of Sylvius.

Cerebral cortex

Each hemisphere of the cerebrum consists of three portions: cerebral cortex, tracts, and basal ganglia. The *cerebral cor-*

Fig. 129

Scheme to show development of the major parts of the brain from three divisions of the embryological neural tube. The names most commonly used are indicated by capital letters.

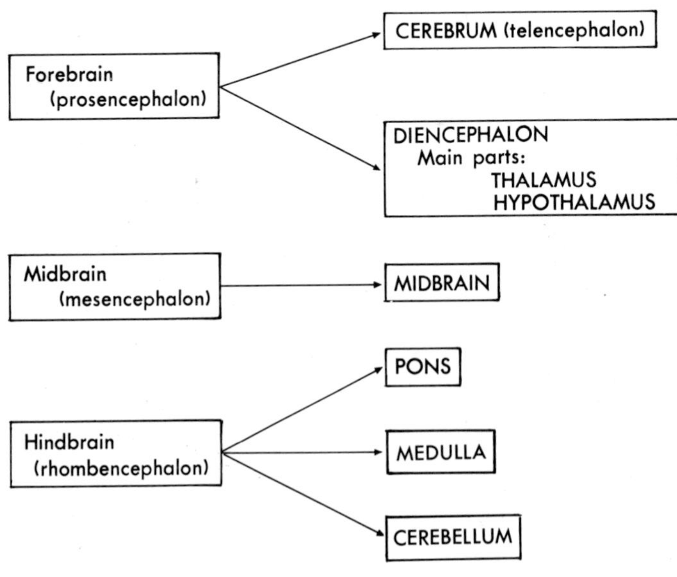

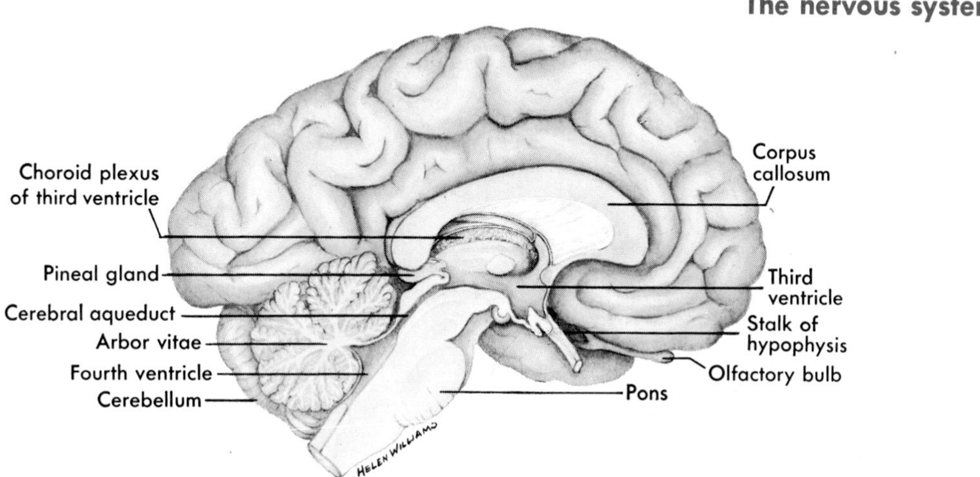

Fig. 130

Sagittal section through the midline of the brain showing the medial surface of the left half of the brain (for more detailed structure, see Fig. 131). (From Francis and Farrell: Integrated anatomy and physiology, St. Louis, The C. V. Mosby Co.)

Fig. 131

Sagittal section of the brain showing structures around the third ventricle.

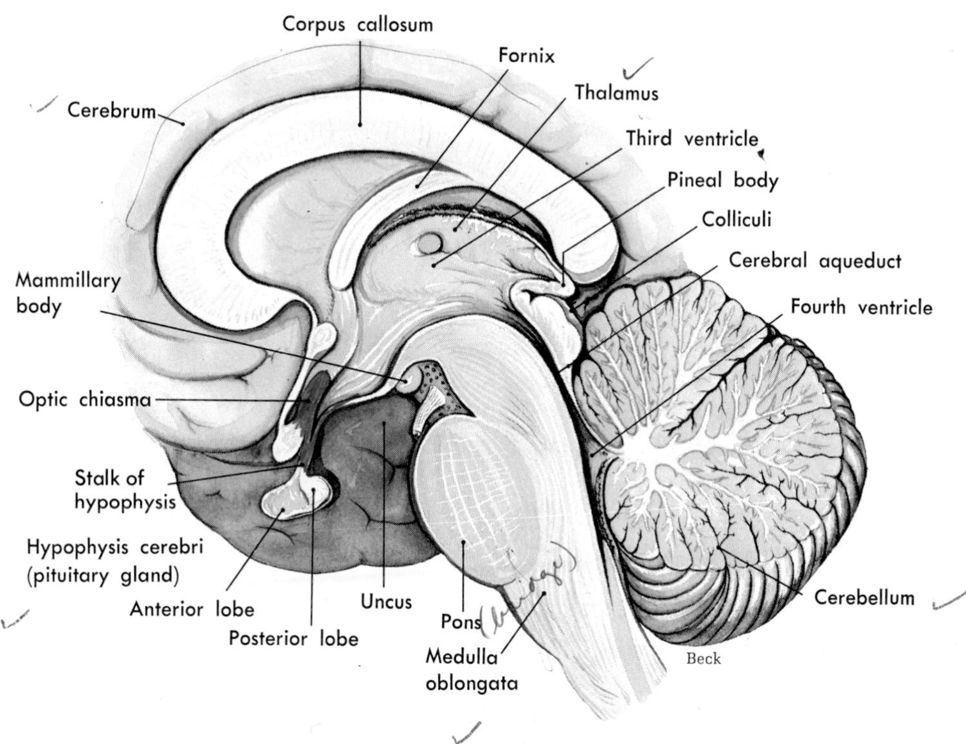

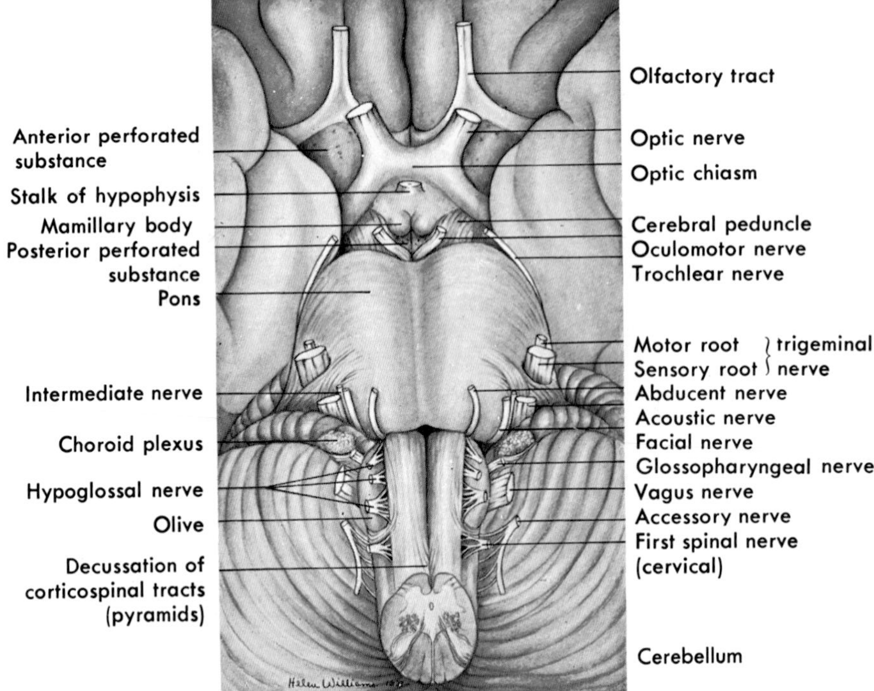

Fig. 132

Inferior or ventral surface of the brain stem showing attachment of the cranial nerves. (From Francis and Farrell: Integrated anatomy and physiology, St. Louis, The C. V. Mosby Co.)

tex is the thin surface layer of the cerebrum. *Gray matter* (that is, mostly neuron dendrites and cell bodies) composes the cortex, whereas *white matter* (mainly myelinated axons) makes up the part of the cerebrum directly underneath the cortex. No doubt, when early anatomists observed the outer darker layer, it reminded them of tree bark, hence their choice of the name cortex, which comes from Latin for bark.

Provided one uses a little imagination, the surface of the cerebrum looks like a group of small sausages. Each "sausage" represents a convolution or *gyrus*. Between adjacent gyri lie shallow grooves called *sulci* or deeper crevices called *fissures*.

Cerebral tracts

Cerebral tracts lie interior to the cortex and are composed of great numbers of nerve fibers (axons). Tracts and nerves are comparable structures. Both consist of bundles of nerve fibers. However, whereas tracts are bundles of axons located in the brain and spinal cord, nerves are bundles of dendrites or axons, or both, located outside the brain and cord.

The first part of a tract's name indicates the location of the dendrites and cell bodies of the neurons whose axons compose the tract. The last part of its name indicates the structure in which the axons terminate. For example, axons making up the corticospinal tract originate from cell bodies in the cerebral cortex and terminate in the spinal cord. In short, a tract's name tells you, in order, from where and to where its fibers conduct impulses. If you apply this

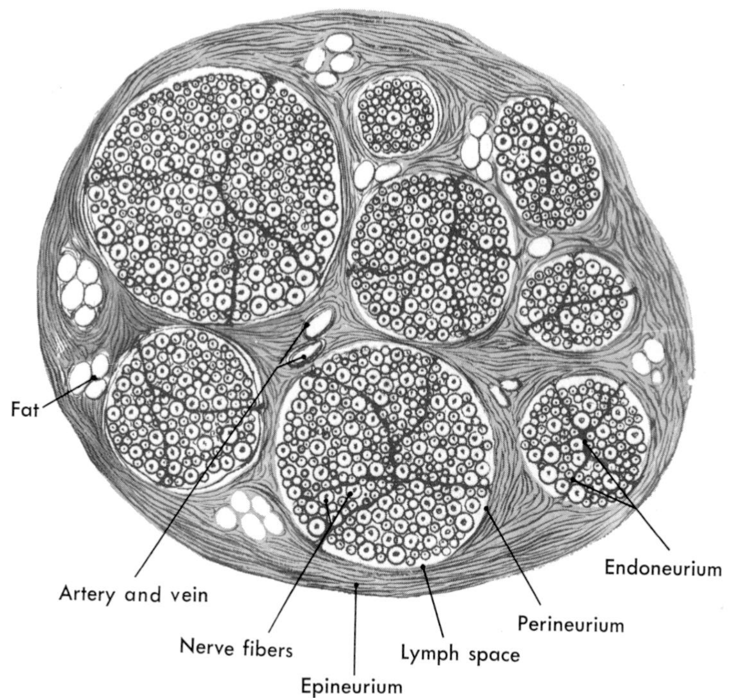

Fig. 133

Cross section of a nerve trunk. The fibers are medulated and are separated by a perineural sheath. The endoneurium is an extension of the perineurium which runs into the interior of the fasciculi.

principle to the spinothalamic tract, where do you deduce its fibers begin and end?

Tracts that conduct impulses upward are called sensory or *ascending projection tracts,* and those that conduct downward are referred to as motor or *descending projection tracts.* In one part of the interior of the cerebrum a group of sensory and motor projection tracts forms a large irregular mass of white matter known as the *internal capsule.* It lies between the thalamus on one side and the caudate and lentiform nuclei on the other (Figs. 146 and 148). Some tracts are short, extending from one convolution to another in the same hemisphere. These are called *association tracts.*

Basal ganglia

Basal ganglia (or cerebral nuclei*) are islands of gray matter deep inside the cerebrum (Fig. 134). Names of the three main basal ganglia are the caudate nucleus, the lentiform nucleus, and the amygdaloid body. The lentiform nucleus has two parts—a larger, more laterally located section named the *putamen,* and a smaller, more medially placed part named the globus pallidus but commonly called the *pallidum.* The caudate nucleus, the lentiform nucleus, and the internal capsule (a band of white fibers located between the caudate and

*When applied to the nervous system, the term *nucleus* means an area of gray matter in the brain or cord (composed mainly, as is all gray matter, of neuron cell bodies and dendrites). Such a cluster located outside the brain and cord is called a *ganglion.* So cerebral nuclei is a more accurate (but less common) name than basal ganglia.

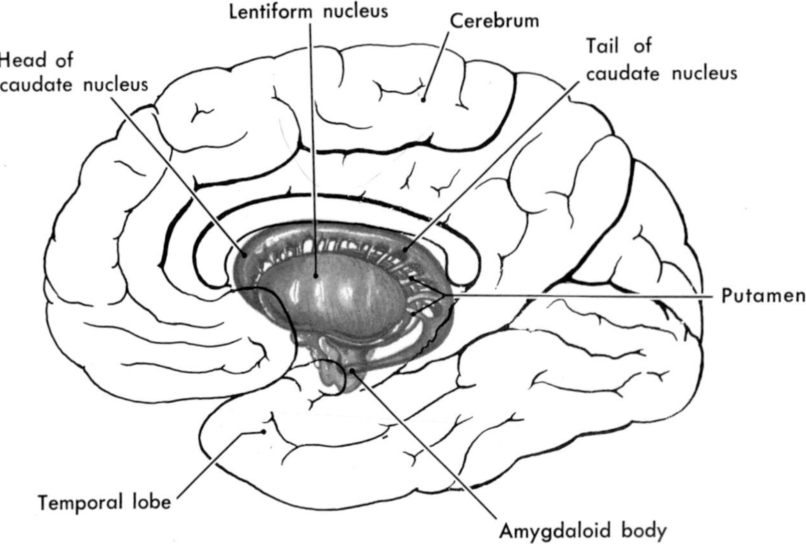

Fig. 134

Basal ganglia (caudate, lentiform, and amygdaloid) within a cerebral hemisphere. The claustrum is not shown.

lentiform nuclei) together compose the *corpus striatum*. As its name suggests, this region has a striped appearance. The stripes are narrow strips of gray matter that extend across the white internal capsule between the caudate and lentiform nuclei. Basal ganglia play an essential role in producing movements (see pp. 223 to 227).

Functions

Knowledge of cerebral function has accumulated in various ways: by studying symptoms of patients known to have brain lesions, by studying the effects of removing or destroying various cerebral areas in animals, by stimulating various cerebral areas in animals and human beings and recording results, and, more recently, by studying brain action potentials as recorded on electroencephalograms (EEG's). Another approach to investigating cerebral function has been to study the microscopic structure of the cerebrum. It was discovered, for example, that several layers of neurons and neuroglia compose the cerebral cortex and that the number of layers and type and arrangement of cells differ in different areas. These findings led to the postulate that different areas of the cortex perform different functions—that cortical functions, in other words, are localized in different cortical areas. The current view differs somewhat. It holds that not one but many cortical areas take part in the performance of probably all cerebral functions. But, as we shall see, certain areas apparently do play a major role in the carrying out of certain functions.

What functions does the cerebral cortex perform? A concise, general answer is this: the cerebral cortex performs all mental functions and many essential motor, sensory, and visceral functions. For example, conduction by cortical neurons occurs when we remember or imagine anything, when we experience sensations or emotions of any kind, and when we will to make any movements. Conduction by certain cortical neurons may even lead to visceral changes such as dilatation or constriction of facial blood vessels (blushing with embarrassment or turning pale with fear). Data presently available suggest that it is neurons in the frontal and temporal lobes that somehow produce our memories and our feelings of emotion. Neurons in the frontal lobe (precentral gyrus) initiate our willed movements, those in the parietal lobe (postcentral gyrus) are responsible for our general sensations, and those in certain gyri of the temporal and occipital lobes are responsible for our special senses of hearing, smelling, and vision. Neurons in widely scattered areas of the cortex perform visceral functions.

Sensations. Complex nervous mechanisms function to produce our sensations. Many gross structures are involved—nerves, ganglia, cord, medulla, pons, midbrain, thalamus, and cerebral cortex. Complex discriminative sensations depend upon the cerebral cortex, especially the *somesthetic area* or general sensory area and the visual and auditory areas (Fig. 135). These regions of the cortex do more than just register separate and simple sensations. They compare them and evaluate them. They integrate them into meaningful concepts. Suppose, for example, that someone blindfolded you and then put an ice cube in your hand. You would, of course, sense something cold touching your hand. But also, you would probably know that it was an ice cube because you would sense a total impression compounded of many sensations such as temperature, shape, size, weight, texture, and movement and position of body parts.

Note the following locations in Fig. 135:

1. General or *somesthetic sensory area* —parietal lobe, postcentral gyrus (areas 3, 1, 2)
2. *Primary auditory area*—temporal lobe, transverse gyrus along the fissure of Sylvius (areas 41, 42)
3. *Primary visual area*—occipital lobe (area 17)
4. *Primary olfactory area*—not precisely located but in temporal lobe (ventral or undersurface)
5. *Primary gustatory (taste) area*—not precisely located; good evidence that parietal lobe (lower part of postcentral convolution) is one taste area

Voluntary movements. Mechanisms that control voluntary movements are extremely complex and are imperfectly understood. Many parts of the nervous system are involved, and certain areas of the cerebral cortex play an essential part in the production of normal movements. The precentral or pre-Rolandic gyrus (that is, the most posterior gyrus of the frontal lobe; area 4, Fig. 135) constitutes the *primary motor area.* However, the gyrus immediately anterior to the precentral gyrus contains motor neurons. So, too, do many other regions, including even the somatic sensory area. Neurons in the precentral gyrus are said to exert control over individual muscles, especially those that produce movements of distal joints (wrist, hand, finger, ankle, foot, and toe movements). Neurons in the gyrus just anterior to the precentral gyrus, on the other hand, are thought to activate groups of muscles simultaneously.

Mental functions. Included in the category of mental functions are many diverse functions such as memory, foresight, emotional feelings, personality traits, speech functions, and intelligence. These and other mental and psychic functions depend more on widespread cortical activity than on localized regions. Memory, for example, once considered a function of the temporal lobes, now is viewed as a complex neural process dependent on many parts. Visual memories, stored (in some as yet unknown manner) in the occipital lobe, auditory memories in the temporal lobe, and general sensory experiences in the parietal lobe are all linked together and synthesized into complex memories by numerous association tracts between lobes. Foresight and personality traits depend largely on the prefrontal lobes. Evidence of this lies in the changes observed in patients who have undergone a

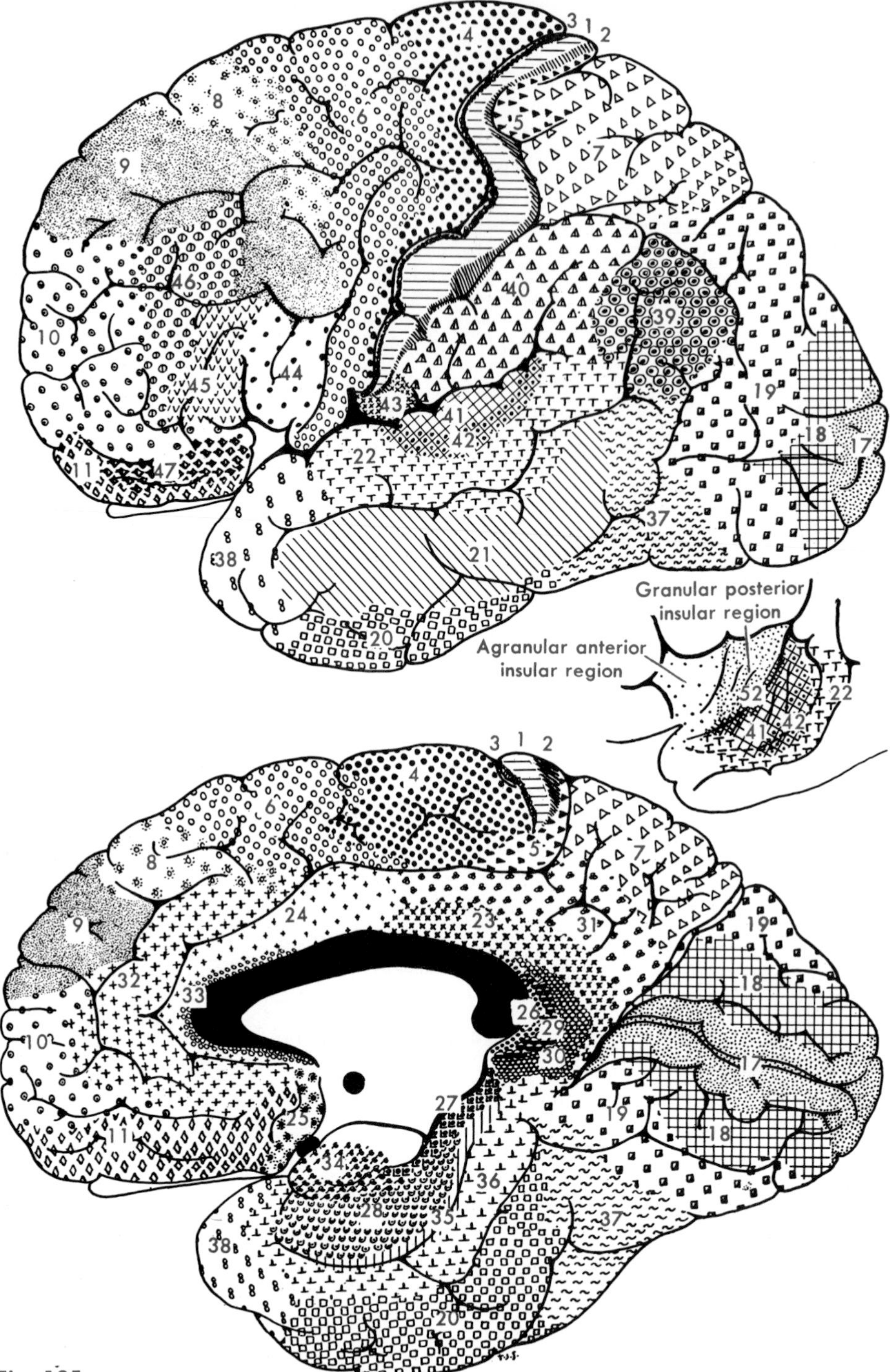

Fig. 135

Map of human cortex according to Brodmann. Each numbered area shows different cellular structure. Some areas whose functions are best understood are the following: areas 3, 1, and 2, general somatic sensory area; area 17, primary visual area; areas 18 and 19, secondary visual areas; areas 41 and 42, primary auditory areas; area 22, secondary auditory area; area 4, primary motor area; area 6, secondary motor area. Area 44 and part of area 45 constitute the approximate location of Broca's motor speech area. (From Mettler: Neuroanatomy, St. Louis, The C. V. Mosby Co.)

prefrontal lobectomy. Most noticeable are their loss of initiative and planning ability and their lack of restraint. A housewife might, for example, become almost unable to plan a simple meal. And probably she would become boastful and aggressive—personality changes indicative of a decreased ability to restrain behavior.

Speech functions consist of the use of language (speaking and writing) and the understanding of language (spoken and written). Today these faculties are believed to depend on highly integrated cortical processes, with certain areas in the frontal, parietal, and temporal lobes called speech centers serving as the focal points for integration. Lesions in different ones of these areas are associated with different types of speech defects or *aphasias.* For example, with a lesion in *Broca's motor speech area* in the frontal lobe, the individual becomes unable to express his ideas in spoken words although he is not actually unable to speak. This condition is known as *motor aphasia.* With a lesion in the parietal lobe speech center, on the other hand, the individual has trouble finding the right names for things.

Diencephalon—thalamus, epithalamus, subthalamus, and hypothalamus

The diencephalon is the part of the brain located between the cerebrum and the midbrain. It consists of structures around the third ventricle: the thalamus, epithalamus, subthalamus, and hypothalamus. We shall confine our discussion to the thalamus and hypothalamus.

Thalamus

Structure and location

The right thalamus is a rounded mass of gray matter about ½ inch wide and 1½ inches long, bulging into the right lateral wall of the third ventricle. The left thalamus is a similar mass in the left lateral wall. Each thalamus consists of numerous nuclei. One of these, for example, is called the posterior ventral nucleus. Here, axons of the spinothalamic tracts terminate and synapse with neurons whose axons extend in thalamocortical tracts to the general sensory area of the cerebral cortex. Thus, this nucleus serves as a relay station for sensory impulses. In another nucleus of the thalamus, impulses from basal ganglia are relayed to the motor area of the cerebral cortex, and, vice versa, impulses from the motor area are relayed to basal ganglia. Still other thalamic nuclei relay impulses from the hypothalamus to various areas of the cortex and from these areas to the hypothalamus.

Functions

The thalamus performs the following functions:

1. It plays two parts in the mechanism responsible for sensations:

(a) It produces conscious recognition of the cruder, less critical sensations of pain, temperature, and touch.

(b) It relays all kinds of sensory impulses, except possibly olfactory, to the cerebrum.

2. It plays a part in the mechanism responsible for emotions by associating sensory impulses with feelings of pleasantness and unpleasantness.

3. It plays a part in the arousal or alerting mechanism.

4. It plays a part in mechanisms that produce complex reflex movements.

Hypothalamus

Structure and location

The hypothalamus consists of several structures which form the floor and the lower part of the sidewall of the third ventricle (Fig. 131). More specifically, the anterior part of the hypothalamus consists of gray matter around the optic chiasma. The supraoptic nuclei are located in the anterior hypothalamus, just above and on either side of the optic chiasma. The midportion of the hypothalamus consists of the stalk of the pituitary gland and the posterior lobe of the pituitary gland (neurohypophysis). The medial part of the hypothalamus contains the paraventricular nuclei, so-called because of their location close to the wall of the third ventricle. The posterior part of the hypothalamus consists mainly of the mamillary bodies (Fig. 132), in which are located the mamillary nuclei.

Tracts connect the hypothalamus with various parts of the central nervous system. Some are afferent (conduct impulses into the hypothalamus) and others are efferent (conduct impulses away from it). Some have actually been traced and therefore are known to exist. Others are inferred from laboratory and clinical findings. For example, the hypothalamus receives impulses via tracts from the cerebral cortex, the thalamus, and basal ganglia. It sends impulses out over other tracts to many structures, notably to the following: to parasympathetic centers in the brainstem and sacral segments of the cord, to sympathetic centers in the thoracic and lumbar segments of the cord (Fig. 152), and to the neurohypophysis. Neurons whose dendrites and cell bodies lie in the parasympathetic and sympathetic centers in the brainstem and spinal cord send out impulses that eventually reach visceral effectors, namely, cardiac muscle, smooth muscle (in blood vessels, digestive tract, etc.), and glands.

Functions

The hypothalamus is a small but functionally mighty area of the brain. It weighs little more than a quarter of an ounce, yet it performs many functions of the greatest importance both for survival and for the enjoyment of life. For instance, it functions as a link between the psyche (mind) and the soma (body). It also links the nervous system to the endocrine system. And if indications of recent experiments prove true, certain areas of the hypothalamus function as pleasure centers or reward centers for the primary drives such as eating, drinking, and mating. The following paragraphs give a brief summary of hypothalamic functions:

1. The hypothalamus functions as a higher autonomic center or, rather, as several higher autonomic centers. By this we mean that it sends impulses to lower autonomic centers. Tracts extend from the hypothalamus to both parasympathetic and sympathetic centers in the brainstem and cord. Thus impulses from the hypothalamus can simultaneously or successively stimulate or inhibit few or many lower autonomic centers. In other words, the hypothalamus serves as a regulator and coordinator of autonomic activities. It helps control and integrate the responses made by visceral effectors all over the body.

2. The hypothalamus functions as the major relay station between the cerebral cortex and lower autonomic centers. Tracts conduct impulses from various centers in the cortex to the hypothalamus. Then, via numerous synapses in the hypothalamus, these impulses are relayed to other tracts that conduct them on down to autonomic centers in the brainstem and cord and also to spinal cord somatic centers (anterior horn motor neurons). In short, the hypothalamus is the link between the cerebral cortex and lower centers—hence, between the psyche and the soma. It provides a crucial part of the route by which emotions can express themselves in changed bodily functions. It is the all-important relay station in the neural pathways which make possible the mind's influence over the body—sometimes, unfortunately, even to the profound degree of producing "psychosomatic disease."

3. Neurons in the supraoptic and paraventricular nuclei of the hypothalamus synthesize the hormones secreted by the pos-

terior pituitary gland. They also help regulate the rate at which the posterior pituitary gland secretes these hormones. Therefore, the hypothalamus plays an essential role in maintaining water balance (see Fig. 329, p. 534).

4. The hypothalamus functions as an important part of the mechanism for controlling hormone secretion by the anterior pituitary gland—hence it helps control the functioning of every cell in the body (see pp. 498 to 500).

5. The hypothalamus plays an essential role in maintaining the waking state. Presumably it functions as part of an arousal or alerting mechanism (p. 222). Clinical evidence of this is that somnolence characterizes some hypothalamic disorders.

6. The hypothalamus functions as a crucial part of the mechanism for regulating appetite and therefore the amount of food intake. Experimental and clinical findings seem to indicate the presence of a "feeding or appetite center" in the lateral part of the hypothalamus and a "satiety center" located medially. For example, an animal with an experimental lesion in the ventromedial nucleus of the hypothalamus will consume tremendous amounts of food. Similarly, a human being with a tumor in this region of the hypothalamus may eat insatiably and gain an enormous amount of weight.

7. The hypothalamus probably helps control various reproductive functions (see pp. 498 to 500).

8. The hypothalamus functions as a crucial part of the mechanism for maintaining normal body temperature. Hypothalamic neurons whose fibers connect with autonomic centers for vasoconstriction and dilatation and sweating and with somatic centers for shivering constitute heat-regulating centers. Marked elevation of body temperature frequently characterizes injuries or other abnormalities of the hypothalamus.

Cerebellum

Structure and location

The cerebellum, the second largest part of the brain, is located just below the posterior portion of the cerebrum and is partially covered by it. A transverse fissure separates the cerebellum from the cerebrum. These two parts of the brain have several characteristics in common. The exterior of the cerebellum is composed of gray matter and its interior of white matter, although there is proportionately less white matter in the cerebellum, where it follows a pattern similar to the veins of a leaf, described as the *arbor vitae*. Like the cerebrum, the cerebellar surface is grooved with numerous sulci, but its convolutions are much more slender and less prominent than those of the cerebrum. The cerebellum has two large lateral masses, the cerebellar hemispheres, and a central section called the vermis because in shape it resembles a worm coiled upon itself. (For a detailed description of the several subdivisions of the cerebellum, consult a textbook on neuroanatomy.)

The internal white matter of the cerebellum is composed of some short and some long tracts. The short association tracts connect the cerebellar cortex with nuclei located in the interior of the cerebellum. The longer projection tracts connect the cerebellum with other parts of the brain and with the spinal cord. These enter or leave the cerebellum by way of its three pairs of peduncles as follows:

1. *inferior cerebellar peduncles* (or *restiform bodies*)—composed chiefly of tracts into the cerebellum from the medulla and cord (notably, spinocerebellar, vestibulocerebellar, and reticulocerebellar tracts)
2. *middle cerebellar peduncles* (or *brachia pontis*)—composed almost entirely of tracts into the cerebellum from the pons (that is, pontocerebellar tracts)

3. *superior cerebellar peduncles* (or *brachia conjunctivum cerebelli*)—composed principally of tracts from dentate nuclei through the red nucleus of the midbrain to the thalamus.

An important pair of cerebellar nuclei are the *dentate nuclei,* one of which lies in each hemisphere. Tracts connect these nuclei with motor areas of the cerebral cortex (the dentatorubrothalamic tracts to the thalamus and thalamocortical tracts to the cortex). By means of these tracts, cerebellar impulses influence the motor cortex. Impulses also travel the reverse direction. Corticopontine and pontocerebellar tracts enable the motor cortex to influence the cerebellum.

Functions

The cerebellum performs three general functions, all of which have to do with the control of skeletal muscles. It acts with the cerebral cortex to produce skilled movements by coordinating the activities of groups of muscles. It controls skeletal muscles so as to maintain equilibrium. It helps control posture. It functions below the level of consciousness to make movements smooth instead of jerky, steady instead of trembling, and efficient and coordinated instead of ineffective, awkward, and uncoordinated (asynergic).

There have been many theories about cerebellar functions. One theory, based on comparative anatomy studies and substantiated by experimental methods, regards the cerebellum as three organs, each with a somewhat different function: synergic control of muscle action, excitation and inhibition of postural reflexes, and maintenance of equilibrium.

Synergic control of muscle action. Synergic control of muscle action, which is ascribed to the neocerebellum (superior vermis and hemispheres), is closely associated with cerebral motor activity. Normal muscle action, it is known, involves groups of muscles, the various members of which function together as a unit. In any given action, for example, the prime mover contracts, the antagonist relaxes but contracts weakly at the proper moment to act as a brake, checking the action of the prime mover, the synergists contract to assist the prime mover, and the fixation muscles of the neighboring joint contract. Through such harmonious coordinated group action normal movements are smooth, steady, and precise as to force, rate, and extent. Achievement of such movements results from cerebellar activity added to cerebral activity. Impulses from the cerebrum start the action, but those from the cerebellum synergize or coordinate the contractions and relaxations of the various muscles once they have begun. Some physiologists consider this the main, if not the sole, function of the cerebellum.

Postural reflexes. One part of the cerebellum is thought to be concerned with both exciting and inhibiting postural reflexes.

Equilibrium. Part of the cerebellum presumably discharges impulses important to the maintenance of equilibrium. Afferent impulses from the labyrinth of the ear reach the cerebellum. Here connections are made with the proper efferent fibers for contraction of the necessary muscles for equilibrium.

Cerebellar disease (abscess, hemorrhage, tumors, trauma, etc.) produces certain characteristic symptoms, among which asynergia, hypotonia, tremors, and disturbances of gait and equilibrium predominate. As examples of asynergia may be mentioned overshooting a mark or stopping before reaching it when asked to touch a given point on the body (finger-to-nose test) and drawling, scanning, or singsong speech because of asynergic action of phonation and articulation muscles. Tremors are particularly pronounced toward the end of movements and with the exertion of effort. Disturbances of gait and equilibrium vary, depending upon the muscle groups involved, but the walk is often characterized by staggering or lurching and by a clumsy manner of raising the foot too high and bringing it down with a clap. Paralysis does not result from loss of cerebellar function.

Medulla oblongata

Structure and location

The medulla or bulb is the part of the brain that attaches to the spinal cord. It is, in fact, an enlarged extension of the cord located just above the foramen magnum. It measures only slightly more than an inch in length and is separated from the pons above by a horizontal groove. It is composed mainly of white matter (projection tracts) and *reticular formation,* a term that means the interlacement of gray and white matter present in the cord, brainstem, and diencephalon. Nuclei in the reticular formation of the medulla include such important centers as respiratory and vasomotor centers.

On each side of the lower posterior part of the medulla are two prominent nuclei, the *nucleus gracilis* and the *nucleus cuneatus.* Here, afferent fibers from the posterior white columns (fasciculi gracilis and cuneatus) of the cord synapse with neurons whose axons extend to the thalamus and cerebellum.

The pyramids (Fig. 132) are two bulges of white matter located on the anterior surface of the medulla formed by fibers of the pyramidal projection tracts.

The olive (Fig. 132) is an oval projection appearing one on each side of the anterior surface of the medulla. It contains the *inferior olivary nucleus* and two accessory olivary nuclei. Fibers from the cells of these nuclei run through the inferior cerebellar peduncles (restiform bodies) into the cerebellum. Nuclei of the ninth to the twelfth cranial nerve are also located in the medulla.

Functions

Nuclei in the medulla contain a number of reflex centers. Some of these perform functions so necessary for survival that they are called the *vital centers.* They are the cardiac, vasomotor, and respiratory centers. As their names suggest, they serve as the centers for various reflexes controlling heart action, blood vessel diameter, and respirations. Because the medulla contains these centers, it is the most vital part of the entire brain—so vital, in fact, that injury or disease of the medulla often proves fatal. Blows at the base of the skull and bulbar poliomyelitis, for example, cause death if they interrupt impulse conduction by the vital respiratory centers.

The medulla functions in many nonvital reflexes. For example, it contains centers for vomiting, coughing, sneezing, hiccoughing, and swallowing.

All projection tracts between the cord and brain necessarily pass through the medulla. Hence it functions in a great many sensory and motor mechanisms. Fibers of the crossed corticospinal tracts decussate, that is, cross from one side to the other in the pyramids of the medulla—an anatomical fact that explains why one side of the brain is said to control the other side of the body.

Pons varolii

Structure and location

Just above the medulla lies the pons, composed like the medulla of white matter and a few nuclei. Fibers that run transversely across the pons and through the brachia pontis (middle cerebellar peduncles) into the cerebellum make up the external white matter of the pons and give it its bridgelike appearance. The reticular formation extends into the pons from the medulla. One important reticular nucleus in the pons is called the *pneumotaxic center.* It functions in the control of respirations. Nuclei of the fifth to eighth cranial nerve are located in the upper part of the pons.

Functions

For functions of the pons varolii, see below under the heading midbrain.

Midbrain

Structure and location

The midbrain lies below the inferior surface of the cerebrum and above the pons. It consists mainly of white matter with some internal gray matter around the cerebral aqueduct, the cavity within the midbrain. The *cerebral peduncles* form the ventral part of the midbrain, and the corpora *quadrigemina* or *colliculi* form the dorsal part. The cerebral peduncles are two ropelike masses of white matter that extend divergently from the pons to the undersurface of the cerebral hemispheres (Fig. 132). In other words, the cerebral peduncles are made up of tracts that constitute the main connection between the forebrain and hindbrain. Hence the midbrain, by function as well as by location, is well named.

The *corpora quadrigemina* consist of four rounded eminences, the two superior and the two inferior colliculi (Fig. 131) which form the dorsal part of the midbrain. Certain auditory reflex centers lie in the inferior colliculi and visual centers in the superior colliculi.

An important nucleus in the midbrain reticular formation is the *red nucleus,* a large gray mass ventral to the superior colliculi. Fibers from the cerebellum and from the frontal lobe of the cerebral cortex end here, whereas fibers that extend into the rubrospinal tracts of the cord have their cells of origin here. Nuclei of the third and fourth cranial nerves and the anterior part of the nucleus of the fifth cranial nerve are located deep in the midbrain. Also, as mentioned in the preceding paragraph, nuclei for certain auditory and visual reflexes lie in the colliculi of the midbrain.

Functions of pons and midbrain

The upper part of the brainstem serves as conduction pathways (projection tracts) between the cord and other parts of the brain. In addition, the pons functions as the reflex center for reflexes mediated by the fifth, sixth, seventh, and eighth cranial nerves (see Table 25 for functions). And because the pons contains the pneumotaxic centers, it helps regulate respirations (discussed on p. 369).

Like the pons, the midbrain also functions as a reflex center for certain cranial nerve reflexes—for example, pupillary reflexes and eye movements, mediated by the third and fourth cranial nerves, respectively.

SPINAL CORD

Location

The spinal cord lies within the spinal cavity, extending from the foramen magnum to the lower border of the first lumbar vertebra, a distance of 17 or 18 inches in the average body. The meninges of the cord, however, continue on down for some distance. The pia mater forms a slender filament known as the *filum terminale,* which blends with the dura mater at the level of the third segment of the sacrum, forming a fibrous cord that disappears in the periosteum of the coccyx. This extension of the meninges beyond the cord is an anatomical feature of great convenience in performing lumbar punctures. By inserting the needle between the third and fourth or fourth and fifth lumbar vertebrae into the subarachnoid space, cerebrospinal fluid can be withdrawn without danger of injuring the spinal cord, which ends more than an inch above that point. The fourth lumbar vertebra is easily located because it lies on a line with the iliac crest. Placing the patient on his side and arching his back by drawing the knees and chest together separates the vertebra sufficiently to introduce the needle. The cord does not completely fill the spinal cavity, which also contains the meninges, spinal fluid, a cushion of adipose tissue, and blood vessels.

Structure

The spinal cord is an oval-shaped cylinder which tapers slightly from above downward and has two bulges, one in the cervical region and the other in the lumbar region. Gray matter, shaped roughly like a three-dimensional letter H, composes the inner core of the cord, that is, the anterior, posterior, and lateral columns or horns of gray matter. Six lengthwise grooves divide the white matter into long columns. The deepest of these grooves, the *anterior median fissure,* together with the somewhat shallower *posterior median sulcus,* just misses dividing the cord into separate symmetrical halves. The anterolateral sulcus and posterolateral sulcus subdivide each half of the cord into three *columns* (or funiculi): the anterior, posterior, and lateral white columns. These consist of large bundles of nerve fibers arranged in tracts.

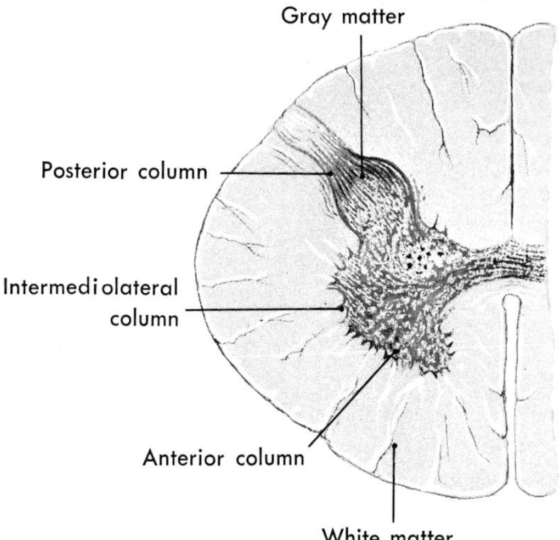

Fig. 136

Distribution of gray and white matter in a section of the spinal cord at the thoracic level.

Fig. 137

Location in the spinal cord of some major projection tracts. Black areas, motor tracts. Shaded areas, sensory tracts. Also refer to Tables 23 and 24.

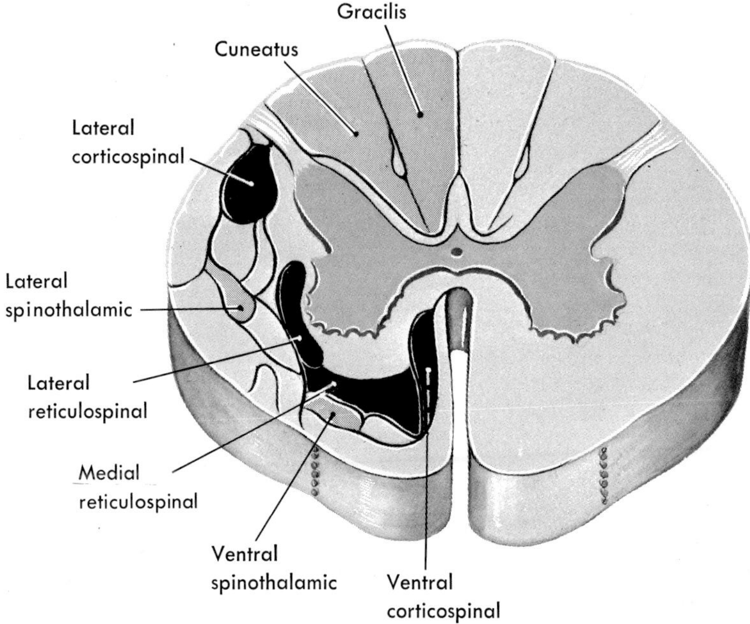

Table 23. Major ascending tracts of spinal cord

Name	*Function*	*Location*	*Origin**	*Termination†*
Lateral spinothalamic	Pain, temperature opposite side	Lateral white columns	Posterior gray column opposite side	Thalamus
Ventral spinothalamic	Crude touch	Anterior white columns	Same	Same
Fasciculus gracilis and cuneatus	Conscious kinesthesia, sensations of vibration, stereognosis, deep touch and pressure, two-point discrimination	Posterior white columns	Spinal ganglia same side	Medulla
Spinocerebellar	Unconscious kinesthesia	Lateral white columns	Posterior gray column	Cerebellum

*Location of cell bodies of neurons from which axons of tract arise.
†Structure in which axons of tract terminate.

Table 24. Major descending tracts of spinal cord

Name	*Function*	*Location*	*Origin**	*Termination†*
Lateral corticospinal (or crossed pyramidal)	Voluntary movement, contraction of individual or small groups of muscles, particularly those moving hands, fingers, feet, and toes of opposite side	Lateral white columns	Motor areas cerebral cortex (mainly areas 4 and 6) opposite side from tract location in cord	Intermediate or anterior gray column
Ventral corticospinal (direct pyramidal)	Same as lateral corticospinal except mainly muscles of same side	Same as lateral corticospinal	Motor cortex but on same side as tract location in cord	Same as lateral corticospinal
Lateral reticulospinal	Mainly facilitatory influence on motoneurons to skeletal muscles	Lateral white columns	Reticular formation midbrain, pons, and medulla	Intermediate or anterior gray columns
Medial reticulospinal	Mainly inhibitory influence on motoneurons to skeletal muscles	Anterior white columns	Reticular formation medulla mainly	Intermediate or anterior gray columns

*Location of cell bodies of neurons from which axons of tract arise.
†Structure in which axons of tract terminate.

Important tracts of each white column are given in Tables 23 and 24; also refer to Fig. 137.

Functions

The spinal cord performs sensory, motor, and reflex functions. The following paragraphs describe these functions briefly.

Sensory and motor functions. Spinal cord tracts serve as two-way conduction paths between peripheral nerves and the brain. Both ascending and descending tracts compose the white matter of the cord. Tracts are structural organizations—that is, they are made up of groups of axons, all of which originate in the same structure and terminate in the same structure. For example, all fibers of the spinothalamic tract are axons which originate from neuron cell bodies located in the spinal cord and terminate in the thalamus. But tracts are also functional organizations. Any one tract is a group of fibers that serves one general function. For instance, fibers of the lateral spinothalamic tract serve a sensory function. They transmit the impulses that produce our sensations of pain and of temperature.

Because so many different tracts make up the white columns of the cord, we shall mention only a few that seem most important in man. Locate each tract in Fig. 137. Table 23 and Table 24 include more information about tracts. Four important ascending or sensory tracts and their functions, stated very briefly, are as follows:

1. *lateral spinothalamic tracts*—pain and temperature
2. *ventral spinothalamic tracts*—crude touch
3. *fasciculi gracilis and cuneatus*—discriminating touch and conscious kinesthesia
4. *spinocerebellar tracts* — unconscious kinesthesia

Further discussion of the sensory neural pathways may be found on pp. 218 to 222.

Four important descending or motor tracts and their functions in brief are as follows:

1. *lateral corticospinal tracts*—voluntary movement; contraction of individual or small groups of muscles, particularly those moving hands, fingers, feet, and toes on opposite side of body
2. *ventral corticospinal tracts*—same as preceding except mainly muscles of same side of body
3. *lateral reticulospinal tracts*—mainly facilitatory impulses to anterior horn motoneurons to skeletal muscles
4. *medial reticulospinal tracts*—mainly inhibitory impulses to anterior horn motoneurons to skeletal muscles

Further discussion of the motor neural pathways may be found on pp. 222 to 228.

Reflex functions. The spinal cord functions in all reflexes except those mediated by cranial nerves. Gray matter of the cord contains innumerable reflex centers. To mention just one example, gray matter of the second, third, and fourth lumbar segments contains the centers for the knee jerk reflex. The term reflex center means literally the center of a reflex arc or the place in the arc at which incoming sensory impulses become outgoing motor impulses. Some reflex centers are merely synapses between sensory and motoneurons, whereas others are interneurons interposed between sensory and motoneurons.

CRANIAL NERVES

Twelve pairs of nerves arise from the undersurface of the brain, some from each division with the exception of the cerebellum, and pass through small foramina in the skull to their respective destinations. They are numbered in the order in which they emerge from front to back and, in addition, bear names descriptive of their distribution or of their function. Some of these nerves consist of afferent fibers only, some of efferent fibers mainly, and some

Table 25. Cranial nerves

	Sensory fibers†			*Motor fibers†*		
*Nerve**	*Receptors*	*Cell bodies*	*Termination*	*Cell bodies*	*Termination*	*Functions‡*
I. Olfactory	*Nasal mucosa*	*Nasal mucosa*	Olfactory bulbs (new relay of neurons to olfactory cortex)			*Sense of smell*
II. Optic	*Retina*	*Retina*	*Nucleus in thalamus (lateral geniculate body); some fibers terminate in superior colliculus of midbrain*			*Vision*
III. Oculomotor	*External eye muscles except superior oblique and lateral rectus*	?	?	**Midbrain (oculomotor nucleus and Edinger-Westphal nucleus)**	**External eye muscles except superior oblique and lateral rectus; fibers from E-W nucleus terminate in ciliary ganglion and thence to ciliary and iris muscles**	**Eye movements, regulation of size of pupil, accommodation,** *proprioception (muscle sense)*
IV. Trochlear	*Superior oblique*	?	?	**Midbrain**	**Superior oblique muscle of eye**	***Eye movements,*** *proprioception*
V. Trigeminal	*Skin and mucosa of head, teeth*	*Gasserian ganglion*	*Pons (sensory nucleus)*	**Pons (motor nucleus)**	**Muscles of mastication**	*Sensations of head and face,* **chewing movements,** *muscle sense*
VI. Abducens	*Lateral rectus*			**Pons**	**Lateral rectus muscle of eye**	***Abduction of eye,*** *proprioception*

VII. Facial	*Taste buds of anterior two-thirds of tongue*	*Geniculate ganglion*	*Medulla (nucleus solitarius)*	**Pons**	**Superficial muscles of face and scalp**	**Facial expressions, secretion of saliva,** *taste*
VIII. Acoustic 1. Vestibular branch	*Semicircular canals and vestibule (utricle and saccule)*	*Vestibular ganglion*	*Pons and medulla (vestibular nuclei)*			*Balance or equilibrium sense*
2. Cochlear or auditory branch	*Organ of Corti in cochlear duct*	*Spiral ganglion*	*Pons and medulla (cochlear nuclei)*			*Hearing*
IX. Glossopharyngeal	*Pharynx; taste buds and other receptors of posterior one-third of tongue*	*Jugular and petrous ganglia*	*Medulla (nucleus solitarius)*	**Medulla (nucleus ambiguus)**	**Muscles of pharynx**	*Taste and other sensations of tongue,* **swallowing movements, secretion of saliva, aid in reflex control of blood pressure and respirations**
	Carotid sinus and carotid body	*Same*	*Medulla (respiratory and vasomotor centers)*	**Medulla at junction of pons (nucleus salivatorius)**	**Otic ganglion and thence to parotid gland**	

*The first letters of the words in the following sentence are the first letters of the names of the cranial nerves. Many generations of anatomy students have used this sentence as an aid to memorizing these names. It is, "On Old Olympus Tiny Tops, A Finn And German Viewed Some Hops." (There are several slightly differing versions of this sentence.)

†Italics indicate sensory fibers and functions. Boldface type indicates motor fibers and functions.

‡An aid for remembering the general function of each cranial nerve is the following twelve-word saying: "Some say marry money but my brothers say bad business marry money." Words beginning with S indicate sensory function. Words beginning with M indicate motor function. Words beginning with B indicate both sensory and motor functions. For example, the first, second, and eighth words in the saying start with S, which indicates that the first, second, and eighth cranial nerves perform sensory functions.

Continued.

Table 25. Cranial nerves—cont'd

	Sensory fibers†			**Motor fibers**†		
*Nerve**	*Receptors*	*Cell bodies*	*Termination*	*Cell bodies*	*Termination*	*Functions*‡
X. Vagus	*Pharynx, larynx, carotid body, and thoracic and abdominal viscera*	*Jugular and nodose ganglia*	*Medulla (nucleus, solitarius), pons (nucleus of fifth cranial nerve)*	**Medulla (dorsal motor nucleus)**	**Ganglia of vagal plexus and thence to muscles of pharynx, larynx and thoracic and abdominal viscera**	*Sensations* and **movements** of organs supplied; for example, **slows heart, increases peristalsis, and contracts muscles for voice production**
XI. Spinal accessory	?	?	?	**Medulla (dorsal motor nucleus of vagus and nucleus ambiguus)** **Anterior gray column of first five or six cervical segments of spinal cord**	**Muscles of thoracic and abdominal viscera and pharynx and larynx** **Trapezius and sternocleidomastoid muscle**	**Shoulder movements, turning movements of head, movements of viscera, voice productions,** *proprioception*?
XII. Hypoglossal	?	?	?	**Medulla (hypoglossal nucleus)**	**Muscles of tongue**	**Tongue movements,** *proprioception*?

*The first letters of the words in the following sentence are the first letters of the names of the cranial nerves. Many generations of anatomy students have used this sentence as an aid to memorizing these names. It is, "On Old Olympus Tiny Tops, A Finn And German Viewed Some Hops." (There are several slightly differing versions of this sentence.)

†Italics indicate sensory fibers and functions. Boldface type indicates motor fibers and functions.

‡An aid for remembering the general function of each cranial nerve is the following twelve-word saying: "Some say marry money but my brothers say bad business marry money." Words beginning with S indicate sensory function. Words beginning with M indicate motor function. Words beginning with B indicate both sensory and motor functions. For example, the first, second, and eighth words in the saying start with S, which indicates that the first, second, and eighth cranial nerves perform sensory functions.

of both afferent and efferent fibers, in which case they are called mixed nerves. Cell bodies of the efferent fibers lie in the various nuclei of the brainstem. Cell bodies of the afferent fibers, with few exceptions, are located in ganglia (for example, the semilunar or gasserian ganglion of the fifth cranial nerve) outside the brainstem. The first, second, and eighth pairs are purely afferent. Information about cranial nerves is summarized in Table 25.

First (olfactory)

The olfactory nerves are composed of axons of neurons whose dendrites and cell bodies lie in the nasal mucosa, high up along the septum and superior conchae (turbinates). Axons of these neurons form about twenty small fibers which pierce each cribriform plate and terminate in the olfactory bulbs, where they synapse with olfactory neurons II whose axons comprise the olfactory tracts. Summarizing:

Olfactory neurons I
- Dendrites, Cell body — In nasal mucosa
- Axons — In small fibers which extend through cribriform plate to olfactory bulb

Olfactory neurons II
- Dendrites, Cell body — In olfactory bulb
- Axons — In olfactory tracts

Second (optic)

Axons from the third and innermost layer of neurons of the retina compose the second cranial nerves. After entering the cranial cavity through the optic foramina, the two optic nerves unite to form the *optic chiasma,* in which some of the fibers of each nerve cross to the opposite side and continue in the *optic tract* of that side. Thus each optic nerve contains only fibers from the retina of the same side, whereas each optic tract has fibers in it from both retinae, a fact of importance in interpreting certain visual disorders (Fig. 171, p. 263). Most of the optic tract fibers terminate in the thalamus (in the portion known as the lateral geniculate body). From here a new relay of fibers runs to the visual area of the occipital lobe cortex. A few optic tract fibers terminate in the superior colliculi of the midbrain, where they synapse with motor fibers to the external eye muscles (third, fourth, and sixth cranial nerves).

Third (oculomotor)

Fibers of the third cranial nerve originate from cells in the oculomotor nucleus in the ventral part of the midbrain and extend to the various external eye muscles, with the exception of the superior oblique and the lateral rectus. Autonomic fibers whose cells lie in a nucleus of the midbrain (the Edinger-Westphal nucleus) are also contained in the oculomotor nerves. These fibers terminate in the ciliary ganglion, where they synapse with cells whose postganglionic fibers supply the intrinsic eye muscles (ciliary and iris). Still a third group of fibers are found in the third cranial nerves, namely, sensory fibers from proprioceptors in the eye muscles.

Fourth (trochlear)

Motor fibers of the fourth cranial nerve have their origin in cells in the midbrain, from whence they extend to the superior oblique muscles of the eye. Afferent fibers from proprioceptors in these muscles are also contained in the trochlear nerves.

Fifth (trifacial or trigeminal)

Three sensory branches (ophthalmic, maxillary, and mandibular nerves) carry afferent impulses from the skin and mucosa of the head and from the teeth to cell bodies in the semilunar or gasserian ganglion (a swelling on the nerve, lodged in the petrous portion of the temporal bone) (Fig. 138). Fibers extend from the ganglion to the main sensory nucleus of the fifth cra-

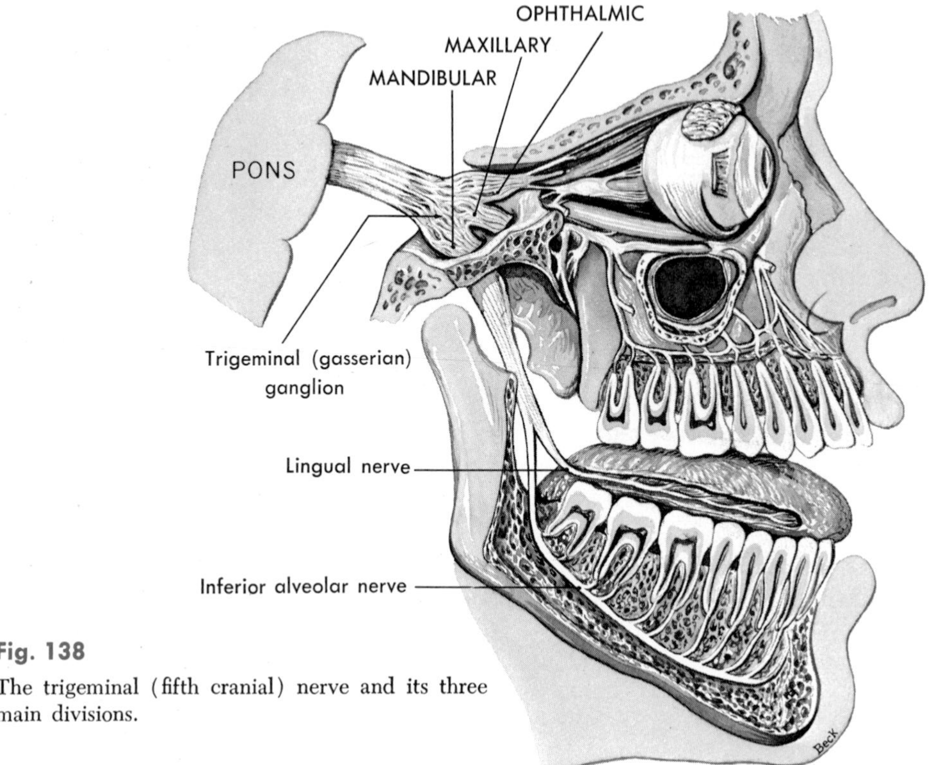

Fig. 138

The trigeminal (fifth cranial) nerve and its three main divisions.

nial nerve situated in the pons. A smaller motor root of the trigeminal nerve originates in the trifacial motor nucleus located in the pons just medial to the sensory nucleus. Fibers run from the motor root to the muscles of mastication by way of the mandibular nerve.

Sixth (abducens)

The sixth cranial nerve is a motor nerve with fibers originating from a nucleus in the pons in the floor of the fourth ventricle and extending to the lateral rectus muscles of the eyes. It contains also some afferent fibers from proprioceptors in the lateral rectus muscles.

Seventh (facial)

The motor fibers of the seventh cranial nerve arise from a nucleus in the lower part of the pons, whence they extend by way of several branches to the superficial muscles of the face and scalp and to the submaxillary and sublingual glands. Sensory fibers from the taste buds of the anterior two-thirds of the tongue run in the facial nerve to cell bodies in the geniculate ganglion, a small swelling on the facial nerve, where it passes through a canal in the temporal bone. From the ganglion, fibers extend to the nucleus solitarius in the medulla.

Eighth (acoustic or auditory)

The eighth cranial nerve has two distinct divisions: the vestibular nerve and the cochlear nerve. Both are sensory. Fibers from the semicircular canals run to the vestibular ganglion (in the internal auditory meatus) where their cell bodies are located and whence fibers extend to the vestibular nuclei in the pons and medulla. Together these fibers constitute the *vestibular nerve.* Some of its fibers run to the cerebellum. The *cochlear nerve* consists of fibers which start in the organ of Corti in the cochlea, have their cell bodies in the spiral ganglion in the cochlea, and terminate in the cochlear nuclei located between the medulla and pons. The vestibular nerve transmits impulses which result in sensations of balance or imbalance. Conduction by the cochlear nerve results in sensations of hearing.

Ninth (glossopharyngeal)

Both sensory and motor fibers compose the ninth cranial nerve. This nerve supplies fibers not only to the tongue and pharynx, as its name implies, but also to other structures, for example, to the carotid sinus. The latter plays an important part in the control of blood pressure. Sensory fibers, with their receptors in the pharynx and posterior third of the tongue, have their cell bodies in the jugular (superior) and petrous (inferior) ganglia, located respectively in the jugular foramen and the petrous portion of the temporal bone. From these, fibers extend to the nucleus solitarius in the medulla. The motor fibers of the ninth cranial nerve originate in cells in the nucleus ambiguus in the medulla and run to muscles of the pharynx. There are also secretory fibers in this nerve, with cells of origin in the nucleus salivatorius (at the junction of the pons and medulla). These fibers run to the otic ganglion, whence postganglionic fibers extend to the parotid gland.

Tenth (vagus or pneumogastric)

The tenth cranial nerve is widely distributed and contains both sensory and motor fibers. Its sensory fibers supply the pharynx, larynx, trachea, heart, carotid body, lungs, bronchi, esophagus, stomach, small intestine, and gallbladder. Cell bodies for these sensory dendrites lie in the jugular and nodose ganglia, located respectively in the jugular foramen and just inferior to it on the trunk of the nerve. Centrally the sensory axons terminate in the medulla (in the nucleus solitarius) and in the pons (in the nucleus of the trigeminal nerve). Motor fibers of the vagus originate in cells in the medulla (in the dorsal motor nucleus of the vagus) and extend to various autonomic ganglia in the vagal plexus, whence postganglionic fibers run to muscles of the pharynx, larynx, and thoracic and abdominal viscera.

Eleventh (accessory or spinal accessory)

The eleventh cranial nerve is a motor nerve. Part of its fibers originates in cells in the medulla (in the dorsal motor nucleus of the vagus and in the nucleus ambiguus) and pass by way of vagal branches to thoracic and abdominal viscera. The rest of the fibers have their cells of origin in the anterior gray column of the first five or six segments of the cervical spinal cord and extend through the spinal root of the accessory nerve to the trapezius and sternocleidomastoid muscles.

Twelfth (hypoglossal)

Motor fibers with cell bodies in the medulla (in the hypoglossal nucleus) compose the twelfth cranial nerve. They supply the muscles of the tongue. According to some anatomists, this nerve also contains sensory fibers from proprioceptors in the tongue.

• • •

The main facts about the distribution and function of each of the cranial nerve pairs are summarized in Table 25.

Neuralgia of the trifacial nerve, known as tic douloureux, is an extremely painful condition which can be relieved by removing the gasserian (or semilunar) ganglion, the large ganglion on the posterior root

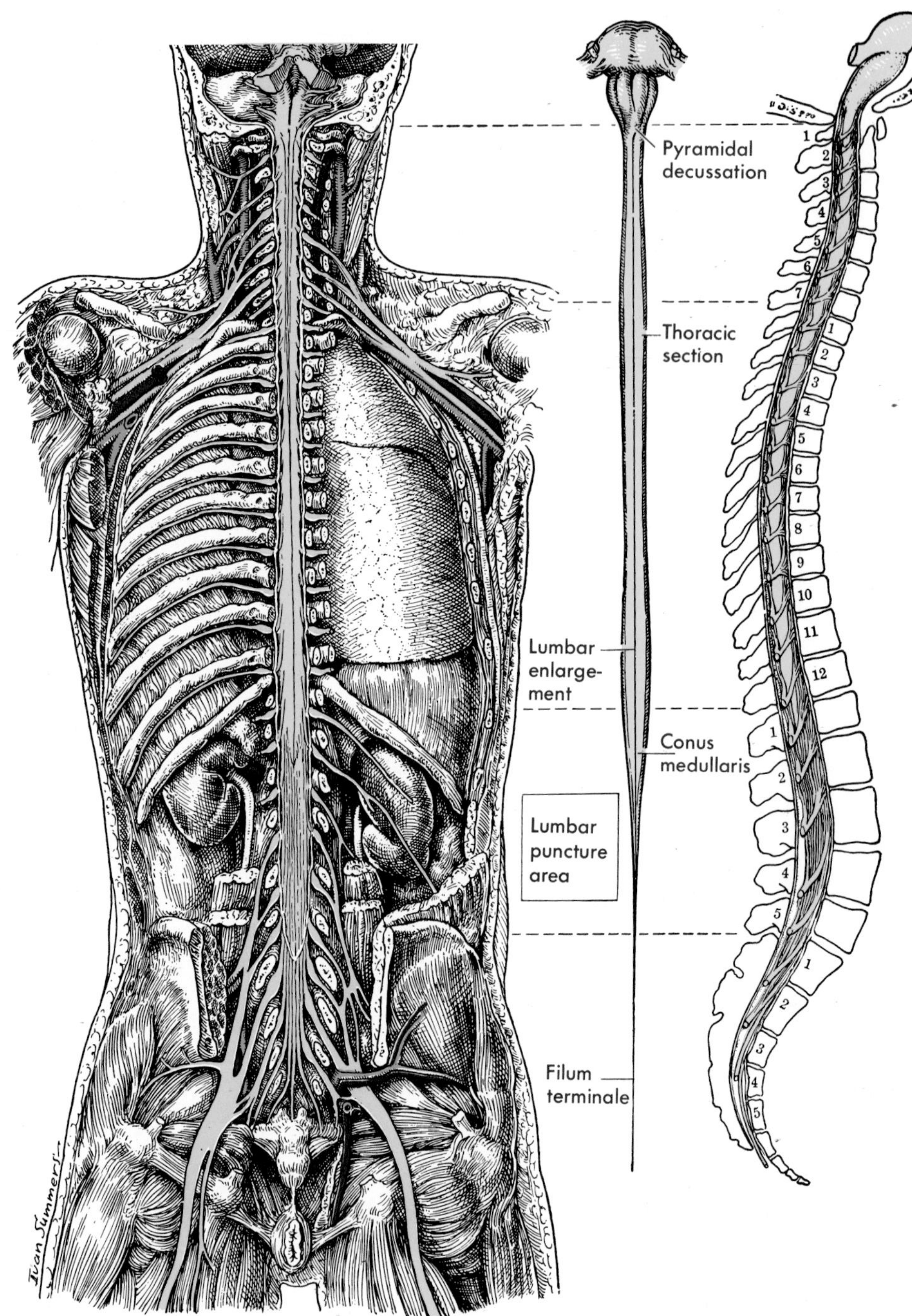

Fig. 139

Relation of the spinal cord, part of the brain, and some of the spinal nerves to surrounding structures. (From Mettler: Neuroanatomy, St. Louis, The C. V. Mosby Co.)

of the nerve (Fig. 138) containing the cell bodies of the nerve's afferent fibers. After such an operation, the patient's face, scalp, teeth, and conjunctiva on the side treated show anesthesia. Special care, such as wearing protective goggles and irrigating the eye frequently, is therefore prescribed. The patient is instructed also to visit his dentist regularly since he can no longer experience a toothache as a warning of diseased teeth.

Severe head injuries often damage one or more of the cranial nerves, producing symptoms analogous to the functions of the nerve affected. For example, injury of the sixth cranial nerve causes the eye to turn in, due to paralysis of the abducting muscle of the eye, whereas injury of the eighth cranial nerve produces deafness. Injury to the facial nerve results in a poker-faced expression and a drooping of the corner of the mouth due to paralysis of the facial muscles.

An aneurysm of one of the middle cerebral arteries with resulting pressure on the nearby oculomotor nerve is not uncommon. In such cases the pupil on the same side remains dilated. In addition, the eye may turn outward and the lid may droop.

The second cranial nerve is particularly susceptible to atrophy, resulting in total blindness on the affected side.

SPINAL NERVES

Origin

Thirty-one pairs of nerves have their origin on the spinal cord. Unlike the cranial nerves, they have no special names but are merely numbered according to the level of the spinal column at which they emerge from the spinal cavity. Thus, there are eight cervical, twelve thoracic, five lumbar, and five sacral pairs and one coccygeal pair of spinal nerves. The first cervical nerves emerge from the cord in the spaces above the first cervical vertebra (between it and the occipital bone). The rest of the cervical and all the thoracic nerves pass out of the spinal cavity horizontally through the intervertebral foramina of their respective vertebrae. For example, the second cervical nerves emerge through the foramina above the second cervical vertebra.

Lumbar, sacral, and coccygeal nerves, on the other hand, have to descend from their point of origin at the lower end of the cord (which terminates at the level of the first lumbar vertebra) before reaching the intervertebral foramina of their respective vertebrae, through which they then emerge. This gives the lower end of the cord, with its attached spinal nerves, the appearance of a horse's tail. In fact, it bears the name *cauda equina* (Latin equivalent for horse's tail).

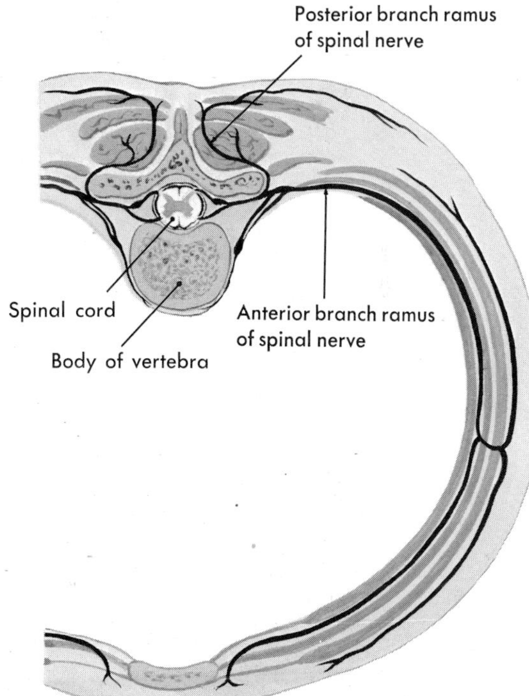

Fig. 140

Diagram showing branchings of a spinal nerve. The anterior and posterior roots of the nerve can be seen within the vertebral foramen.

Table 26. Spinal nerves and peripheral branches

Spinal nerves	*Plexuses formed from anterior rami*	*Spinal nerve branches from plexuses*	*Parts supplied*
Cervical 1, 2, 3, 4	Cervical plexus	Lesser occipital Great auricular Cutaneous nerve of neck Anterior supraclavicular Middle supraclavicular Posterior supraclavicular Branches to numerous neck muscles	Sensory to back of head, front of neck, and upper part of shoulder; motor to numerous neck muscles
Cervical 5, 6, 7, 8; *Thoracic* (*or dorsal*) 1	Brachial plexus	Suprascapular and dorsoscapular	Superficial muscles* of scapula
		Thoracic nerves, medial and lateral anterior	Pectoralis major and minor
		Long thoracic nerve	Serratus anterior
		Thoracodorsal	Latissimus dorsi
		Subscapular	Subscapular and teres major muscles
		Axillary (circumflex)	Deltoid and teres minor muscles and skin over deltoid
		Musculocutaneous	Muscles of front of arm (biceps brachii, coracobrachialis, and brachialis) and skin on outer side of forearm
		Ulnar	Flexor carpi ulnaris and part of flexor digitorum profundus; some of muscles of hand; sensory to medial side of hand, little finger, and medial half of fourth finger
		Median	Rest of muscles of front of forearm and hand; sensory to skin of palmar surface of thumb, index, and middle fingers
		Radial	Triceps muscle and muscles of back of forearm; sensory to skin of back of forearm and hand
		Medial cutaneous	Sensory to inner surface of arm and forearm
		Phrenic (branches from cervical nerves before formation of plexus; most of its fibers from fourth cervical nerve)	Diaphragm
Thoracic 2, 3, 4, 5, 6, 7, 8, 9, 10, 11, 12	No plexus formed; branches run directly to intercostal muscles and skin of thorax		

*Although nerves to muscles are considered motor, they do contain some sensory fibers that transmit proprioceptive impulses.

Table 26. Spinal nerves and peripheral branches—cont'd

Spinal nerves	*Plexuses formed from anterior rami*	*Spinal nerve branches from plexuses*	*Parts supplied*
		Iliohypogastric (Sometimes fused)	Sensory to anterior abdominal wall
		Ilioinguinal (Sometimes fused)	Sensory to anterior abdominal wall and external genitalia; motor to muscles of abdominal wall
		Genitofemoral	Sensory to skin of external genitalia and inguinal region
Lumbar 1		Lateral cutaneous of thigh	Sensory to outer side of thigh
2, 3, 4, 5		Femoral	Motor to quadriceps, sartorius, and iliacus muscles; sensory to front of thigh and to medial side of lower leg (saphenous nerve)
Sacral 1, 2	Lumbosacral plexus	Obturator	Motor to adductor muscles of thigh
3, 4, 5		Tibial* (medial popliteal)	Motor to muscles of calf of leg; sensory to skin of calf of leg and sole of foot
Coccygeal 1		Common peroneal (lateral popliteal)	Motor to evertors and dorsiflexors of foot; sensory to lateral surface of leg and dorsal surface of foot
		Nerves to hamstring muscles	Motor to muscles of back of thigh
		Gluteal nerves, superior and inferior	Motor to buttocks muscles and tensor fasciae latae
		Posterior cutaneous nerve	Sensory to skin of buttocks, posterior surface of thigh, and leg
		Pudendal nerve	Motor to perineal muscles; sensory to skin of perineum

*Sensory fibers from the tibial and peroneal nerves unite to form the *medial cutaneous* (or sural) *nerve* that supplies the calf of the leg and the lateral surface of the foot. In the thigh the tibial and common peroneal nerves are usually enclosed in a single sheath to form the *sciatic nerve*, the largest nerve in the body with its width of approximately three-quarters of an inch. About two-thirds of the way down the posterior part of the thigh, it divides into its component parts. Branches of the sciatic nerve extend into the hamstring muscles.

Each spinal nerve, instead of attaching directly to the cord, attaches indirectly by means of two short roots, anterior and posterior. The posterior roots are readily recognized by the presence on them of a swelling, the posterior root ganglion or *spinal ganglion*. The roots lie within the spinal cavity with the ganglia in the intervertebral foramina (Fig. 61, p. 88). Like all ganglia, spinal ganglia are made up of cell bodies of sensory neurons.

Distribution

After each spinal nerve emerges from the spinal cavity, it divides into two main branches, the anterior and posterior rami

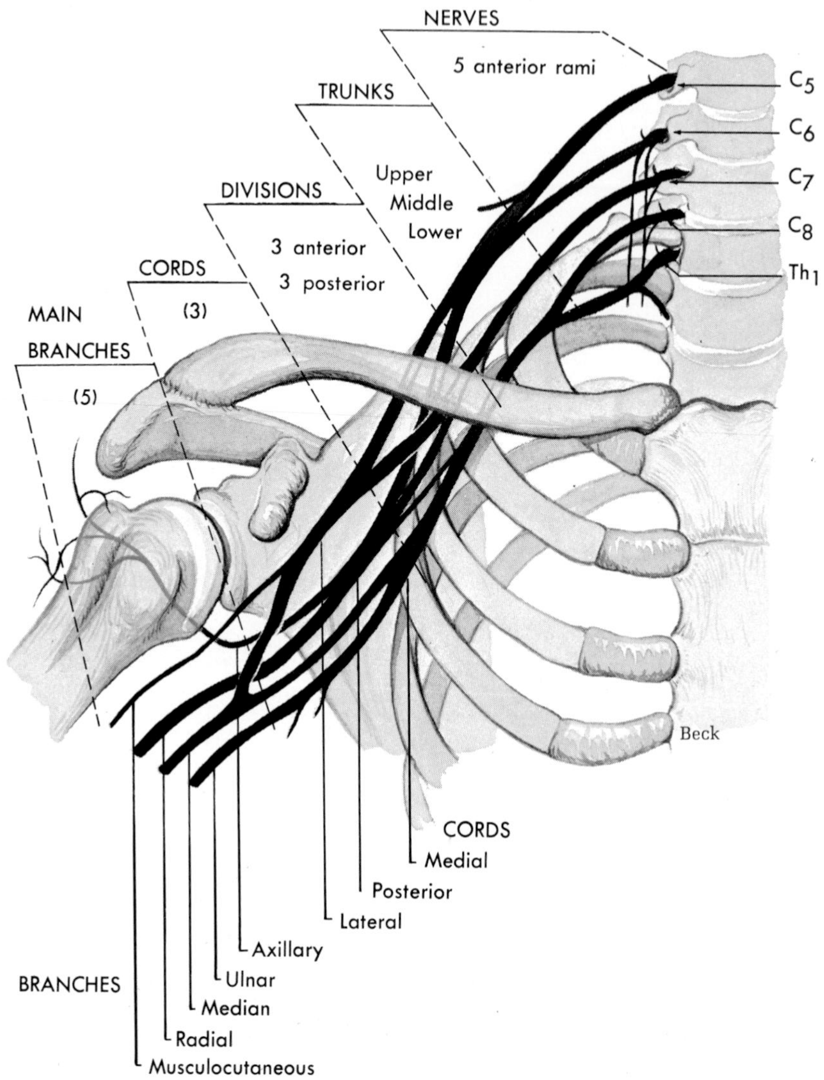

Fig. 141

Brachial plexus. Intermixing of fibers from the lower four cervical and the first thoracic nerves.

(Fig. 140). The posterior rami then subdivide into lesser nerves that extend into the muscles and skin of the posterior surface of the head, neck, and trunk.

The anterior rami (except those of the thoracic nerves) subdivide in a more complicated fashion, forming plexuses or complex networks of nerves (Table 26). For example, fibers from the lower four cervical and first thoracic nerves intermix in such a way as to form a fairly definite, although apparently hopelessly confused, pattern called the *brachial plexus* (Fig. 141). Emerging from this plexus are smaller nerves bearing names descriptive of their locations, such as the median nerve, the musculocutaneous nerve, and the ulnar nerve. These nerves (each containing fibers from more than one spinal nerve) divide

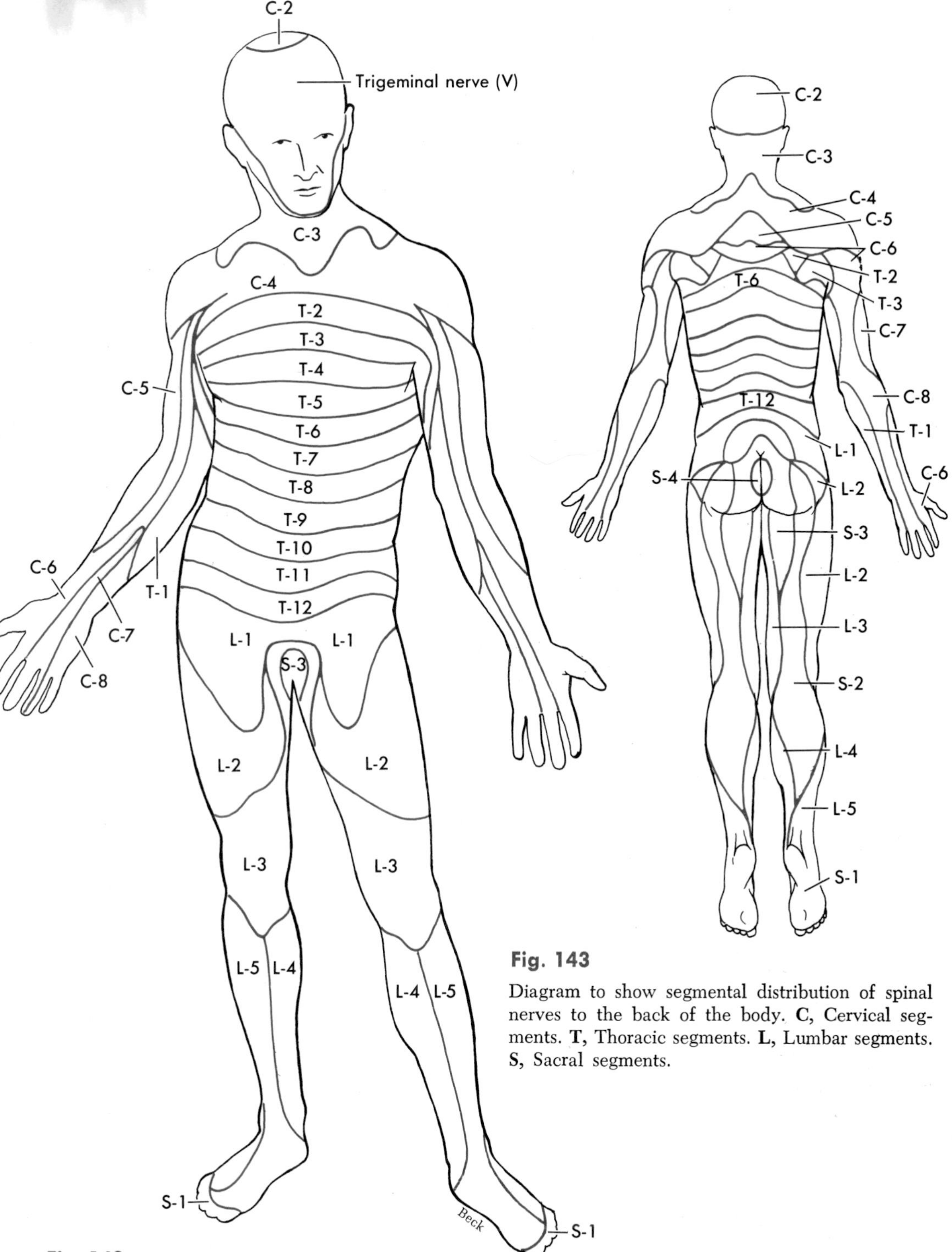

Fig. 143

Diagram to show segmental distribution of spinal nerves to the back of the body. **C**, Cervical segments. **T**, Thoracic segments. **L**, Lumbar segments. **S**, Sacral segments.

Fig. 142

Diagram to show segmental distribution of spinal nerves to the front of the body. **C**, Cervical segments. **T**, Thoracic segments. **L**, Lumbar segments. **S**, Sacral segments.

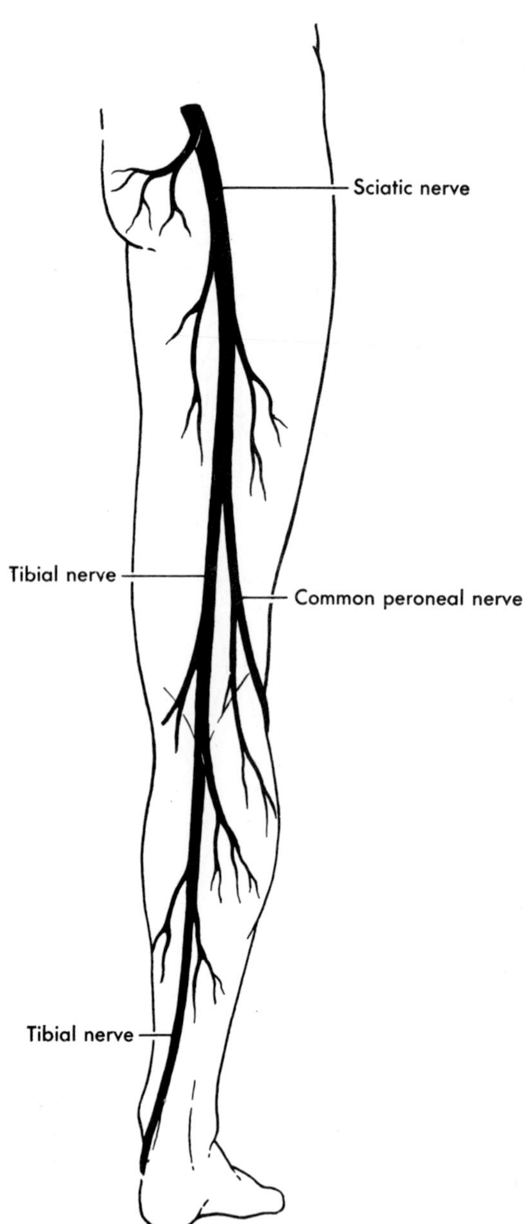

Fig. 144

Main nerves of the lower extremity.

further into smaller and smaller branches, resulting ultimately in the complete innervation of the hand and most of the arm. The brachial plexus is located in the shoulder region from the neck to the axilla. It is of clinical significance since it is sometimes stretched or torn at birth, causing paralysis and numbness of the baby's arm on that side. If untreated, it results in a withered arm. Branching from this plexus are several nerves to the skin and to voluntary muscles.

The right and left phrenic nerves whose fibers come from the third and fourth or fourth and fifth cervical spinal nerves before formation of the brachial plexus have considerable clinical interest since they supply the diaphragm muscle. If the neck is broken in a way that severs or crushes the cord above this level, nerve impulses from the brain can, of course, no longer reach the phrenic nerves, and therefore the diaphragm stops contracting. Unless artificial respiration of some kind is provided, the patient dies of respiratory paralysis as a result of the broken neck. Poliomyelitis that attacks the cord between the third and fifth cervical segments also paralyzes the phrenic nerve and, therefore, the diaphragm.

Another spinal nerve plexus is the *lumbar plexus,* formed by the intermingling of fibers from the first four lumbar nerves. This network of nerves is located in the lumbar region of the back in the psoas muscle. The large femoral nerve is one of several nerves emerging from the lumbar plexus. It divides into many branches which supply the thigh and leg.

Fibers from the fourth and fifth lumbar nerves and the first, second, and third sacral nerves form the *sacral plexus,* located in the pelvic cavity on the anterior surface of the piriformis muscle. Among other nerves which emerge from the sacral plexus are the tibial and common peroneal nerves which, in the thigh, form the largest nerve

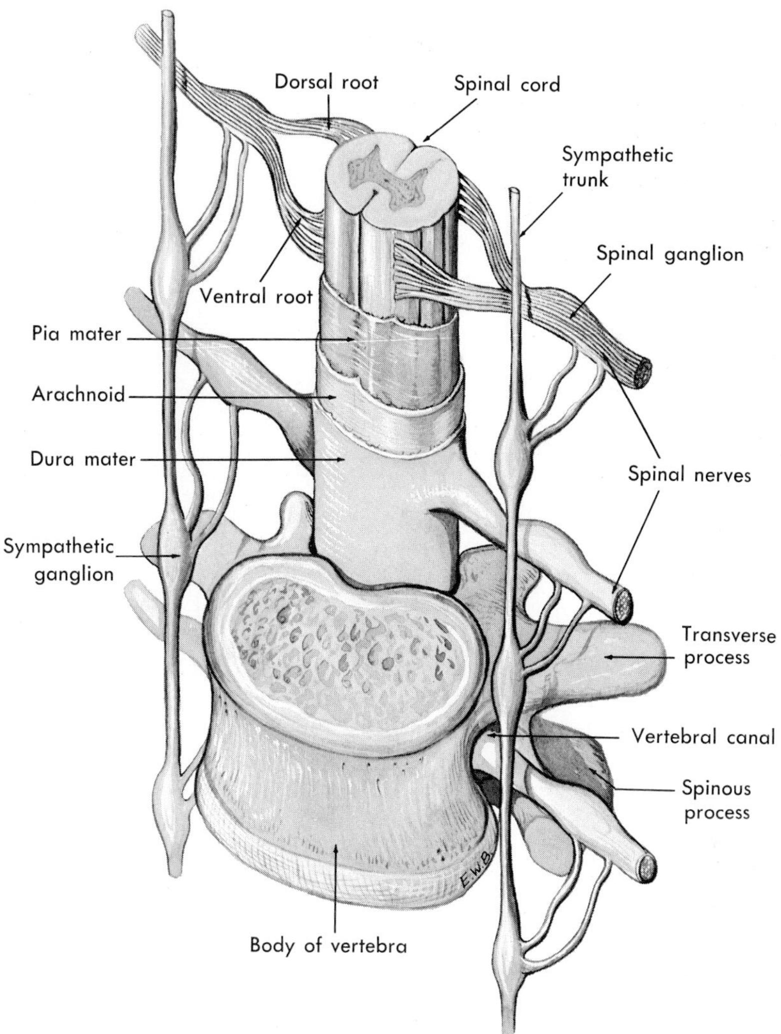

Fig. 145

Diagram of the spinal cord showing meninges, formation of the spinal nerves, and relations to a vertebra and to the sympathetic trunk and ganglia.

in the body, namely, the great sciatic nerve. It pierces the buttocks and runs down the back of the thigh. Its many branches supply nearly all the skin of the leg, the posterior thigh muscles, and the leg and foot muscles. Sciatica or neuralgia of the sciatic nerve is a fairly common and very painful condition.

Microscopic structure

Unlike cranial nerves, all spinal nerves are *mixed nerves.* As shown in Fig. 122, spinal nerves are composed of both sensory fibers (dendrites) and motor axons. Note that the sensory dendrite shown in this figure comes from a cell body located in the ganglion on the posterior root of the spinal nerve. The motor axon shown originates from a cell body located in the anterior gray column of the cord. These

Table 27. Cranial nerves contrasted with spinal nerves

	Cranial nerves	*Spinal nerves*
Origin	Base of brain	Spinal cord
Distribution	Mainly to head and neck	Skin, skeletal muscles, joints, blood vessels, sweat glands, and mucosa except of head and neck
Structure	Some composed of sensory fibers only; some of both motor axons and sensory dendrites; some motor fibers belong to voluntary nervous system, some to autonomic	All of them composed of both sensory dendrites and motor axons; some of latter, somatic or voluntary, some autonomic
Function	Vision, hearing, sense of smell, sense of taste, eye movements, etc.	Sensations, movements, and sweat secretion

neurons whose cell bodies lie in the anterior gray columns and whose axons terminate in skeletal muscle are called *somatic motor neurons.* Spinal nerves also contain axons of autonomic motor neurons (p. 232).

Functions

Because spinal nerves contain both sensory and motor fibers, they serve as two-way conduction paths between the periphery and the spinal cord and perform the general functions of making possible both our sensations and our movements. The sensory dendrites in spinal nerves constitute the first part of the neural pathway traveled by sensory impulses. And the motor axons in spinal nerves constitutes the last part of the neural pathway, the *"final common path,"* traveled by motor impulses to skeletal muscles. Consequently, anything that interferes with the functioning of a spinal nerve produces both anesthesia and paralysis of the part innervated by that nerve. Spinal nerve *branches,* however, may be purely sensory or motor, or they may be mixed nerves (Table 26).

Sensory neural pathways

Here are some important general principles about sensory neural pathways (also see Table 28).

1. The sensory neural pathway to the cerebral cortex consists of a chain of at least three sensory neurons. We shall call them sensory neurons I, II, and III.

(a) Sensory neuron I of the relay conducts from the periphery to the spinal cord, where it synapses wtih sensory neuron II. (If the receptors of sensory neuron I lie in regions supplied by cranial nerves, then its axon enters the brainstem instead of the cord.) Examine Fig. 146 and then try to answer question 40(a), p. 245. Check your answer with Table 28.

(b) Sensory neuron II conducts from the cord or brainstem up to the thalamus, where it synapses with sensory neuron III. Answer question 40(b), after again examining Fig. 146.

(c) Sensory neuron III conducts from the thalamus to the general sensory area of the cerebral cortex (postcentral gyrus, parietal lobe). Look once more at Fig. 146 and then answer questions 40(c) and 43.

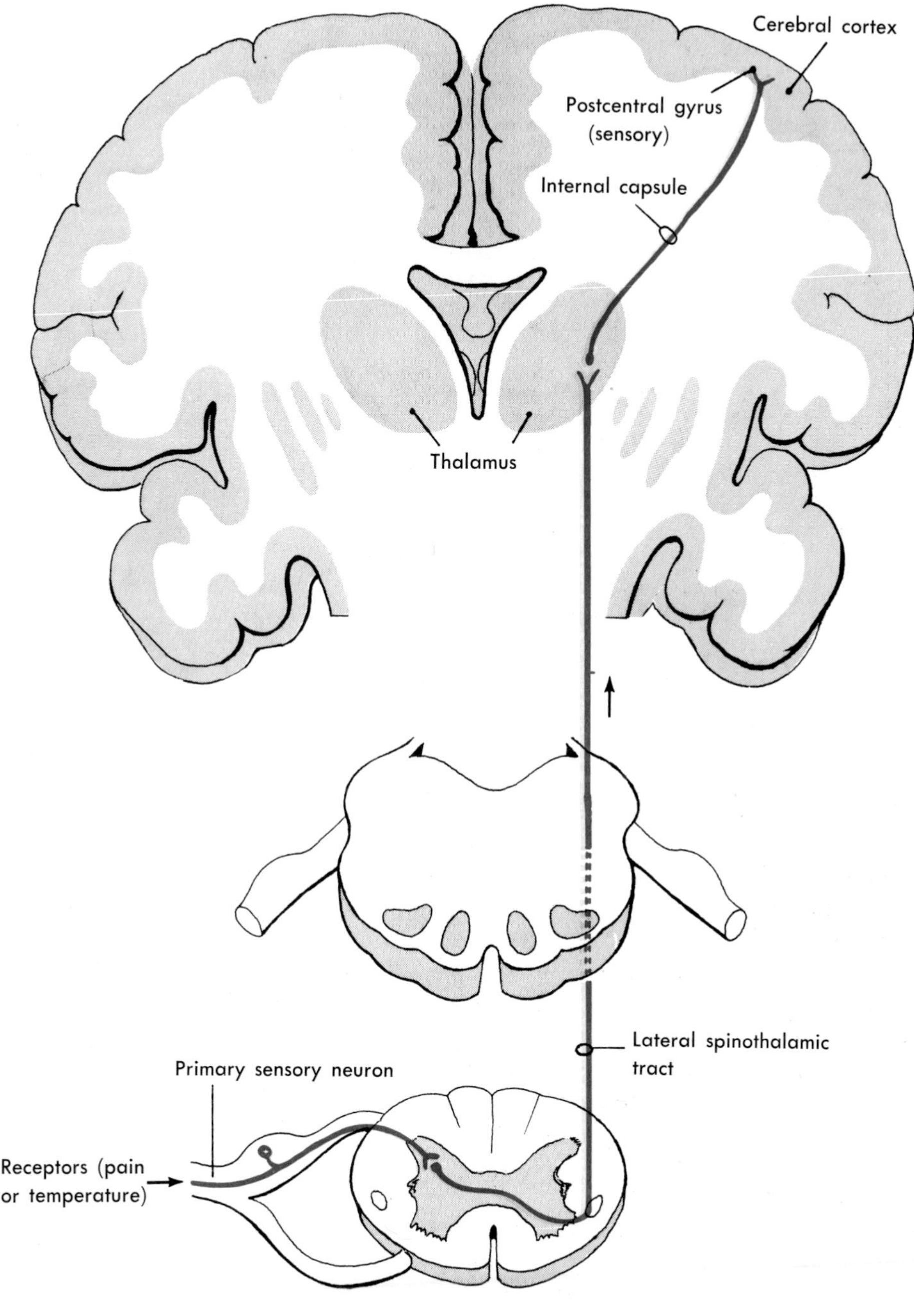

Fig. 146

The lateral spinothalamic tract relays sensory impulses from pain and temperature receptors.

Table 28. Sensory neural pathways

Neurons	*Gross structures in which neuron parts are located*
1. **Pain and temperature**	
Sensory neuron I	
Receptors	In skin, mucosa, muscles, tendons, viscera
Dendrite	In spinal nerve and branch of spinal nerve
Cell body	In spinal ganglion, on posterior root of spinal nerve
Axon	In posterior root of spinal nerve; terminates in posterior gray column of cord
Sensory neuron II	
Dendrite	Posterior gray column
Cell body	Posterior gray column
Axon	Decussates and ascends in lateral spinothalamic tract (Figs. 137 and 146); terminates in thalamus
Sensory neuron III	
Dendrite	Thalamus
Cell body	Thalamus
Axon	Thalamus via thalamocortical tract in internal capsule to general sensory area of cerebral cortex, i.e., post-central gyrus in parietal lobe
2. **Crude touch stimuli**	
Sensory neuron I	Same as sensory neuron I for pain and temperature stimuli
Sensory neuron II	
Dendrite Cell body	Posterior gray column; same as sensory neuron II for pain and temperature
Axon	In ventral spinothalamic tract (Fig. 137) to thalamus
Sensory neuron III	Same as sensory neuron III for pain and temperature stimuli (i.e., lateral spinothalamic tract)
3. **Discriminating touch** (two-point discrimination, vibrations) **deep touch,** and **pressure and conscious proprioception**	
Sensory neuron I	Same as sensory neuron I for pain, temperature, and crude touch stimuli, except that axon extends up cord in posterior white columns (fasciculi gracilis and cuneatus, Fig. 137) to nuclei gracilis or cuneatus in medulla instead of terminating in posterior gray columns of cord
Sensory neuron II	
Dendrite Cell body	In nuclei gracilis or cuneatus of medulla
Axon	Decussates and ascends in medial lemniscus (broad band of fibers extending up through medulla and midbrain) and terminates in thalamus
Sensory neuron III	Same as sensory neuron III for pain, temperature, and crude touch stimuli

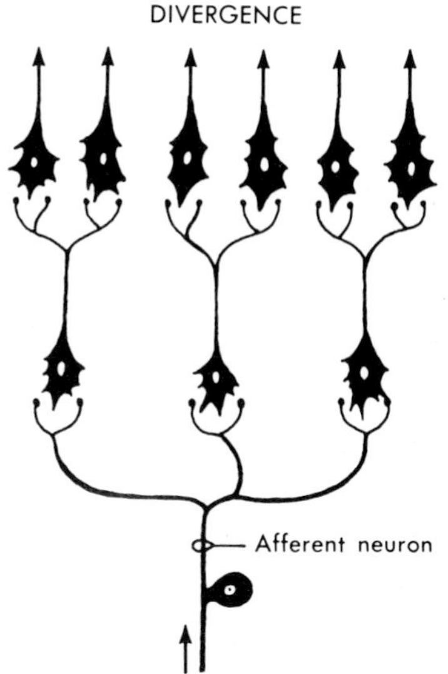

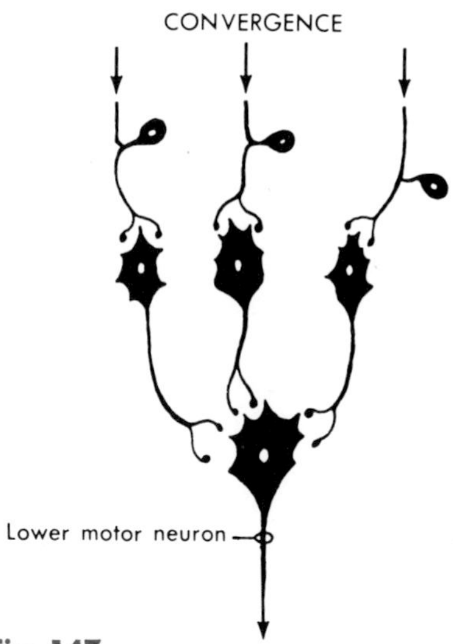

Fig. 147

Diagrams demonstrating principles of divergence (a single stimulus initiating multiple responses) and convergence (many neurons activating a single lower motoneuron). (Adapted from Starling.)

2. Crude awareness of a sensation occurs when sensory impulses reach the thalamus. By crude awareness we mean that the individual is conscious both of the kind of sensation (for example, heat, cold, pain) he is experiencing and of whether it feels pleasant or unpleasant to him to a mild, moderate, or marked degree.

3. Full consciousness of sensations occurs when sensory impulses reach the cerebral cortex. Then the individual not only recognizes the kind of sensation present, but he also knows exactly where it is coming from. He can localize it accurately and can discriminate as to its intensity.

4. For the most part, sensory pathways to the cerebral cortex are crossed pathways. This means that each side of the brain registers sensations from the opposite side of the body. Usually it is the axon of sensory neuron II that decussates at some point in its ascent to the thalamus.

5. Most sensory neurons form synapses with many other neurons located at various levels of the cord and brain. This fact, sometimes referred to as the *principle of divergence,* makes it possible for impulses initiated in any one receptor to be conducted to many different effectors almost simultaneously. Such an arrangement can have great survival value—somewhat as if a single line into a telephone exchange were to connect with a hospital, doctor's office, and police and fire departments all at the same time.

6. The neural pathway for sensations of *pain* and *temperature* is called the *lateral spinothalamic pathway.*

7. Two neural pathways conduct impulses that produce sensations of touch and pressure, namely, the medial lemniscal system and the ventral spinothalamic pathway. The *medial lemniscal system* consists of the tracts that make up the posterior white columns of the cord (the fasciculi cuneatus and gracilis) plus the *medial lemniscus,* a flat band of white fibers extending through the medulla, pons, and midbrain. (Derivation of the name lemniscus may interest you. It comes from the Greek work *lemniskos* meaning "woolen band." Apparently, to some early anatomist, the medial lemniscus looked like a

band of woolen material running through the brainstem.)

The fibers of the medial lemniscus, like those of the spinothalamic tracts, are axons of sensory neurons II. They originate from cell bodies in the medulla, decussate, and then extend upward to terminate in the thalamus on the opposite side. The function of the medial lemniscal system is to transmit impulses that produce our more discriminating touch and pressure sensations. These include stereognosis (awareness of an object's size, shape, and texture), precise localization (sense of exact location of stimuli), and sense of vibrations.

The function of the *ventral spinothalamic pathway* is to transmit impulses that result in crude touch and pressure sensations—knowing when something touches the skin, for example.

8. The neural pathway for *conscious proprioception* or *kinesthesia* (sense of the position of body parts and of their movements) is also the medial lemniscal system. See Table 28 for a brief summary of the sensory neural pathways named in items 6, 7, and 8.

Arousal or alerting mechanism

According to an older theory, consciousness was the result of sufficient numbers of sensory impulses reaching the cerebral cortex, presumably via the great sensory pathways (mainly spinothalamic, auditory, and visual). Now, however, it is known that these impulses alone can neither arouse the cortex to wakefulness nor maintain it in the conscious state. Instead, consciousness results from impulses reaching the cortex via the so-called *reticular activating system.* It is these impulses that arouse or alert the cortex and maintain consciousness and not those over the more direct great sensory paths.

The reticular activating system consists of nuclei in the brainstem reticular formation and tracts to and from it. Impulses continually feed into the brainstem reticular formation by direct spinoreticular tracts and by collaterals from spinothalamic, auditory, and visual tracts. Impulses also continually leave the reticular formation for the cortex. But presumably the pathways from the brainstem reticular formation to the cortex are long and multisynaptic routes. They probably include relays to the hypothalamus, thalamus, and possibly other parts of the brain too before the final relay to the cerebral cortex. At any rate, it is now an accepted concept that impulses over this system are the ones that arouse or alert the cortex and maintain consciousness.

Conversely, if anything blocks conduction by the reticular activating system, unconsciousness results. General anesthetics, for example, are thought to produce unconsciousness by inhibiting conduction by the reticular activating system. And certain drugs, notably amphetamines and Adrenalin, produce the opposite effect. They stimulate the reticular activating system and thereby produce wakefulness.

In addition to its arousal function, the reticular formation also serves motor functions (see p. 223).

Motor neural pathways to skeletal muscles

Because neural pathways to skeletal muscles are extremely complex and because there are still so many unknowns about them, we shall confine our discussion to basic facts related to two major principles about these pathways: the principle of the final common path and the principle of convergence.

The *principle of the final common path* might be stated this way: motoneurons whose dendrites and cells lie in the anterior gray horns of the spinal cord constitute the final common path which all impulses to skeletal muscles must traverse. In other words, axons of anterior horn neurons (or lower motoneurons as they are called) are the only motor fibers terminating in skeletal muscles. Therefore, any condition which damages anterior horn neurons enough to make them unable to conduct causes paralysis of the associated muscles. The individual can then no longer contract these muscles at will. And reflex contraction, of course, also becomes impossible when impulses cannot travel over these final common paths to skeletal muscle cells. The poliomyelitis virus, probably the best known virus in the world today, produces paralysis by destroying anterior horn neurons.

The *principle of convergence,* briefly stated, holds that axons of a great many neurons converge upon, that is, synapse with, each lower motoneuron. Hence, many impulses from diverse sources continually bombard it, and together their combined or summated effect controls its functioning.

Motor pathways from the cerebral cortex down to anterior horn motoneurons are numerous and complex. Two methods are used to classify them—one based on the location of their fibers in the medulla and the other on their influence on the lower motoneurons. The first method divides them into pyramidal and extrapyramidal tracts, and the second classifies them as facilitatory and inhibitory tracts.

Pyramidal tracts are those whose fibers come together in the medulla to form the pyramids—hence their name. Because axons composing the pyramidal tracts originate from neuron cell bodies located in the cerebral cortex (presumably mainly from giant pyramidal cells of Betz in the primary motor area), pyramidal tracts are also called corticospinal tracts. Their fibers terminate at various levels of the cord in synapses with interneurons which, in turn, synapse with anterior horn neurons. (A few corticospinal fibers may synapse directly with the anterior horn neurons. Authorities disagree about this.) More than two-thirds of the fibers in the pyramidal tracts decussate in the medulla and extend down the cord in the lateral corticospinal tract on the opposite side. The remaining fibers do not cross over from one side of the medulla to the other. They extend down the cord in the ventral corticospinal tract located on the same side of the cord as the cerebral motor area from which they came. Hence another name for ventral corticospinal tract is direct or uncrossed pyramidal tract, and another name for lateral corticospinal tract is crossed pyramidal tract. Impulses over these tracts stimulate anterior horn cells which, in turn, stimulate individual muscles (mainly of the hands and feet) to contract and produce small, discrete movements. In fact, stimulation of anterior horn cells by pyramidal tract impulses must occur in order for willed movements to occur. This means that paralysis results whenever pyramidal tract conduction is interrupted. For instance, the paralysis that so often follows cerebral vascular accidents comes from pyramidal neuron injury—sometimes of their cell bodies in the primary motor area, sometimes of their axons in the internal capsule (Fig. 148).

Extrapyramidal tracts are much more complex than pyramidal tracts. They consist of all pathways between the motor cortex and anterior horn cells except pyramidal tracts. Complicated incompletely worked out relays between the cortex, basal ganglia, thalamus, and brainstem form the upper portions of extrapyramidal tracts, and reticulospinal tracts constitute one of the main lower portions.

Fibers of the *reticulospinal tracts* originate from cell bodies in the reticular formation of the brainstem and terminate in gray matter of the spinal cord, where they synapse with interneurons that synapse with lower motoneurons. Some reticulospinal fibers constitute facilitatory tracts, while others form inhibitory tracts (see below).

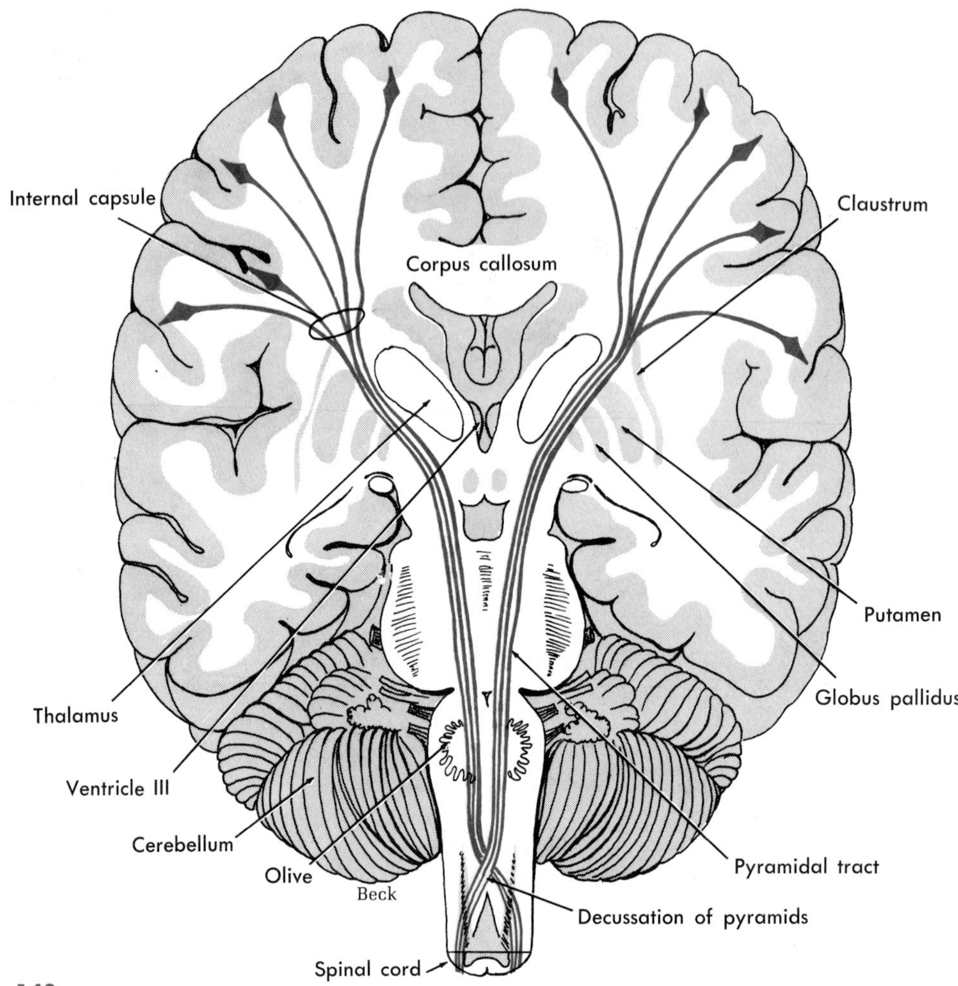

Fig. 148

The crossed pyramidal tracts (lateral corticospinal), the main motor tracts of the body. Most fibers of these tracts decussate in the medulla as shown here. Some decussate in the cord as shown in Fig. 149.

Extrapyramidal tracts conduct impulses important for muscle tone, automatic movements, and emotional expressions.

1. Impulses over some extrapyramidal fibers (for example, over facilitatory reticulospinal fibers) facilitate lower motoneurons and thereby tend to increase muscle tone. But impulses over other extrapyramidal fibers produce the opposite effect—they inhibit lower motoneurons and tend to decrease muscle tone.
2. Conduction by extrapyramidal tracts plays a crucial part in producing our larger, more automatic movements because they cause groups of muscles to contract in sequence or simultaneously. Such muscle action occurs, for example, in swimming and walking and, in fact, in all normal voluntary movements.
3. Conduction by extrapyramidal tracts plays an important part in our emo-

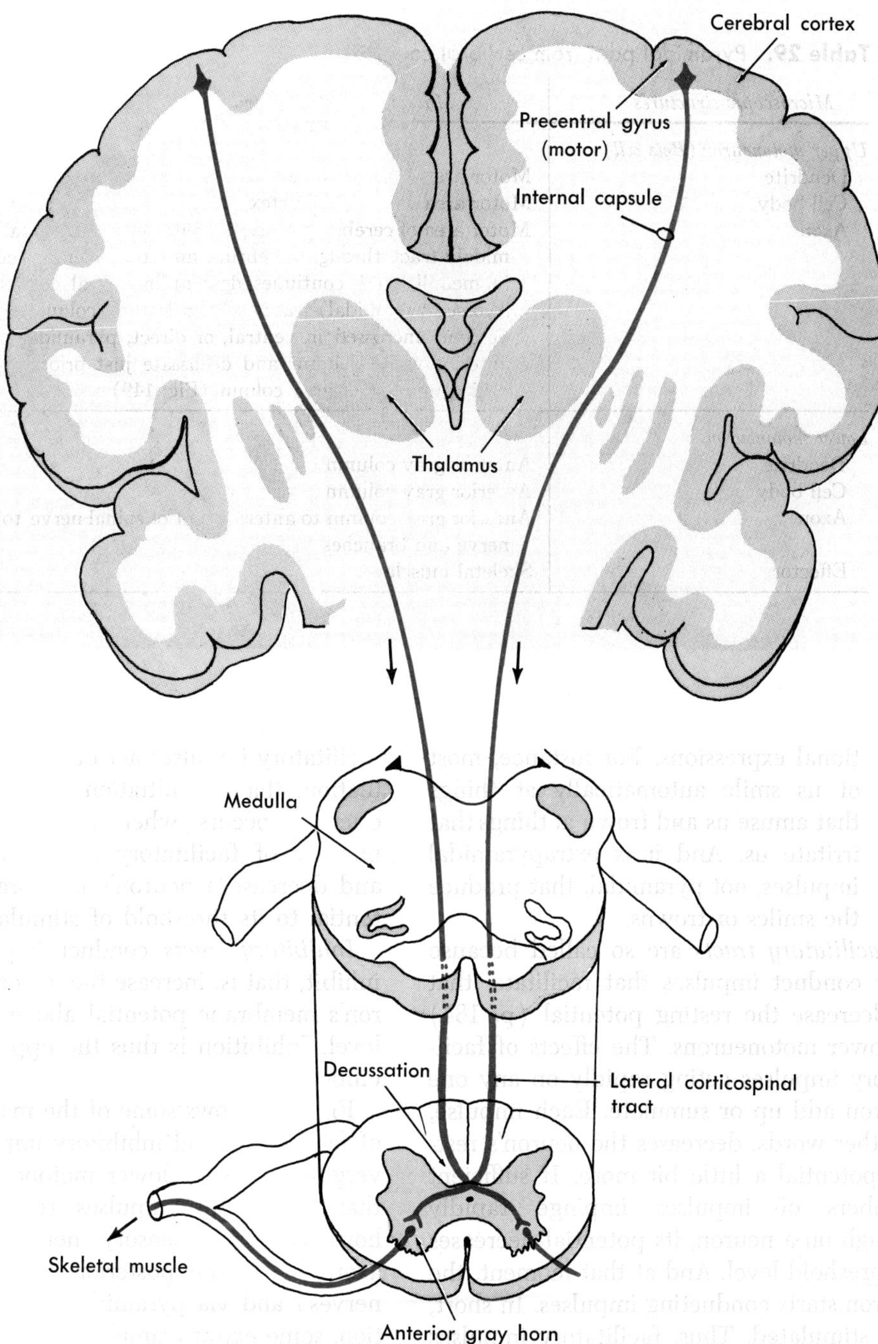

Fig. 149

Crossed pyramidal tract (decussation) below the level of the medulla (also see Fig. 148).

Table 29. Pyramidal path from cerebral cortex

Microscopic structures	*Macroscopic structures in which neurons located*
Upper motoneuron (*Betz cell*)	
Dendrite	Motor area of cerebral cortex
Cell body	Motor area of cerebral cortex
Axon	Motor area of cerebral cortex; descends in corticospinal (pyramidal) tract through cerebrum and brainstem; decussates in medulla and continues descent in lateral corticospinal (crossed pyramidal) tract in lateral white column; or may descend uncrossed in ventral, or direct, pyramidal tract in anterior white column and decussate just prior to terminating in anterior gray column (Fig. 149)
Lower motoneuron	
Dendrite	Anterior gray column
Cell body	Anterior gray column
Axon	Anterior gray column to anterior root of spinal nerve to spinal nerve and branches
Effector	Skeletal muscle

tional expressions. For instance, most of us smile automatically at things that amuse us and frown at things that irritate us. And it is extrapyramidal impulses, not pyramidal, that produce the smiles or frowns.

Facilitatory tracts are so called because they conduct impulses that facilitate, that is, decrease the resting potential (p. 184) of lower motoneurons. The effects of facilitatory impulses acting rapidly on any one neuron add up or summate. Each impulse, in other words, decreases the neuron's resting potential a little bit more. If sufficient numbers of impulses impinge rapidly enough on a neuron, its potential decreases to threshold level. And at that moment, the neuron starts conducting impulses. In short, it is stimulated. Thus, facilitatory impulses can either facilitate or stimulate a neuron. Facilitation—a decrease in a neuron's resting potential to some point above its threshold level—occurs when relatively few facilitatory impulses act on a neuron. Stimulation, that is, initiation of impulse conduction, occurs when a relatively large number of facilitatory impulses summate and decrease a neuron's membrane potential to its threshold of stimulation.

Inhibitory tracts conduct impulses that inhibit, that is, increase the lower motoneuron's membrane potential above its resting level. Inhibition is thus the opposite of facilitation.

Fig. 150 shows some of the main sources of facilitatory and inhibitory impulses converging upon the lower motoneuron. Note that facilitatory impulses reach anterior horn cells via sensory neurons (whose axons lie in the posterior roots of spinal nerves) and via pyramidal tracts. In addition, some extrapyramidal tract fibers bring facilitatory impulses to anterior horn cells. Facilitatory extrapyramidal fibers are believed to come mainly from neuron cell bodies located in the so-called *facilitatory area* in the lateral reticular formation of the brainstem. According to recent evidence, impulses over these facilitatory reticulospinal fibers facilitate the lower motoneurons that supply extensor muscles. And at the same time they reciprocally inhibit the lower motoneurons that supply flexor muscles. Hence, facilitatory reticulospinal impulses tend to increase the tone of extensor muscles and decrease the tone of flexor muscles.

Inhibitory impulses reach lower motoneurons mainly via inhibitory reticulospinal fibers that originate from cell bodies located in the *bulbar inhibitory area* in the medulla. They inhibit the lower motoneurons to extensor muscles (and reciprocally stimulate those to flexor muscles). Hence, inhibitory reticulospinal impulses tend to decrease extensor muscle tone and increase flexor muscle tone—opposite effects from facilitatory reticulospinal impulses.

Brainstem inhibitory and facilitatory areas receive impulses from various higher motor centers—notably from the cerebral cortex, cerebellum, and basal ganglia. But the pathways which transmit impulses from these centers to the brainstem centers are complex and poorly understood. Normally, the ratio of facilitatory and inhibitory

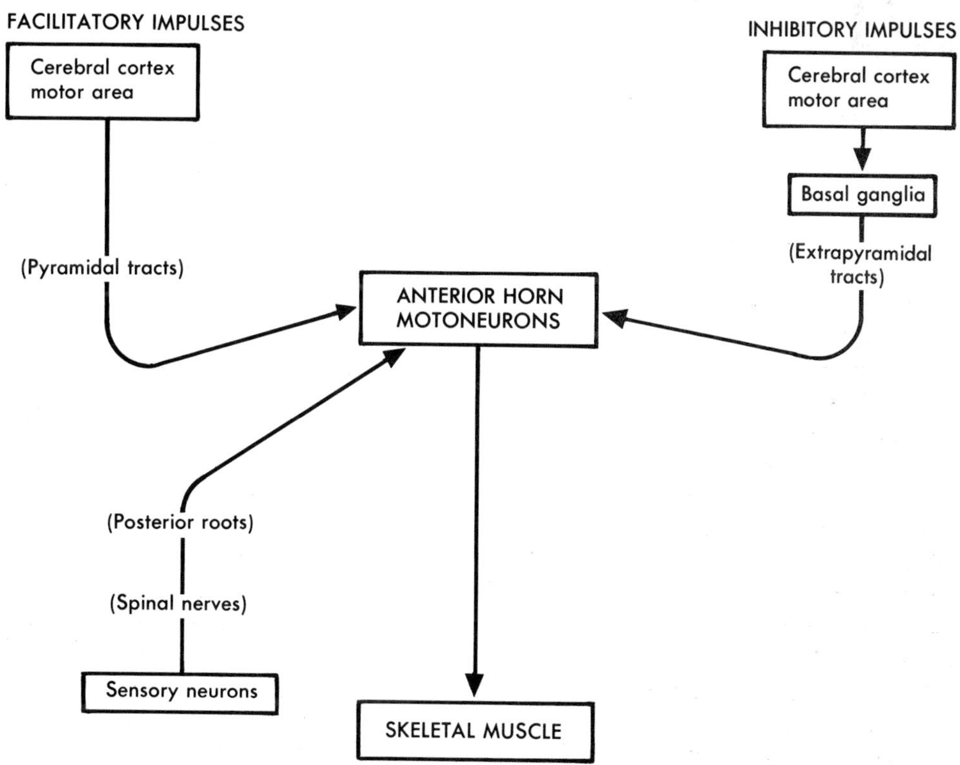

Fig. 150

The main sources of impulses converging on the lower motoneuron. Impulses via the pyramidal tracts and via proprioceptive and other sensory neurons exert a stimulating or facilitatory effect on the lower motoneuron. Impulses relayed through the basal ganglia and some extrapyramidal tracts—notably inhibitory reticulospinal fibers—exert an inhibitory effect on these cells. Not shown, for example, are facilitatory extrapyramidal tracts, including some reticulospinal fibers.

impulses converging upon lower motoneurons is such as to maintain normal muscle tone. In other words, facilitatory impulses normally somewhat exceed inhibitory impulses. But disease sometimes alters this ratio. Parkinson's disease and "strokes," for example, may interrupt transmission by inhibitory extrapyramidal paths through basal ganglia to bulbar inhibitory centers. Facilitatory impulses then predominate, and excess muscle tone (rigidity or spasticity) develops. Injury of *upper motoneurons* (those whose axons lie in either pyramidal or extrapyramidal tracts) produces symptoms frequently referred to as "pyramidal signs," notably a spastic type of paralysis, exaggerated deep reflexes, and a positive Babinski reflex (see p. 230). Actually, pyramidal signs result from interruption of both pyramidal and extrapyramidal pathways. The paralysis stems mainly from interruption of pyramidal tracts, whereas the spasticity (rigidity) and exaggerated reflexes come from interruption of inhibitory extrapyramidal pathways.

Injury of lower motoneurons produces different symptoms from upper motoneuron injury. Anterior horn cells or lower motoneurons, you will recall, constitute the final common path by which impulses reach skeletal muscles. This means that if they are injured, impulses can no longer reach the muscles they supply. This, in turn, means that reflexes involving these muscles are no longer possible and that these muscles cannot be moved at the patient's will and that they therefore lose their normal tone and become soft and flabby (flaccid). In short, absence of reflexes and flaccid paralysis are the chief "lower motoneuron signs."

Reflexes

Definition

The action that results from a nerve impulse passing over a reflex arc is called a *reflex*. In other words, a reflex is a response to a stimulus. It may or may not be conscious. Usually the term is used to mean only involuntary responses rather than those directly willed (that is, involving cerebral cortex activity).

Some reflexes of clinical importance

Clinical interest in reflexes stem from the fact that they deviate from normal in certain diseases. So the testing of reflexes is a valuable diagnostic aid. Physicians frequently test the following reflexes: knee jerk, ankle jerk, Babinski reflex, corneal reflex, and abdominal reflex.

Knee jerk. The knee jerk or patellar reflex is an extension of the lower leg in response to tapping of the patellar tendon. The tap stretches both the tendon and its muscles, the quadriceps femoris, and thereby stimulates muscle spindles (receptors) in the muscle and initiates conduction over the following two-neuron reflex arc (Fig. 122):

1. *Sensory neurons*
   (a) Dendrites—in femoral nerves and in second, third, and fourth lumbar nerves
   (b) Cell bodies—second, third, and fourth ganglia
   (c) Axons—in posterior roots of second, third, and fourth lumbar nerves; terminate in spinal cord, anterior gray columns; synapse directly with lower motoneurons
2. *Reflex center*—synapses in anterior gray column between axons of sensory neurons and dendrites and cell bodies of lower motoneurons
3. *Motoneurons*
   (a) Dendrites and cell bodies—in spinal cord anterior gray column
   (b) Axons—in anterior roots of second, third, and fourth lumbar spinal nerves, these spinal nerves, and femoral nerves; terminate in quadriceps femoris muscle

Table 30. Correlation of microscopic and macroscopic structures of a spinal cord reflex arc*

Microscopic structures	*Macroscopic structures in which neurons located*
Sensory neuron	
Receptor	In skin or mucosa
Dendrite	In spinal nerve and branches
Cell body	In spinal ganglion on posterior root of spinal nerve
Axon	Posterior root of spinal nerve; terminates in posterior gray column of cord
Central neuron	
Dendrite	Posterior gray column
Cell body	Posterior gray column
Axon	Central gray matter of cord, extending into anterior gray column
Motoneuron	
Dendrite	Anterior gray column
Cell body	Anterior gray column
Axon	Anterior gray column, extending into anterior root of spinal nerve, spinal nerve, and its branches
Effector	In skeletal muscles

*See Figs. 123 and 124; Fig. 122 shows the two-neuron cord arc.

The knee jerk can be classified in various ways as follows:

1. As a *spinal cord reflex*—because the center of the reflex arc (which transmits the impulses that activate the muscles which produce the knee jerk) lies in the spinal cord gray matter
2. As a *segmental reflex*—because impulses that mediate it enter and leave the same segment of the cord
3. As an *ipsilateral reflex*—because the impulses that mediate it come from and go to the same side of the body
4. As a *stretch reflex,* or *myotatic reflex* (Greek, *mys,* muscle; + *tasis,* stretching)—because of the kind of stimulation used to evoke it
5. As an *extensor reflex*—because produced by extensor muscles of lower leg
6. As a *tendon reflex*—because tapping of a tendon is the stimulus that elicits it
7. *Deep reflex*—because of the deep location (in tendon and muscle) of the receptors stimulated to produce this reflex (*superficial reflexes*—those elicited by stimulation of receptors located in the skin or mucosa)

When a physician tests a patient's reflexes, he interprets the test results on the basis of what he knows about the reflex arcs which must function to produce normal reflexes.

To illustrate, suppose that a patient has been diagnosed as having poliomyelitis. In examining him, the physician finds that he cannot elicit the knee jerk when he taps the patient's patellar tendon. He knows that the poliomyelitis virus attacks anterior horn motoneurons. And he also knows the information previously related about which cord segments contain the reflex centers for the knee jerk. On the basis of this knowledge, therefore, he deduces that in this patient the poliomyelitis virus has damaged which segments of the spinal cord? Do you think that this patient's leg would be paralyzed, that he would be unable to move it voluntarily? What neurons would not be able to function which must function to produce voluntary contractions?

Ankle jerk. Ankle jerk or Achilles reflex is an extension (plantar flexion) of the foot in response to tapping of the Achilles tendon. It is a deep reflex mediated by two-neuron spinal arcs with centers in the first and second sacral segments of the cord.

Babinski reflex. The Babinski reflex is an extension of the great toe, with or without fanning of the other toes, in response to stimulation of the outer margin of the sole of the foot. Normal babies, up until they are about 1½ years old, show this positive Babinski reflex. By about this time corticospinal fibers have become fully myelinated and the Babinski reflex becomes suppressed. Just why this is so is not clear. But at any rate it is, and a positive Babinski reflex after this age is abnormal. The normal response to stimulation of the outer edge of the sole is the *plantar reflex*. It consists of a curling under of all the toes (plantar flexion) plus a slight turning in and flexion of the anterior part of the foot. A positive Babinski reflex is one of the pyramidal signs (p. 228) and is interpreted to mean destruction of pyramidal tract (corticospinal) fibers.

Corneal reflex. The corneal reflex is winking in response to touching the cornea. It is mediated by reflex arcs with sensory fibers in the ophthalmic branch of the fifth cranial nerve, centers in the pons, and motor fibers in the seventh cranial nerve.

Abdominal reflex. The abdominal reflex is drawing in of the abdominal wall in response to stroking the side of the abdomen. It is mediated by arcs with sensory and motor fibers in the ninth to twelfth thoracic spinal nerves and centers in these segments of the cord and is classified as a superficial reflex. A decrease in this reflex or its absence occurs in lesions involving pyramidal tract upper motor neurons.

Autonomic nervous system

Definition

By definition, the autonomic nervous system consists microscopically of motoneurons only and only those whose impulses reach visceral effectors. The term *visceral effectors* may be defined in two ways: in terms of tissues or of organs. In terms of tissues, visceral effectors consist of cardiac muscle, smooth muscle, and glandular epithelium. In terms of organs, visceral effectors consist of the heart, blood vessels, iris, ciliary muscles, hair muscles, various thoracic and abdominal organs, and the body's many glands. Note that all of these structures innervated by the autonomic nervous system are ones we think of as involuntary. They lie beyond our conscious control. They are our automatic parts. They function without our willing them to and, for the most part, without our even being conscious of them.

Even though the autonomic nervous system consists, by definition, of only motoneurons (specifically, those that conduct impulses to visceral effectors), nevertheless sensory neurons also take part in autonomic functioning. The autonomic nervous system functions on the reflex arc principle just as the voluntary nervous system does. But any sensory neuron can theoretically function in both autonomic and somatic reflex arcs. For example, stimulation of cold receptors in the skin can initiate both an autonomic reflex (vasoconstriction of skin blood vessels) and a somatic reflex (shivering). In short, any one sensory neuron can function in both somatic and autonomic arcs, whereas any one motoneuron can function in either a somatic arc or an autonomic arc but not in both.

Divisions

Two anatomically and physiologically separate divisions compose the autonomic nervous system: the sympathetic (or thoracolumbar) division and the parasympathetic (or craniosacral) division. Both divisions consist macroscopically of ganglia and fibers and microscopically, as we have mentioned, of motoneurons.

Macroscopic structure

Sympathetic ganglia lie lateral to the anterior surface of the spinal column. Because short fibers extend between the sympathetic ganglia, connecting them to each other, they look a little like two chains of beads (one chain on each side of the spinal col-

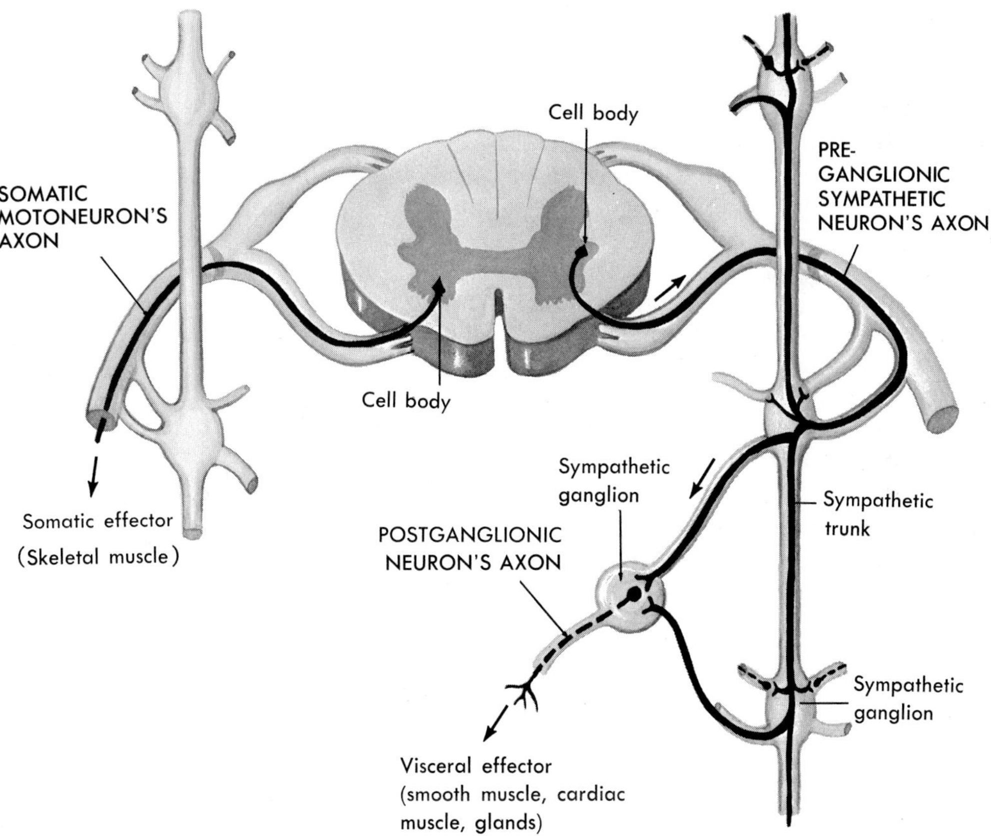

Fig. 151

Diagram showing difference between the neural pathways from the central nervous system to visceral effectors and to somatic effectors. A relay of two autonomic neurons—preganglionic and postganglionic—conduct from cord (or brainstem) to visceral effectors. Note that, in contrast, only one somatic motoneuron (anterior horn neuron) conducts from cord to somatic effectors with no intervening synapses. Note the location of the preganglionic neuron's cell body and axon. Where are the postganglionic neuron's cell body and axon located?

umn from the level of the second cervical vertebra to the coccyx) and are often referred to as the "sympathetic chain ganglia."*

Parasympathetic ganglia lie in or near visceral effectors, not near the spinal column, as do sympathetic ganglia. One example is the ciliary ganglion located in the posterior part of the orbit near the iris and ciliary muscle.

Microscopic structure

Microscopically, the autonomic nervous system consists of preganglionic neurons, postganglionic neurons, and synapses between them. *Preganglionic neurons,* as their name suggests, conduct impulses before they reach the autonomic ganglia. Specifically, preganglionic neurons conduct impulses from either the cord or the brainstem out to autonomic ganglia. Here in the ganglia, the axons of preganglionic neurons synapse with the dendrites and cell bodies of postganglionic neurons. *Postganglionic neurons* are those that conduct impulses from autonomic ganglia to visceral effectors. Note then that a relay of two autonomic neurons conducts impulses from the central nervous system to visceral effectors —a fact noteworthy because it is the most fundamental difference between visceral effector and somatic effector innervation. Only one motoneuron, you will recall, conducts from the central nervous system to a skeletal muscle cell (Fig. 151).

Preganglionic neurons of sympathetic system. The preganglionic neurons of the sympathetic system (Figs. 151 and 152 and Table 31) have their cell bodies in the lateral gray columns of the thoracic and first three or four lumbar segments of the cord. Axons from these cells extend through the anterior roots of the corresponding spinal nerves and through small side branches (the white rami) to the respective sympathetic ganglia. Here, some of them synapse with postganglionic neurons (each axon synapsing with several postganglionic neurons). Other preganglionic axons send branches up and down the sympathetic chain to terminate in ganglia above and below their point of origin. Still others extend through the sympathetic ganglia, out through the splanchnic nerves,* and terminate in the collateral ganglia.

But no matter which course a sympathetic preganglionic axon follows, it synapses with many postganglionic neurons, and these frequently terminate in widely separated organs. This anatomical fact explains a well-known physiological principle—sympathetic responses are usually widespread, involving many organs and not just one.

Postganglionic neurons of sympathetic system. The postganglionic neurons of the sympathetic system have their dendrites and cell bodies in the sympathetic chain ganglia or in collateral ganglia. Their axons are distributed by both spinal nerves and separate autonomic nerves. They reach the spinal nerves via small filaments (gray rami) that connect the sympathetic ganglia with the spinal nerves. They then travel in the spinal nerves to blood vessels, sweat

---

**Sympathetic ganglia*—There are three cervical, ten or eleven thoracic, four lumbar, and four sacral ganglia in each sympathetic chain.

A few sympathetic ganglia, notably the celiac, superior, and inferior mesenteric ganglia, are located a short distance from the cord and therefore are called *collateral ganglia.*

Celiac ganglia (solar plexus)—two fairly large, flat ganglia located on either side of the celiac artery just below the diaphragm.

Superior mesenteric ganglion—small ganglion located near the beginning of the superior mesenteric artery.

Inferior mesenteric ganglion—small ganglion located close to the beginning of the inferior mesenteric artery.

*The three splanchnic nerves constitute the main branches from the thoracic sympathetic trunk. Since their fibers synapse in the celiac and other collateral ganglia with postganglionic neurons to abdominal structures, they form the main route for sympathetic stimulation of abdominal viscera.

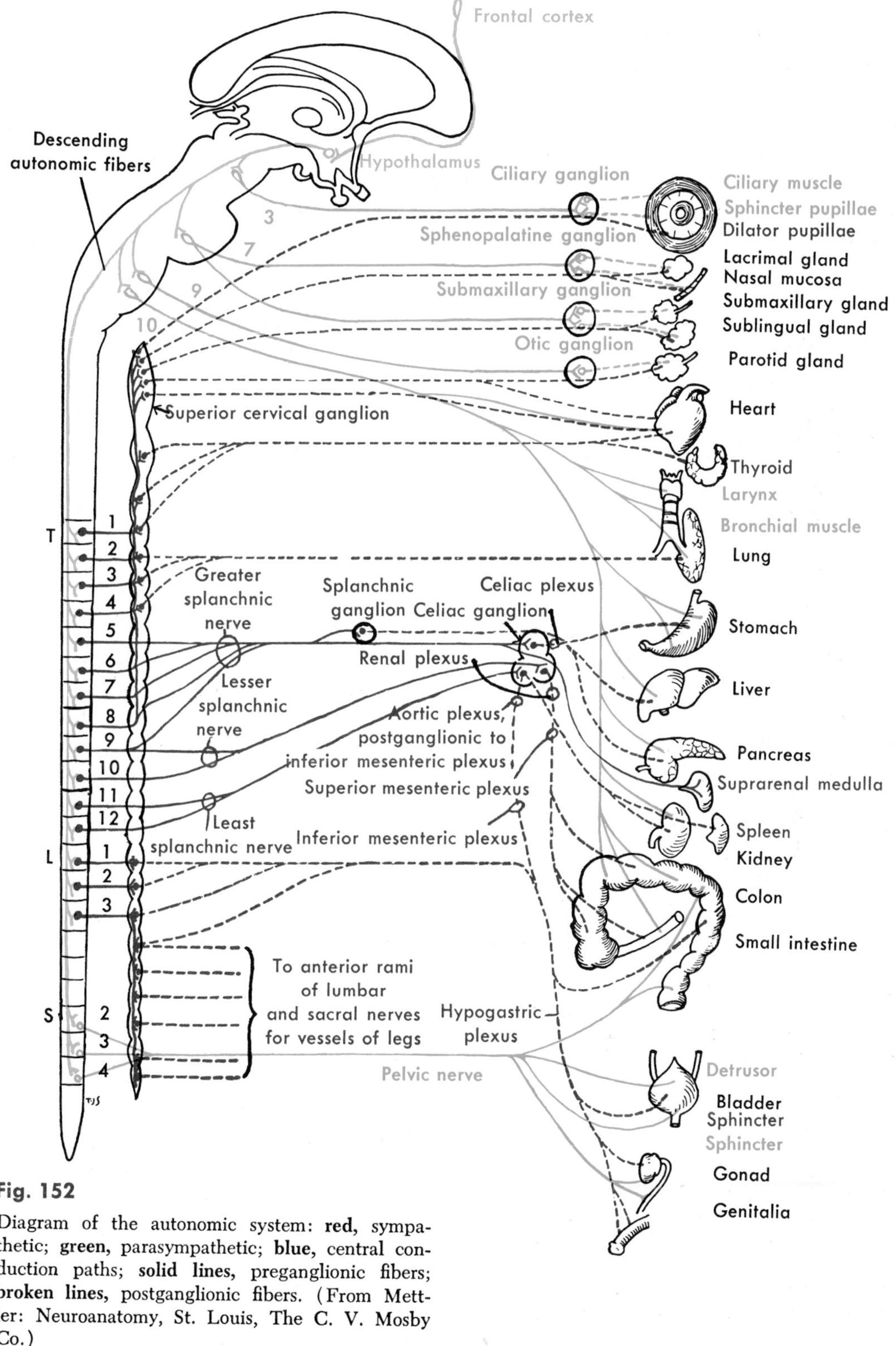

Fig. 152

Diagram of the autonomic system: **red,** sympathetic; **green,** parasympathetic; **blue,** central conduction paths; **solid lines,** preganglionic fibers; **broken lines,** postganglionic fibers. (From Mettler: Neuroanatomy, St. Louis, The C. V. Mosby Co.)

Table 31. Locations of autonomic neurons

Autonomic neurons (motoneurons)	*Macroscopic structures in which located*
Sympathetic division	
Preganglionic neurons	
Dendrites and cell bodies	In lateral gray columns of thoracic and first four lumbar segments of spinal cord
Axons (preganglionic fibers)	In anterior roots of spinal nerves to spinal nerves (thoracic and first four lumbar) to white rami and thence in any of three following pathways: (1) through white rami to sympathetic ganglia, where they synapse with several postganglionic neurons; (2) through white rami to and through sympathetic ganglia, thence up or down sympathetic trunk before synapsing in a sympathetic ganglion with several postganglionic neurons; (3) through white rami to and through sympathetic ganglia, to and through splanchnic nerves to collateral ganglia (celiac, superior, and inferior mesenteric ganglia), where they synapse with several postganglionic neurons
Postganglionic neurons	
Dendrites and cell bodies	In sympathetic or collateral ganglia
Axons (postganglionic fibers)	In autonomic nerves that form various plexuses before supplying thoracic and abdominal viscera and blood vessels in these body cavities, or Through gray rami to spinal nerves to cutaneous blood vessels, sweat glands, and smooth muscles of hair follicles
Parasympathetic division	
Preganglionic neurons	
Dendrites and cell bodies	In midbrain, pons, or medulla (or lateral gray columns of sacral cord)
Axons (preganglionic fibers)	From midbrain to third cranial nerve to ciliary ganglion or From pons to seventh cranial nerve to sphenopalatine ganglion or submaxillary ganglion or From medulla to (1) ninth cranial nerve to otic ganglion or (2) tenth and eleventh cranial nerves to cardiac and celiac ganglia
Postganglionic neurons	
Dendrites and cell bodies	In various ganglia (ciliary, sphenopalatine, submaxillary, otic, cardiac, and celiac) located in or near organs
Axons (postganglionic fibers)	In short nerve filaments to various viscera, glands, blood vessels, and intrinsic eye muscles

glands, and arrector hair muscles all over the body.

The course of postganglionic axons through autonomic nerves is somewhat more complex. These nerves form complicated plexuses before fibers are finally distributed to their respective destinations. For example, postganglionic fibers from the celiac and superior mesenteric ganglia pass through the celiac plexus before reaching the abdominal viscera, those from the inferior mesenteric ganglion pass through the hypogastric plexus on their way to the lower abdominal and pelvic viscera, and those from the cervical ganglion pass through the cardiac nerves and the cardiac plexus at the base of the heart and are then distributed to the heart.

Preganglionic neurons of parasympathetic system. The preganglionic neurons of the parasympathetic system have their cell bodies in nuclei in the brainstem or in the lateral gray columns of the sacral cord. Their axons are contained in cranial nerves III, VII, IX, X, and XI and in some pelvic nerves. They extend a considerable distance before synapsing with postganglionic neurons. For example, axons arising from cell bodies in the vagus nuclei (located in the medulla) travel in the vagus nerve for a distance of a foot or more before reaching their terminal ganglia in the chest and abdomen (Fig. 152 and Table 31).

Postganglionic neurons of parasympathetic system. The postganglionic neurons of the parasympathetic system have their dendrites and cell bodies in the outlying parasympathetic ganglia and send short axons into the nearby structures. Each parasympathetic preganglionic neuron synapses, therefore, only with postganglionic neurons to a single structure. For this reason, parasympathetic stimulation frequently involves response by only one organ as contrasted with sympathetic responses which, as noted before, usually involve numerous organs.

Some general principles

Following are some general principles about the autonomic nervous system.

1. *Principle of dual autonomic innervation.* Most visceral effectors receive both sympathetic and parasympathetic fibers. Examples are cardiac muscle, smooth muscle of the iris, ciliary body, bronchial tubes, and digestive tract, and some glands (Fig. 152).

2. *Principle of single autonomic innervation.* Some visceral effectors are believed to receive only sympathetic fibers. Examples are the adrenal medulla, sweat glands, and probably the smooth muscle of hairs and most blood vessels.

3. *Principle of autonomic chemical transmitters.* Terminals of autonomic axons, like those of all axons, release chemicals that transmit impulses across synapses and neuroeffector junctions. Autonomic axons fall into two classifications based on the chemical transmitters that they release. Some release acetylcholine so are classified as cholinergic fibers. Others release norepinephrine (and lesser amounts of epinephrine) so are classified as adrenergic fibers.

The following are cholinergic autonomic fibers:

(a) All preganglionic axons
(b) All (or almost all) parasympathetic postganglionic axons
(c) A few sympathetic postganglionic axons, namely, those to sweat glands, and also those to smooth muscle in the walls of certain blood vessels (that is, blood vessels in skeletal muscles and some parts of the skin)

The only adrenergic nerve fibers are sympathetic postganglionic axons. But not even all of these fibers are adrenergic. Sympathetic postganglionic axons to sweat glands, skeletal muscle blood vessels, and some skin vessels are cholinergic as mentioned in (c).

4. *Principle of autonomic antagonism and summation.* Both sympathetic and parasympathetic impulses continually play on

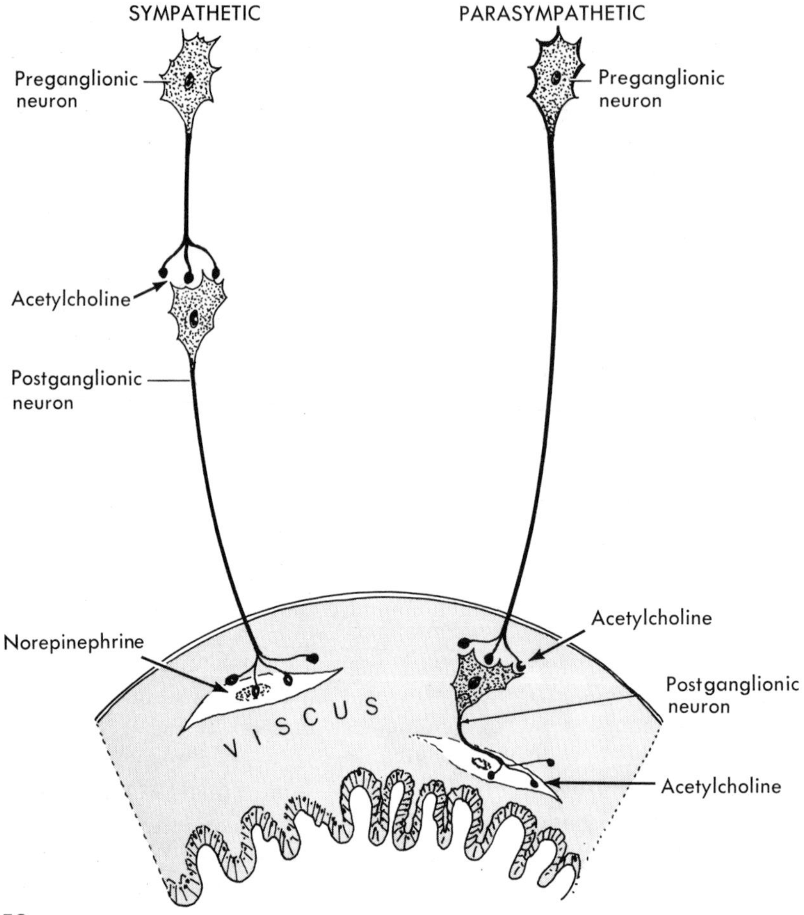

Fig. 153

Diagram of cholinergic fibers (those which release acetylcholine at their terminals) and adrenergic fibers (those which release norepinephrine and some epinephrine). Acetylcholine normally is destroyed almost immediately by cholinesterase, an enzyme.

doubly innervated visceral effectors and tend to produce antagonistic effects on them. Stated differently, acetylcholine and its antagonists, norepinephrine and epinephrine, are continually released at the neuroeffector junctions of doubly innervated structures. Acetylcholine tends to make them respond in one way, while norepinephrine and epinephrine tend to make them respond in the opposite way. Hence, the algebraic sum of these opposing chemicals determines the actual response. Here is one example of this principle of autonomic antagonism in operation: parasympathetic fibers to the heart release acetylcholine whch tends to slow the heart rate. At the same time, sympathetic fibers to the heart release norepinephrine and epinephrine, and these chemicals tend to accelerate the heart rate. Therefore, at any one moment, the algebraic sum of these antagonists determines the actual rate of the heartbeat. If sympathetic impulses increase, the heart rate increases. If parasympathetic impulses increase, the heart rate decreases.

5. *Principle of autonomic functioning*

and homeostasis. Together, summated, parasympathetic and sympathetic impulses regulate the activities of visceral effectors under normal conditions so that their responses maintain or quickly restore homeostasis.

6. *Principle of parasympathetic dominance of digestive tract glands and smooth muscle.* Under normal conditions, parasympathetic impulses to the digestive glands and to the smooth muscle of the digestive tract dominate over sympathetic impulses to them. As shown in Table 32, parasympathetic impulses tend to increase digestive gland secretions and to stimulate the smooth muscle of the digestive tract. In short, parasympathetic impulses tend to promote digestion and peristalsis. They also tend to promote elimination (defecation and also urination).

7. *Principle of sympathetic dominance under stress conditions.* Under stress conditions, from either physical or emotional causes, sympathetic impulses to most visceral effectors increase greatly and cause them to respond in ways which enable the body to put forth its greatest physical effort, to expend its maximal amount of energy. Sympathetic dominance, to use Cannon's now classic phrase, prepares the body for "fight or flight." In fact, one of the very first steps in the body's complex defense mechanism against stress is a sudden and marked increase in sympathetic activity. Note the sympathetic effects listed in Table 32 and see if you can deduce the role each would play in making the body ready to fight or take flight.

Psychosomatic disorders illustrate an interesting principle—that emotions not outwardly expressed tend to be inwardly expressed. In other words, emotions not expressed through somatic effectors tend to be expressed through visceral effectors. You may have seen this principle operate in your own body. You have if, for example, you have ever been angry and gone for a walk to "work it off" and afterward felt "calmed down." Before your emotion expressed itself through your somatic effectors (skeletal muscle contractions during walking), it undoubtedly was expressing itself through your visceral effectors—your heart was probably beating faster than usual, your blood pressure may have increased, and your salivary glands probably were secreting less saliva than usual, perhaps so little that you were conscious of your mouth feeling dry.

Sympathetic impulses usually dominate the control of most visceral effectors in times of stress. But not always. Curiously enough, parasympathetic impulses frequently become excessive to some effectors at such times. For instance, one of the first symptoms of emotional stress in many individuals is that they feel hungry and want to eat more than usual. Presumably this is party caused by increased parasympathetic impulses to the smooth muscle of the stomach. This stimulates increased gastric contractions which, in turn, may cause the feeling of hunger. The most famous disease of parasympathetic excess is peptic ulcer. In some individuals (presumably those born with certain genes), chronic stress leads to excessive parasympathetic stimulation of hydrochloric acid glands, with eventual development of peptic ulcer.

8. *Principle of nonautonomy.* The autonomic nervous system is not autonomous. It is neither anatomically nor physiologically independent of the rest of the nervous system. It and all parts of the nervous system work together as a single functional unit. As evidence of the nonautonomy of the autonomic system, consider the following facts. All preganglionic neurons have their dendrites and cells located in the brain and cord gray matter, in the "lower autonomic centers." Moreover, fibers of numerous descending spinal cord tracts synapse with preganglionic neurons. And therefore impulses from various higher cen-

Table 32. Autonomic functions

Visceral effectors	*Parasympathetic effects*	*Sympathetic effects*
Cardiac muscle	Slows heart rate	Accelerates rate
Smooth muscle		
1. Of bronchi	Stimulates → Bronchial constriction	Inhibits → Bronchial dilatation
2. Of blood vessels in skin and most viscera	No parasympathetic innervation	Stimulates → Vasoconstriction
3. Of blood vessels in skeletal muscles	No parasympathetic innervation	Cholinergic sympathetic fibers → Vasodilatation
4. Of coronary arteries	Authorities disagree	Authorities disagree
5. Of digestive tract	Stimulates → Increased peristalsis	Inhibits → Decreased peristalsis
6. Of anal sphincter	Inhibits → Opens sphincter for defecation	Stimulates → Closes sphincter
7. Of eye		
(a) Iris	Stimulates circular fibers → Constriction of pupil	Stimulates radial fibers → Dilation of pupil
(b) Ciliary	Stimulates → Accommodation for near vision (bulging of lens)	Inhibits → Accommodation for far vision (flattening of lens)
8. Of hairs (pilomotor muscles)	Inhibits	Stimulates → "Goose pimples"
9. Of urinary bladder	Stimulates	Inhibits
10. Of urinary sphincters	Inhibits → Opens sphincter for urination	Stimulates → Closes sphincter
Glands		
1. Sweat	None	Cholinergic sympathetic fibers stimulate sweat glands
2. Digestive (salivary, gastric, etc.)	Stimulates secretion	Vasoconstriction; decreased secretion
3. Pancreas, including islets	Stimulates secretion	Vasoconstriction; decreased secretion
4. Liver	None	Stimulates glycogenolysis which tends to increase blood sugar
5. Adrenal medulla	None	Stimulates adrenalin secretion which tends to increase blood sugar, blood pressure, and heart rate and to produce many other sympathetic effects

ters impinge upon and control the lower autonomic centers.

You may be wondering why the name autonomic system was ever chosen in the first place if the system is really not autonomous. Originally the term seemed appropriate. The autonomic system seemed to be self-regulating and independent of the rest of the nervous system. Common observations furnished abundant evidence of its independence from cerebral control, from direct control by the will, that is. But later even this was found to be not entirely true. Some rare and startling exceptions were discovered. I have seen one such exception—a man who sat in a brightly lighted amphitheater in front of a class of medical students and made his pupils change from small, constricted dots (normal response to bright light) to widely dilated circles. This same man also willed gooseflesh to appear on his arms by contracting the smooth muscles of the hairs.

Higher autonomic centers

Reflex centers of the autonomic nervous system are classified as lower and higher centers depending upon their locations in the central nervous system. Lower autonomic centers lie in gray matter of the spinal cord or brainstem (medulla, pons, and midbrain). They consist essentially of synapses with dendrites and cell bodies of preganglionic neurons. Higher autonomic centers lie in various parts of the brain located above the brainstem— notably, in the hypothalamus and in the limbic system. Impulses from these centers are conducted to lower autonomic centers via various pathways. Hence, higher autonomic centers help control both sympathetic and parasympathetic functioning.

The term limbic comes from a word meaning border or fringe. And the *limbic system** consists mainly of cerebral cortex located on the medial surface of the brain and forming a border around the corpus callosum. The higher autonomic centers of the limbic system and hypothalamus function as important parts of the neural mechanisms for producing the responses characteristic of different emotions. As yet, however, these mechanisms are not clearly understood.

*Rhinencephalon (literally, "nose brain") is an older name for about the same structures now known as the limbic system.

Outline summary— The nervous system

Cells

NEUROGLIA

1. Types—astrocytes, microglia, oligodendroglia
2. Structure and function
   a. astrocytes—star-shaped; numerous processes twine around neurons and attach them to blood vessels; support neurons and may carry on phagocytosis
   b. microglia—small cells but enlarge and move about in inflamed brain tissue; carry on phagocytosis
   c. oligodendroglia—fewer processes than other two types of neuroglia; support neurons, connect them to blood vessels

NEURONS

1. Classification
   a. classification according to function
      1. sensory or afferent-transmit impulses to cord or brain
      2. motoneurons (efferent)—conduct away from brain or cord
      3. interneurons (internuncial or intercalated)—conduct from sensory to motoneurons
   b. classification according to structure
      1. multipolar—several dendrites, one axon
      2. bipolar—one dendrite, one axon
      3. unipolar—one process comes off neuron cell body but divides almost immediately into dendrite and axon

2. Structure—see Figs. 119 and 120
3. Function—respond to stimulation by conducting impulses

Nerve impulse

1. Nature
   a. when neuron not conducting, outer surface of its membrane about 70 mv. positive to inner surface; this difference in electrical charge called resting potential
   b. stimulus increases permeability of neuron membrane to sodium ions
   c. rapid inward diffusion of sodium ions causes outer surface of membrane to become negative to inner surface; this difference in charge called action potential or nerve impulse
2. Conduction
   a. initiation of conduction
      1. normally, impulse conduction starts with stimulation of receptors (distal ends of sensory neurons)
      2. threshold stimulus—just strong enough to decrease receptor potential to critical level—threshold of stimulation
      3. subthreshold stimulus – decreases membrane potential below resting level but not down to threshold level
   b. course of conduction
      1. generally, nerve impulse initiated in receptors, conducted over reflex arcs, and terminates in effectors (muscles and glands), causing reflex response
      2. two-neuron or monosynaptic reflex arc—simplest arc possible; consists of at least one sensory neuron, one synapse, and one motoneuron (synapse is contact point between axon terminals of one neuron and dendrites or cell body of another neuron)
      3. three-neuron arc—consists of at least one sensory neuron, synapse, interneuron, synapse, and motoneuron
      4. complex, multisynaptic neural pathways also exist; many not clearly understood
   c. rate of conduction—see Table 22, p. 182
   d. conduction across synapses
      1. when impulse reaches axon terminals, they eject chemical transmitter substance into synaptic cleft
      2. chemical released by axon terminals of some neurons lowers the postsynaptic neuron's resting potential; threshold or larger amounts of chemical excite neuron, i.e., stimulate impulse conduction; subthreshold amounts of chemical produce excitatory postsynaptic potential, i.e., facilitate neuron but do not stimulate it to conduct; acetylcholine is chemical released by some facilitatory axons
      3. chemical released by terminals of some axons produces inhibitory postsynaptic potential, i.e., increases resting potential or inhibits postsynaptic neuron; inhibitory chemical unknown

Brain and cord coverings

1. Bony—cranial bones around brain; vertebrae around cord
2. Membranous—called meninges and consist of three layers
   a. dura mater—white fibrous tissue outer layer
   b. arachnoid membrane—cobwebby middle layer
   c. pia mater—transparent; adherent to outer surface of brain and cord; contains blood vessels; therefore, nutritive layer

Brain and cord fluid spaces

1. Subarachnoid space around brain
2. Subarachnoid space around cord
3. Ventricles and cerebral aqueduct inside brain—four cavities within brain
   a. first and second lateral ventricles—large cavities, one in each cerebral hemisphere
   b. third ventricle—vertical slit in cerebrum beneath corpus callosum and longitudinal fissure
   c. fourth ventricle—diamond-shaped space between cerebellum and medulla and pons; is expansion of central canal of cord
4. Central canal inside cord

Formation and circulation of cerebrospinal fluid

1. Formed by plasma filtering from network of capillaries (choroid plexus) in each ventricle
2. Circulates from lateral ventricles to third ventricle, cerebral aqueduct, fourth ventricle, central canal of cord, subarachnoid space of cord and brain; venous sinuses

Organs

BRAIN

See Fig. 129 for names of major parts of brain

Cerebrum

1. Hemispheres, fissures, and lobes—longitudinal fissure divides cerebrum into two hemispheres, connected only by corpus callosum; each cerebral hemisphere divided by fissures into five lobes: frontal, parietal, temporal, occipital, and island of Reil (insula)
2. Cerebral cortex—outer layer of gray matter arranged in ridges called convolutions or gyri
3. Cerebral tracts—bundles of axons compose white matter in interior of cerebrum; ascending projection tracts transmit impulses toward or to brain; descending projection tracts transmit impulses down from brain to cord; commissural tracts transmit from one hemisphere to other; association tracts transmit from one convolution to another in same hemisphere
4. Basal ganglia (or cerebral nuclei)—masses of gray matter embedded deep inside white matter in interior of cerebrum; caudate, lentiform nucleus (pallidum and putamen), and amygdaloid main basal ganglia
5. Functions—in general, all conscious functions; e.g., analysis, integration, and interpretation of sensations, control of voluntary movements, use and understanding of language, and all other mental functions

Diencephalon—thalamus, epithalamus, subthalamus, and hypothalamus

Thalamus

1. Structure and location—large rounded mass of gray matter in each cerebral hemisphere, lateral to third ventricle; composed of many nuclei
2. Functions
   a. relays afferent impulses to cerebral cortex
   b. conscious recognition of crude sensations of pain, temperature, and touch
   c. involved in emotional component of sensations; feelings of pleasantness or unpleasantness
   d. involved in alerting or arousal mechanism
   e. involved in production of complex reflex movements

Hypothalamus

1. Structure and location
   a. gray matter around optic chiasma, pituitary stalk, posterior lobe of pituitary, mamillary bodies, and adjacent regions; made up of many nuclei, notably supraoptic, paraventricular, and mamillary
   b. afferent tracts conduct impulses to hypothalamus from cerebral cortex, thalamus, and basal ganglia
   c. efferent tracts conduct from hypothalamus to thalamus and to autonomic centers in brainstem and cord
2. Functions
   a. higher autonomic center; helps control and integrate autonomic functions
   b. relay station between cerebral cortex and lower autonomic centers; crucial part of neural paths by which emotions influence bodily functions
   c. crucial part of mechanism for maintaining water balance
   d. important part of mechanism for controlling anterior pituitary gland
   e. essential part of arousal or alerting mechanism; essential for maintaining waking state
   f. crucial part of mechanism for regulating appetite and food intake
   g. crucial part of mechanism for maintaining normal body temperature
   h. probably helps control various reproductive functions

Cerebellum

Second largest part of human brain

1. Structure and location
   a. has two hemispheres and center section, vermis
   b. surface grooved with sulci
   c. slightly raised, slender convolutions
   d. internal white matter arranged in pattern like veins of leaf
   e. three pairs of tracts in cerebellum—inferior, middle, and superior cerebellar peduncles
   f. most important cerebellar nucleus—dentate nucleus
2. Functions
   a. synergic control of muscle action
   b. postural reflexes
   c. equilibrium

Medulla oblongata

1. Structure and location
   a. part of brain formed by enlargement of cord as it enters cranial cavity

b. mainly white matter (projection tracts); also reticular formation (interlacement of gray and white matter, containing many nuclei)
c. various autonomic centers in reticular formation, e.g., cardiac and vasomotor; also respiratory, vomiting, coughing, hiccoughing, sneezing, and swallowing centers

2. Functions
   a. helps control heartbeat, blood pressure, and respirations
   b. mediates reflexes of vomiting, coughing, hiccoughing, etc.
   c. conducts impulses between cord and brain

Pons varolii

1. Structure and location
   a. located just above medulla
   b. white matter with few nuclei
2. Functions
   a. contains projection tracts between cord and various parts of brain
   b. centers for fifth to eighth cranial nerves

Midbrain

1. Location and structure
   a. located above pons, below cerebrum and diencephalon
   b. white matter with few nuclei
   c. cerebral aqueduct within midbrain
   d. cerebral peduncles are two tracts composing ventral part of midbrain and connecting pons to cerebrum
   e. corpora quadrigemina — four rounded eminences (two superior and two inferior colliculi) on dorsal surface of midbrain
   f. important nucleus—red nucleus
2. Functions
   a. projection tracts function in sensations and movements
   b. centers for third and fourth cranial nerves, hence for pupillary reflexes and eye movements

SPINAL CORD

1. Location
   a. in spinal cavity, from foramen magnum to first lumbar vertebra
   b. meninges continue below that point
2. Structure
   a. core of gray matter shaped like three-dimensional letter H
   b. white matter present in columns, anterior, lateral, and posterior, composed of numerous projection tracts
3. Functions
   a. sensory and motor conduction pathways between peripheral nerves and brain; for names and functions of tracts see Fig. 137, p. 201
   b. composite of reflex centers—for all spinal cord reflexes

CRANIAL NERVES

1. Twelve pairs
2. See Table 25, p. 204, for distribution and function

SPINAL NERVES

1. Thirty-one pairs
2. Origin—originate by anterior and posterior roots from cord, emerge through intervertebral foramina; spinal ganglion on each posterior root
3. Distribution—branches distributed to skin, mucosa, skeletal muscles; branches form plexuses, such as brachial plexus, from which nerves emerge to supply various parts
4. Microscopic structure—consist of sensory dendrites and motor axons; i.e., are mixed nerves; also contain autonomic postganglionic fibers; see Table 26, p. 212, for peripheral branches
5. Functions—see Table 27, p. 218

Sensory neural pathways

See Table 28, p. 220

1. Three-neuron relay conducts impulses from periphery to cerebral cortex
   a. sensory neuron I conducts from periphery to cord or to brainstem
   b. sensory neuron II conducts from cord or brainstem to thalamus
   c. sensory neuron III conducts from thalamus to general sensory area of cerebral cortex (areas 3, 1, 2)
2. Crude awareness of sensations occurs when impulses reach thalamus
3. Full consciousness of sensations with accurate localization and discrimination occurs when impulses reach cerebral cortex
4. Most sensory neuron II axons decussate; so one side of brain registers mainly sensations for opposite side of body
5. Principle of divergence applies to sensory impulse conduction; each sensory neuron synapses with more than one neuron;

hence impulses over any sensory neuron diverge and may activate many effectors

6. Pain and temperature—lateral spinothalamic tracts to thalamus
7. Touch and pressure
   a. discriminating touch and pressure (stereognosis, precise localization, vibratory sense)—medial lemniscal system (fasciculi cuneatus and gracilis to medulla; medial lemniscus to thalamus)
   b. crude touch and pressure—ventral spinothalamic tracts
8. Conscious proprioception or kinesthesia—medial lemniscal system to thalamus

Arousal or alerting mechanism

Cerebral cortex stimulated by impulses from reticular formation which is stimulated by sensory impulses of all kinds reaching it

Motor neural pathways to skeletal muscles

1. Principle of the common path—motor neurons in anterior gray horns of cord constitute final common path for impulses to skeletal muscles; are only neurons transmitting impulses into skeletal muscles
2. Principle of convergence—axons of many neurons synapse with each anterior horn motoneuron
3. Motor pathways from cerebral cortex to anterior horn cells classified according to way fibers enter cord:
   a. pyramidal tracts (or corticospinal tracts)—dendrites and cells in cortex, axons enter cord by way of pyramids of medulla, synapse directly with anterior horn cells or indirectly via internuncial neurons; impulses via pyramidal tracts essential for voluntary contractions of individual muscles to produce small discrete movements; also help maintain muscle tone
   b. extrapyramidal tracts—all pathways between motor cortex and anterior horn cells, except pyramidal tracts; upper extrapyramidal tracts relay impulses between cortex, basal ganglia, thalamus, and brainstem; reticulospinal tracts main lower extrapyramidal tracts; impulses via extrapyramidal tracts essential for large, automatic movements; also for facial expressions and movements accompanying many emotions
4. Motor pathways from cerebral cortex to anterior horn cells also classified according to influence on anterior horn cells:
   a. facilitatory tracts—have facilitating or stimulating effect on anterior horn cells; all pyramidal tracts and some extrapyramidal tracts facilitatory, notably facilitatory reticulospinal fibers
   b. inhibitory tracts—have inhibiting effect on anterior horn cells; inhibitory reticulospinal fibers main inhibitory tracts
5. Ratio of facilitatory and inhibitory impulses impinging on anterior horn cells controls activity; normally, slight predominance of facilitatory impulses maintains muscle tone

Reflexes

1. Definition—action resulting from conduction over reflex arc; reflex is response (either muscle contraction or glandular secretion) to stimulus; usually term reflex used to mean only involuntary responses
2. Some reflexes of clinical importance—see pp. 228 to 230

Autonomic nervous system

1. Definition—part of nervous system that sends efferent fibers to visceral effectors; specifically, to smooth muscle, cardiac muscle, and glands
2. Divisions—sympathetic (or thoracolumbar) and parasympathetic (or craniosacral)
3. Macroscopic structure
   a. sympathetic division consists of two chains of ganglia (one on either side of backbone) and fibers that connect ganglia with each other and with thoracic and lumbar segments of cord; other fibers extend from sympathetic ganglia out to visceral effectors
   b. parasympathetic division consists of ganglia located on or near viscera with fibers between ganglia and brainstem and between ganglia and sacral region of cord; also fibers from ganglia into viscera and glands
4. Microscopic structure
   a. cell bodies of preganglionic neurons of sympathetic system in lateral gray columns of thoracic and lumbar segments of cord; lower sympathetic centers also located here
   b. cell bodies of postganglionic neurons of sympathetic system in sympathetic chain ganglia or in collateral ganglia

(celiac, superior, and inferior mesenteric)

   c. cells of preganglionic neurons of parasympathetic system in various nuclei of brainstem and in gray matter of sacral segments of cord; lower parasympathetic centers also located here
   d. cells of postganglionic neurons of parasympathetic system in ganglia on or near organs innervated

5. Some general principles
   a. dual autonomic innervation: both sympathetic and parasympathetic fibers supply most visceral effectors
   b. single autonomic innervation: sympathetic fibers but not parasympathetic fibers to adrenal medulla, sweat glands, and probably to smooth muscles of hairs and most blood vessels
   c. autonomic chemical transmitters: autonomic axon terminals release acetylcholine at synapses and either acetylcholine or norepinephrine and epinephrine at neuroeffector junctions; those which release acetylcholine called cholinergic fibers; those which release norepinephrine and epinephrine called adrenergic fibers
      1. all preganglionic axons cholinergic fibers, as are all (or almost all) parasympathetic postganglionic axons and few sympathetic postganglionic axons (to sweat glands and to smooth muscle in walls of blood vessels in skeletal muscles and some parts of skin)
      2. only adrenergic fibers sympathetic postganglionic axons but even few of these cholinergic (see preceding item)
   d. autonomic antagonism and summation: sympathetic and parasympathetic impulses tend to produce opposite effects; algebraic sum of two opposing tendencies determines response made by doubly innervated visceral effector
   e. autonomic functioning and homeostasis: normally, parasympathetic and sympathetic impulses together so regulate activities of visceral effectors that their responses maintain or quickly restore homeostasis
   f. parasympathetic dominance of digestive tract: normally, parasympathetic impulses to glands and smooth muscle of digestive tract dominate over sympathetic impulses to them; parasympathetic impulses promote digestive gland secretion, peristalsis, and defecation
   g. sympathetic dominance in stress: under stress conditions, sympathetic impulses to most visceral effectors increase greatly, causing them to respond in ways which enable body to expend maximal amount of energy; sympathetic dominance one of first defenses against stress; parasympathetic impulses, however, may become excessive to some effectors under stress conditions.
   h. nonautonomy: autonomic nervous system not autonomous with relation to rest of nervous system; partly controlled by higher autonomic centers, notably in hypothalamus and limbic system

6. Higher autonomic centers
   a. located in various parts of brain above brainstem, notably in hypothalamus and limbic system
   b. help control both sympathetic and parasympathetic functioning; play part in expression of emotion

Review questions

1. In a word or two, what general function does the nervous system perfom?
2. What other system serves the same general function?
3. Compare neurons and neuroglia.
4. Make an identifying statement about each of the three types of neurons.
5. What function does the neurilemma serve?
6. What neurons do not have a neurilemma?
7. What microscopic structures compose gray matter? White matter?
8. Agree or disagree with the following statement and give your reasons: Neurons located in the brain or cord, once destroyed, do not regenerate.
9. Briefly explain the following terms: (a) resting potential, (b) action potential, (c) potential difference, (d) depolarized.
10. What term in the preceding question is a synonym for nerve impulse?
11. What are receptors? Effectors?
12. What is a synapse?
13. Name the chemical transmitter known to be released at some synapses. What is its function?
14. What function does cholinesterase serve?
15. Where is a lumbar puncture done? Why?

16. What general name is given to the membranous coverings of the brain and cord? What three layers compose this covering?
17. What are the cavities inside the brain called? How many are there? What do they contain?
18. Describe the circulation of cerebrospinal fluid.
19. What is the function of the cerebrospinal fluid?
20. What name is given to the outer portion of the cerebrum? Describe its appearance. What structure connects its hemispheres?
21. Compare nerves and tracts.
22. What are cerebral nuclei?
23. State at least one specific function performed by each of the lobes of the cerebral cortex: frontal, parietal, temporal, and occipital.
24. Explain the system for naming individual tracts.
25. Based on your explanation in answer to question 20, what is a spinothalamic tract?
26. Compare nucleus and ganglion.
27. What general functions does the cerebral cortex perform?
28. What is the diencephalon? What are its two main parts?
29. What general function does the thalamus perform?
30. What general functions does the hypothalamus perform?
31. What general functions does the cerebellum perform?
32. What general functions does the medulla perform?
33. What general functions does the spinal cord perform?
34. Name several ascending or sensory tracts in the spinal cord.
35. Name two descending or motor tracts in the spinal cord.
36. What is a reflex center?
37. Which cranial nerves transmit impulses that result in vision? In eye movements? Hearing? Taste sensations? Slowing of the heart?
38. What is the great sensory nerve of the head?
39. Digitalis, a drug said to have a stimulating effect on the vagus nerve, has been administered to a patient. What effect, if any, would you expect it to have on the patient's pulse rate?
40. Locate the dendrite, cell body, and axon of sensory neurons (a) I, (b) II, and (c) III.
41. Explain briefly the arousal or alerting mechanism.
42. Explain each of the following: lower motoneuron, upper motoneuron, and final common path.
43. Name the tracts that transmit impulses from each of the following types of receptors to the brain and state in which column of the cord each tract is located: pain and temperature receptors, crude touch receptors, proprioceptors, (name two tracts for these), and discriminating touch receptors (two tracts).
44. Compare pyramidal tract and extrapyramidal tract functions.
45. Explain briefly the general function of the autonomic nervous system; of the sympathetic system; of the parasympathetic system.
46. Sympathetic stimulation produces massive, widespread responses, whereas reactions to parasympathetic stimulation are often highly localized. What anatomical differences between the two systems explain this physiological difference?
47. Contrast these two neural paths: from the central nervous system to somatic effectors; from the central nervous system to visceral effectors.
48. Classify the following structures as somatic effectors, visceral effectors, or neither: adrenal glands, biceps femoris muscle, heart, iris, and skin.
49. Which of the following would indicate an increase in sympathetic impulses and which might indicate an increase in parasympathetic impulses to visceral effectors?

    constipation
    dilated pupils
    dry mouth
    goose pimples
    "I'm always hungry and eat too much when I am upset."
    rapid heartbeat
50. What is the limbic system, and what general function does it perform?

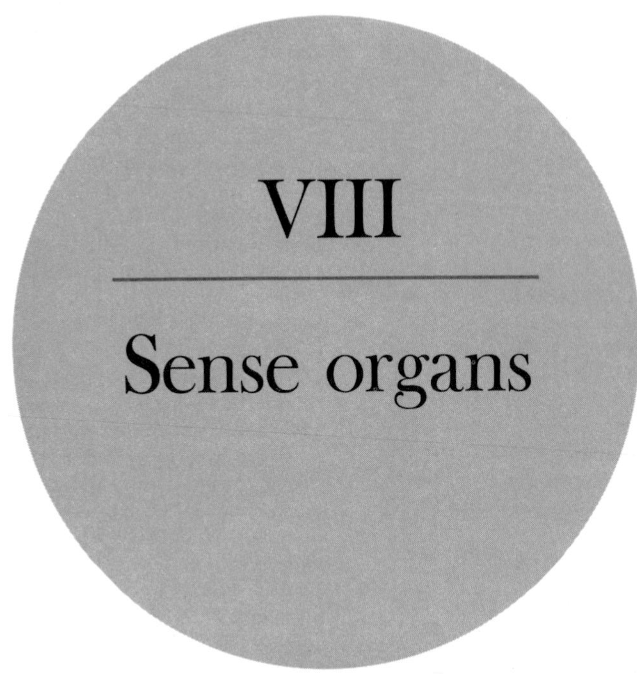

VIII Sense organs

General remarks

The body has millions of sense organs. All of its receptors, the beginnings of dendrites of all its sensory neurons, are its sense organs. They serve two vital general functions—sensations and reflexes. All sensations and all reflexes result from stimulation of receptors. In short, receptors are the structures that detect changes in our external and internal environment and that initiate the responses necessary for adjusting the body to these changes so as to maintain or restore homeostasis. One more point —a matter more of interest than importance—we have more than just the "five senses," vision, hearing, taste, smell, and touch. For example, some of our other senses are warmth, cold, pain, and proprioception.

Receptors are located all over the body, inside as well as on its surfaces. Sherrington classified receptors according to their location as exteroceptors, visceroceptors, and proprioceptors. Exteroceptors are surface receptors. They are located in the skin, mucosa, eye, and ear. Visceroceptors and proprioceptors are both located internally. Visceroceptors are found, for example, in the walls of blood vessels, stomach, intestines, and various other organs. Proprioceptors are located in muscles, tendons, joints, and the internal ear.

Structurally, receptors differ considerably. Some, such as those in the eye and ear, constitute highly specialized sense organs. Others are simply naked or free nerve fibers, and still others are encapsulated nerve fibers. (Fig. 154.)

According to the principle of specificity of receptors, specific kinds of receptors mediate specific sensations because they are sensitive to specific kinds of stimuli. Although generally accepted, this principle is now questioned by some investigators who think one kind of receptor may mediate more than one kind of sensation and that one kind of sensation may be mediated by

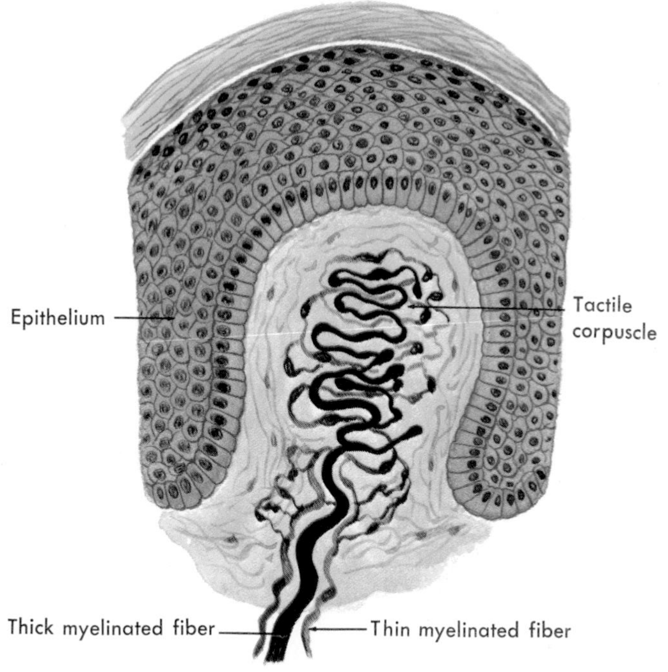

Fig. 154

A Meissner's corpuscle (tactile corpuscle) found in the connective tissue papillae of the skin. It is an example of an encapsulated specialized nerve ending found in the hairless portions of the skin.

Table 33. Receptors and sensations which they mediate

Sensations	*Receptors*
Touch	Meissner's corpuscles (Fig. 154) Merkel's disks Basketlike arrangements around bases of hairs
Pressure	Vater-Pacinian corpuscles
Heat	Corpuscles of Ruffini
Cold	Krause end bulbs
Pain	Naked nerve fibers
Proprioception	Neuromuscular spindles Neurotendinous spindles Ruffini endings in joint capsules

more than one kind of receptor. Generally accepted ideas about which types of receptors mediate which sensations are included in Table 33.

Somatic, visceral, and referred pain

Because stimulation of pain receptors may give warning of potentially harmful environmental changes, pain receptors are also called *nociceptors* (L. *noceo,* to injure). Any type of stimulus, provided that it be sufficiently intense, seems to be adequate for stimulating nociceptors in the skin and mucosa. In contrast, only marked changes in pressure and certain chemicals can stimulate nociceptors located in the viscera. Sometimes this knowledge proves useful. For example, it enables a physician to cauterize the uterine cervix without giving an anesthetic but with assurance that the patient will not suffer pain from the intense heat. On the other hand, he knows that if the intestine becomes markedly distended (as it sometimes does following surgery), the patient will experience pain. So, too, will the individual whose heart becomes ischemic due to coronary occlusion. Presumably, the resulting cellular oxygen deficiency leads to the formation or accumulation of chemicals that stimulate nociceptors in the heart.

Two main types of pain are recognized: somatic and visceral.

Somatic pain may be *superficial,* as when it arises from stimulation of skin receptors, or it may be *deep,* as when it results from stimulation of receptors in the skeletal muscles, fascia, tendons, and joints.

Visceral pain results from stimulation of receptors located in the viscera. Impulses are conducted from these receptors to the cord primarily by sensory fibers in sympathetic nerves and only rarely in parasympathetic nerves.

The cerebrum does not always interpret the source of pain accurately. Sometimes it erroneously refers the pain to a surface area instead of to the region in which the stimulated receptors actually are located. This phenomenon is called *referred pain.* It occurs only as a result of stimulation of pain receptors located in deep structures (skeletal muscles and viscera, for example)—never from stimulation of skin receptors. In other words, deep somatic pain and visceral pain may be referred but not superficial somatic pain.

According to one theory, pain originating in the viscera and other deep structures is interpreted as coming from the skin area whose sensory fibers enter the same segment of the spinal cord as the sensory fibers from the deep structure. For example, sensory fibers from the heart enter the first to fourth thoracic segments. And so do sensory fibers from the skin areas over the heart and on the inner surface of the left arm. Pain originating in the heart, therefore, is referred to those skin areas. Several other theories have also been advanced to explain referred pain.

Eye

ANATOMY

Coats of eyeball

Approximately five-sixths of the eyeball lies recessed in the orbit, protected by this bony socket. Only its small anterior surface is exposed. Three layers of tissues or coats compose the eyeball. From the outside in they are the sclera, the chorioid,* and the retina. Both the sclera and the chorioid coats consist of an anterior and a posterior portion.

Tough white fibrous tissue fashions the *sclera.* Deep within the anterior part of the sclera at its junction with the cornea lies a ring-shaped venous sinus, the *canal*

*The spelling *chorioid* is considered etymologically preferable to the widely used choroid.

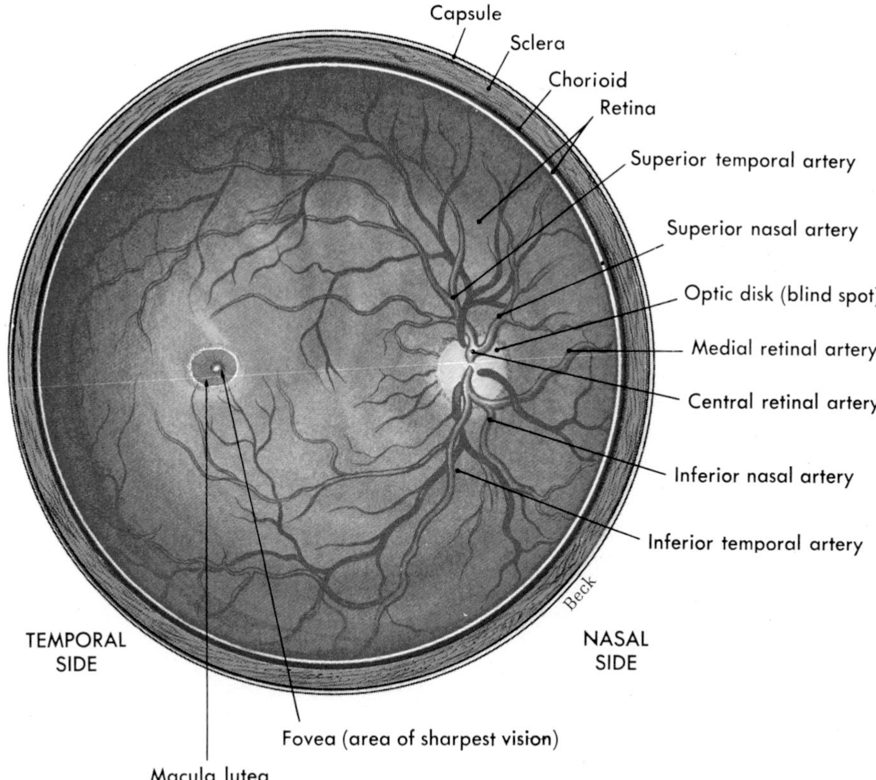

Fig. 155

The right eyeground (fundus) showing vessels, optic disk, the macula lutea, and layers of the eyeball.

of Schlemm (see Figs. 159 to 161). The anterior portion of the sclera is called the *cornea* and lies over the colored part of the eye (iris). The cornea is transparent, whereas the rest of the sclera is white and opaque, a fact which explains why the visible anterior surface of the sclera is usually spoken of as the "whites" of the eyes. No blood vessels are found in the cornea, in the aqueous and vitreous humors, or in the lens.

The middle or *chorioid coat* of the eye contains a great many blood vessels and a large amount of pigment. Its anterior portion is modified into three separate structures: the ciliary body, the suspensory ligament, and the iris.

The *ciliary body* is formed by a thickening of the chorioid and fits like a collar into the area between the anterior margin of the retina and the posterior margin of the iris. The small *ciliary muscle,* composed of both radial and circular smooth muscle fibers, lies in the anterior part of the ciliary body. Attached to the ciliary body is the *suspensory ligament,* which blends with the elastic capsule of the *lens* and holds it suspended in place.

The *iris* or colored part of the eye consists of circular and radial smooth muscle fibers arranged so as to form a doughnut-shaped structure. (The hole in the middle is called the *pupil.*) The iris attaches to the ciliary body.

The *retina* is the incomplete innermost coat of the eyeball—incomplete in that it

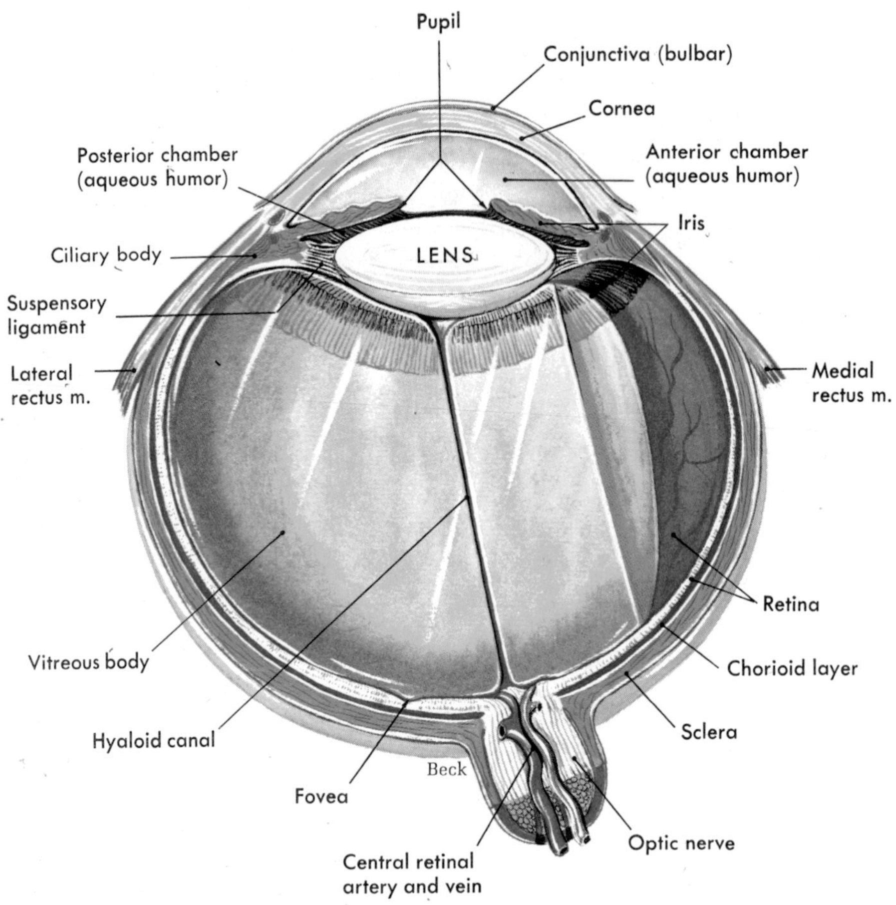

Fig. 156

Horizontal section through the left eyeball.

has no anterior portion. It consists mainly of nervous tissue and contains three layers of neurons (Fig. 158). Named in the order in which they conduct impulses, they are photoreceptor neurons, bipolar neurons, and ganglion neurons. The beginning of the dendrites of the photoreceptor neurons have been given names descriptive of their shapes. Because some look like tiny rods and others like cones, they are called *rods* and *cones,* respectively. They constitute our visual receptors, structures highly specialized for stimulation by light rays (discussed on p. 262). They differ as to numbers, distribution, and function. The estimated number of cones is 7,000,000 and that of rods, somewhere between 10 and 20 times as many. Cones are most densely concentrated in the *fovea centralis,* a small depression in the center of a yellowish area the *macula lutea* found near the center of the retina. They become less and less dense from the fovea outward. Rods, on the other hand, are absent entirely from the fovea and macula and increase in density toward the periphery of the retina. How these anatomical facts relate to rod and cone functions is revealed on p. 262.

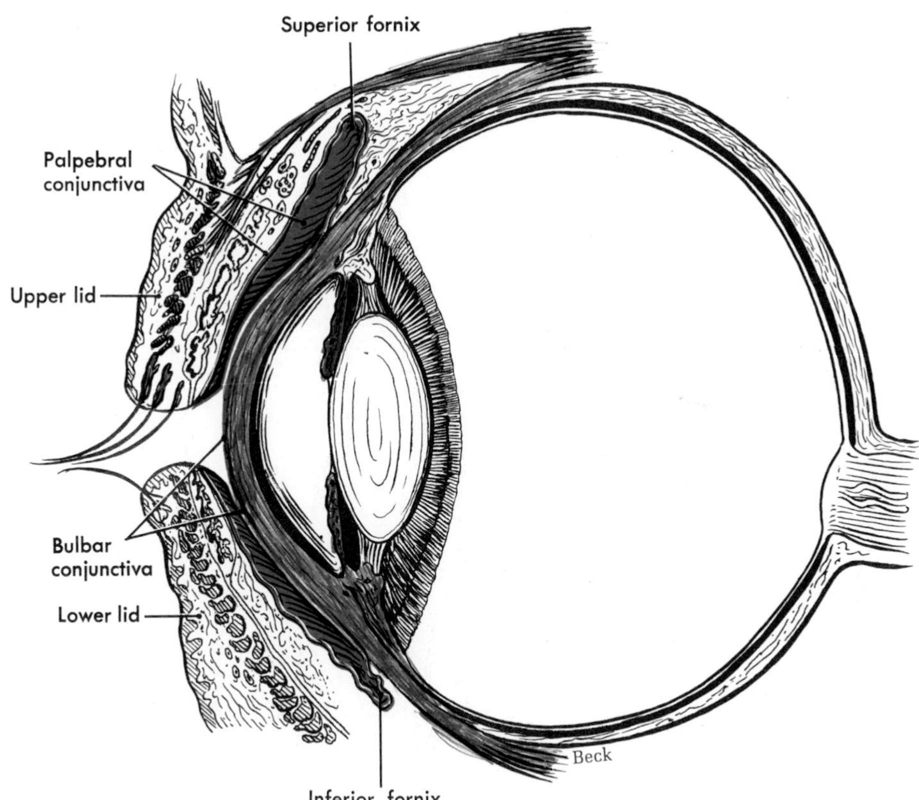

Fig. 157

Longitudinal section through the eyeball and eyelids showing the conjunctiva, a lining of mucous membrane. Conjunctiva which covers the cornea is called bulbar, and that which lines the posterior surface of the eyelids is called palpebral.

All the axons of ganglion neurons extend back to a small circular area in the posterior part of the eyeball known as the *optic disk* or papilla. This part of the sclera contains perforations through which the fibers emerge from the eyeball as the *optic nerves.* The optic disk is also called the *blind spot* because light rays striking this area cannot be seen since it contains no rods or cones, only nerve fibers.

An outline summary of the coats of the eyeball is presented in Table 34.

Cavities and humors

The eyeball is not a solid sphere but contains a large interior cavity that is divided into two cavities, anterior and posterior.

The *anterior cavity* has two subdivisions known as the *anterior* and *posterior chambers.* The entire anterior cavity lies in front of the lens. The posterior chamber of the anterior cavity consists of the space directly posterior to the iris but anterior to the lens. And the anterior chamber of the anterior cavity is the small space anterior to the iris but posterior to the cornea. *Aqueous humor* fills both chambers of the anterior cavity. This substance is clear and watery and often leaks out when the eye is injured.

The *posterior cavity* of the eyeball is considerably larger than the anterior since it

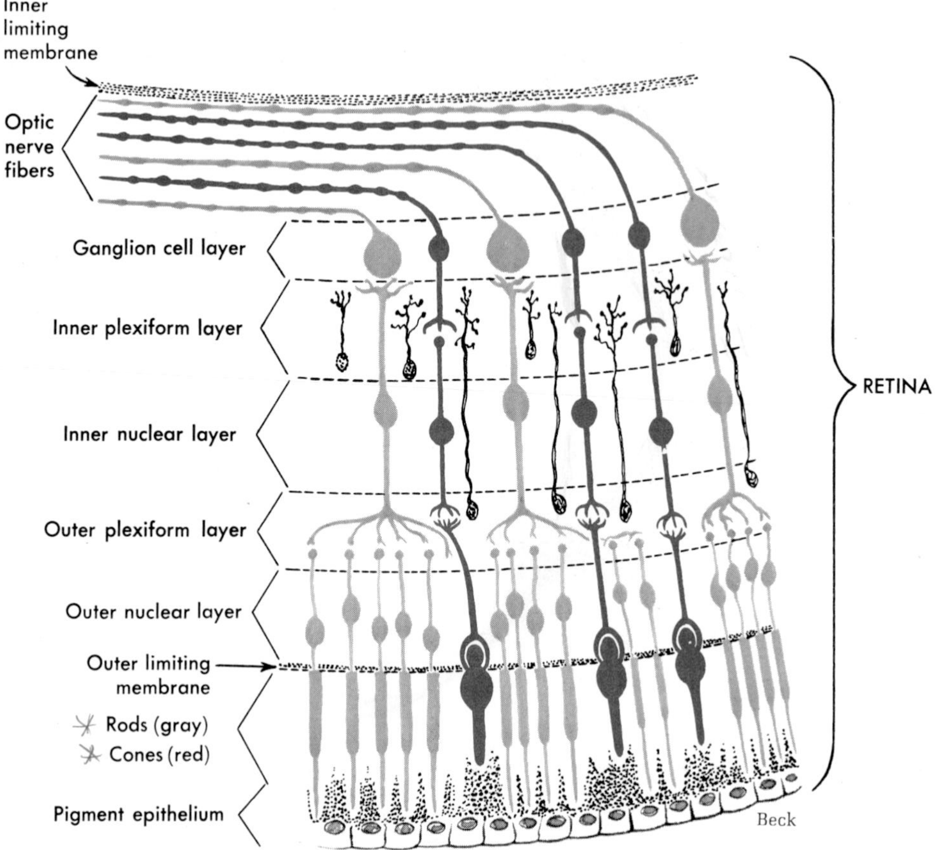

Fig. 158

Schematic diagram of layers that compose the retina. The inner limiting membrane lies nearest the inside of the eyeball. It adheres to the vitreous humor. The pigment epithelium lies farthest from the inside of the eyeball. It adheres to the chorioid coat. Note relay of three neurons in the retina: photoreceptor, bipolar, and ganglion neurons (named in order of impulse transmission). Light rays pass through the vitreous humor and various layers of retina to stimulate rods and cones, the receptors of the photoreceptor neurons.

occupies all the space posterior to the lens, suspensory ligament, and ciliary body. It contains *vitreous humor,* a substance with a consistency comparable to soft gelatin. This semisolid material helps maintain sufficient intraocular pressure to prevent the eyeball from collapsing. (An obliterated artery, the hyaloid canal, runs through the vitreous humor between the lens and optic disk.)

An outline summary of the cavities of the eye is included in Table 35 (also see Fig. 156).

Still not established is the mechanism by which aqueous humor forms. It comes from blood in capillaries (located mainly in the ciliary body). Presumably, the capillaries actively secrete aqueous humor into the posterior chamber. But also passive filtration from capillary blood may contribute to

Table 34. Coats of the eyeball

Location	*Posterior portion*	*Anterior portion*	*Characteristics*
Outer coat (sclera)	Sclera proper	Cornea	Protective fibrous coat; cornea transparent; rest of coat white and opaque
Middle coat (chorioid)	Chorioid proper	Ciliary body; suspensory ligament; iris (pupil is hole in iris); lens suspended in suspensory ligament	Vascular, pigmented coat
Inner coat (retina)	Retina	No anterior portion	Nervous tissue; rods and cones (receptors for second cranial nerve) located in retina

Table 35. Cavities of the eye

Cavity	*Divisions*	*Location*	*Contents*
Anterior	Anterior chamber Posterior chamber	Anterior to iris and posterior to cornea Posterior to iris and anterior to lens	Aqueous humor Aqueous humor
Posterior	None	Posterior to lens	Vitreous humor

aqueous humor formation. From the posterior chamber, aqueous humor moves between the iris and the lens and on through the pupil into the anterior chamber (Fig. 159). From here it drains into the canal of Schlemm and moves on into small veins. Normally, aqueous humor drains out of the anterior chamber at the same rate at which it enters the posterior chamber. So the amount of aqueous humor in the eye remains relatively constant. And so, too, does intraocular pressure. But sometimes something happens to upset this balance and intraocular pressure increases above the normal level of about 20 to 25 mm. Hg pressure. The individual then has the eye disease known as glaucoma (Figs. 159 to 161). Either excess formation or, more often, decreased absorption is seen as an immediate cause of this condition, but underlying causes are unknown.

Muscles

Eye muscles are of two types: extrinsic and intrinsic.

Extrinsic muscles are those that attach to the outside of the eyeball and to the bones of the orbit. They move the eyeball in any desired direction and are, of course, voluntary muscles. Four of them are

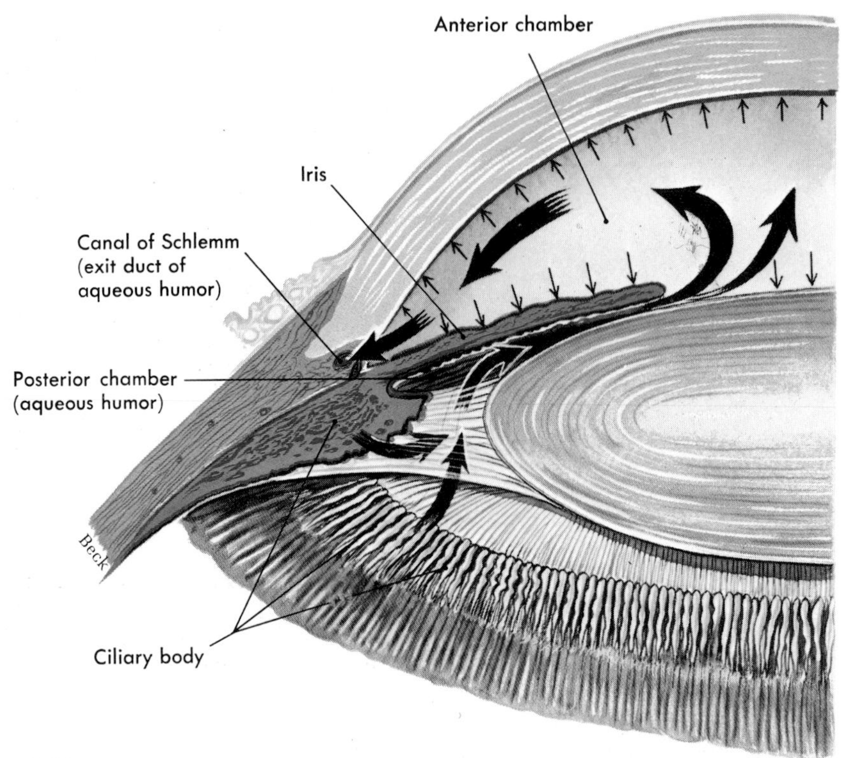

Fig. 159

Aqueous humor (heavy arrows) is believed to be formed mainly by secretion by the ciliary body into the posterior chamber. It passes into the anterior chamber through the pupil, from which it is drained away by the canal of Schlemm and finally into the anterior ciliary veins. Small arrows indicate pressure of the aqueous humor.

straight muscles and two are oblique. Their names describe their positions on the eyeball. They are the superior, inferior, mesial, and lateral rectus muscles and superior and inferior oblique muscles.

Intrinsic eye muscles are those located within the eye. Their names are the iris and the ciliary muscles, and they are involuntary. Incidentally, the eye is the only organ in the body in which both voluntary and involuntary muscles are found. The iris regulates the size of the pupil. The ciliary muscle controls the shape of the lens. As the ciliary muscle contracts, it releases the suspensory ligament from the backward pull usually exerted upon it. And this allows the elastic lens, suspended in the ligament, to bulge or become more convex—a necessary accommodation for near vision (p. 260). Some essential facts about eye muscles are summarized in Table 36.

Accessory structures

Accessory structures of the eye include the eyebrows, eyelashes, eyelids, and lacrimal apparatus.

Eyebrows and eyelashes. The eyebrows and eyelashes serve a cosmetic purpose and give some protection against the entrance of foreign objects into the eyes. Small glands located at the base of the lashes secrete a lubricating fluid. They are of interest because they frequently become infected, forming a *stye*.

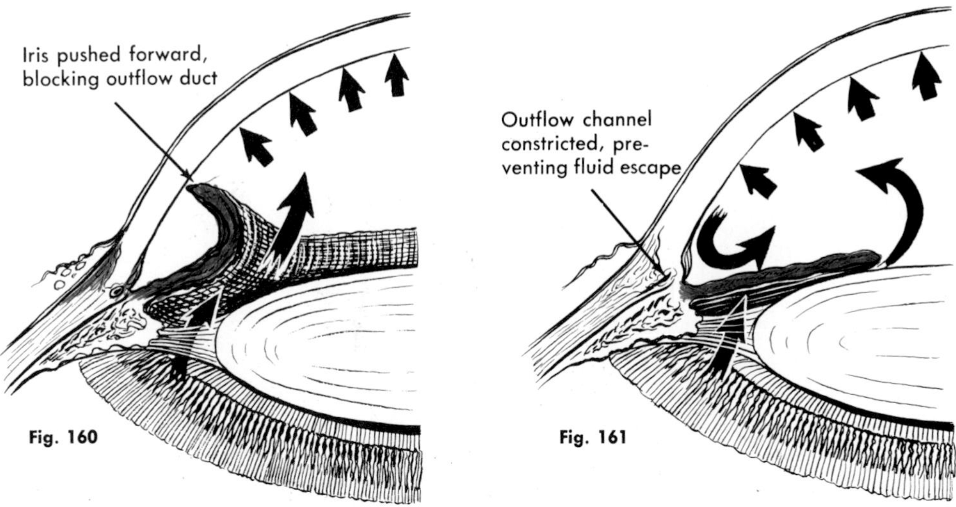

Figs. 160 and 161

Acute glaucoma. When pressure of the aqueous humor in the anterior chamber becomes extreme, the iris is pushed forward and blocks the canal of Schlemm from draining the fluid. In most instances, proper eyedrop medication will dilate the duct, permitting excess fluid escape. When medication fails, a new outflow duct can be created surgically.

Table 36. Eye muscles

	Extrinsic muscles	*Intrinsic muscles*
Names	Superior rectus Inferior rectus Lateral rectus Mesial rectus Superior oblique Inferior oblique	Iris Ciliary muscle
Kind of muscle	Voluntary (striated, skeletal)	Involuntary (smooth, visceral)
Location	Attached to eyeball and bones of orbit	Modified anterior portion of chorioid coat of eyeball; iris doughnut-shaped, sphincter muscle; pupil, hole in center of iris
Functions	Eye movements	Iris regulates size of pupil, therefore, amount of light entering eye; ciliary muscle controls shape of lens (accommodation), therefore, its refractive power
Innervation	Somatic fibers of third, fourth, and sixth cranial nerves	Autonomic fibers of third and fourth cranial nerves

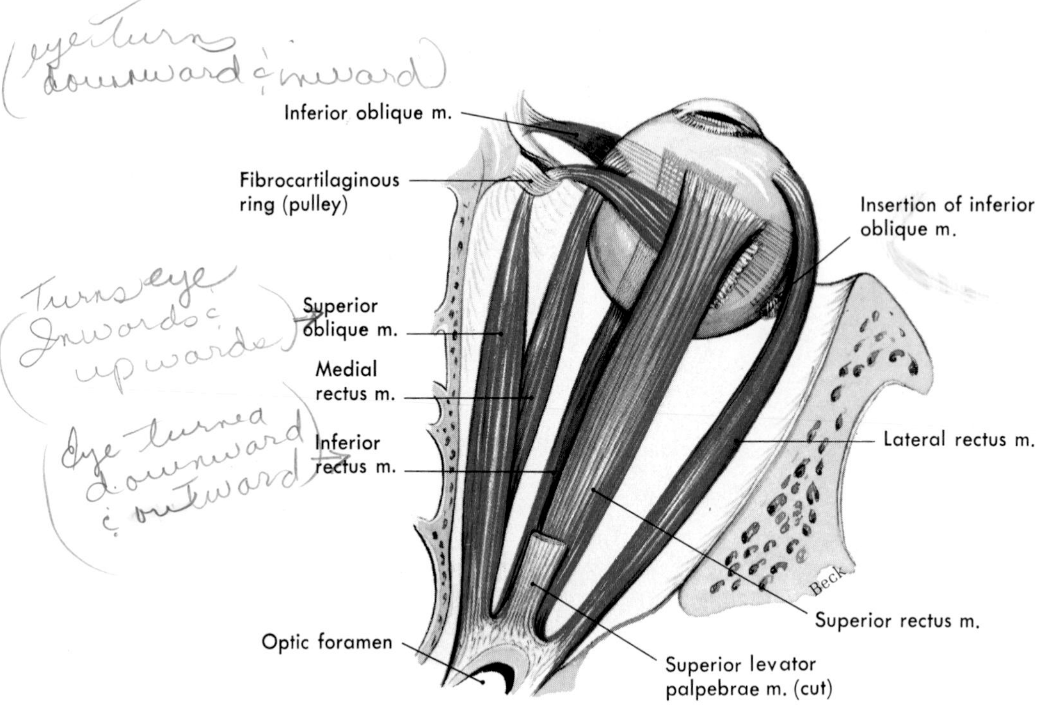

Fig. 162

Muscles that move the right eye as viewed from above.

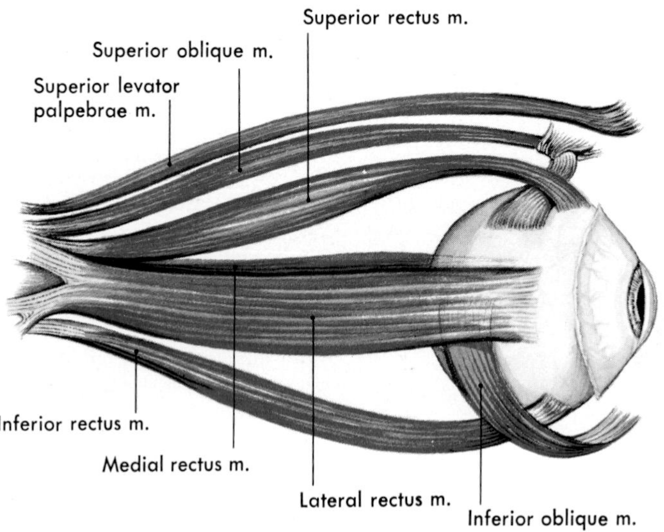

Fig. 163

Muscles of the right orbit as viewed from the side.

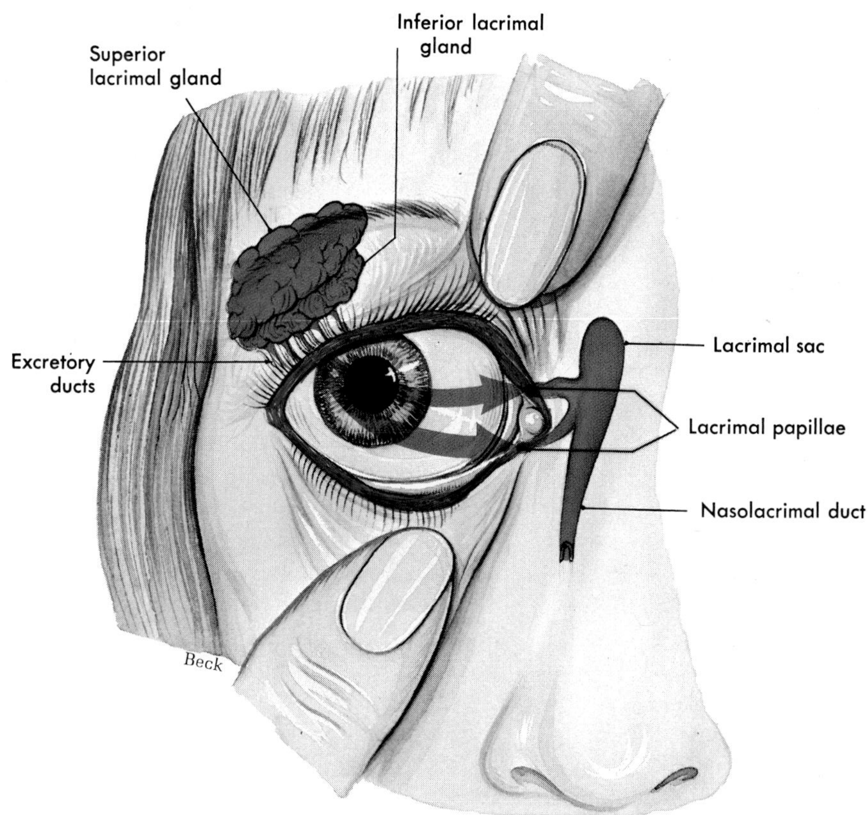

Fig. 164

The lacrimal apparatus. Arrows indicate direction of drainage from the excretory ducts of the lacrimal glands across the eye to the nasolacrimal duct.

Eyelids. The eyelids or palpebrae consist mainly of voluntary muscle and skin, with a border of thick connective tissue at the free edge of each lid known as the tarsal plate. One can feel the tarsal plate as a ridge when turning back the eyelid to remove a foreign object. Mucous membrane called conjunctiva lines each lid and continues over the surface of the eyeball, where it is modified to give transparency. Inflammation of the conjunctiva (conjunctivitis) is a fairly common infection. It is often called pinkeye because it produces a pinkish discoloration of the eye's surface.

The opening between the eyelids bears the technical name of palpebral fissure. The height of this fissure determines the apparent size of the eyes. In other words, if the eyelids are habitually held widely opened, the eyes appear large. Keeping the lids only partially open, on the other hand, gives the illusion of small eyes. Actually, there is very little difference in size between eyeballs of different adults. The upper and lower eyelids join, forming an angle or corner known as a *canthus,* the inner canthus being the mesial corner of the eye and the outer canthus the lateral corner.

Lacrimal apparatus. The lacrimal apparatus consists of the structures that secrete tears and drain them from the surface of the eyeball. They are the lacrimal glands, lacrimal ducts, lacrimal sacs, and nasolacrimal ducts.

The *lacrimal glands,* comparable in size and shape to a small almond, are located in a depression of the frontal bone at the upper outer margin of each orbit. Approximately a dozen small ducts lead from each gland, draining the tears onto the conjunctiva at the upper outer corner of the eye.

The *lacrimal canals* are small channels, one above and the other below each *caruncle* (small red body at inner canthus). They empty into the lacrimal sacs. The openings into the canals are called *punctae* and can be seen as two small dots at the inner canthus of the eye. The *lacrimal sacs* are located in a groove in the lacrimal bone. The *nasolacrimal ducts* are small tubes that extend from the lacrimal sac into the inferior meatus of the nose. All the tear ducts are lined with mucous membrane, an extension of the mucosa that lines the nose. When this membrane becomes inflamed and swollen, the nasolacrimal ducts become plugged, causing the tears to overflow from the eyes instead of draining into the nose as they do normally. Hence, when we have a common cold, "watering" eyes add to our discomforts.

PHYSIOLOGY OF VISION

In order for vision to occur, the following conditions must be fulfilled: an image must be formed on the retina to stimulate its receptors (rods and cones), and the resulting nerve impulses must be conducted to the visual areas of the cerebral cortex.

Formation of retinal image

Four processes focus light rays so that they form a clear image on the retina: *refraction* of the light rays, *accommodation* of the lens, *constriction* of the pupil, and *convergence* of the eyes.

Refraction of light rays. Refraction means the deflection or bending of light rays. It is produced by light rays passing obliquely from one transparent medium into another of different optical density, and the more convex the surface of the medium, the greater is its refractive power. The refracting media of the eye are the cornea, aqueous humor, lens, and vitreous humor. Light rays are bent or refracted at the anterior surface of the cornea as they pass from the rarer air into the denser cornea, at the anterior surface of the lens as they pass from the aqueous humor into the denser lens, and at the posterior surface of the lens as they pass from the lens into the rarer vitreous humor.

When an individual goes to an ophthalmologist for an eye examination, the doctor does a "refraction." In other words, by various specially designed methods, he measures the refractory or light-bending power of that person's eyes.

In a normal (emmetropic) eye when it is relaxed, the four refracting media together bend light rays sufficiently to bring to a focus on the retina the parallel rays reflected from an object 20 or more feet away. Of course a normal eye can also focus objects located much nearer than 20 feet from the eye. This is accomplished by a mechanism known as accommodation (discussed on pp. 260 to 262). Many eyes, however, show *errors of refraction;* that is, they are not able to focus the rays on the retina under the stated conditions. Some common errors of refraction are *nearsightedness* (myopia), *farsightedness* (hypermetropia), and *astigmatism.*

The nearsighted eye sees distant objects as blurred images because it focuses rays from the object at a point in front of the retina (Fig. 166). According to one theory, this occurs because the eyeball is too long and the distance too great from the lens to the retina in the myopic eye. Concave glasses, by lessening refraction, can give

Fig. 165

In the normal eye, light rays from an object are refracted by the cornea, aqueous humor, lens, and vitreous humor and are converged on the fovea of the retina, where an inverted image is clearly formed.

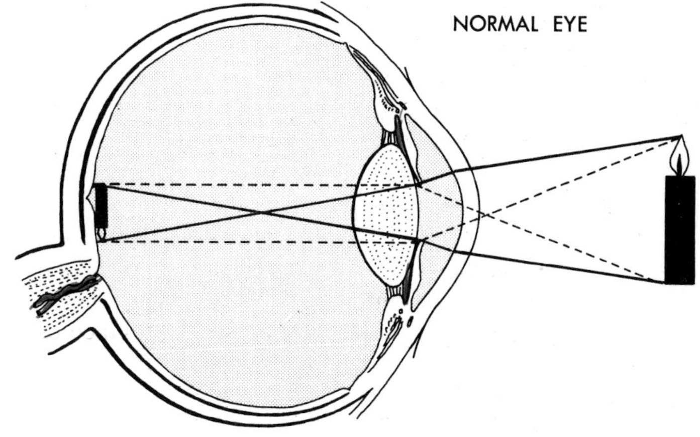

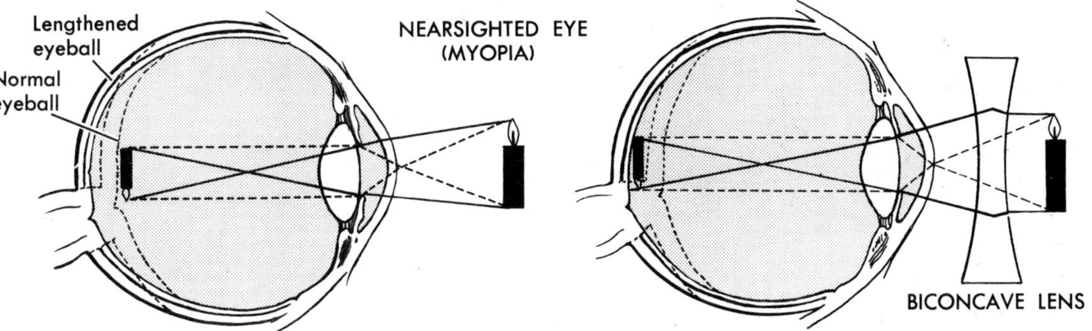

Fig. 166

The nearsighted or myopic eye focuses the image in front of the retina. This may occur when the eyeball is too long or the lens is too thick. Correction is by concave lens.

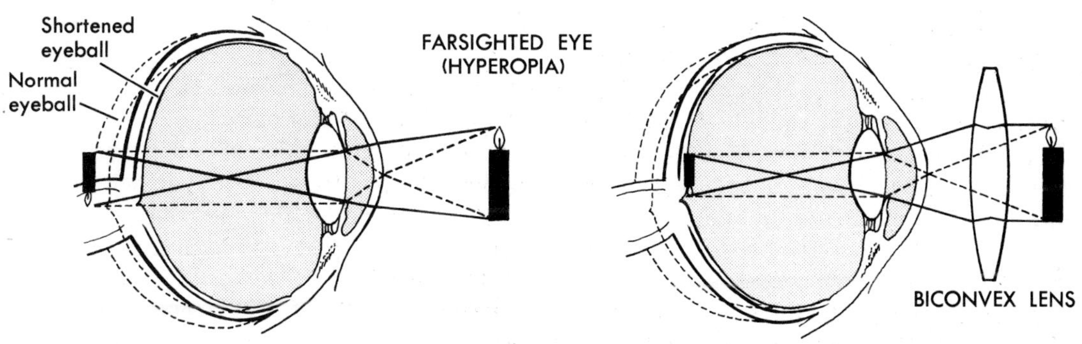

Fig. 167

The farsighted or hypermetropic eye focuses the image behind the retina. This may occur when the eyeball is too short or the lens is too thin. Correction is by convex lens.

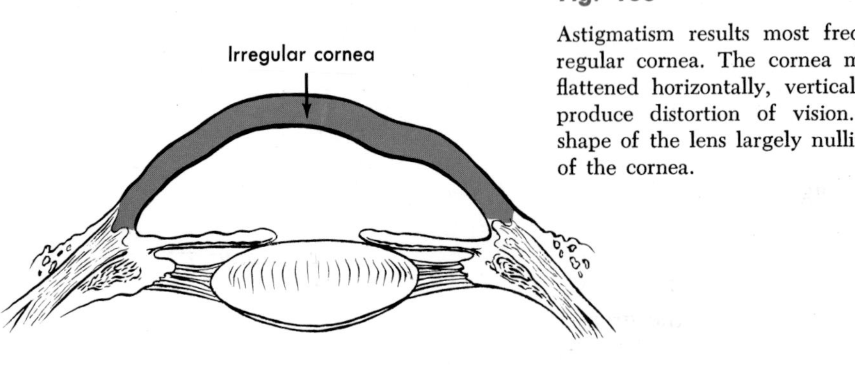

Fig. 168

Astigmatism results most frequently from an irregular cornea. The cornea may be only slightly flattened horizontally, vertically, or diagonally to produce distortion of vision. The compensating shape of the lens largely nullifies the irregularities of the cornea.

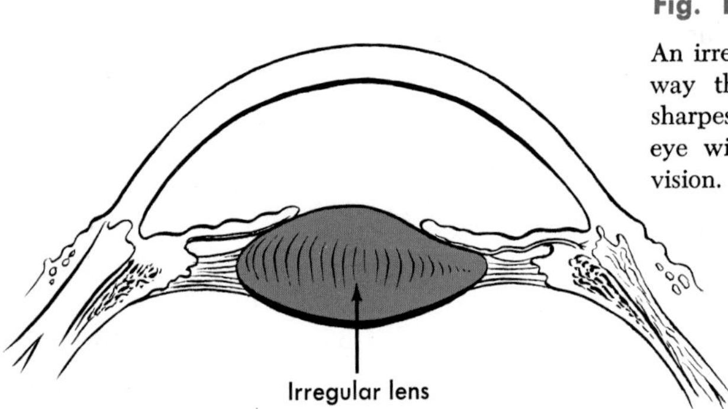

Fig. 169

An irregular lens causes light to be bent in such a way that it does not focus the image on the sharpest area of vision on the retina. An astigmatic eye with this defect causes distorted or blurred vision.

clear distant vision to nearsighted individuals. Presumably opposite conditions exist in the farsighted eye.

Astigmatism is a more complicated condition in which the curvature of the cornea or of the lens is uneven, causing horizontal and vertical rays to be focused at two different points on the retina (Figs. 168 and 169). Instead of the curvature of the cornea being a section of a sphere, it is more like that of a teaspoon with horizontal and vertical arcs uneven. Suitable glasses correct the refraction of such an eye.

Visual acuity or the ability to distinguish form and outline clearly is indicated by a fraction that compares the distance at which an individual sees an object (usually letters of a definite size and shape) clearly with the distance at which the normal eye would see the object. Thus, if he sees clearly at 20 feet an object that the normal eye would be able to see clearly at 20 feet, his visual acuity is said to be 20/20 or normal, but if he sees an object clearly at 20 feet which the normal eye sees clearly at 30 feet, then his visual acuity is 20/30 or two-thirds of normal.

As people grow older, they become farsighted due to the lenses losing their elasticity and therefore their ability to bulge and to accommodate for near vision. This condition is called *presbyopia*.

Accommodation of lens. Accommodation for near vision necessitates three changes: increase in the curvature of the lens, constriction of the pupils, and convergence of the two eyes. Light rays from objects 20 or more feet away are practically parallel. The normal eye, as previously noted, refracts such rays sufficiently to focus them clearly on the retina. But light rays from nearer objects are divergent rather than parallel. So obviously they must be bent more acutely to bring them to a focus on the retina. Accommodation of the lens or, in other words, an increase in its curvature takes place to achieve this greater refraction. (It is a physical fact that the greater the convexity of a lens, the greater is its refractive power.) Most observers accept Helmholtz' theory about the mechanism that produces accommodation of the lens. According to his theory, the ciliary muscle contracts, pulling the ciliary body and chorioid forward toward the lens. This releases the tension on the suspensory ligament and therefore on the lens which, being elastic, immediately bulges. For near vision, then, the ciliary muscle is contracted, and the lens is bulging, whereas for far vision the ciliary muscle is relaxed and the lens is comparatively flat. Continual use of the eyes for near work produces eyestrain because of the prolonged contraction of the ciliary muscle. Some of the strain can be avoided by looking into the distance at intervals while doing close work.

Constriction of pupil. The muscles of the iris play an important part in the formation of clear retinal images. Part of the accommodation mechanism consists of contraction of the circular fibers of the iris which constricts the pupil. This prevents divergent rays from the object from entering the eye through the periphery of the cornea and lens. Such peripheral rays could not be brought to a focus on the retina (due to spherical aberration of the lens) and therefore would cause a blurred image. Constriction of the pupil for near vision is called the *near reflex* of the pupil and occurs simultaneously with accommodation of the lens in near vision. The pupil constricts also in bright light *(photopupil reflex or pupillary light reflex)* to protect the retina from too intense or too sudden stimulation.

Convergence of eyes. Single binocular vision (seeing only one object instead of two when both eyes are used) occurs when light rays from an object fall on corresponding points of the two retinas. The foveas and all points lying equidistant and in the same direction from the foveas are corresponding points. Whenever the eyeballs move in unison, either with the visual axes parallel (for far objects) or converging upon a common point (for near objects), light rays strike corresponding points of the two retinas. Convergence is the movement of the two eyeballs inward so that their visual axes come together or converge at the object viewed. The nearer the object, the greater is the degree of convergence necessary to maintain single vision. A simple procedure serves to demonstrate the fact that single binocular vision results from stimulation of corresponding points of the two retinas. Gently press one eyeball out of line while viewing an object. Instead of one object, you will then see two. In order to achieve unified movement of the two eyeballs, a functional balance between the antagonistic extrinsic muscles must exist. If, for example, the right internal rectus muscle should contract more forcefully than its antagonist, the right external rectus, the right eye would be pulled in toward the nose instead of its visual axis being held parallel to that of the left eye in distant vision or converged upon the same point in near vision. Light rays from an object would then fall on noncorresponding points of the two retinas, and the object would be seen double (diplopia). Sometimes the individual can overcome the deviation of the visual axes by muscular effort (extra innervation of the weak muscle) and thereby achieve single vision, but only at the expense of muscular and nervous strain. The condition in which the imbalance of the eye muscles can be overcome by extra innervation of the weak muscle is called *heterophoria* (*esophoria* if the internal rectus is stronger and pulls the eye nasalward and *exophoria* if the external rectus is stronger and pulls the eye temporalward). *Strabismus* (cross-eye or squint) is an exaggerated esophoria which cannot be overcome by neuromuscular effort. An individual with strabismus usually does not have double vision, as would be expected, because he learns to suppress one of the images.

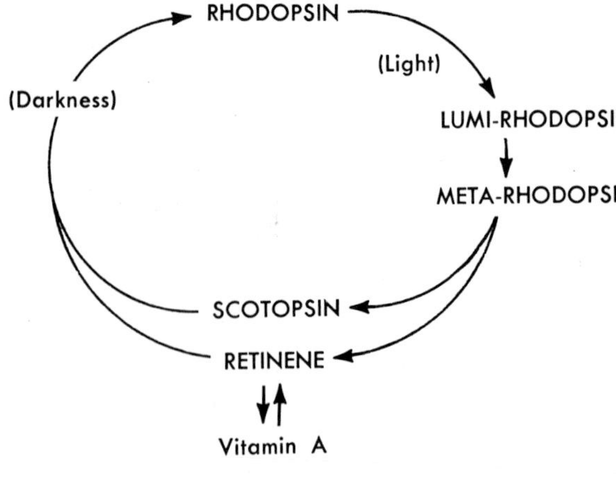

Fig. 170

The rhodopsin cycle.

Stimulation of retina

Rods are known to contain *rhodopsin* (visual purple), a pigmented compound. As shown in Fig. 170, it forms by a protein scotopsin combining with retinene, a derivative of vitamin A. Rhodopsin is highly light-sensitive, so that when light rays strike a rod, its rhodopsin rapidly breaks down (also shown in Fig. 170). And in some way this chemical change initiates impulse conduction by the rod. Then if the rod is exposed to darkness for a short time, rhodopsin reforms from the scotopsin and retinene and is ready to function again. *Cones* also contain photosensitive chemicals. Just what they are, however, is not established. (Recent work suggests that there may be three major substances: iodopsin, chlorolabe, and erythrolabe.) Presumably, the cone compounds are less sensitive to light than rhodopsin. Brighter light seems necessary for their breakdown. Cones, therefore, are considered to be the receptors responsible for daylight and color visions. Rods, on the other hand, are believed to be the receptors for night vision because their rhodopsin quickly becomes almost depleted in bright light due to its rapid breakdown but slow regeneration. This explains why you cannot see for a little while after you go from a bright light to darkness. But when rhodopsin has had time to reform, the rods again start functioning and dark adaptation has occurred. Or as we say, we "can see in the dark once we get used to it." Night blindness occurs in marked vitamin A deficiency. Why? Fig. 170 contains a clue. The fovea contains the greatest concentration of cones and is, therefore, the point of clearest vision in good light. For this reason when we want to see an object clearly in the daytime, we look directly at it so as to focus the image on the fovea. But in dim light or darkness we see an object better if we look slightly to the side of it, thereby focusing the image nearer the periphery of the retina where rods are more plentiful.

Conduction to visual area

Fibers that conduct impulses from the rods and cones reach the visual cortex in the occipital lobes via the optic nerves, optic chiasma, optic tracts, and optic radiations. Those fibers that originate in the medial half of each retina cross over in the optic chiasma and continue through the optic tract and radiation on the opposite side. This anatomical arrangement explains certain peculiar visual abnormalities seen occasionally in persons with brain tumors or other intracranial lesions (Fig. 171).

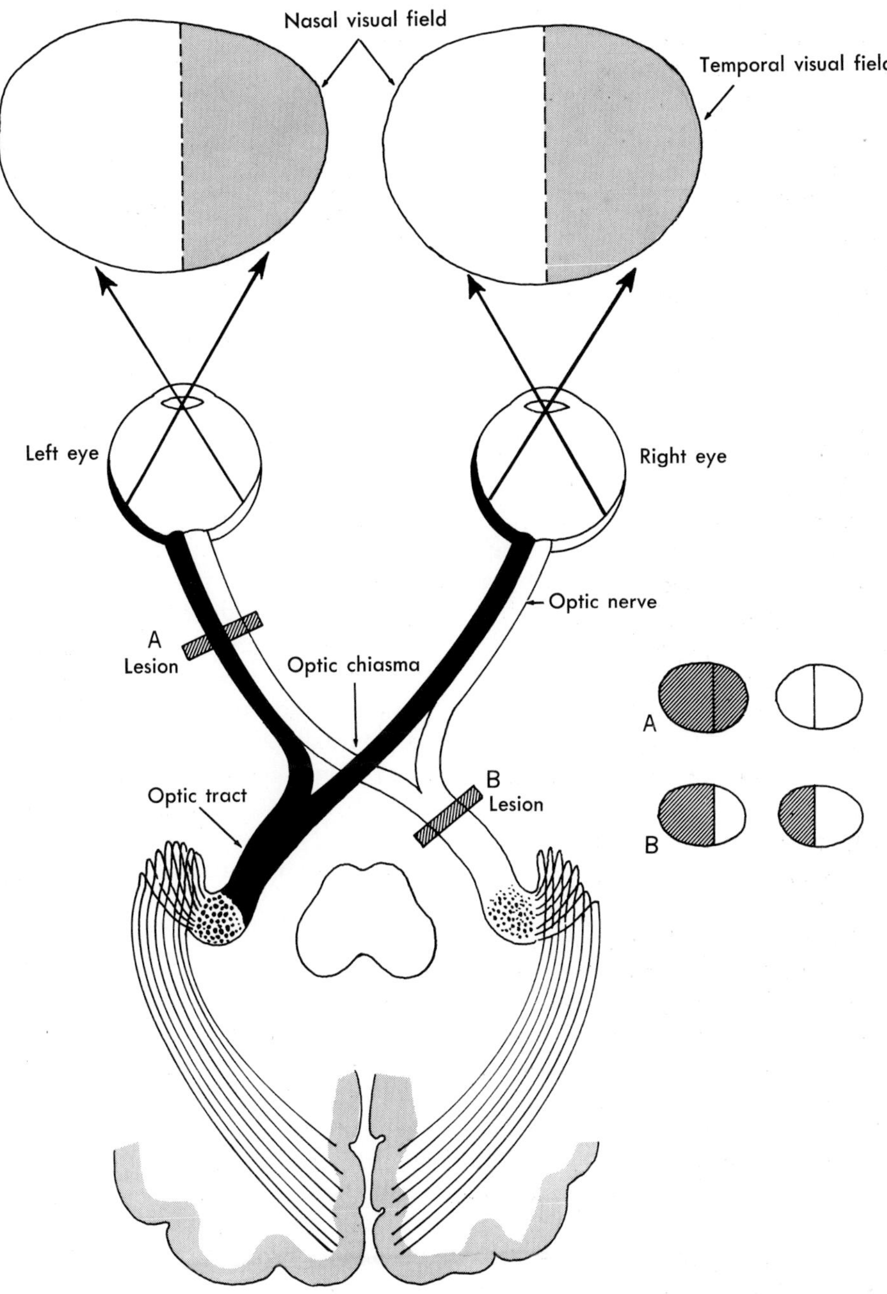

Fig. 171

Diagram of the visual pathways. **A,** Left optic nerve destruction causes complete blindness of the same eye. **B,** Right optic tract destruction causes blindness of the nasal visual field of the same eye and of the temporal visual field of the opposite eye.

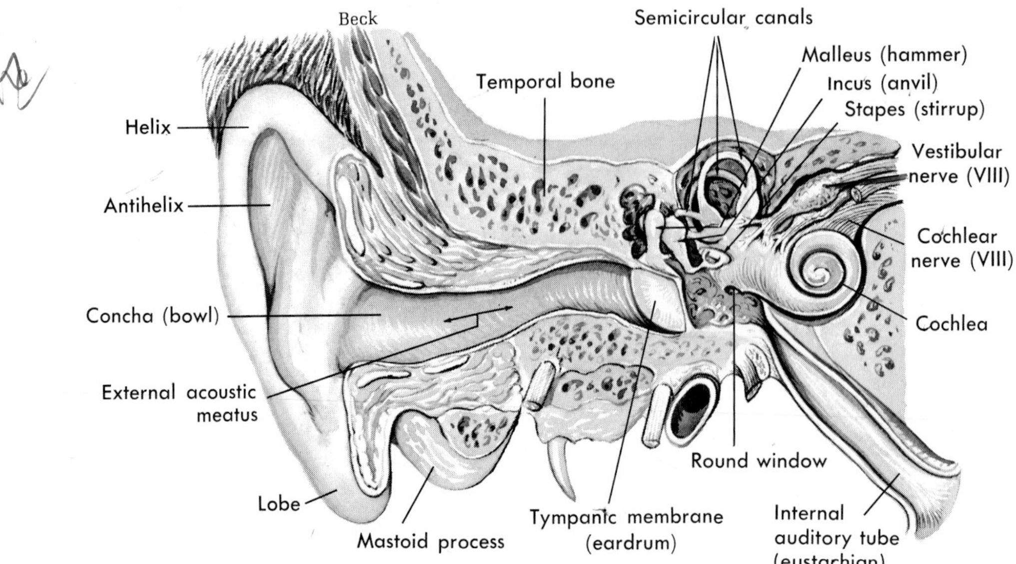

Fig. 172

Components of the ear. The external ear consists of the auricle (pinna), external acoustic meatus (ear canal), and the tympanic membrane (eardrum). The middle ear includes the malleus (hammer), incus (anvil), and stapes (stirrup) and the tympanic cavity. The inner ear contains the organs of balance and hearing.

Auditory apparatus

ANATOMY

The ears, auditory nerves, and auditory areas of the temporal lobes of the cerebrum compose the auditory apparatus. Each ear consists of three parts: external ear, middle ear, and inner ear (Fig. 172).

External ear

The external ear has two divisions: the flap or modified trumpet on the side of the head called the *auricle* or *pinna* and the tube leading from the auricle into the temporal bone and named the *external acoustic meatus (ear canal)*. This canal is about 1¼ inches long and takes, in general, an inward, forward, and downward direction, although the first portion of the tube slants upward and then curves downward. Because of this curve in the auditory canal, the auricle should be pulled up and back to straighten the tube when medications are to be dropped into the ear. Modified sweat glands in the auditory canal secrete *cerumen* (waxlike substance) which occasionally becomes impacted and may cause pain and deafness. The *tympanic membrane* (eardrum) stretches across the inner end of the auditory canal, separating it from the middle ear.

Middle ear

The middle ear (tympanic cavity), a tiny epithelial-lined cavity hollowed out of the temporal bone, contains the three auditory ossicles: the malleus, incus, and stapes. The names of these very small bones describe their shapes (hammer, anvil, and stirrup). The "handle" of the malleus is attached to the inner surface of the tympanic membrane, whereas the "head" attaches to the incus, which, in turn, attaches to the stapes. There are several openings into the middle ear cavity: one from the external auditory meatus, covered over with the tympanic membrane; two into the internal ear, the fenestra ovalis (oval window), into which the stapes fits, and the fenestra rotunda (round window), which is covered by a membrane; and one into the eustachian tube.

Posteriorly, the middle ear cavity is continuous with a number of mastoid cells in the temporal bone. The clinical importance of these openings is that they provide routes for infection to travel. Head colds, for example, especially in children, may lead to middle ear or mastoid infections via the nasopharynx–eustachian tube–middle ear–mastoid path.

The *eustachian* or *auditory tube* is composed partly of bone and partly of cartilage and fibrous tissue and is lined with mucosa. It extends downward, forward, and inward from the middle ear cavity to the nasopharynx (the part of the throat behind the nose).

In the preceding paragraph we called attention to the disadvantage of this anatomical connection between the nasopharynx and middle ear. But the eustachian tube also serves a useful function. It makes possible equalization of pressure against inner and outer surfaces of the tympanic membrane and therefore prevents membrane rupture and the discomfort that marked pressure differences produce. The way the eustachian tube equalizes tympanic membrane pressures is this. When one swallows or yawns, air spreads rapidly through the open tube. Atmospheric pressure then presses against the inner surface of the tympanic membrane. And since atmospheric pressure is continually exerted against its outer surface, the pressures are equal. You might test this mechanism sometime when you are ascending or descending in an airplane—start chewing gum to increase your swallowing and observe whether this relieves the discomfort in your ears.

Inner ear

The inner ear is also called the labyrinth because of its complicated shape. It consists of two main parts, a bony labyrinth and inside this a membranous labyrinth. The bony labyrinth consists of three parts: vestibule, cochlea, and semicircular canals. The membranous labyrinth consists of the utricle and saccule inside the vestibule, the cochlear duct inside the cochlea, and the membranous semicircular canals inside the bony ones (Fig. 173).

Vestibule, utricle, and saccule

The vestibule constitutes the central section of the bony labyrinth. Into it open both the oval and round windows from the middle ear as well as the three semicircular canals of the inner ear. The membranous utricle and saccule are suspended within the vestibule. They are separated from the bony walls of the vestibule by fluid (perilymph), and both utricle and saccule contain a fluid called endolymph.

Located within the utricle (and also within the saccule) lies a small structure called the *macula.* It consists mainly of hair cells and a gelatinous membrane that contains *otoliths* (tiny ear "stones"; that is, small particles of calcium carbonate). A few delicate hairs protrude from the hair cells and are embedded in the gelatinous membrane. Receptors for the vestibular branch of the eighth cranial nerve contact the hair cells of the macula located in the utricle. Changing the position of the head causes a change in the amount of pressure on the gelatinous membrane and causes the otoliths to pull on the hair cells. This stimulates the adjacent receptors of the vestibular nerve. Its fibers conduct impulses to the brain which produce a sense of the position of the head and also a sensation of a change in the pull of gravity (for example, a sensation of acceleration). In addition, stimulation of the macula in the utricle evokes *righting reflexes,* muscular responses to restore the body and its parts to their normal position when they have been displaced. (Impulses from proprioceptors and from the eyes also activate righting reflexes.

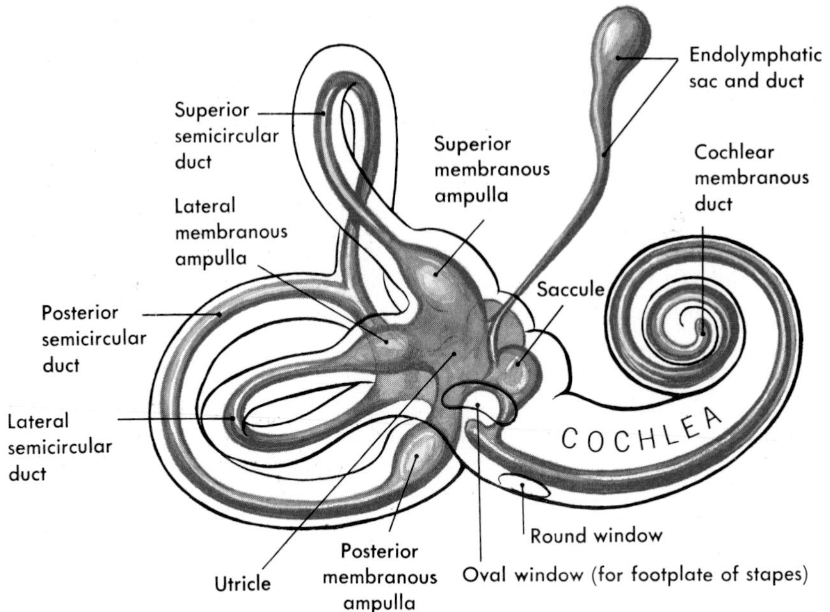

Fig. 173

The membranous labyrinth (red) of the inner ear shown in relation to the bony labyrinth.

And interruption of the vestibular or visual or proprioceptive impulses that initiate these reflexes may cause disturbances of equilibrium, nausea, vomiting, and other symptoms.)

Cochlea and cochlear duct

The word cochlea, which means snail, describes the outer appearance of this part of the bony labyrinth. When sectioned, the cochlea resembles a tube wound spirally around a cone-shaped core of bone, the *modiolus.* The modiolus houses the spiral ganglion which consists of cell bodies of the first sensory neurons in the auditory relay. Inside the cochlea lies the membranous *cochlear duct.* This structure is shaped like a tube but is a triangular rather than a round tube. It forms a shelf across the inside of the bony cochlea, dividing it into upper and lower sections all along its winding course (Figs. 174 and 175). The upper section (above the cochlear duct, that is) is called the *scala vestibuli,* whereas the lower section below the cochlear duct is the *scala tympani.* The roof of the cochlear duct is known as *Reissner's membrane* or the vestibular membrane. *Basilar membrane* is the name given the floor of the cochlear duct. It is supported by bony and fibrous projections from the wall of the cochlea. Perilymph fills the scala vestibuli and scala tympani and endolymph the cochlear duct.

The hearing sense organ, the *organ of Corti,* rests on the basilar membrane throughout the whole length of the cochlear duct. The structure of the organ of Corti resembles that of the equilibrium sense organ (that is, the macula in the utricle). It consists of supporting cells plus the important *hair cells* which project into the endolymph and are topped by an adherent gelatinous membrane called the *tectorial membrane.* Dendrites of the sensory neurons whose cells lie in the spiral ganglion in the modiolus have their beginnings around the bases of the hair cells of the organ of Corti. Axons of these neurons extend in the cochlear nerve (a branch

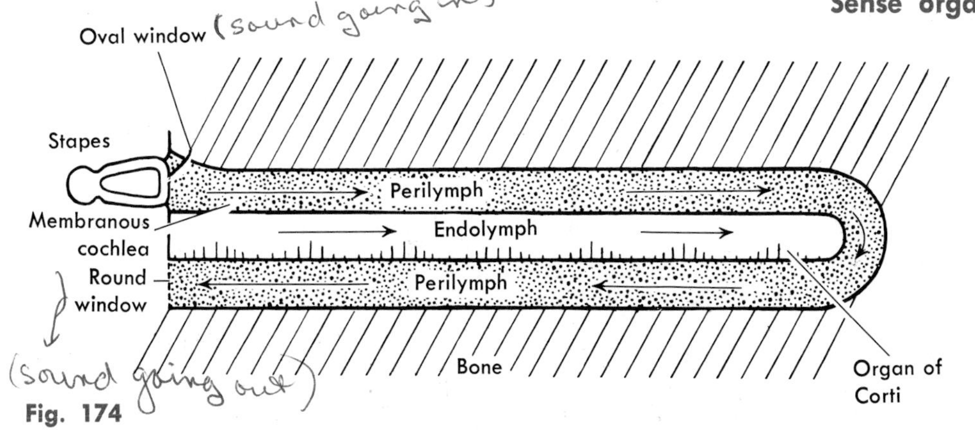

Fig. 174

Diagram of the bony and membranous cochlea, uncoiled. Note the end organ of Corti projecting into the endolymph contained in the membranous cochlea. The perilymph indicated above the endolymph occupies the scala vestibuli. That in the lower compartment lies in the scala tympani (see also Fig. 175). (Modified from Williams: Textbook of anatomy and physiology, Philadelphia, W. B. Saunders Co.)

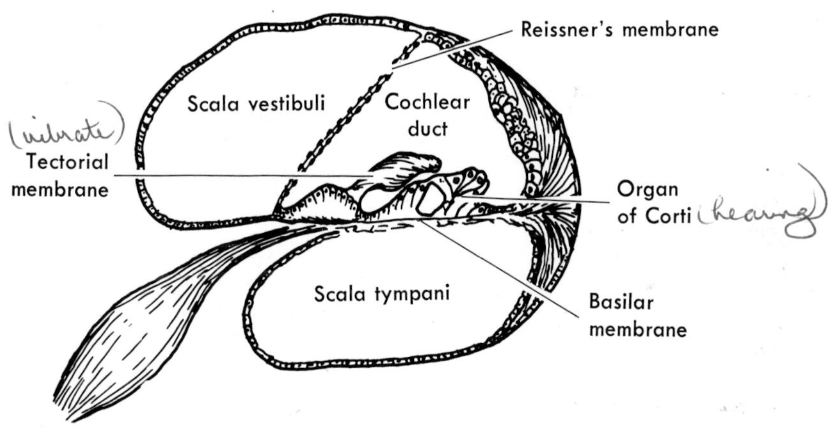

Fig. 175

Section through one of the coils of the cochlea. Perilymph fills the scala vestibuli and scala tympani. Endolymph fills the cochlear duct (membranous cochlea). A part of the spiral ganglion is shown (bulging stemlike structure at left of diagram). (Modified from Rasmussen.)

of the eighth cranial nerve) to the brain. They conduct impulses that produce the sensation of hearing.

Semicircular canals

Three semicircular canals, each in a plane approximately at right angles to the others, are found in each temporal bone. Within the bony semicircular canals and separated from them by perilymph are the membranous semicircular canals. Each contains endolymph and connects with the utricle, one of the membranous sacs inside the bony vestibule. Near its junction with the utricle the canal enlarges into an *ampulla*. Some of the receptors for the vestibular branch of the eighth cranial nerve lie in each ampulla. Like all receptors for both vestibular and auditory branches of this nerve, these receptors, too, lie in contact with hair cells in a supporting structure. Here in the ampulla, the hair cells and supporting structure together are named the *crista ampullaris,* whereas in the utricle and saccule they are called the macula and in the cochlear duct, the organ of Corti. Sitting atop the crista is a gelatinous structure called the *cupula.*

The crista with its vestibular nerve endings presumably functions as the end organ for sensations of head movements, whereas the macula in the utricle serves as the end organ for sensations of head positions. Hence both the crista and the macula of the utricle function as end organs for the sense of equilibrium.

The function of the macula in the saccule is not known but is postulated to play some part in the sense of hearing rather than in the sense of equilibrium.

PHYSIOLOGY

Hearing

Hearing results from stimulation of the auditory area of the cerebral cortex (temporal lobe, Fig. 135). Before reaching this area of the brain, however, sound waves must be projected through air, bone, and fluid to stimulate nerve endings and set up impulse conduction over nerve fibers.

Sound waves in the air enter the external auditory canal, probably without much aid from the pinna in collecting and reflecting them because of its smallness in man. At the inner end of the canal they strike against the tympanic membrane, setting it in vibration. Vibrations of the tympanic membrane move the malleus, whose handle attaches to the membrane. The head of the malleus attaches to the incus, and the incus attaches to the stapes. So when the malleus vibrates, it moves the incus, which moves the stapes against the oval window into which it fits so precisely. At this point fluid conduction of sound waves begins. To understand this, you will probably need to refer to Figs. 172 to 175 frequently as you read the next few sentences. When the stapes moves against the oval window, pressure is exerted inward into the perilymph in the scala vestibuli of the cochlea. This starts a "ripple" in the perilymph which is transmitted through Reissner's membrane (the roof of the cochlear duct) to endolymph inside the duct and thence to the organ of Corti and to the basilar membrane that supports the organ of Corti and forms the floor of the cochlear duct. From the basilar membrane the ripple is next transmitted to and through the perilymph in the scala tympani and finally expends itself against the round window—on a much reduced scale, like an ocean wave expending itself as it breaks against the shore. Dendrites (of neurons whose cell bodies lie in the spiral ganglion and whose axons make up the cochlear nerve) terminate around the bases of the hair cells of the organ of Corti, and the tectorial membrane adheres to their upper surfaces. The movement of the hair cells against the adherent tectorial membrane somehow stimulates these dendrites and initiates impulse conduction by the cochlear nerve to the brainstem. Before reaching the auditory area of the temporal lobe, impulses pass through "relay stations" in nuclei in the medulla, pons, midbrain, and thalamus.

Equilibrium

In addition to hearing, the inner ear aids in the maintenance of equilibrium by making possible sensations of position and movements of the head (discussed earlier on this page and on p. 265).

Olfactory sense organs

The receptors for the fibers of the olfactory (first) cranial nerves lie in the mucosa of the upper part of the nasal cavity. Their location here explains the necessity for sniffing or drawing air forcefully up into the nose in order to smell delicate odors. The olfactory sense organ consists of hair cells and is relatively simple compared with the complex visual and auditory organs. Whereas the olfactory receptors are extremely sensitive, that is, are stimulated by even very slight odors, they are also easily fatigued—a fact which explains why odors which are at first very noticeable are not sensed at all after a short time.

Gustatory sense organs

The receptors for the taste nerve fibers (in branches of the seventh and ninth cranial nerves) are known as *taste buds* or taste corpuscles. They are located in the papillae of the tongue. Not all taste receptors are stimulated by the same kinds of substances. Four different tastes are recognized, each resulting from stimulation of a different set of taste buds—for sweet, sour, bitter, and salt substances. All the other flavors experienced are a result of fusions of two or more of the four tastes named and as a result of stimulation of the olfactory receptors. In other words, the myriads of tastes recognized are not tastes alone but tastes plus odors. For this reason a cold that interferes with the stimulation of the olfactory receptors by odors from foods in the mouth markedly dull one's taste sensations.

The four kinds of taste corpuscles are not evenly distributed over the tongue. Most of those sensitive to bitter are located at the back of the tongue, those sensitive to sweet at the tip, and those sensitive to sour and to salt along the sides and tip. So, if you take a bitter medicine by placing it on the tip of your tongue and swallowing it quickly with water, you will experience less of the bitter taste than if you placed it on the back of your tongue where there is a concentration of bitter-sensitive taste buds.

Outline summary—Sense organs

General remarks

1. Millions of receptors constitute sense organs
2. For receptors and sensations they mediate, see Table 33, p. 247

Somatic, visceral, and referred pain

1. Somatic—results from stimulation of pain receptors (nociceptors) in skin or in deep structures (skeletal muscles, tendons, or joints)
2. Visceral—results from stimulation of pain receptors in viscera by pressure or chemical stimuli; conducted almost exclusively by sensory fibers in sympathetic nerves
3. Referred—pain interpreted as coming from skin area when it actually originates in deep structure

Eye

ANATOMY

Coats of eyeball

1. Outer coat (sclera)
2. Middle coat (chorioid)
3. Inner coat (retina)
4. For outline summary, see Table 34, p. 253

Cavities and humors

1. Anterior cavity
2. Posterior cavity
3. For outline summary, see Table 35, p. 253

Muscles

1. Extrinsic
   a. attach to outside of eyeball and to bones of orbit
   b. voluntary muscles; move eyeball in desired directions

c. four straight (rectus) muscles—superior, inferior lateral, and mesial; two oblique muscles—superior and inferior
2. Intrinsic
   a. within eyeball; named iris and ciliary muscles
   b. involuntary muscles
   c. iris regulates size of pupil
   d. ciliary muscle controls shape of lens, making possible accommodation for near and far objects
3. For outline summary, see Table 36, p. 255

Accessory structures

1. Eyebrows and eyelashes—protective and cosmetic
2. Eyelids
   a. lined with mucous membrane which continues over surface of eyeball; called conjunctiva
   b. opening between eyelids called palpebral fissure
   c. corners where upper and lower eyelids join called canthus, mesial and lateral
3. Lacrimal apparatus—lacrimal glands, lacrimal canals, lacrimal sacs, and nasolacrimal ducts

PHYSIOLOGY OF VISION

Fulfillment of following conditions results in conscious experience known as vision: formation of retinal image, stimulation of retina, and conduction to visual area

Formation of retinal image

1. Accomplished by four processes:
   a. refraction or bending of light rays as they pass through eye
   b. accommodation or bulging of lens—normally occurs if object viewed lies nearer than 20 feet from eye
   c. constriction of pupil; occurs simultaneously with accommodation for near objects and also in bright light
   d. convergence of eyes for near objects so light rays from object fall on corresponding points of two retinas; necessary for single binocular vision

Stimulation of retina

Accomplished by light rays producing photochemical change in rods and cones

Conduction to visual area

Fibers that conduct impulses from rods and cones reach visual cortex in occipital lobes via optic nerves, optic chiasma, optic tracts, and optic radiations

Auditory apparatus

ANATOMY

External ear

1. Auricle or pinna
2. External acoustic meatus (ear canal)

Middle ear

1. Separated from external ear by tympanic membrane
2. Contains auditory ossicles (malleus, incus, and stapes) and openings from external acoustic meatus, internal ear, eustachian tube, and mastoid sinuses
3. Eustachian tube, collapsible tube, lined with mucosa, extending from nasopharynx to middle ear
   a. equalizes pressure on both sides of eardrum
   b. open when yawning or swallowing

Inner ear

1. Consists of bony and membranous portions, latter contained within former
2. Bony labyrinth has three divisions—vestibule, cochlea, and semicircular canals
3. Membranous cochlear duct contains receptors for cochlear branch of eighth cranial nerve (sense of hearing)
4. Utricle and membranous semicircular canals contain receptors for vestibular branch of eighth cranial nerve (sense of equilibrium)

PHYSIOLOGY

Hearing

Hearing results from stimulation of auditory area of temporal lobes by impulses over auditory nerves, which are stimulated by sound waves being projected through air, bone, and fluid before reaching auditory receptors (organ of Corti)

Equilibrium

Stimulation of receptors in semicircular canals and utricle leads to sense of equilibrium; also initiates righting reflexes essential for balance

Olfactory sense organs

1. Receptors for olfactory (first) cranial nerve located in nasal mucosa high along septum
2. Receptors very sensitive but easily fatigued

Gustatory sense organs

1. Receptors for taste nerve fibers (in branches of seventh and ninth cranial nerves) called

taste corpuscles or taste buds and located in papillae of tongue
2. Four different kinds of taste corpuscles or taste buds—those sensitive to sweet, salt, sour, and bitter
3. All other tastes result from fusion of two or more of these tastes or from olfactory stimulation

Review questions

1. What two general functions do sense organs perform?
2. Explain briefly the principle of specificity of receptors.
3. Describe briefly one theory about the mechanism of referred pain.
4. Explain briefly the mechanism for accommodation for near vision.
5. Define briefly the term refraction. Name the refractory media of the eye.
6. Concave glasses are prescribed for nearsighted vision. Upon what principle is this based?
7. What is the name of the receptors for vision in dim light? For bright light?
8. Distinguish between exteroceptors, proprioceptors, and visceroceptors.
9. Describe the main features of middle ear structure.
10. Name the parts of the bony and membranous labyrinths and describe the relationship of membranous labyrinth parts to those of the bony labyrinth.
11. In what ear structure(s) is the hearing sense organ located? The equilibrium sense organs?
12. What is the name of the hearing sense organ? Of the equilibrium sense organs?

UNIT FOUR

Maintaining the metabolism of the body

Functions

Blood

- Blood cells
  - Erythrocytes
  - Leukocytes
  - Platelets
- Blood types (or blood groups)
- Blood plasma
  - Composition
- Blood clotting
  - Purpose
  - Mechanism
  - Factors that oppose clotting
  - Factors that hasten clotting
  - Pharmaceutical preparations that retard clotting
  - Clot dissolution
  - Clinical methods of hastening clotting

Heart

- Covering
  - Structure
  - Function
- Structure
  - Wall
  - Cavities
  - Valves and openings
  - Blood supply
  - Conduction system
  - Nerve supply
- Physiology
  - Function
  - Cardiac cycle

Blood vessels

- Kinds
- Structure
- Functions

Main blood vessels

- Systemic circulation
  - Arteries
  - Veins
- Portal circulation
- Fetal circulation

Circulation

- Definitions
- How to trace
- Functions of control mechanisms
- Principles
- Local control of arterioles
- Special factors influencing venous return to heart

Blood pressure

- How arterial blood pressure measured clinically
- Relation to arterial and venous bleeding

Velocity of blood

Pulse
- Definition
- Cause
- Pulse wave
- Where pulse can be felt
- Venous pulse

Lymphatic system
- Definition
- Lymph and interstitial fluid (tissue fluid)
  - Definition
- Lymphatics
  - Formation and distribution
  - Structure
  - Function
- Lymph circulation
- Lymph nodes
  - Structure
  - Location
  - Functions
- Spleen
  - Location
  - Structure
  - Functions

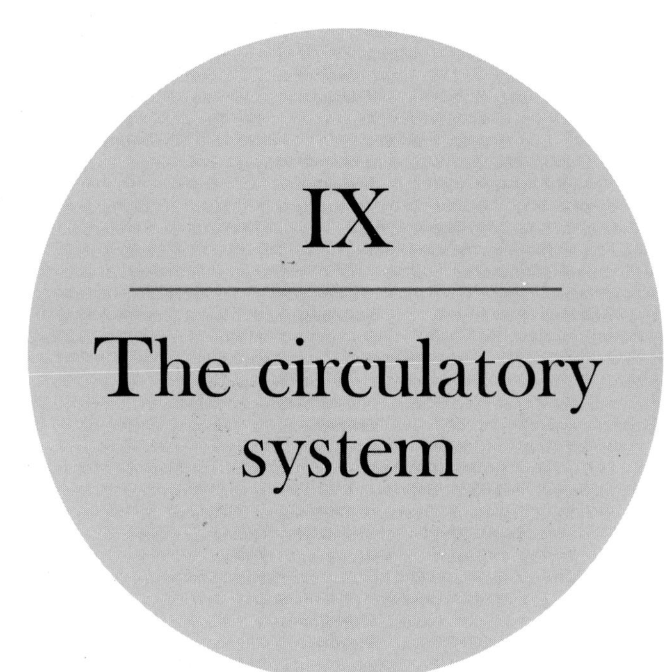

IX The circulatory system

Functions

Transportation is the primary function of the circulatory system. Its secondary functions—the functions to which it contributes—are every function of every cell and every function of the body as a whole. This is a sweeping statement and is therefore suspect, but we shall try to support it with substantial evidence as this and the remaining chapters of the book unfold. For now, just a few examples: the circulatory system transports food and oxygen to all cells so plays a vital part in cellular metabolism and in all cellular functions. It transports water and electrolytes so makes vital contributions to the maintenance of homeostasis—homeostasis of fluid volume and pH and even of body temperature. It transports hormones and enzymes so takes part in the control and integration of countless functions. It transports antibodies so contributes heavily to the body's defense against microorganisms. Our discussion in this chapter will center around the following main topics: blood, heart, blood vessels, circulation, blood pressure, velocity of blood, pulse, lymphatic system, and spleen.

Blood

Blood plasma is one of the body's three major fluids (interstitial fluid and intracellular fluid are the other two). Water, solutes, and cells compose the blood. We shall discuss blood cells first and then blood plasma, the fluid portion of blood, in which solutes are dissolved.

BLOOD CELLS

Three main kinds of blood cells are recognized: red blood cells (erythrocytes), white blood cells (leukocytes), and platelets (thrombocytes). Leukocytes are further divided as shown in the following classifications of blood cells:

1. Red blood cells or erythrocytes

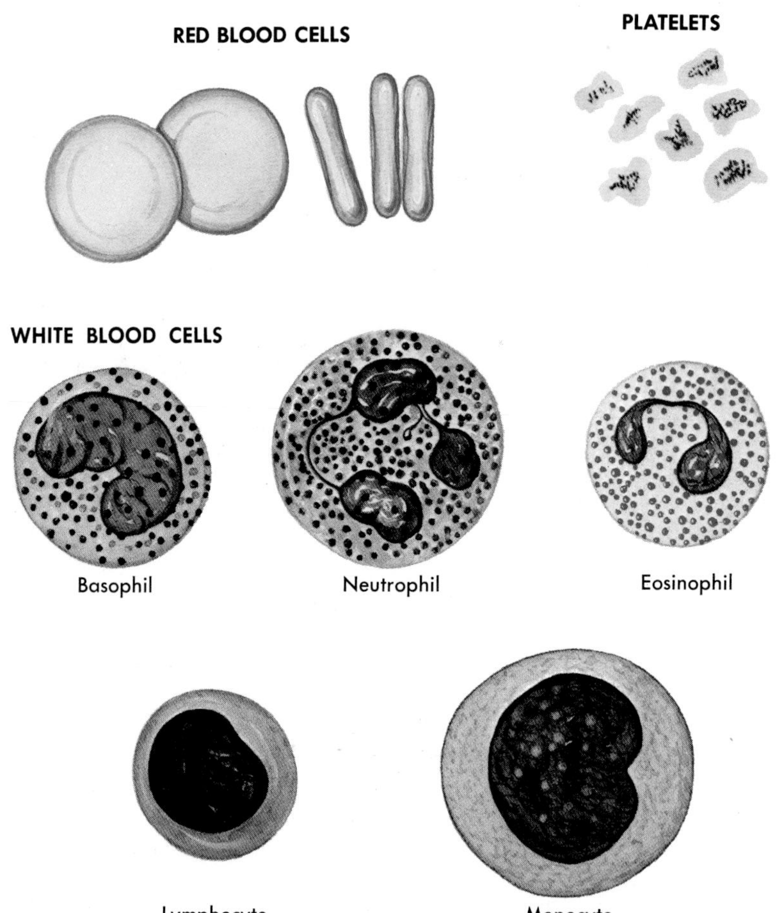

Fig. 176

Human blood cells. There are close to 30 trillion red blood cells in the adult. Each cubic millimeter of blood contains from 4½ to 5½ million red blood cells and an average total of 7,500 white blood cells.

2. White blood cells or leukocytes
   (a) Granular leukocytes: basophils, neutrophils, and eosinophils
   (b) Nongranular leukocytes: lymphocytes and monocytes
3. Platelets (thrombocytes)

In another method of classification, blood cells are divided into two main types according to origin:

1. Myeloid cells (formed in myeloid tissue, that is, in red bone marrow)
   (a) Erythrocytes
   (b) Granular leukocytes: neutrophils, eosinophils, and basophils
   (c) Platelets
2. Lymphoid cells (or lymphatic cells; formed mainly in lymphatic tissue in lymph nodes, thymus, and spleen)
   (a) Lymphocytes
   (b) Monocytes

Erythrocytes

Appearance and size. Facts about normal red cell size and shape hold more than

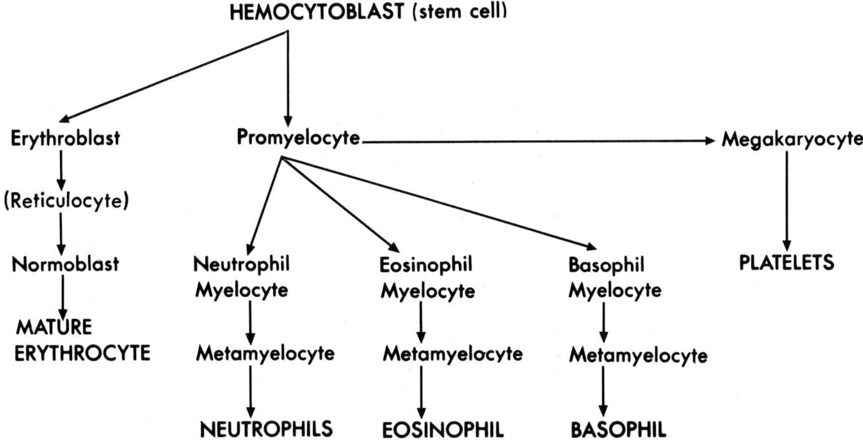

Fig. 177

Stages of development of erythrocytes (red blood cells), granular leukocytes, and platelets in red bone marrow. Under ordinary conditions when the need for red cells is not greater than normal, most erythroblasts develop directly into normoblasts without going through the reticulocyte stage.

academic interest. They are also clinically important. For example, an increase in red cell size characterizes one type of anemia. And a decrease in red cell size characterizes another type. Red cells are extremely small. More than 3,000 of them could be placed side by side in one inch since they measure only about 7 microns in diameter. A normal mature red cell has no nucleus. Just before the cell reaches maturity and enters the bloodstream from the bone marrow, the nucleus is extruded and the cell becomes caved in on both sides. So normal mature red cells are shaped like tiny biconcave disks.

Structure and functions. Red blood cell functions (namely, the transport of oxygen and carbon dioxide) illustrate the familiar principle that structure determines function. Packed within one tiny red cell are an estimated 200 to 300 million molecules of the complex compound *hemoglobin.* One hemoglobin molecule consists of a protein molecule (globin) combined with four molecules of a pigmented compound (heme). Because each molecule of heme contains one atom of iron, one hemoglobin molecule contains four iron atoms. And this is the structural fact that enables one hemoglobin molecule to unite with four oxygen molecules to form oxyhemoglobin (a reversible reaction). Hemoglobin can also combine with carbon dioxide to form carbaminohemoglobin (also reversible). But in this reaction the structure of the globin part of the hemoglobin molecule rather than of its heme part makes the combining possible. Further discussion of oxygen and carbon dioxide transport appears in Chapter X.

Formation (erythropoiesis). Erythrocytes are formed in the red bone marrow* from nucleated cells known as hemocytoblasts or stem cells. The main stages of red cell

*Locations of red bone marrow are given on p. 72. Before birth, the liver and spleen produce red blood cells, but by birth and from that time on only the red bone marrow performs this function. An exception to this principle is that the liver and spleen may again produce red cells under some markedly abnormal conditions. With increased age comes decreased marrow productivity, a fact that may partially account for the anemia so common in old age.

development (Fig. 177) are as follows: hemocytoblast, erythroblast, normoblast, and erythrocyte (mature red cell). But, curiously, when for some reason the body needs faster red cell production, another stage, reticulocytes, occurs between the erythroblast and normoblast stages. Hemoglobin synthesis starts during the erythroblast stage. Extrusion of the nucleus occurs sometimes from erythroblasts (to form reticulocytes) but more often from normoblasts (to form mature red cells).

Frequently a physician needs information about the rate of erythropoiesis to help him make a diagnosis or prescribe treatment. A *reticulocyte count* gives this information. For example, a lower than normal reticulocyte count is one of the signs of anemia due to decreased red cell production. A higher than normal reticulocyte count, on the other hand, indicates accelerated red cell production such as may occur following treatment of anemia.

Destruction. The life span of a red blood cell circulating in the bloodstream is now believed to be about 120 days, based on studies using radioactive substances (isotopes) to "tag" red cells. Apparently as red cells grow older, their membranes become increasingly fragile and eventually rupture, causing the cell to break apart or fragment within the capillaries. Following this, reticuloendothelial cells in the liver, spleen, and bone marrow phagocytose the red cell fragments and break down their hemoglobin to yield an iron-containing pigment (hemosiderin) and bile pigments (bilirubin and biliverdin). Eventually the bone marrow uses most of the iron over again for new red cell synthesis, and the liver excretes the bile pigments in the bile.

Erythrocyte homeostatic mechanism. Red cells are formed and destroyed at a breathtaking rate. Millions are destroyed while millions of others are formed every second of every day of our lives! Obviously some kind of homeostatic mechanism operates to balance the number of cells formed against the number destroyed, since, in health, the number of red cells remains relatively constant at about 4½ to 5½ million per cubic millimeter of blood. The exact mechanism responsible for this constancy is not known. It is known, however, that the rate of red cell production speeds up very soon after tissue hypoxia develops for any reason. The stimulus for starting the mechanism, in other words, appears to be tissue hypoxia. Whether or not it acts as a direct stimulant of the bone marrow is not known. Experimental evidence suggests that it acts indirectly, that is, that tissue hypoxia acts as a stimulant to some structure, causing it to secrete a substance (erythropoietin) which, in turn, stimulates the bone marrow (Fig. 178). Still unknown is the source of erythropoietin. The kidneys and pituitary gland have both been suggested as possible sources.

Note that for the red blood cell homeostatic mechanism to succeed in maintaining a normal number of red cells, the bone marrow must function adequately. To do this the blood must supply it with adequate amounts of several substances with which to form the new red cells—iron and amino acids, for example, and also copper, vitamin B compounds, and possibly cobalt to serve as catalysts. In addition, the gastric mucosa must provide some unidentified intrinsic factor necessary for absorption of vitamin B_{12} (called extrinsic factor because of its external source in foods; also called antianemic principle). The chain of reactions necessary for normal red cell production might be summarized as follows:

normal gastric mucosa
supplies
intrinsic factor
which
promotes absorption of vitamin B (extrinsic factor)
which
stimulates bone marrow
to produce
normal number of mature red blood cells

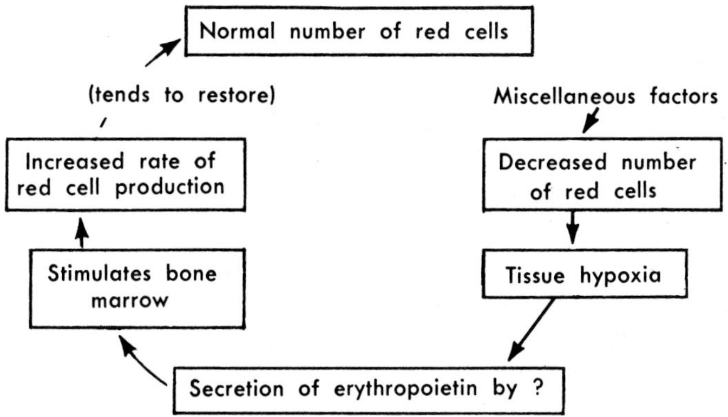

Fig. 178

Postulated red blood cell homeostatic mechanisms. Hypoxia may stimulate bone marrow directly instead of indirectly by erythropoietin as shown.

Failure to maintain homeostasis of red blood cells may result from interference at some point in the foregoing chain of reactions. For example, pernicious anemia develops when the gastric mucosa fails to produce sufficient intrinsic factor. Inadequate absorption of vitamin B_{12} then follows, and the bone marrow, deprived of stimulation by vitamin B_{12}, produces fewer but larger red cells than normal. Many of these cells are immature with overly fragile membranes, a fact which leads to their more rapid destruction.

A clinical example of failure of red cell homeostasis seen in recent years is anemia due to bone marrow injury by x-ray or gamma ray radiations.

Other factors may also cause marrow damage. To help diagnose this condition, a sample of marrow is removed from the sternum by means of a sternal puncture and is studied microscopically for abnormalities. When damaged marrow can no longer keep red cell production apace with destruction, red cell homeostasis is not maintained. The red cell count falls below normal, and the individual has anemia.

Can you deduce other ways anemia might develop other than by a decrease in the rate of red cell production? It does sometimes happen that an individual becomes anemic even though his bone marrow produces red cells at a normal rate or faster. How?*

The number of red blood cells is determined by the *"red count"* or is estimated by the hematocrit. The *hematocrit* is the percentage of red cells in whole blood. For example, a hematocrit of 47 means that in every 100 ml. of whole blood there are 47 ml. of blood cells and 53 ml. of fluid (plasma). Normally, the average hematocrit for a man is about 47 ($\pm$ 7, normal range) and for a woman about 42 ($\pm$ 5).

Leukocytes

Appearance and size. Consult Fig. 176. Note particularly the differences in color of the cytoplasmic granules and in the shapes of the nuclei of the granular leukocytes. Neutrophils take their name from the fact that they stain with neutral dyes. And because their nuclei have two to five or more lobes, neutrophils are also called *polymorphonuclear leukocytes* or, to avoid that tongue twister, simply "polymorphs." Eosinophils stain with acid dyes. Their

*When red cells are being destroyed faster than bone marrow can replace them even by increasing its red cell production as much as possible.

nuclei have two oval lobes. Basophils stain with basic dyes. Their nuclei are roughly S shaped.

Lymphocytes and monocytes do not contain granules in their cytoplasm, a characteristic indicated by the classification of these cells as nongranular leukocytes.

Functions. White blood cells constitute part of the important defense mechanisms of the body. Most of them carry on *phagocytosis,* a process in which they ingest and digest microorganisms and other foreign particles. Neutrophils and monocytes are most actively phagocytic, whereas eosinophils are only moderately so. All leukocytes are motile cells. This characteristic enables them to move out of capillaries by squeezing through the intercellular spaces of the capillary wall (a process called *diapedesis)* and to migrate by ameboid movement toward microorganisms or other injurious particles that may have invaded the tissues. Neutrophils are highly motile, whereas lymphocytes, monocytes, and eosinophils are sluggishly so.

You may recall that reticuloendothelial cells (p. 55) also perform the function of phagocytosis. In general, however, they do this work within more localized areas than white cells, which can be transported by the blood to any part of the body. One more point—white blood cells carry on their function of phagocytosis in the tissues. Where do red cells perform their functions?

Small lymphocytes may play a part in the development of immunity. Evidence now available suggests the following sequence of events. An antigen invades body tissues. Its presence stimulates certain specific small lymphocytes to multiply and differentiate into plasma cells. The plasma cells produce antibodies. Finally, the antibodies destroy or inactivate the particular antigen—the one that originally stimulated the particular small lymphocytes to multiply and become plasma cells.

Formation. All three types of granular leukocytes originate, as do erythrocytes, in myeloid tissue. In contrast, nongranular leukocytes derive from lymphatic tissue—mainly in the lymph nodes and spleen.

Myeloid tissue (bone marrow) and lymphatic tissue together constitute the hemopoietic or blood cell-forming tissues of the body. Red bone marrow is myeloid tissue that is actually producing blood cells. Its red color comes from the red cells it contains. Yellow marrow, on the other hand, is yellow because it stores considerable fat. It is not active in the business of blood cell formation so long as it remains yellow. Sometimes, however, it becomes active and red in color when an extreme and prolonged need for red cell production occurs.

Granular leukocytes, like erythrocytes, pass through several recognized stages before becoming mature cells: hemocytoblast (or myeloblast), promyelocyte, myelocyte, metamyelocyte, and mature leukocyte (Fig. 177).

Destruction and life span. The life span of white blood cells is not known. But presumably lymphocytes live the shortest time, probably less than twenty-four hours, and monocytes the longest time. Granular leukocytes are thought to live perhaps three days or less or possibly as long as about twelve days. Some of them are probably destroyed by phagocytosis and some by microorganisms. Many lymphocytes leave the body in the feces. Many others may degenerate in the lymphatic tissue where they are formed.

Numbers. A cubic millimeter of blood normally contains about 5,000 to 9,000 leukocytes, with definite percentages of each type (Table 37). Because these percentages change in certain abnormal conditions, they have clinical significance. In acute appendicitis, for example, the percentage of neutrophils increases and so, too, does the total white count. In fact, these

Table 37. White blood cells

Class	Differential count* — Normal range (%)	Differential count* — Typical normal (%)
Those with nongranular cytoplasm and regular nucleus		
Lymphocytes (large and small)	20 to 25	25
Monocytes	3 to 8	6
Those with granular cytoplasm and irregular nuclei—leukocytes		
Eosinophils (acid staining)	2 to 5	3
Basophils (basic staining)	½ to 1	1
Neutrophils (neutral staining)	65 to 75	65
Total		100

*In any differential count the sum of the percentages of the different kinds of leukocytes must, of course, total 100%

Table 38. Blood cells

Cells	Number	Function	Formation (hemopoiesis)	Destruction
Red blood cells (erythrocytes)	4½ to 5½ million per c.mm. (total of approximately 30 trillion in adult body)	Transport oxygen and carbon dioxide	Red marrow of bones (myeloid tissue)	By fragmentation in circulating blood and by macrophages of spleen, liver, and red bone marrow; thought to live about 120 days in bloodstream
White blood cells (leukocytes)	5,000 to 9,000 per c.mm.	Defense against microorganisms and other injurious factors—by phagocytosis	Granular leukocytes in red marrow; nongranular leukocytes in lymphatic tissue	Not known definitely; probably some destroyed by phagocytosis and some by microorganisms
Platelets (thrombocytes)	250,000 to 450,000 per c.mm.; wide variation with different counting methods	Initiate blood clotting	Red marrow	Unknown

characteristic changes may be the deciding points for surgery.

The procedure in which the different types of leukocytes are counted and their percentage of the total white count is computed is known as a *differential count.* In other words, a differential count is a percentage count of white cells. The different kinds of white cells and a normal differential count are listed in Table 37. A decrease in the number of white blood cells is *leukopenia.* An increase in the number of white cells is *leukocytosis. (Leukemia* is a malignant disease characterized by a marked increase in the number of white blood cells.)

Platelets

Appearance and size. Platelets are small fragments of cells.

Functions. These important little blood cells help set in operation the blood-clotting mechanism (p. 283).

Formation and life span. Platelets are formed in the red bone marrow presumably by fragmentation of very large cells known as megakaryocytes (Fig. 177). Their life span is not definitely known but is thought to be only a few days. A summary of the basic facts about blood cells is given in Table 38.

BLOOD TYPES (OR BLOOD GROUPS)

The term blood type refers to the type of antigens* present on or in red blood cell membranes. Most common are those known as factors A and B and the Rh factor. Many other factors have also been identified, but they are less important clinically and are too complex to discuss here. Since blood types are named according to the antigens present on red cells, the main blood types are the following:

1. *type A*—A factor antigen on red cells
2. *type B*—B factor antigen on red cells
3. *type AB*—both A and B factor antigens on red cells
4. *type O*—neither A nor B antigen factor on red cells
5. *Rh positive*—Rh factor antigen on red cells, with or without A or B factors
6. *Rh negative*—Rh factor antigen absent from red cells

Blood plasma may or may not contain antibodies that can react with red cell antigens A, B, and Rh. An important principle about this is that plasma never contains antibodies against the antigens present on its own red blood cells—for obvious reasons. If it did, the antibody would react with the antigen and thereby destroy the red cells. But (and this is an equally important principle) plasma does contain antibodies against the main antigens *not* present on its red cells. Applying these two principles: plasma of type A blood contains b antibodies but does not contain a antibodies (small letters distinguish antibodies from antigens designated by capital letters). Type B blood contains a antibodies but not b antibodies. Rh-negative blood contains Rh antibodies (but no Rh factor on its red cells). Suppose you have type AB blood, Rh positive. Which antigens would be present on your red blood cell membranes? What antibodies would be present in your blood plasma?*

Practical use is made of knowledge about blood types in the typing and cross matching of blood before transfusions. Type O blood is referred to as *universal donor* blood. Not only can it be transfused safely into a person whose blood is also type O, but it can be given as well to one who has

*Antigen—substance capable of stimulating formation of antibodies which can react with the antigen, for example, to agglutinate or clump it or to dissolve it.

*Type AB blood—antigens A and B and Rh factor all present on red cells; no a or b or Rh antibodies in plasma.

type A, B, or AB blood. Why? Because type O blood cells contain neither A nor B antigens to react with either or both types of antibodies that might be present in the recipient's blood. Therefore, the type O donor blood cells will not be agglutinated (clumped) or hemolyzed by the recipient's blood. *Universal recipient* blood contains neither a nor b antibodies so supposedly cannot agglutinate any donor's red cells. What type, therefore, is universal recipient blood? A? B? AB? or O?

BLOOD PLASMA

Plasma is the liquid part of blood or whole blood minus its cells. It can be prepared simply by allowing blood removed from the body to stand for some time after a chemical has been added to it to prevent clotting. Blood cells, being heavier than water, sink to the bottom of the container and clear, straw-colored plasma lies above them. A more rapid way of forming plasma is to centrifuge whole blood, a very rapid whirling process that hurls cells to the bottom of the tube.

Composition

Plasma is approximately 90% water and 10% solutes. These may be classified in several ways.

Classification according to size of solute particles

1. *crystalloids*—particles less than 1 millimicron in diameter (for example, mineral salts)
2. *colloids*—particles 1 to about 100 millimicrons in diameter (for example, proteins—albumin, globulins, and fibrinogen)

Classification according to whether or not solute ionizes

1. *electrolytes*—molecules ionize in solution; for example, the mineral salts and proteins in blood are electrolytes. Because salt molecules dissociate very rapidly to yield positive ions (cations) and negative ions (anions), almost all the salt in blood is present as ions rather than as molecules. Proteins, on the other hand, ionize to a much lesser extent so that many more protein molecules than protein ions are present in blood.
2. *nonelectrolytes*—molecules do not ionize in solution; for example, lipids, glucose, and various metabolic wastes exist as molecules in blood, not as ions.

Classification according to function

1. *nutrients*—glucose, amino acids, and fats
2. *metabolic wastes*—urea, uric acid, creatinine, and lactic acid
3. *respiratory gases*—oxygen and carbon dioxide
4. *regulatory substances*—hormones, enzymes, and mineral salts
5. *protective substances*—antibodies

BLOOD CLOTTING

Purpose

The purpose of blood clotting is obvious—to plug up ruptured vessels and prevent excessive loss of the body's vital fluid.

Consult Figs. 179 and 180.

Mechanism

Because of the function of clotting, the mechanism for producing it must be swift and sure when needed, as when a vessel is cut or ruptured. Equally important, however, clotting needs to be prevented from happening when it is not needed because clots can plug up vessels that must stay open if cells are to receive blood's life-sustaining cargo of oxygen. Essentially, clotting is a mechanism whereby the soluble blood protein fibrinogen is changed into the insoluble protein fibrin. The nature of this mechanism has long been and

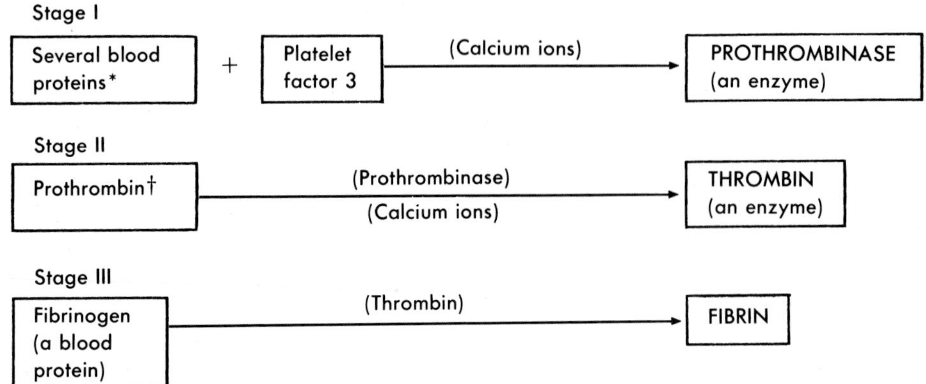

*Some of the main blood proteins (all globulins in type) involved in clotting are AHF (antihemophilic factor; factor VIII), Hageman factor, PTA (plasma thromboplastin antecedent), PTC (plasma thromboplastin component; Christmas factor), proaccelerin (factor V), proconvertin (factor VII), and Stuart factor.
†Prothrombin synthesized by liver cells. Vitamin K acts as a catalyst for this synthesis. Vitamin K, a fat-soluble vitamin, is absorbed from the intestine when adequate amounts of bile are present. Vitamin K is contained in foods and also is synthesized by certain bacteria normally present in the intestine.

Fig. 179

Stages in blood clotting (also see Fig. 180). (From Mosby's comprehensive review of nursing, St. Louis, The C. V. Mosby Co.

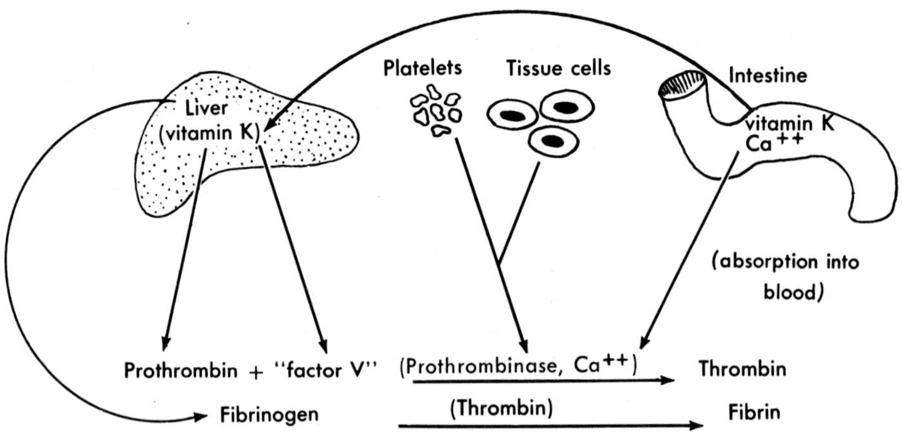

Fig. 180

Diagram to show source of substances that take part in blood clotting. Note that vitamin K catalyzes liver synthesis of prothrombin and that both injured platelets and tissue cells lead to prothrombinase formation by a step not shown in this diagram. When platelets contact a rough surface, they disintegrate, releasing platelet factor 3, which reacts with several blood proteins and calcium ions to form prothrombinase (Fig. 179, stage I).

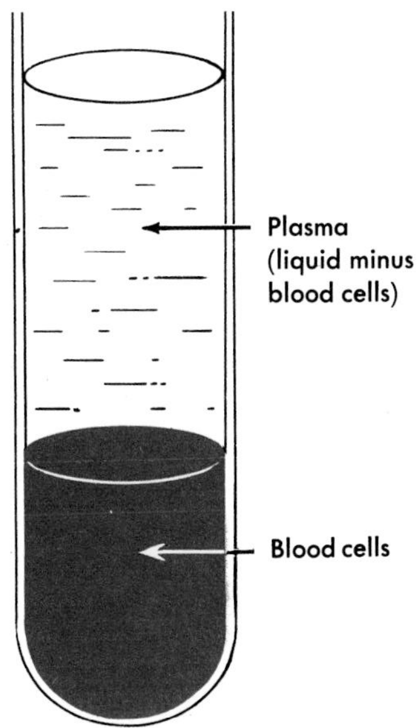

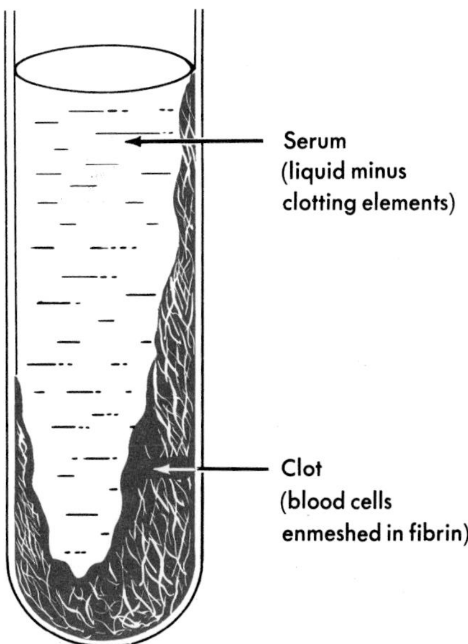

Fig. 181

Diagram to show the difference between blood plasma and blood serum. Plasma is whole blood minus cells. Serum is whole blood minus the clotting elements. Plasma is prepared by centrifuging blood. Serum is prepared by clotting blood.

still is the subject of numerous investigations and theories.

In fact, it is one of the most, if not the most, complex confused fields in physiology. To try to find our way through this maze, a good method seems to be to think of the clotting mechanism as consisting of the three following major stages and to discuss each.

1. Prothrombinase (active thromboplastin) formation
2. Thrombin formation
3. Fibrin formation

Prothrombinase (active thromboplastin) formation. The first stage of blood clotting, prothrombinase formation consists of a number of imperfectly understood chemical reactions. The trigger that sets off these reactions, although not completely clear, is known to involve contact of blood with wettable or rough surfaces (surfaces that are not perfectly smooth).

When platelets contact a wettable surface, they tend to disintegrate, releasing granules of a substance known as *platelet factor 3*. Platelet factor 3 then reacts with several blood proteins and calcium ions to form prothrombinase.

Thrombin formation. One of the complex globulin proteins in blood is *prothrombin.* Prothrombin combines with prothrombinase (formed in stage 1) and several blood proteins and calcium ions to form thrombin. Vitamin K catalyzes prothrombin synthesis by liver cells. Although a balanced diet includes foods that contain vitamin K, synthesis of it in the body also occurs—not by body cells but by certain bacteria normally present in the intestines (except for a time in newborn infants). But even though foods and synthesis supply ample amounts of this vitamin, a person still may have a vitamin K deficiency. Explanation of this paradox lies in the fact of inadequate absorption of vitamin K in the presence of too little bile in the intestine. Vitamin K is fat soluble so that its absorption requires bile. And, therefore, patients whose bile ducts become obstructed or whose liver is too severely diseased to produce adequate amounts of bile cannot absorb enough vitamin K for normal prothrombin synthesis. As a result, their blood does not clot normally. They have a bleeding tendency. As a preoperative safeguard, they are generally given some kind of vitamin K preparation.

Fibrin formation. Another blood protein synthesized by liver cells and involved in blood clotting is *fibrinogen.* Its molecules are long, fiberlike, and large—they have a molecular weight of over 400,000. The enzyme thrombin, formed in stage 2, catalyzes the formation of the gel fibrin from the sol fibrinogen. Fibrin appears as an entangled network of fine threads. Red cells catch in this entanglement, producing the red color of clotted blood. The pale yellowish liquid left after a clot forms is *blood serum.* Serum should not be confused with plasma, which is whole blood minus the cells (Fig. 181).

Factors that oppose clotting

Although blood clotting probably goes on continuously and concurrently with clot dissolution (fibrinolysis), several factors do operate to oppose clot formation and enlargement in intact vessels. For one thing, the normal endothelial lining of blood vessels is a smooth nonwettable surface. Therefore, platelets do not readily adhere to it and disintegrate to release thromboplastin. For another thing, blood contains some substances that tend to prevent clotting—*antithrombins,* for example, that inactivate thrombin and make it unable to catalyze stage 3, fibrin formation. *Heparin* is one substance that acts as an antithrombin. Its normal concentration in blood, however, is too low to have much effect in keeping blood fluid. Where it comes from is not definitely known. Mast cells are known to contain considerable amounts of heparin, although they may not themselves synthesize it but only store it. It was first prepared from liver (hence its name), but various other organs also contain heparin.

Factors that hasten clotting

Two conditions particularly favor thrombus formation: a rough spot in the endothelium (blood vessel lining) and abnormally slow blood flow. Atherosclerosis, for example, is associated with an increased tendency toward thrombosis because of endothelial rough spots in the form of plaques of accumulated lipid material. Immobility, on the other hand, may lead to thrombosis because blood flow slows down as movements decrease. Incidentally, this fact is one of the major reasons why physicians insist that bed patients must either move or be moved frequently. Presumably, sluggish blood flow allows thromboplastin to accumulate sufficiently to reach a concentration adequate for clotting.

Once started, a clot tends to grow. Platelets enmeshed in the fibrin threads disintegrate, releasing more thromboplastin which, in turn, causes more clotting, which enmeshes more platelets, and so on, in a vicious circle. Clot-retarding substances, available in recent years, have proved valuable for retarding this process.

Pharmaceutical preparations that retard clotting

The anticoagulant *Dicumarol* has become well known because of its clinical value in lessening thrombus and embolus formation. It is thought to decrease prothrombin synthesis by the liver, perhaps by blocking vitamin K action (Fig. 180). Commercial preparations of heparin are also used as anticoagulants. These are useful to prevent clotting in the body or outside of it. Blood to be used for transfusions is usually treated with a citrate compound. The latter combines with calcium ions. Therefore, citrate prevents coagulation by blocking formation of what substances? (If you are not sure, consult Fig. 179 for the answer.)

Clot dissolution

Fibrinolysis is the physiological mechanism that dissolves clots. Newer evidence indicates that the two opposing processes of clot formation and fibrinolysis go on continuously. Dr. George Fulton of Boston University has presented one bit of dramatic evidence. He took micromovies that show tiny blood vessels rupturing under apparently normal circumstances and clots forming to plug them. Blood contains an enzyme, fibrinolysin, which catalyzes the hydrolysis of fibrin, causing it to dissolve. Many other factors, however, presumably also take part in clot dissolution—for instance, substances that activate profibrinolysin, the inactive form of fibrinolysin. Streptokinase, an enzyme from certain streptococci, can act this way and so can cause clot dissolution and even hemorrhage.

Clinical methods of hastening clotting

One way of treating excessive bleeding is to speed up the blood-clotting mechanism. The principle involved is apparent—to increase any of the substances essential for clotting. Application of this principle is accomplished in the following ways:

1. By applying a rough surface such as gauze, or by applying heat, or by gently squeezing the tissues around a cut vessel. Each of these procedures causes more platelets to disintegrate and release more platelet factor 3. And this, in turn, accelerates stage I of the clotting mechanism.
2. By applying purified thrombin (in the form of sprays or impregnated gelatin sponges which can be left in a wound). Which stage of the clotting mechanism does this accelerate? See Fig. 179.
3. By applying fibrin foam, films, etc.

Heart

The human heart is a four-chambered muscular organ, shaped and sized roughly like a man's closed fist. It lies in the mediastinum, with approximately two-thirds of its mass to the left of the midline of the body and one-third to the right.

The lower border of the heart, which forms a blunt point known as the *apex*, lies on the diaphragm, pointing toward the left. To count the apical beat, one must place a stethoscope directly over the apex, that is, in the space between the fifth and sixth ribs (fifth intercostal space) on a line with the midpoint of the left clavicle.

The upper border of the heart, or its base, lies just below the second rib. The boundaries, which, of course, indicate its size, have considerable clinical importance since a marked increase in heart size accompanies certain types of heart disease. Therefore, when diagnosing heart disorders, the doctor charts the boundaries of the heart.

COVERING

Structure

The heart has its own special covering, a loose-fitting inextensible sac called the *pericardium.* The pericardium consists of two parts: a fibrous portion and a serous portion (Fig. 182). The sac itself is made of tough white fibrous tissue but is lined with smooth, moist serous membrane—the parietal layer of the serous pericardium. The same kind of membrane covers the entire outer surface of the heart. This covering layer is known as the visceral layer of the serous pericardium or as the *epicardium.* The fibrous sac attaches to the large blood vessels emerging from the top of the heart but not to the heart itself. Therefore, it fits loosely around the heart with a slight space between the visceral layer adhering to the heart and the parietal layer adhering to the inside of the fibrous sac. This space

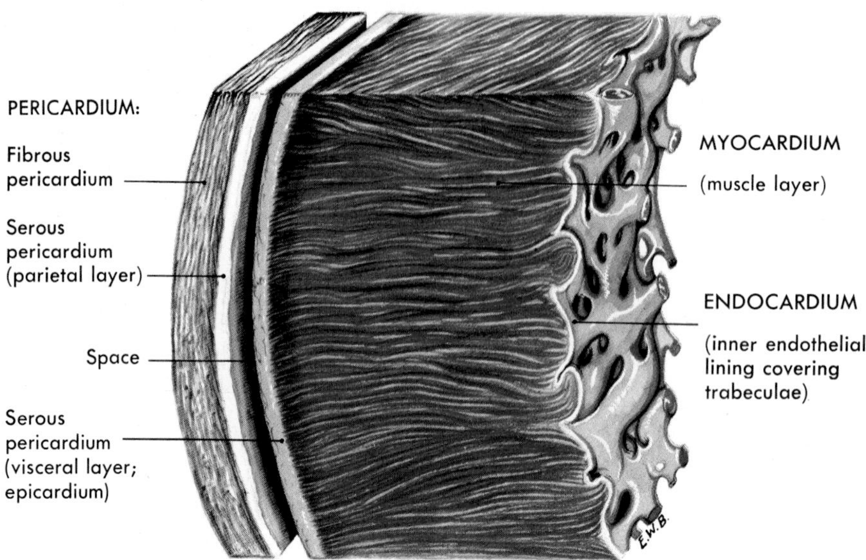

Fig. 182

Section of the heart wall showing the components of the outer pericardium (heart sac), muscle layer (myocardium), and inner lining (endocardium).

is called the *pericardial space.* It contains a few drops of lubricating fluid secreted by the serous membrane and is called *pericardial fluid.*

The structure of the pericardium can be summarized in outline form as follows:

1. *fibrous pericardium*—loose-fitting sac around the heart
2. *serous pericardium*—consisting of two layers
   (a) *parietal layer*—lining inside of the fibrous pericardium
   (b) *visceral layer (epicardium)*—adhering to the outside of the heart; between visceral and parietal layers is a potential space, the pericardial space, which contains a few drops of pericardial fluid

Function

The fibrous pericardial sac with its smooth, well-lubricated lining provides protection against friction. The heart moves easily in this loose-fitting jacket with no danger of irritation from friction between the two surfaces so long as the serous pericardium remains normal. If, however, it becomes inflamed (pericarditis) and too much pericardial fluid or fibrin or pus develops in the pericardial space, the visceral and parietal layers may adhere to each other in spots, interfering with the normal contractions of the heart. In such cases it sometimes becomes necessary to remove the fibrous pericardium with its lining of parietal serous membrane in order for the heart to continue functioning. This operation, a spectacular procedure, is called a *pericardectomy.*

STRUCTURE

Wall

Three distinct layers of tissue make up the heart wall (Fig. 182). The bulk of the wall consists of specially constructed muscle tissue known as cardiac muscle or the *myocardium.* Covering the myocardium on the outside and adherent to it is the visceral layer of the *serous pericardium* (or *epicardium*) already described. Lining the interior of the myocardial wall is a delicate layer of endothelial* tissue known as the *endocardium*. On its inner surface the myocardium is raised into ridgelike projections, the papillary muscles.

Cavities

The interior of the heart is divided into four chambers, two upper and two lower. The upper cavities are named *atria*† and the lower ones *ventricles*. Of these, the ventricles are considerably larger and thicker walled than the atria because they carry a heavier pumping burden than the atria. Also, the left ventricle has thicker walls than the right because it has to pump blood through all the vessels of the body, except those to and from the lungs, whereas the right ventricle sends blood only through the lungs.

Valves and openings

The heart valves are mechanical devices that permit the flow of blood in one direction only. Four sets of valves are of importance to the normal functioning of the heart. Two of these, the cuspid (atrioventricular) valves, are located in the heart, guarding the openings between the atria and ventricles (atrioventricular orifices). The other two, the semilunar valves, are located inside the pulmonary artery and the great aorta just as they arise from the right and left ventricles, respectively.

The cuspid valve guarding the right atrioventricular orifice consists of three flaps of endocardium anchored to the papillary muscles of the right ventricle by several cordlike structures called *chordae tendineae*. Because this valve has three flaps, it is appropriately named the *tricuspid valve*. The valve that guards the left atrioventricular orifice is similar in structure to the tricuspid except that it has only two flaps and is, therefore, called the *bicuspid* or, more commonly, the *mitral valve*. (An easy way to remember which valve is on the right and which is on the left is to remember that the names whose first letters come nearest together in the alphabet go together—thus, L and M for *l*eft side, *mi*tral valve, and R and T for *r*ight side, *t*ricuspid.)

The construction of both cuspid valves allows blood to flow from the atria into the ventricles but prevents it from flowing back up into the atria from the ventricles. Ventricular contraction forces the blood in the ventricles hard against the cuspid valves, closing them and thereby ensuring the movement of the blood upward into the pulmonary artery and aorta as the ventricles contract.

The *semilunar valves* consist of half-moon-shaped flaps growing out from the lining of the pulmonary artery and great aorta. When these valves are closed, blood fills the spaces between the flaps and the vessel wall, giving each flap the appearance of a tiny filled bucket. Inflowing blood smooths the flaps against the blood vessel wall, collapsing the buckets and thereby opening the valves.

Like the cuspid valves, the semilunar valves, by preventing backflow of blood, cause it to flow forward in places where there would otherwise be considerable blackflow. Whereas the cuspid valves prevent blood from flowing back up into the atria from the ventricles, the semilunar valves prevent it from flowing back down into the ventricles from the aorta and pulmonary artery.

*Endothelial tissue resembles simple squamous epithelial tissue in that it consists of a single layer of flat cells. It differs from epithelial tissue in that it arises from the mesoderm layer of the embryo, whereas epithelial tissue arises from the ectoderm.

†The atria are sometimes called auricles. Strictly speaking, the latter term means the earlike flaps protruding from the atria, although the two terms are often used synonymously.

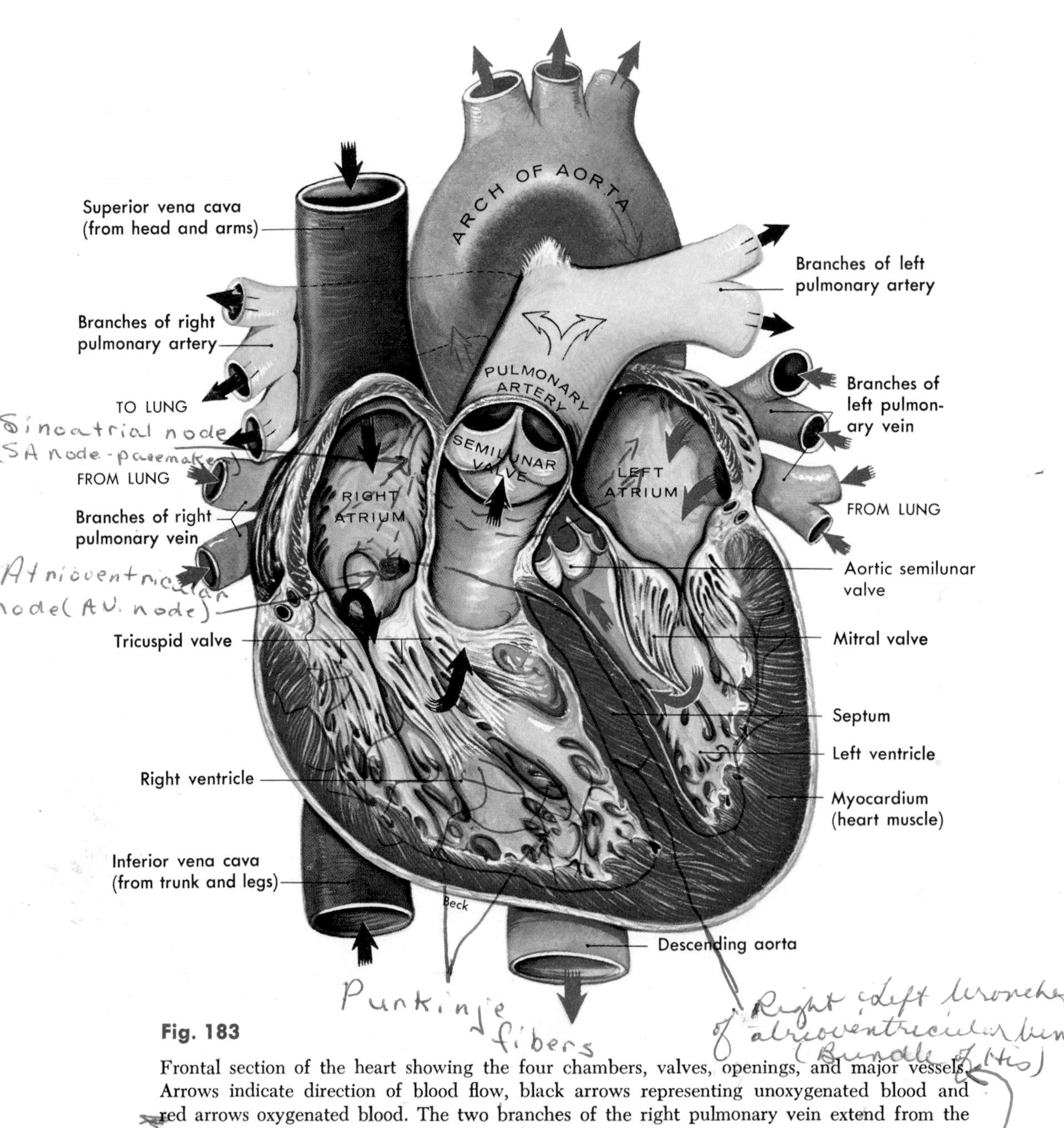

Fig. 183

Frontal section of the heart showing the four chambers, valves, openings, and major vessels. Arrows indicate direction of blood flow, black arrows representing unoxygenated blood and red arrows oxygenated blood. The two branches of the right pulmonary vein extend from the right lung behind the heart to enter the left atrium.

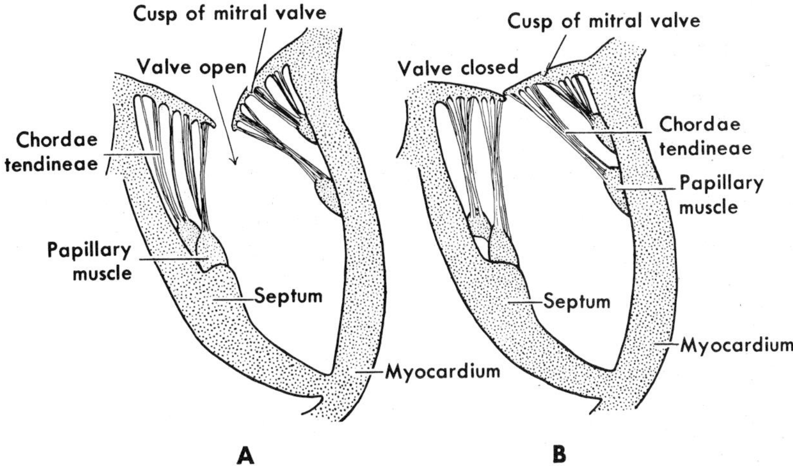

Fig. 184

Action of the cuspid (atrioventricular) valves. **A,** When the valves are open, blood passes freely from the atria to the ventricles. **B,** Filling of the ventricles closes the valves and prevents a back flow of blood into the atria when the ventricles contract.

Fig. 185

The valves of the heart viewed from above. The atria are removed to show the mitral and tricuspid valves.

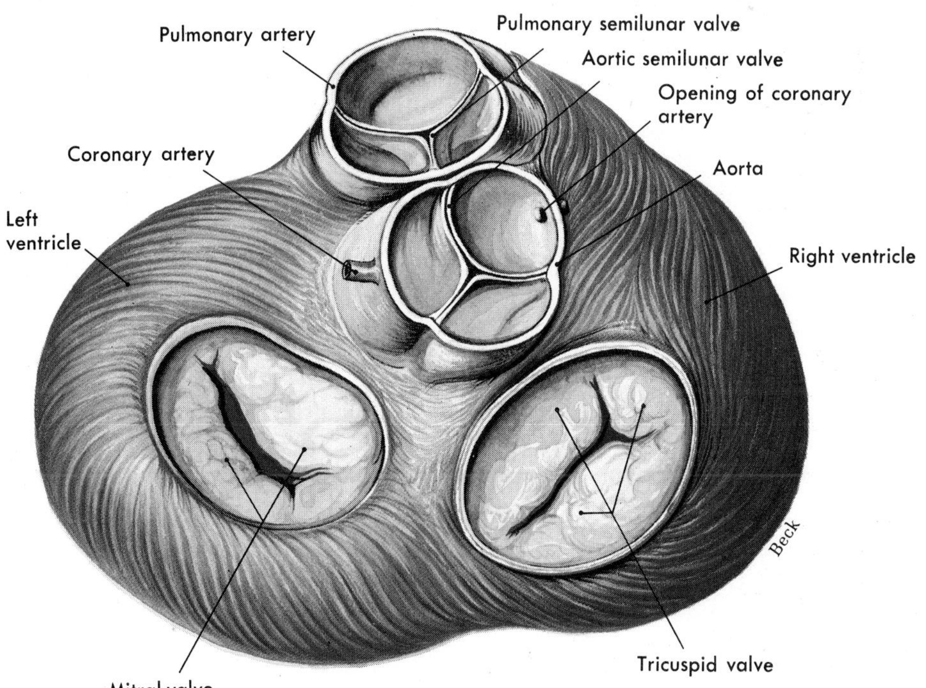

Table 39. Branches of coronary arteries

Left coronary artery	*Right coronary artery*
1. Anterior descending artery—supplies branches to left and right ventricles 2. Circumflex artery—supplies branches to left atrium and left ventricle	1. Posterior descending artery—supplies branches to both left and right ventricles 2. Marginal artery—supplies branches to right atrium and right ventricle

Any one of the four valves may lose its ability to close tightly. Such a condition is known as *valvular insufficiency* or, because it permits blood to "leak" back into the part of the heart from which it came, "leakage of the heart." *Mitral stenosis* is an abnormality in which the left atrioventricular orifice becomes narrowed by scar tissue that forms as a result of disease and therefore hinders the passage of blood from the left atrium to the left ventricle.

Blood supply

Myocardial cells receive blood by way of two small vessels, the right and left coronary arteries. Since the openings into these vitally important vessels lie behind flaps of the aortic semilunar valve, they come off of the aorta at its very beginning and are its first branches. Both right and left coronary arteries have two main branches, as shown in Table 39.

Note that each ventricle receives blood from both major branches of its respective coronary artery and from the descending branch of the opposite coronary artery, whereas each atrium receives blood from only one source. More specifically, the left ventricle receives blood from the anterior descending and circumflex branches of the left coronary artery and from the posterior descending branch of the right coronary artery. The left atrium, on the other hand, receives blood only from the left circumflex artery. This structural fact seems appropriate in relation to function. The ventricles do more work than the atria and therefore need more blood.

Another fact about the heart's own blood supply—and one of life-and-death importances—is the fact that only a few anastomoses exist between the larger branches of the coronary arteries. An *anastomosis* consists of one or more branches from the proximal part of an artery to a more distal part of itself or of another artery. Thus, anastomoses provide detours which arterial blood can travel if the main route becomes obstructed. They provide the means for collateral circulation to a part. This explains why the scarcity of anastomoses between larger coronary arteries looms as so large a threat to life. If, for example, a blood clot plugs one of the larger coronary artery branches, as it frequently does in coronary thrombosis or embolism, too little or no blood can reach some of the heart muscle cells. In other words, they become ischemic. Deprived of oxygen, they release too little energy for their own survival. Myocardial infarction (death of ischemic heart muscle cells) soon results. There is another anatomical fact, however, which brightens the picture somewhat—many anastomoses do exist between very small arterial vessels in the heart, and, given time, new ones develop and provide collateral circulation to ischemic areas. In recent years several surgical procedures have been devised to aid this process.*

*Artery link helps heart, Sci. Newsletter **90**:8, 1966.

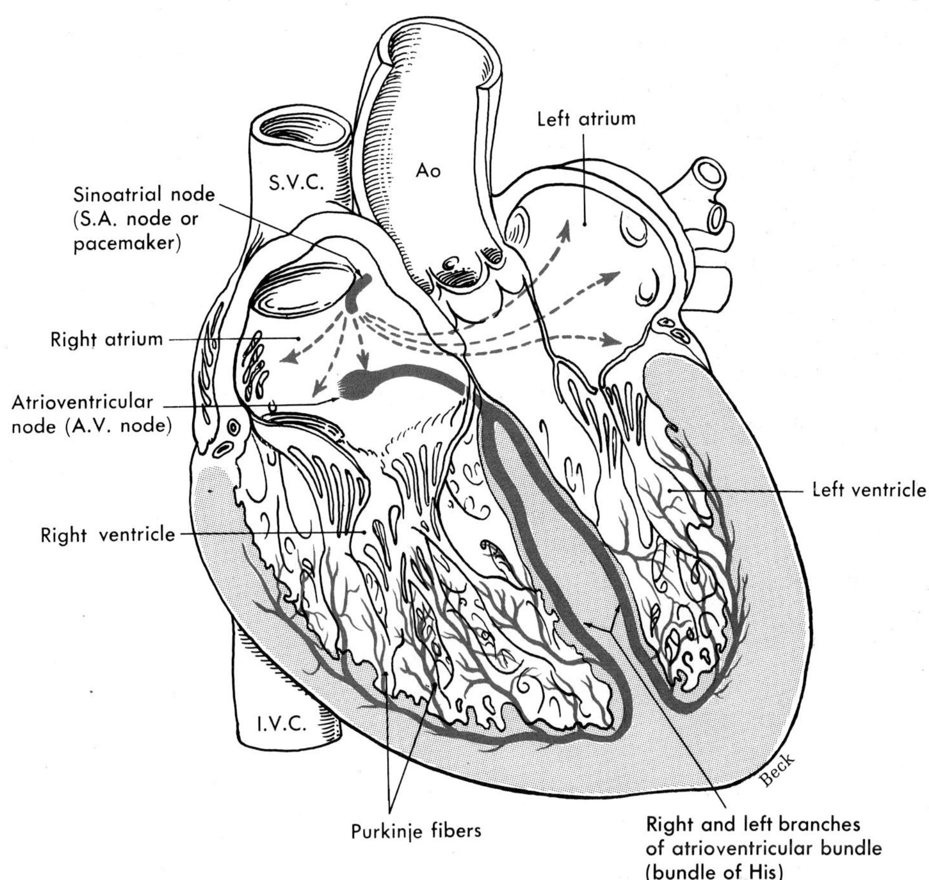

Fig. 186

The conduction system of the heart. The sinoatrial node in the wall of the right atrium sets the pace of the heart's rhythm so is called the "pacemaker."

Conduction system

Four structures—the sinoatrial node, atrioventricular node, atrioventricular bundle, and Purkinje fibers—compose the conduction system of the heart (Fig. 186). Each of these structures consists of cardiac muscle modified enough in structure to differ in function from ordinary cardiac muscle. The main specialty of ordinary cardiac muscle is contraction. In this it is like all muscle and, like all muscle, ordinary cardiac muscle can also conduct impulses. But conduction alone is the specialty of the modified cardiac muscle that composes the conduction system structures.

Sinoatrial node. The sinoatrial node (S.A. node, Keith-Flack node, or pacemaker) is a small mass of modified cardiac muscle fibers located in the right atrial wall near the opening of the superior vena cava (Fig. 186). It is abundantly supplied with both sympathetic and parasympathetic fibers. Normally, the S.A. node, stimulated by impulses over these fibers, initiates each heartbeat—hence its designation as the pacemaker.

Atrioventricular node. The atrioventricular node (A.V. node or node of Tawara) is a small mass of special cardiac muscle tissue in the lower part of the interatrial septum (Figs. 186 and 187).

Atrioventricular bundle and Purkinje fibers. The atrioventricular bundle (bundle

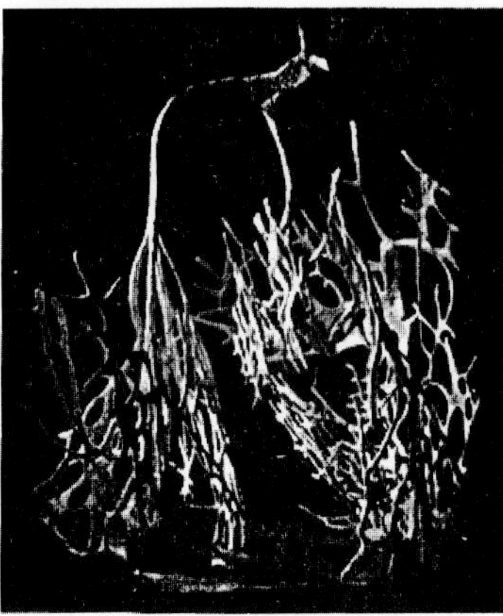

Fig. 187

Model of the atrioventricular node and bundle of His, two of the important neuromuscular structures of the heart. (From Howell: A textbook of physiology, Philadelphia, W. B. Saunders Co.)

of His) is a bundle of special cardiac muscle fibers which originate in the A.V. node and which extend by two branches down the two sides of the interventricular septum. From there, they continue as the Purkinje fibers (Figs. 186 and 187). The latter extend out to the papillary muscles and lateral walls of the ventricles.

Impulse conduction through the heart normally starts in the S.A. node and spreads through atrial muscle fibers in all directions, causing atrial contraction. When impulses reach the A.V. node, it relays them by way of the bundle of His and Purkinje fibers to the ventricles, causing their contraction. Impulse conduction generates tiny electrical currents in the heart that spread through surrounding tissues to the surface of the body. This fact has great clinical importance. Why? Because from the skin, visible records of heart conduction can be made with the electrocardiograph or oscillograph.

Nerve supply

Both divisions of the autonomic nervous system send fibers to the heart. Sympathetic fibers (contained in the middle, superior, and inferior cardiac nerves) and parasympathetic fibers (in branches of the vagus) combine to form *cardiac plexuses* located close to the arch of the aorta. From the cardiac plexuses, fibers accompany the right and left coronary arteries to enter the heart. Here, most of the fibers terminate in the S.A. node, but some end in the A.V. node and in the atrial myocardium. Sympathetic nerves to the heart are also called accelerator nerves. Vagus fibers to the heart serve as inhibitory or depressor nerves.

PHYSIOLOGY

Function

The function of the heart is to pump blood in sufficient amounts to meet the varying needs of the cells of the body for the substances it transports. Mechanisms that accomplish this function of pumping different volumes of blood per minute under different conditions are discussed on pp. 312 to 325 and on p. 328.

Cardiac cycle

The term cardiac cycle means a complete heartbeat consisting of contraction (systole) and relaxation (diastole) of both atria plus contraction and relaxation of both ventricles. The two atria contract simultaneously. Then, as they relax, the two ventricles contract and relax, instead of the entire heart contracting as a unit. This gives a kind of milking action to the movements of the heart. The atria remain relaxed during part of the ventricular relaxation and then start the cycle over again. The events occurring during the cycle are described in Table 40. Note the following facts:

1. The contracting force of the atria completes the emptying of blood out of the atria into the ventricles. Cuspid valves are necessarily open during this phase, the ventricles relaxed, filling with blood, and the semilunar valves closed so that blood does

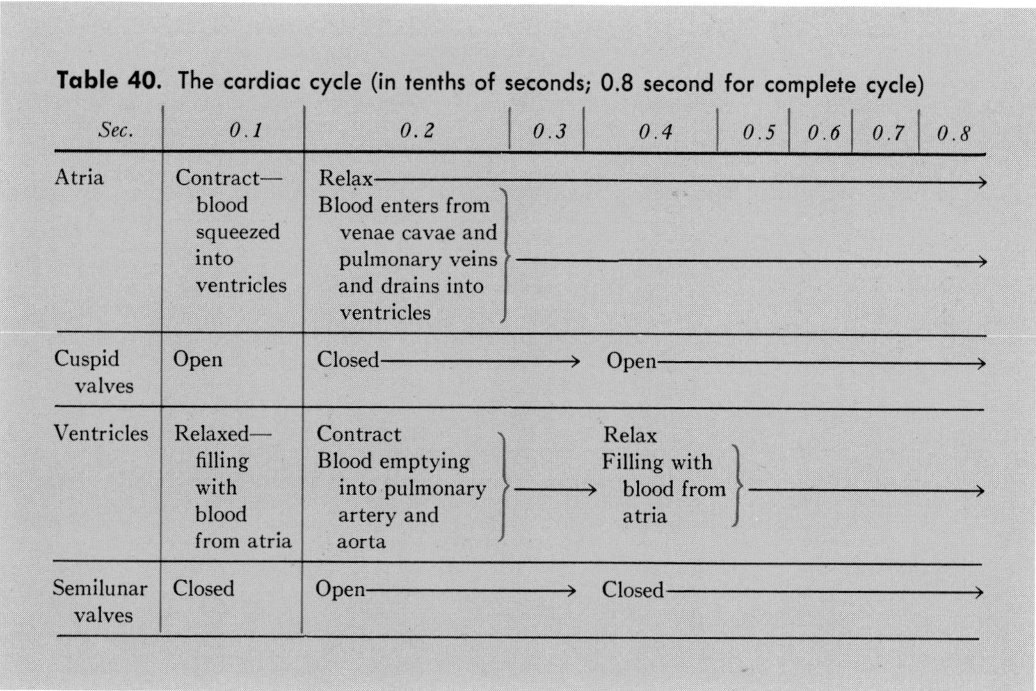

Table 40. The cardiac cycle (in tenths of seconds; 0.8 second for complete cycle)

Sec.	*0.1*	*0.2*	*0.3*	*0.4*	*0.5*	*0.6*	*0.7*	*0.8*
Atria	Contract—blood squeezed into ventricles	Relax→ Blood enters from venae cavae and pulmonary veins and drains into ventricles	→	→	→	→	→	→
Cuspid valves	Open	Closed→	→	Open→	→	→	→	→
Ventricles	Relaxed—filling with blood from atria	Contract Blood emptying into pulmonary artery and aorta	→	Relax Filling with blood from atria	→	→	→	→
Semilunar valves	Closed	Open→	→	Closed→	→	→	→	→

not flow on out into the pulmonary artery or aorta.

2. The atria relax, and blood enters them from the veins during the first part of their diastole and starts draining out into the ventricles during the latter part of it. The cuspid valves are closed during the first part of the diastole (while the ventricles are contracting, squeezing blood through the open semilunar valves into the pulmonary artery and aorta) but open as the ventricles relax, the semilunar valves close, and the ventricles start to fill with blood from the atria. About what percent of the time are the atria relaxed or resting? The ventricles? Consult Table 40 to find the answers.

Heart sounds during cycle. The heart makes certain typical sounds during each cycle that are described as sounding like lubb-dupp through a stethoscope. The first or systolic sound is believed to be due to the contraction of the ventricles and to vibrations of the closing cuspid valves. It is longer and lower than the second or diastolic sound, which is thought to be caused by vibrations of the closing semilunar valves.

Both of these sounds have clinical significance since they give information about the valves of the heart. Any variation from normal in the sounds indicates imperfect functioning of the valves. *Heart murmur* is one type of abnormal sound frequently heard and may signify incomplete closing of the valves (valvular insufficiency) or stenosis of them.

Blood vessels

Kinds

There are three kinds of blood vessels: arteries, veins, and capillaries. By definition an *artery* is a vessel that carries blood away from the heart. All arteries except the pulmonary artery and its branches carry oxy-

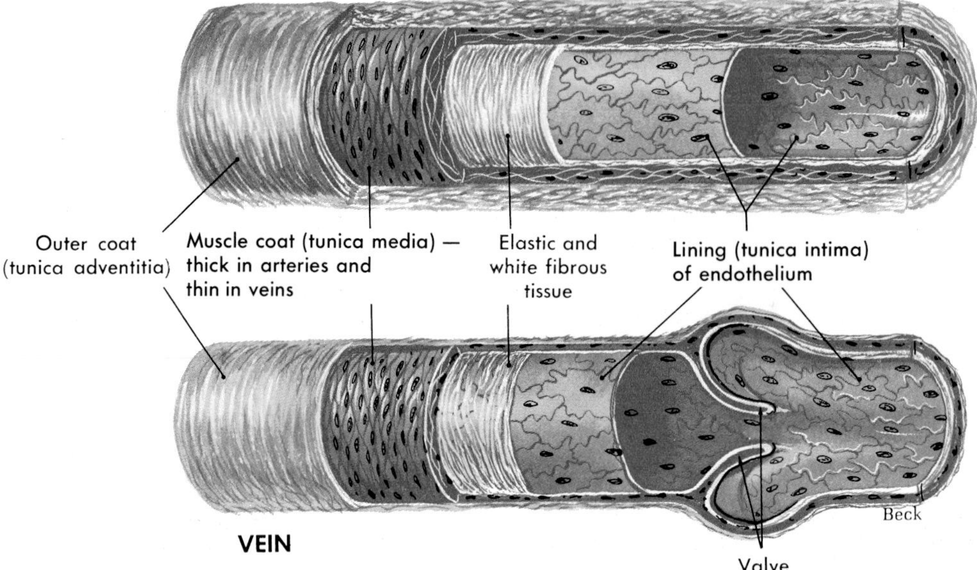

Fig. 188

Schematic drawings of an artery and vein showing comparative thicknesses of the three coats: outer coat (tunica adventitia), muscle coat (tunica media), and lining of endothelium (tunica intima). Note that the muscle and outer coats are much thinner in veins than in arteries and that veins have valves.

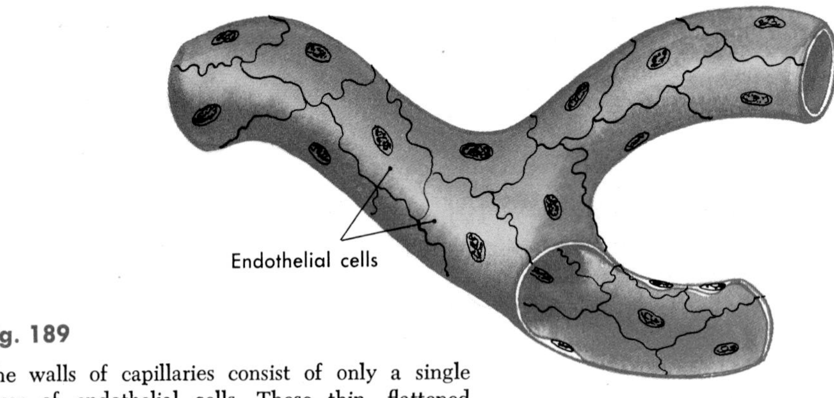

Fig. 189

The walls of capillaries consist of only a single layer of endothelial cells. These thin, flattened cells permit the rapid movement of substances between blood and interstitial fluid. Note that capillaries have no smooth muscle layer, elastic fibers, or surrounding adventitia.

Table 41. Structure of blood vessels

	Arteries	*Veins*	*Capillaries*
Coats	Outer coat (tunica adventitia or externa) of white fibrous tissue; causes artery to stand open instead of collapsing when cut (see Fig. 188) Lining (tunica intima) of endothelium Muscle coat (tunica media) of smooth muscle, elastic, and some white fibrous tissues; this coat permits constriction and dilatation	Same three coats but thinner and fewer elastic fibers; veins collapse when cut; semilunar valves present at intervals	Only lining coat present; therefore walls only one-cel! thick
Blood supply Endothelial lining cells supplied by blood flowing through vessels; exchange of oxygen, etc., between cells of middle coat and blood by diffusion; outer coat supplied by tiny vessels known as *vasa vasorum* or "vessels of vessels"			
Nerve supply Smooth muscle cells of tunica media innervated by autonomic fibers			
Abnormalities *Arteriosclerosis*—hardening of walls of arteries *Aneurysm*—saclike dilatation of artery wall *Varicose veins*—stretching of walls, particularly around semilunar valves *Phlebitis*—inflammation of vein; "milk leg," phlebitis of femoral vein of women after childbirth			

genated blood. Small arteries are called *arterioles.*

A *vein,* on the other hand, is a vessel that carries blood toward the heart. All of the veins except the pulmonary contain deoxygenated blood. Small veins are called *venules.* Both arteries and veins are macroscopic structures. *Capillaries* are microscopic vessels that carry blood from small arteries to small veins—that is, from arterioles to venules. They represented the "missing link" in the proof of circulation for many years—from the time William Harvey first declared that blood circulated from the heart through arteries to veins and back to the heart until the time that microscopes made it possible to find these connecting vessels between arteries and veins. Many people rejected Harvey's theory of circulation on the basis that there was no possible way for blood to get from arteries to veins. The discovery of the capillaries formed the final proof that the blood actually does circulate from the heart into arteries to arterioles, to capillaries, to venules, to veins, and back to the heart.

Structure

Consult Table 41 for structure of the blood vessels.

Functions

The capillaries, though seemingly the most insignificant of the three kinds of

Table 42. Main arteries

Artery	*Branches (only largest ones named)*
Ascending aorta	Coronary arteries (two, to myocardium)
Aortic arch	Innominate artery Left subclavian Left common carotid
Innominate artery	Right subclavian Right common carotid
Subclavian (right and left)	Vertebral* Axillary (continuation of subclavian)
Axillary	Brachial (continuation of axillary)
Brachial	Radial Ulnar
Radial and ulnar	Palmar arches (superficial and deep arterial arches in hand formed by anastomosis of branches of radial and ulnar arteries; numerous branches to hand and fingers)
Common carotid (right and left)	Internal carotid (brain, eye, forehead, and nose)* External carotid (thyroid, tongue, tonsils, ear, etc.)
Descending thoracic aorta	Visceral branches to pericardium, bronchi, esophagus, mediastinum Parietal branches to chest muscles, mammary glands, and diaphragm
Descending abdominal aorta	Visceral branches 1. Celiac axis (or artery), which branches into gastric, hepatic, and splenic arteries (stomach, liver, and spleen) 2. Right and left suprarenal arteries (suprarenal glands) 3. Superior mesenteric artery (small intestine) 4. Right and left renal arteries (kidneys) 5. Right and left spermatic (or ovarian) arteries (testes or ovaries) 6. Inferior mesenteric artery (large intestine) Parietal branches to lower surface of diaphragm, muscles and skin of back, spinal cord, and meninges Right and left common iliac arteries—abdominal aorta terminates in these vessels in an inverted **Y** formation

*The right and left vertebral arteries extend from their origin as branches of the subclavian arteries up the neck, through foramina in the transverse processes of the cervical vertebrae, and through the foramen magnum into the cranial cavity and unite on the undersurface of the brainstem to form the *basilar artery*, which shortly branches into the right and left *posterior cerebral arteries*. The internal carotid arteries enter the cranial cavity in the midpart of the cranial floor, where they become known as the *anterior cerebral arteries*. Small vessels, the *communicating arteries*, join the anterior and posterior cerebral arteries in such a way as to form an arterial circle (the *circle of Willis*) at the base of the brain, a good example of arterial anastomosis (Fig. 193).

Table 42. Main arteries—cont'd

Artery	*Branches (only largest ones named)*
Right and left common iliac arteries	Internal iliac or hypogastric (pelvic wall and viscera) External iliac (to leg)
External iliac (right and left)	Femoral (continuation of external iliac after it leaves abdominal cavity)
Femoral	Popliteal (continuation of femoral)
Popliteal	Anterior tibial Posterior tibial
Anterior and posterior tibial	Plantar arch (arterial arch in sole of foot formed by anastomosis of terminal branches of anterior and posterior tibial arteries; small arteries lead from arch to toes)

blood vessels because of their diminutive size, nevertheless are the most important vessels functionally. Since the prime function of blood is to transport essential materials to and from the cells and since the actual delivery and collection of these substances take place in the capillaries, the capillaries must be regarded as the most important blood vessels functionally. Arteries serve merely as "distributors," carrying the blood to the capillaries. Veins function simply as "collectors." They return blood from the capillaries to the heart. And the heart acts as a "pump," keeping the blood moving through this circuit of vessels. In short, the entire circulatory mechanism pivots around this one essential, that of keeping the capillaries supplied with an amount of blood adequate to the changing needs of the cells. All the factors governing circulation operate to this one end.

Although capillaries are very tiny (on the average, only 1 mm. long or about 1/25 inch), they are so numerous as to be incomprehensible. Someone has calculated that if these microscopic tubes were joined end to end, they would extend 62,000 miles, in spite of the fact that it takes twenty-five of them to reach a single inch! According to one estimate, one square inch of muscle tissue contains over 1½ million of these important little vessels. None of the billions of cells composing the body lie very far removed from a capillary. The reason for this lavish distribution of capillaries is of course apparent in view of their function of keeping the cells supplied with needed materials and rid of injurious wastes.

MAIN BLOOD VESSELS

Systemic circulation

Arteries

Locate the arteries listed in Table 42 (see also Figs. 190 to 193). The names of blood vessels and the relation of the vessels to each other are more easily learned from diagrams than from descriptions.

As you learn the names of the main arteries, keep in mind that these are only the major pipelines distributing blood from the heart to the various organs and that in each organ the main artery resembles a tree

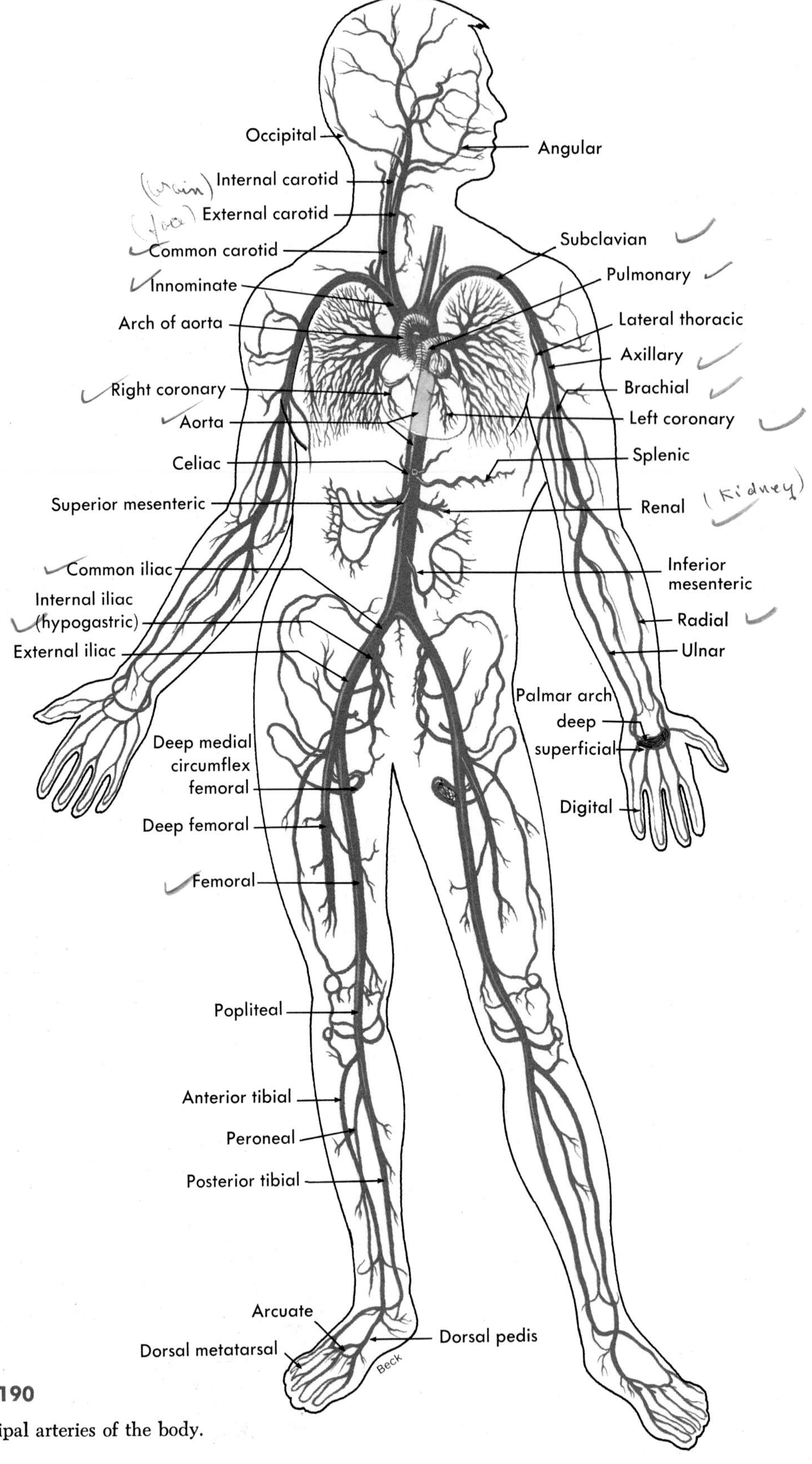

Fig. 190

Principal arteries of the body.

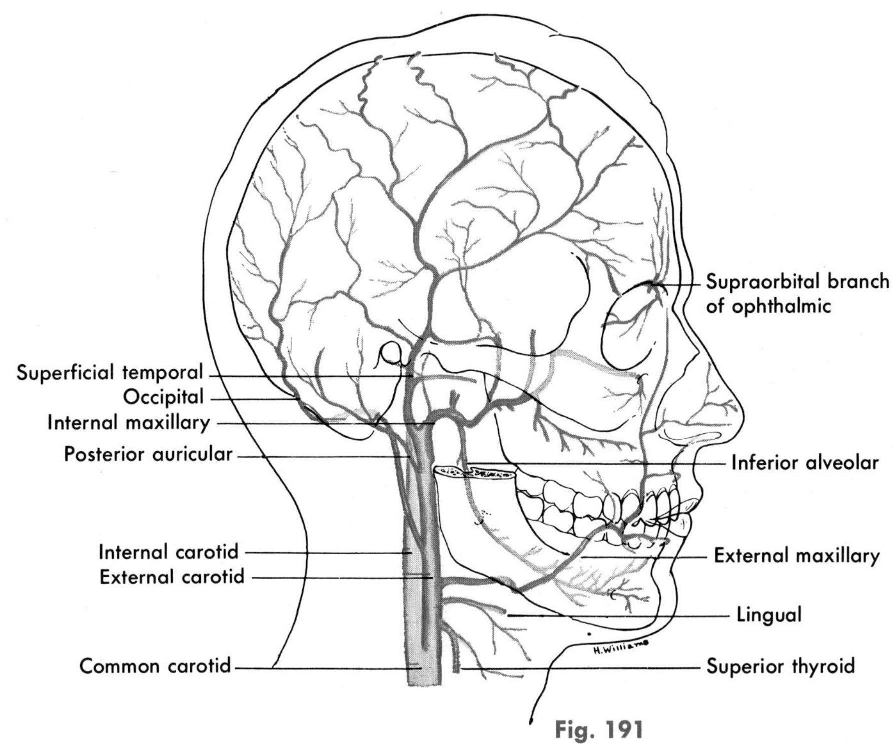

Fig. 191

Main arteries of the face and head. Superficial vessels are shown in brighter color than deep vessels. (From Francis and Farrell: Integrated anatomy and physiology, St. Louis, The C. V. Mosby Co.)

trunk in that it gives off numerous branches that continue to branch and rebranch, forming ever smaller vessels (arterioles), which also branch, forming microscopic vessels, the capillaries. In other words, any artery eventually ramifies into capillaries.

A few arteries open into other branches of the same or other arteries. Such a communication is termed an *arterial anastomosis.* Anastomoses, we have already noted, fulfill an important protective function in that they provide detour routes for blood to travel in the event of obstruction of a main artery. Examples of arterial anastomoses are the circle of Willis at the base of the brain and the palmar and plantar arches. Other examples are found around several joints as well as in other locations.

Veins

Several facts should be borne in mind while learning the names of veins.

1. Veins are the ultimate extensions of capillaries just as capillaries are the eventual extensions of arteries. Whereas arteries branch into vessels of decreasing size to form arterioles and eventually capillaries, capillaries unite into vessels of increasing size to form venules and eventually veins.

2. Many of the main arteries have corresponding veins bearing the same name and located alongside or near the arteries. These veins, like the arteries, lie in deep, well-protected areas, for the most part close along the bones. Example: femoral artery and femoral vein, both located along the femur bone.

3. Veins found in the deep parts of the body are called *deep veins* in contradistinction to *superficial veins,* which lie near the

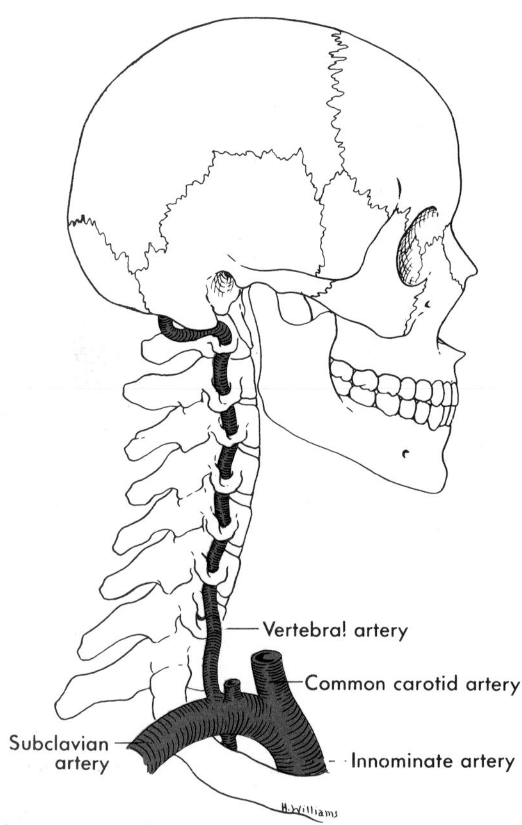

Fig. 192

Location of the vertebral artery.

surface. The latter are the veins that can be seen through the skin.

4. The large veins of the cranial cavity, formed by the dura mater, are not called veins but *sinuses*. They should not be confused with the bony sinuses of the skull.

The following list identifies the major veins. Locate each one as named on Figs. 194 to 198.

Veins of upper extremities (Figs. 194 and 195)
- Deep
  - Palmar (volar) arch (also superficial)
  - Radial (partially deep, partially superficial)
  - Ulnar (partially deep, partially superficial)
  - Brachial
  - Axillary (continuation of brachial)
  - Subclavian (continuation of axillary)
- Superficial
  - Veins of hand from dorsal and volar venous arches which, together with complicated network of superficial veins of lower arm, finally pour their blood into two large veins—cephalic (thumb side) and basilic (little finger side); these two veins empty into deep axillary vein

Veins of lower extremities (Figs. 194, 196, and 197)
- Deep
  - Plantar arch
  - Anterior tibial
  - Posterior tibial
  - Popliteal
  - Femoral
  - External iliac
- Superficial
  - Dorsal venous arch of foot
  - Great (or internal or long) saphenous
  - Small (or external or short) saphenous
- (Great saphenous terminates in femoral vein in groin; small saphenous terminates in popliteal vein)

Veins of head and neck (Figs. 198 and 199)
- Deep (in cranial cavity)
  - Longitudinal (or sagittal) sinus
  - Inferior sagittal and straight sinus
  - Numerous small sinuses
  - Right and left transverse (or lateral) sinuses
  - Internal jugular veins, right and left (in neck); continuations of transverse sinuses
  - Innominate veins, right and left; formed by union of subclavian and internal jugulars
- Superficial
  - External jugular veins, right and left (in neck); receive blood from small superficial veins of face, scalp, and neck; terminate in subclavian veins (small emissary veins connect veins of scalp and face with blood sinuses of cranial cavity, a fact of clinical interest as a possible avenue for infections to enter cranial cavity)

Veins of abdominal organs (Fig. 194)
- Spermatic (or ovarian), Renal, Hepatic, Suprarenal } Drain into inferior vena cava
- Left spermatic and left suprarenal veins usually drain into left renal vein instead of into inferior vena cava; for return of blood from abdominal digestive organs, see discussion of portal circulation, p. 303; also Fig. 200

Veins of thoracic organs
- Several small veins, such as bronchial, esophageal, pericardial, etc., return blood from chest organs (except lungs) directly into superior vena cava or into azygos vein; azygos vein

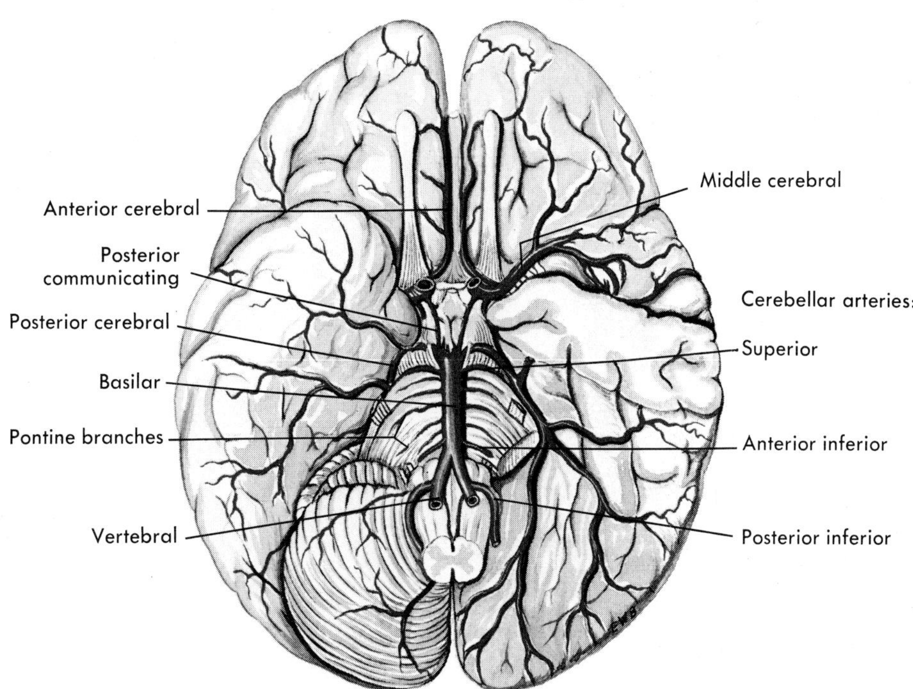

Fig. 193

Arteries at base of the brain. Those arteries that compose the circle of Willis are the two anterior cerebral arteries joined by the slender posterior communicating arteries to the posterior cerebral arteries.

lies to right of spinal column and extends from inferior vena cava (at level of first or second lumbar vertebra) to terminal part of superior vena cava; hemiazygos vein lies to left of spinal column, extending from lumbar level of inferior vena cava through diaphragm to terminate in azygos vein; accessory hemiazygos vein connects some of superior intercostal veins with azygos or hemiazygos vein

Correlations. Middle ear infections sometimes cause infection of the transverse sinuses with the formation of a thrombus. In such cases the internal jugular vein may be ligated to prevent the development of a fatal cardiac or pulmonary embolism.

Intravenous injections are most often given into the median basilic vein at the bend of the elbow. Blood that is to be used for various laboratory tests is also usually removed from this vein. In an infant, however, the longitudinal sinus is more often punctured (through the anterior fontanel) because the superficial arm veins are too tiny for the insertion of a needle.

Portal circulation

Veins from the spleen, stomach, pancreas, and intestines do not pour their blood directly into the inferior vena cava as do the veins from other abdominal organs. Instead, they send their blood to the liver by means of the portal vein. Here, the blood mingles with the arterial blood in the capillaries and is eventually drained from the liver by the hepatic veins that join the inferior vena cava. The reason for this detouring of the blood through the liver before it returns to the heart will be discussed in the chapter on the digestive system.

Fig. 200 shows the plan of the portal system. The portal vein is formed by the

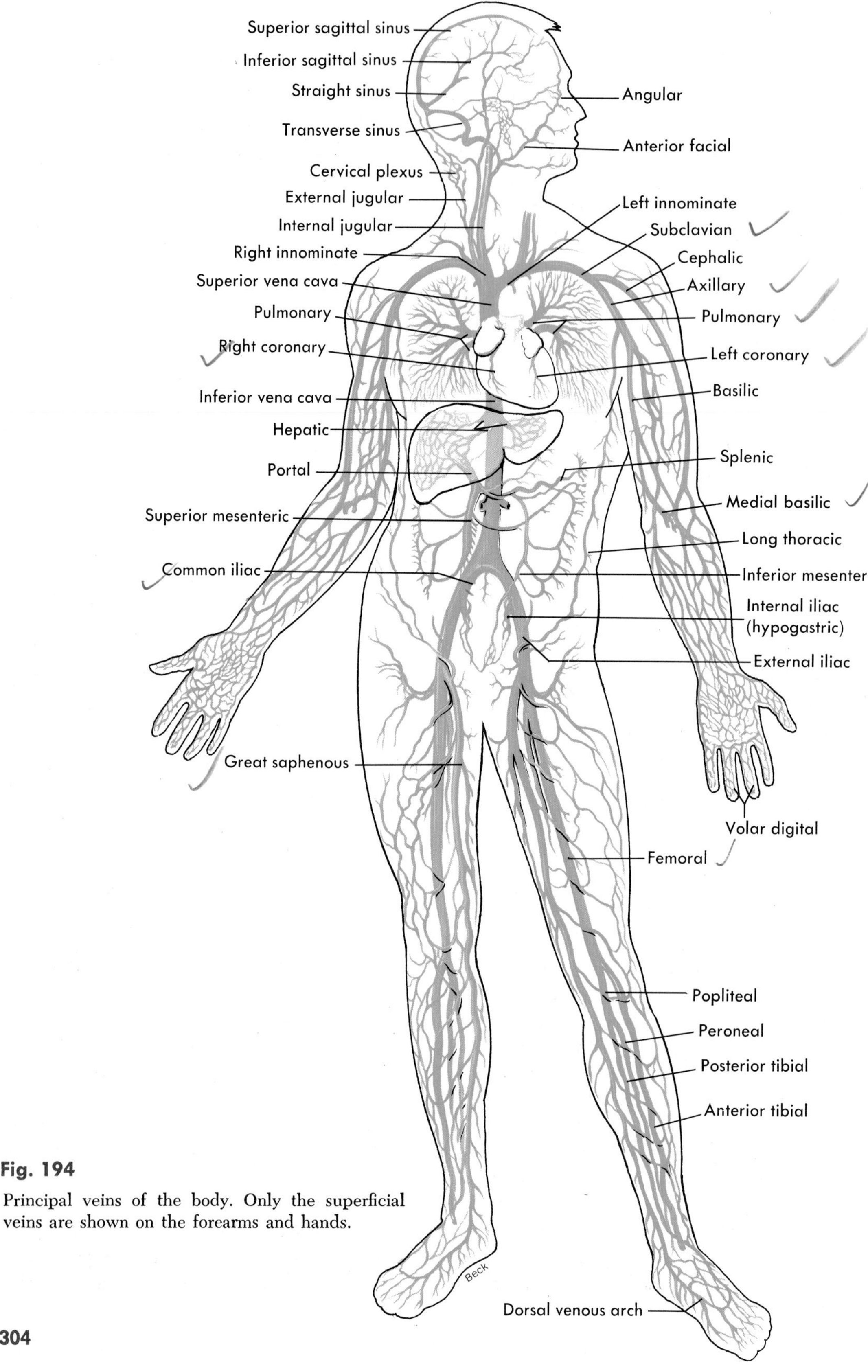

Fig. 194

Principal veins of the body. Only the superficial veins are shown on the forearms and hands.

union of the splenic and superior mesenteric veins, but blood from the gastric, pancreatic, and inferior mesenteric veins drains into the splenic vein before it merges with the superior mesenteric vein.

If either portal circulation or venous return from the liver is interfered with (as they often are in certain types of liver or heart disease), then venous drainage from most of the other abdominal organs is necessarily obstructed also. The accompanying increased capillary pressure accounts at least in part for the occurrence of ascites ("dropsy" of abdominal cavity) under these conditions.

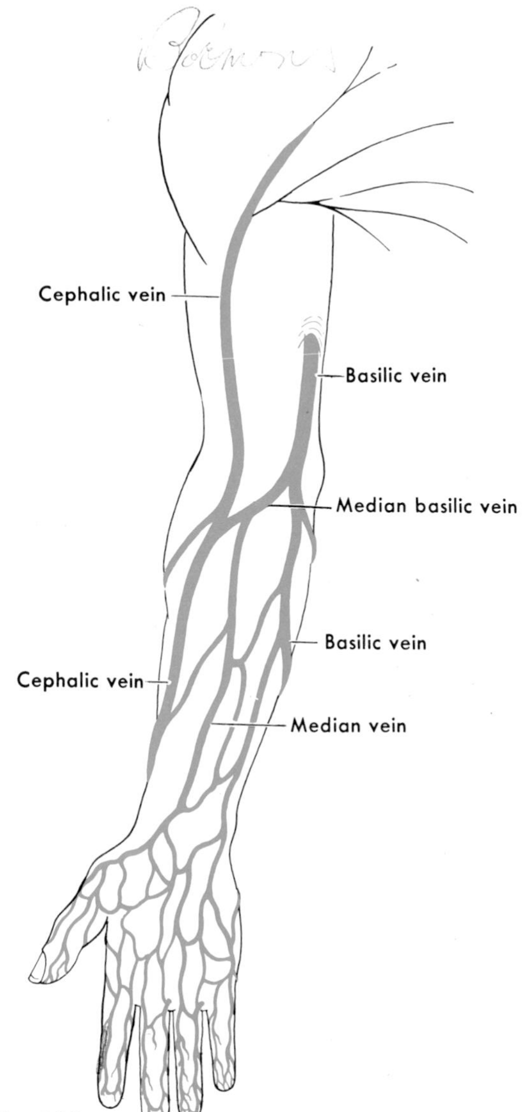

Fig. 195

Main superficial veins of the upper extremity, anterior view.

Fetal circulation

Circulation in the body before birth necessarily differs from circulation after birth for one main reason—because fetal blood secures oxygen and food from maternal blood instead of from its own lungs and digestive organs respectively. Obviously, then, there must be additional blood vessels in the fetus to carry the fetal blood into close approximation with the maternal blood and to return it to the fetal body. These structures are the two *umbilical arteries,* the *umbilical vein,* and the *ductus venosus.* Also, there must be some structure to function as the lungs and digestive organs do postnatally—that is, a place where an interchange of gases, foods, and wastes between the fetal and maternal blood can take place. This structure is the *placenta.* The exchange of substances occurs without any actual mixing of maternal and fetal bloods since each flows in its own capillaries.

In addition to the placenta and umbilical vessels, three structures located within the fetus' own body play an important part in fetal circulation. One of them (ductus venosus) serves as a detour by which most of the blood returning from the placenta bypasses the fetal liver. The other two (foramen ovale and ductus arteriosus) provide detours by which blood bypasses the lungs. A brief description of each of the six structures necessary for fetal circulation follows (also see Fig. 201).

1. The *two umbilical arteries* are extensions of the internal iliac (hypogastric) arteries and carry fetal blood to the placenta.

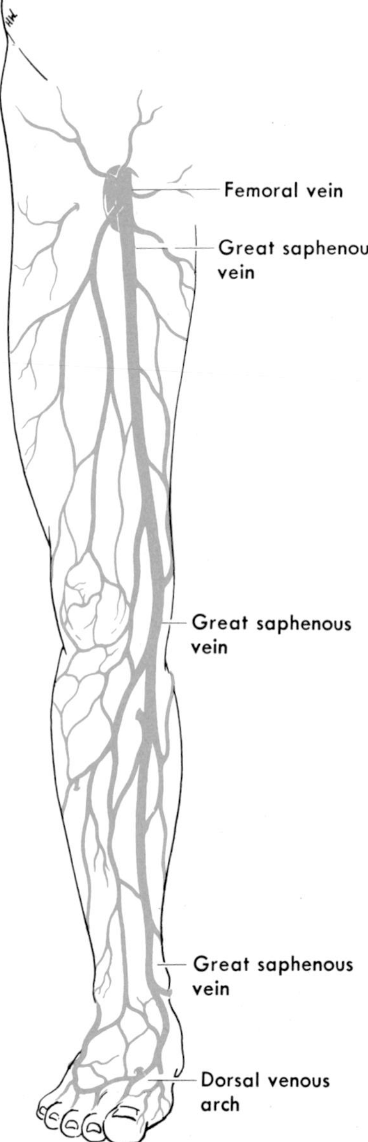

Fig. 196

Main superficial veins of the lower extremity, anterior view.

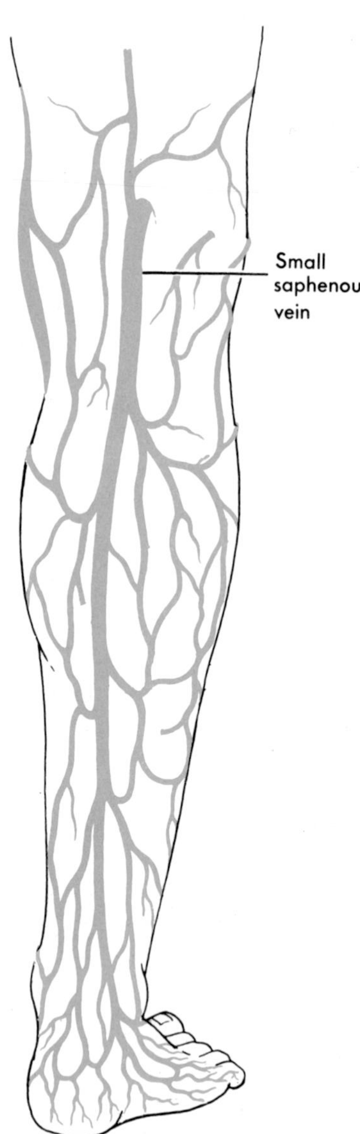

Fig. 197

Main superficial veins of the lower extremity, posterior view.

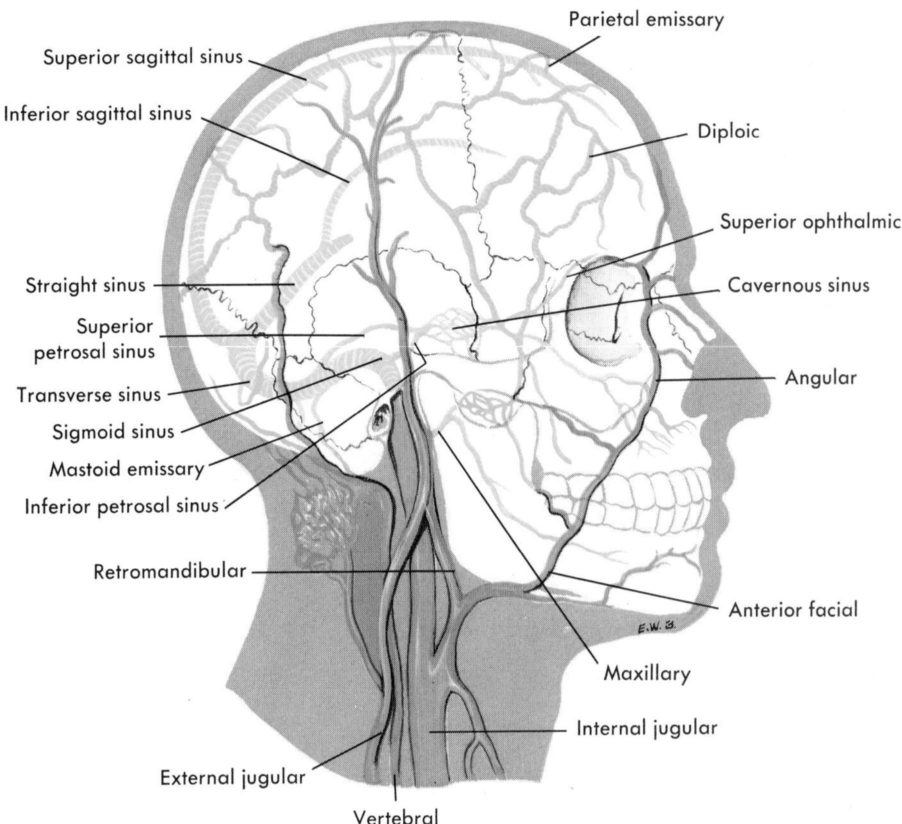

Fig. 198

Semischematic projection of the large veins of the head. Deep veins and dural sinuses are projected on the skull. Note connections (emissary veins) between the superficial and deep veins.

2. The *placenta* is a structure attached to the uterine wall. Exchange of oxygen and other substances between maternal and fetal blood takes place in the placenta.

3. The *umbilical vein* returns oxygenated blood from the placenta, enters the fetal body through the umbilicus, extends up to undersurface of the liver where it gives off two or three branches to the liver, and then continues on as the ductus venosus. Two umbilical arteries and the umbilical vein together constitute the *umbilical cord* and are shed at birth along with the placenta.

4. The *ductus venosus* is a continuation of the umbilical vein along the undersurface of the liver and drains into the inferior vena cava. Most of the blood returning from the placenta bypasses the liver. Only a relatively small amount enters the liver by way of the branches from the umbilical vein into the liver.

5. The *foramen ovale* is an opening in the septum between the right and left atria. A valve at the opening of the inferior vena cava into the right atrium directs most of the blood through the foramen ovale into the left atrium so that it bypasses the fetal lungs. A small percent of the blood leaves the right atrium for the right ventricle and pulmonary artery. But even most of this does not flow on into the lungs. Still another detour, the ductus arteriosus, diverts it.

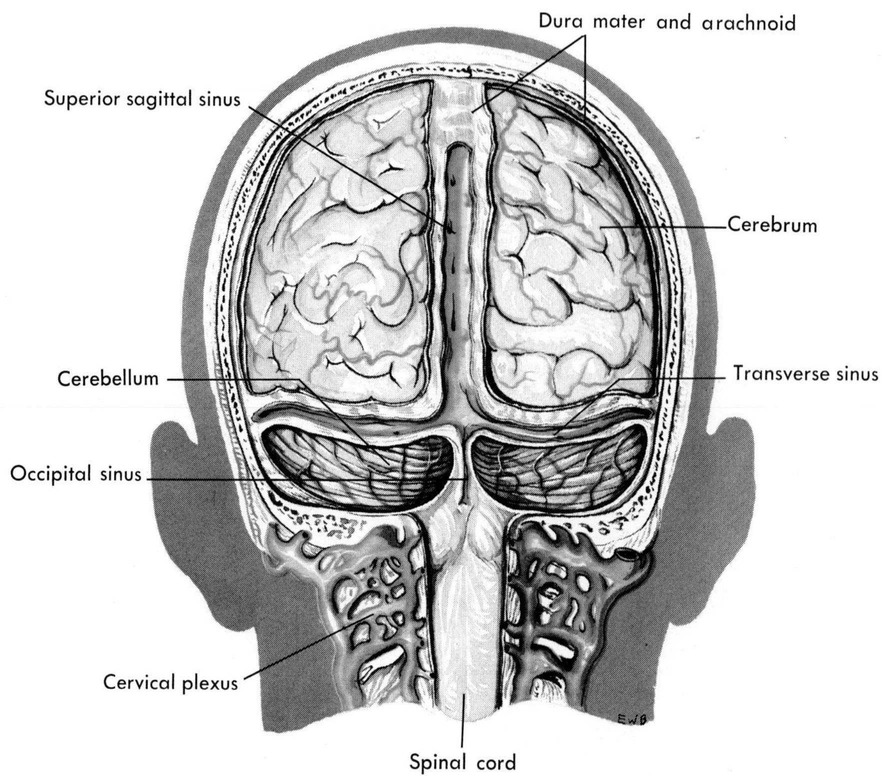

Fig. 199

Venous sinuses shown in relation to the brain and skull.

6. The *ductus arteriosus* is a small vessel connecting the pulmonary artery with the descending thoracic aorta. It therefore enables another portion of the blood to detour into the systemic circulation without going through the lungs.

Almost all fetal blood is a mixture of oxygenated and deoxygenated blood. Examine Fig. 201 carefully to determine why this is so. What happens to the oxygenated blood returned from the placenta via the umbilical vein? It flows into what vessel?

Since the six structures that serve fetal circulation are no longer needed after birth, several changes take place. As soon as the umbilical cord is cut, the two umbilical arteries, the placenta, and the umbilical vein obviously no longer function. The placenta is shed from the mother's body as the afterbirth with part of the umbilical vessels attached. The sections of these vessels remaining in the infant's body eventually become fibrous cords which remain throughout life (the umbilical vein becomes the round ligament of the liver). The ductus venosus, no longer needed to bypass blood around the liver, eventually becomes the ligamentum venosum of the liver. The foramen ovale normally becomes functionally closed soon after a newborn baby takes his first breath and full circulation through his lungs becomes established. Complete structural closure, however, requires longer. According to Gray, the foramen ovale "gradually decreases in size during the first month, but a small opening usually persists until the last third of the first year and

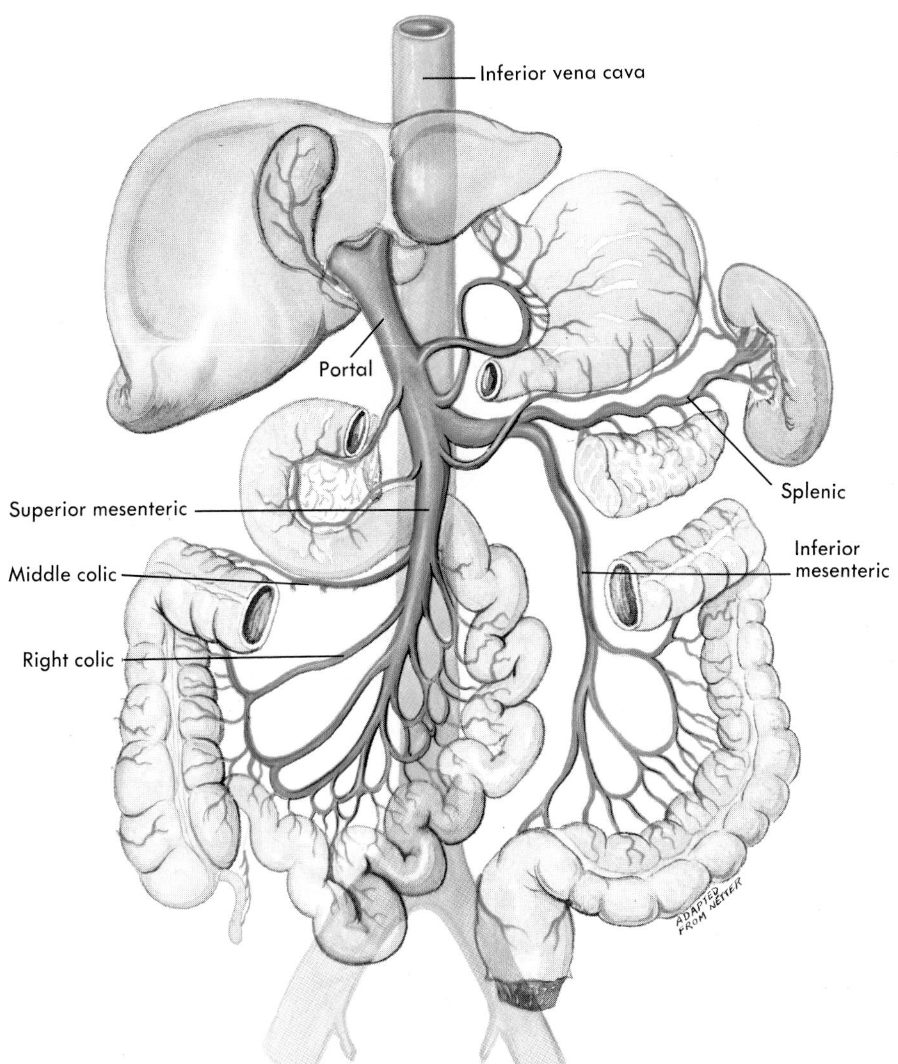

Fig. 200

Tributaries of the portal vein (diagrammatic).

often later."* Eventually the foramen ovale becomes a mere depression (fossa ovalis) in the wall of the right atrial septum. About the ductus arteriosus, Gray writes that it "begins to contract immediately after respiration is established, and its lumen slowly becomes obliterated."* Eventually it also turns into a fibrous cord.

*From Goss, Charles M. (editor): Gray's anatomy of the human body, ed. 27, Philadelphia, 1959. Lea & Febiger, p. 579.

Circulation

Definitions

The term circulation of blood suggests its meaning, namely, blood flow through vessels arranged to form a circuit or circular pattern. Blood flow from the heart (left ventricle) through all blood vessels except those of the lungs and back to the

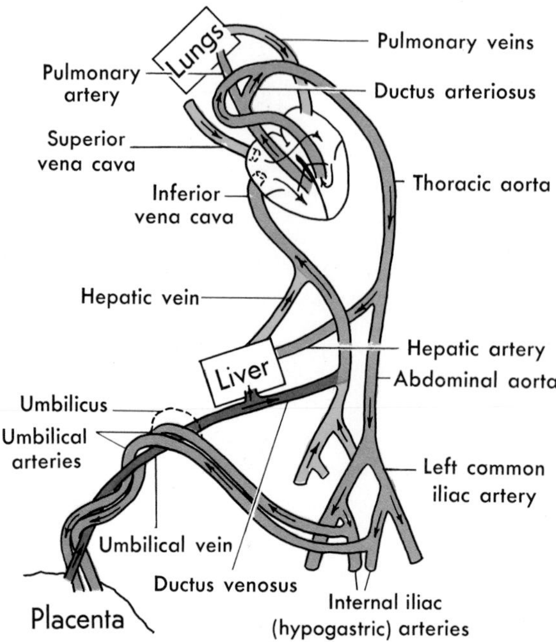

Fig. 201

Scheme to show the plan of fetal circulation. Note the following essential features: (1) two umbilical arteries, extensions of the internal iliac arteries, carry blood to (2) the placenta, which is attached to the uterine wall; (3) one umbilical vein returns blood, rich in oxygen and food, from the placenta; (4) the ductus venosus, a small vessel which connects the umbilical vein with the inferior vena cava; (5) the foramen ovale, an opening in the septum between the right and left atria; and (6) the ductus arteriosus, a small vessel which connects the pulmonary artery with the thoracic aorta.

heart (to the right atrium) is spoken of as *systemic circulation.* The left ventricle pumps blood into the ascending aorta. From here it flows into arteries that carry it into the various tissues and organs of the body. Within each structure blood moves from arteries to arterioles to capillaries. Here, the vital two-way exchange of substances occurs between blood and cells. Blood flows next out of each organ by way of its venules and then its veins to drain eventually into the inferior or superior vena cava. These two great veins of the body return venous blood to the heart to the right atrium to complete systemic circulation. But the blood has not quite come full circle back to its starting point, the left ventricle. To do this and start on its way again, it must first flow through another circuit, the *pulmonary circulation.* Venous blood moves from the right atrium to the right ventricle to the pulmonary artery to lung arterioles and capillaries. Here, exchange of gases between blood and air takes place, converting venous blood to arterial blood. This oxygenated blood then flows on through lung venules into four pulmonary veins and returns to the left atrium of the heart. From the left atrium it enters the left ventricle to be pumped again through the systemic circulation.

How to trace

In order to enumerate the vessels through which blood flows in reaching a designated part of the body or in returning

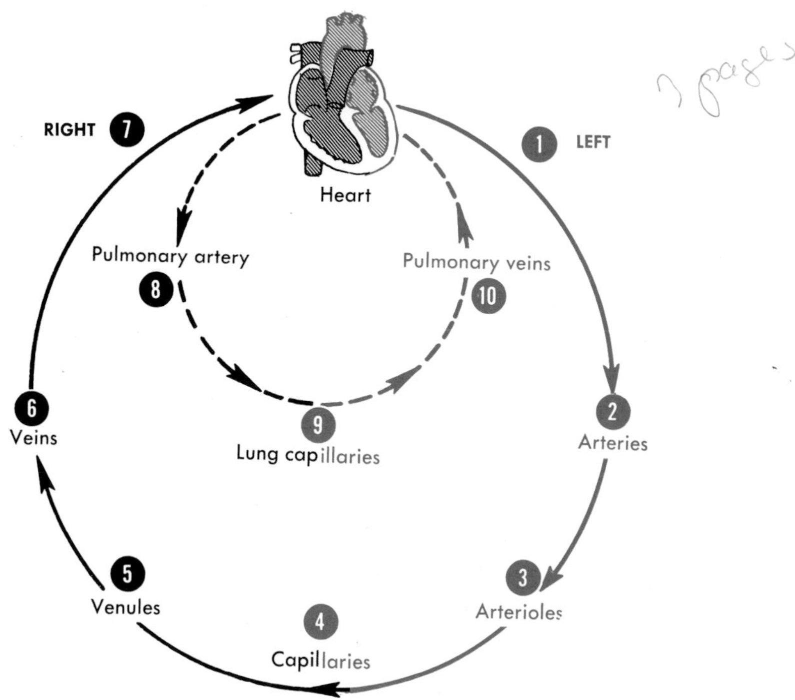

Fig. 202

Diagram showing the relation of systemic and pulmonary circulation. As indicated by the numbers, blood circulates from the left side of the heart to arteries, to arterioles, to capillaries, to venules, to veins, to the right side of the heart, to the lungs, and back to the left side of the heart, thereby completing a circuit. Refer to this diagram when tracing the circulation of blood to or from any part of the body.

to the heart from a part, one must remember the following:

1. That blood always flows in this direction—from *left ventricle* of heart to *arteries,* to *capillaries* of each body part, to *veins,* to *right atrium, right ventricle, pulmonary artery, lung capillaries, pulmonary veins, left atrium,* and back to left ventricle (Fig. 202)
2. That when blood is in capillaries of abdominal digestive organs, it must flow through portal system before returning to heart
3. Names of main arteries and veins of body

For example, suppose glucose were instilled into the rectum. To reach the cells of the right little finger, the vessels through which it would pass after absorption from the intestinal mucosa into capillaries would be as follows: *capillaries* into venules of large intestine into inferior mesenteric *vein,* splenic vein, portal vein, capillaries of liver, hepatic veins, inferior vena cava, *right atrium* of heart, *right ventricle, pulmonary artery, lung capillaries, pulmonary veins, left atrium, left ventricle, ascending aorta,* aortic arch, innominate artery, right subclavian artery, right axillary artery, right brachial artery, right ulnar artery, arteries of palmar arch, arterioles, and *capillaries* of right little finger.

Note: The structures italicized show the direction of blood flow as described in points 1 and 2 and illustrated in Fig. 202. Follow this course of circulation first on

Fig. 200 and then on Figs. 194 and 190. Try to answer question 37 of the review questions at the end of this chapter, using the plan outlined. For circulation to and from various parts of the body, see Fig. 215.

Functions of control mechanisms

Circulation is, of course, a vital function. It constitutes the only means by which cells can receive materials needed for energy and growth and can have their wastes removed. Not only is circulation necessary, but circulation of different volumes of blood per minute is also essential for healthy survival. More active cells need more blood per minute than less active cells. The reason underlying this principle is obvious. The more work cells do, the more energy they use and the more substances they need to supply this energy. Only arterial blood can deliver these energy suppliers (oxygen and foods). So the more active any part of the body is, the greater the volume of blood circulated to it per minute must be. And this requires that circulation control mechanisms accomplish two functions: maintain circulation (keep blood flowing, that is) and vary circulation (that is, change the volume of blood circulating per minute and the volume circulating to different tissues as their activity changes). At the right time, the right amount of blood must be shifted from the right tissues to the right tissues—must be transferred, in other words, from the more active tissues to the less active ones.

To achieve these two ends, a great many factors must operate together. Incidentally, this is an important physiological principle that you have no doubt observed by now—that every body function depends upon many other functions. A constellation of separate processes or mechanisms act as a single integrated mechanism. Together they perform some one large function. For example, many mechanisms together accomplish the large function we call circulation. To try to make the complexities of circulation mechanisms a little more understandable, we shall use a question and answer method for our discussion of the principles of circulation.

Principles

Why does blood circulate? What makes it keep moving over and over again as long as life lasts, from the left side of the heart through the systemic vessels to the right side of the heart, to the lungs, and back to the left heart?

Answer: Blood flows for the same reason that any fluid flows—whether it be water in a river or in a garden hose or in hospital tubing or blood in vessels. A fluid flows because a pressure gradient exists between different parts of its bed. This primary fluid flow principle derives from Newton's first and second laws of motion. In essence, these laws state the following principles:

1. That a fluid does not flow when the pressure is the same in all parts of it
2. That a fluid flows only when its pressure is higher in one area than in another, and it flows always from the higher pressure area toward the lower pressure area

In brief, then, the answer to our first question about circulation is that blood circulates because a blood pressure gradient exists within the circulatory system.

What is blood pressure gradient?

Answer: Blood pressure gradient is blood pressure difference. For example, if blood pressure in the aorta averages 100 mm. Hg and pressure in a vein is 5 mm. Hg, a blood pressure gradient of 95 mm. Hg exists between the two areas. A blood pressure gradient might be thought of a blood pressure hill down which blood flows. The symbol $(P_1 - P_2)$ is often used to stand for a pressure gradient, with P_1 the symbol for the higher pressure and P_2 the symbol for the lower pressure.

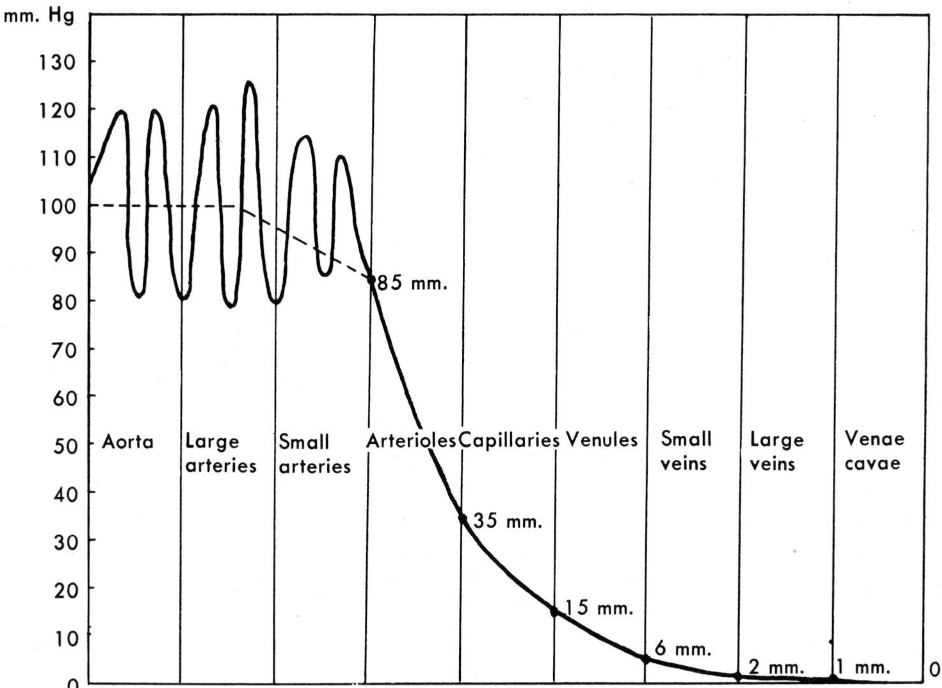

Fig. 203

Blood pressure gradient. Dotted line indicates the average or mean systolic pressure in arteries.

Suppose, for instance, that the average capillary pressure in the capillaries of your arm muscles is 25 mm. Hg and the average pressure in the arterioles from which these capillaries branch is 60 mm. Hg. Which is P_1? P_2? What is the blood pressure gradient? In which direction would blood necessarily flow?

Fig. 203 shows a typical blood pressure gradient. What is the gradient for systemic circulation taken as a whole? P_1 in this gradient is the average systolic pressure in the aorta and P_2 is the pressure in the venae cavae at their junction with the right atrium.

What factors determine arterial blood pressure?

Answer: The primary determinant is the volume of blood in the arteries. A direct relation exists between arterial blood volume and arterial pressure. This means that an increase in arterial blood volume tends to increase arterial pressure, and conversely a decrease in arterial volume tends to decrease arterial pressure. Many factors together indirectly determine arterial pressure through their influence on arterial volume. Two of the most important are cardiac minute output (CMO) and peripheral resistance. A change in either tends to change the volume of blood within the arteries and thereby to change the blood pressure in the same direction. More specifically, anything that increases cardiac minute output tends to increase arterial blood volume and thereby to increase arterial blood pressure. Anything that decreases cardiac minute output tends to decrease arterial blood volume and pressure. Anything that increases peripheral resistance tends to increase arterial blood volume and pressure,

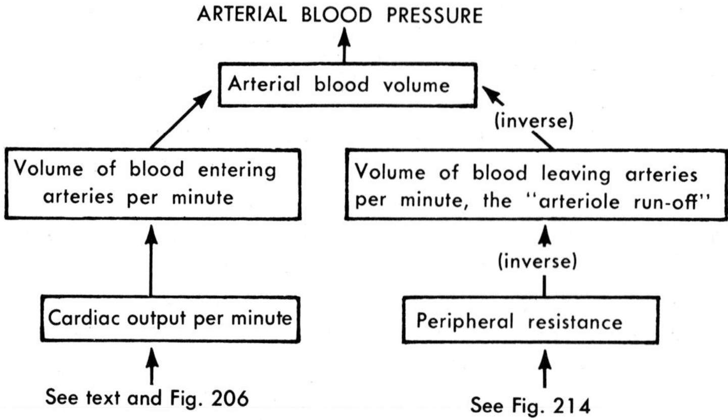

Fig. 204

Scheme to show how cardiac minute output and peripheral resistance affect arterial blood pressure. If cardiac minute output increases, the amount of blood entering the arteries increases and tends to increase the volume of blood in the arteries. The resulting increase in arterial volume increases arterial blood pressure. If peripheral resistance increases, it tends to decrease the amount of blood leaving the arteries, which tends to increase the amount of blood left in them. The increase in arterial volume increases arterial blood pressure.

and anything that decreases peripheral resistance tends to decrease arterial volume and pressure. Now let us examine these terms cardiac minute output and peripheral resistance a little further.

Cardiac minute output means what you would guess—the volume of blood pumped out of the left ventricle into the aorta each minute. How big this volume is, of course, depends both upon the number of heart contractions per minute and upon the amount of blood pumped per contraction. Contraction of the heart is called *systole.* Therefore, the volume of blood pumped by one contraction is known as *systolic discharge. Stroke volume* means the same thing, the amount of blood pumped by one stroke (contraction) of the ventricle. Stroke volume reflects the force or strength of ventricular contraction—the stronger the contraction, the greater the stroke volume tends to be. Cardiac minute output can be computed by the following simple equation:

$$\text{Stroke volume} \times \text{Heart rate} = \text{CMO}$$

From this equation we can derive the following principles. Anything that changes either the rate of the heartbeat or its stroke volume tends to change cardiac minute output, arterial blood volume, and blood pressure in the same direction. In other words, anything that makes the heart beat faster or anything that makes it beat stronger, increasing its stroke volume, tends to increase cardiac minute output and, therefore, arterial blood volume and pressure. Conversely, anything that causes the heart to beat more slowly or more weakly tends to decrease cardiac minute output, arterial volume, and blood pressure. But do not overlook the word *tend* in the preceding sentences. A change in heart rate or in stroke volume does not always change the heart's output, or the amount of blood in the arteries, or the blood pressure. To see whether this is true, do the following simple arithmetic, using the formula just given for computing CMO. Assume a normal rate and stroke volume of 72 beats per minute and 70 ml., respectively. Next, suppose the rate drops to 60 and the stroke volume increases to 100. Does the decrease in heart rate actually cause a decrease in cardiac minute output in this case? Clearly not—the cardiac minute output increases. Do you think it is valid, however, to say that a slower rate *tends* to decrease the heart's minute output? By itself, without any change in any other factor, would not a slowing of the heartbeat cause cardiac minute volume, arterial volume, and blood pressure to fall?

Peripheral resistance, another factor that helps determine arterial blood pressure, is resistance to blood flow imposed by the force of friction between blood and the walls of its vessels. Friction develops partly because of a characteristic of blood—its viscosity or stickiness—and partly from the small diameter of arterioles and capillaries. Peripheral resistance helps determine arterial pressure by controlling the rate of "arteriole runoff," the amount of blood that runs out of the arteries into the arterioles. The greater the resistance, the less the arteriole runoff tends to be. And, therefore, the more blood left in the arteries, and the higher the arterial pressure tends to be.

Summarized, arterial blood pressure is determined directly by arterial blood volume which is determined by many factors but especially by the heart's output and peripheral resistance (see Fig. 204).

What factors regulate the stroke volume of the heart?

Answer: The main regulator of the strength of the heartbeat and therefore of its stroke volume is now believed to be the ratio of sympathetic-parasympathetic impulses to the heart. An increase in sympathetic impulses tends to make the heart contract more forcefully and to increase its stroke volume. On the other hand, an increase in parasympathetic impulses tends to produce opposite results—weaker contraction and smaller stroke volume.

Many years ago Starling described a principle later made famous as Starling's law of the heart. In this principle he stated the factor he had observed as the main regulator of heartbeat strength in experiments performed on denervated animal hearts. He wrote, "the energy set free at each contraction of the heart is a simple function of the length of the fibers composing its muscular walls." Interpreted, this means that within limits, the longer or more stretched the heart fibers at the beginning of contraction, the stronger will be their contraction.

The factor determining how stretched the animal hearts were at the beginning of contractions was, as you might deduce, the amount of blood in the hearts at the end of diastole. The more blood returned to the hearts per minute, the more stretched were their fibers, the stronger were their contractions, and the larger was the volume of blood they ejected with each contraction. If, however, too much blood stretched the hearts too far, beyond a certain critical point, they seemed to lose their elasticity. They then contracted less vigorously—much as a rubber band, stretched too much, rebounds with less force.

Starling's law of the heart is valid under experimental conditions. But under normal physiological conditions, neural and hormonal mechanisms exert the dominant control over the heart's contracting force and its stroke volume. More specifically, in the normal body, the main regulators of heart contractility and stroke volume are the ratio of sympathetic-parasympathetic impulses to the heart and the blood concentration of epinephrine. An increase in the sympathetic-parasympathetic ratio (more sympathetic, or fewer parasympathetic impulses) causes an increase in the force of the heart's contractions and in its stroke volume. An increase in blood epinephrine concentration produces the same effects.

What factors regulate the heart rate?

Answer: *Pressoreflexes* constitute the dominant heart rate control mechanism, although various other factors also influence heart rate.

Cardiac pressoreflexes. Pressoreceptors (Fig. 205) are located in the aortic arch and the carotid sinus. (The carotid sinus is a small dilatation at the beginning of the internal carotid artery just above the bifurcation of the common carotid artery to form the internal and external carotid arteries.) The sinus lies just under the sternocleidomastoid muscle at the level of the upper margin of the thyroid cartilage. Sensory fibers extend from the aortic pressoreceptors in the vagus (tenth cranial nerve) to terminate in the medulla in its cardiac and vasomotor centers. Sensory fibers from carotid sinus pressoreceptors, on the other hand, run through the carotid sinus nerve (of Hering) and on through the glossopharyngeal (or ninth cranial) nerve to the cardiac and vasomotor centers.

If blood pressure within the aorta or carotid sinus increases suddenly, it stimulates the aortic or carotid pressoreceptors. As shown in Fig. 205, this leads to stimulation of the cardioinhibitory centers and reciprocal inhibition of the accelerator centers, which in turn leads to more impulses per second over parasympathetic fibers in the vagus and fewer impulses over the sympathetic fibers in the cardioaccelerator nerves

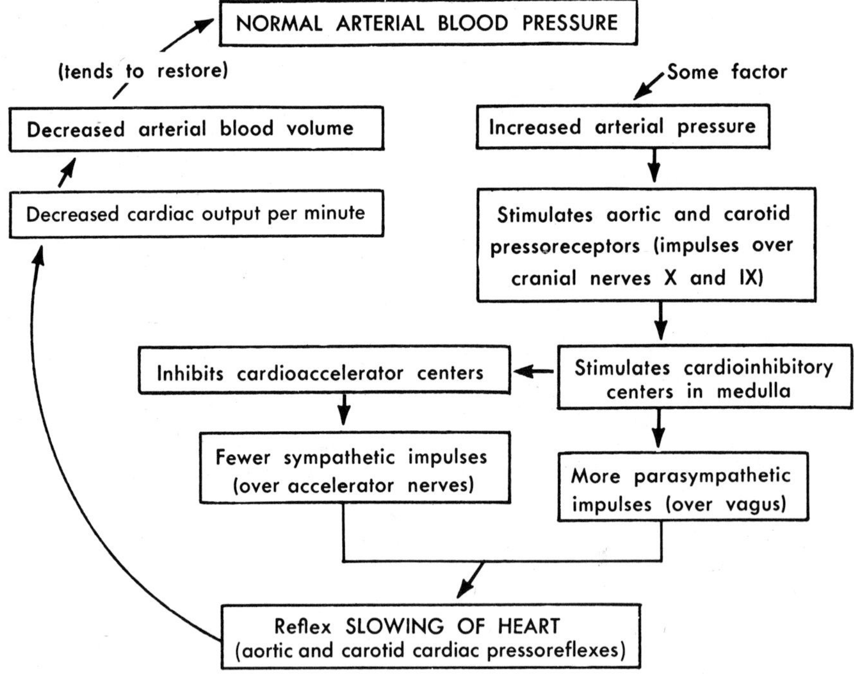

Fig. 205

The aortic and carotid cardiac pressoreflexes, a mechanism that tends to maintain or restore homeostasis of arterial blood pressure by regulating the rate of the heartbeat. Note that by this mechanism an increase in arterial blood pressure leads to reflex slowing of the heart and tends to lower blood pressure. The converse is also true. A decrease in blood pressure leads to reflex acceleration of the heart and tends to raise the pressure upward toward normal.

to the heart. As a result, reflex slowing of the heart occurs.

On the other hand, a decrease in aortic or carotid blood pressure usually initiates reflex acceleration of the heart. The lower blood pressure stimulates pressoreceptors less strongly. Hence, the cardioinhibitory center receives fewer stimulating impulses and the cardioaccelerator center fewer inhibitory impulses with the net result that the heart beats faster.

Pressoreceptors located in the right atrium of the heart may respond to changes in right atrial pressure. An increase in this pressure results in reflex acceleration of the heart, and a decrease in right atrial pressure produces reflex slowing.

Almost fifty years ago the noted physiologist Bainbridge demonstrated reflex heart acceleration in dogs following injection of saline solution or blood intravenously but did not establish the mechanism involved. But since then some have postulated that this Bainbridge reflex (accelerated heartbeat following increased venous return) is initiated by stimulation of pressoreceptors in the vena cava or right atrium. Others deny that such a reflex exists at all.

Miscellaneous factors that influence heart rate. Included in this category are such important factors as emotions, exercise, hormones, blood temperature, and stimulation of various exteroceptors. Anxiety, fear, and anger often make the heart beat faster. Grief, in contrast, tends to slow it. Presumably, emotions produce changes in the heart rate through the influence of impulses from the cerebrum via the hypothalamus to cardiac centers in the medulla and cord.

In exercise, the heart normally accelerates. The mechanism is not definitely known. But it is thought to include impulses from the cerebrum through the hypothalamus to cardiac centers. Epinephrine is the hormone most noted as a cardiac accelerator.

Increased blood temperature or stimulation of skin heat receptors tends to increase the heart rate, and decreased blood temperature or stimulation of skin cold receptors tends to slow it. Sudden intense stimulation of pain receptors also tends to decrease the heart rate. The major factors controlling the rate of the heartbeat are summarized in Fig. 206.

What factors determine peripheral resistance?

Answer: Viscosity is the characteristic of a fluid that results from attraction forces between its molecules or other small particles and that causes it to resist flowing. Blood viscosity stems mainly from the red cells but also partly from the protein molecules present in blood. An increase in either blood protein concentration or in the red cell count tends to increase viscosity, and a decrease in either tends to decrease it. Under normal circumstances blood viscosity changes very little. But under certain abnormal conditions, such as marked anemia or hemorrhage, a decrease in blood viscosity may be the crucial factor lowering peripheral resistance and arterial pressure even to the point of circulatory failure.

What factors regulate arteriole diameter?

Answer: Factors that control arteriole diameter might be said to constitute the vasomotor control mechanism. Like most physiological mechanisms, it consists of many parts (Figs. 207 to 212). A change in either arterial blood pressure or in arterial blood's oxygen or carbon dioxide content sets vasomotor control mechanisms in operation. A change in arterial blood pressure initiates a *vasomotor pressoreflex.* A change in arterial oxygen or carbon dioxide content acts in two ways to bring about a change in arteriole diameter—by stimulating chemoreceptors and thereby initiating a *vasomotor chemoreflex* and by stimulating the medulla's vasomotor centers directly

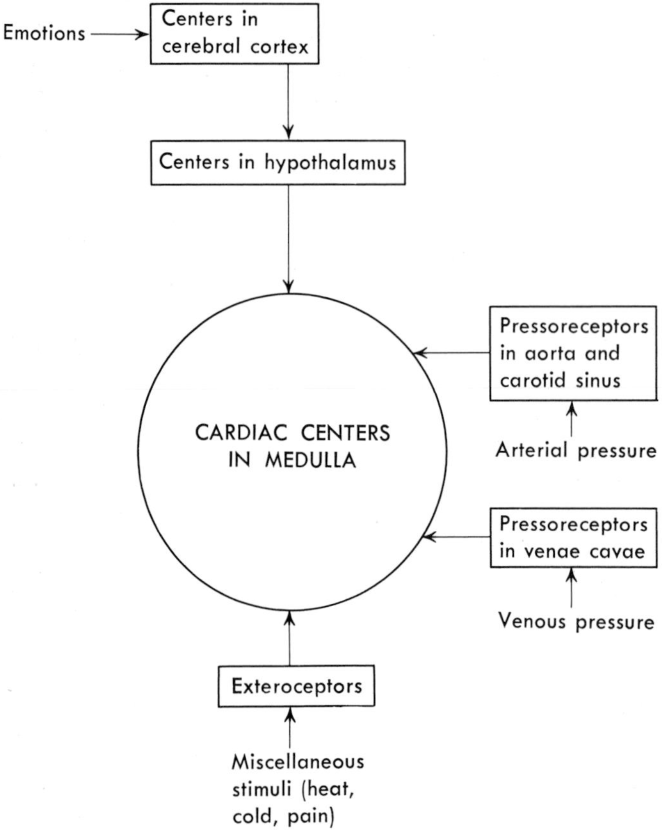

Fig. 206

Scheme to show some of the many parts of the heart rate control mechanism. Impulses from various receptors are conducted by sensory fibers which terminate in synapses with neurons in cardiac centers. Motor fibers from the centers relay impulses to sympathetic and parasympathetic neurons which transmit them to the heart. Also streaming into the cardiac centers are impulses from the hypothalamus, presumably part of the pathway by which emotions influence heart rate.

and thereby initiating what we shall call the *medullary ischemic reflex.*

Vasomotor pressoreflexes (Fig. 207). A sudden increase in arterial blood pressure stimulates aortic and carotid pressoreceptors—the same ones that initiate cardiac reflexes. Not only does this lead to stimulation of cardioinhibitory centers but also to inhibition of vasoconstrictor centers. More impulses per second go out to the heart over parasympathetic vagal fibers and fewer over sympathetic fibers to blood vessels. As a result, the heartbeat slows, and arterioles and venules of the "blood reservoirs" dilate. Since sympathetic vasoconstrictor impulses predominate at normal arterial pressures, inhibition of these is considered the major mechanism of vasodilatation.

The main blood reservoirs are the venous plexuses and sinuses in the skin and abdominal organs (especially in the liver and spleen). In other words, blood reservoirs are the venous networks in most parts of the body—all but those in the skeletal muscles, heart, and brain. The term reser-

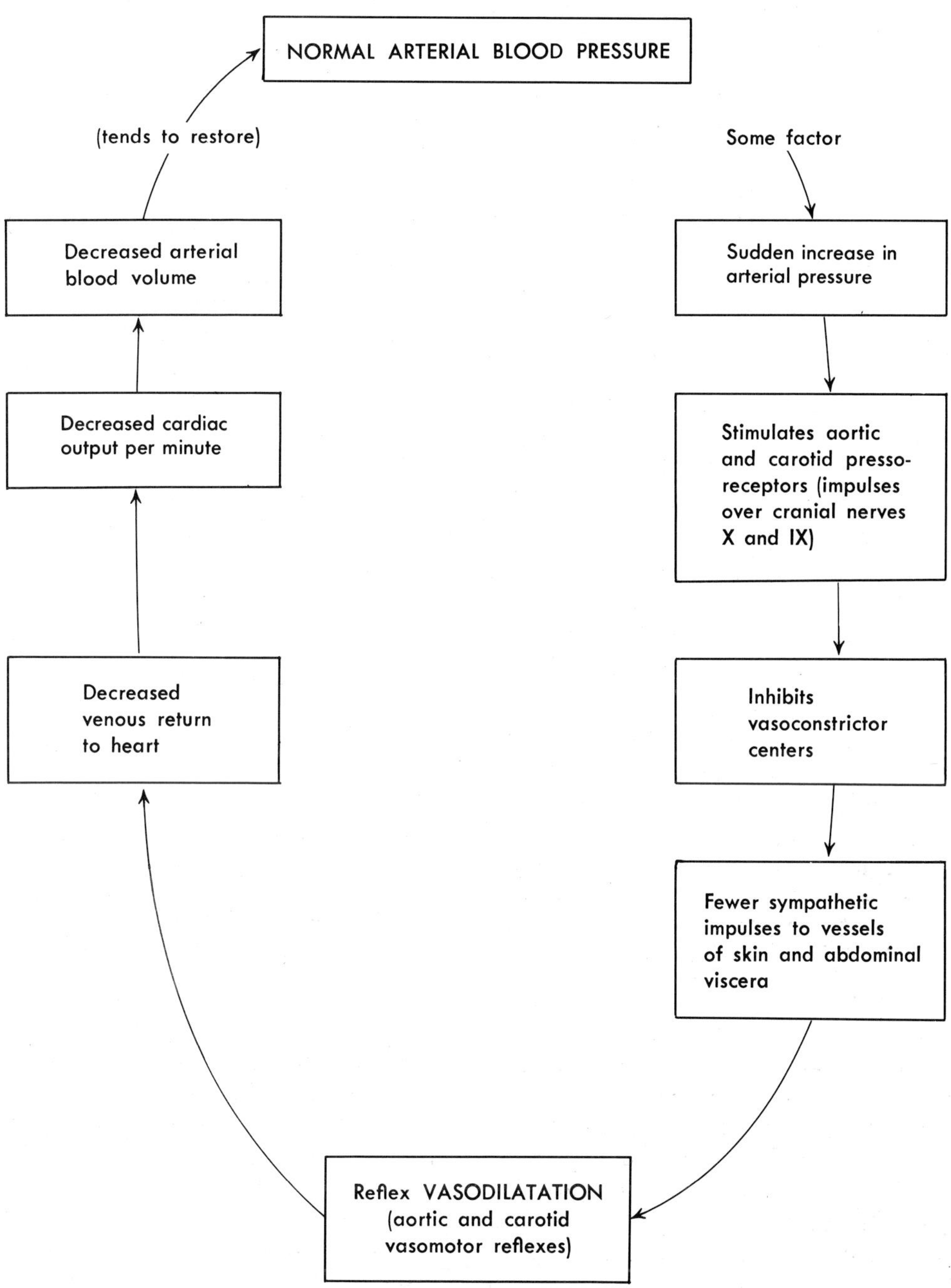

Fig. 207

The aortic and carotid vasomotor pressoreflex mechanism shown here is set in operation when some factor causes a sudden increase in arterial blood pressure. This mechanism and the aortic and carotid cardiac pressoreflexes (Fig. 205) operate simultaneously to maintain or restore homeostasis of arterial blood pressure.

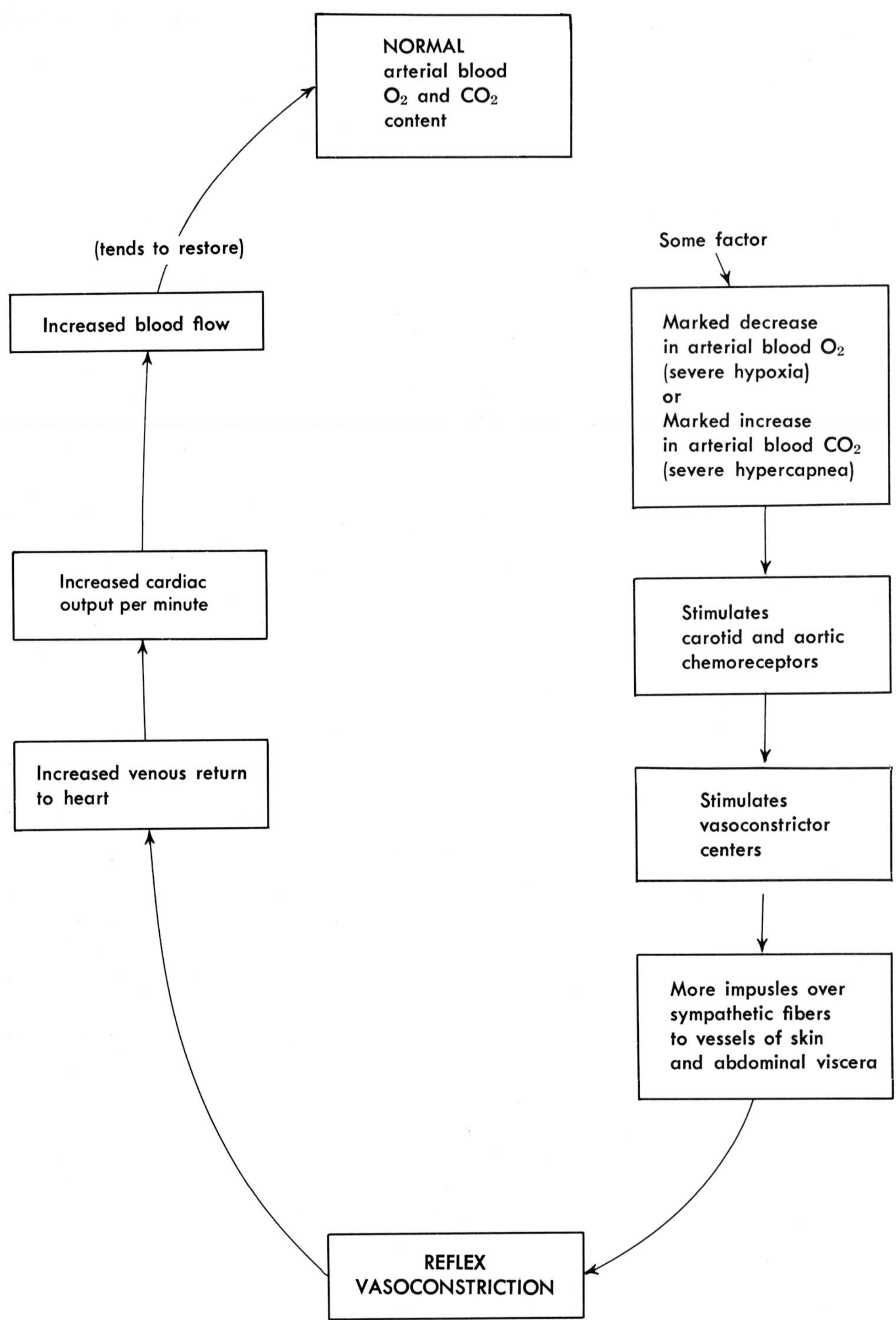

Fig. 208

The vasomotor chemoreflex shown here serves mainly to maintain homeostasis of blood oxygen and carbon dioxide. But, because it brings about reflex vasoconstriction, it also tends to increase peripheral resistance and arterial blood pressure. (Also see Fig. 209.)

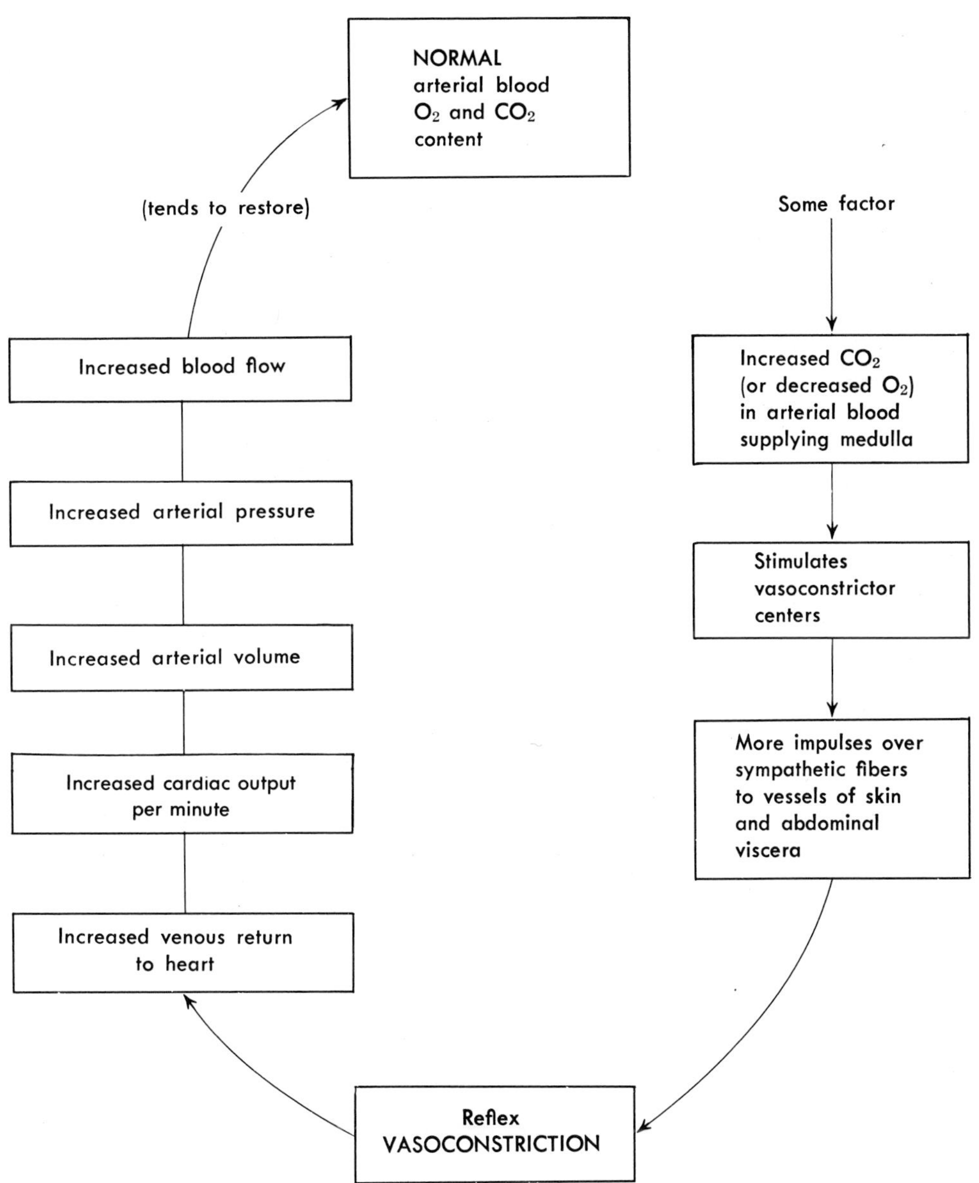

Fig. 209

The medullary ischemic reflex, a mechanism that tends to restore homeostasis of blood oxygen and carbon dioxide content.

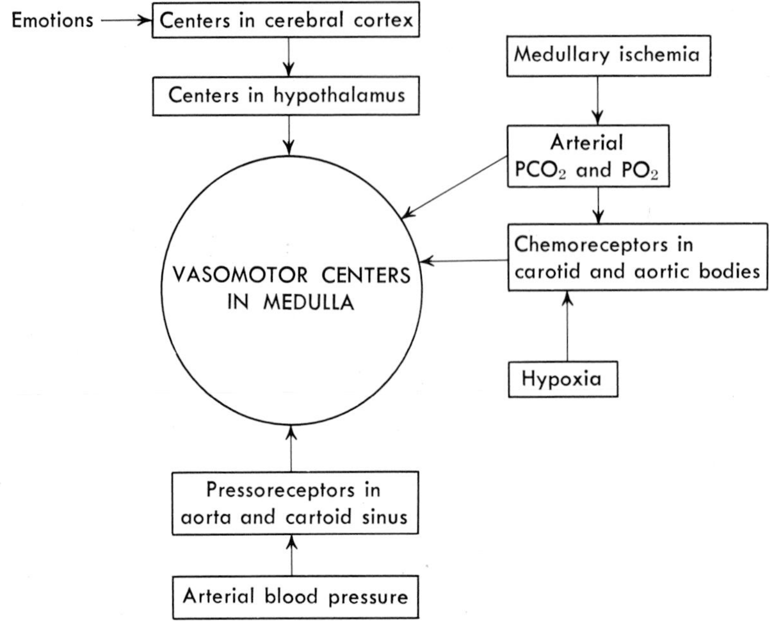

Fig. 210

Scheme to show some of the many parts of the vasomotor control mechanism. Impulses from chemoreceptors and pressoreceptors are conducted by sensory fibers that terminate in synapses with neurons in vasomotor centers. From the centers sympathetic neurons relay impulses to smooth muscle in blood vessels. More impulses cause vessels to constrict. Fewer impulses cause them to dilate. Also streaming into the vasomotor centers are impulses from the hypothalamus, presumably part of the pathway by which emotions influence blood pressure.

voir is apt, since these veins serve as storage depots for blood. It can quickly be moved out of them and "shifted" to heart and skeletal muscles when increased activity demands. The reflex vasoconstrictor mechanism that accomplishes this operates as follows.

A decrease in arterial pressure causes the aortic and carotid pressoreceptors to send fewer impulses to the medulla's vasodilator centers, thereby depressing them and reciprocally stimulating the vasoconstrictor centers. The latter then send more impulses via sympathetic fibers to the smooth muscle in the arterioles, venules, and veins of the blood reservoirs, causing their constriction. This squeezes more blood out of them, increasing the amount of venous return to the heart. Eventually this extra blood is redistributed to more active structures such as skeletal muscles and heart because their arterioles become dilated due largely to operation of a local mechanism (p. 323). Thus, the vasoconstrictor pressoreflex and the local vasodilating mechanism together serve as an important device for shifting blood from reservoirs to structures that need it more. It is an especially valuable mechanism during exercise.

Vasomotor chemoreflexes (Fig. 208). Chemoreceptors located in the aortic and carotid bodies are particularly sensitive to a deficiency of blood oxygen (hypoxia) and somewhat less sensitive to excess blood carbon dioxide (hypercapnia) and to decreased arterial blood pH. When one or more of these conditions stimulates the chemoreceptors, their fibers transmit more

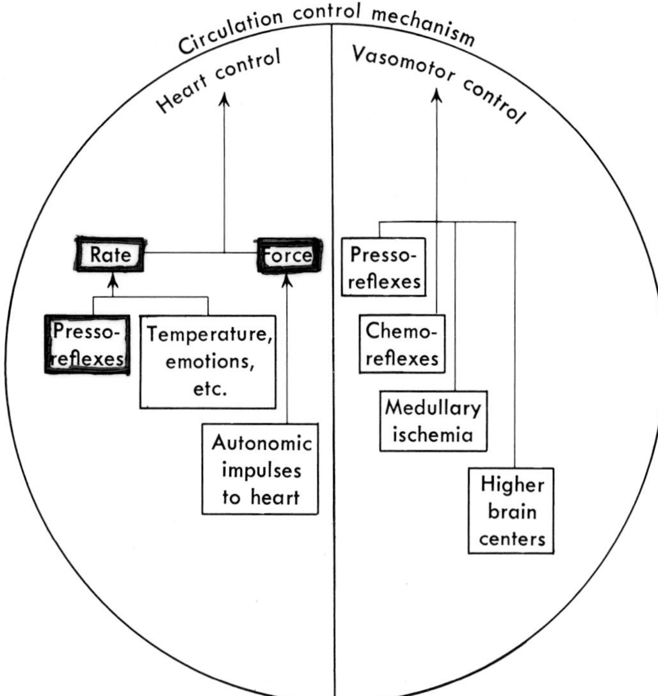

Fig. 211

Scheme to show some of the many parts of the complex circulation control mechanism.

impulses to the medulla's vasoconstrictor centers, and vasoconstriction of arterioles and venous reservoirs soon follows. This mechanism functions as an emergency device when severe hypoxia or hypercapnea develops.

The medullary ischemic reflex (Fig. 209). The medullary ischemic reflex mechanism is said to exert the most powerful control of all on small blood vessels. When the blood supply to the medulla becomes inadequate (ischemia), its neurons suffer from both oxygen deficiency and carbon dioxide excess. But, presumably, it is the latter, the hypercapnea, that intensely and directly stimulates the vasoconstrictor centers to bring about marked arteriole and venous constriction.

Vasomotor control by higher brain centers (Fig. 210). Impulses from centers in the cerebral cortex and in the hypothalamus are believed to be transmitted to the vasomotor centers in the medulla and to thereby help control vasoconstriction and dilatation. One evidence supporting this view, for example, is the fact that vasoconstriction and a rise in arterial blood pressure characteristically accompany emotions of intense fear or anger. Also, laboratory experiments on animals in which stimulation of the posterior or lateral parts of the hypothalamus leads to vasoconstriction support the belief that higher brain centers influence the vasomotor centers in the medulla.

Local control of arterioles

Some kind of local mechanism operates to produce vasodilatation in localized areas. Although the mechanism is not clear, it is known to function in times of increased tissue activity. For example, it probably accounts for the increased blood flow into

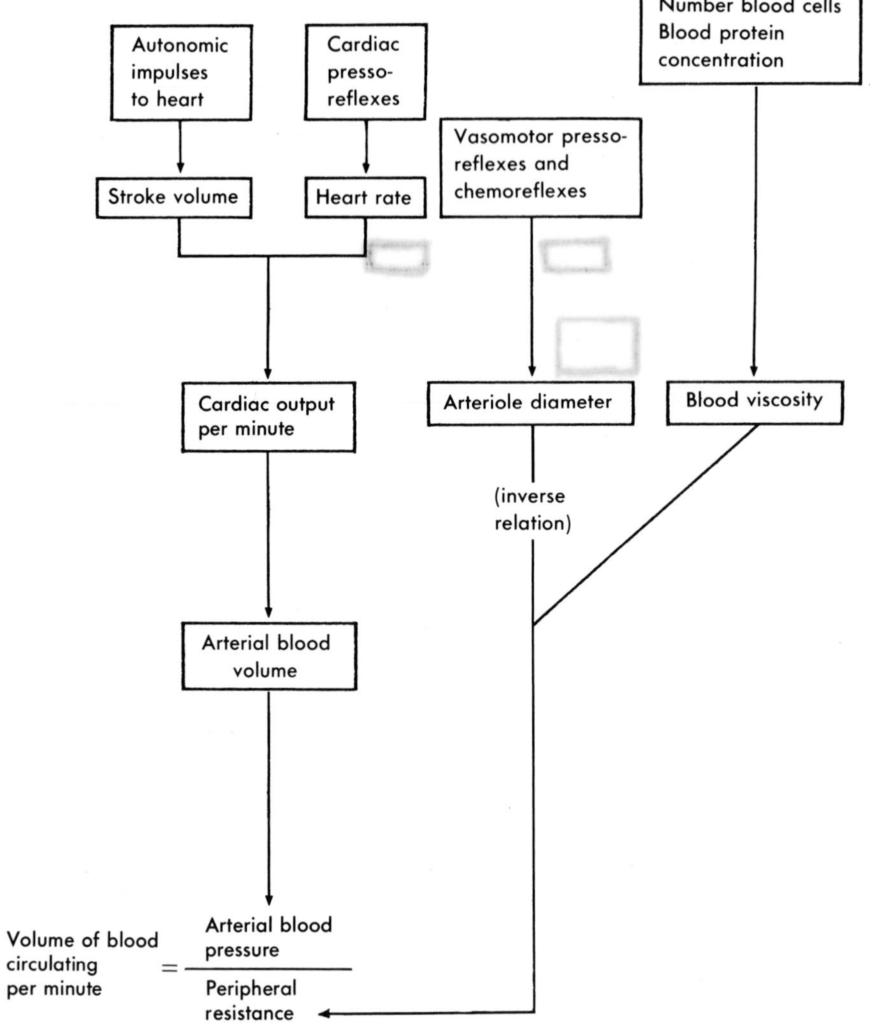

Fig. 212

Another scheme to show some of the many parts of the complex circulation control mechanism. The volume of blood circulating through the body per minute is directly related to arterial blood pressure and inversely related to peripheral resistance. Note, however, that a great many factors act together to regulate these two factors. (Slightly modified from Mosby's comprehensive review of nursing, St. Louis, The C. V. Mosby Co.)

skeletal muscles during exercise. It also operates in ischemic tissues, serving as a homeostatic mechanism that tends to restore normal blood flow. Norepinephrine, histamine, lactic acid, and other locally produced substances have been suggested as the stimuli that activate the local vasodilator mechanism. Local vasodilation is also referred to as *reactive hyperemia.*

What factors determine the volume of blood flow per minute? Or, stated differently, what makes circulation increase or decrease from time to time?

Answer: The answer to this question lies

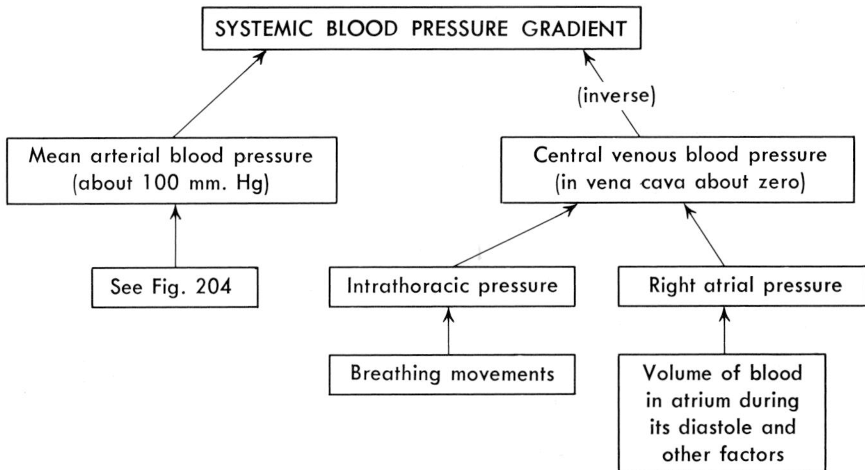

Fig. 213

Factors that determine the systemic blood pressure gradient.

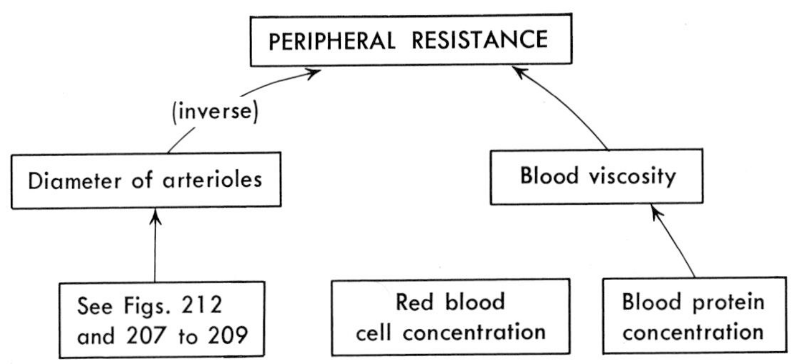

Fig. 214

The main determinants of peripheral resistance.

within the answers to all of the preceding questions about circulation. In most abbreviated form it might be stated this way: the amount of blood flowing through the body per minute is determined by both the blood pressure gradient and peripheral resistance.

A nineteenth century physiologist and physicist, Poiseuille, described the relationship between these three factors—pressure gradient, resistance, and volume of fluid flow per minute—with a mathematical equation known as *Poiseuille's law*. Because the systemic blood pressure gradient (mean arterial pressure–central venous pressure) normally equals the mean or average arterial blood pressure, we can write Poiseuille's law as applied to circulation in the simplest terms as follows: the volume of blood circulated per minute is directly related to arterial pressure and inversely related to resistance or:

$$\text{Volume of blood circulated per minute} = \frac{\text{Arterial pressure}}{\text{Resistance}}$$

The preceding statement and equation need qualifying with regard to the influence of peripheral resistance on circula-

ARTERIAL SUPPLY—FROM LEFT VENTRICLE | BODY PART | VENOUS DRAINAGE—INTO RIGHT ATRIUM OF HEART

Ascending aorta → Coronary → Heart muscle → Coronary → Coronary sinus → Right atrium

Same → Aortic arch → Left common carotid → External carotid → Various branches → Head and neck (exclusive of brain) → External jugular → Subclavian → Innominate → Superior vena cava

Same → Same → Same → Internal carotid → Circle of Willis → Brain → Longitudinal sinus → Transverse sinus → Internal jugular → Same → Same

Brain → Other cranial sinuses

Same → Same → Innominate → Right common carotid → Same → Same → Same → Longitudinal sinus; Other cranial sinuses → Same → Same → Same

Same → Same → Subclavian → Vertebral → Basilar → Same → Same → Same → Same → Same → Same

Same → Same → Same → Axillary → Brachial → Ulnar → Superficial volar arch → Hand; Brachial → Radial → Deep volar arch → Hand

Hand → Superficial and deep volar venous arches → Radial or ulnar → Brachial → Axillary → Subclavian → Same → Same

Superficial and deep volar venous arches → Cephalic or basilic → Axillary → Subclavian → Same → Same

Same → Same → Thoracic aorta → Pericardial → Pericardium → Pericardial → Same

Same → Same → Same → Bronchial → Bronchi, lungs → Bronchial → Azygos → Same

Same → Same → Same → Esophageal → Esophagus → Esophageal → Same → Same

Same → Same → Same → Intercostal → Skin and muscles of chest wall, pleurae, spinal cord, spine → Intercostal → Azygos → Same

Same → Same → Same → Superior phrenic → Upper surface of diaphragm → Superior phrenic → Same → Same

Same → Same → Same → Abdominal aorta → Inferior phrenic → Undersurface of diaphragm → Inferior phrenic → Inferior vena cava

Same → Same → Same → Same → Celiac → (1) Left gastric → Stomach, esophagus → Gastric → Portal → Liver → Hepatic → Same

Ascending aorta → Aortic arch → Thoracic aorta → Abdominal aorta → Celiac → (2) Hepatic → Liver → Hepatic → Inferior vena cava

(a) Right gastric → Stomach → Gastric → Portal → Liver → Hepatic → Same

(b) Gastroduodenal → Stomach, duodenum → Same → Same → Same → Same → Same

(c) Cystic → Gallbladder → Cystic → Same → Same → Same → Same

(3) Splenic → Stomach, pancreas, spleen → Splenic → Same → Same → Same → Same

Ascending aorta → Aortic arch → Thoracic aorta → Abdominal aorta → Superior mesenteric → Jejunum, ileum, cecum, ascending and transverse colon → Superior mesenteric → Same → Same → Same → Same

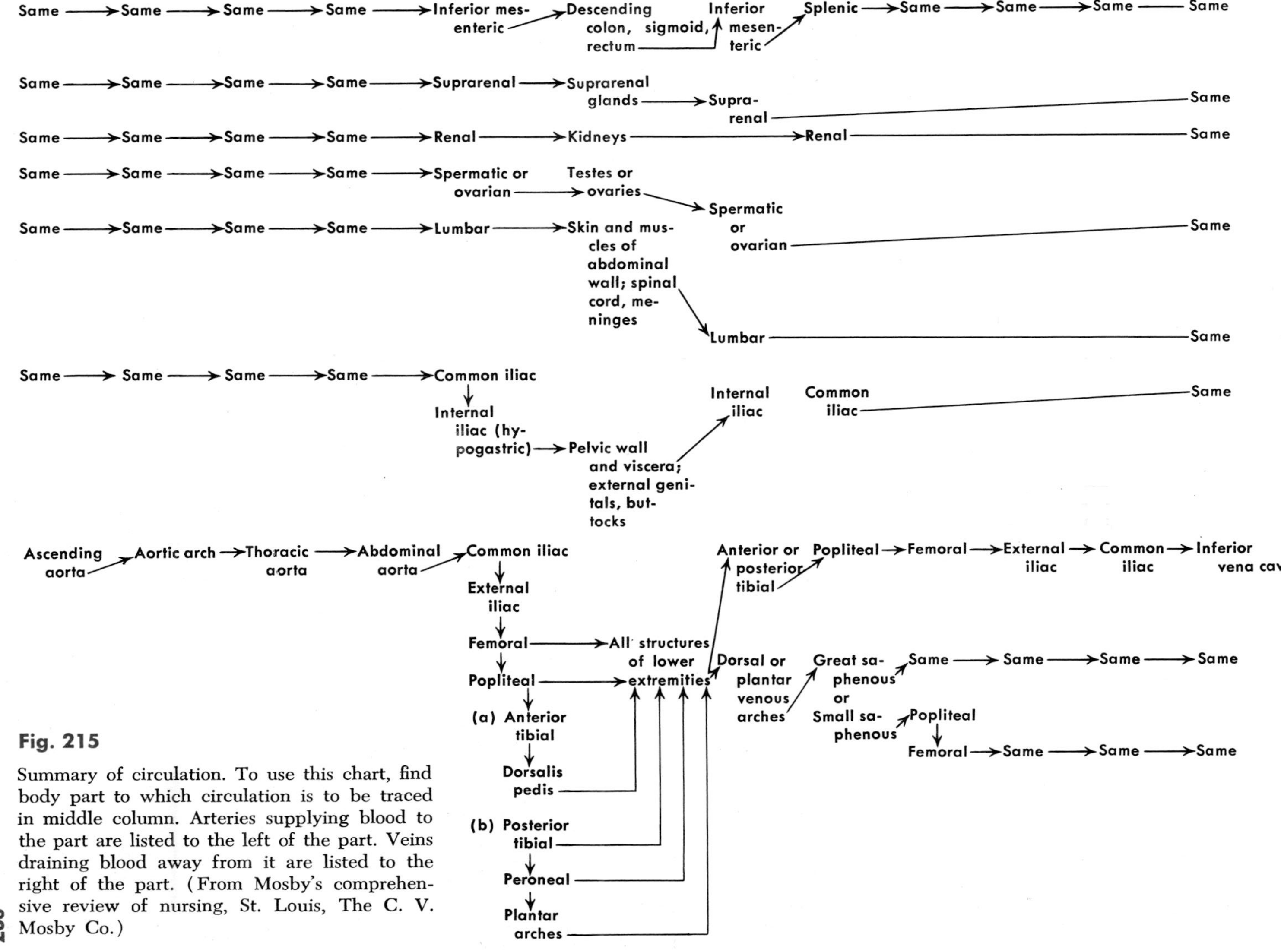

Fig. 215

Summary of circulation. To use this chart, find body part to which circulation is to be traced in middle column. Arteries supplying blood to the part are listed to the left of the part. Veins draining blood away from it are listed to the right of the part. (From Mosby's comprehensive review of nursing, St. Louis, The C. V. Mosby Co.)

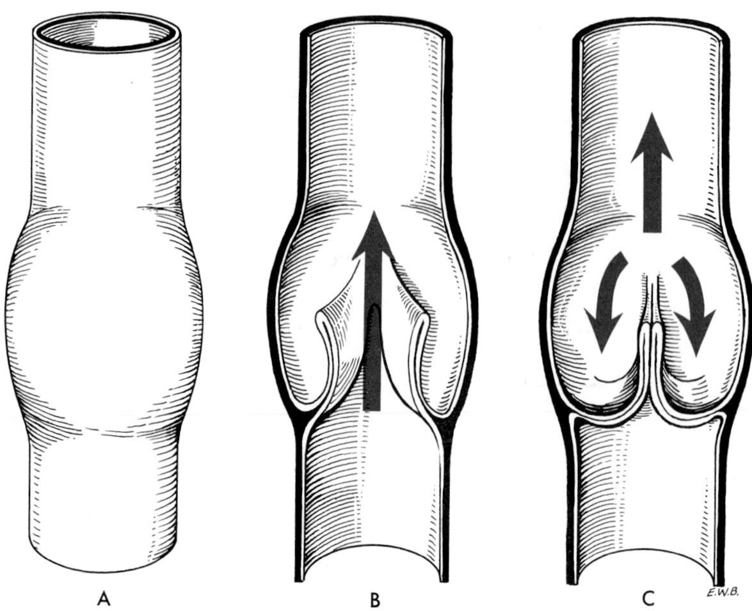

Fig. 216

Diagram showing the action of venous valves. **A,** External view of vein showing dilation at site of the valve. **B,** Interior of vein with the semilunar flaps in open position, permitting flow of blood through the valve. **C,** Valve flaps approximating each other, occluding the cavity and preventing the backflow of blood.

tion. For instance, according to the equation, an increase in peripheral resistance would tend to decrease blood flow. (Why? Increasing peripheral resistance increases the denominator of the fraction in the preceding equation. And increasing the denominator of any fraction necessarily does what to its value?) Increased peripheral resistance, however, has a secondary action that acts against its primary tendency to decrease blood flow. An increase in peripheral resistance hinders or decreases arteriole runoff. And this, of course, tends to increase the volume of blood left in the arteries so tends to increase arterial pressure. Note also that increasing arterial pressure tends to increase the value of the fraction in Poiseuille's equation. Therefore, it tends to increase circulation. In short, to say unequivocally what the effect of an increased peripheral resistance will be on circulation is impossible. It depends also upon arterial blood pressure—whether it increases, decreases, or stays the same when peripheral resistance increases. The clinical condition arteriosclerosis with hypertension (high blood pressure) illustrates this point. Both peripheral resistance and arterial pressure are increased in this condition. As a result, circulation may decrease if resistance increases more than arterial pressure. If arterial pressure increases proportionately to resistance, it may remain normal.

Special factors influencing venous return to heart

Two special factors that promote the return of venous blood to the heart are respirations and skeletal muscle contractions. Both produce their facilitating effect on venous return by increasing the pressure gradient between peripheral veins and venae cavae.

The process of breathing increases the pressure gradient between peripheral and central veins by both increasing peripheral venous pressure and decreasing central venous pressure. Each time the diaphragm contracts, enlarging the thoracic cavity and compressing the abdominal cavity, the pressure in the thoracic cavity and therefore in the thoracic portion of the vena cava and in the atria decreases, whereas that in the abdominal cavity and the abdominal veins increases. Deeper respirations intensify these effects and therefore tend to increase venous return to the heart more than do normal respirations. This is part of the reason why the principle is true that increased respirations and increased circulation tend to go hand in hand.

Skeletal muscle contractions operate in the following way to promote venous return; as each skeletal muscle contracts, it squeezes the soft veins scattered through its interior, thereby milking the blood in them upward or toward the heart. And the closing of the semilunar valves present in veins prevents blood from falling back as the muscle relaxes. Their flaps catch the blood as gravity pulls backward on it (Fig. 216). The net effect of skeletal muscle contraction and venous valvular action, therefore, is to move venous blood toward the heart, to increase the venous return.

The value of skeletal muscle contractions in moving blood through veins is illustrated by a common experience. Who has not noticed how much more uncomfortable and tiring standing still is than walking? After several minutes of standing quietly, the feet and legs feel "full" and swollen. Blood has accumulated in the veins because the skeletal muscles are not contracting and squeezing it upward. The repeated contractions of the muscles when walking, on the other hand, keep the blood moving in the veins and prevent the discomfort of distended veins.

Blood pressure

How arterial blood pressure measured clinically

Blood pressure is measured with the aid of an apparatus known as a sphygmomanometer which makes it possible to measure the amount of air pressure equal to the blood pressure in an artery. The measurement is made in terms of how many millimeters high the air pressure raises a column of mercury in a glass tube.

The sphygmomanometer consists of a rubber cuff attached by a rubber tube to a compressible bulb and by another tube to a column of mercury that is marked off in millimeters. The cuff is wrapped around the arm over the brachial artery, and air is pumped into the cuff by means of the bulb. In this way air pressure is exerted against the outside of the artery. Air is added until the air pressure exceeds the blood pressure within the artery or, in other words, until it compresses the artery. At this time no pulse can be heard through a stethoscope placed over the brachial artery at the bend of the elbow along the inner margin of the biceps muscle. By slowly releasing the air in the cuff, the air pressure is decreased until it approximately equals the blood pressure within the artery. At this point the vessel opens slightly and a small spurt of blood comes through, producing the first sound, one with a rather sharp, taplike quality. This is followed by increasingly louder sounds which suddenly change, becoming more muffled, then disappearing altogether. The nurse must train herself to hear these different sounds and simultaneously to read the column of mercury since the first taplike sound represents the *systolic blood pressure.* Systolic pressure is the force with which the blood is pushing against the artery walls when the ventricles are contracting. The lowest point at which the sounds can be heard, just before they disappear, is approximately equal to the *diastolic pressure* or the force of the blood when the ventricles are relaxed. Systolic pressure gives valuable information about the force of the left ventricular contraction, and diastolic pressure gives valuable information about the resistance of the blood vessels. Clinically, diastolic pressure is considered more important than systolic pressure because it indicates the pressure or strain to which blood vessel walls are constantly subjected. It also reflects the condition of the peripheral vessels since diastolic pressure rises or falls with the peripheral resistance. If, for instance, arteries are sclerosed, peripheral resistance and diastolic pressure both increase.

Blood in the arteries of the average adult exerts a pressure equal to that required to raise a column of mercury about 120 mm. (or a column of water over 5 feet) high in a glass tube during systole of the ventricles and 80 mm. high during their diastole. For the sake of brevity, this is expressed as a blood pressure of 120 over 80 (120/80). The first or upper figure represents systolic pressure and the second diastolic pressure. From the figures just given, we observe that blood pressure fluctuates considerably during each heartbeat. During ventricular systole the force is great enough to raise the mercury column 40 mm. higher than during ventricular diastole. This difference between systolic and diastolic pressure is called *pulse pressure.* It characteristically increases in arteriosclerosis due mainly to increased systolic pressure. Pulse pressure increases even more markedly in aortic valve insufficiency due both to a rise in systolic and a fall in diastolic pressure.

Relation to arterial and venous bleeding

Because blood exerts a comparatively high pressure in arteries and a very low pressure in veins, it gushes forth with considerable force from a cut artery but seeps in a slow, steady stream from a vein. As we have just seen, each ventricular contraction raises arterial blood pressure to the systolic level, and each ventricular relaxation lowers it to the diastolic level. As the ventricles contract, then, the blood spurts forth forcefully due to increased pressure in the artery, but as the ventricles relax, the flow ebbs to almost nothing due to the fall in pressure. In other words, blood escapes from an artery in spurts because of the alternate raising and lowering of arterial blood pressure but flows slowly and steadily from a vein because of the low, practically constant pressure. A uniform instead of a pulsating pressure exists in the capillaries and veins because the arterial walls, being elastic, continue to squeeze the blood forward while the ventricles are in diastole. Therefore, blood enters capillaries and veins under a steady pressure.

Velocity of blood

The speed with which blood flows (that is, distance per minute) through its vessels is governed in part by the physical principle that when a liquid flows from an area of one cross-section size to an area of larger size, its velocity will be slower in the area with the larger cross section. For example, a narrow river whose bed widens flows more slowly through the wider section than through the narrow. In terms of blood vascular system, the total cross-section area of all arterioles together is greater than that of the arteries. Therefore, blood flows more slowly through arterioles than through arteries. Likewise, the total cross-section area of all capillaries together is greater than that of all arterioles and, therefore, capillary flow is slower than arteriole. Venule cross-section area, on the other hand, is smaller than capillary cross-section area. Therefore, the blood velocity increases in venules and again in veins, which have a still smaller cross-section area. In short, the most rapid blood flow takes place in arteries and the slowest in capillaries.

Pulse

Definition

Pulse is defined as the alternate expansion and recoil of an artery.

Cause

Two factors are responsible for the existence of a pulse which can be felt:

1. Intermittent injections of blood from the heart into the aorta, which alternately increase and decrease the pressure in that vessel. If blood poured steadily out of the heart into the aorta, the pressure there would remain constant and there would be no pulse.

2. The elasticity of the arterial walls, which makes it possible for them to expand with each injection of blood and then recoil. If the vessels were fashioned from rigid material such as glass, there would still be an alternate raising and lowering of pressure within them with each systole and diastole of the ventricles, but the walls could not expand and recoil and, therefore, no pulse could be felt.

Pulse wave

Each ventricular systole starts a new pulse which proceeds as a wave of expansion throughout the arteries and is known as the pulse wave. It gradually lessens as it travels, disappearing entirely in the capillaries. The pulse felt in the radial artery at the wrist does not coincide with the contraction of the ventricles but rather follows each contraction by an appreciable interval (the length of time required for the pulse wave to travel from the aorta to the radial artery). The farther from the heart the pulse is taken, therefore, the longer that interval is.

Any nurse has only to think of the number of times she has counted pulses to become aware of the diagnostic importance of the pulse. It reveals important information about the cardiovascular system, about heart action, blood vessels, and circulation.

Where pulse can be felt

In general, the pulse can be felt whereever an artery lies near the surface and over a bone or other firm background. Some of the specific locations where the pulse is most easily felt are as follows:

1. *radial artery*—at wrist
2. *temporal artery*—in front of ear or above and to outer side of eye
3. *common carotid artery*—along anterior edge of sternocleidomastoid muscle at level of lower margin of thyroid cartilage
4. *facial artery*—at lower margin of lower jawbone on a line with corners of mouth and in a groove in mandible about one-third of way forward from angle
5. *brachial artery*—at bend of elbow along inner margin of biceps muscle
6. *femoral artery*—in middle of groin where artery passes over pelvic bone
7. *popliteal artery*—in popliteal space behind knee

Note: The so-called pressure points or points at which pressure may be applied to stop arterial bleeding are roughly related to the points where the pulse may be felt in that they both are found where an artery lies near the surface and near a bone which can act as a firm background for pressure. There are six important pressure points:

1. *temporal artery*—in front of ear
2. *facial artery*—same place as pulse is taken
3. *common carotid artery*—point where pulse is taken, with pressure back against spinal column
4. *subclavian artery*—behind mesial third of clavicle, pressing against first rib
5. *brachial artery*—few inches above el-

bow on inside of arm, pressing against humerus

6. *femoral artery*—where pulse is taken

In trying to stop arterial bleeding by pressure, one must always remember to apply the pressure at the pressure point that lies between the bleeding part and the heart, since the blood flows from the heart through the arteries to the part. Pressure between the heart and bleeding point, therefore, cuts off the source of the blood flow.

Venous pulse

A pulse exists in the large veins only, particularly in those near the heart, due to changes in venous blood pressure brought about by alternate contraction and relaxation of the atria of the heart. Venous pulse does not have as great clinical significance as arterial pulse and is only rarely recorded.

Lymphatic system

Definition

The lymphatic system is actually part of the circulatory system since it consists of a moving fluid (lymph and tissue fluid) derived from the blood and a group of vessels (lymphatics) which return the lymph to the blood.

LYMPH AND INTERSTITIAL FLUID (TISSUE FLUID)

Definition

Lymph is the clear watery-appearing fluid found in the lymphatic vessels, whereas interstitial fluid is located intercellularly in the microscopic spaces between cells. In some tissues it is part of a semifluid ground substance. In others it is the bound water in a gelatinous ground substance. Interstitial fluid and blood together constitute the extracellular fluid or, in the words of Claude Bernard, the internal environment of the body—the fluid environment of cells in contrast to the atmosphere or external environment of the body. Both lymph and tissue fluid closely resemble blood plasma in composition. The main difference is that they contain a lower percentage of proteins than does plasma. (The term lymph is sometimes used to mean both the fluid in the lymphatics and that in the tissue spaces.)

LYMPHATICS

Formation and distribution

Lymphatic vessels originate as microscopic blind-end vessels called *lymphatic capillaries.* These tiny vessels are located in the intercellular spaces and are widely distributed throughout the body. As twigs of a tree join to form branches and branches join to form larger branches, and large branches join to form the tree trunk, so do lymphatic capillaries merge, forming slightly larger lymphatics that join other lymphatics to form still larger vessels, which merge to form the main lymphatic trunks: the *right lymphatic ducts* and the *thoracic duct.* Lymph from the entire body, except the upper right quadrant (Fig. 220), drains eventually into the thoracic duct, which drains into the left subclavian vein at the point where it joins the left internal jugular vein. Lymph from the upper right quadrant of the body empties into the right lymphatic duct (or, more commonly, into three collecting ducts) and thence into the right subclavian vein. Since most of the lymph of the body returns to the bloodstream by way of the thoracic duct, this vessel is considerably larger than the other main lymph channels, the right lymphatic ducts, but is much smaller than the large veins, which it resembles in structure. It has a diameter about the size of a goose quill and a length of from 15 to 18 inches. It originates as a dilated structure, the *cisterna chyli,* in the lumbar region of the abdominal cavity and ascends by a flexuous course to the root of the neck, where it joins the subclavian vein as just

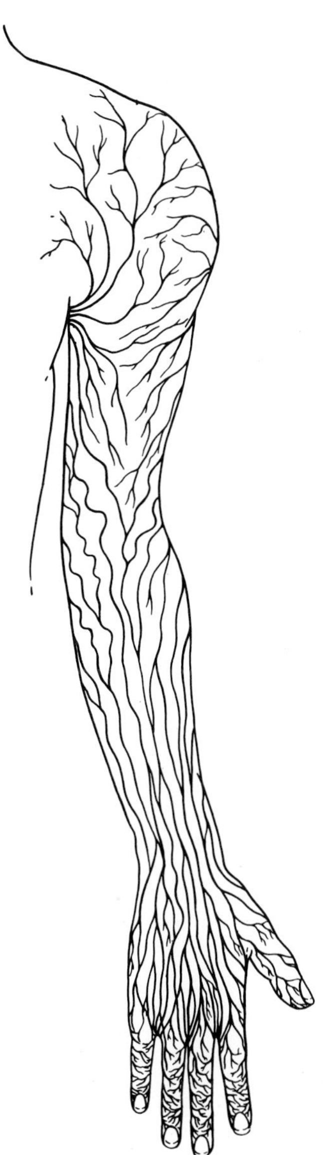

Fig. 217

Superficial lymphatics of the upper extremity, posterior surface. (After Sappey; from Francis and Farrell: Integrated anatomy and physiology, St. Louis, The C. V. Mosby Co.)

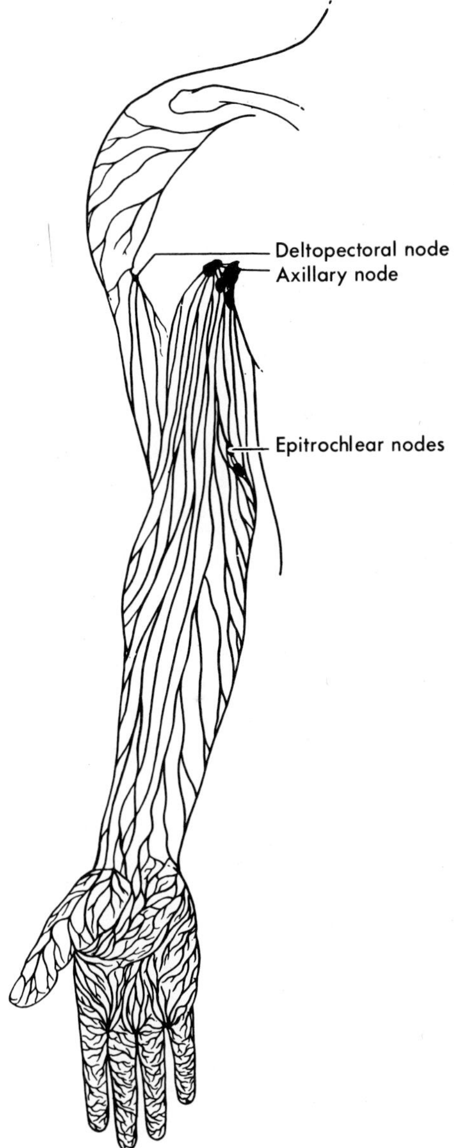

Fig. 218

Superficial lymphatics of the upper extremity, anterior surface. (After Sappey; from Francis and Farrell: Integrated anatomy and physiology, St. Louis, The C. V. Mosby Co.)

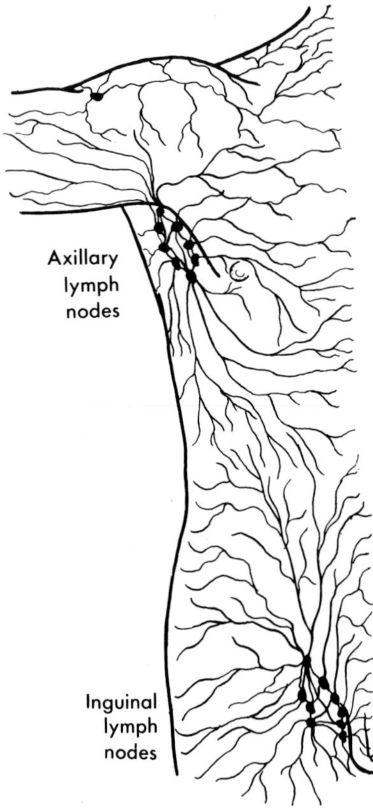

Fig. 219

Distribution of the superficial lymphatics and lymph nodes of the front of the trunk.

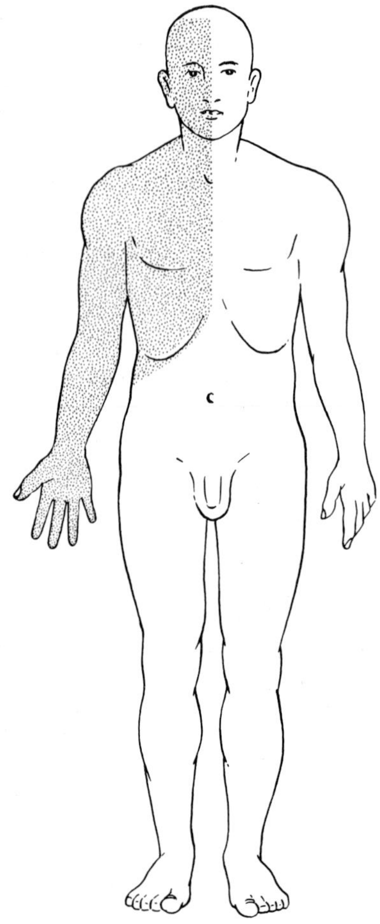

Fig. 220

Lymph drainage. The right lymphatic ducts drain lymph from the part of the body indicated by the stippled area. Lymph from all the rest of the body enters the general circulation by way of the thoracic duct.

described (see Fig. 221). The presence of semilunar valves at frequent intervals along the duct gives it a somewhat varicose appearance.

Structure

Lymphatics resemble veins in structure with these exceptions: (1) lymphatics have thinner walls, (2) they contain more valves, and (3) they contain lymph nodes (or glands) located at certain intervals along their course. Lymphatics originating in the villi of the small intestine are called *lacteals,* whereas the milky fluid found in them after digestion is *chyle.*

Function

The function of lymphatics is the return of water and proteins from the interstitial fluid to blood from which they came. Proteins can return to blood only via lymphatics. This fact has great clinical importance. For instance, if anything blocks lymphatic return, blood protein concentration and blood osmotic pressure soon fall below

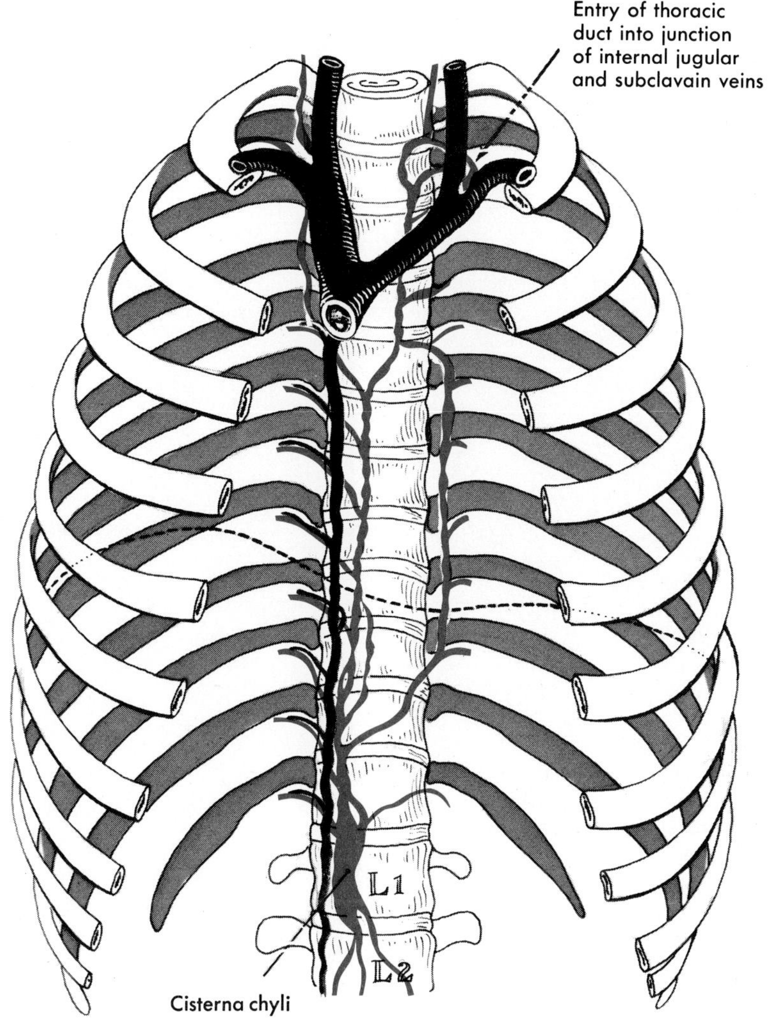

Fig. 221

Position of the cisterna chyli and the thoracic duct and its tributaries and the entry of the duct into the junction of the internal jugular and subclavian veins.

normal and fluid imbalance results (see Chapter XV).

LYMPH CIRCULATION

Water and solutes continually filter out of capillary blood into the interstitial fluid. To balance this outflow, fluid continually reenters blood from the interstitial fluid. Some osmoses back into the capillaries, and a much smaller amount enters lymphatic capillaries by a method not yet clearly understood. For more details about fluid exchange between blood and interstitial fluid, see Chapter XV. From lymphatic capillaries, lymph flows through progressively larger lymphatic vessels to eventually reenter blood at the junction of the internal jugular and subclavian veins (Fig. 221).

Although there is no pump connected with the lymphatic vessels to force lymph onward as the heart does blood, still lymph moves slowly and steadily along in its vessels. And this occurs despite the fact that

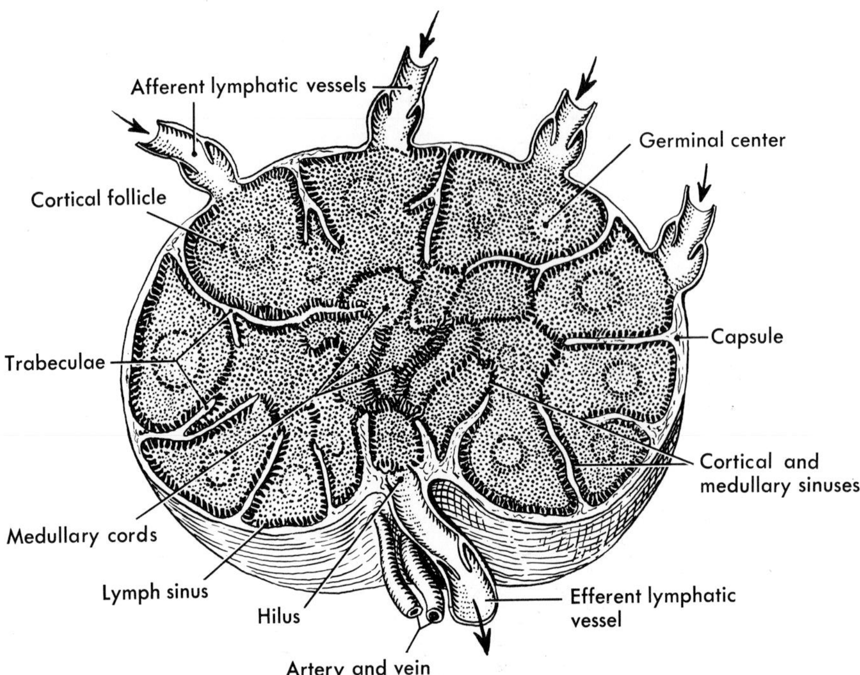

Fig. 222

Structure of a lymph node (diagrammatic). Several afferent valved lymphatics bring lymph to the node. An efferent lymphatic leaves the node at the hilus. Note that the artery and vein enter and leave at the hilus.

most of the flow is uphill. What mechanisms establish the pressure gradient required by the basic law of fluid flow? Two of the same mechanisms that contribute to the blood pressure gradient also establish a lymph pressure gradient. These are breathing movements and skeletal muscle contractions.

The mechanism of inspiration, due to the descent of the diaphragm, causes intra-abdominal pressure to increase as intrathoracic pressure decreases. And this causes pressure to increase in the abdominal portion of the thoracic duct and to decrease in the thoracic portion. In other words, the process of inspiring establishes a pressure gradient in the thoracic duct that causes lymph to flow upward through it.

In addition, contracting skeletal muscles exert pressure on the lymphatics to push the lymph forward because valves within the lymphatics prevent backflow.

LYMPH NODES

Structure

Lymph nodes or glands, as they are often called, are oval or bean-shaped structures. Some are as small as a pinhead and others as large as a lima bean. As shown in Fig 222, lymph moves into the nodes via several afferent lymphatic vessels. Here it moves slowly through sinus channels lined with phagocytic reticuloendothelial cells and emerges usually by one efferent vessel. Lymphatic tissue, densely packed with lymphocytes, composes the substance of the node.

Location

With the exception of comparatively few single nodes, most of the lymph nodes are arranged in groups or clusters in certain

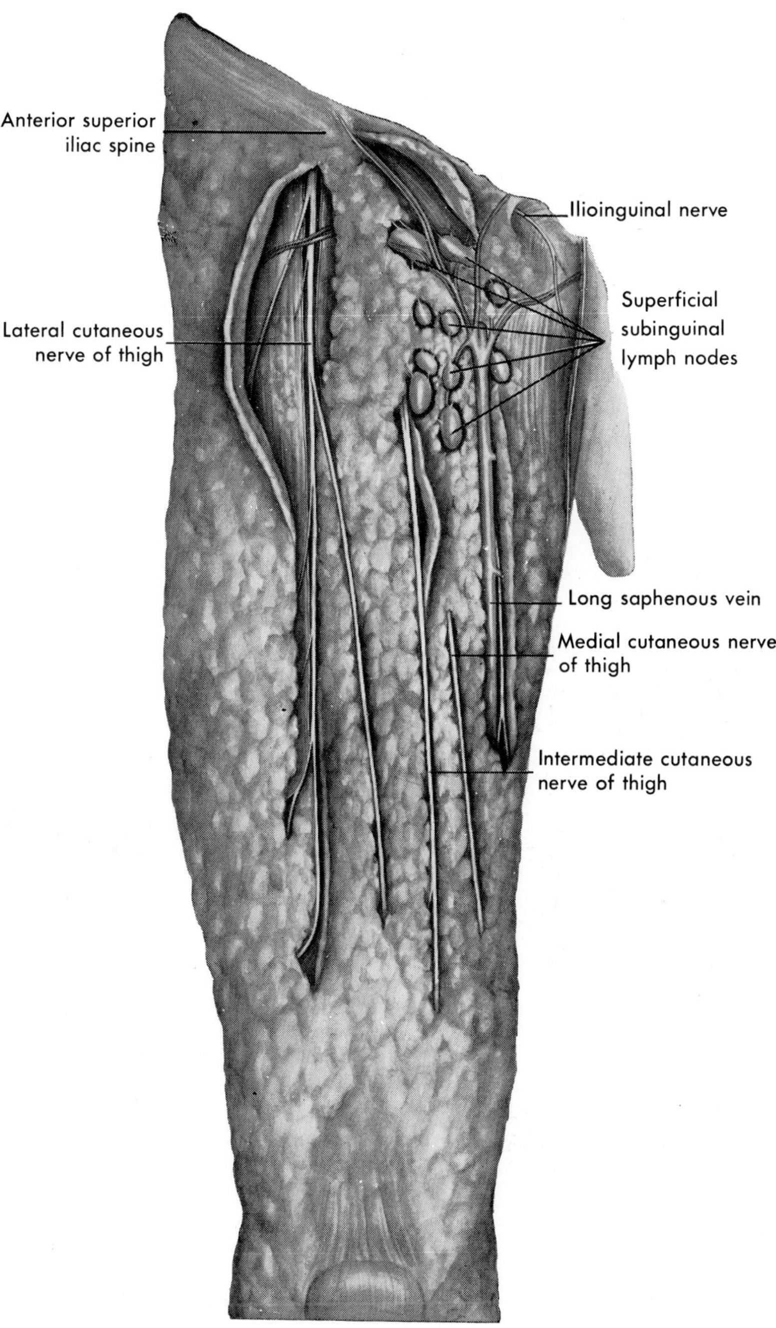

Fig. 223

Location of the superficial inguinal lymph nodes. The skin has been removed from this specimen, showing the deposits of subcutaneous fat. (From Francis and Farrell: Integrated anatomy and physiology, St. Louis, The C. V. Mosby Co.)

areas. The group locations of greatest clinical importance are as follows:

1. *submental and submaxillary groups* in the floor of the mouth—lymph from the nose, lips, and teeth drains through these nodes.
2. *superficial cervical glands* in the neck along the sternocleidomastoid muscle—these nodes drain lymph from the head (which has already passed through other nodes) and neck.
3. *superficial cubital or supratrochlear nodes* located just above the bend of the elbow—lymph from the forearm passes through these nodes.
4. *axillary nodes*—(twenty to thirty

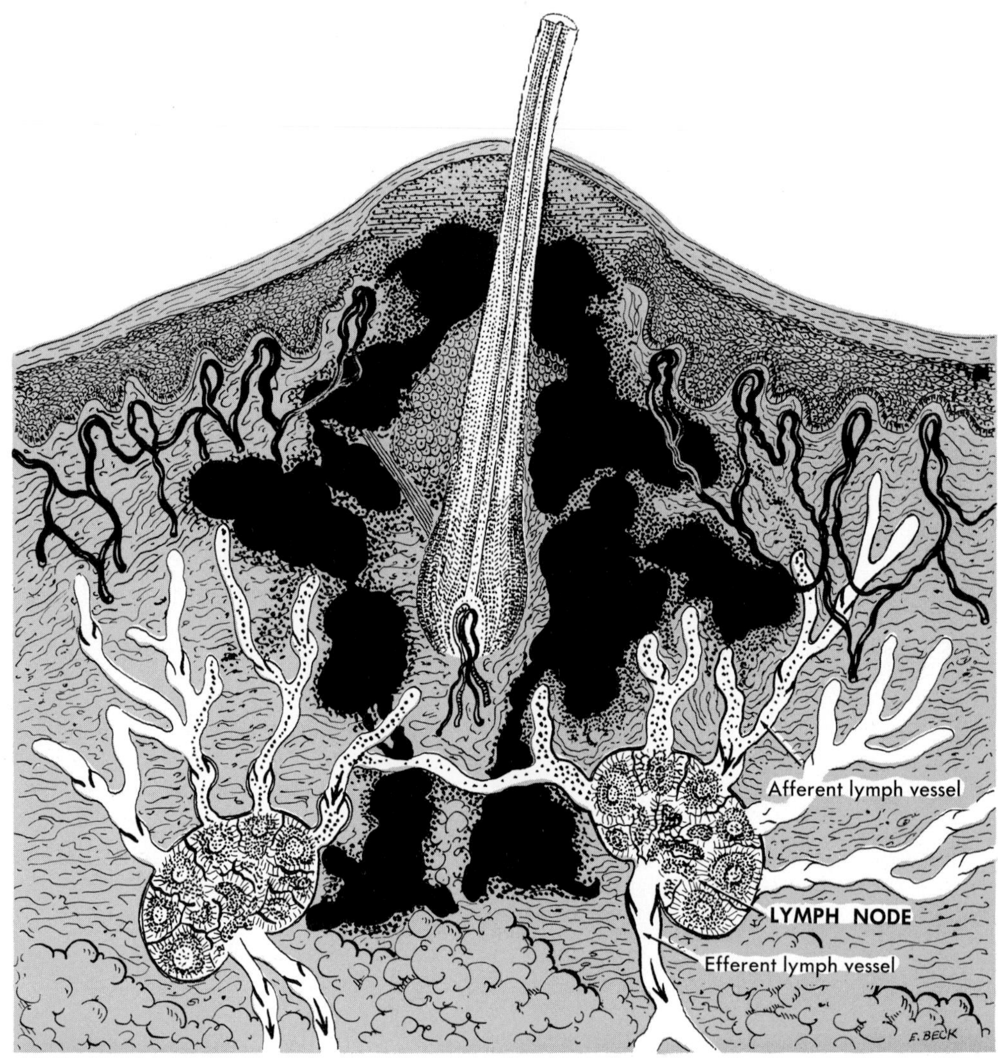

Fig. 224

Diagrammatic representation of a skin section in which an infection surrounds a hair follicle. The black areas represent dead and dying cells (pus). Black dots around the black areas represent bacteria. Leukocytes engulf the bacteria and carry them to the lymph nodes by way of afferent lymphatics. The nodes filter and destroy most of the bacteria by enzymatic action.

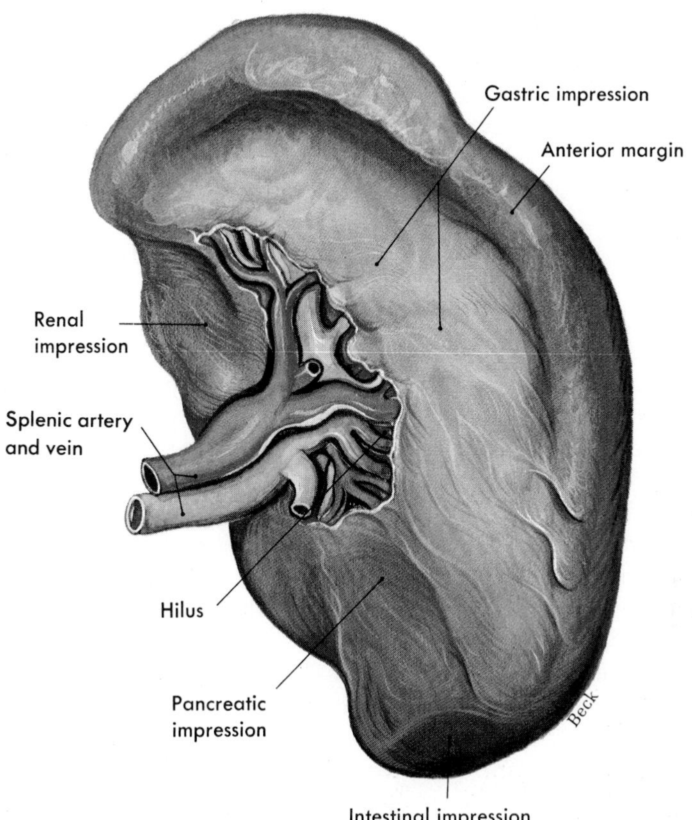

Fig. 225

Spleen, medial aspect. Arrangement of the vessels at the hilus is highly variable.

large nodes clustered deep within the underarm and upper chest regions)—lymph from the arm and upper part of the thoracic wall, including the breast, drains through these nodes.

5. *inguinal nodes* (Fig. 223) in the groin—lymph from the leg and external genitals drains through these.

Functions

Lymph nodes perform two unrelated functions, defense and hemopoiesis.

1. *Defense functions: filtration and phagocytosis.* The structure of the sinus channels within lymph nodes slows the lymph flow through them, giving the reticuloendothelial cells that line the channels time to remove microorganisms and other injurious particles—cancer cells and soot, for example—from the lymph and phagocytose them. Sometimes, however, such hordes of microorganisms enter the nodes that the phagocytes cannot destroy enough of them to prevent their injuring the node. An infection of the node, adenitis, then results. Also, because cancer cells often break away from a malignant tumor and enter lymphatics, they travel to the lymph nodes where they may set up new growths. This may leave too few channels for lymph to return to the blood. For example, if tumors block axillary node channels, fluid accumulates in the interstitial spaces of the arm,

causing the arm to become markedly swollen.

2. *Hemopoiesis.* The lymphatic tissue of lymph nodes forms lymphocytes and monocytes, the nongranular white blood cells, and plasma cells, the antibody-forming cells of the body.

SPLEEN

Location

The spleen is located in the left hypochondrium directly below the diaphragm, above the left kidney and descending colon, and behind the fundus of the stomach.

Structure

The spleen is roughly ovoid in shape, and its size varies greatly in different individuals and in the same individual at different times. For example, it hypertrophies during infectious diseases and atrophies in old age. Within the spleen are numerous areas of lymphatic tissue and many venous sinuses.

Functions

The spleen has long puzzled physiologists who have ascribed many and sundry functions to it. According to present-day knowledge, it performs the following functions:

1. *Defense.* The spleen's reticuloendothelial cells, like all such cells, carry on phagocytosis. Therefore, the spleen plays a part in the body's defense against microorganisms.

2. *Hemopoiesis.* Nongranular leukocytes, that is, monocytes and lymphocytes, and plasma cells are formed in the spleen. Before birth, red blood cells are also formed in the spleen but after birth the spleen is said to form red cells only in extreme hemolytic anemia.

3. *Red blood cell destruction.* The spleen's reticuloendothelial cells also phagocytose fragments of old worn-out red blood cells.

4. *Blood reservoir.* The pulp of the spleen and its venous sinuses store considerable blood. Its normal volume of about 350 ml. is said to decrease about 200 ml. in less than a minute's time following sympathetic stimulation that produces marked constriction of its smooth capsule.

5. *Platelet destruction.* An interesting hypothesis about the spleen is that sometimes it removes too many blood platelets from circulation, causing a platelet deficiency *(thrombocytopenia)* and consequent tiny capillary hemorrhages. Surgical removal of the spleen has been tried on some patients with thrombocytopenia. Some surgeons report cures following this treatment.

Outline summary—The circulatory system

Functions

1. Primary function—transportation of various substances to and from body cells
2. Secondary functions—contributes to all bodily functions, for example:
   a. cellular metabolism
   b. homeostasis of fluid volume
   c. homeostasis of pH
   d. homeostasis of temperature
   e. defense against microorganisms

Blood

BLOOD CELLS

Three main kinds—red blood cells (erythrocytes), white blood cells (leukocytes), platelets (thrombocytes)

Erythrocytes (red blood cells)

1. Size and appearance—biconcave disks about 7 microns in diameter
2. Structure and functions—millions of molecules of hemoglobin inside each red cell

makes possible red cell functions of oxygen and carbon dioxide transport
3. Formation (erythropoiesis)—by myeloid tissue (red bone marrow); see Fig. 177 for stages of red cell development
4. Destruction—by fragmentation in capillaries; reticuloendothelial cells phagocytose red cell fragments and break down hemoglobin to yield iron containing pigment and bile pigments; bone marrow reuses most of iron for new red cell synthesis; liver excretes bile pigments; life span of red cells about 120 days according to studies made with radioactive isotopes
5. Erythrocyte (red blood cell) homeostatic mechanism—stimulus thought to be tissue hypoxia; for description of mechanisms, see Fig. 178; clinical applications (pernicious anemia, vitamin B_{12}, bone marrow damage, reticulocyte count, red count, hematocrit, and sternal punctures) discussed on p. 279

Leukocytes (white blood cells)

1. Appearance and size—vary; some relatively large cells (e.g., monocytes) and some small cells (e.g., small lymphocytes); nuclei vary from spherical to S shaped to lobulated; cytoplasm of neutrophils, eosinophils, and basophils contain granules that take neutral, acid, and basic stains, respectively
2. Functions—defense or protection since carry on phagocytosis
3. Formation—in myeloid tissue (red bone marrow) for granular leukocytes; nongranular leukocytes (lymphocytes and monocytes) in lymphatic tissue, i.e., mainly in lymph nodes and spleen
4. Destruction and life span—some destroyed by phagocytosis; life span unknown
5. Numbers—about 5,000 to 10,000 leukocytes per cubic millimeter of blood; differential count on p. 282

Platelets

1. Appearance and size—platelets are small fragments of cells
2. Functions—disintegrating platelets release factor that combines with blood proteins and calcium ions to form prothrombinase, which initiates blood clotting
3. Formation and life span—formed in red bone marrow by fragmentation of large cells (megakaryocytes, Fig. 177); life span not known, probably only few days

BLOOD TYPES (OR BLOOD GROUPS)

1. Names—indicate type of antigen on or in red cell membranes
2. Plasma does not contain antibodies against antigens present on its red cells but does contain antibodies against other major blood cell antigens not present on its red cells
3. Universal donor: type O; universal recipient: type AB

BLOOD PLASMA

1. Liquid part of blood or whole blood minus its cells
2. Composition
   a. about 90% water and 10% solutes
   b. most solutes crystalloids but some colloids
   c. most solutes electrolytes but some nonelectrolytes
   d. solutes include foods, wastes, gases, hormones, enzymes, vitamins, and antibodies and other proteins

BLOOD CLOTTING

1. Purpose—to plug up ruptured vessels and thus prevent fatal hemorrhage
2. Mechanism—see Figs. 179 and 180
   a. stage 1—prothrombinase (active thromboplastin) formation
   b. stage 2—thrombin formation
   c. stage 3—fibrin formation
3. Factors that oppose clotting
   a. smoothness of endothelium that lines blood vessels prevents platelets' adherence and consequent disintegration; some platelet disintegration continuously despite this preventive
   b. blood normally contains certain anticoagulants, e.g., antithrombins, substances which inactivate thrombin so that it cannot catalyze fibrin formation
4. Factors that hasten clotting
   a. endothelial "rough" spots (e.g., lipoid plagues in atherosclerosis)
   b. sluggish blood flow
5. Pharmaceutical preparations that retard clotting—commercial heparin, Dicumarol, citrates (for transfusion blood)
6. Clot dissolution—process called fibrinolysis; presumably this and the opposing process (clot formation) go on all the time
7. Clinical methods of hastening clotting
   a. apply rough surfaces to wound to stimulate platelets and tissues to liberate more thromboplastin

b. apply purified thrombin
c. apply fibrin foam, film, etc.

Heart

1. Four-chambered muscular organ
2. Lies in mediastinum with apex on diaphragm, two-thirds of its bulk to left of midline of body and one-third to right
3. Apical beat may be counted by placing stethoscope in fifth intercostal space on line with left midclavicular point

COVERING

1. Structure
   a. loose-fitting, inextensible sac (fibrous pericardium) around heart, lined with serous pericardium (parietal layer), which also covers outer surface of heart (visceral layer or epicardium)
   b. small space between parietal and visceral layers of serous pericardium contains few drops of pericardial fluid
2. Function—protection against friction

STRUCTURE

Wall

1. Myocardium, name of muscular wall
2. Endocardium, lining
3. Pericardium, covering

Cavities

1. Upper two—atria
2. Lower two—ventricles

Valves and openings

1. Openings between atria and ventricles—atrioventricular orifices, guarded by cuspid valves, tricuspid on right and mitral or bicuspid on left; valves consist of three parts: flaps, chordae tendineae, and papillary muscle
2. Opening from right ventricle into pulmonary artery guarded by semilunar valves
3. Opening from left ventricle into great aorta guarded by semilunar valves

Blood supply

From coronary arteries; branch from ascending aorta behind semilunar valves

1. Left ventricle receives blood via both major branches of left coronary artery and from one branch of right coronary artery
2. Right ventricle receives blood via both major branches of right coronary artery and from one branch of left coronary artery
3. Each atrium receives blood only from one branch of its respective coronary artery
4. Usually only a few anastomoses between larger branches of coronary arteries, so that occlusion of one of these produces areas of myocardial infarction; if not fatal, anastomoses between smaller vessels grow and provide collateral circulation

Conduction system

1. Sinoatrial node (pacemaker of heart)—small mass of modified cardiac muscle at junction of superior vena cava and right atrium; numerous sympathetic and parasympathetic fibers terminate here, initiating each heartbeat
2. Atrioventricular node—small mass of modified cardiac muscle in septum between the two atria
3. Atrioventricular bundle (bundle of His)—special cardiac muscle fibers originating in A.V. node and extending down interventricular septum
4. Purkinje fibers—extension of bundle of His fibers out into walls of ventricles

Nerve supply

1. Sympathetic fibers (in cardiac nerves) and parasympathetic fibers (in vagus) form cardiac plexuses
2. Fibers from plexuses terminate mainly in S.A. node
3. Sympathetic fibers tend to accelerate and strengthen heartbeat
4. Vagal fibers slow it

PHYSIOLOGY

1. Primary functions of circulatory system—maintain blood flow and vary rate of flow according to energy needs of cells
2. Cardiac cycle
   a. nature—consists of systole and diastole of atria and of ventricles; atria contract and as they relax, ventricles contract
   b. time required for cycle—about 4/5 second or from 70 to 80 times per minute
   c. events of cycle
      1. atria contracted—cuspid valves open; ventricles relaxed; semilunar valves closed
      2. atria relaxed—cuspid valves closed during first part of atrial diastole while ventricles are contracted and then open as ventricles relax; semilunar valves open during ventricular contraction

d. heart sounds during cycle–lubb due to contraction of ventricles and closure of cuspid valves; dupp due to closure of semilunar valves

Blood vessels

1. Kinds
   a. arteries–vessels that carry blood away from heart; all except pulmonary artery carry oxygenated blood
   b. veins–vessels that carry blood toward heart; all except pulmonary veins carry deoxygenated blood
   c. capillaries–microscopic vessels that carry blood from small arteries (arterioles) to small veins (venules)
2. Structure–see Table 41
3. Functions
   a. arteries and arterioles–carry blood away from heart to capillaries
   b. capillaries–deliver materials to cells (by way of tissue fluid) and collect substances from them; vital function of entire circulatory system
   c. veins and venules–carry blood from capillaries back to heart

MAIN BLOOD VESSELS

Systemic circulation

1. Arteries–see pp. 298 and 299 and Fig. 190
2. Veins–see p. 302 and Fig. 194

Portal circulation

See p. 303 and Fig. 200

Fetal circulation

See p. 305 and Fig. 201

Circulation

1. Definitions
   a. circulation–blood flow through closed circuit of vessels
   b. systemic circulation–blood flow from left ventricle into aorta, other arteries, arterioles, capillaries, venules, and veins to right atrium of heart
   c. pulmonary circulation–blood flow from right ventricle to pulmonary artery to lung arterioles, capillaries, and venules, to pulmonary veins, to left atrium
2. Functions of control mechanisms
   a. maintain circulation
   b. vary circulation; increase blood flow per minute when activity increases and decreases blood flow when activity decreases
3. Principles
   a. blood circulates because blood pressure gradient exists within its vessels; systemic blood pressure gradient (mean arterial pressure minus central venous pressure) equals about 100 mm. Hg
   b. arterial blood pressure determined primarily by volume of blood in arteries; other factors remaining constant–greater arterial blood volume, greater arterial blood pressure
   c. arterial blood volume determined mainly by cardiac minute output and peripheral resistance–directly related to cardiac output and inversely related to resistance
   d. cardiac minute output determined by heart's rate of contraction and its systolic discharge and directly related to both factors
   e. heart's systolic discharge regulated mainly by ratio of sympathetic-parasympathetic impulses
   f. heart rate regulated by pressoreflexes and by many miscellaneous factors; increased arterial pressure in aorta or carotid sinus tends to produce reflex slowing of heart, whereas increased right atrial pressure tends to produce reflex cardiac acceleration
   g. peripheral resistance determined mainly by blood viscosity and by arteriole diameter; in general, less blood viscosity, less peripheral resistance, but smaller diameter of arterioles, greater peripheral resistance
   h. blood viscosity determined by concentration of blood proteins and of blood cells and directly related to both
   i. arteriole diameter regulated mainly by pressoreflexes and chemoreflexes; in general, increase in arterial pressure produces reflex dilatation of arterioles, whereas hypoxia and hypercapnea cause constriction of arterioles in blood reservoir organs but dilatation of them in local structures, notably in skeletal muscles, heart, and brain
   j. volume of blood circulating per minute determined by blood pressure gradient and peripheral resistance; according to Poiseuille's law, directly related to pressure gradient and inversely related to peripheral resistance
   k. respirations and skeletal muscle contractions tend to increase venous return to heart

Blood pressure

1. How arterial blood pressure measured clinically
   a. sphygmomanometer
   b. systolic pressure normally about 120 mm. Hg and diastolic pressure about 80 mm. Hg
2. Relation to arterial and venous bleeding
   a. arterial bleeding in spurts due to difference in amounts of systolic and diastolic pressures
   b. venous bleeding—slow and steady due to low, practically constant venous pressure

Velocity of blood

1. Speed with which blood flows
2. Most rapid in arteries and slowest in capillaries

Pulse

1. Definition—alternate expansion and recoil of artery
2. Cause—intermittent injections of blood from heart into aorta with each ventricular contraction; pulse can be felt because of elasticity of arterial walls
3. Pulse wave—pulse starts at beginning of aorta and proceeds as wave of expansion throughout arteries
4. Where pulse can be felt—radial, temporal, common carotid, facial, brachial, femoral, and popliteal arteries; where near surface and over firm background, such as bone; pressure points, points where bleeding can be stopped by pressure, roughly related to places where pulse can be felt
5. Venous pulse—in large veins only; due to changes in venous pressure brought about by alternate contraction and relaxation of atria

Lymphatic system

Part of circulatory system—consists of lymph, tissue fluid, lymphatics, and lymph nodes

LYMPH AND INTERSTITIAL FLUID (TISSUE FLUID)

1. Definition
   a. lymph—clear, watery fluid found in lymphatic vessels
   b. interstitial fluid (tissue fluid)—clear liquid in tissue spaces

LYMPHATICS

1. Formation and distribution
   a. start as capillaries in tissue spaces
   b. widely distributed throughout body
   c. two or more main lymphatic ducts—thoracic duct, which drains into left subclavian vein at junction of internal jugular and subclavian, and one or more right lymphatic ducts which drain into right subclavian vein
2. Structure
   a. similar to veins except thinner walled
   b. contain more valves and contain lymph nodes located at intervals
3. Function—return of water and proteins from interstitial fluid to blood from which they came

LYMPH CIRCULATION

Water and solutes from capillary blood to interstitial fluid, to lymphatics, to blood at junction of internal jugular and subclavian veins

LYMPH NODES

1. Structure
   a. lymphatic tissue, separated into compartments by fibrous partitions
   b. afferent lymphatics enter each node and efferent lymphatic leaves each node
2. Location—usually in clusters (see pp. 336 to 339)
3. Functions
   a. defense functions—filter out injurious substances and phagocytose them
   b. hemopoiesis—formation of lymphocytes and monocytes

SPLEEN

1. Location—left hypochondrium
2. Structure
   a. similar to lymph nodes, ovoid in shape
   b. size varies
   c. contains numerous venous blood spaces that serve as blood reservoir
3. Functions
   a. defense—protection by phagocytosis by reticuloendothelial cells and possibly antibody formation by lymphocytes
   b. hemopoiesis of nongranular leukocytes (monocytes and lymphocytes) and of red cells before birth
   c. red blood cell destruction—reticuloendothelial cells phagocytose fragments of old worn-out red blood cells
   d. blood reservoir

e. hypothesis that spleen sometimes removes too many thrombocytes from blood, causing platelet deficiency that leads to pinpoint capillary hemorrhages

Review questions

1. Name the three kinds of blood cells.
2. Compare different kinds of blood cells as to (1) appearance and size, (2) functions, (3) formation, destruction, and life span, and (4) number per cubic millimeter of blood.
3. State a general rule for estimating blood volume. About how much blood is there in your body? (See Chapter XV.)
4. What is the normal pH range for blood?
5. Differentiate between blood plasma and blood serum.
6. Briefly describe the chemical composition of blood.
7. Explain the blood-clotting mechanism. Show the main parts of the mechanism by diagram.
8. On what principles do the mechanisms that oppose blood clotting operate?
9. Why and how does a vitamin K deficiency affect blood clotting?
10. Explain some principles and methods by which blood clotting may be hastened.
11. Describe the structure of the heart and its location. Where should a stethoscope be placed to listen to the apical beat?
12. Describe the pericardium, differentiating between the fibrous and serous portions.
13. Exactly where is pericardial fluid found? Explain its function.
14. Describe the heart's own blood supply. Explain the structural reason why occlusion of a large coronary artery branch has serious consequences.
15. Explain the innervation of the heart. Include a description of sensory and motor nerves to the heart and cardiac centers.
16. Name and describe the special neuromuscular structures of the heart, including their location and function, and impulse conduction through the heart.
17. Compare arteries, veins, and capillaries as to structure and functions.
18. Differentiate between systemic, pulmonary, and portal circulation.
19. Explain the differences between fetal and postnatal circulation and the functional reasons for these differences.
20. Explain the heart control mechanism. Include control of both rate and force. Devise a diagram to indicate the different parts of the mechanism.
21. Explain the vasomotor mechanism. Devise a diagram to indicate its various parts.
22. Explain reactive hyperemia and one theory about the mechanism producing it.
23. State in your own words the basic principle of fluid flow.
24. State in your own words Poiseuille's law. Give an example of increased circulation to illustrate application of this law. Give an example of decreased circulation to illustrate application of this law.
25. What mechanisms control arterial blood pressure? Cite an example of the operation of one or more of these mechanisms to increase arterial pressure; to decrease it.
26. What mechanisms control peripheral resistance? Cite an example of the operation of one or more parts of this mechanism to increase resistance; to decrease it.
27. What two factors determine blood viscosity? What does viscosity mean? Give an example of a condition in which blood viscosity decreases. Explain its effect on circulation.
28. What effect, if any, would a respiratory stimulant drug have on circulation. Explain why it would or would not affect circulation.
29. Describe and explain the effects of exercise on circulation.
30. Explain the principles of the clinical method used to measure blood pressure.
31. Explain why a pulse can be felt in certain vessels. In which vessel is there a palpable pulse?
32. Specify places where pulse can be felt.
33. What and where is lymph? Describe its circulation.
34. Compare lymphatics and lymph nodes as to structure and location and function.
35. Describe the location and function of the spleen. What functions is it thought to perform?
36. If cancer cells from breast cancer were to enter the lymphatics of the breast, where do you think they might lodge and start new growths? Explain, using your knowledge of the anatomy of the lymphatic and circulatory systems.
37. Starting with the left ventricle of the heart, list the vessels through which

blood would flow in reaching (1) the small intestine, (2) the large intestine, (3) the liver (two ways), (4) the spleen, (5) the stomach, (6) the kidneys, (7) the suprarenal glands, (8) the ovaries or testes, (9) the anterior part of the base of the brain, and (10) the little finger of the right hand. List the vessels through which the blood returns from these parts to the right atrium of the heart (see Figs. 190, 194, and 202).

38. Name and explain the action of the heart and its valves.
39. Trace the flow of blood through the heart.
40. Give two reasons why blood is considered a protective agent against infection.
41. Describe one or more mechanisms that probably operate to return circulation to normal a short time after exercise ceases.
42. Give the general location of the following veins: longitudinal sinus, internal jugular vein, innominate vein, portal vein, great saphenous vein, inferior vena cava, and basilic vein.
43. Define the following terms briefly.

adenitis	leukopenia
anemia	lymphocyte
aneurysm	monocyte
atherosclerosis	myocardium
basophils	neutrophil
blood pressure	pH
diastole	phagocytosis
differential count	phlebitis
embolus	plasma
endocardium	peripheral resistance
eosinophil	pulse pressure
erythrocyte	sphygmomanometer
heart block	thrombocyte
hemophilia	thrombus
leukemia	systole
leukocyte	

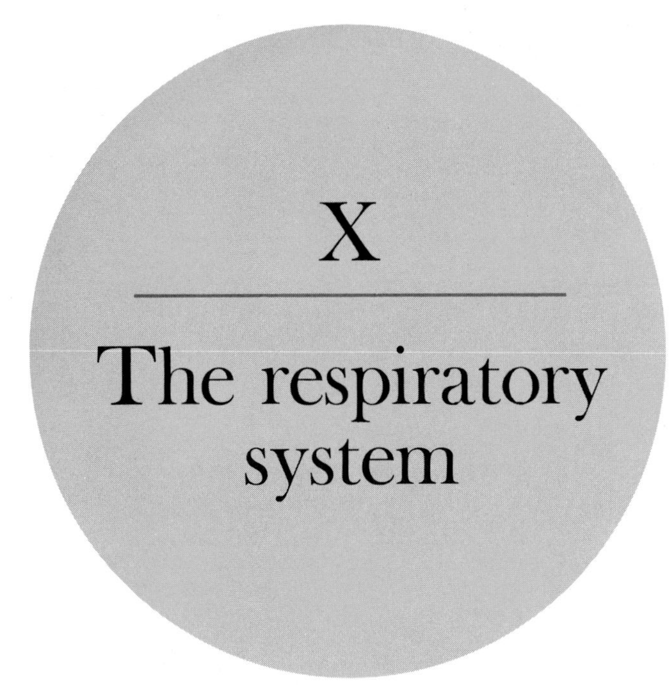

X

The respiratory system

Functions and importance

The respiratory system consists of those organs that make it possible for blood to exchange gases with air. They are the nose, pharynx, larynx, trachea, bronchi, and lungs. This group of organs constitutes the lifeline of the body. If anything interferes with the functioning of this anatomical lifeline, death ensues in a very short time.

The exchange of gases between the blood and air is known as respiration, but actually it is only one phase of respiration. The transportation of gases between the lungs and tissues constitutes another phase, and the exchange of gases between the blood and tissues still another. The first phase is a function of the respiratory system, whereas the second and third phases are functions of the circulatory system. The first and second phases are vital only because they make possible the third phase. The all-important requisite is that cells receive oxygen and rid themselves of carbon dioxide—in short, that they "breathe." But most of our billions of cells cannot exchange these gases directly with air. They lie far too distant from it. Hence they need special structures to make the exchange for them and other structures to transport the gases to and from them. The respiratory and circulatory systems fulfill these needs.

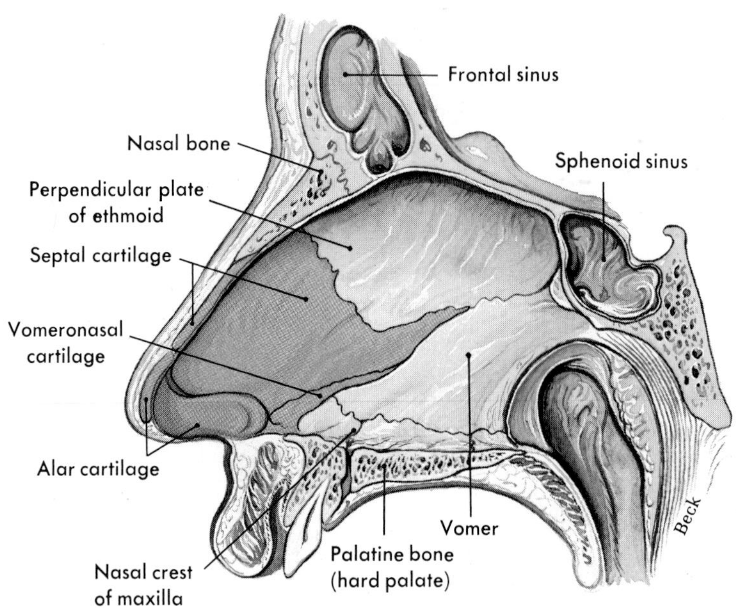

Fig. 226

The nasal septum consists of the perpendicular plate of the ethmoid bone, the vomer, and the septal and vomeronasal cartilages. The cartilages are shown in pink.

Organs

NOSE

Structure

The nose consists of an internal and an external portion. The external portion, that is, the part that protrudes from the face, is considerably smaller than the internal portion, which lies over the roof of the mouth. The interior of the nose is hollow and is separated by a partition, the *septum,* into a right and left cavity. The palatine bones, which form both the floor of the nose and the roof of the mouth, separate the nasal cavities from the mouth cavity. Sometimes the palatine bones fail to unite completely, producing a condition known as *cleft palate* (Fig. 306). When this abnormality exists, the mouth is only partially separated from the nasal cavity, and difficulties arise in swallowing.

Each nasal cavity is divided into three passageways (superior, middle, and inferior meati) by the projection of the turbinates (conchae) from the lateral walls of the internal portion of the nose (Figs. 227 and 228). The superior and middle turbinates are processes of the ethmoid bone, while the inferior turbinates are separate bones.

The external openings into the nasal cavities (nostrils) have the technical name of *anterior nares.* The posterior nares (or choanae) are openings from the internal nose into the nasopharynx.

Ciliated mucous membrane lines the nose and the rest of the respiratory tract down as far as the smaller bronchioles.

Four pairs of sinuses drain into the nose. These paranasal sinuses are the frontal, maxillary, ethmoidal, and sphenoidal. They drain as follows:

1. Into the middle meatus (passageway below middle turbinate)—frontal, maxillary, and anterior ethmoidal sinuses

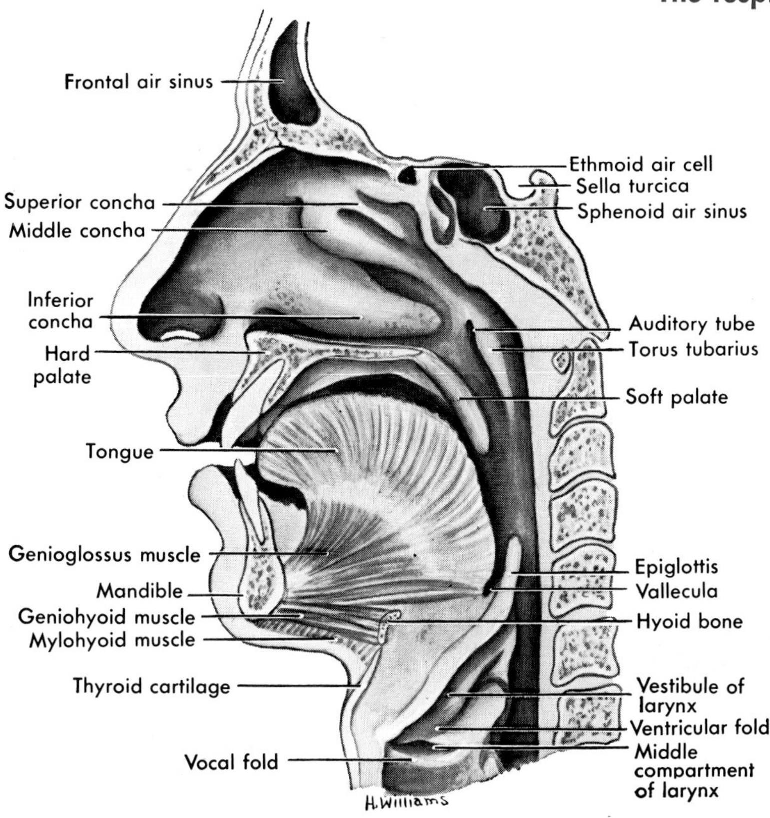

Fig. 227

Sagittal section through the face and neck. The nasal septum has been removed, exposing the lateral wall of the nasal cavity. Note the position of the conchae (turbinates). (From Francis and Farrell: Integrated anatomy and physiology, St. Louis, The C. V. Mosby Co.)

2. Into the superior meatus—posterior ethmoidal sinuses
3. Into the space above the superior turbinates (sphenoethmoidal recess) —sphenoid sinuses

Functions

The nose serves as a passageway for air going to and from the lungs, filtering it of impurities and warming, moistening, and chemically examining it for substances that might prove irritating to the mucous lining of the respiratory tract. It serves as the organ of smell, since olfactory receptors are located in the nasal mucosa, and it aids in phonation.

PHARYNX

Structure

Another name for the pharynx is the throat. It is a tubelike structure about 5 inches long that extends from the base of the skull to the esophagus and lies just anterior to the cervical vertebrae. It is made of muscle, is lined with mucous membrane, and has three parts: one located behind the nose, the *nasopharynx;* one behind the mouth, the *oropharynx;* and another behind the larynx, the *laryngopharynx.*

Seven openings are found in the pharynx (Fig. 227):

1. Two from the auditory (eustachian) tubes into the nasopharynx

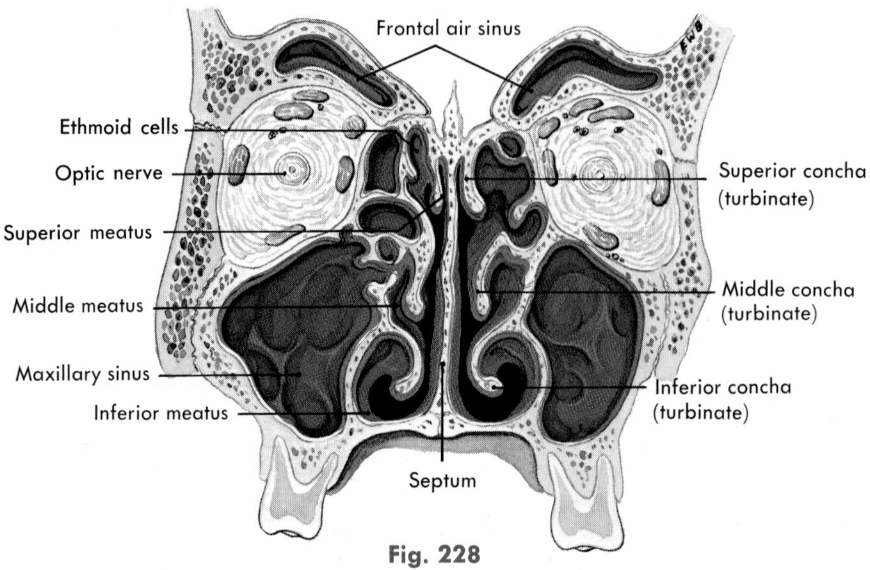

Fig. 228

Frontal section through the face viewed from behind. The sinus cavities are shown in red.

2. Two posterior nares into the nasopharynx
3. The opening from the mouth, known as the *fauces,* into the oropharynx
4. The opening into the larynx from the laryngopharynx
5. The opening into the esophagus from the laryngopharynx

The *adenoids* or pharyngeal tonsils are located in the nasopharynx, on its posterior wall opposite the posterior nares. If the adenoids become enlarged, they fill the space behind the posterior nares, making it difficult or impossible for air to travel from the nose into the throat. When this happens, the individual keeps his mouth open to breathe and is described as having an "adenoidy" appearance.

Two pairs of organs are found in the oropharynx: the faucial or *palatine tonsils,* located behind and below the pillars of the fauces, and the *lingual tonsils,* located at the base of the tongue. The palatine tonsils are the ones most commonly removed by a tonsillectomy. Only rarely are the lingual ones also removed.

Functions

The pharynx serves as a hallway for the respiratory and digestive tracts, since both air and food must pass through this structure before reaching the appropriate tubes. It also plays an important part in phonation. For example, only by the pharynx changing its shape can the different vowel sounds be formed.

LARYNX

Location

The larynx or voice box lies at the upper end of the trachea and just below the pharynx. It might be described as a kind of vestibule opening into the trachea from the pharynx.

Structure

The larynx consists of nine pieces of cartilage so joined that they make a box-

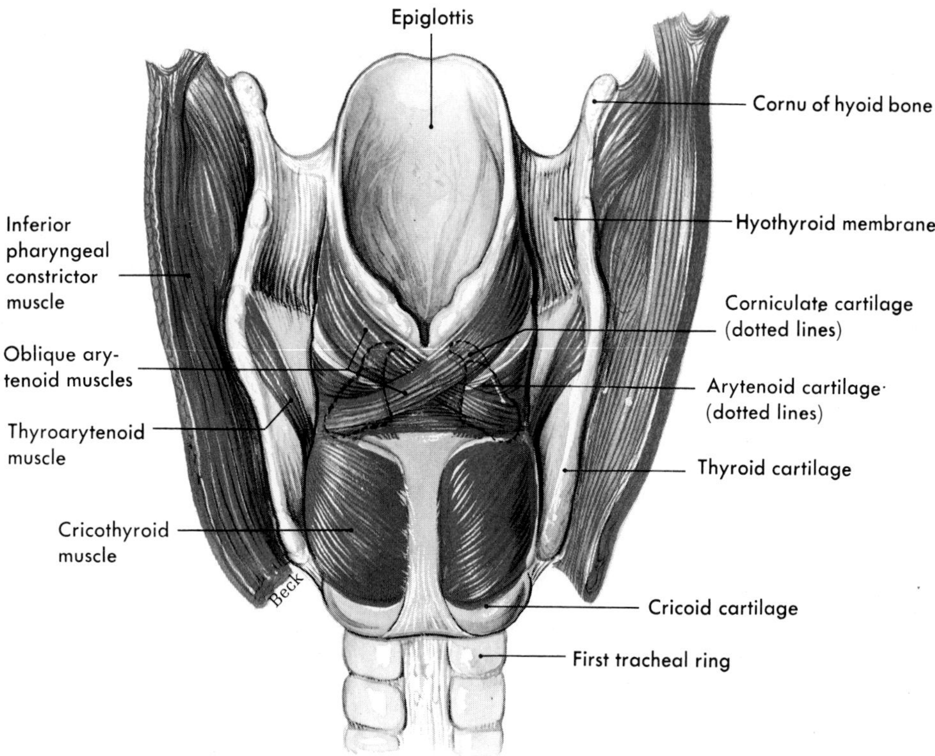

Fig. 229
Posterior view of the larynx (voice box) showing many of the muscles that function to alter its shape.

like structure. Three of them are prominent enough to warrant mention:

1. The largest and the one that gives the characteristic triangular shape to the anterior wall of the larynx is called the *thyroid cartilage* or, by lay people, the Adam's apple. This cartilage is usually larger in men than in women and has less of a fat pad lying over it, two reasons for its protruding more noticeably in the male neck.

2. A small cartilage, attached along one edge to the thyroid cartilage but free on its other borders, giving it a hingelike action, is named the *epiglottis* or the lid cartilage because during the swallowing act it forms a kind of lid over the opening into the larynx. When the epiglottis fails to close, food or liquids enter the larynx instead of the esophagus, and we say we have "swallowed down our Sunday throat."

3. The *cricoid* or signet ring cartilage, so called because its shape resembles a signet ring (turned so the signet forms part of the posterior wall of the larynx), is the most inferiorly placed of the nine cartilages.

The mucous membrane lining of the larynx forms two horizontal folds known as the *false vocal cords.* The *true vocal* cords are fibrous bands stretched across the hollow interior of the larynx. The space between the true vocal cords (or vocal folds) is called the *glottis.*

Function

The function of the larynx is voice production. The length and tension of the vocal cords determines the pitch of the voice. Short tense cords produce high notes and long relaxed cords low notes. Several other structures aid the larynx in voice production by acting as sounding boards or resonating chambers. Thus, the size and shape of the nose, mouth, pharynx, and bony sinuses help to determine the quality of the voice.

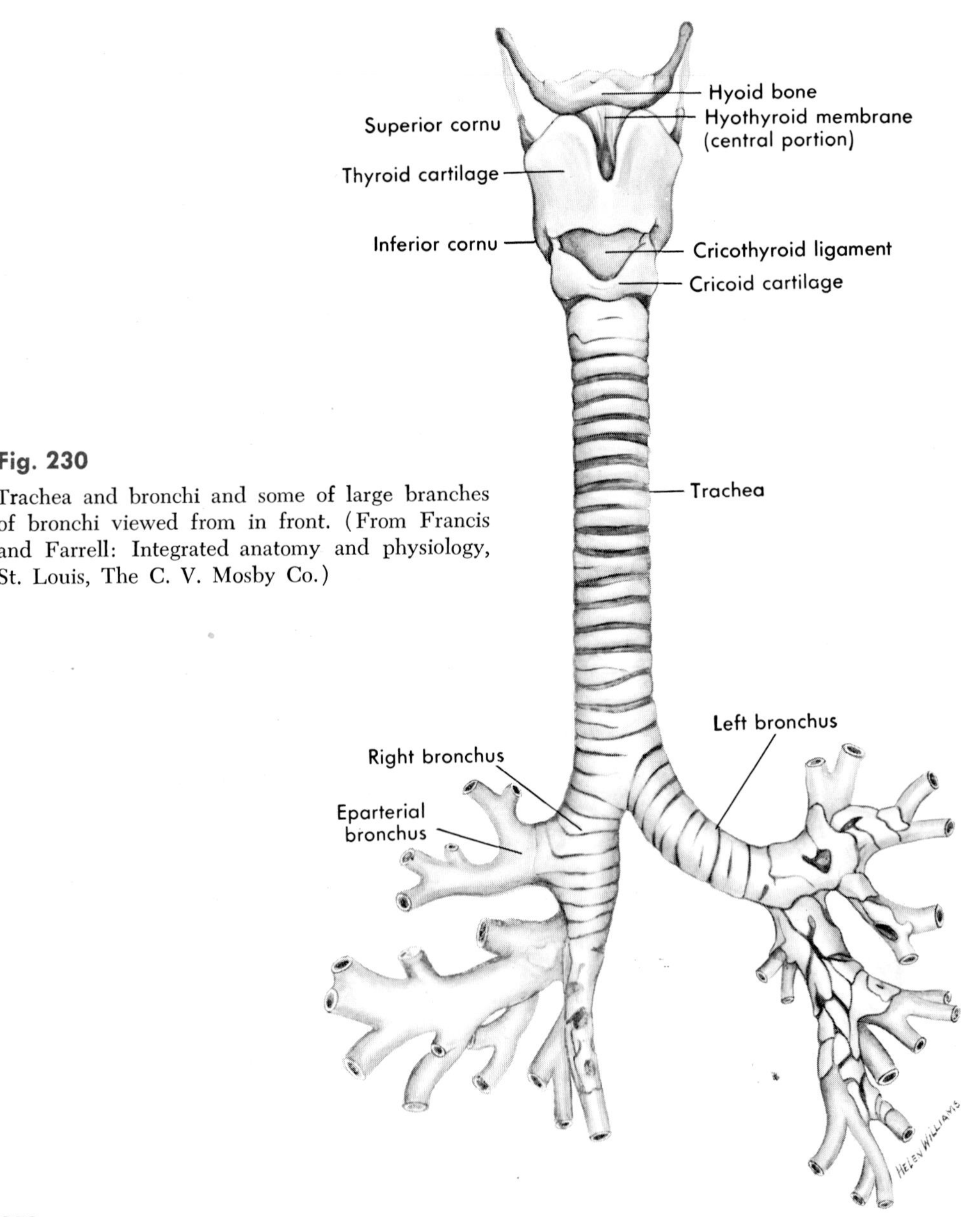

Fig. 230

Trachea and bronchi and some of large branches of bronchi viewed from in front. (From Francis and Farrell: Integrated anatomy and physiology, St. Louis, The C. V. Mosby Co.)

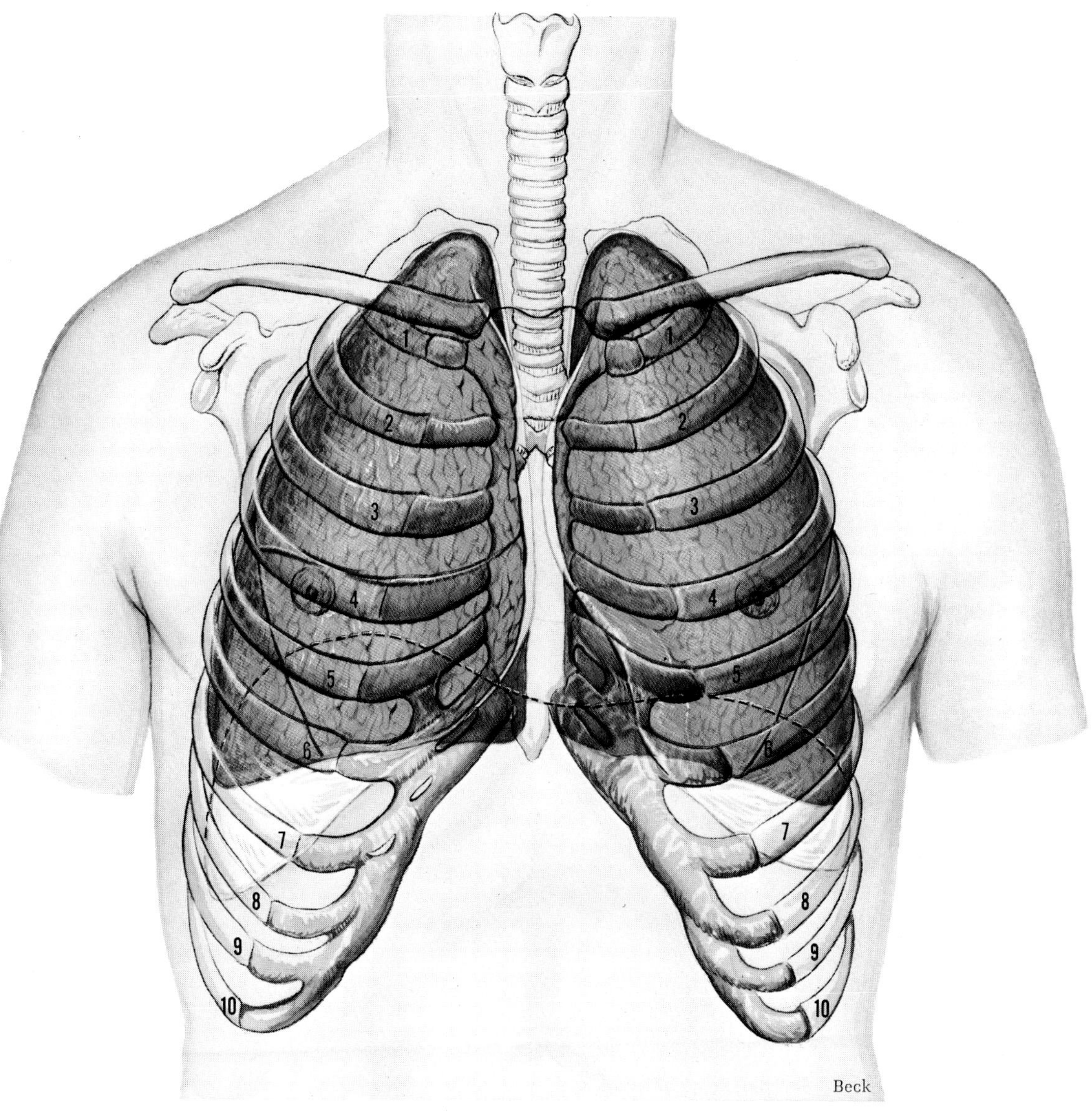

Fig. 231

Projection of the lungs and trachea in relation to the rib cage and clavicles. Dotted line indicates location of the dome-shaped diaphragm at the end of expiration and before inspiration.

TRACHEA

Structure

Smooth muscle, in which are embedded C-shaped rings of cartilage at regular intervals, fashions the walls of the trachea or windpipe. The cartilaginous rings are incomplete on the posterior surface. They give firmness to the wall, tending to prevent it from collapsing and shutting off the vital airway. Occasionally, certain conditions, such as cervical adenitis, may obstruct the trachea, making necessary emergency measures to open it. Two methods are used. Either an incision is made into the trachea (tracheotomy) and a double metal tube inserted through the opening in the neck, or the tube is inserted by way of the mouth and larynx (intubation).

The trachea is about 4½ inches long and extends from the larynx to the bronchi. It is cylindrical in shape with a diameter of approximately 1 inch.

Function

The trachea performs a simple but vital function—it furnishes part of the open passageway through which air can reach the lungs from the outside. Obstruction of this airway for even a few minutes causes death from asphyxiation.

BRONCHI

Structure

The trachea divides at its lower end into two *primary bronchi,* of which the right bronchus is slightly larger and more vertical than the left. This anatomical fact explains why aspirated foreign objects frequently lodge in the right bronchus. In structure the bronchi resemble the trachea, their walls containing the same type of cartilaginous rings and the same ciliated mucous lining.

Each primary bronchus enters the lung on its respective side and immediately divides into smaller branches called *secondary bronchi.* The secondary bronchi continue to branch, forming small *bronchioles.* The trachea and the two primary bronchi and their many branches resemble an inverted tree trunk with its branches and are, therefore, spoken of as the bronchial tree. The bronchioles subdivide into smaller and smaller tubes, eventually terminating in microscopic branches that divide into *alveolar ducts,* which terminate in several alveolar sacs, the walls of which consist of numerous *alveoli.* The structure of an alveolar duct with its branching alveolar sacs can be likened to a bunch of grapes—the stem represents the alveolar duct, each cluster of grapes represents an alveolar sac, and each grape represents an alveolus.

The structure of the secondary bronchi and bronchioles shows some modification of the primary bronchial structure. The cartilaginous rings become irregular and disappear entirely in the smaller bronchioles. By the time the branches of the bronchial tree have dwindled sufficiently to form the alveolar ducts and sacs and the alveoli, only the internal surface layer of cells remains. In other words, the walls of these microscopic structures consist of a single layer of simple, squamous epithelial tissue. As we shall see, this structural fact makes possible the performance of their function.

Function

The tubes composing the bronchial tree perform the same function as the trachea—that of furnishing a passageway by which air can reach the interior of the lung. The alveoli, enveloped as they are by networks of capillaries, provide spaces where gases can diffuse between air and blood. Someone has observed that "the lung passages all serve the alveoli" just as "the circulatory system serves the capillaries." Certain diseases may block the passage of air through the bronchioles or through the alveoli. For example, in pneumonia the al-

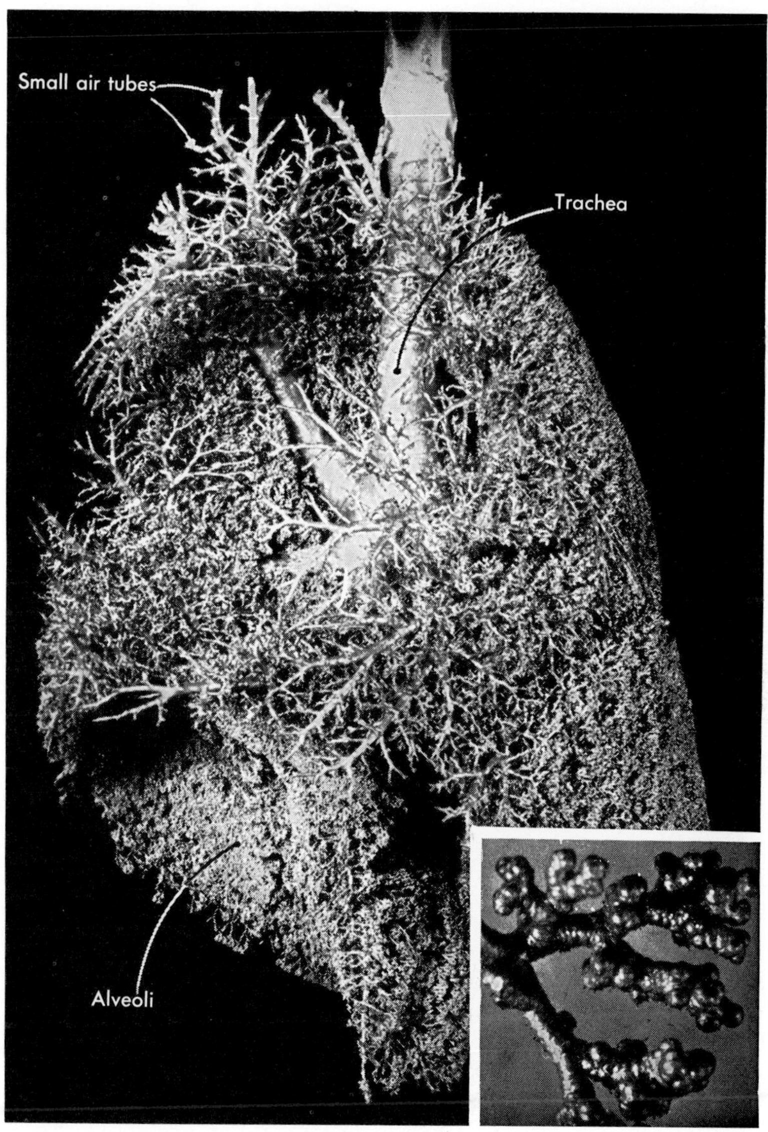

Fig. 232

Metal cast of air spaces of the lungs of a dog. The inset shows a cast of clusters of alveoli at the terminations of tiny air tubes. The magnification of the inset is about eleven times the actual size (also see Fig. 233). (From Carlson and Johnson: The machinery of the body, Chicago, The University of Chicago Press.)

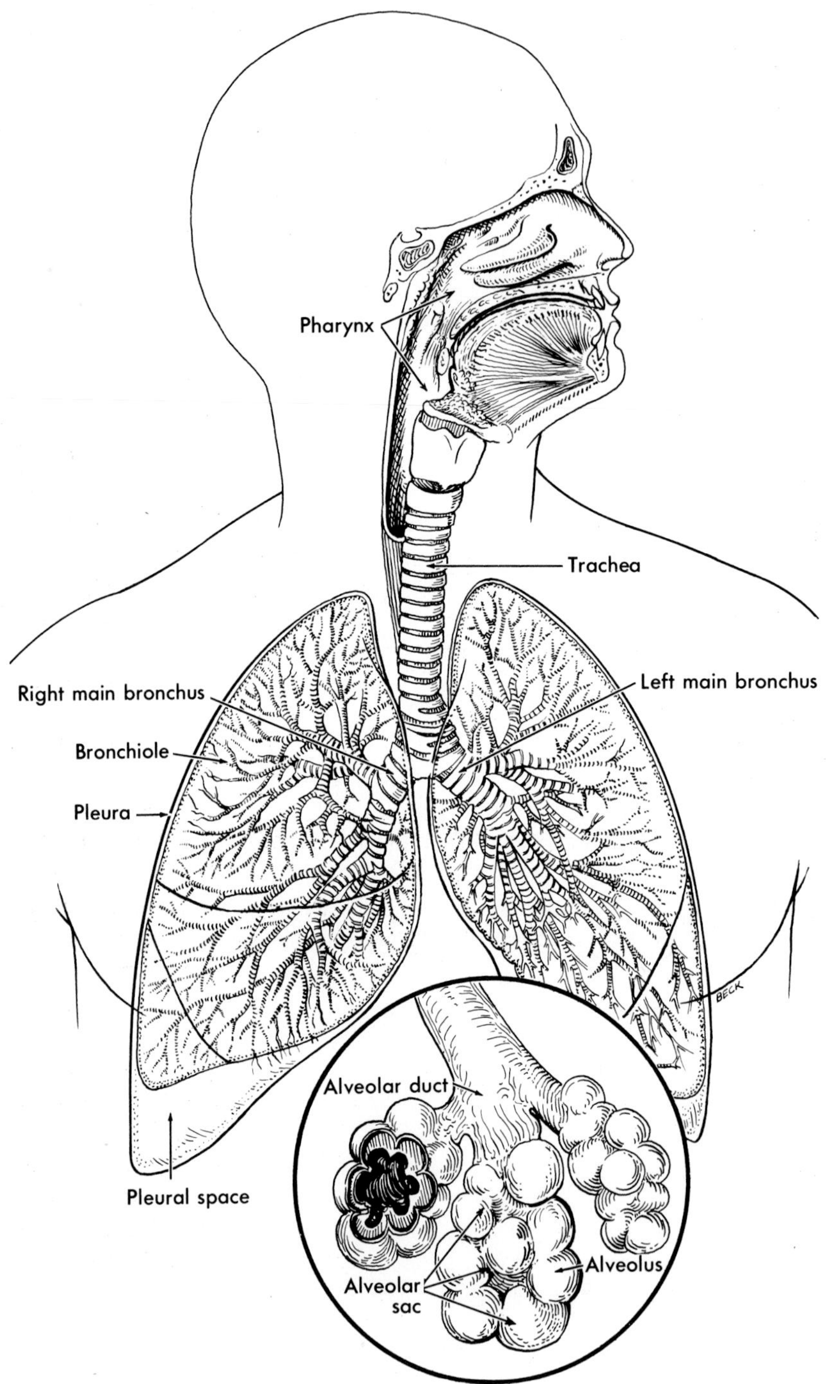

Fig. 233

The pharynx, trachea, and lungs. The inset shows the grapelike alveolar sacs where interchange of oxygen and carbon dioxide takes place through the thin walls of the alveoli. Capillaries (not shown) surround the alveoli.

veoli become inflamed, and the accompanying wastes plug up these minute air spaces, making the affected part of the lung solid. Whether the victim survives depends largely upon the extent of the solidification.

LUNGS

Structure

The lungs are cone-shaped organs, large enough to fill the pleural portion of the thoracic cavity completely. They extend from the diaphragm to a point slightly above the clavicles and lie against the ribs both anteriorly and posteriorly. The medial surface of each lung is roughly concave to allow room for the mediastinal structures and for the heart, but concavity is greater on the left than on the right because of the position of the heart. The primary bronchi and pulmonary blood vessels (bound together by connective tissue to form what is known as the *root* of the lung) enter each lung through a slit on its medial surface called the *hilum.*

The broad inferior surface of the lung, which rests on the diaphragm, constitutes the *base,* whereas the pointed upper margin is the *apex.*

The left lung is partially divided by fissures into two *lobes* (upper and lower) and the right lung into three lobes (superior, middle, and inferior). Internally, each lung consists of millions of microscopic alveoli with their related ducts and bronchioles and bronchi, as described in the discussion of the structure of the bronchi.

Visceral pleura covers the outer surfaces of the lungs and adheres to them much as the skin of an apple adheres to the apple.

Function

The lungs provide a place where an exchange of gases can take place between blood and air. Lung structure makes possible this function. Because an open airway branches into millions of thin-walled alveoli, enveloped by networks of capillaries, large amounts of oxygen can be quickly loaded into blood and large amounts of carbon dioxide quickly unloaded from it.

Thorax

The thorax is the chest.

Structure

As described on p. 4, the thoracic cavity has three divisions, separated from each other by partitions of pleura. The part of the cavity occupied by the lungs is the pleural division, the space between the lungs occupied by the esophagus, trachea, large blood vessels, etc. is the mediastinum and the part occupied by the heart and its enveloping sac is the pericardial portion.

The parietal layer of the pleura lines the entire thoracic cavity, meaning the internal surface of the ribs, the superior surface of the diaphragm, and the mediastinum. A separate pleural sac thus encases each lung. Since the outer surface of each lung is covered by the visceral layer of the pleura, the visceral pleura lies against the parietal pleura, separated only by a potential space (pleural space) which contains just enough pleural fluid for lubrication. Thus, when the lungs inflate with air, the smooth, moist visceral pleura coheres to the smooth, moist parietal pleura. Friction is thereby avoided and respirations are painless. In pleurisy, on the other hand, the pleura is inflamed and respirations become painful.

Function

The thorax plays a major role in respirations. Because of the elliptical shape of the ribs and the angle of their attachment to the spine, the thorax becomes larger when the chest is raised and smaller when it is lowered. And it is these changes in thorax size which bring about inspiration and expiration (discussed below). Lifting up the chest raises the ribs so they no longer slant downward from the spine, and because of their elliptical shape, this enlarges both depth (from front to back) and width of the thorax. (If this does not sound convincing to you, examine a skeleton to see why it is so.)

Physiology

Kinds of respirations

There are two kinds of respiration: external or "lung breathing" and internal or "cell breathing." Lung breathing is important only because it makes possible cell breathing. It is the necessary preliminary to cell breathing. And it is this—the continual supply of oxygen to cells—that is essential for life.

Mechanism of respirations

Air moves in and out of the lungs for the same basic reason that blood flows in vessels—because of a pressure gradient—a gas pressure gradient in the case of air movement and a blood pressure gradient in the case of blood flow. When atmospheric pressure is greater than pressure within the lung, air flows down this gas pressure gradient. Then air moves from the atmosphere into the lungs. Inspiration occurs, in other words. And when pressure in the lungs is greater than atmospheric pressure, air again moves down a gas pressure gradient. But now, this means that it moves in the opposite direction. This time air moves outward from the lungs into the air. The respiratory mechanism, therefore, must somehow establish these two gas pressure gradients—one in which intrapulmonic pressure (pressure within the lungs) is lower than atmospheric pressure to produce inspiration and one in which it is higher than atmospheric pressure to produce expiration.

These pressure gradients are established by changes in the size of the thoracic cavity, which, in turn, is produced by contraction and relaxation of respiratory muscles. When the diaphragm contracts, for example, it descends, and this enlarges the vertical length of the thorax. Other muscles may also contract at the same time, elevating the sternum and ribs and enlarging the thorax from front to back and from side to side. The increase in size of the thorax causes intrapleural (intrathoracic) pressure to decrease—due to operation of the familiar principle known as Boyle's law. At the end of an expiration and before the beginning of the next inspiration, intrathoracic pressure is about 2.5 mm. Hg less than atmospheric pressure, or, in other words, it is −2.5 mm. Hg. During quiet inspiration intrathoracic pressure decreases further to −6 mm. Hg. That is, it becomes more negative than it was at the beginning of inspiration. This decrease in intrathoracic pressure and the cohesion of the lungs to the inner wall of the thorax together bring about the expansion of the lungs and a decrease in their inside or intrapulmonic pressure. It decreases from atmospheric level to a subatmospheric level, namely, to −2 mm. Hg. With this, the gas pressure gradient necessary for causing air to move into the lungs is established. Figs. 234 and 235 show the mechanisms of inspiration and of expiration in diagrammatic form.

To apply some of the information just discussed about the respiratory mechanism, let us suppose that a surgeon makes an incision through the chest wall into the pleural space, as he would in doing one of the dramatic, modern "open chest" operations. Air would then be present in the thoracic cavity, a condition known as *pneumothorax*. What change, if any, do you think would take place in respirations?

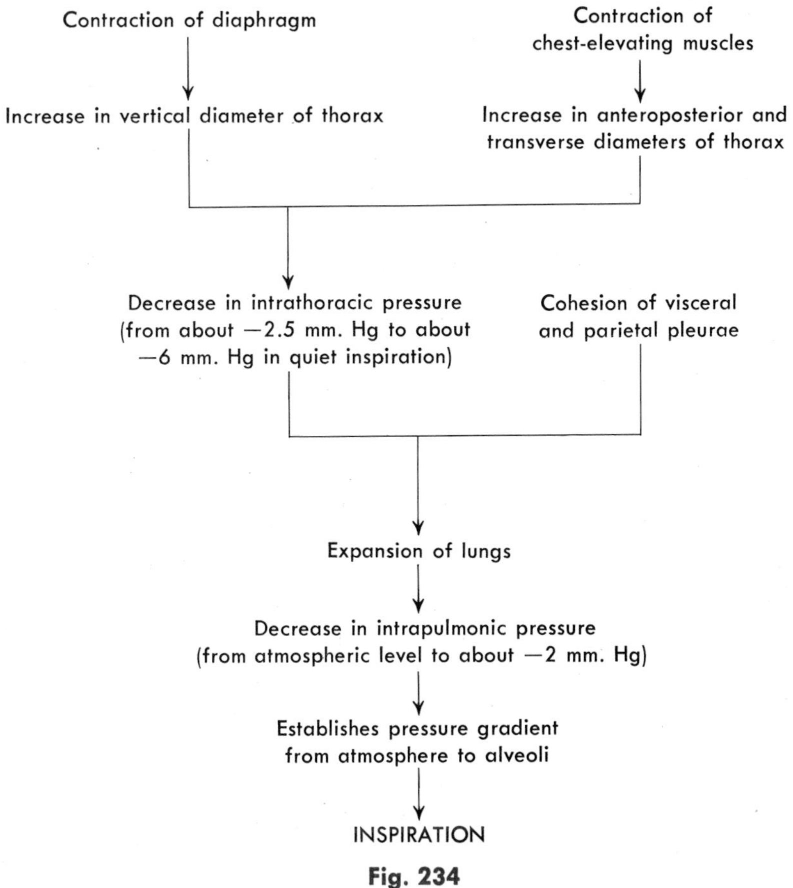

Fig. 234

The mechanism of inspiration.

Intrathoracic pressure would, of course, immediately increase from its normal subatmospheric level to atmospheric level. More pressure than normal would, therefore, be exerted upon the outer surface of the lung and would cause its collapse. It could even collapse the other lung. This is because the mediastinum is a mobile rather than a rigid partition between the two pleural sacs. This anatomical fact allows the increased pressure in the side of the chest that is open to push the heart and other mediastinal structures over toward the intact side where they exert pressure on the other lung. Pneumothorax results in many respiratory and circulatory changes. They are of great importance in determining medical and nursing care but lie beyond the scope of this book.

Amount of air exchanged in respirations

Poiseuille's law (p. 325) applies to the flow of gases as well as of liquids. This means that the volume of air inspired is directly related to the gas pressure gradient between the atmosphere and the lung alveoli and is inversely related to the resistance opposing air flow. In general, the deeper the inspiration, the lower the intrapulmonic pressure, the greater the pressure gradient from atmosphere to alveoli, and the larger the volume of air inspired.

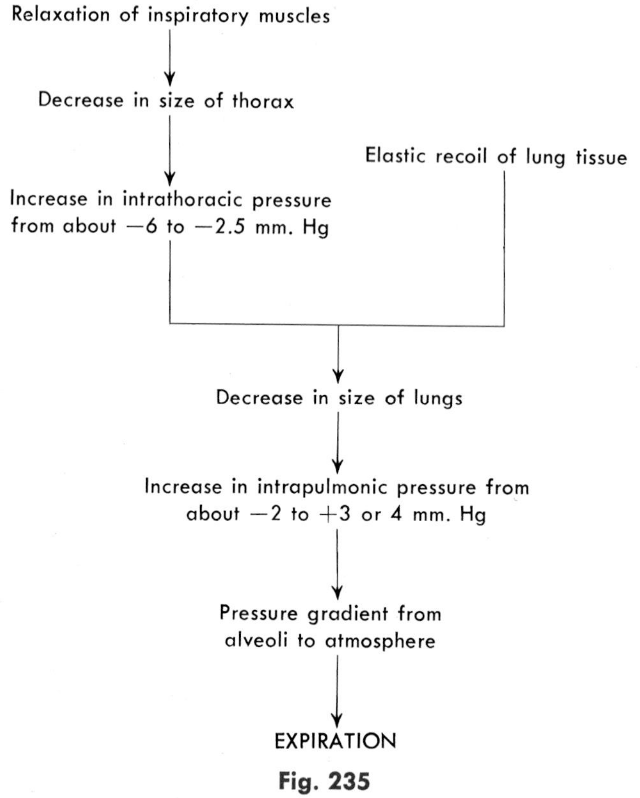

Fig. 235

The mechanism of expiration.

Obstruction of the airway has the opposite effect. For example, if the tongue falls back into the throat, as it may do in an unconscious patient, this obviously increases resistance and slows air flow. It may even prevent any air at all from moving down into the alveoli.

An apparatus called a *spirometer* is used to measure the amount of air exchanged in breathing. The amount of air exhaled normally after a normal inspiration is termed *tidal air.* The average individual has a tidal air of approximately 500 ml. (about 1 pint). A forcible expiration after a normal inspiration represents the *supplemental air* (or *expiratory reserve volume*). *Complemental air* (or *inspiratory reserve volume*) is the amount that can be forcibly inspired over and above a normal inspiration. It is measured by having the individual exhale normally after a forced inspiration. Both supplemental and complemental air average about 1,500 ml. No matter how forcefully an individual exhales, he cannot squeeze all the air out of his lungs. Some of it remains trapped in the alveoli. This amount of air that cannot be forcibly expired is known as *residual air* and amounts to about 1,000 ml. If, after death, the thoracic cavity is opened and the lungs are collapsed by atmospheric pressure, a small amount of air still remains in the alveoli *(minimal air).* Its presence can be demonstrated by placing a small piece of lung in water. It will float due to the presence of the minimal air, whereas any other soft tissue will sink.

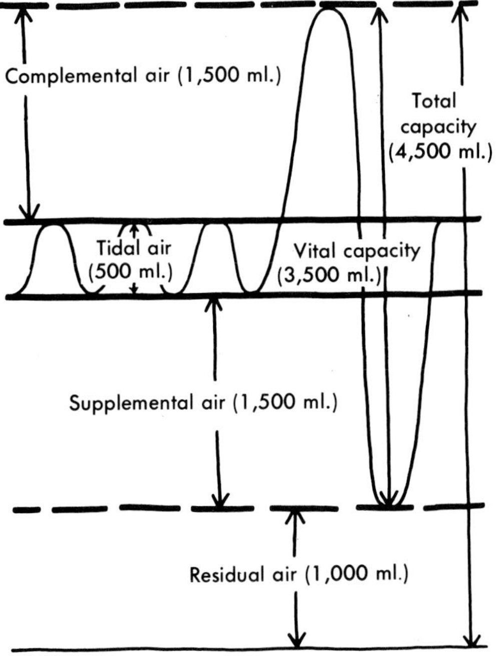

Fig. 236

During normal, quiet respirations, about 500 ml. of air (tidal air) is exchanged between the atmosphere and lungs. With a forcible inspiration, about 1,500 ml. more air can be inhaled (complemental air). After a normal inspiration, approximately 1,500 ml. of air can be forcibly expired (supplemental air). Vital capacity is the amount of air that can be forcibly expired after a maximum inspiration and indicates, therefore, the largest amount of air that can be exchanged during respiration. Residual air is that which remains trapped in the alveoli.

Because of this property, the lungs of an animal are known as the "lights" in slaughterhouses. The demonstration of minimal air in the lungs sometimes has legal importance in proving whether or not a child has lived at all or was born dead. If he has once filled his lungs with air, minimal air can be demonstrated at autopsy by the simple method described.

The term *vital capacity* means the approximate volume of the lungs as determined by measuring the largest possible expiration after the largest possible inspiration. It equals the sum of the tidal air, plus the complemental air, plus the supplemental air. Vital capacity depends upon the size of the thoracic cavity which, in turn, depends upon the size of the rib cage, posture, and various other factors. For example, if the lungs contain more blood than normal, alveolar air space is encroached upon and vital capacity accordingly decreases. This becomes a very important factor in congestive heart disease and probably explains also the smaller vital capacity in normal individuals in the supine position. Excess fluid in the pleural or abdominal cavities also decreases vital capacity, as does the disease emphysema. In the latter condition, alveolar walls become stretched, that is, lose their elasticity, and are unable to collapse normally for expiration. This leads to a great increase in the amount of residual air—so much so, in fact, that the chest occupies the inspiratory position even at rest. Excessive muscular effort is necessary, therefore, for inspiration, and because of the loss of elasticity of lung tissue, greater effort is required, too, for expiration.

Types of respirations

Respirations, when normal, are of either of two types or a combination of both: abdominal or costal. *Abdominal breathing,* sometimes called diaphragmatic or deep breathing, is characterized by an outward movement of the abdominal wall due to the contraction and descent of the diaphragm. *Costal,* shallow, or chest *breathing* is characterized by an upward, outward movement of the chest due to contraction of the external intercostals and other chest-elevating muscles. Normal quiet breathing of either the abdominal or costal type is known as *eupnea.*

There are various types of abnormal respirations, a few of which will be described. *Apnea* is a temporary cessation of respirations. *Dyspnea* is difficult or labored breathing. *Orthopnea* is inability to breathe in the horizontal position. *Cheyne-Stokes* respirations are characterized by a period of dyspnea followed by a period of apnea. The latter type of respiration often precedes death.

Some principles about gases

Before discussing respirations further, we need to understand the following principles.

1. *Dalton's law* (or the law of partial pressures). The term *partial pressure* means the pressure exerted by any one gas in a mixture of gases or in a liquid. The partial pressure of a gas in a mixture of gases is directly related to the concentration of that gas in the mixture and to the total pressure of the mixture. Suppose we apply this principle to compute the partial pressure of oxygen in the atmosphere. The concentration of oxygen in the atmosphere is 20.96% and the total pressure of the atmosphere is 760 mm. Hg under standard conditions. Therefore:

Atmospheric $Po_2 = 20.96\% \times 760 = 159.2$ mm. Hg

The symbol used to designate partial pressure is the capital letter P preceding the chemical symbol for the gas. Examples: alveolar air Po_2 is about 100 mm. Hg; arterial blood Po_2 is also about 100 mm. Hg; venous blood Po_2 is about 37 mm. Hg. The word *tension* is often used as a synonym for the term partial pressure—oxygen tension means the same thing as Po_2.

2. The partial pressure of a gas in a liquid is directly determined by the amount of that gas dissolved in the liquid, which, in turn, is determined by the partial pressure of the gas in the environment of the liquid. Gas molecules diffuse into a liquid from its environment and dissolve in the liquid until the partial pressure of the gas in solution becomes equal to its partial pressure in the environment of the liquid. For example, alveolar air constitutes the environment of blood moving through pulmonary capillaries. Standing between the blood and the air are only the very thin alveolar and capillary membranes, and both of these are highly permeable to oxygen and carbon dioxide. By the time blood leaves the pulmonary capillaries as arterial blood, diffusion and approximate equilibration of oxygen and carbon dioxide across the membranes has occurred. Arterial blood Po_2 and Pco_2, therefore, usually equal or very nearly equal alveolar Po_2 and Pco_2 (see Table 43).

How blood transports gases

Blood transports oxygen and carbon dioxide as solutes and as parts of molecules of certain chemical compounds. Immediately upon entering the blood, both oxygen and carbon dioxide dissolve in the plasma. But, because fluids can hold only small amounts of gas in solution, most of the oxygen and carbon dioxide rapidly form a chemical union with some other blood constituent. In this way comparatively large volumes of the gases can be transported. For example, every 100 ml. of arterial blood contains about 20 ml. of oxygen instead of a mere 0.5 ml., which is all that can stay in solution in that amount of blood. About 19 ml. of oxygen combines chemically with the hemoglobin present in 100 ml. of blood to form oxyhemoglobin. Since each gram of hemoglobin can unite with about 1.3 ml. of oxygen, the exact amount of oxygen in blood depends mainly upon the amount of hemoglobin present—15 grams of hemoglobin per 100 ml. of blood is a typical normal blood hemoglobin content. With this amount of hemoglobin, 100 ml. of arterial blood, when 100% saturated with oxygen, contains the following:

19.5 ml. oxygen as oxyhemoglobin (15×1.3 ml.)
0.5 ml. oxygen in solution in plasma

20.0 ml. total oxygen content

Table 43. Oxygen and carbon dioxide pressure gradients

	Atmosphere	*Alveolar air*	*Arterial blood*	*Venous blood*
Po_2	160*	100	100	37
Pco_2	0.3	40	40	46

*All figures indicate approximate mm. Hg pressure under usual conditions.

Perhaps a more common way of expressing blood oxygen content is in terms of volume per cent. Normal arterial blood, for example, contains about 20 vol.% O_2 (meaning 20 ml. of oxygen in each 100 ml. of blood).

Blood that contains more hemoglobin can, of course, transport more oxygen and that which contains less hemoglobin can transport less oxygen. Hence, hemoglobin deficiency anemia decreases oxygen transport and may be responsible for marked cellular hypoxia (inadequate oxygen supply).

In order to combine with hemoglobin, oxygen must, of course, diffuse from plasma into the red cells where millions of hemoglobin molecules are located. Several factors influence the rate at which hemoglobin combines with oxygen in lung capillaries. For instance, an increasing blood Po_2 and a decreasing Pco_2 both accelerate hemoglobin association with oxygen.

$$Hb + O_2 \xrightarrow[\text{(Decreasing } Pco_2)]{\text{(Increasing } Po_2)} HbO_2$$

Decreasing Po_2 and increasing Pco_2, on the other hand, accelerate oxygen dissociation from oxyhemoglobin—that is, the reverse of the preceding equation. Oxygen associates with hemoglobin rapidly—so rapidly, in fact, that about 97% of the blood's hemoglobin has united with oxygen

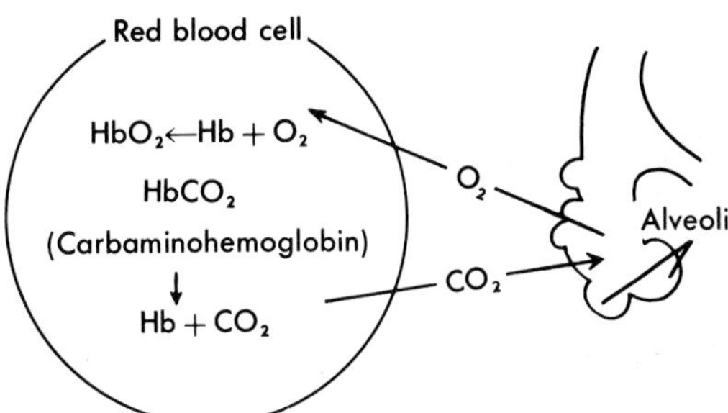

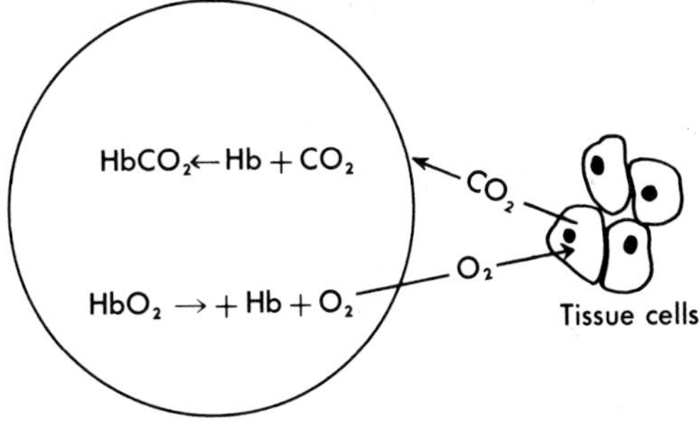

Fig. 237

Diagram showing main facts about oxygen and carbon dioxide transport. In *lung capillaries* oxygen pressure increases and carbon dioxide pressure decreases—conditions that accelerate both oxygen association with hemoglobin and carbon dioxide dissociation from carbaminohemoglobin. In *tissue capillaries* oxygen pressure decreases and carbon dioxide pressure increases—conditions that accelerate both oxygen dissociation from oxyhemoglobin and carbon dioxide association with hemoglobin.

by the time the blood leaves the lung capillaries to return to the heart. In other words, the average *oxygen saturation* of arterial blood is about 97%.

Carbon dioxide is carried in the blood in several ways, the most important of which are described briefly as follows:

1. A small amount dissolves in plasma and is transported as a solute (dissolved carbon dioxide produces the Pco_2 of blood).

2. More than one-half of the carbon dioxide is carried in the plasma as bicarbonate ions.*

3. Somewhat less than one-third of blood carbon dioxide unites with the NH_2 group of hemoglobin and certain other proteins to form carbamino compounds. Most of these are formed and transported in the red cells since hemoglobin is the main protein to combine with carbon dioxide. The compound formed has a tongue-twisting name —carbaminohemoglobin. Carbon dioxide association with hemoglobin is accelerated by an increasing Pco_2 and a decreasing Po_2 and is slowed by the opposite conditions. How do the conditions that accelerate carbon dioxide association affect the rate of oxygen association with hemoglobin?

*As a preliminary to sodium bicarbonate formation from carbon dioxide, a phenomenon known as the chloride shift occurs. Part of the CO_2 that diffuses into red cells combines with water (because of the catalytic action of the enzyme carbonic anhydrase) to form carbonic acid. Some of the latter immediately ionizes.

$$CO_2 + H_2O \xrightarrow[\text{anhydrase)}]{\text{(Carbonic}} H_2CO_3$$

$$H_2CO_3 \longrightarrow H^+ + HCO_3^-$$

HCO_3 ions diffuse out of the red cell into the plasma, while Cl ions from the plasma diffuse into the red cell to take their place. The advantage of this arrangement is that it helps maintain the normal alkaline pH of the blood. When venous blood, with its high $NaHCO_3$ content, reaches the lungs, these reactions reverse and CO_2 is released into the alveolar air. Only about 10% of venous CO_2 is normally eliminated. The other 90% remains in the blood. Whole venous blood has a Pco_2 of about 45 mm. and whole arterial blood has a Pco_2 of about 40 mm. This level of Pco_2 in arterial blood is essential for continued activation of the respiratory center and, therefore, for continued respirations. If blood Pco_2 falls to around 19 to 24 mm., respirations cease.

Exchange of gases between alveolar air and venous blood

The exchange of gases between alveolar air and venous blood occurs in lung capillaries, across the alveolar-capillary membrane. Oxygen enters blood from the alveolar air because the Po_2 of alveolar air is greater than the Po_2 of venous blood.

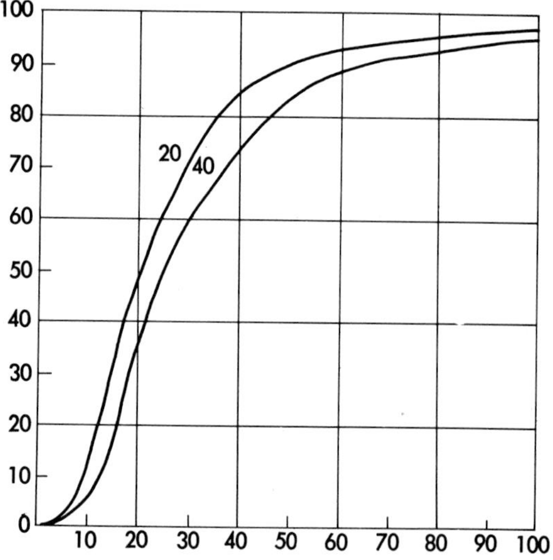

Fig. 238

Oxygen association curves of human blood showing that the percent of hemoglobin associated with oxygen depends upon both the oxygen and carbon dioxide pressures of the blood. *Vertical coordinate,* Po_2 $\%O_2$ saturation (% of hemoglobin combined with oxygen). *Horizontal coordinate,* Po_2 in mm. Hg pressure. *Numbers on curves,* Pco_2 in mm. Hg pressure. *Interpretation:* When blood Po_2 is 40 and Pco_2 is also 40, almost 75% of the hemoglobin is combined with O_2 (that is, blood has about a 75% O_2 saturation). *Questions:* What is $\%O_2$ saturation with blood Po_2 40 and Pco_2 20? Is it true that the less CO_2 dissolved in blood, the greater its O_2 saturation can be?

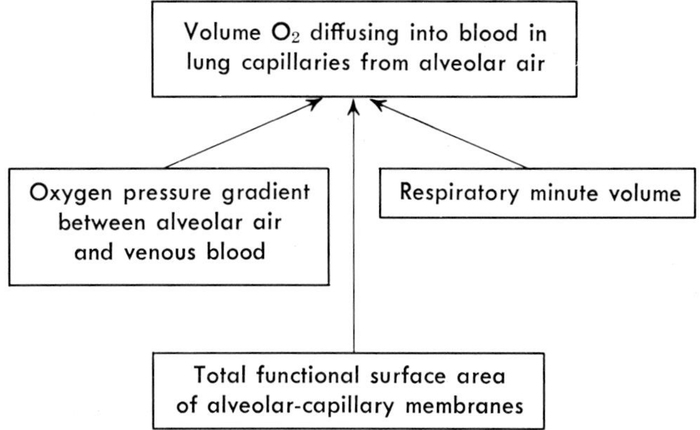

Fig. 239

Factors determining volume of oxygen entering lung capillary blood. An increase in any of the factors tends to increase oxygenation of blood. A decrease in one of them tends to decrease blood oxygenation. Respiratory minute volume means the volume of air inspired per minute.

Another way of saying this is that oxygen diffuses "down" its pressure gradient. Simultaneously, carbon dioxide molecules exit from the blood by diffusing down the carbon dioxide pressure gradient out into the alveolar air. The Pco_2 of venous blood is much higher than the Pco_2 of alveolar air. This two-way exchange of gases between alveolar air and venous blood converts venous blood to arterial blood.

The amount of oxygen that diffuses into blood each minute depends upon several factors, notably upon these three: (1) the oxygen pressure gradient between alveolar air and venous blood (alveolar Po_2-venous blood Po_2), (2) the total functional surface area of the alveolar-capillary membrane, and (3) the respiratory minute volume (respiratory rate per minute times volume of air inspired per respiration). All three of these factors bear a direct relation to oxygen diffusion. Anything that decreases alveolar Po_2, for instance, tends to decrease the alveolar-venous oxygen pressure gradient and therefore tends to decrease the amount of oxygen entering the blood. Application: alveolar air Po_2 decreases as altitude increases, and therefore less oxygen enters the blood at high altitudes. At a certain high altitude, alveolar air Po_2 equals venous blood Po_2. How would this affect oxygen diffusion into blood?

Anything that decreases the total functional surface area of the alveolar-capillary membrane also tends to decrease oxygen diffusion into the blood (by functional surface area is meant that which is freely permeable to oxygen). Application: in emphysema, this total functional area decreases and is one of the factors responsible for poor blood oxygenation in the condition.

Anything that decreases the respiratory minute volume also tends to decrease blood oxygenation. Application: morphine slows respirations and therefore decreases the respiratory minute volume (volume of air inspired per minute) and tends to lessen the amount of oxygen entering the blood. The main factors influencing blood oxygenation are shown in Fig. 239.

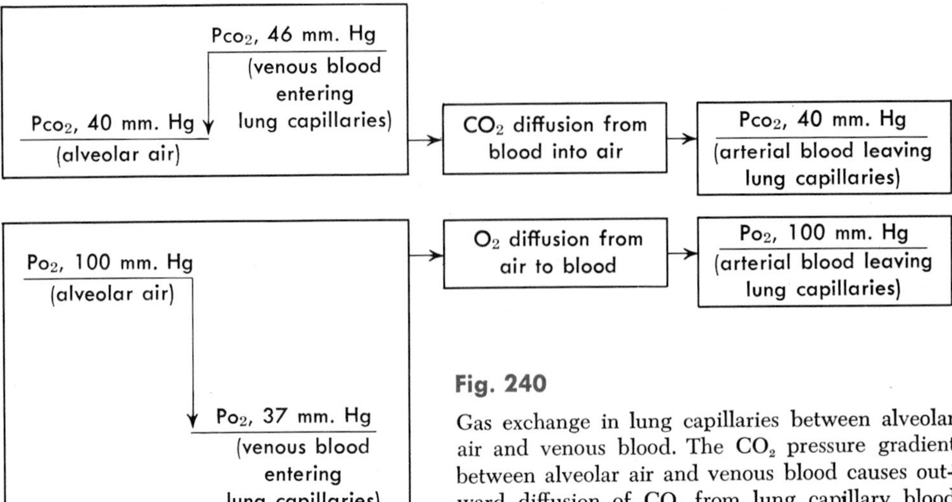

Fig. 240

Gas exchange in lung capillaries between alveolar air and venous blood. The CO_2 pressure gradient between alveolar air and venous blood causes outward diffusion of CO_2 from lung capillary blood and lowers blood Pco_2 from its venous level to its arterial level. The O_2 pressure gradient between alveolar air and venous blood causes inward diffusion of O_2 into lung capillary blood and raises blood Pco_2 from its venous level up to its arterial level.

Several times we have stated the principle that structure determines functions. You may find it interesting to note the application of this principle to gas exchange in the lungs. Several structural facts facilitate oxygen diffusion from the alveolar air into the blood in lung capillaries:

1. The fact that the walls of the alveoli and of the capillaries together form a very thin barrier for the gases to cross (estimated at not more than 0.004 mm. thick)
2. The fact that both alveolar and capillary surfaces are extremely large
3. The fact that the lung capillaries accommodate a large amount of blood at one time (about 900 ml.)
4. The fact that the blood is distributed through the capillaries in a layer so thin (equal only to the diameter of one red corpuscle) that each corpuscle comes in close proximity to alveolar air

Exchange of gases between arterial blood and cells

The exchange of gases between arterial blood and cells takes place because of the principle already noted that gases move down a gas pressure gradient. More specifically, in the tissue capillaries oxygen diffuses out of arterial blood because the oxygen pressure gradient favors its outward diffusion. Arterial blood Po_2 is about 100 mm. Hg, interstitial fluid Po_2 is considerably lower, and intracellular fluid Po_2 is still lower. Although interstitial fluid and intracellular fluid Po_2 are not definitely established, they are thought to vary considerably—perhaps from around 60 mm. Hg down to about 1 mm. Hg. As activity increases in any structure, its cells necessarily utilize oxygen more rapidly. This decreases intracellular and interstitial Po_2 which, in turn, tends to increase the oxygen pressure gradient between blood and tissues and to accelerate oxygen diffusion out of the tissue capillaries. In this way, the rate of oxygen utilization by cells automatically tends to regulate the rate of oxygen delivery to cells. As dissolved oxygen diffuses out of arterial blood, blood Po_2 decreases, and this ac-

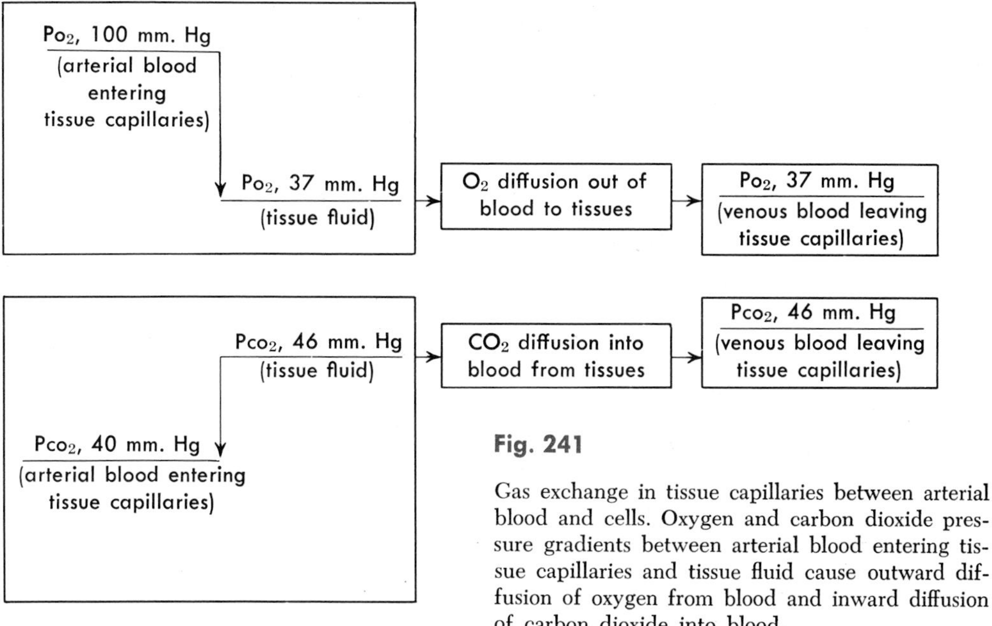

Fig. 241

Gas exchange in tissue capillaries between arterial blood and cells. Oxygen and carbon dioxide pressure gradients between arterial blood entering tissue capillaries and tissue fluid cause outward diffusion of oxygen from blood and inward diffusion of carbon dioxide into blood.

celerates oxyhemoglobin dissociation to release more oxygen into the plasma for diffusion out to cells, as indicated in the following equation.

$$Hb + O_2 \xleftarrow[\text{(Increasing } Pco_2)]{\text{(Decreasing } Po_2)} HbO_2$$

Because of oxygen release to tissues from tissue capillary blood, Po_2, oxygen saturation, and total oxygen content are all less in venous blood than in arterial blood, as shown in Table 44.

Carbon dioxide exchange between tissues and blood takes place in the opposite direction from oxygen exchange. Catabolism produces large amounts of carbon dioxide inside cells. So, intracellular and interstitial Pco_2 are higher than arterial blood Pco_2. This means that the carbon dioxide pressure gradient causes diffusion of carbon dioxide from the tissues into the blood flowing along through tissue capillaries. Consequently, the Pco_2 of blood increases in tissue capillaries from its arterial level of about 40 mm. Hg to its venous level of about 46 mm. Hg. This increasing Pco_2 and decreasing Po_2 together produce two effects—they favor both oxygen dissociation from oxyhemoglobin and carbon dioxide association with hemoglobin to form carbaminohemoglobin.

Control of respirations

The mechanism for controlling respirations has many parts. A brief description of its main features follows.

1. The Pco_2, Po_2, and pH of *arterial blood* all influence respirations. The Pco_2 influences respiratory centers in the medulla directly and indirectly via its action on chemoreceptors. The normal range for arterial Pco_2 is about 38 to 40 mm. Hg. When it increases even slightly above this, it stimulates the inspiratory centers (clusters of neurons located bilaterally in the medulla). Faster breathing results, with a greater volume of air moving in and out of the lungs per minute. Decreased arterial

Table 44. Blood oxygen

	Venous blood	*Arterial blood*
Po_2	37 mm. Hg	100 mm. Hg
Oxygen saturation	75%	97%
Oxygen content	15 ml. O_2 per 100 ml. blood	20 ml. O_2 per 100 ml. blood*

*Oxygen utilization by tissues = difference between oxygen contents of arterial and venous blood (20-5) = 5 ml. O_2 per 100 ml. blood circulated per minute.

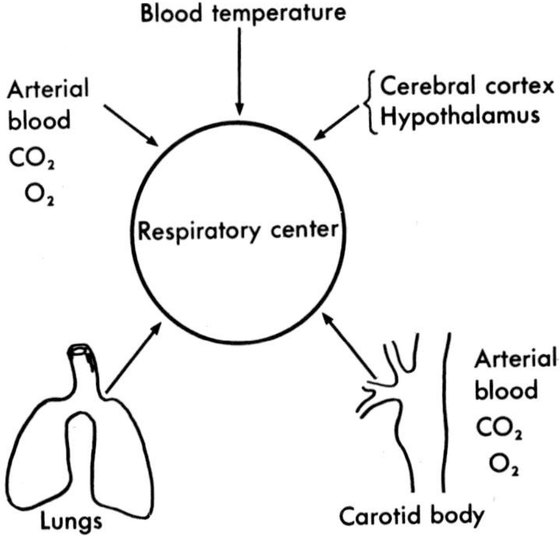

Fig. 242

Respiratory control mechanism. Scheme to show the main factors that influence the respiratory center and thereby control respirations. A moderate increase in blood CO_2 stimulates respiratory centers in the medulla directly, and also indirectly by stimulating chemoreceptors in the carotid body (small structure at bifurcation of common carotid artery to form internal and external carotid arteries). A moderate decrease in arterial blood oxygen stimulates carotid chemoreceptors. Either a marked excess of arterial blood CO_2 or a deficiency of it depresses the respiratory centers, as does marked oxygen lack. See text for a discussion of other factors.

Pco_2 produces the opposite effects, inhibiting medullary respiratory centers and slowing respirations. In fact, breathing stops entirely for a few moments (apnea) when arterial Pco_2 drops moderately—to about 35 mm. Hg, for example.

Arterial blood Pco_2, in addition to acting on respiratory centers directly, also influences them indirectly via its effect on carotid and aortic chemoreceptors. Moderate increases in arterial Pco_2 stimulate these receptors, and this leads to stimulation of inspiratory centers and faster breathing. Conversely, decreased arterial Pco_2 results in reflex slowing of respirations. There has been much debate over the question of which is the more important regulator of respirations—arterial Pco_2 acting directly on respiratory centers or reflexly on them via the chemoreceptors. The majority seems to favor the view that the direct influence of arterial Pco_2 on respiratory centers is primary.

The role of *arterial blood* Po_2 in controlling respirations is not entirely clear. Presumably it has little influence as long as it stays above a certain level. But, neurons of the respiratory centers, like all body cells, require adequate amounts of oxygen in order to function optimally. Consequently, if they become hypoxic, they become depressed and send fewer impulses to respiratory muscles. Respirations then decrease or fail entirely. This principle has important clinical significance. For example, the respiratory centers cannot respond to stimulation by an increasing blood CO_2 if, at the same time, blood Po_2 falls below a critical level—a fact that may become of life and death importance during anesthesia.

However, a decrease in arterial blood Po_2 to a point above the critical level stimulates chemoreceptors in the carotid and aortic bodies and causes reflex stimulation of the inspiratory center. This constitutes an emergency respiratory control mechanism. It does not help regulate respirations under usual conditions when arterial blood Po_2 remains above the level necessary to stimulate the chemoreceptors. But during strenuous exercise, for example, a moderate decrease in arterial blood Po_2 may act as the stimulus for faster respirations.

A decrease in *arterial blood* pH (increase in acid), within certain limits, has a stimulating effect on carotid and aortic chemoreceptors and also on respiratory centers and therefore tends to increase respirations.

2. *Arterial blood pressure* helps control respirations through the respiratory pressoreflex mechanism. A sudden rise in arterial pressure, by acting on aortic and carotid pressoreceptors, results in reflex slowing of respirations. And a sudden drop in arterial pressure brings about a reflex increase in rate and depth of respirations. The pressoreflex mechanism is probably not of great importance in the control of respirations. It is, however, as you will recall, of major importance in the control of circulation.

3. The *Hering-Breuer reflexes* help control respirations—particularly their depth and rhythmicity. They are believed to regulate the normal depth of respirations (extent of lung expansion) and, therefore, the volume of tidal air in the following way. Presumably when the tidal volume of air has been inspired, the lungs are expanded enough to stimulate pressoreceptors located within them. The pressoreceptors then send inhibitory impulses to the inspiratory center, relaxation of inspiratory muscles occurs, and expiration follows—the Hering-Breuer expiratory reflex. Then, when the tidal volume of air has been expired, the lungs are sufficiently deflated to inhibit the lung pressoreceptors and allow inspiration to start again—the Hering-Breuer inspiratory reflex.

4. The *pneumotaxic center* in the upper part of the pons is postulated to function mainly to maintain rhythmicity of respirations. Whenever the inspiratory center is stimulated, it sends impulses to the pneumotaxic center as well as to inspiratory muscles. The pneumotaxic center, after a moment's delay, stimulates the expiratory center which then feeds back inhibitory impulses to the inspiratory center. Inspiration, therefore, ends and expiration starts. Lung deflation soon initiates the Hering-Breuer inspiratory reflex, and inspiration starts again. In short, the pneumotaxic center and Hering-Breuer reflexes together constitute an automatic device for producing rhythmic respirations.

5. The *cerebral cortex* helps control respirations. Impulses to the respiratory center from the motor area of the cerebrum may either increase or decrease the rate and strength of respirations. In other words, an individual may voluntarily speed up or slow down his breathing rate. This voluntary control of respirations, however, has certain limitations. For example, one may will to stop breathing and do so for a few minutes. But holding the breath results in an increase in the carbon dioxide content of the blood since it is not being removed by respirations. Carbon dioxide is a powerful respiratory stimulant. So when arterial blood Pco_2 increases to a certain level, it stimulates the inspiratory center both directly and reflexly to send motor impulses to the respiratory muscles,

and breathing is resumed even though the individual may still will contrarily. This knowledge that the carbon dioxide content of the blood is a more powerful regulator of respirations than cerebal impulses is of practical value when dealing with a child who holds his breath to force the granting of his wishes. The best treatment is to ignore such behavior, knowing that respirations will start again as soon as the amount of carbon dioxide in arterial blood increases to a certain level.

6. Miscellaneous factors also influence respirations. Among these are blood temperature and sensory impulses from skin thermal receptors and from superficial or deep pain receptors.

(a) *Sudden painful stimulation* produces a reflex apnea, but continued painful stimuli cause faster and deeper respirations.

(b) *Sudden cold stimuli* applied to the skin cause temporary apnea.

(c) *Afferent impulses* initiated by stretching the anal sphincter produce reflex acceleration and deepening of respirations. Use has sometimes been made of this mechanism as an emergency measure to stimulate respirations during surgery.

(d) *Stimulation of the pharynx or larynx* by irritating chemicals or by touch causes a temporary apnea. This is the choking reflex, a valuable protective device. It operates, for example, to prevent aspiration of food or liquids during swallowing.

Control of respirations during exercise. Respirations increase greatly during strenuous exercise. The mechanism that accomplishes this, however, is not the one that produces more moderate increases in breathing. A number of studies have shown that arterial blood P_{CO_2}, P_{O_2}, and pH do not change enough during exercise to produce the degree of hyperpnea (faster, deeper respirations) observed. Venous blood P_{CO_2}, however, is known to increase with strenuous muscle exertion. Krahl and Armstrong reported finding chemoreceptors in the walls of the pulmonary artery—a strategic location for them to be acted on by changes in venous blood.* It may be, they suggest, that the higher venous P_{CO_2} present during exercise acts as a stimulant to these receptors and helps bring about the characteristic faster, deeper breathing.

*Krahl, Vernon, and Armstrong, Bruce: Breathing regulated by blood composition, Sci. Newsletter **82**:56 (July 28), 1962.

Outline summary— The respiratory system

Functions and importance

Exchange of gases between blood and air; of vital importance

Organs

NOSE

1. Structure
   - a. portions—internal, in skull, above roof at mouth; external, protruding from face
   - b. cavities
     1. divisions—right and left
     2. meati—superior, middle, and lower; named for turbinate located above each meatus
     3. openings—to exterior, anterior nares; to nasopharynx, posterior nares
     4. turbinates (conchae)—superior and middle, processes of ethmoid bone; inferior turbinates separate bones; divide internal nasal cavities into three passageways or meati
     5. floor—formed by palatine bones that also act as roof of mouth
   - c. lining—ciliated mucous membrane
   - d. sinuses draining into nose (or paranasal sinuses)—frontal, maxillary (or antrum of Highmore), sphenoidal, and ethmoidal
2. Functions
   - a. serves as passageway for incoming and outgoing air, filtering, warming, moistening, and chemically examining it
   - b. organ of smell because olfactory receptors located in nasal mucosa
   - c. aids in phonation (talking)

PHARYNX

1. Structure—made of muscle with mucous lining
   a. divisions—nasopharynx, behind nose; oropharynx, behind mouth; laryngopharynx, behind larynx
   b. openings—four in nasopharynx: two auditory tubes and two posterior nares; one in oropharynx: fauces from mouth; and two in laryngopharynx: into esophagus and into larynx
   c. organs in pharynx—adenoids or pharyngeal tonsils in nasopharynx; palatine and lingual tonsils in oropharynx
2. Functions—serves both respiratory and digestive tracts as passageway for air, food, and liquids; aids in phonation

LARYNX

1. Location—at upper end of trachea, just below pharynx
2. Structure
   a. cartilages—nine pieces arranged in box-like formation; thyroid largest, known as "Adam's apple"; epiglottis, "lid" cartilage; cricoid, "signet ring" cartilage
   b. vocal cords—false cords, folds of mucous lining; true cords, fibroelastic bands stretched across hollow interior of larynx; glottis, opening between true vocal cords
   c. lining—ciliated mucous membrane
   d. sexual differences—male larynx larger, covered with less fat, and therefore more prominent than female larynx
3. Function—expired air causes true vocal cords to vibrate, producing voice; pitch determined by length and tension of cords

TRACHEA

1. Structure
   a. walls—smooth muscle; contain C-shaped rings of cartilage at intervals, which keeps the tube open at all times; lining—ciliated mucous membrane
   b. extent—from larynx to bronchi; about 4½ inches long
2. Function—furnishes open passageway for air going to and from lungs

BRONCHI

1. Structure—formed by division of trachea into two tubes; right bronchus slightly larger and more vertical than left; same structure as trachea; each primary bronchus branches as soon as enters lung into secondary bronchi which branch into bronchioles, which branch into microscopic alveolar ducts, which terminate in cluster of blind sacs called alveoli; trachea and two primary bronchi and all their branches compose the "bronchial tree"; alveolar walls composed of single layer of cells
2. Function—bronchi and their many branching tubes furnish passageway for air going to and from lungs; alveoli provide large, thin-walled surface area where blood and air can exchange gases

LUNGS

1. Structure
   a. size, shape, location—large enough to fill pleural divisions of thoracic cavity; cone-shaped; extend from base, on diaphragm, to apex, located slightly above clavicle
   b. divisions—three lobes in right lung, two in left; root of lung consists of primary bronchus and pulmonary artery and veins, bound together by connective tissue; hilum is vertical slit on mesial surface of lung through which root structures enter lung; base is broad, inferior surface of lung; apex is pointed upper margin
   c. covering—visceral layer of pleura
2. Function — furnish place where large amounts of air and blood can come in close enough contact for rapid exchange of gases to occur

Thorax

1. The chest
2. Structure
   a. has three divisions
      1. pleural portion—contains lungs
      2. mediastinum — area between two lungs; contains esophagus, trachea, great blood vessels, etc.
      3. pericardial portion—space occupied by heart and pericardial sac
   b. lining
      1. parietal layer of pleura lines entire chest cavity and covers superior surface of diaphragm
      2. forms separate sac encasing each lung
      3. separated from visceral pleura, covering lungs, only by potential space, the pleural space, which contains few drops of pleural fluid

c. shape of ribs and angle of their attachment to spine such that elevation of rib cage enlarges two dimensions of thorax, its width and depth from front
3. Function
   a. increase in size of thorax leads to inspiration
   b. decrease in size of thorax leads to expiration

Physiology

1. Kinds of respirations
   a. external or lung breathing
   b. internal or cell breathing
2. Mechanism of respirations
   a. contraction of diaphragm and chest elevating muscles enlarges thorax, thereby decreases intrathoracic pressure, which causes expansion of lungs, which decreases intrapulmonic pressure to subatmospheric level, which establishes gas pressure gradient, which causes air to move into lungs
   b. relaxation of inspiratory muscles produces opposite effects; see Fig. 235
3. Amount of air exchanged in respirations
   a. directly related to gas pressure gradient between atmosphere and lung alveoli and inversely related to resistance opposing air flow
      1. measured by apparatus called spirometer
      2. tidal air – average amount expired after normal inspiration; approximately 500 ml. or 1 pint
      3. supplemental air—amount that can be forcibly expired after normal inspiration
      4. complemental air—amount that can be forcibly inspired after normal inspiration; measured by having individual expire normally after forced inspiration
      5. residual air—that which cannot be forcibly expired from lungs
      6. minimal air—that which can never be removed from alveoli, even when lungs subjected to atmospheric pressure
      7. vital capacity—approximate capacity of lungs (limited by size of thoracic cavity and various other factors, such as amount of blood in lungs and condition of alveoli); air that can be forcibly expired after forcible inspiration represents vital capacity
4. Types of respirations
   a. normal (eupnea)
      1. abdominal (also called deep or diaphragmatic breathing)—characterized by outward movement of abdominal wall due to contraction and descent of diaphragm
      2. costal (also called shallow or chest breathing) – characterized by upward, outward movement of chest due to contraction of chest-elevating muscles
   b. abnormal
      1. apnea—temporary cessation of respirations
      2. dyspnea—difficult or painful respirations
      3. orthopnea – inability to breathe in horizontal position
      4. Cheyne-Stokes – alternate periods of dyspnea and apnea
5. Some principles about gases
   a. Dalton's law—partial pressure of gas in mixture of gases directly related to concentration of that gas in mixture and to total pressure of mixture
   b. partial pressure of gas in liquid directly related to amount of gas dissolved in liquid; becomes equal to partial pressure of that gas in environment of liquid
6. How blood transports gases
   a. oxygen
      1. about 0.5 ml. transported as *solute,* i.e., dissolved in 100 ml. blood
      2. about 19.5 ml. O_2 per 100 ml. blood transported as *oxyhemoglobin* in red blood cells
      3. about 20 ml. = *total O_2 content* per 100 ml. blood (100% saturation of 15 grams hemoglobin)
   b. carbon dioxide
      1. small amount dissolves in plasma and transported as true *solute*
      2. more than half of CO_2 transported as *bicarbonate ion* in plasma
      3. somewhat less than one-third of CO_2 transported in red blood cells as *carbaminohemoglobin*
7. Exchange of gases between alveolar air and venous blood
   a. where it occurs—in lung capillaries; across alveolar-capillary membrane
   b. what exchange consists of—oxygen diffuses out of alveolar air into venous

blood; carbon dioxide diffuses in opposite direction

c. why it occurs—oxygen pressure gradient causes inward diffusion of oxygen; carbon dioxide pressure gradient causes outward diffusion of carbon dioxide

	Alveolar air	*Venous blood*
Po_2	100 mm. Hg	37 mm. Hg
Pco_2	40 mm. Hg	46 mm. Hg

d. results of gas exchange
   1. Po_2 of blood increases to arterial blood level as blood moves through lung capillaries
   2. Pco_2 of blood decreases to arterial blood level as blood moves through lung capillaries
   3. oxygen association with hemoglobin to form oxyhemoglobin and carbon dioxide dissociation from carbaminohemoglobin both accelerated by increasing Po_2 and decreasing Pco_2

8. Exchange of gases between arterial blood and cells
   a. where it occurs—tissue capillaries
   b. what exchange consists of—oxygen diffuses out of arterial blood into interstitial fluid and on into cells, whereas carbon dioxide diffuses in opposite direction
   c. why it occurs—O_2 pressure gradient causes outward diffusion of O_2; CO_2 pressure gradient causes inward diffusion of CO_2

	Arterial blood	*Interstitial fluid*
Po_2	100 mm. Hg	60 (?) mm. Hg down to 1 (?) mm. Hg
Pco_2	46 mm. Hg	50 (?) mm. Hg

   d. results of oxygen diffusion out of blood and carbon dioxide diffusion into blood
      1. Po_2 blood decreases as blood moves through tissue capillaries; arterial Po_2, 100 mm. Hg, becomes venous Po_2, 40 mm. Hg (figures vary)
      2. Pco_2 blood increases; arterial Pco_2, 40 mm. Hg, becomes venous Pco_2, 46 mm. Hg (figures vary)
      3. oxygen dissociation from hemoglobin and carbon dioxide association with hemoglobin to form carbaminohemoglobin both accelerated by decreasing Po_2 and increasing Pco_2

9. Control of respirations (see Fig. 242)
   a. respiratory centers – inspiratory and expiratory centers in medulla; pneumotaxic center in pons
   b. control of respiratory centers
      1. carbon dioxide major regulator of respirations; increased blood carbon dioxide content, up to certain level, stimulates respiration and above this level depresses respirations; decreased blood carbon dioxide decreases respirations
      2. oxygen content of blood influences respiratory center—decreased blood O_2, down to a certain level, stimulates respirations and below this critical level depresses them; O_2 control of respirations nonoperative under usual conditions
      3. Hering-Breuer mechanism helps control rhythmicity of respirations; increased alveolar pressure inhibits inspiration and starts expiration; decreased alveolar pressure stimulates inspiration and ends expiration
      4. miscellaneous factors influence respiratory center—e.g., body temperature, pain, emotions, etc.
   c. control of respirations during exercise—not established but evidence that increased venous blood Pco_2 stimulates chemoreceptors in pulmonary artery, thereby initiating reflex acceleration of respirations

Review questions

1. What anatomical feature favors the spread of the common cold through the respiratory passages and into the middle ear and mastoid sinus?
2. How are the turbinates arranged in the nose? What are they?
3. What organs are found in the nasopharynx?
4. What tubes open into the nasopharynx?
5. Make a diagram showing the termination of a bronchiole in an alveolar duct with alveoli.
6. What kind of membrane lines the respiratory system?
7. What is the serous covering of the lungs called? Where else, besides covering the lungs, is this same membrane found?

8. The pharynx is common to what two systems?
9. Are the lungs active or passive organs during breathing? Explain.
10. What is the main inspiratory muscle?
11. How is inspiration accomplished? Expiration?
12. If an opening is made into the pleural cavity from the exterior, what happens? Why?
13. What is the pleural space? What does it contain?
14. What substance found in blood is the natural chemical stimulant for the respiratory center?
15. Compare mechanisms that achieve internal and external respiration.
16. Respirations increase during exercise. Explain the mechanisms involved.
17. What is the voice box? Of what is it composed? What is the Adam's apple?
18. What is the epiglottis? What is its function?
19. What are the true vocal cords? Where are they? What name is given to the opening between the cords?
20. Name the three divisions of the thorax and their contents.
21. One gram of hemoglobin combines with how many milliliters of oxygen?
22. Suppose your blood has a hemoglobin content of 15 grams per 100 ml. and an oxygen saturation of 97%. How many milliliters of oxygen would 100 ml. of your arterial blood contain?
23. Compare the mechanisms that accelerate respiration with those that accelerate circulation during exercise.
24. Make a generalization about the effect of a moderate increase in the amount of blood CO_2 on circulation and respiration. What advantage can you see in this effect?
25. Make a generalization about the effect of a moderate decrease in blood O_2 on circulation and respiration.
26. Define the following terms briefly:

alveolus	Po_2
apnea	pleurisy
asphyxia	residual air
complemental air	respiration
cyanosis	spirometer
dyspnea	supplemental air
minimal air	thorax
orthopnea	tidal air
Pco_2	vital capacity

Functions and importance

Organs
Walls of organs
  Coats
  Modifications of coats
Mouth (buccal cavity)
Salivary glands
Teeth
Pharynx
Esophagus
Stomach
  Size, shape, and position
  Divisions
  Curves
  Sphincter muscles
  Coats
  Glands
  Functions
Small intestine
  Size and position
  Divisions
  Coats
  Functions
Large intestine (colon)
  Size
  Divisions
  Coats
  Functions
Liver
  Location and size
  Lobes
  Ducts
  Functions
Gallbladder
  Size, shape, and location
  Structure
  Functions
  Correlations
Pancreas
  Size, shape, and location
  Structure
  Functions
Vermiform appendix
  Size, shape, and location
  Structure

Digestion
Definition
Purpose
Kinds
Control of digestive gland secretion

Absorption
Definition
How accomplished

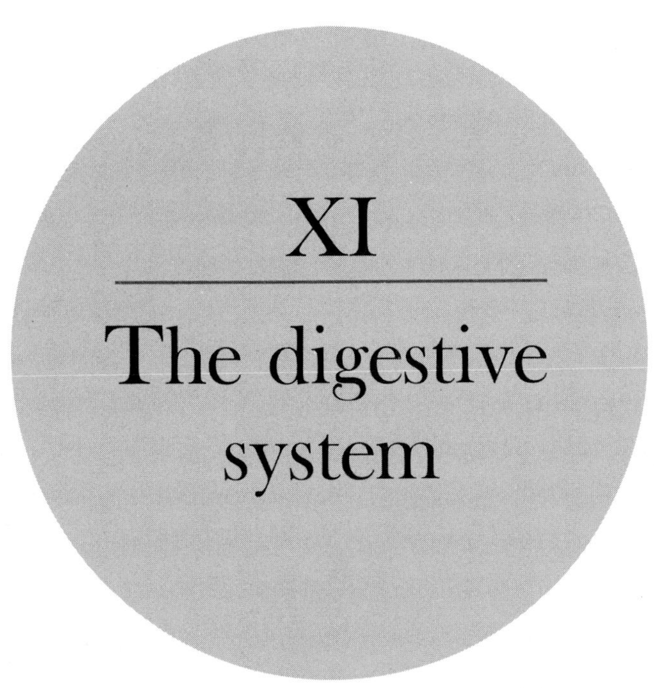

Functions and importance

The organs of the digestive system together perform a vital function—that of preparing food for absorption and for use by the millions of body cells. Most food when eaten is in a form that cannot reach the cells (because it cannot pass through the intestinal mucosa into the bloodstream) nor could it be used by the cells even if it could reach them. It must, therefore, be modified as to both chemical composition and physical state. This process of altering the chemical and physical composition of food so that it can be absorbed and utilized by body cells is known as digestion and is the function of the digestive system. Part of the digestive system, the large intestine, serves also as an organ of elimination, ridding the body of the wastes resulting from the digestive process.

Organs

The main organs of the digestive system form a tube all the way through the ventral cavities of the body. It is open at both ends. This tube is usually referred to as the *alimentary canal* (or tract) or the *gastrointestinal* or GI tract. The following organs form the gastrointestinal tract: mouth, pharynx, esophagus, stomach, and intestines. Several accessory organs are

Fig. 243

Section of the small bowel showing the circular folds (valvulae conniventes) and layers of the bowel wall.

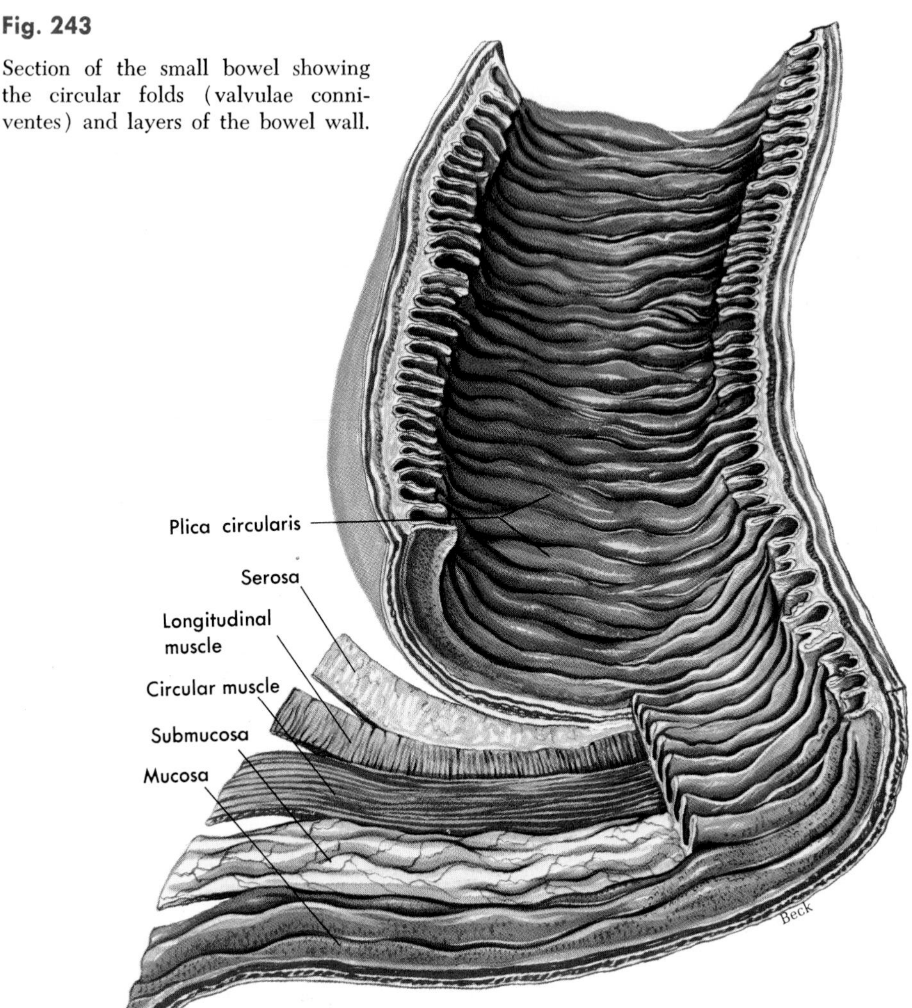

located in the main digestive organs or open into them. They are the salivary glands, teeth, liver, gallbladder, pancreas, and vermiform appendix.

WALLS OF ORGANS

Coats

The alimentary canal is essentially a tube whose walls are fashioned of four layers of tissues: a mucous lining, a submucous coat of connective tissue in which are embedded the main blood vessels of the tract, a muscular coat, and a fibroserous coat.

Modifications of coats

Although the same four tissue coats form the various organs of the alimentary tract, their structure varies in different organs. Some of these modifications are listed in Table 45.

The parietal peritoneum, which lines the posterior wall of the abdominal cavity, projects from the lumbar region into the abdominal cavity in a double fold, shaped like a plaited fan. It is named the *mesentary* (Fig. 245). The loose outer edge of this great fan measures approximately 20

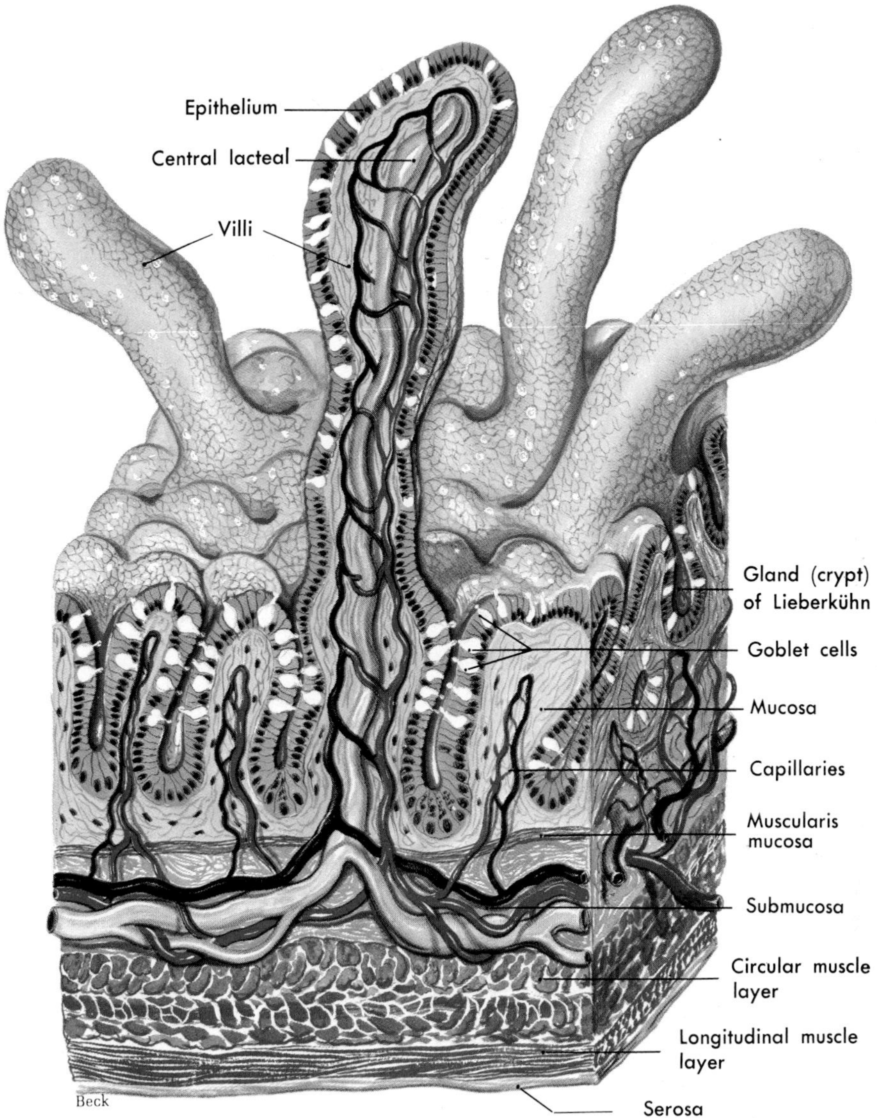

Fig. 244

Section of the intestinal mucosa showing villi, central lacteal, and glands.

feet, whereas its attached posterior border has a length of from only 6 to 8 inches. Most of the small intestine is attached to its outer edge. The mesentery, then, may be defined as a fan-shaped double fold of parietal peritoneum by which the small intestine is anchored to the posterior abdominal wall. It should not be confused with the *greater omentum,** an apron-shaped double fold of peritoneum that is

*The *lesser omentum* is a fold of peritoneum that attaches the liver to the lesser curvature of the stomach and beginning of the duodenum.

Table 45. Modifications of coats of digestive tract

Organ	*Mucous coat*	*Muscle coat*	*Fibroserous coat*
Esophagus		Two layers—inner one of circular fibers and outer one of longitudinal fibers; striated muscle in upper part and smooth in lower part of esophagus and in rest of tract	Outer coat fibrous; serous around part of esophagus in thoracic cavity
Stomach	Arranged in temporary longitudinal folds called *rugae;* allow for distention (Fig. 251) Contains microscopic gastric and hydrochloric acid glands	Has three layers instead of usual two, circular, longitudinal, and oblique fibers; two sphincters—cardiac at entrance of stomach and pyloric at its exit formed by circular fibers	Outer coat visceral peritoneum; hangs in double fold from lower edge of stomach over intestines, forming apronlike structure, *greater omentum,* or "lace apron" (Fig. 246)
Small intestine	Contains permanent circular folds, *valvulae conniventes* (or plica circularis) (Fig. 243) Microscopic fingerlike projections, *villi* (Fig. 244) Microscopic intestinal glands (of Lieberkühn) Microscopic duodenal (Brunner's) glands Clusters of lymph nodes, *Peyer's patches* Numerous single lymph nodes called solitary nodes	Two layers—inner one of circular fibers and outer one of longitudinal fibers	Outer coat visceral peritoneum
Large intestine	Solitary nodes Intestinal glands	Incomplete outer longitudinal coat; present only in three tapelike strips (taenia libera).; small sacs (haustra) give rest of wall of large intestine puckered appearance (Fig. 252); internal anal sphincter formed by circular smooth fibers and external anal sphincter by striated fibers	Outer coat visceral peritoneum

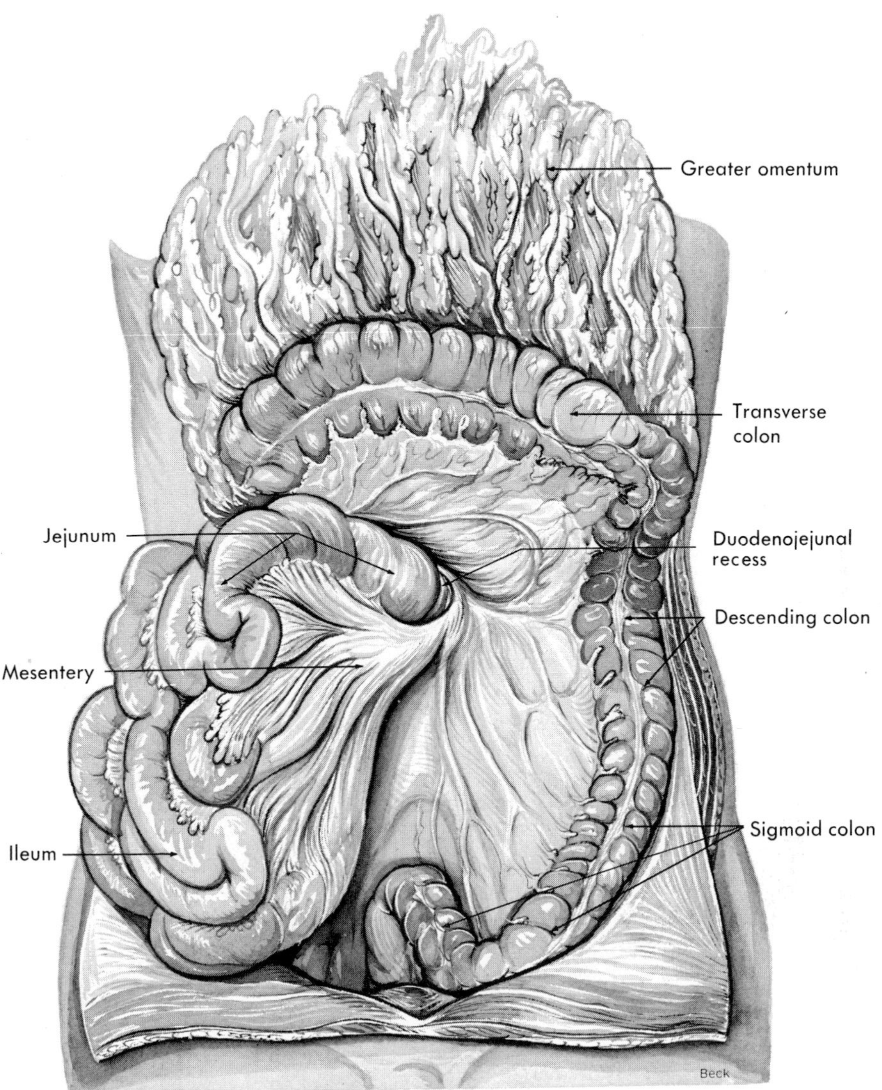

Fig. 245

The transverse colon and omentum are raised to demonstrate the duodenojejunal recess. The small intestine is pulled to the side to show the mesentery. Also see Fig. 246.

attached at its upper border to the first part of the duodenum, the lower edge of the stomach, and the transverse colon and hangs down loosely over the intestines. In case of a localized abdominal inflammation, such as appendicitis, the omentum envelops the inflamed area, walling it off from the rest of the abdomen. Spotty deposits of fat accumulate in the omentum, giving it a lacy appearance (Fig. 246).

MOUTH (BUCCAL CAVITY)

The following structures form the buccal cavity: the cheeks (sidewalls), the tongue and its muscles (floor), and the hard and soft palates (roof). Of these, only the pal-

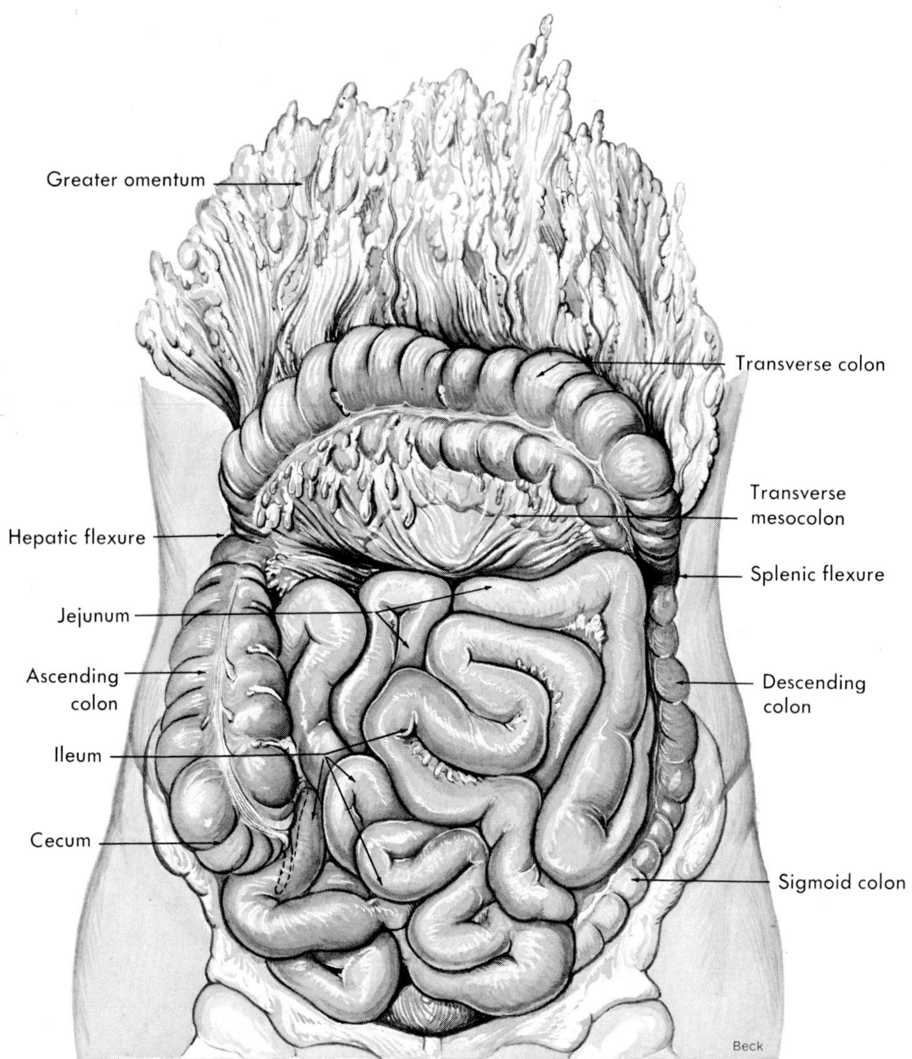

Fig. 246

Abdominal viscera from the front. The transverse colon and the omentum are elevated to reveal the loops of the small intestine.

ates and the tongue will be included in this discussion.

The *hard palate* consists of the two palatine bones and parts of the two superior maxillary bones. The *soft palate,* which forms a partition between the mouth and nasopharynx, is fashioned of muscle arranged in the shape of an arch. The opening in the arch leads from the mouth into the oropharynx and is named the *fauces,* whereas the two vertical side portions of the arch are appropriately termed the pillars of the fauces. Suspended from the midpoint of the posterior border of the arch is a small cone-shaped process, the *uvula.*

The entire buccal cavity, like the rest of the digestive tract, is lined with mucous membrane.

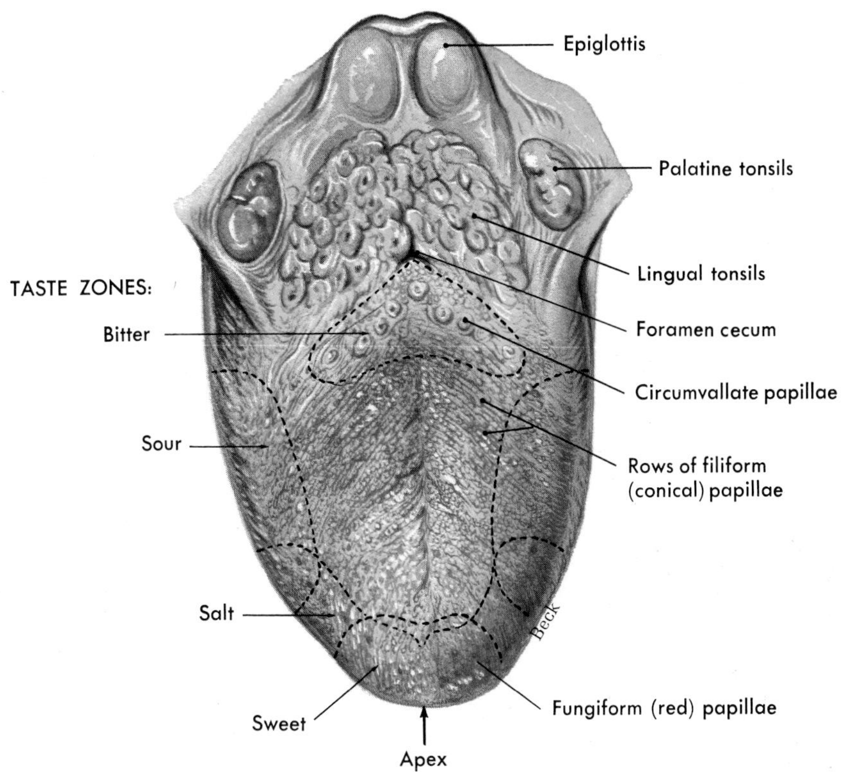

Fig. 247
The human tongue showing various papillae that contain taste buds. Note overlapping of the taste zones.

The salivary glands and teeth are accessory organs of the mouth.

Skeletal muscle covered with mucous membrane composes the *tongue.* Several muscles that originate on skull bones insert into the tongue. The rough elevations on the tongue's surface are called *papillae.* They contain the taste buds. Three types, filiform, fungiform, and circumvallate, can be observed.

The filiform papillae are numerous threadlike structures distributed over the anterior two-thirds of the tongue. Fungiform papillae are knoblike elevations most numerous near the edges of the tongue. Circumvallate papillae form an inverted V at the posterior part of the tongue.

The *frenum* (or frenulum) is a fold of mucous membrane in the midline of the undersurface of the tongue that helps to anchor the tongue to the floor of the mouth. If the frenum is too short for freedom of tongue movements, the individual is said to be tongue-tied, and his speech is faulty.

SALIVARY GLANDS

See Table 46 for the names, location, and duct openings of the salivary glands.

Mumps is an acute infection of the parotid glands characterized by swelling of the glands. The act of opening the mouth causes pain because it squeezes that part of the gland that projects between the temporomandibular joint and the mastoid process.

Table 46. Salivary glands

Name of gland	*Location*	*Duct openings*
Parotid	Below and in front of ear	On inside of cheek, opposite upper second molar tooth; known as Stensen's duct
Submaxillary	Posterior part of floor of mouth	Floor of mouth, at sides of frenum; known as Wharton's duct
Sublingual	Anterior part of floor of mouth, under tongue	Several ducts open into floor of mouth

Table 47. Dentition

Name of tooth	*Number per jaw*	
	Deciduous set	*Permanent set*
Central incisors	2	2
Lateral incisors	2	2
Cuspids (canines)	2	2
Premolars (bicuspids)	0	4
Molars (tricuspids)	4	6
Total per jaw	10	16
Total per set	20	32

TEETH

The so-called baby teeth or the set that appears first and is later shed are technically known as the *deciduous teeth,* whereas the set that replaces these are the *permanent teeth.* The names and numbers of teeth present in both sets are given in Table 47. Also see Figs. 249 and 250.

The first deciduous tooth erupts usually at the age of about 6 months. The rest follow at the rate of one or more a month until all twenty have appeared. There is, however, great individual variation in the age at which teeth erupt. Deciduous teeth are shed generally between the ages of 6 and 13 years. The third molars (wisdom teeth) are the last to appear, erupting usually sometime after 17 years of age.

Intact enamel resists bacterial attack, but once it is broken, the softer dentine decays. Pyorrhea is an inflammation of the gums (gingiva) and periodontal membrane (Fig. 248).

PHARYNX

For a discussion of the pharynx, see pp. 349 and 350.

ESOPHAGUS

The esophagus, a collapsible tube about 10 inches long, extends from the pharynx to the stomach, piercing the diaphragm in

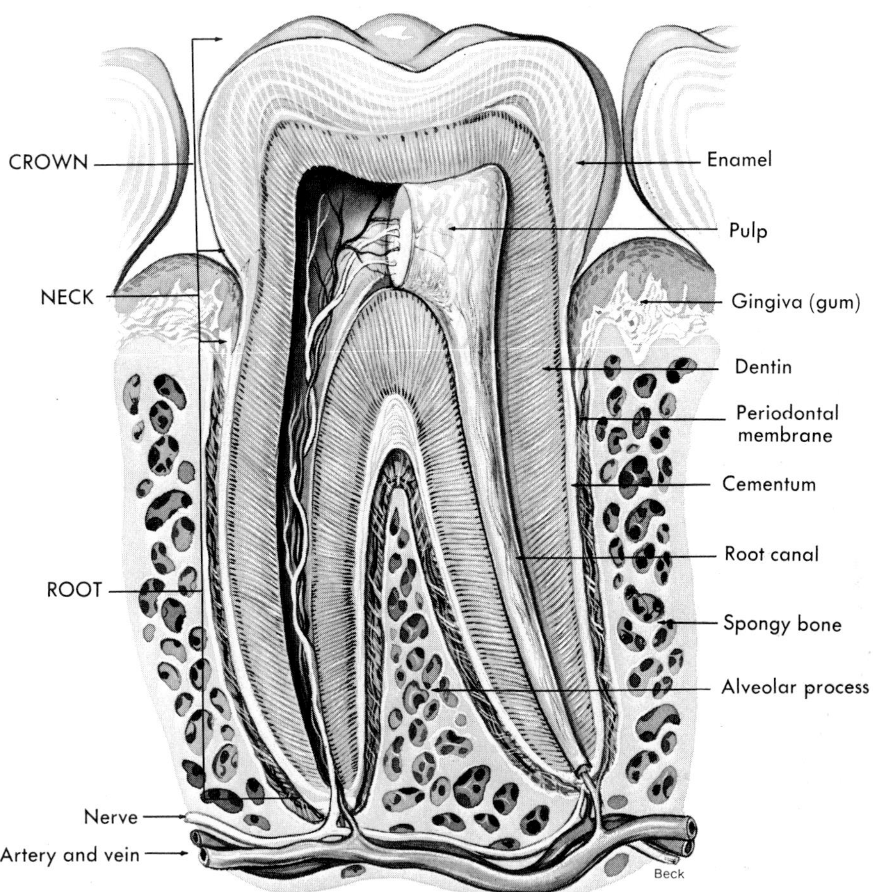

Fig. 248

A molar tooth sectioned to show its bony socket and details of its three main parts: crown, neck, and root. The pulp contains nerves and blood vessels.

its descent from the thoracic to the abdominal cavity. It lies posterior to the trachea and heart.

Unlike the trachea, the esophagus is a collapsible tube, its muscle walls lacking the cartilaginous rings found in the trachea (Table 45).

STOMACH

Size, shape, and position

Just below the diaphragm, the alimentary tube dilates into an elongated pouchlike structure, the stomach (see Fig. 251), the size of which varies according to several factors, notably sex and the amount of distention. In general, the female stomach is usually more slender and smaller than the male stomach. For some time after a meal, the stomach is enlarged due to distention of its walls, but as food leaves, the walls partially collapse, leaving the organ about the size of a large sausage.

The stomach lies in the upper part of the abdominal cavity under the liver and diaphragm, with approximately five-sixths of its mass to the left of the median line. In other words, it is described as lying in the

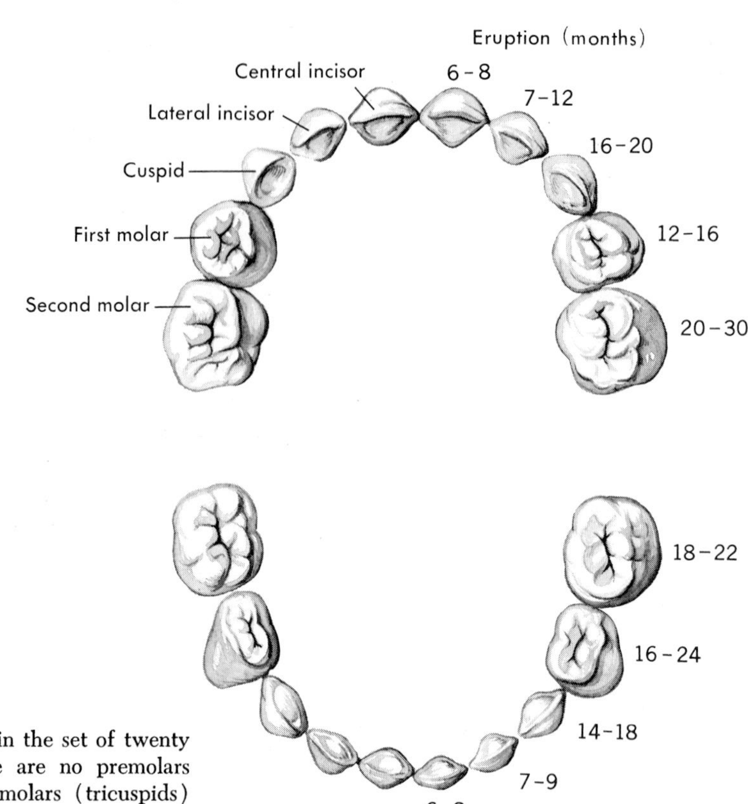

Fig. 249

The deciduous arch. Note that in the set of twenty temporary primary teeth there are no premolars (bicuspids) and two pairs of molars (tricuspids) in each jaw. Compare with permanent teeth (Fig. 250).

epigastrium and left hypochondrium (Fig. 3, p. 7). Its position, however, alters frequently. For example, it is pushed downward with each inspiration and upward with each expiration. When it is greatly distended from an unusually large meal, its size interferes with the descent of the diaphragm on inspiration, producing the familiar feeling of dyspnea that accompanies overeating. In this state the stomach also pushes upward against the heart, giving rise to the sensation that the heart is being crowded.

Divisions

The *fundus*, the *body*, and the *pylorus* are the three divisions of the stomach. The fundus is the enlarged portion to the left and above the opening of the esophagus into the stomach. The body is the central part of the stomach, and the pylorus is its lower portion (Fig. 251).

Curves

The upper right border of the stomach presents what is known as the *lesser curvature* and the lower left border the *greater curvature.*

Sphincter muscles

Sphincter muscles guard both stomach openings. A sphincter muscle consists of circular fibers so arranged that there is an opening in the center of them (like the hole in a doughnut) when they are relaxed and no opening when they are contracted.

The *cardiac sphincter* guards the opening of the esophagus into the stomach and

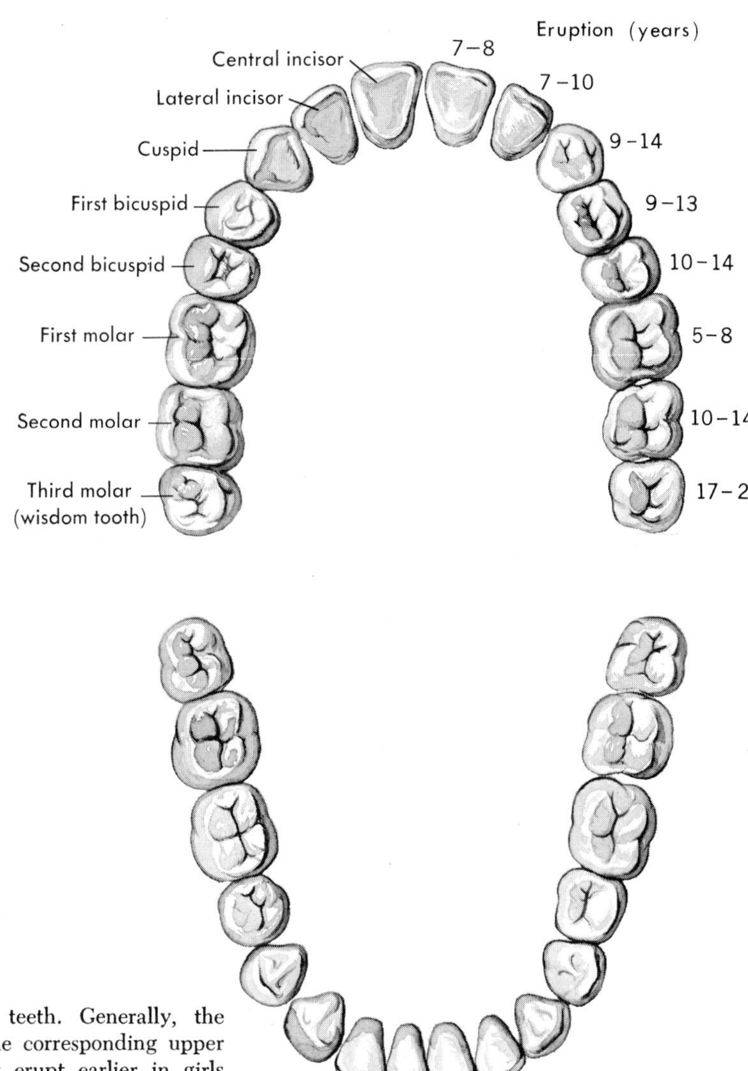

Fig. 250

The thirty-two permanent teeth. Generally, the lower teeth erupt before the corresponding upper teeth and all teeth usually erupt earlier in girls than in boys.

the *pyloric sphincter* the opening from the pyloric portion of the stomach into the first part of the small intestine (duodenum). This latter muscle is of clinical importance because *pylorospasm* is a fairly common condition in babies. The pyloric fibers do not relax normally to allow food to leave the stomach, and the baby vomits his food instead of digesting and absorbing it. The condition is relieved by administering a drug that relaxes smooth muscle. Another abnormality of the pyloric sphincter is pyloric stenosis, an obstructive narrowing of its opening.

Coats

See Table 45 for information on coats of the stomach.

Glands

Numerous microscopic tubular glands are embedded in the gastric mucosa. Those in

Fig. 251

Muscle layers and interior of the stomach.

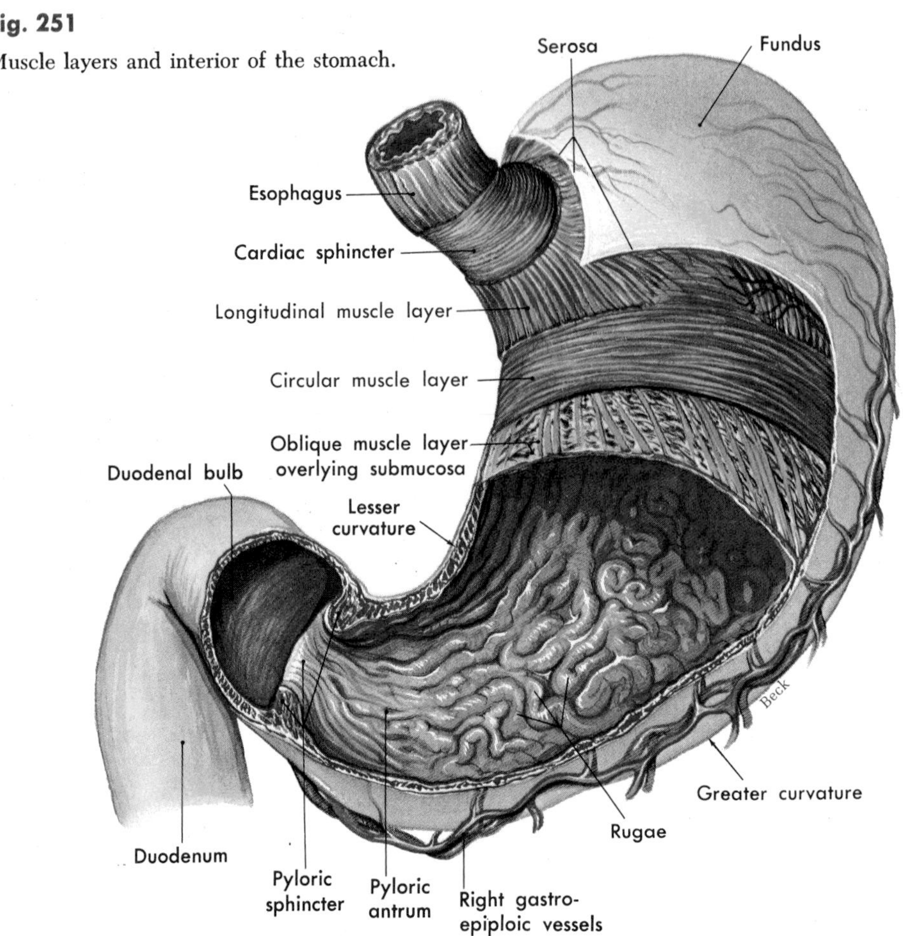

the mucosa that lines the fundus and body of the stomach secrete most of the gastric juice, a fluid composed of mucus, enzymes, and hydrochloric acid. *Epithelial cells* that form the surface of the gastric mucosa (next to the lumen of the stomach) secrete mucus. *Parietal cells* secrete hydrochloric acid, and *chief cells* (or zymogen cells) secrete the enzymes of the gastric juice. In pernicious anemia, the gastric mucosa atrophies with the result that hydrochloric acid and a mysterious substance known as the intrinsic factor are not produced. Achlorhydria, therefore, is a characteristic finding in pernicious anemia. Absence of the intrinsic factor produces anemia. Without it vitamin B_{12} cannot be absorbed, and without vitamin B_{12} the red bone marrow is not sufficiently stimulated to produce enough normal red blood cells.

Functions

The stomach carries on the following functions:

1. It serves as a reservoir, storing food until it can be partially digested and moved farther along the gastrointestinal tract.
2. It secretes gastric juice, one of the juices whose enzymes digest food.
3. Through contractions of its muscular coat, it churns the food, breaking it into small particles and mixing them well with

the gastric juice. In due time it moves the gastric contents on into the duodenum.

4. It secretes the intrinsic factor just mentioned.

5. It carries on a limited amount of absorption—of some water, alcohol, and certain drugs.

SMALL INTESTINE

Size and position

The small intestine is a tube measuring approximately 1 inch in diameter and 20 feet in length. Its coiled loops fill most of the abdominal cavity.

Divisions

The small intestine consists of three divisions: the duodenum, the jejunum, and the ileum. The *duodenum** is the uppermost division and is the part to which the pyloric end of the stomach attaches. It is about 10 inches long and is shaped roughly like the letter C. The duodenum becomes *jejunum* at the point where the tube turns abruptly forward and downward. The jejunal portion continues for approximately the next 8 feet, where it becomes *ileum,* but without any clear line of demarcation between the two divisions. The ileum is about 12 feet long.

Coats

See Table 45 for information on the coats of the small intestine.

Functions

The small intestine carries on three main functions as follows:

1. It completes the digestion of foods. The digestive intestinal juice contains mucus and many digestive enzymes. The glands of Lieberkühn secrete the digestive enzymes, whereas the glands of Brunner and innumerable goblet cells secrete the mucus.

2. It absorbs the end products of digestion into blood and lymph.

3. It secretes hormones—for example, some which help control the secretion of pancreatic juice, bile, and intestinal juice.

*Derivation of the word duodenum may interest you. It comes from words which means 12 fingerbreadths, a distance of about 11 inches, the approximate length of the duodenum.

LARGE INTESTINE (COLON)

Size

The lower part of the alimentary canal bears the name *large intestine* because its diameter is noticeably larger than that of the small intestine. Its length, however, is much less, being about 5 or 6 feet. Its average diameter is approximately 2½ inches but decreases toward the lower end of the tube.

Divisions

The large intestine is divided into the cecum, colon, and rectum.

Cecum. The first two or three inches of the large intestine are named the cecum. It is located in the lower right quadrant of the abdomen (Fig. 253).

Colon. The colon is divided into the following portions, ascending, transverse, descending, and sigmoid.

1. The *ascending colon* lies in the vertical position, on the right side of the abdomen, extending up to the lower border of the liver. The ileum joins the large intestine at the junction of the cecum and ascending colon, the place of attachment resembling the letter T in formation (Fig. 252). The ileocecal valve guards the opening of the ileum into the large intestine, permitting material to pass from the former into the latter but not in the reverse direction.

2. The *transverse colon* passes horizontally across the abdomen, below the liver and stomach and above the small intestine.

3. The *descending colon* lies in the vertical position, on the left side of the abdo-

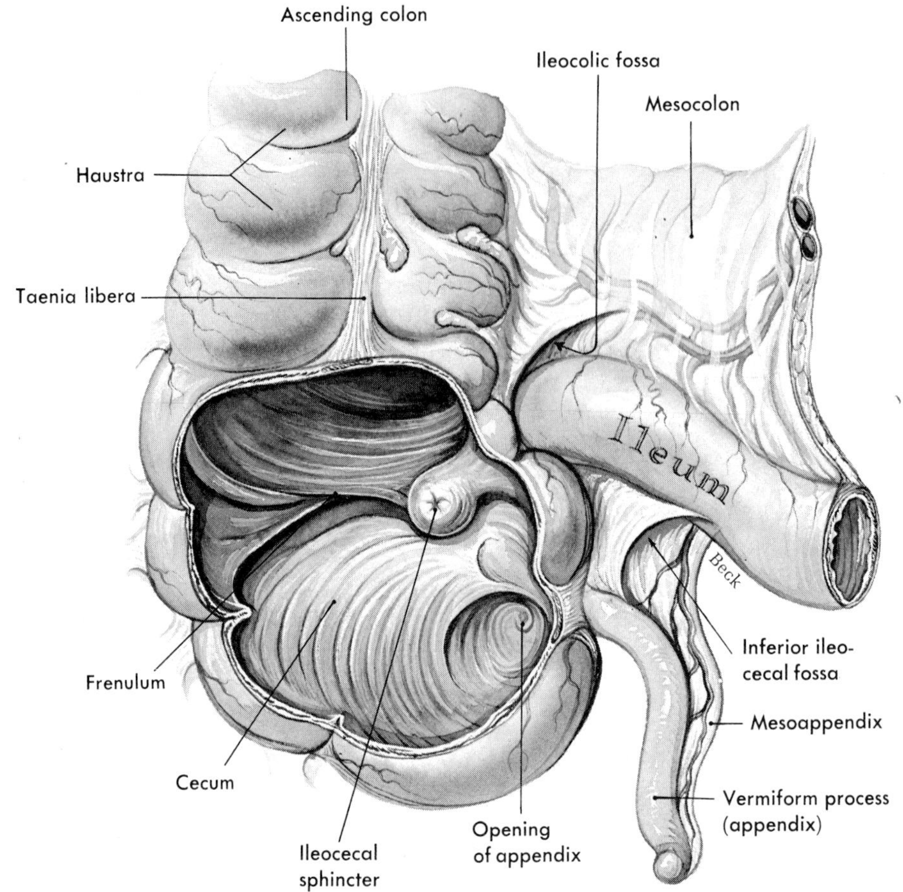

Fig. 252

The vermiform process (appendix) and the ileocecal region. The cecum is opened to reveal the papillary form of ileocecal sphincter.

men, extending from a point below the stomach to the level of the iliac crest.

4. The *sigmoid colon* is that portion of the large intestine that courses downward below the iliac crest. It describes an S-shaped curve. The lower part of the curve, which joins the rectum, bends toward the left, the anatomical reason for placing a patient on the left side when giving an enema. In this position gravity aids the flow of the water from the rectum into the sigmoid flexure.

Rectum. The last seven or eight inches of the intestinal tube is called the rectum. The terminal inch of the rectum is called the *anal canal.* Its mucous lining is arranged in numerous vertical folds known as *rectal columns,* each of which contains an artery and a vein. *Hemorrhoids* (or piles) are enlargements of the veins in the anal canal. The opening of the canal to the exterior is guarded by two sphincter muscles—an internal one of smooth muscle and an external one of striated muscle. The opening itself is called the *anus.* The general direction of the rectum is up, in, and back.

Coats

See Table 45 for information on the coats of the large intestine.

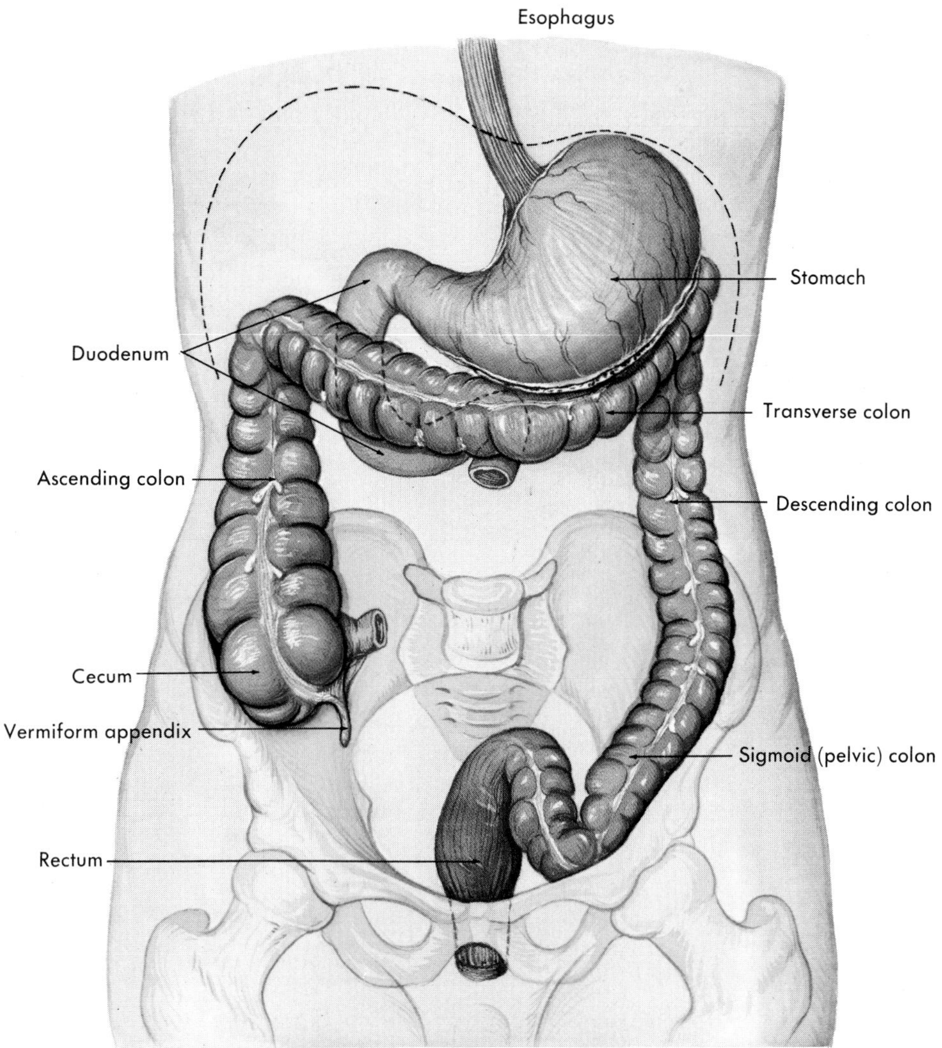

Fig. 253

Position of the stomach and large intestine in relation to the diaphragm (dotted lines) and the bony pelvis.

Functions

The main functions of the large intestine are absorption of water and elimination of the wastes of digestion.

LIVER

Location and size

The liver is the largest gland in the body. It weighs between 3 and 4 pounds, lies immediately under the diaphragm, and occupies most of the right hypochondrium and part of the epigastrium.

Lobes

The falciform ligament divides the liver into two main lobes, right and left, with the right lobe having three parts designated as the right lobe proper, the caudate lobe (a small four-sided area on the posterior surface), and the quadrate lobe (an approximately oblong section on the undersurface). Each lobe is divided into numerous lobules by small blood vessels and by fibrous strands that form a supporting framework (the capsule of Glisson) for them. The capsule of Glisson is an extension of the heavy connective tissue capsule that envelops the entire liver. The hepatic lobules, the anatomical units of the liver, are tiny hexagonal or pentagonal cylinders about 2 mm. high and 1 mm. in diameter. A small branch of the hepatic vein extends through the center of each lobule. Around this central (intralobular) vein, in columns radiating outward, are arranged the hepatic cells. Three separate sets of tiny tubes—branches of the hepatic artery, of the portal vein (interlobular veins), and of the hepatic duct (interlobular bile ducts)—are arranged around each lobule. From these, irregular branches (sinusoids) of the interlobular veins extend between the radiating columns of hepatic cells to join the central vein. Branches of the interlobular bile ducts also run between each two rows of hepatic cells.

Ducts

The small bile ducts within the liver join to form two larger ducts which emerge from the undersurface of the organ as the right and left hepatic ducts but which immediately join to form one *hepatic duct*. The hepatic duct merges with the *cystic duct* from the gallbladder, forming the *common bile duct* (Fig. 254) which opens into the duodenum in a small raised area, called the *ampulla* or *papilla of Vater*, or duodenal papilla. This papilla is located three to four inches below the pyloric opening from the stomach.

Functions

The liver is one of the most vital organs of the body. Although its cells are merely microscopic dots in size, they do so many things at once as to seem incredible—or perhaps miraculous would be a better word. Because of the diversity of its activities, a single liver cell might be likened to a *factory* (it makes many chemical compounds), a *warehouse* (it stores such valuables as glycogen, iron, and certain vitamins), a *waste disposal plant* (it excretes bile pigments, urea, and various detoxication products), and a *power plant* (its catabolism produces considerable heat).

Here, in brief, are the liver's main functions:

1. It secretes about a pint of bile a day. Bile contains bile salts that facilitate fat digestion and absorption and various waste products.

2. The liver plays an essential role in the metabolism of all three kinds of foods.

(a) For its special part in carbohydrate metabolism, the liver carries on three processes: glycogenesis, glycogenolysis, and gluconeogenesis (pp. 404 and 405). Briefly, by these processes, the liver plays an important part in maintaining homeostasis of blood sugar—helped, as we shall see, by various other processes.

(b) Liver cells, more than any others, carry out the first step in both protein and fat catabolism (see pp. 411 to 416).

(c) Liver cells perform an essential part of protein anabolism by synthesizing various blood proteins such as prothrombin and fibrinogen, albumins, and many globulins. This function alone stamps the liver as one of the highly essential workers for bodily welfare and survival. Consider these three vital functions of the blood proteins synthesized by the liver: (1) prothrombin and fibrinogen are, as you already know, essential for blood clotting, (2) all blood proteins contribute to blood osmotic pressure and therefore are important for maintaining water balance, and (3) all blood proteins contribute to blood viscosity and therefore are essential for normal circulation.

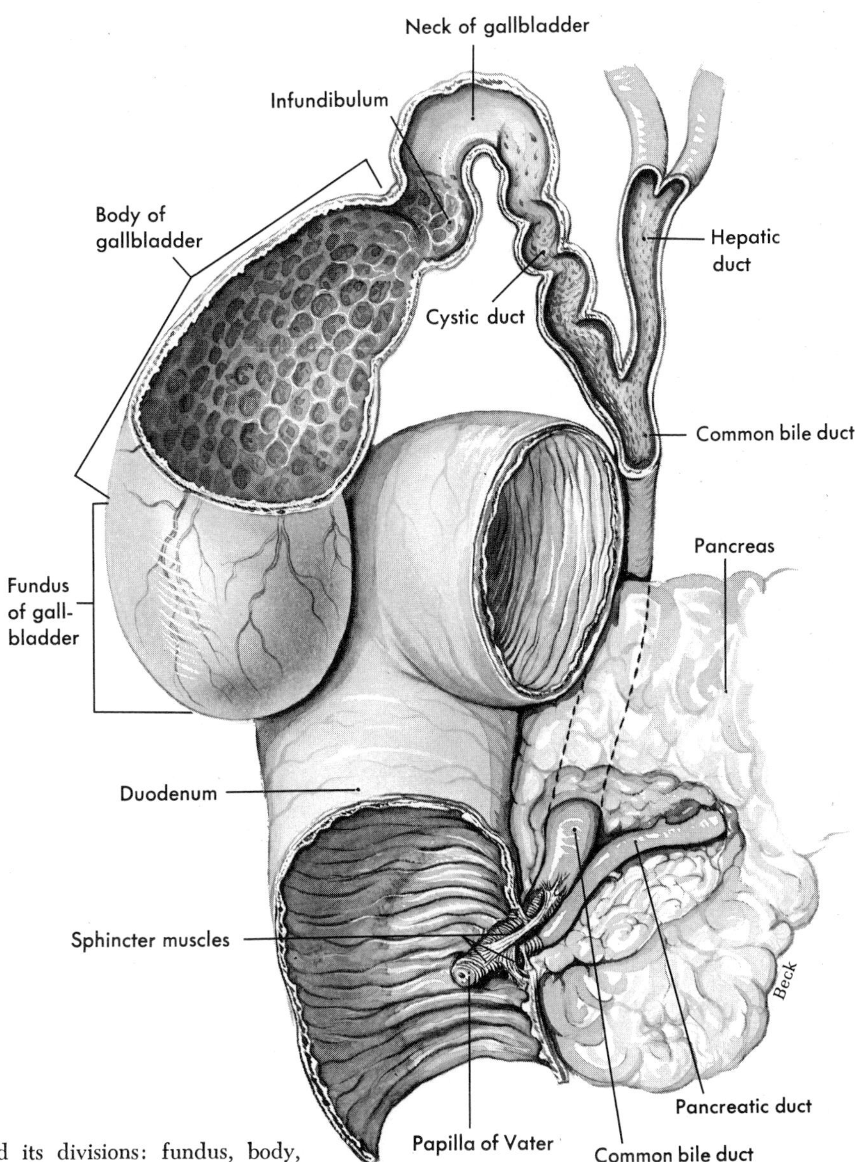

Fig. 254

The gallbladder and its divisions: fundus, body, infundibulum, and neck. Obstruction of either the hepatic or common bile duct by stone or spasm blocks the exit of bile from the liver where it is formed and prevents bile from ejecting into the duodenum.

GALLBLADDER

Size, shape, and location

The gallbladder is a pear-shaped sac from 3 to 4 inches long and an inch or more wide. It lies on the undersurface of the liver and is attached to this organ by areolar tissue.

Structure

Serous, muscular, and mucous coats compose the wall of the gallbladder. The mucosal lining is arranged in rugae, similar in structure and function to those of the stomach.

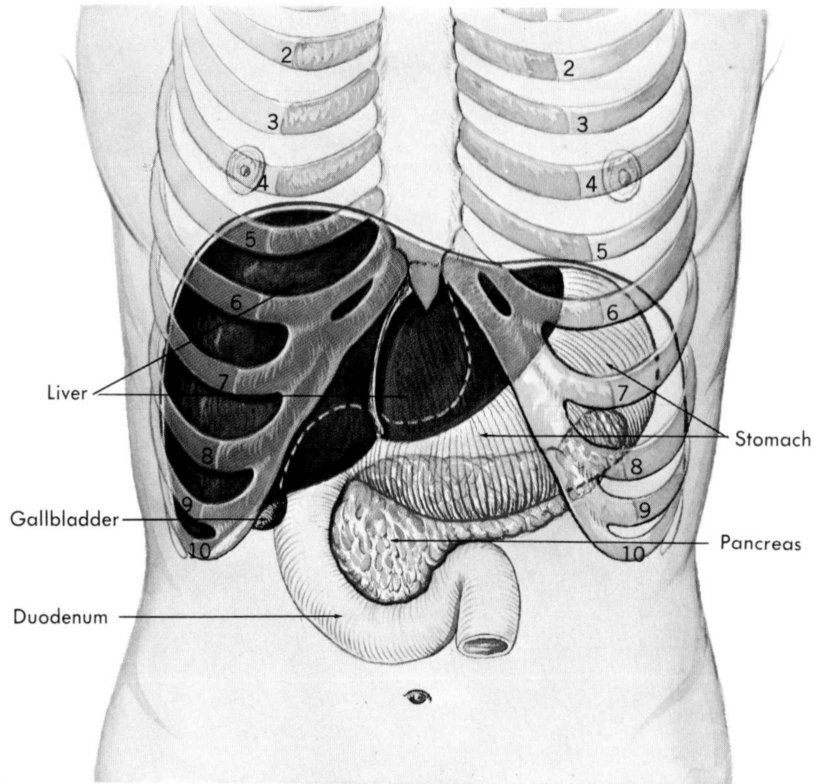

Fig. 255

The liver and pancreas in their normal positions relative to the rib cage, diaphragm, and stomach.

Functions

The gallbladder concentrates and stores the bile which enters it by way of the hepatic and cystic ducts. Then later, when digestion is going on in the stomach and intestines, the gallbladder contracts, ejecting the concentrated bile into the duodenum.

Correlations

Inflammation of the lining of the gallbladder is called *cholecystitis. Cholecystectomy* is the surgical removal of the gallbladder. *Jaundice,* a yellow discoloration of the skin and mucosa, results whenever obstruction of the hepatic or common bile ducts occurs. Bile is thereby denied its normal exit from the body in the feces. Instead, it is absorbed into the blood. As the more bile pigments than normal accumulate in blood, the latter takes on a yellow hue, and the feces, lacking the normal amount of bile pigments, become clay colored.

PANCREAS

Size, shape, and location

The pancreas is roughly fish shaped. It lies behind the stomach, with its head and neck in the C-shaped curve of the duodenum, its body extending horizontally across the posterior abdominal wall, and its tail touching the spleen. According to an old anatomical witticism, the "romance of the abdomen" is the pancreas lying "in the arms of the duodenum."

This gland varies in size according to sex

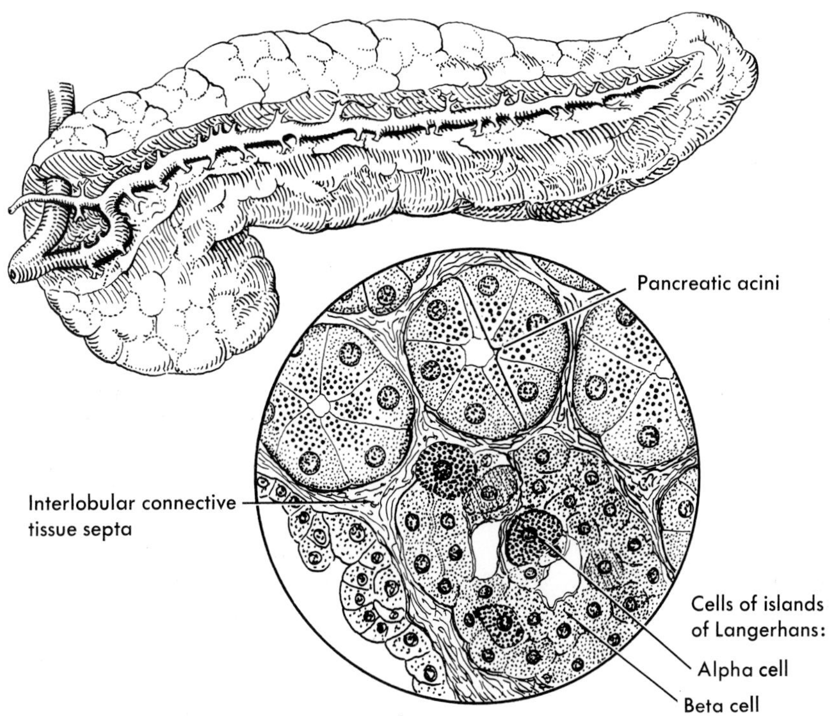

Fig. 256

The top drawing shows the pancreas dissected to expose the pancreatic duct. Note the slender accessory duct crossing the common bile duct just above its union with the main pancreatic duct. The ducts empty into the duodenum at the ampulla of Vater. The lower drawing shows cells of the pancreas. Cells of the islands of Langerhans are little glands of internal secretion (endocrine). Cells of the acini are exocrine.

and individuals, being larger in men than in women. Usually its length is 6 to 9 inches, its width 1 to 1½ inches, and its thickness ½ to 1 inch. It weighs about 3 ounces.

Structure

The pancreas is classified as a compound tubuloacinar gland. The word compound tells us that the gland has a branching duct. The term tubuloacinar, on the other hand, tells us that some of the secreting units of the pancreas resemble tiny tubes and some tiny grapes in shape. Secreting cells constitute the walls of these tubular and acinar units. These are exocrine glands since they release their secretion into the microscopic duct within each unit. These tiny ducts unite to form larger ducts that eventually join the main pancreatic duct, the *duct of Wirsung,* which extends throughout the length of the gland from its tail to its head. It empties into the duodenum at the same point as the common bile duct, that is, at the ampulla of Vater. (An accessory duct, the *duct of Santorini,* is frequently found extending from the head of the pancreas into the duodenum, about an inch above the duodenal papilla.)

In between the tubuloacinar units of the pancreas, like so many little islands isolated from one another and from the ducts of the pancreas, lie clusters of cells called *islets* or *islands of Langerhans.* Special staining techniques have revealed that two kinds of cells—alpha cells and beta cells—

chiefly compose the islands of Langerhans. They are secreting cells, but their secretion passes into blood capillaries rather than into ducts. Thus the pancreas is a dual gland—an exocrine or duct gland because of the tubuloacinar units and an endocrine or ductless gland because of the islands of Langerhans.

Functions

1. The tubuloacinar units of the pancreas secrete the digestive enzymes found in pancreatic juice. Hence the pancreas plays an important part in digestion (p. 398).
2. Beta cells of the pancreas secrete *insulin,* a hormone that exerts a major control over carbohydrate metabolism (p. 406).
3. Alpha cells, as indicated by considerable evidence, secrete *glucagon,* another hormone involved in carbohydrate metabolism (p. 406).

VERMIFORM APPENDIX

Size, shape, and location

The appendix is a blind tube branching from the lower portion of the cecum (Fig. 252). As its name suggests, it resembles a large angle worm in size and shape, although its size varies greatly in different individuals.

Structure

The structure of the appendix is similar to that of the rest of the intestine. Its mucous lining frequently becomes inflamed, a condition well known as *appendicitis.*

Digestion

Definition

Digestion is the sum of all the changes food undergoes in the alimentary canal.

Purpose

The purpose of digestion as suggested in the dictionary definition is "the conversion of food into assimilable matter." Digestion is necessary because foods, as eaten, are too complex in physical and chemical composition to pass through the intestinal mucosa into the blood or for cells to utilize them for energy and tissue building. In other words, digestion is the necessary preliminary to both absorption and metabolism of foods.

Kinds

Since both the physical and chemical composition of ingested food makes its absorption impossible, two kinds of digestive changes are necessary, *mechanical* and *chemical.*

Mechanical digestion. Mechanical digestion consists of all those movements of the alimentary tract that bring about the following:

1. Change the physical state of ingested food from comparatively large, solid pieces into minute dissolved particles, thereby facilitating chemical digestion
2. Propel the food forward along the alimentary tract, finally eliminating the digestive wastes from the body
3. Churn the intestinal contents in such a way that it becomes well mixed with the digestive juices and that all parts of it come in contact with the surface of the intestinal mucosa, thereby facilitating absorption

A list of definitions of the different processes involved in mechanical digestion, together with the organs that accomplish them, are given in Table 48. Swallowing, the movement of food out of the stomach, and defecation are considered in more detail below.

Swallowing consists of three steps: movement of the food through the mouth into the pharynx, through the pharynx into the esophagus, and through the esophagus into the stomach. Only the first act is voluntary, that is, can be controlled by the will. The other two actions are reflexes that occur

Table 48. Processes in mechanics of digestion

Organ	*Mechanical process*	*Nature of process*
Mouth (teeth and tongue)	Mastication	Chewing movements—reduce size of food particles and mix them with saliva
	Deglutition	Swallowing—movement of food from mouth to stomach
Pharynx	Deglutition	
Esophagus	Deglutition	
	Peristalsis	Wormlike movements that squeeze food downward in tract; constricted ring forms first in one section, the next, etc., causing waves of contraction to spread throughout canal
Stomach	Churning	Forward and backward movement of gastric contents; peristalsis propels it forward; closed pyloric sphincter deflects it backward
	Peristalsis	Moves material through stomach and at intervals into duodenum
Small intestine	Churning (rhythmic segmentation)	Forward and backward movement within segment of intestine; purpose, to mix food and digestive juices thoroughly and to bring all digested food in contact with intestinal mucosa to facilitate absorption; purpose of peristalsis, on the other hand, to propel intestinal contents along digestive tract
	Peristalsis	
Large intestine		
Colon	Haustral churning	Churning movements within haustral sacs
	Peristalsis	
Descending colon	Mass peristalsis	Entire contents moved into sigmoid colon and rectum; usually occurs after a meal
Rectum	Defecation	Emptying of rectum, so-called bowel movement

automatically after food enters the pharynx. Stimulation of the mucosa of the back of the mouth, pharynx, or laryngeal region initiates the second step by producing contractions of the muscular pharyngeal walls. Consequently, paralysis of the sensory nerves to the mucosa of the back of the mouth, pharynx, or laryngeal region by a drug such as Novocain makes swallowing impossible. Since the pharynx serves both the digestive and respiratory systems, it has connections with the parts of the digestive tract above and below it (mouth and esophagus) and with the parts of the respiratory tract above and below (nasal cavity and larynx). When food enters the pharynx and its walls contract, theoretically its contents could be squeezed in any of these four directions, that is, back up into the nose or mouth or downward into the larynx or esophagus. That it takes only one of these routes (into the esophagus) is due to the fact that the openings into the other organs become blocked off during swallowing. Elevation of the tongue (so that it presses against the roof of the mouth) bars entry into the mouth, elevation of the soft palate obstructs the passageway into the nose, and elevation of the larynx closes over the opening into this organ. As the larynx moves upward, the base of the tongue pushes the epiglottis downward over the laryngeal opening like a lid. If solids or liquids enter the larynx and lower respiratory tract, they can bring on fatal consequences (either from asphyxiation or infection). But an additional mechanism prevents such an occurrence. Stimulation of the mucosa of the back of the mouth, pharynx, and laryngeal region produces not only the second phase of the swallowing act, but also momentary inhibition of respirations. Obviously, prevention of inspiration during swallowing greatly lessens the danger of foods entering the respiratory tract.

Stimulation of the esophageal mucosa by material entering it from the pharynx initiates the reflex of esophageal peristalsis. Liquids and well-chewed foods are precipitated down the esophagus to the cardiac sphincter by the force of pharyngeal contraction and by gravity. They are then moved through the sphincter into the stomach by means of esophageal peristalsis. The latter is responsible for propelling large solid particles throughout the length of the esophagus.

Emptying of the stomach after a meal requires a considerable period of time (about one to four hours for the average meal). Many theories have been proposed about the mechanism regulating gastric emptying. It is now known that as small amounts of gastric contents become liquefied they are ejected bit by bit every twenty seconds or so into the duodenum until a certain amount has accumulated there. From then on the emptying process slows down due to operation of a mechanism known as the *enterogastric reflex.* Both nerve impulses and a hormone initiate this reflex. Fats and sugars present in the small intestine stimulate the intestinal mucosa to release a hormone (called enterogastrone) into the bloodstream. When it circulates to the stomach wall, it has an inhibitory effect on gastric muscle, decreasing its peristalsis (the enterogastric reflex) and thereby slowing down stomach emptying. Proteins and acid also initiate the enterogastric reflex but not by means of a hormone. They stimulate vagal nerve receptors in the intestinal mucosa.

Defecation is a reflex brought about by stimulation of receptors in the rectal mucosa. Recent distention of the rectum constitutes the usual stimulus. Normally the rectum is empty until mass peristalsis moves fecal matter out of the colon into the rectum. This distends the rectum and produces the desire to defecate. Also, it stimulates colonic peristalsis and initiates reflex relaxation of the internal sphincter of the anus. Voluntary straining efforts and relaxation of the external anal sphincter may then follow as a result of the desire to defecate. And together these several responses bring about defecation. Note that this is a reflex partly under voluntary control. If it is voluntarily inhibited, rectal receptors soon become depressed and the urge to defecate is usually not reexperienced until about twenty-four hours later, when mass peristalsis again takes place. During the interim, water is absorbed from the fecal mass, producing a hardened or constipated stool.

Chemical digestion. Chemical digestion consists of all the changes in chemical composition that foods undergo in their travel through the alimentary canal. These changes result from the hydrolysis of foods. (*Hydrolysis* is a chemical process in which a compound unites with water and then splits into simpler compounds.) Numerous enzymes* present in the various digestive juices catalyze the hydrolysis of foods. (See Table 49.)

---

*The term enzyme means literally "in yeast." It was derived from the fact that these substances were first discovered in yeast cells. Enzymes are usually defined simply as "organic catalysts"; that is, they are organic compounds, and they accelerate chemical reactions without appearing in the final products of the reaction. Enzymes are vital substances. Without them, the chemical reactions necessary for life could not take place. So important are they that someone has even defined life as the "orderly functioning of hundreds of enzymes."

Chemical structure: Enzymes are proteins. Frequently their molecules also contain a nonprotein part called the *prosthetic group* of the enzyme molecule (if this group readily detaches from the rest of the molecule, it is spoken of as the *coenzyme*). Some prosthetic groups contain inorganic ions (Ca^{++}, Mg^{++}, Mn^{++}, etc.). Many of them contain vitamins. In fact, every vitamin of known function constitutes part of a prosthetic group of some enzyme. Nicotinic acid, thiamin, riboflavin, and other B complex vitamins, for example, function in this way.

Classification and naming: Two of the systems used for naming enzymes are as follows: suffix *ase* is used either with the root name of the substance whose chemical reaction is catalyzed (the substrate chemical, that is) or with the word that describes the kind of chemical reaction catalyzed. Thus, according to the first method, sucrase is an enzyme that catalyzes a chemical reaction in which sucrose takes part. According to the second method, sucrase might also be called hydrolase because it hydrolyzes sucrose. Enzymes investigated before these methods of nomenclature were adopted still are called by older names, such as ptyalin, pepsin, trypsin, etc.

Classified according to the kind of chemical reactions catalyzed, enzymes fall into several groups:

1. *Oxidation-reduction enzymes.* These are known as oxidases, hydrogenases, and dehydrogenases. Energy release for muscular contraction and all physiological work depends upon these enzymes.
2. *Hydrolyzing enzymes* or hydrolases. Digestive enzymes belong to this group. These are generally named after the substrate acted upon: for example, lipase, sucrase, maltase, etc.
3. *Phosphorylating enzymes.* These add or remove phosphate groups and are known as phosphorylases or phosphatases.
4. *Enzymes that add or remove carbon dioxide.* They are known as carboxylases or decarboxylases.
5. *Enzymes that rearrange atoms within a molecule.* These are known as mutases or isomerases.
6. *Hydrases.* These add water to a molecule without splitting it, as hydrolases do.

Enzymes are also classified as intracellular or extracellular, depending upon whether they act within cells or outside of them in the surrounding medium. Most enzymes act intracellularly in the body, an important exception being the digestive enzymes.

Properties: In general, the properties of enzymes are the same as those of proteins, since enzymes are proteins. For example, they form colloidal solutes in water and are precipitated or coagulated by various agents, such as high temperatures and salts of heavy metals. Hence, these agents inactivate enzymes. Other important enzyme properties are as follows.

1. Most enzymes are *specific in their action,* that is, act only on a specific substrate. This is attributed to a "key-in-a-lock" kind of action, the configuration of the enzyme molecule fitting the configuration of some part of the substrate molecule.

2. Enzymes *function optimally at a specific pH* and become inactive if this deviates beyond narrow limits.

3. A *variety of physical and chemical agents inactivate or inhibit enzyme action:* for example, x-rays and radium rays (this presumably accounts for some of the ill effects of excessive radiation), certain antibiotic drugs, unfavorable pH, etc.

4. *Most enzymes catalyze a chemical reaction in both directions,* the direction and rate of the reaction being governed by the law of mass action. An accumulation of a product slows the reaction and tends to reverse it. A practical application of this fact is the slowing of digestion when absorption is interfered with and the products of digestion accumulate.

5. *Enzymes are continually being destroyed in the body* and therefore have to be continually synthesized, even though they are not used up in the reactions they catalyze.

6. *Many enzymes are synthesized in an inactive form* that must be activated by some other substance before the enzyme can function. The kinases are such enzyme activators. For example, thrombokinase (thromboplastin) converts inactive prothrombin into active thrombin and enterokinase changes inactive trypsinogen into active trypsin, etc. *(End of footnote.)*

Table 49. Chemical digestion

Digestive juices and enzymes	*Food enzyme digests (or hydrolyzes)*	*Resulting product**
Saliva		
Amylase (ptyalin)	Starch (polysaccharide or complex sugar)	Maltose (a disaccharide or double sugar)
Gastric juice		
Protease (pepsin) plus hydrochloric acid	Proteins, including casein	Proteoses and peptones (partially digested proteins)
Lipase (of little importance)	Emulsified fats (butter, cream, etc.)	*Fatty acids and glycerol*
Bile contains no enzymes	Large fat droplets (unemulsified fats)	Small fat droplets or emulsified fats
Pancreatic juice		
Protease (trypsin)†	Proteins (either intact or partially digested)	Proteoses, peptides, and *amino acids*
Lipase (steapsin)	Bile-emulsified fats	*Fatty acids and glycerol*
Amylase (amylopsin)	Starch	Maltose
Intestinal juice (succus entericus)		
Peptidases	Peptides	*Amino acids*
Sucrase	Sucrose (cane sugar)	*Glucose and fructose*‡ (simple sugars or monosaccharides)
Lactase	Lactose (milk sugar)	*Glucose and galactose* (simple sugars)
Maltase	Maltose (malt sugar)	*Glucose* (grape sugar)

*Substances in italics are end products of digestion or, in other words, completely digested foods ready for absorption.
†Secreted in inactive form (trypsinogen); activated by enterokinase, an enzyme in the intestinal juice.
‡Glucose is also called dextrose; fructose is called levulose.

Although we eat six kinds of chemical substances (carbohydrates, proteins, fats, vitamins, mineral salts, and water), only the first three named have to be chemically digested in order to be absorbed.

Different enzymes require different hydrogen ion concentrations in their environment for optimal functioning. Ptyalin, the main enzyme in saliva, functions best in the neutral to slightly acid pH characteristic of saliva. It is gradually inactivated by the marked acidity of gastric juice. In contrast, pepsin, an enzyme in gastric juice, is inactive unless sufficient hydrochloric acid is present. Therefore, in diseases characterized by gastric hypoacidity (pernicious anemia, for example) hydrochloric acid is given orally before meals.

Carbohydrate digestion (Fig. 257). Carbohydrates are saccharide compounds. This means that their molecules contain one or more saccharide groups ($C_6H_{10}O_5$). Polysaccharides, notably starches, contain many of these groups, disaccharides (su-

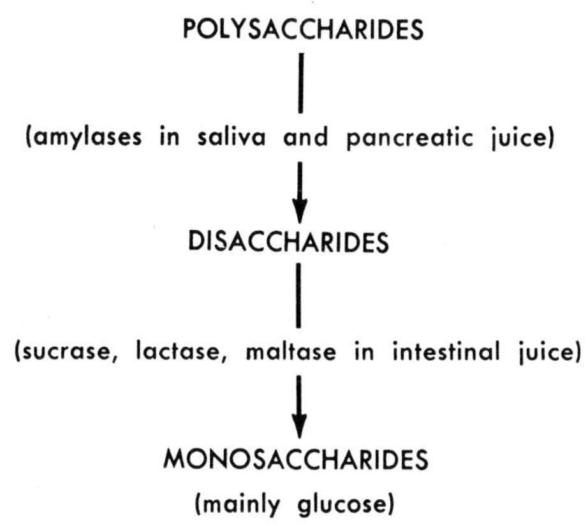

Fig. 257

Carboyhdrate digestion.

crose, lactose, and maltose) contain two of them, and monosaccharides (glucose, fructose, and galactose) contain only one. Polysaccharides are hydrolyzed to disaccharides by enzymes known as *amylases* found in saliva and pancreatic juice (salivary amylase is also called ptyalin and pancreatic amylase is also known as amylopsin). Disaccharides are hydrolyzed to monosaccharides by the intestinal juice enzymes sucrase, lactase, and maltase.

Protein digestion (Fig. 258). Protein compounds have very large molecules made up of amino acids. Enzymes called *proteases* catalyze the hydrolysis of proteins into intermediate compounds, for example, proteoses and peptides, and finally into amino acids. The main proteases are pepsin in gastric juice, trypsin in pancreatic juice, and peptidases in intestinal juice.

Fat digestion (Fig. 259). Because fats are insoluble in water, they must be emulsified, that is, dispersed as very small droplets before they can be digested. Bile emulsifies fats in the small intestine. This facilitates fat digestion by providing a greater contact area between fat molecules and pancreatic lipase, the main fat-digesting enzyme (pancreatic lipase was formerly known as steapsin). For a summary of the actions of each digestive juice, see Table 49.

Residues of digestion. Certain components of food resist digestion and are eliminated from the intestines in the feces. These *residues of digestion* are cellulose from carbohydrates, undigested connective tissue and toxins from meat proteins, and undigested fats. In addition to these wastes, feces consists of bacteria, pigments, water, and mucus.

Control of digestive gland secretion

Digestive glands secrete when food is present in the alimentary tract or when it

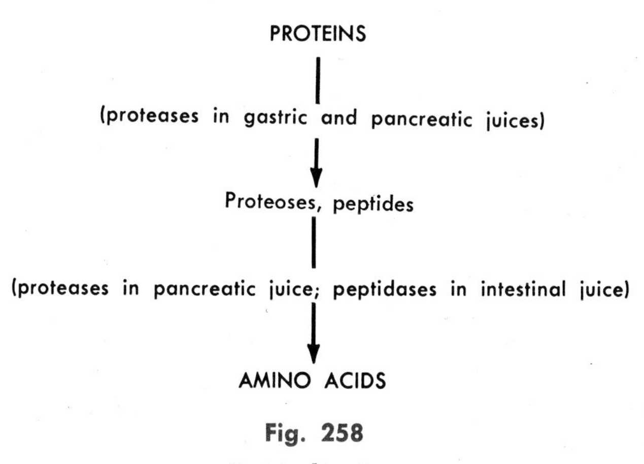

Fig. 258

Protein digestion.

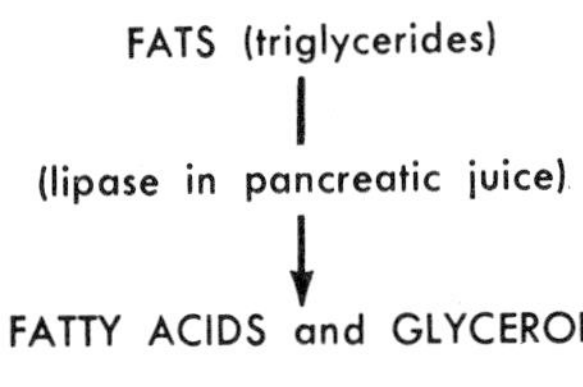

Fig. 259

Fat digestion by lipase, facilitated first by emulsion by bile.

is seen, smelled, or imagined. Complicated reflex and chemical (hormonal) mechanisms control the flow of digestive juices in such a way that they appear in proper amounts when and for as long as needed.

Saliva. As far as is known, only reflex mechanisms control the secretion of saliva. Chemical, mechanical, olfactory, and visual stimuli initiate afferent impulses to centers in the brainstem that send out efferent impulses to salivary glands, stimulating them. Chemical and mechanical stimuli come from the presence of food in the mouth, and olfactory and visual stimuli come from the smell and sight of food.

Gastric secretion. Stimulation of gastric juice secretion occurs in three phases controlled by reflex and chemical mechanisms. Because stimuli that activate these mechanisms arise in the head, stomach, and intestines, the three phases are known as the cephalic, gastric, and intestinal phases, respectively.

The *cephalic phase* is also spoken of as the reflex phase and as the psychic phase because a reflex mechanism controls gastric juice secretion at this time and psychic factors activate the mechanism. For example, the sight or smell or taste of food that is pleasing to an individual stimulates various head receptors and thereby initiates reflex stimulation of the gastric glands. Parasympathetic fibers in branches of the vagus nerve conduct the stimulating efferent impulses to the glands.

During the *gastric phase* of gastric juice secretion, the following chemical control mechanism dominates. Substances (such as meat extractives and products of protein digestion) in foods that have reached the pyloric portion of the stomach stimulate its mucosa to release a hormone called *gastrin* into the blood in stomach capillaries. When it circulates to the gastric glands, it greatly accelerates their secretion of gastric juice which has a high pepsin and hydrochloric acid content (see Table 50). Hence, this seems to be a device for ensuring that when food is in the stomach there will be enough enzymes there to digest it.

The *intestinal phase* of gastric juice secretion is less clearly understood than the other two. A chemical control mechanism, however, is believed to operate. And it is known, too, that the hormone *enterogastrone* (released by intestinal mucosa when fat is in the intestine) causes a lessening of both gastric secretion and motility.

Pancreatic secretion. Chemical control of pancreatic secretion has been established. Also, reflex control is postulated. Chemical control ensures continued pancreatic secretion while food is in the duodenum. The presence in the small intestine of hydrochloric acid, protein, and fat digestion products causes the intestinal mucosa to release a hormone, *secretin,* into the blood. When secretin circulates to the pancreas, it stimulates pancreatic cells to secrete at a faster rate. But the juice they produce has a low enzyme content. Another hormone, pancreozymin, stimulates them to produce enzymes. The presence of hydrochloric acid and partially digested proteins in the intestine serves as the stimulus for pancreozymin release by the intestinal mucosa.

Secretin has an interesting claim to fame. Not only was it the first hormone to be discovered, but its discovery gave rise to the broad concept of hormonal control of body activities.

Secretion of bile. Chemical mechanisms

Table 50. Actions of some digestive hormones summarized

Hormone	*Source*	*Action*
Gastrin	Formed by gastric mucosa in presence of partially digested proteins	Stimulates secretion of gastric juice rich in pepsin and HCl
Secretin	Formed by action of hydrochloric acid on prosecretin (chemical normally present in intestinal mucosa)	Stimulates secretion of pancreatic juice low in enzymes Stimulates secretion of bile by liver May stimulate secretion of intestinal juice
Pancreozymin	Formed by intestinal mucosa in presence of hydrochloric acid and partially digested proteins	Stimulates pancreatic cells to produce enzymes
Cholecystokinin	Formed by intestinal mucosa in presence of fats	Stimulates ejection of bile from gallbladder

dominate the control of bile. Secretin, the same hormone that stimulates pancreatic activity, stimulates the liver to secrete bile. The ejection of bile, however, from the gallbladder into the duodenum is largely controlled by another hormone, *cholecystokinin,* which is formed by the intestinal mucosa when fats are present in the duodenum.

Intestinal secretion. Knowledge concerning the regulation of the secretion of *intestinal juice* is still somewhat obscure. It is thought that the intestinal mucosa, stimulated by hydrochloric acid and food products, releases into the blood a hormone, *enterocrinin,* which brings about increased intestinal juice secretion. Presumably, neural mechanisms also help control the secretion of this digestive juice.

Absorption

Definition

The passage of substances (notably digested foods, water, salts, and vitamins) through the intestinal mucosa into the blood or lymph.

How accomplished

Absorption is not entirely a passive process explainable on the basis of the physical laws of diffusion, filtration, and osmosis alone. Investigation has shown that these phenomena play a part in absorption but that they are aided by active transport mechanisms. These are not clearly understood processes carried on by epithelial cells of the intestinal mucosa. They move substances in the opposite direction from that expected according to the laws of osmosis and diffusion.

The mechanism postulated for glucose absorption (Fig. 260) consists of these steps:

1. Glucose moves into cells of the intestinal mucosa presumably by diffusion and active transport.
2. Inside the mucosal cells, phosphorylation of the glucose molecule occurs immediately, presumably by the fol-

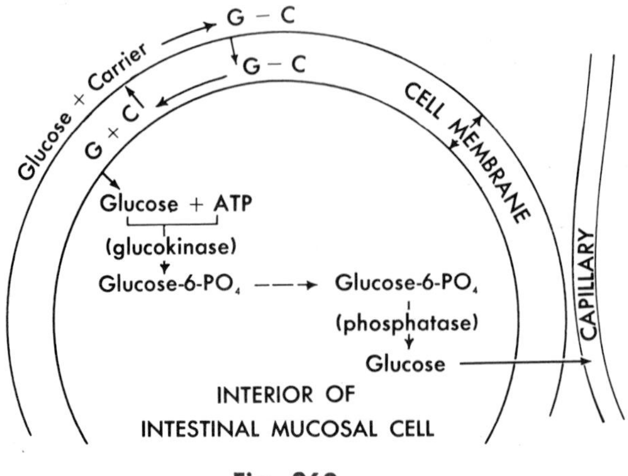

Fig. 260

Mucosal cell of villus actively transporting glucose from lumen of intestine into capillary.

lowing reaction catalyzed by the enzyme glucokinase:

$$\text{Glucose} + \text{ATP} \xrightarrow{\text{(Glucokinase)}} \text{Glucose-6-phosphate} + \text{ADP}$$

3. Glucose-6-phosphate diffuses across the mucosal cell, and near its surface adjacent to a blood capillary, the preceding equation is reversed, but by another enzyme, phosphatase. Glucose then moves out of the cell into the blood.

That an active transport mechanism operates for the absorption of amino acids is a conclusion supported by considerable evidence. But a definite description of the mechanism is still lacking. And the mechanism for fat absorption is also not clear, although it, too, is thought to involve some kind of active transport. It is known, however, that some fatty acids and glycerol enter intestinal mucosal cells and there recombine to form neutral fats which then move out of the cells into lymphatic capillaries (lacteals) in the intestinal villi. In addition, some fatty acids are absorbed as such into blood capillaries. Also, some neutral fats are absorbed without first being hydrolyzed to fatty acids and glycerol.

Active transport mechanisms seem to be available also for water and salt absorption. And apparently some sort of mechanism exists for preventing absorption of certain substances. Magnesium sulfate (Epsom salts), for example, is not absorbed from the intestine even though its molecules are smaller than glucose molecules which can diffuse through the intestinal mucosa. In fact, it is this nonabsorbability of magnesium sulfate that makes it an effective cathartic. (Since magnesium sulfates do not diffuse freely through the intestinal mucosa, do you think their presence in intestinal fluid would create an osmotic pressure gradient between the intestinal fluid and blood? If so, what effect would this have on water movement between these two fluids? Reread pp. 24 to 29 if you need help in answering these questions.)

Note that after absorption food does not pass directly into the general circulation. Instead it is first carried via the portal system to the liver. During intestinal absorption, blood entering the liver via the portal

Table 51. Food absorption

Form absorbed	*Structures into which absorbed*	*Circulation*
Protein—as amino acids Perhaps minute quantities of some whole proteins absorbed—e.g., in allergic reactions	Blood in intestinal capillaries	Portal vein, liver, hepatic vein, inferior vena cava to heart, etc.
Carbohydrates—as simple sugars	Same as amino acids	Same as amino acids
Fats Glycerol Fatty acids combine with bile salts to form water-soluble substance Some finely emulsified undigested fats absorbed	Lymph in intestinal lacteals Lymph in intestinal lacteals Small fraction enters intestinal blood capillaries	During absorption, i.e., while in epithelial cells of intestinal mucosa, glycerol and fatty acids recombine to form microscopic particles of fats (chylomicrons); lymphatics carry them by way of thoracic duct to left subclavian vein, superior vena cava, heart, etc. Some fats transported by blood in form of phospholipids or cholesterol esters

vein contains greater concentrations of glucose, amino acids, and fats than does blood leaving the liver via the hepatic vein for the systemic circulation. Clearly, the excess of these food substances, over and above the normal blood levels, has remained behind in the liver.

What the liver does with them is part of the story of metabolism, our next topic for discussion.

Metabolism

MEANING

Foods are first digested, then absorbed, and, finally, metabolized. Metabolism, as the word is usually defined, means the chemical changes absorbed foods undergo within the body cells. More simply, metabolism is the body's utilization of foods. Digestion and absorption are merely preliminary steps or preparations for metabolism.

WAYS IN WHICH FOODS METABOLIZED

Foods consist of six kinds of chemical compounds: carbohydrates, proteins, fats, vitamins, inorganic salts (or minerals), and water. The body utilizes or metabolizes these substances in two general ways—catabolizes them to make their stored energy available for cellular work and anabolizes them to build protoplasm, enzymes, hormones, and other complex compounds.

Research has unlocked some of the secrets of anabolism. Brilliant work by many investigators has disclosed some of the actual events that take place inside cells as they build the small, simple food molecules up into the large, complex molecules of enzymes and hosts of other compounds. A full description of this does not seem appropriate in a book of this kind. But if you enjoy reading exciting though not easy material, by all means read the articles cited in the footnote.* And for a brief description of protein anabolism, see p. 414. Anabolism is one of the most important kinds of work that cells do. Such vital functions as cell growth and repair and reproduction, for example, are achieved through the process of anabolism.

The relationship between anabolism and catabolism is worth noting. Anabolism depends upon catabolism. Catabolism must occur in order that anabolism may occur. Why? Because catabolism provides the energy for the work of anabolism. Energy is stored in ATP molecules during catabolism and is released from them during anabolism.

CARBOHYDRATE METABOLISM

A physiological principle worth noting is that carbohydrates are the body's "preferred fuel." Normally, body cells "burn," that is, catabolize carbohydrates in order to carry on their many kinds of work and survive. They use fats and proteins as secondary or supplementary fuels if their glucose supply becomes inadequate for one reason or another. Physiologists sometimes express this idea by saying that cells "shift" from carbohydrate to fat or protein utilization when the amount of glucose entering them proves too meager for their energy needs. This most commonly occurs when a person goes without food for many hours or when he has untreated diabetes mellitus. How the shift from carbohydrate to fat or protein utilization is brought about is discussed on pp. 407 and 414. Now we shall consider the processes involved in carbohydrate metabolism and then turn to the mechanisms that control them.

Glucose transport through cell membranes and phosphorylation

Carbohydrate metabolism starts with the active transport of glucose through cell membranes. Immediately upon reaching the interior of the cell, glucose reacts with ATP to produce glucose-6-phosphate. The reaction is referred to as glucose phosphorylation and is catalyzed by the enzyme glucokinase (or glucose hexokinase). Next, glucose-6-phosphate is either anabolized or catabolized.

Glycogenesis and glycogenolysis

Glycogenesis is a process of glucose anabolism. Simply defined, glycogenesis is the formation of glycogen from glucose. Notice in Fig. 261 that glycogenesis consists of a series of chemical reactions, each one catalyzed by a different enzyme. Glycogen molecules do not remain permanently in the cell but from time to time are broken down or hydrolyzed back to glucose-6-phosphate or, in certain cells, all the way back to glucose. This reversal of the process of glycogenesis, this hydrolysis of glycogen, is called *glycogenolysis*. Now look at Fig. 262. Phosphorylase, the enzyme that catalyzes the first reaction of glycogenolysis, is presumably present in all cells. But phosphatase (glucose phosphatase), the enzyme that catalyzes the final step of glycogenolysis—the changing of glucose-6-phosphate back to glucose—is lacking in most cells. Only liver cells, intestinal mucosal cells, and kidney tubule cells contain glucose phosphatase. Therefore, the term glycogenolysis means different things in different cells. *Muscle cell glycogenolysis*, for example, means the conversion of glycogen to glucose-6-phosphate, but *liver glycogenolysis* means the chang-

---

*Rich, Alexander: Polyribosomes, Sci. Amer. **209**:44 (Dec.), 1963; Nossal, G. J. V.: How cells make antibodies, Sci. Amer. **211**:106 (Dec.), 1964; Hurwitz, J., and Furth, J. J.: Messenger RNA, Sci. Amer. **206**:41 (Feb.), 1962.

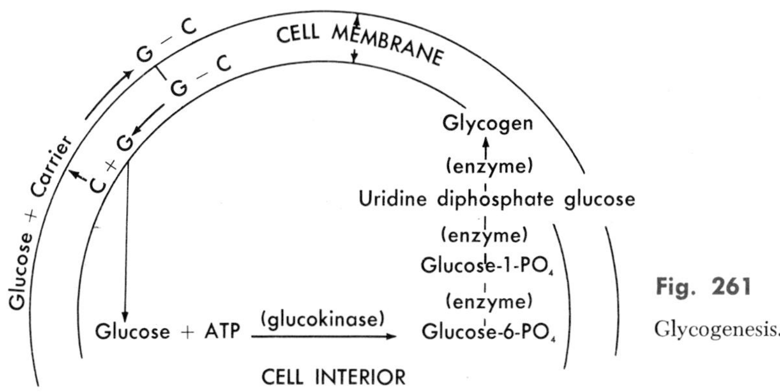

Fig. 261
Glycogenesis.

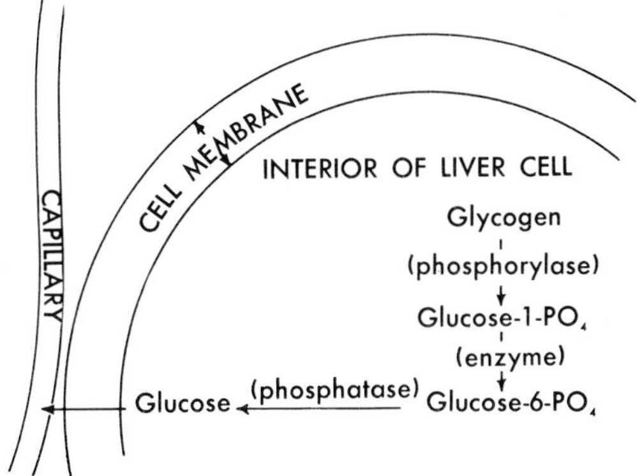

Fig. 262
Glycogenolysis in a liver cell.

ing of glycogen to glucose and the addition of this glucose to the bloodstream. Carbohydrate catabolism was described on pp. 33 to 38. Reread these pages carefully if you are not sure of the answers to the following questions:

1. What two processes make up the larger process of glucose catabolism?
2. What overall chemical change occurs in glycolysis? In the citric acid cycle?
3. What energy change occurs in glycolysis? In the citric acid cycle?
4. Where do glycolysis and the citric acid cycle occur?

Gluconeogenesis

Gluconeogenesis means literally the formation of "new" glucose—"new" in the sense that it is made from proteins or fats, not from carbohydrates. The process, which occurs in the liver, consists of many complex chemical reactions. The new glucose produced from fats or proteins by gluconeogenesis diffuses out of liver cells into the blood (Fig. 263). Gluconeogenesis, therefore, can add glucose to the blood when needed, as can the process of liver glycogenolysis. Obviously, then, the liver is a most important organ for maintaining blood glucose homeostasis.

Control of glucose metabolism

The complex mechanism that normally maintains homeostasis of blood glucose concentration consists of hormonal and neural devices. At least five endocrine

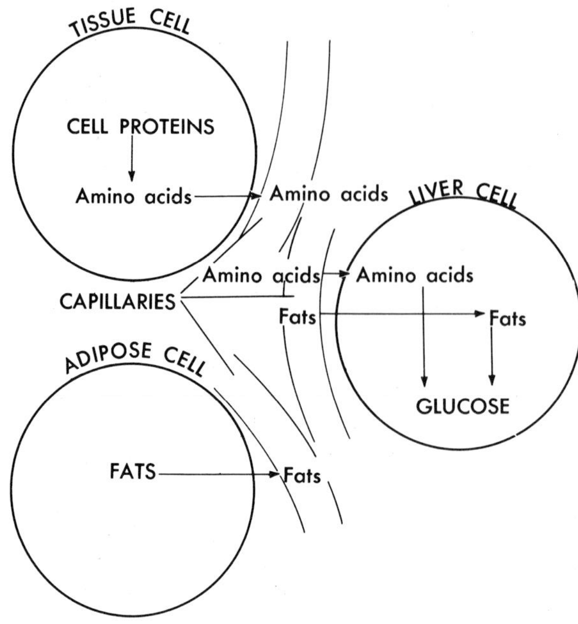

Fig. 263

Liver gluconeogenesis from mobilized tissue proteins and fats.

glands—islands of Langerhans, anterior pituitary gland, adrenal cortex, adrenal medulla, and thyroid gland—and at least eight hormones secreted by those glands function as key parts of the glucose homeostatic mechanism.

Beta cells of the islands of Langerhans in the pancreas secrete the most famous sugar-regulating hormone of them all, *insulin.* Although no one yet knows exactly how insulin acts, several of its effects are well known. For instance, insulin is known to act in some way to accelerate glucose transport through cell membranes and to increase the activity of the enzyme glucokinase. As shown in Fig. 261, glucokinase catalyzes glucose phosphorylation, the reaction which must occur before either glycogenesis or glucose catabolism can take place. By applying these facts, you can deduce for yourself some of the prominent metabolic defects resulting from insulin deficiency such as occurs in diabetes mellitus. Slow glycogenesis with resulting low glycogen storage, decreased glucose catabolism, and increased blood glucose all result from the slower glucose transport into cells and the decreased glucokinase activity produced by insulin deficiency.

The islands of Langerhans secrete two sugar-regulating hormones—insulin from the beta cells and glucagon from the alpha cells. Whereas insulin tends to decrease blood glucose, glucagon tends to increase it. *Glucagon* increases the activity of the enzyme phosphorylase (Fig. 262), and this necessarily accelerates liver glycogenolysis and releases more of its product, glucose, into the blood.

The anterior pituitary gland (adenohypophysis) also secretes three hormones that help regulate carbohydrate metabolism particularly in times of stress. Growth hormone, adrenocorticotrophin hormone (ACTH), and thyroid-stimulating hormone are their names.

Growth hormone tends to bring about a shift from carbohydrate utilization to fat utilization. Less glucose, therefore, leaves the blood to enter cells or, stated the other way around, more glucose remains in the blood. In other words, blood glucose tends to increase. Growth hormone presumably brings about this shift to fat utilization by influencing several processes. It appears to act in some way to decrease the deposition of fats in adipose tissue, to increase the mobilization of fats from adipose tissue, and to decrease carbohydrate utilization by all tissues.

ACTH also tends to increase blood glucose concentration, but it does it in a different and an even more indirect way than does growth hormone. ACTH stimulates the adrenal cortex to increase its secretion of glucocorticoids. Glucocorticoids accelerate the mobilization of proteins, that is, the breakdown or hydrolysis of tissue proteins to amino acids. More amino acids enter the circulation and are carried to the liver. Liver cells step up their production of "new" glucose from the mobilized amino acids. Gluconeogenesis accelerates, if you prefer more technical language. More glucose streams out of liver cells into the blood and adds to the blood glucose level. In short, growth hormone and glucocorticoids are hyperglycemic hormones. They both tend to increase blood glucose concentration, in other words. And ACTH also is hyperglycemic, but only indirectly through its effects on glucocorticoid secretion.

The anterior pituitary gland's thyroid-stimulating hormone (thyrotrophin) stimulates the thyroid gland to increase its secretion of thyroid hormone. Thyroid hormone accelerates catabolism—usually glucose catabolism since glucose is the body's "preferred fuel."

Epinephrine is a hormone secreted in large amounts by the adrenal medulla in times of emotional or physical stress. Like the hormone glucagon secreted by the alpha islet cells, epinephrine increases phosphorylase activity (Fig. 262). This makes liver glycogenolysis go on at a faster rate and causes more of its product, glucose, to enter the blood. Epinephrine accelerates both liver and muscle glycogenolysis, whereas glucagon accelerates only liver glycogenolysis.

In summary, glucose metabolism is regulated mainly by the following hormones:

1. *Insulin,* a hypoglycemic hormone—that is, it tends to decrease blood glucose
2. Glucagon, epinephrine, growth hormone, ACTH, glucocorticoids, and hyperglycemic hormones—that is, they tend to increase blood glucose
3. Thyroid-stimulating hormone and thyroid hormone—ordinarily tend to decrease blood glucose

• • •

Some important principles about normal carbohydrate metabolism may be summarized as follows.

1. *Principle of "preferred energy fuel."* All body cells catabolize glucose for their needed energy supply when the amount of glucose and the amount of insulin in the blood are adequate. Glucose is the "preferred energy fuel" of human cells—preferred to fat and protein, that is. Therefore, cells get their energy first from glucose—for as long as enough of it continues to enter them—then next from fats, and last from proteins.

2. *Principle of glycogenesis.* The process of glycogenesis is part of a homeostatic mechanism that operates when blood glucose concentration increases above the midpoint of its normal range. When blood glucose concentration increases, glycogenesis also increases. This soon decreases blood

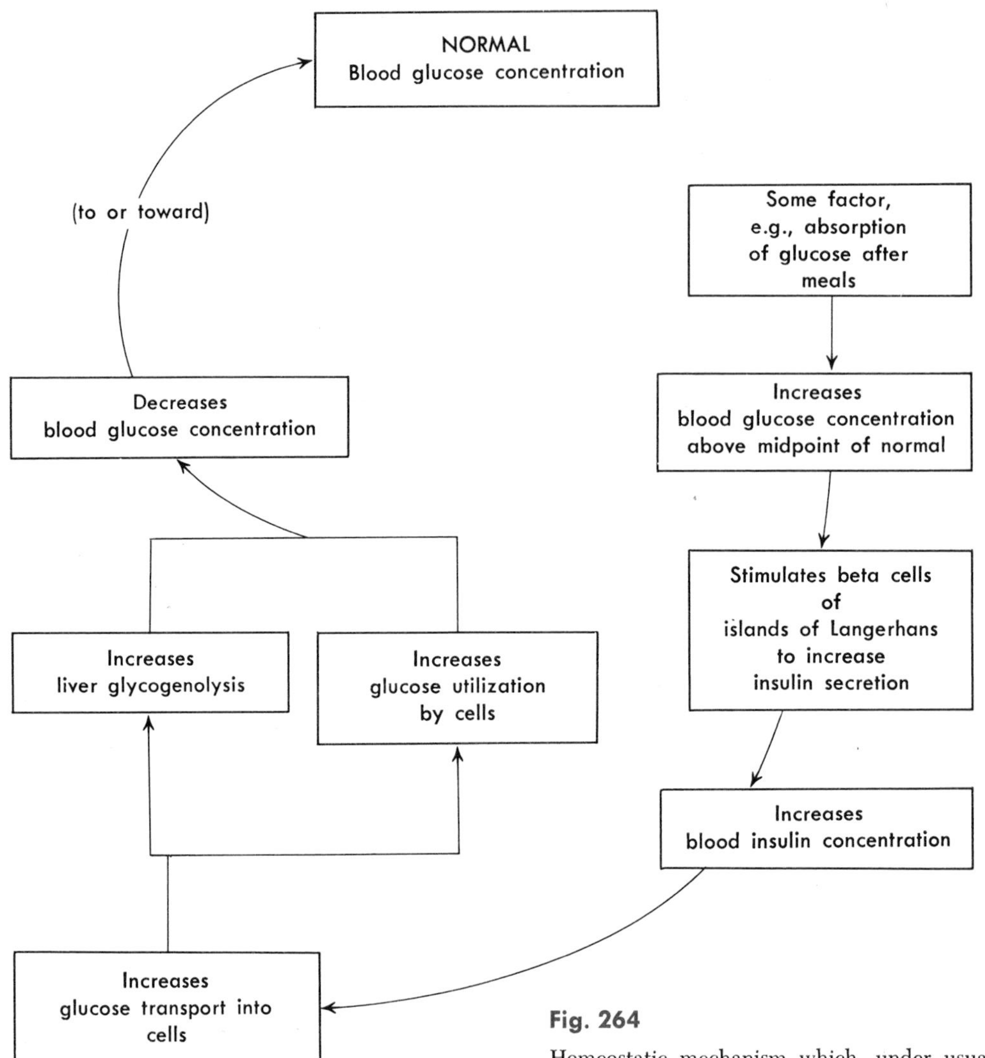

Fig. 264

Homeostatic mechanism which, under usual conditions, prevents blood glucose concentration from increasing above the upper limit of normal. This mechanism and the one shown in Fig. 265 operate together to maintain homeostasis of blood glucose under usual circumstances in the normal body.

glucose, ordinarily enough to maintain its normal level. Example: soon after meals, while glucose is being absorbed rapidly, a great many glucose molecules leave the blood for storage as glycogen—mainly in liver cells but also in muscle and various other cells (see Fig. 264).

3. *Principle of glycogenolysis.* The process of liver glycogenolysis is part of a homeostatic mechanism that operates when blood glucose concentration decreases below the midpoint of its normal range. When blood glucose concentration decreases, liver glycogenolysis increases (see Fig. 265). Example: a few hours after meals, when blood glucose decreases below the midpoint of normal, liver glycogenolysis accelerates. This, of course, adds glu-

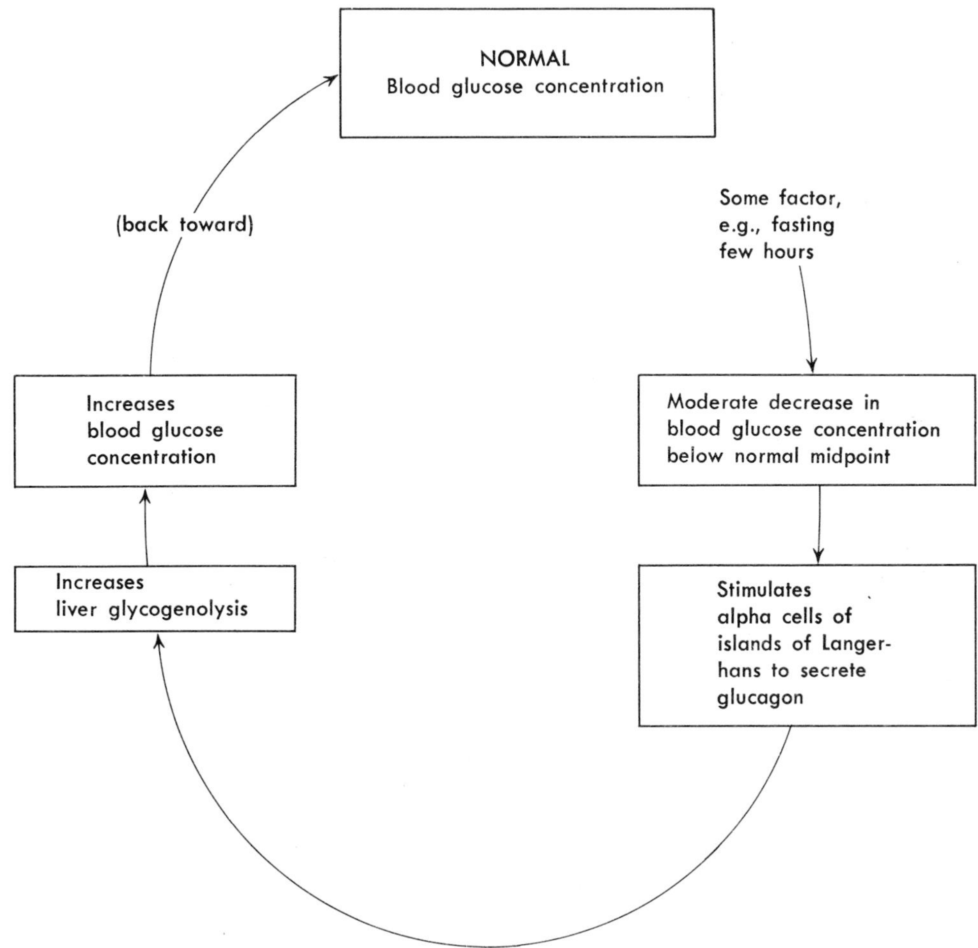

Fig. 265

Homeostatic mechanism which, under usual conditions, is chiefly responsible for preventing blood glucose from falling below the lower limit of normal. This mechanism and the one shown in Fig. 264 work together to maintain homeostasis of blood glucose in the normal body under usual circumstances. See Fig. 266 for mechanism that controls carbohydrate metabolism under stress conditions.

cose molecules to blood and tends to raise glucose concentration back up to the midpoint of normal. However, glycogenolysis alone can probably maintain homeostasis of blood glucose concentration only a few hours since the body can store only modest amounts of glycogen.

4. *Principle of gluconeogenesis.* Liver gluconeogenesis is another part of the homeostatic mechanism that operates when blood glucose decreases below the midnormal point. When this happens or when the amount of glucose entering cells is inadequate (for example, in diabetes mellitus), liver gluconeogenesis accelerates and tends to raise blood glucose concentration back to normal.

5. *Principle of glucose storage as fat.* If blood glucose still remains higher than nor-

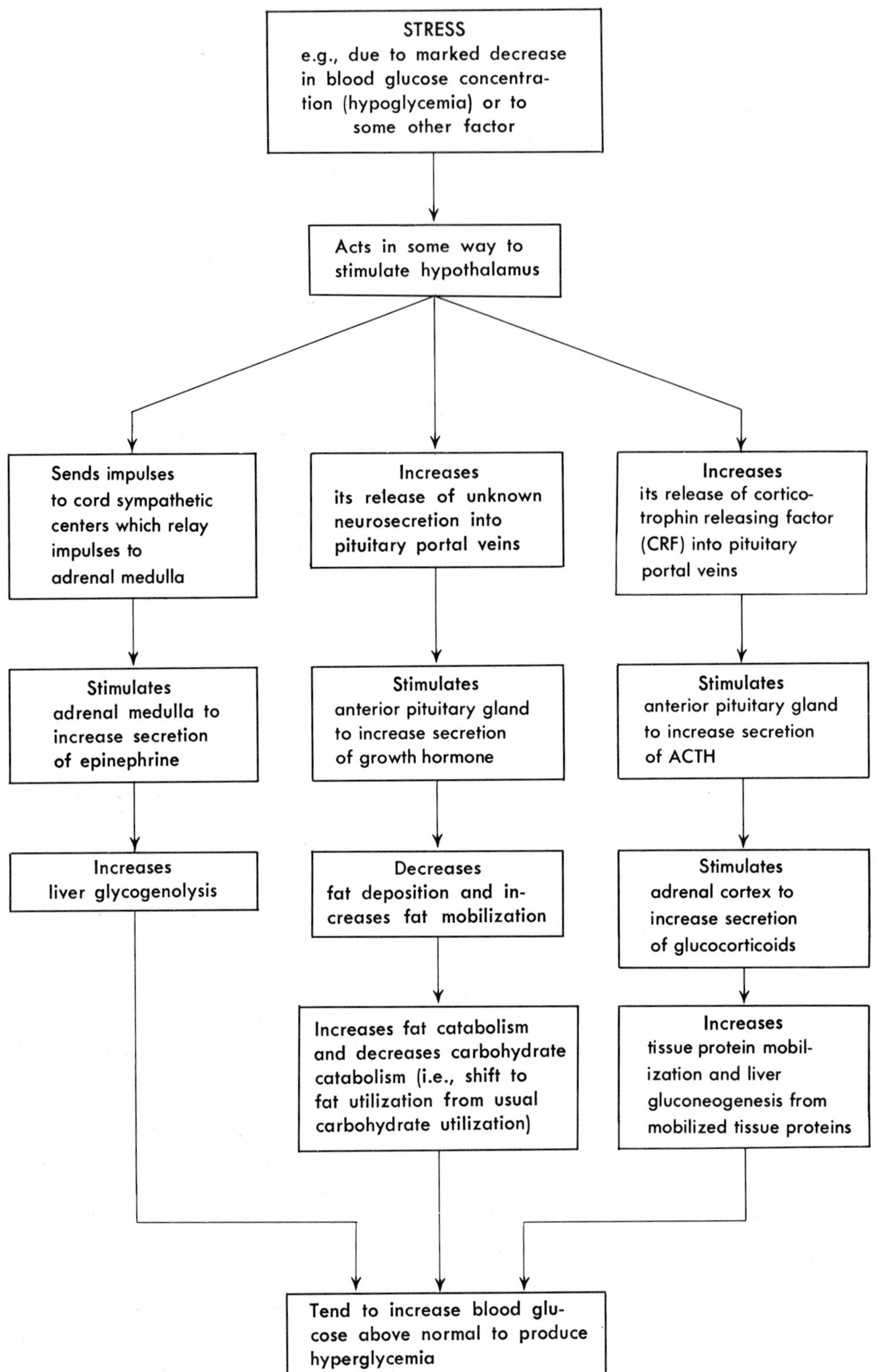

Fig. 266

Mechanism that dominates control of carbohydrate metabolism under conditions of stress and that tends to produce hyperglycemia under these conditions.

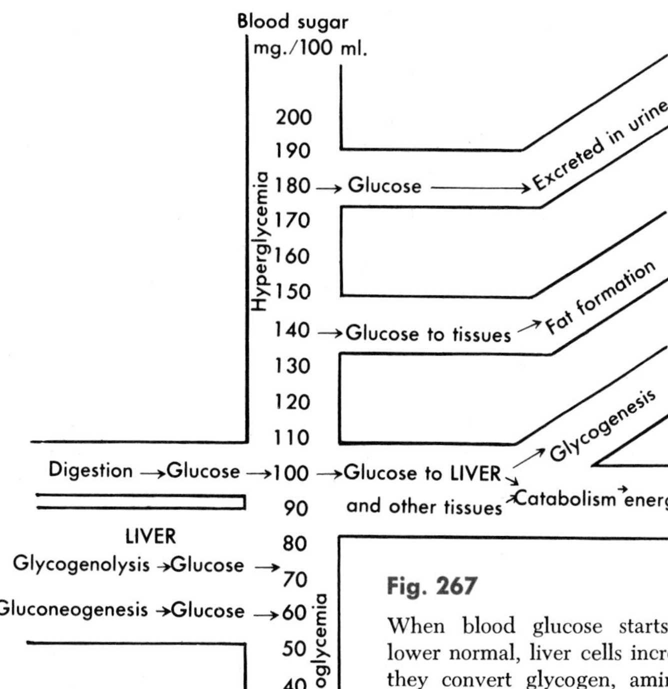

Fig. 267

When blood glucose starts to decrease toward lower normal, liver cells increase the rate at which they convert glycogen, amino acids, and fats to glucose (glycogenolysis and gluconeogenesis) and release it into blood. But when blood glucose increases, liver cells increase the rate at which they remove glucose molecules from blood and convert them to glycogen for storage (glycogenesis). At still higher levels, glucose leaves blood for tissue cells to be anabolized into adipose tissue and at still higher levels is excreted in the urine.

mal after glycogenesis and catabolism and if the blood insulin content is adequate, the excess glucose is converted to fat (mainly by liver cells) and is stored as such in fat depots—in adipose tissue, in other words. Unfortunately from the standpoint of health and beauty, the amount of glucose the body can store as fat is virtually unlimited.

FAT METABOLISM

Body cells both catabolize and anabolize fats. Fats constitute a more concentrated energy food than carbohydrates. Catabolism of 1 gram of fat yields 9 Calories of heat, catabolism of 1 gram of carbohydrates yields only 4.1 Calories. *Fat catabolism*, like carbohydrate catabolism, consists of two main processes each of which, in turn, consists of a series of chemical reactions. The first process in fat catabolism is called *ketogenesis,* which means the formation of ketone bodies. Liver cells carry on most of the ketogenesis for the body. It consists of the following steps: first, the hydrolysis of fat to form fatty acids and glycerol, next, a series of chemical reactions (known as beta oxidations) by which fatty acids are converted to coenzyme A, and, last, the conversion of acetyl coenzyme A to acetoacetic acid (by a process called condensation). Acetoacetic acid is a ketone body. Some of it undergoes a chemical change to become two other ketone bodies, acetone and β-hydroxybutyric acid. Ketone bodies are oxidized via the citric acid cycle. In other

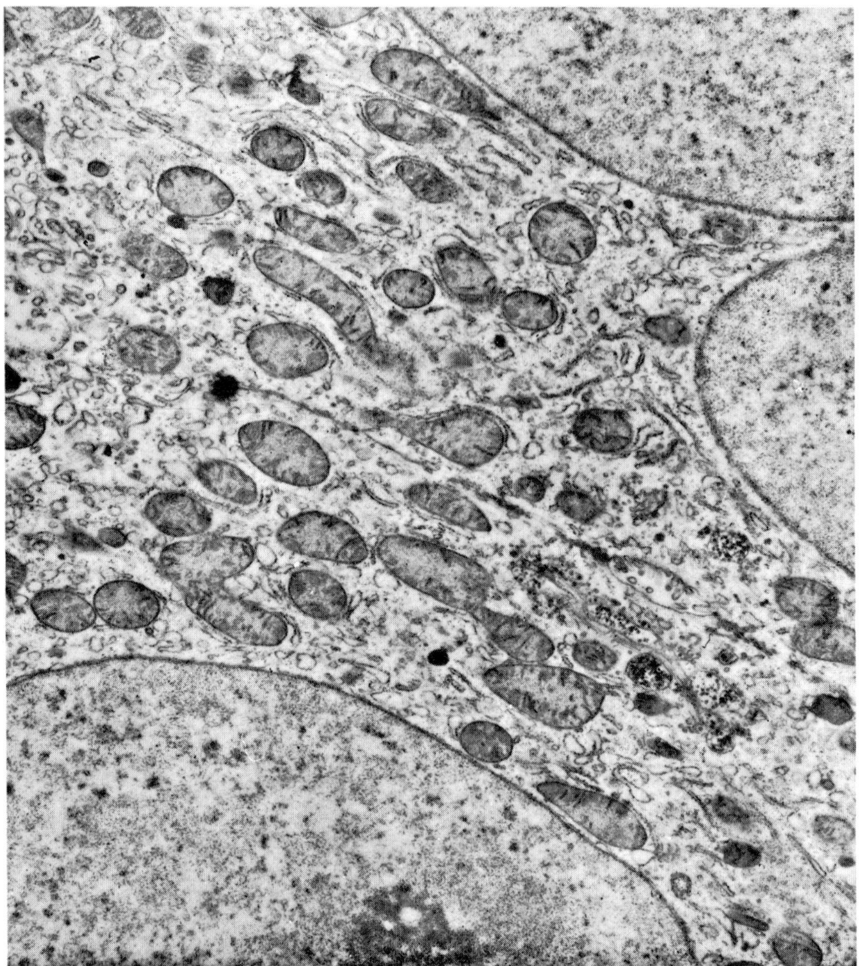

Fig. 268

Electron microphotograph of mouse liver. Numerous mitochondria are visible in the midportion of the photograph. (×25,000.) (Courtesy Department of Pathology, Western Reserve University, Cleveland, Ohio.)

words, the final step of fat catabolism and of glucose catabolism are the same. Liver cells oxidize a small portion of the ketone bodies for their own energy needs, but most of them are transported by the blood to other tissue cells for the final step of catabolism. Glycerol is metabolized similarly to glucose.

Fat anabolism (fat deposition or lipogenesis) consists of the storage of fats mainly in adipose tissue. It also includes the use of fats in the synthesis of protoplasm and various complex compounds. Fats stored in the fat depots constitute the body's largest reserve energy source—too large too often, unfortunately.

Control

Fat metabolism is controlled mainly by the following hormones: insulin, growth hormone, ACTH, and glucocorticoids. You probably recall from our discussion of these

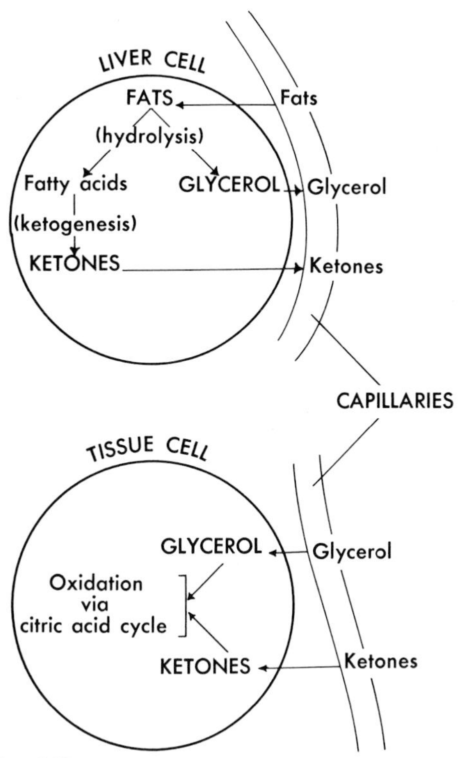

Fig. 269

Fat catabolism consisting of, first, ketogenesis by liver cells and, second, of oxidation by tissue and liver cells.

hormones in connection with carbohydrate metabolism that they regulate fat metabolism in such a way that the rate of fat utilization is inversely related to the rate of carbohydrate utilization. If some condition such as diabetes mellitus causes carbohydrate utilization to decrease below energy needs, increased secretion of growth hormone, ACTH, and glucocorticoids soon follows (see Fig. 266). And these hormones, in turn, bring about an increase in fat utilization. (More details are given on pp. 496 and 506). But when carbohydrate utilization equals energy needs, fats are not mobilized out of storage and catabolized. Instead, they are spared and stored in adipose tissue. "Carbohydrates have a fat-sparing effect," so says an old physiological maxim. Or, a more descriptive way of stating this truth, as anyone who indulges in too many sweets would agree, is "carbohydrates have a 'fat-storing' effect."

PROTEIN METABOLISM

In protein metabolism, anabolism is primary and catabolism is secondary. In carbohydrate and fat metabolism the opposite

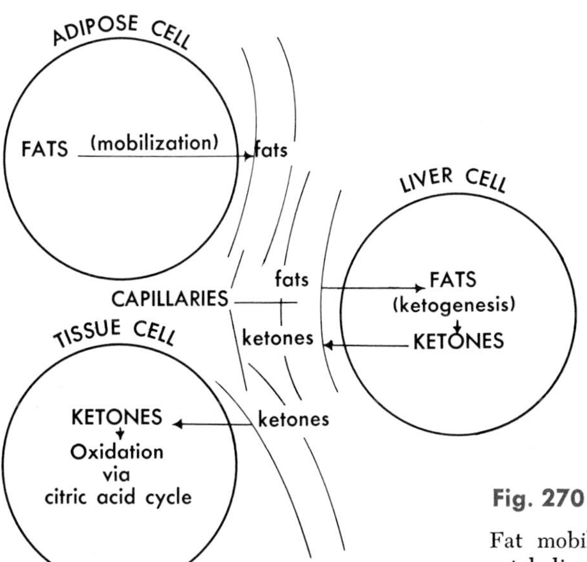

Fig. 270

Fat mobilization from adipose cell followed by catabolism (ketogenesis and citric acid cycle).

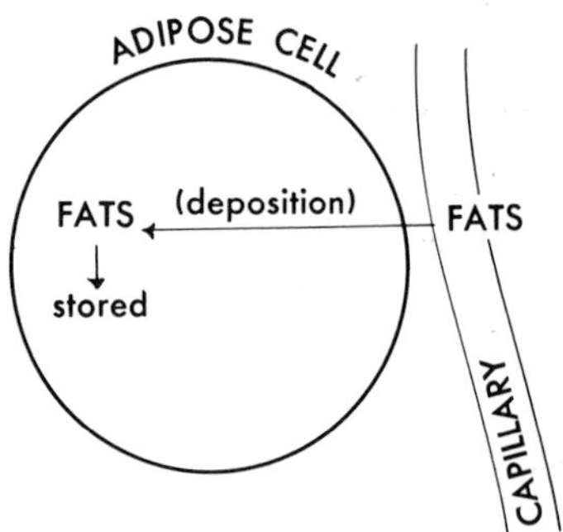

Fig. 271

Fat deposition (lipogenesis or fat anabolism).

is true—catabolism is primary and anabolism is secondary. Proteins are primarily tissue-building foods. Carbohydrates and fats are primarily energy-supplying foods.

The cellular process called protein synthesis (or protein anabolism) produces many substances—enzymes, antibodies, and secretions, to name some noteworthy ones. Protein anabolism plays a major role in the growth and reproduction both of cells and of the body as a whole. And protein anabolism is also the chief process of repair. It accomplishes the healing of wounds, the formation of scar tissue, and the replacement of cells destroyed by daily wear and tear. Protein anabolism is truly "big business" in the body. Red blood cell replacement alone, for instance, runs into millions of cells per second.

A brief synopsis of the process of protein anabolism as now visualized is as follows. First, a gene (a segment of a DNA molecule) directs the formation of a molecule of "messenger RNA," thereby transferring to it the gene's instructions for synthesizing a specific protein. As soon as it is formed, the messenger RNA diffuses out of the nucleus and goes to one of the many ribosomes located in the cytoplasm of the cell. (Ribosomes, you will recall, are the cell's tiny protein factories. They consist of protein and RNA, the latter identified as ribosomal or template RNA.) Next, a molecule of "transfer RNA," present in cytoplasm, attaches itself to a molecule of a specific amino acid and transfers it to a ribosome, where it fits it into its proper position as indicated by the messenger RNA. More transfer RNA molecules, one after the other in rapid sequence, bring more amino acids to the ribosome and fit them into their proper positions. Result? A chain of amino acids joined to each other in a definite sequence—a protein, in other words. Thus is

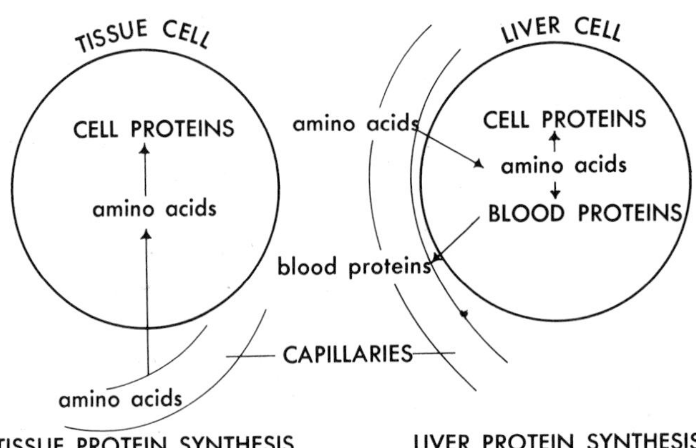

Fig. 272

Protein synthesis (anabolism). Growth hormone and testosterone tend to accelerate the processes shown so are called anabolic hormones.

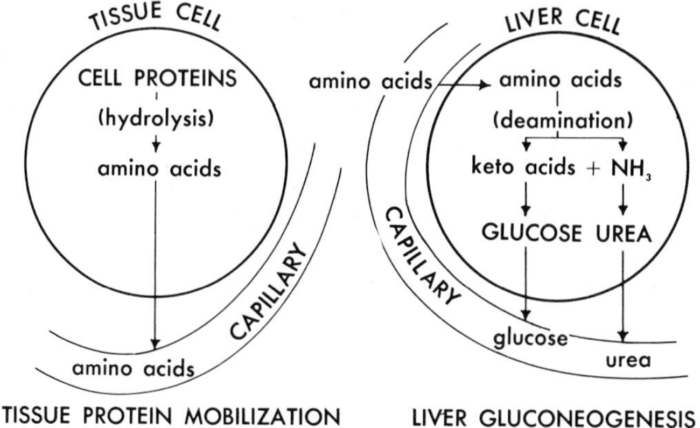

Fig. 273

Protein mobilization and catabolism. Glucocorticoids tend to accelerate these processes so are classed as protein catabolic hormones.

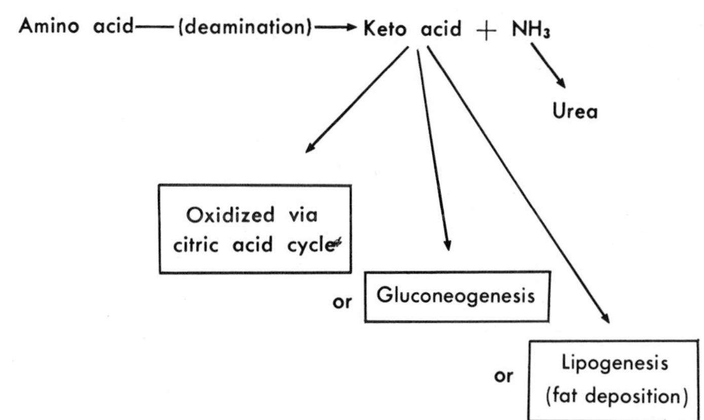

Fig. 274

Protein catabolism. First, liver cells carry on deamination, a process that converts amino acids to keto acids and ammonia. Then keto acids may be changed to glucose by liver cells (gluconeogenesis), or liver and tissue cells may oxidize them (citric acid cycle) or convert them to fat (lipogenesis).

protein anabolism achieved through the combined work of messenger RNA, transfer RNA, and template or ribosomal RNA. Protein anabolism is a major kind of cellular work. One human cell, for example, is estimated to synthesize perhaps two thousand different enzymes. And, in addition, many cells produce special proteins such as antibodies by plasma cells, fibrinogen by liver cells, and various protein hormones by endocrine gland cells.*

Protein catabolism, like the catabolism of fats, consists of two processes. The first takes place mainly in liver cells and the second is the citric acid cycle and occurs in all cells. The first step in protein catab-

*For more details about protein synthesis, see suggested supplementary readings for Chapter XI, reference 5, p. 549.

olism is known as *deamination,* a reaction in which an amino (NH_2) group is split off from an amino acid molecule to form a molecule of ammonia and one of keto acid. Most of the ammonia is converted to urea and is excreted via the urine. The keto acid may be oxidized via the tricarboxylic acid cycle or may be converted to glucose (gluconeogenesis) or to fat (lipogenesis). Formerly, protein catabolism was believed to occur only when the amount of protein ingested exceeded that needed for anabolism. But now it is known that both protein catabolism and anabolism go on continually. Only their rates differ from time to time. With a protein-deficient diet, for example, protein catabolism exceeds protein anabolism. And various hormones, as we shall see, also influence the rates of protein catabolism and anabolism.

Usually a state of *protein balance* exists in the normal healthy adult body. That is, the rate of protein anabolism equals or balances the rate of protein catabolism. And when the body is in protein balance, it is also in a state of *nitrogen balance.* For then, the amount of nitrogen taken into the body (in protein foods) equals the amount of nitrogen in protein catabolic waste products excreted in the urine, feces, and sweat. Two kinds of protein or nitrogen imbalance exist. When protein catabolism exceeds protein anabolism, the amount of nitrogen in the urine exceeds the amount of nitrogen in the protein foods ingested. The individual is then said to be in a state of *negative nitrogen balance.* Or, in a state of "tissue wasting"—because more of his tissue proteins are being catabolized than are being replaced by protein synthesis. Protein-poor diets, starvation, and wasting illnesses, for example, produce a negative nitrogen balance.

A *positive nitrogen balance* (nitrogen intake in foods greater than nitrogen output in urine) indicates that protein anabolism is going on at a faster rate than protein catabolism. A state of positive nitrogen balance, therefore, characterizes any condition in which large amounts of tissue are being synthesized, as during growth, pregnancy, and convalescence from an emaciating illness.

The main facts about protein metabolism are summarized in Figs. 272 to 274. Compare them with Figs. 267 and 269 to 271. Note the important part played by the liver in the metabolism of all three kinds of foods.

Control

Protein metabolism, like that of carbohydrates and fats, is controlled largely by hormones rather than by the nervous system. Growth hormone and the male hormone testosterone both have a stimulating effect on protein synthesis or anabolism. For this reason, they are referred to as anabolic hormones. Protein catabolic hormones of greatest consequence are glucocorticoids. They are thought to act in some way, still unknown, to speed up tissue protein mobilization, that is, the hydrolysis of cell proteins to amino acids, their entry into the blood, and their subsequent catabolism (Fig. 273). ACTH functions indirectly as a protein catabolic hormone because of its stimulating effect on glucocorticoid secretion.

Thyroid hormone is necessary for and tends to promote protein anabolism and, therefore, growth when plenty of carbohydrates and fats are available for energy production. On the other hand, under different conditions, for example, when the amount of thyroid hormone is excessive or when the energy foods are deficient, this hormone may then promote protein mobilization and catabolism.

• • •

Some of the facts about metabolism set forth in the preceding paragraphs are summarized in Table 52.

Table 52. Metabolism

Food	*Anabolism*	*Catabolism*
Carbohydrates	Temporary excess changed into glycogen by liver cells in presence of insulin; stored in liver and skeletal muscles until needed and then changed back to glucose (Figs. 261 and 262) True excess beyond body's energy requirements converted into adipose tissue; stored in various fat depots of body	Oxidized, in presence of insulin, to yield energy (4.1 Calories per gram) and wastes (carbon dioxide and water) $C_6H_{12}O_6 + 6O_2 \longrightarrow$ energy + $6CO_2 + 6H_2O$
Fats	Built into adipose tissue; stored in fat depots of body	Fatty acids ↓ (liver ketogenesis) ketone bodies ↓ (tissues; citric acid cycle) energy (9.3 Calories per gram) + $CO_2 + H_2O$ Glycerol ↓ (liver gluconeogenesis) glucose
Proteins	Temporary excess stored in liver and skeletal muscles Synthesized into tissue proteins, blood proteins, enzymes, hormones, etc.	Deaminated by liver forming ammonia (which is converted to urea) and keto acids (which are either oxidized or changed to glucose or fat)

METABOLISM OF VITAMINS, MINERAL SALTS, AND WATER

Vitamins are substances that were recognized as necessary for life and health before their chemical composition was known. They constitute part of the chemical mechanisms for controlling body activities. All those of known function are components of enzyme molecules. Therefore, they are necessary for numerous physiological reactions. Without adequate amounts of the various vitamins, normal energy production, growth and development, reproduction, resistance to infection, and health in general are not possible. If the diet is too deficient in vitamins, life itself cannot continue. As their name suggests, vitamins are vital.

Mineral salts are also essential for both health and life. Not only do they function as part of the body's chemical control mechanism, but they also constitute structural components of body tissues. For example, calcium and phosphorus are important ingredients of bones and teeth.

Examples of minerals functioning as control mechanisms are the following. Sodium and potassium play critical parts in the maintenance of the acid-base balance of the body and in the maintenance of water balance. Potassium is especially important for normal functioning of muscles (including the heart) and nerves. Calcium salts help sustain rhythmic heart and intestinal contractions and are necessary for normal skeletal muscular action and normal growth. A number of enzymes contain minerals.

Water serves many functions in the body. Some of the chief ones are as follows:

1. Water is an important constituent of every cell in the body. It composes well over one-half of the cells' substance. When dehydrated slightly, cells lose their power to resist infection and die if they are more completely dehydrated.
2. Water plays an essential part in all body functions, for example, in glandular secretion, digestion, absorption, anabolism, elimination of wastes, heat regulation, respiration, circulation, resistance to disease, etc. All cellular activity, and therefore life itself, depends upon the presence of adequate amounts of water. Materials must be dissolved in order to cross the cell membrane and in order to facilitate chemical reactions between them.
3. Water is important for the dilution of toxic wastes, thereby preventing damage of the kidney cells when they eliminate these toxins.

How important water is to life can be estimated by the fact that life can be maintained for a much longer time without food than without water. Men adrift in the ocean, for example, will live much longer with fresh water and no food than they will with food and no water. For a summary of some of the mechanisms involved in maintaining the water balance of the body, see Chapter XV.

METABOLIC RATES

Meaning

The term *metabolic rate* means the amount of energy (heat) released in the body in a given time by catabolism. It represents energy expended or used for accomplishing various kinds of work. In short, metabolic rate actually means catabolic rate or rate of energy release. (It is impossible to measure the rate at which foods are anabolized but fairly easy to determine the

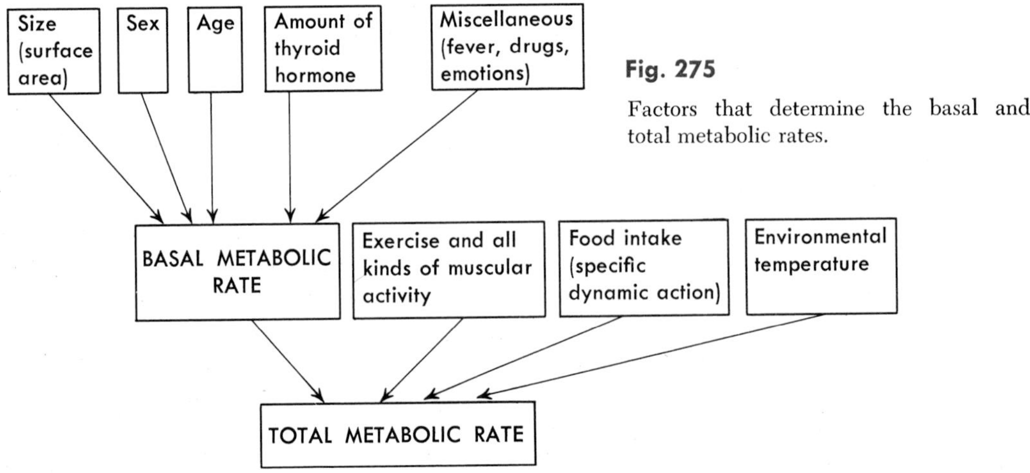

Fig. 275

Factors that determine the basal and total metabolic rates.

rate at which they are catabolized—see p. 420.)

Heat energy is measured in units named calories. One *Calorie* (a so-called "large" calorie or kilocalorie) is the amount of heat used to raise the temperature of 1 kg. (liter) of water 1° C.

Ways of expressing

Metabolic rates are expressed in either of two ways: (1) in terms of the number of Calories of heat energy expended per hour or per day and (2) as normal or as a definite percent above or below normal.

Basal metabolic rate

The basal metabolic rate (BMR) is the body's rate of energy expenditure under "basal conditions," namely, when the individual:

1. Is awake but resting, that is, lying down and, so far as possible, not moving a muscle
2. Is in the postabsorptive state (twelve to eighteen hours after the last meal)
3. Is in a comfortably warm environment

Note that the basal metabolic rate is not the minimum metabolic rate. It does not indicate the smallest amount of energy that must be expended to sustain life. It does, however, indicate the smallest amount of energy expenditure that can sustain life and also maintain the waking state and a normal body temperature in a comfortably warm environment.

Factors influencing

The basal metabolic rate is not identical for all individuals because of the influence of various factors (Fig. 275), some of which are described in the following paragraphs.

Size. In computing the basal metabolic rate, size is usually considered the amount of the body's surface area. It is computed from the individual's height and weight. Per square meter of body surface, if other conditions are equal, a large individual has the same basal metabolic rate as a small one, but because a large individual has more square meters of surface area, his basal metabolism is greater than that of a small individual. For example, the BMR for a man in his twenties is about 40 Calories per square meter of body surface per hour (Table 53). A large man with a body surface area of 1.9 sq.m. would, therefore, have a basal metabolism of 76 Calories per hour, whereas a smaller man with a surface area of perhaps 1.6 sq.m. would have a basal metabolism of only 64 Calories per hour. The average surface area for American adults is 1.6 sq.m. for women and 1.8 sq.m. for men.

Sex. Men oxidize their food approximately 5% to 7% faster than women. Therefore, their basal metabolic rates are about 5% higher for a given size and age. A man 5 feet, 6 inches tall, weighing 140 pounds, for example, has a 5% higher basal metabolic rate than a woman of the same height, weight, and age.

Age. That the fires of youth burn more brightly than those of age is a physiological as well as a psychological fact. In general, the younger the individual, the higher is his basal metabolic rate for a given size and sex. Exception: the BMR is slightly lower at birth than a few years later. That is to say, the rate increases slightly during the first 3 to 6 years and then starts to decrease and continues to do so throughout life. The basal metabolism per hour per square meter of surface area for different age groups is given in Table 53.

Thyroid hormone. Thyroid hormone stimulates basal metabolism. Without a normal amount of this hormone in the blood, a normal basal metabolic rate cannot be maintained. When an excess of thyroid hormone is secreted, foods are catabolized faster, much as coal is burned faster when a furnace draft is open. De-

Table 53. Basal metabolism (Aub-DuBois)

Age (yr.)	*Calories per hour per square meter body surface*	
	Male	*Female*
10–12	51.5	50.0
12–14	50.0	46.5
14–16	46.0	43.0
16–18	43.0	40.0
18–20	41.0	38.0
20–30	39.5	37.0
30–40	39.5	36.5
40–50	38.5	36.0
50–60	37.5	35.0
60–70	36.5	34.0

ficient thyroid secretion, on the other hand, slows the rate of metabolism.

Fever. Fever increases the basal metabolic rate. According to DuBois, metabolism increases about 13% per degree C. rise in body temperature.*

Drugs. Certain drugs, such as caffeine, Benzedrine, and dinitrophenol, increase the basal metabolic rate.

Other factors. Other factors, such as *emotions* and *pregnancy,* also influence basal metabolism. Both of these factors increase the basal rate.

How determined

Originally, basal metabolic rates were determined by a method known as direct calorimetry, which was too time consuming and costly for use on large numbers of people. Now, a rapid, inexpensive method, *indirect calorimetry,* is used in practically all hospitals, as well as in many doctors' offices and nutrition laboratories. This method of determining metabolism consists simply of an oxygen tank into which the patient breathes by means of a rubber tube leading to his mouth, his nose being clamped off. He receives oxygen from the tank and expires carbon dioxide into it, the latter being removed by soda lime contained in a tank within the oxygen tank. The amount of oxygen consumed in a given length of time is measured. Research has shown that for every liter of oxygen consumed, an average of 4.825 Calories of heat are produced under basal conditions. Multiplying the amount of oxygen consumed by 4.825 therefore gives the number of Calories produced in the given time. From that figure the number produced in twenty-four hours can, of course, be readily computed. This number represents the patient's basal metabolic rate per day expressed in Calories. Usually the basal metabolic rate is expressed as normal or as a definite percent above or below normal, the percentage being computed by comparing the actual basal metabolic rate (in Calories) with what is known to be an average basal metabolic rate (in Calories) for normal individuals of the given size, sex, and age. Statistical tables, based on research, give these normal rates for different sizes, sexes, and ages. For instance, you can compute

*Bard, Philip: Medical physiology, ed. 11, St. Louis, 1961, The C. V. Mosby Co., p. 483.

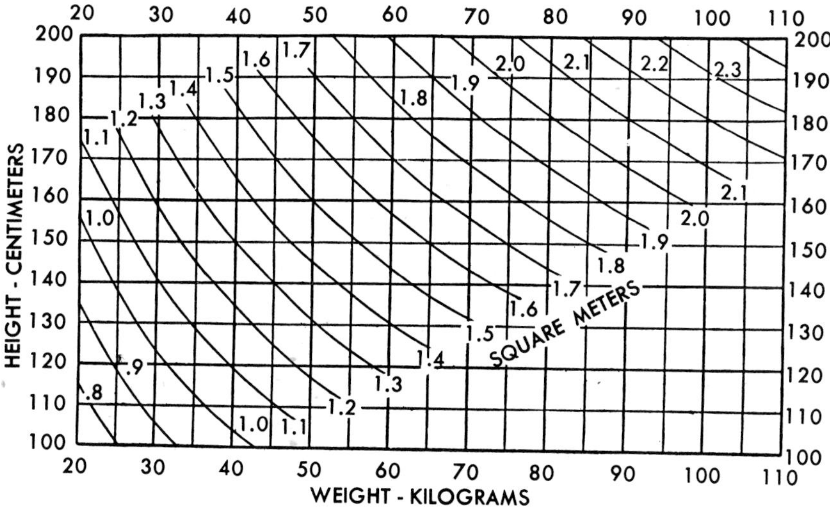

Fig. 276

Chart for determining surface area of man in square meters from weight in kilograms and height in centimeters according to the following formula: area (sq. cm.) = $wt.^{0.425} \times ht.^{0.725} \times 7184$. (From DuBois and DuBois: Arch. Int. Med. 17:863, 1916.)

the average BMR for a person of your own size, sex, and age in this way:

1. Start with your weight in kilograms and your height in centimeters. (Convert pounds to kilograms by dividing pounds by 2.2. Convert inches to approximate centimeters by multiplying inches by 2.5). For example, 110 lb. = 50 kg.; 5 ft., 3 in. = 158 cm.
2. Convert your weight and height to square meters, using Fig. 276. For example, weight 50 kg. and height 158 cm. = about 1.5 sq.m. surface area of body.
3. Find your age and sex on Table 53 and then multiply the number of Calories per square meter per hour given there by your square meters of surface area and then by 24. For example, average BMR per day for a 25-year-old female, weight 110 lb. and height 5 ft., 3 in. = 1332 Calories (37 × 1.5 × 24).

A quick rule of thumb for estimating a young woman's BMR is to multiply her weight in pounds by twelve.

-*Total metabolic rate*

The *total metabolic rate* is the amount of energy used or expended by the body in a given time. It is expressed in Calories per hour or per day. Most of the many factors that together determine the total metabolic rate are shown in Fig. 275. Of these, the main direct determinants are these:

1. The basal metabolic rate, that is, the energy used to do the work of maintaining life under the basal conditions previously described, plus
2. The energy used to do all kinds of skeletal muscle work—from the simplest activities such as feeding oneself or sitting up in bed to the most strenuous kind of physical labor or exercise, plus
3. The energy expended by the specific dynamic action (SDA) of foods.

The SDA of a food is a mysterious action which increases the metabolic rate, which speeds up the rate of energy expenditure. A food starts performing its specific dynamic action soon after ingestion and continues for several hours. Proteins have a SDA of about 30% of their caloric value. More specifically, ingestion of 100 Calories of protein increases the total metabolic rate by 30 calories. Carbohydrates and fats have a much smaller SDA—reportedly about 5% of their caloric value in contrast to protein's 30%. Reducing diets, as you probably know, are often high-protein diets for this reason—that the high SDA of protein increases the total metabolic rate. It increases the amount of energy used or expended by the body, in other words.

Energy balance and its relation to body weight

When we say that the body maintains a state of energy balance, we mean that its energy input equals its energy output. Energy input per day equals the total calories in the food ingested per day. And energy output equals the total metabolic rate expressed in calories. But you may be wondering what energy intake, output, and balance have to do with body weight. "Everything" would be a fairly good one-word answer. Or, to be somewhat more explicit, the following basic principles describe the relationships between these factors:

1. Body weight remains constant (except for possible variations in water content) when the body maintains energy balance—when the total calories in the food ingested equals the total metabolic rate, that is. Example: if you have a total metabolic rate of 2,000 Calories per day and if the food you eat per day yields 2,000 Calories, your body will be maintaining energy balance and your weight will stay constant.

2. Body weight increases when energy input exceeds energy output—when the total calories of food intake per day is greater than the total calories of the metabolic rate. A small amount of the excess energy input is used to synthesize glycogen for storage in the liver and muscles. But the rest of it is used for synthesizing fat and storing it in adipose tissue. If you were to eat 3,000 Calories each day for a week and if your total metabolic rate were 2,000 Calories per day, you would gain weight. How much you would gain, you can discover by doing a little simple arithmetic:

Total energy input for week = 21,000 Calories
Total energy output for week = 14,000 Calories

Excess energy input for week = 7,000 Calories

Approximately 3,500 Calories are used to synthesize one pound of adipose tissue. Hence, at the end of this one week of "over-eating"—of eating 7,000 Calories over and above your total metabolic rate—you would have gained about two pounds.

3. Body weight decreases when energy input is less than energy output—when the total number of calories in the food eaten is less than the total metabolic rate. Suppose you were to eat only a thousand Calories a day for a week and that you have a total metabolic rate of 2,000 Calories per day. By the end of the week your body would have used a total of 14,000 Calories of energy for maintaining life and doing its many kinds of work. All 14,000 Calories of this actual energy expenditure had to come from catabolism of foods since this is the body's only source of energy. Catabolism of ingested food supplied 7,000 Calories and catabolism of stored food supplied the remaining 7,000 Calories. That week your body would not have maintained energy balance. Nor would it have maintained weight balance. It would have incurred an energy deficit paid out of the energy stored in approximately two pounds of body fat. In short, you would have lost about two pounds.

• • •

Anyone who wants to reduce should remember this cardinal principle: eat fewer calories than your total metabolic rate.

Obey this law and you will lose weight. Ignore it and you will not lose weight. Unless caloric intake is less than caloric output (total metabolic rate), weight loss is impossible. But we ought to note one other point about this principle. There are two ways to make your caloric intake less than your total metabolic rate. The approach commonly advised to would-be reducers is simply "cut down on your calories" —a principle that proves easy to understand but difficult to apply. The other approach to weight reduction seems to be thought of or emphasized less often. It is this: increase your total metabolic rate (your caloric output, that is) and also decrease your caloric intake. Simple arithmetic shows which method produces a faster weight loss. Suppose you have a total metabolic rate of 2,000 calories a day and that you ingest 1,500 calories a day for a week. By the end of the week you will have taken in 3,500 calories less than your total metabolic rate. That deficit will have been supplied by the catabolism of about one pound of body fat. Now suppose that the next week you still eat 1,500 calories a day but you also exercise briskly for a half hour each day. Suppose you swim sidestroke at the rate of 1.6 miles per hour for a half hour. This will increase your total metabolic rate from 2,000 to 2,600 calories.* Your calorie deficit will then be 2,600 minus 1,500, or 1,100 calories a day, or 7,700 calories for the week. Catabolism of more than two pounds of body fat will have supplied those 7,700 calories. In short, you will have lost more than twice as much the second week as the first even though you ate the same amount both weeks.

Foods are stored as glycogen, fats, and tissue proteins. And as you will recall, cells catabolize them preferentially in this same order: carbohydrates, fats, and proteins. If there is no food intake, almost all of the glycogen is estimated to be used up in a matter of one or two days. Then, with no more carbohydrate to act as a fat sparer, fat is catabolized. How long it takes to deplete all of this reserve food depends, of course, upon how much adipose tissue the individual has when he starts his starvation diet. Finally, with no more fat available as a protein sparer, tissue proteins are catabolized rapidly, and death soon ensues.

*See suggested supplementary readings for Chapter XI, reference 4, p. 549.

Mechanisms for regulating food intake

The hypothalamus contains the centers that regulate the amount of food we eat. A cluster of cells in the lateral hypothalamus serves as the *appetite center*. And another group of cells, located in the ventral medial nucleus of the hypothalamus, functions as a *satiety center*. What acts directly on these centers to stimulate or depress them is still a matter of theory rather than fact. One theory (the "thermostat theory") holds that it is the temperature of the blood circulating to the hypothalamus that influences the centers. A moderate decrease in blood temperature stimulates the appetite center (and inhibits the satiety center). Result: the individual has an appetite. He wants to eat. And probably does. An increase in blood temperature produces the opposite effects, a depressed appetite (anorexia). One well-known instance of this is the loss of appetite in persons who have a fever.

Another theory (the "glucostat theory") says that it is the blood glucose concentration and rate of glucose utilization that influences the hypothalamic feeding centers. A low blood glucose concentration or low glucose utilization stimulates the appetite center, whereas a high blood glucose concentration inhibits it. Unquestionably, a great many factors operate together as a complex mechanism for regulating food in-

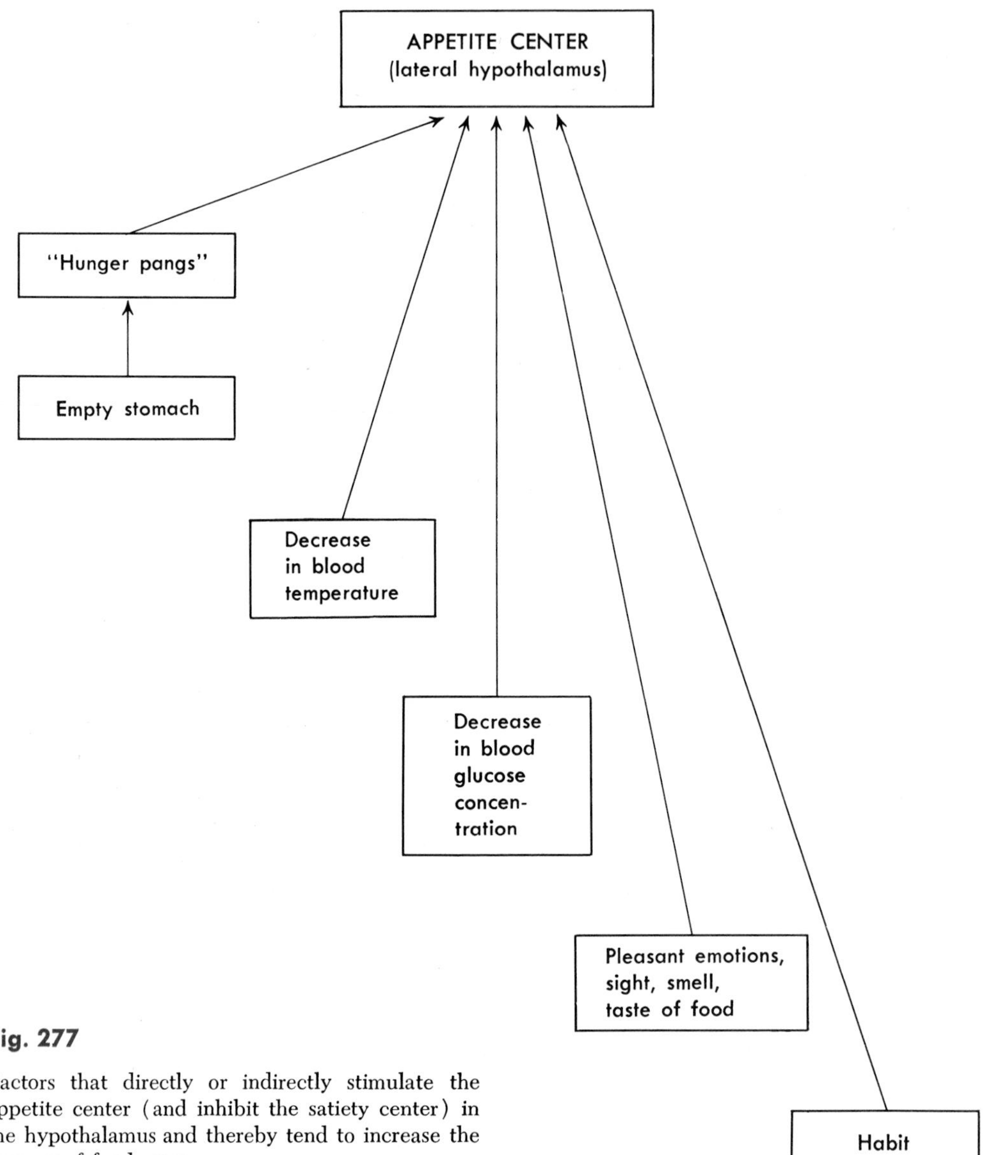

Fig. 277

Factors that directly or indirectly stimulate the appetite center (and inhibit the satiety center) in the hypothalamus and thereby tend to increase the amount of food eaten.

take. Some of these factors are indicated in Fig. 277.

Homeostasis of body temperature

Warm-blooded animals, such as man, maintain a remarkably constant temperature despite sizeable variations in environmental temperatures.

Normally in most people, body temperature moves up and down very little in the course of a day. It hovers close to a midpoint of about 37° C., increasing perhaps to 37.6° C. by late afternoon and decreasing to around 36.2° C. by early morning. This homeostasis of body temperature is of the utmost importance. Why? Because healthy survival depends upon biochemical reactions taking place at certain rates. And these rates, in turn, depend upon normal enzyme functioning, which depends upon body temperature staying within the narrow range of normal.

In order to maintain an even temperature, the body must, of course, balance the amount of heat it produces with the amount it loses. This means that if extra heat is produced in the body, this same amount of heat must then be lost from it. Obviously if this does not occur, if increased heat loss does not follow close upon increased heat production, body temperature will climb steadily upward.

Heat production

Heat is produced by one means—catabolism of foods. Because the muscles and glands (liver, especially) are the most active tissues, they carry on more catabolism and therefore produce more heat than any of the other tissues. So the chief determinant of how much heat the body produces is the amount of muscular work it does. During exercise and shivering, for example, catabolism and heat production increase greatly. But during sleep, when very little muscular work is being done, catabolism and heat production decrease.

Heat loss

Heat is lost from the body by the physical processes of evaporation, radiation, conduction, and convection. Some 80% or more of this heat transfer occurs through the skin. The rest takes place through the mucous membranes of the respiratory, digestive, and urinary tracts.

Evaporation. Heat energy must be expended to evaporate any fluid. Evaporation of water, therefore, constitutes one method by which heat is lost from the body, especially from the skin. At moderate temperatures it accounts for about half as much heat loss as does radiation. But at high environmental temperatures, evaporation constitutes the only method by which heat can be lost from the skin. A humid atmosphere necęssarily retards evaporation and therefore lessens the cooling effect derived from it—the explanation for the fact that the same degree of temperature seems hotter in humid climates than in dry ones.

Radiation. Radiation is the transfer of heat from the surface of one object to that of another without actual contact between the two. Heat radiates from the body surface to nearby objects that are cooler than the skin and radiates to the skin from those that are warmer than the skin. This is, of course, the principle of heating and cooling systems. From surfaces that have been heated to temperatures warmer than the skin, heat radiates to the skin, thereby warming it, whereas with cooled surfaces, heat radiates from the skin to them, thereby cooling the skin. The amount of heat lost by radiation from the skin is made to vary as needed by dilatation of surface blood vessels when more heat needs to be lost and by vasoconstriction when heat loss needs to be decreased. In cool environmental temperatures, radiation accounts for a greater percentage of heat loss from the skin than both conduction and evaporation combined. In hot environments, on the other hand, no heat is lost by radiation but instead may even be gained by radiation from warmer surfaces to the skin.

Conduction. Conduction means the transfer of heat to any substance actually in contact with the body—to clothing or jewelry, for example, or even to cold foods or liquids ingested. This process accounts for a relatively small amount of heat loss compared to the amount lost by evaporation and radiation.

Convection. Convection is the transfer of heat away from a surface by movement of heated air or fluid particles. Usually, convection causes very little heat loss from the body's surface. But it can account for considerable heat loss—as you know from ex-

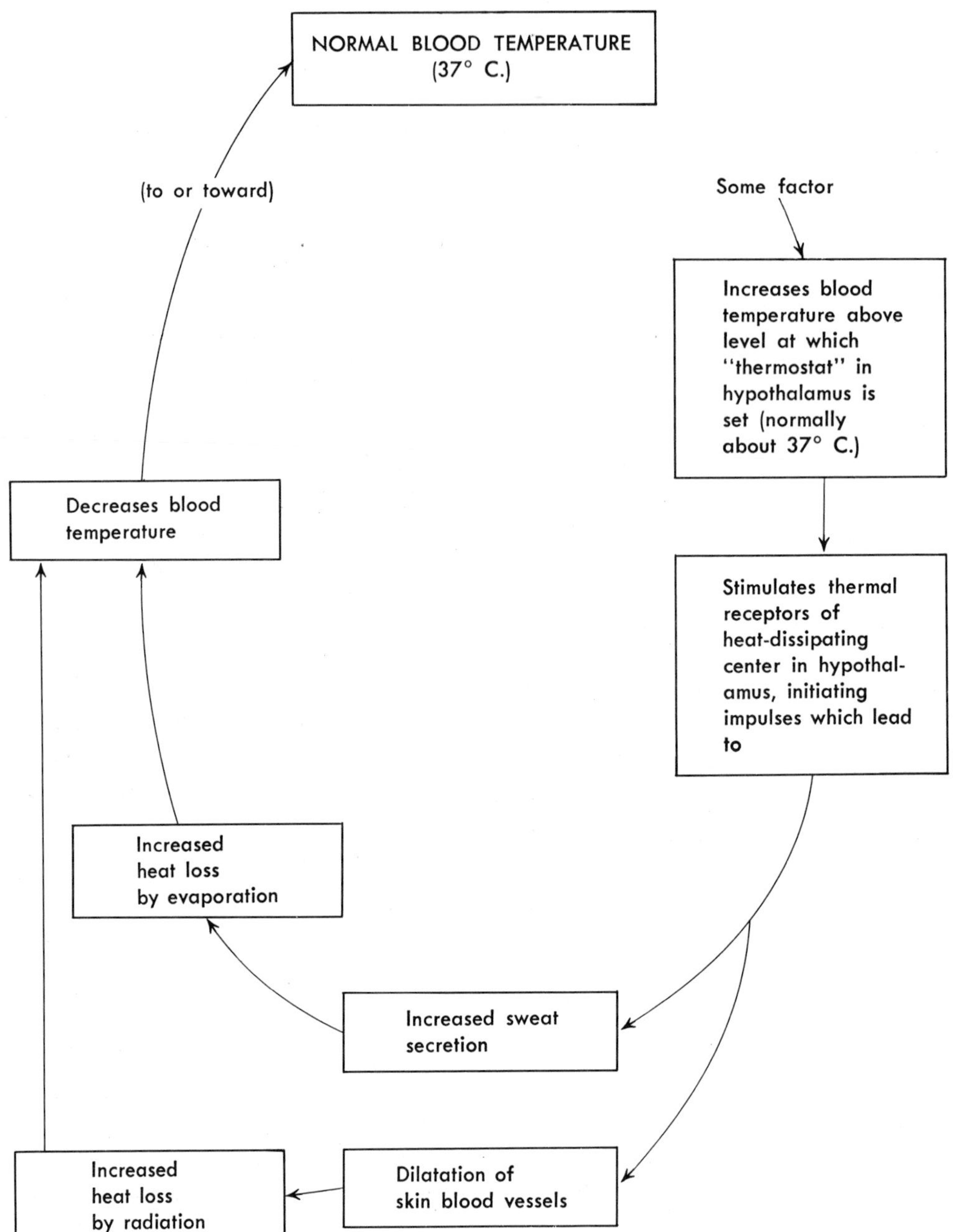

Fig. 278

Scheme to show how heat-dissipating mechanism operates to maintain normal body temperature. In principle, it cancels out any heat gain by bringing about an equal heat loss. Under usual circumstances this mechanism succeeds in preventing body temperature from rising above the upper limit of normal. When it fails, fever develops. According to one theory, certain factors can increase the threshold of stimulation of hypothalamic thermal receptors—in more picturesque language, they reset the hypothalamic thermostat at a higher level than normal. Then, blood temperature rises above normal before it activates the heat-dissipating mechanism shown in this diagram.

perience if you have ever stepped from your bath into even slightly moving air from an open window.

Thermostatic control of heat production and loss

The control mechanism that normally maintains homeostasis of body temperature consists of two parts:

1. A *heat-dissipating mechanism* which acts to increase heat loss when blood temperature increases above a certain point. This mechanism, therefore, prevents body temperature from rising above normal under usual circumstances.
2. A *heat-gaining mechanism* which acts to accelerate catabolism and thereby to increase heat production when blood temperature decreases below a certain point. Under ordinary conditions, this mechanism prevents body temperature from falling below normal.

Heat-dissipating mechanism

In the anterior part of the hypothalamus, behind the sphenoid sinuses, lies a group of cells referred to collectively as the "human thermostat." These neurons are thermal receptors, that is, they are stimulated by a very slight increase in the temperature of the blood above the point at which the human thermostat is set—normally about 37° C. In a sense, one might say that these cells of the hypothalamus take the temperature of the blood circulating to them. Whenever it increases by as little as 0.01° above 37° C.* (or some other set point), these neurons send out impulses that eventually reach sweat glands and blood vessels of the skin. They stimulate the body's two million or more sweat glands to increase their rate of secretion, and they also cause dilatation of surface blood vessels. Evaporation of the larger amount of sweat causes a greater heat loss from the skin. And also more heat is lost by radiation from the larger quantity of blood circulating near the surface in the dilated skin vessels.

Heat-gaining mechanism

In a cold environment, the mechanism that tries to maintain homeostasis of body temperature includes two kinds of responses—those that decrease heat loss and those that increase heat production. Together, they almost always succeed in preventing a decrease in blood temperature below the lower limit of normal. Skin blood vessel constriction decreases the volume of blood circulating near the surface so decreases heat loss by radiation. In addition, shivering and voluntary muscle contractions occur, thereby accelerating catabolism and heat production. Further details about the mechanism for preventing body temperature from falling below normal are not yet established.

Skin thermal receptors

In addition to the thermal receptors in the hypothalamus, there are many heat and cold receptors located in the skin. Impulses initiated in skin thermal receptors travel to the cerebral cortex sensory area. Here, they give rise to sensations of skin temperature and are relayed out over voluntary motor paths to produce skeletal muscle movements that affect skin temperature. For example, on a hot day you "feel hot" because of stimulation of your skin heat receptors. Often you make some sort of movements to "cool yourself off." You may start fanning yourself, or perhaps you turn on an air conditioner or go swimming. And as a result, your skin temperature decreases back to a more comfortable level. Thus, the thermal receptors in the skin will have taken part in a conscious mechanism that helps regulate skin temperature. Convincing evidence supports the view that this is their only

---

*See suggested supplementary readings for Chapter XI, reference 1, p. 549.

function and that impulses from them do not travel to the heat-regulating centers in the hypothalamus and therefore do not take part in the automatic regulation of internal body temperature.

Correlations

When a fever or higher than normal temperature exists, it is thought to be due primarily to inability of the heat-dissipating mechanisms to keep pace with heat production. Some factor—perhaps chemicals from microorganisms or injured tissue cells—stimulates catabolism, thereby producing more heat in the body in a given time. Heat-dissipating mechanisms (Fig. 276) operate in an effort to compensate for the heat gain. But presumably they cannot increase heat loss as much as heat production has increased. So body temperature necessarily increases. The patient "has a fever," in other words.

The heat-regulating centers are present at birth but do not function well for a short time after birth. Therefore, newborn babies need to be kept somewhat warmer than adults. If the baby is born prematurely, the heat-regulating centers do not function for a longer time, perhaps several weeks.

Outline summary— The digestive system

Functions and importance

1. Prepare food for absorption and metabolism
2. Absorption
3. Elimination of wastes
4. Vital importance

Organs

1. Main organs
   a. compose alimentary canal—mouth, pharynx, esophagus, stomach, and intestines
2. Accessory organs
   a. salivary glands, teeth, liver, gallbladder, pancreas, and vermiform appendix

WALLS OF ORGANS

1. Coats
   a. mucous lining
   b. submucous coat of connective tissue—main blood vessels here
   c. muscular coat
   d. fibroserous coat
2. Modifications of coats
   a. mucous lining
      1. rugae and microscopic gastric and hydrochloric acid glands in stomach
      2. circular folds, villi, intestinal glands, Peyer's patches, and solitary lymph nodes in small intestine
      3. solitary nodes and intestinal glands in large intestine
   b. muscle coat
      1. three layers (circular, longitudinal, oblique) in stomach instead of only two layers as in rest of tract
      2. three tapelike strips make up outer, longitudinal layer and pucker large intestine into small sacs called haustra
   c. fibroserous coat
      1. peritoneum covers stomach and intestines
      2. greater omentum or lace apron—double fold of peritoneum, that hangs from lower edge of stomach like an apron over intestines; should not be confused with mesentery, which also is double fold of peritoneum but fan shaped and attached at short side to posterior wall of abdominal cavity; small intestines anchored to posterior abdominal wall by means of mesentery

MOUTH (BUCCAL CAVITY)

1. Formed by cheeks, hard and soft palates, tongue, and muscles
2. Hard palate—formed by two palatine bones and parts of two maxillary bones
3. Soft palate—formed of muscle in shape of arch; forms partition between mouth and nasopharynx; fauces is archway or opening from mouth to oropharynx; uvula is conical-shaped process suspended from midpoint of arch

TONGUE

1. Many rough elevations on tongue's surface called papillae; contain taste buds
2. Frenum—a fold of mucous membrane that helps anchor tongue to mouth floor

SALIVARY GLANDS

1. Parotid—below and in front of ear; duct opens on inside of cheek, opposite upper second molar tooth
2. Submaxillary—posterior part of mouth floor
3. Sublingual—anterior part of mouth floor

TEETH

1. Deciduous or baby teeth—10 per jaw or 20 in set
2. Permanent—16 per jaw or 32 per set
3. Structure of typical tooth (Fig. 248)

PHARYNX

See pp. 349 and 350

ESOPHAGUS

1. Position and extent
   a. posterior to trachea and heart; pierces diaphragm
   b. extends from pharynx to stomach, distance of approximately 10 inches
2. Structure—collapsible, muscle tube

STOMACH

1. Size, shape, and position
   a. size varies in different individuals; also according to whether distended or not
   b. elongated pouch
   c. lies in epigastric and left hypochondriac portions of abdominal cavity
2. Divisions
   a. fundus—portion above esophageal opening
   b. body—central portion
   c. pylorus—constricted, lower portion
3. Curves
   a. lesser—upper, right border
   b. greater—lower, left border
4. Sphincter muscles
   a. cardiac—guarding opening of esophagus into stomach
   b. pyloric—guarding opening of pylorus into duodenum
5. Coats—see Table 45
6. Glands
   a. epithelial cells of gastric mucosa secrete mucus
   b. parietal cells secrete hydrochloric acid
   c. chief cells (zymogen cells) secrete enzymes of gastric juice
7. Functions
   a. serves as food reservoir
   b. secretes gastric juice
   c. contractions break food into small particles, mix them well with gastric juice, and move contents on into duodenum
   d. secretes the antianemic intrinsic factor
   e. carries on a limited amount of absorption—some water, alcohol, and certain other drugs

SMALL INTESTINES

1. Size and position
   a. approximately 1 inch in diameter and 20 feet in length
   b. its coiled loops fill most of abdominal cavity
2. Divisions
   a. duodenum
   b. jejunum
   c. ileum
3. Coats—see Table 45
4. Functions
   a. completes digestion of foods
   b. absorbs end products of digestion
   c. secretes hormones that help control secretion of pancreatic juice, bile, and intestinal juice

LARGE INTESTINE (COLON)

1. Size—approximately 2½ inches in diameter and 5 or 6 feet in length
2. Divisions
   a. cecum
   b. colon
      1. ascending
      2. transverse
      3. descending
      4. sigmoid
   c. rectum
3. Coats—see Table 45
4. Functions
   a. absorption of water
   b. elimination of digestive wastes

LIVER

1. Location and size
   a. occupies most of right hypochondrium and part of epigastrium
   b. largest gland in body
2. Lobes
   a. right lobe, subdivided into three smaller lobes—right lobe proper, caudate, and quadrate
   b. left lobe
   c. lobes divided into lobules by blood vessels and fibrous partitions

3. Ducts
   a. hepatic duct from liver
   b. cystic duct from gallbladder
   c. common bile duct formed by union of hepatic and cystic ducts and opens into duodenum at ampulla of Vater (duodenal papilla)
4. Functions
   a. secretes bile
   b. plays essential role in metabolism of carbohydrates, proteins, and fats, e.g., carries on glycogenesis, glycogenolysis, glycogenesis and gluconeogenesis, deamination, and ketogenesis; synthesizes various blood proteins

GALLBLADDER

1. Size, shape, and location
   a. approximately size and shape of small pear
   b. lies on undersurface of liver
2. Structure—sac of smooth muscle with mucous lining arranged in rugae
3. Functions
   a. concentrates and stores bile
   b. during digestion, ejects bile into duodenum

PANCREAS

1. Size, shape, and location
   a. larger in men than in women but varies in different individuals
   b. shaped something like a fish with head, body, and tail
   c. lies in C-shaped curve of duodenum
2. Structure—similar to salivary glands
   a. divided into lobes and lobules
   b. pancreatic cells pour their secretion into duct that runs length of gland and emties into duodenum at ampulla of Vater
   c. clusters of cells, not connected with any ducts, lie between pancreatic cells—called islets or islands of Langerhans—composed of alpha and beta type cells—latter thought to secrete insulin, former to secrete glucagon
3. Functions
   a. secretes pancreatic juice
   b. beta cells of islands of Langerhans secrete insulin
   c. alpha cells of islands of Langerhans secrete glucagon

VERMIFORM APPENDIX

1. Size, shape, and location
   a. about size and shape of large angle worm
   b. blind-end tube off cecum
2. Structure—similar to rest of intestine

Digestion

1. Definition—all changes food undergoes in alimentary canal
2. Purpose—conversion of foods into chemical and physical forms that can be absorbed and metabolized
3. Kinds
   a. mechanical—movements that change physical state of foods, propel them forward in alimentary tract, eliminate digestive wastes from tract and facilitate absorption (see Table 48 for description of processes involved in mechanical digestion)
      1. mastication (chewing)
      2. swallowing (deglutition)
         a. movement of food through mouth into pharynx—voluntary act
         b. movement of food through pharynx into esophagus—involuntary or reflex act initiated by stimulation of mucosa of back of mouth, pharynx, or laryngeal region; paralysis of receptors here, e.g., by Novocain, makes swallowing impossible
         c. movement of food through esophagus into stomach; accomplished by esophageal peristalsis—reflex initiated by stimulation of esophageal mucosa
      3. peristalsis—wormlike movements that squeeze food downward in tract; emptying of stomach or opening of pyloric sphincter regulated by enterogastric reflex; fats and sugars in intestine stimulate mucosa to release enterogastrone into blood which, in turn, inhibits gastric peristalsis and slows stomach emptying; proteins and acid stimulate vagal nerve receptors in intestinal mucosa and thereby initiate reflex emptying of stomach
      4. churning
      5. mass peristalsis
      6. defecation—reflex initiated by stimulation of rectal mucosa
   b. chemical—series of hydrolytic processes dependent upon specific enzymes (see Table 49 for description of chemical changes)
4. Control of digestive gland secretion—see Table 50

a. saliva—secretion is reflex initiated by stimulation of taste buds, other receptors in mouth and esophagus, olfactory receptors, and visual receptors
b. gastric secretion—controlled reflexly by same stimuli that initiate salivary secretion; also controlled chemically by hormone, gastrin, released by gastric mucosa in presence of partially digested proteins; enterogastrone (hormone just mentioned as slowing stomach emptying) also has inhibitory effect on gastric secretion
c. pancreatic secretion—controlled chemically by hormones secretin and pancreozymin formed by intestinal mucosa when hydrochloric acid enters duodenum
d. bile
   1. secretion of—controlled chemically by same hormone (secretin) that regulates pancreatic secretion
   2. ejection of into duodenum—controlled chemically by hormone cholecystokinin formed by intestinal mucosa when fats present in duodenum
e. intestinal secretion—control still obscure, although believed to be both reflex and chemical

Absorption

1. Definition—passage of substances through intestinal mucosa into blood or lymph
2. How accomplished—probably mainly by active transport mechanisms

Metabolism

MEANING

Chemical changes foods undergo inside cells or utilization of foods by body cells

WAYS IN WHICH FOODS METABOLIZED

1. Catabolism—breaks down food molecules to simpler compounds (carbon dioxide, water, and nitrogenous wastes), transferring some of their energy to phosphate compounds, notably, ATP, and releasing some of it as heat
2. Anabolism—building up food molecules into more complex compounds, notably, glycogen, enzymes and other cell proteins, hormones, etc.

CARBOHYDRATE METABOLISM

1. Glucose transport through cell membranes and phosphorylation
   a. insulin promotes this transport through cell membranes
   b. *glucose phosphorylation*—conversion of glucose to glucose-6-phosphate, catalyzed by enzyme glucokinase; *insulin* increases activity of glucokinase so promotes glucose phosphorylation
2. Glycogenesis—conversion of glucose to glycogen for storage; occurs mainly in liver and muscle cells
3. Glycogenolysis
   a. in muscle cells—glycogen changed back to glucose-6-phosphate, preliminary to catabolism
   b. in liver cells—glycogen changed back to glucose; enzyme, glucose phosphatase, present in liver cells catalyzes final step of glycogenolysis, changing of glucose-6-phosphate to glucose; this enzyme lacking in most other cells; *glucagon* increases activity of phosphorylase so accelerates liver glycogenolysis; *epinephrine* accelerates liver and muscle glycogenolysis
4. Glucose catabolism
   a. *glycolysis*—series of anaerobic reactions that break 1 glucose molecule down into 2 pyruvic acid molecules with conversion of small amount of energy stored in glucose to heat and to ATP
   b. *Krebs' citric acid cycle*—series of aerobic chemical reactions by which 2 pyruvic acid molecules (from 1 glucose molecule) broken down to 6 carbon dioxide and 6 water molecules with release of energy as heat and ATP
5. Gluconeogenesis—sequence of chemical reactions carried on in liver cells; converts protein or fat compounds into glucose; growth hormone, ACTH, and glucocorticoids have stimulating effect on rate of gluconeogenesis
6. *Control of glucose metabolism*
   a. by hormones secreted by islands of Langerhans in pancreas
      1. insulin (from beta cells)—tends to accelerate glucose utilization by cells because it accelerates glucose transport through cell membranes and glucose phosphorylation; hence insulin tends to decrease blood glucose concentration, i.e., has hypoglycemic effect
      2. glucagon (from alpha cells)—increases activity of enzyme phosphorylase, thereby accelerating liver glycogenolysis with release of glucose

into blood; hence glucagon tends to increase blood glucose, i.e, has hyperglycemic effect

b. by hormones secreted by anterior pituitary gland, adrenal cortex, and thyroid gland
   1. growth hormone—decreases fat deposition, increases fat mobilization and catabolism; hence tends to bring about shift to fat utilization from "preferred" glucose utilization
   2. ACTH and glucocorticoids—ACTH stimulates adrenal cortex to increase secretion of glucocorticoids, which accelerate tissue protein mobilization and subsequent liver gluconeogenesis from mobilized proteins; therefore, ACTH and glucocorticoids tend to increase blood glucose, i.e., have hyperglycemic effect
   3. thyrotrophin – stimulates thyroid gland to increase secretion of thyroid hormone which accelerates catabolism, usually glucose catabolism since glucose "preferred fuel"

c. by hormone secreted by adrenal medulla—epinephrine increases phosphorylase activity so accelerates muscle and liver glycogenolysis; hence tends to increase blood glucose, i.e., has hyperglycemic effect

7. Principles about normal carbohydrate metabolism
   a. principle of "preferred energy fuel"—cells catabolize first glucose, sparing fats and proteins; when their glucose supply becomes inadequate, next catabolize fats, sparing proteins, and last catabolize proteins
   b. principle of glycogenesis—glucose in excess of about 120 to 140 mg./100 ml. blood brought to liver by portal veins enters liver cells where it undergoes glycogenesis
   c. principle of glycogenolysis—when blood glucose decreases below midpoint of normal, liver glycogenolysis accelerates and tends to raise blood glucose concentration back toward midpoint of normal
   d. principle of gluconeogenesis – when blood glucose decreases below normal or when amount of glucose entering cells inadequate, liver gluconeogenesis accelerates and tends to raise blood glucose concentration
   e. principle of glucose storage as fat—when blood sugar glucose higher than normal and blood insulin content adequate, excess glucose converted to fat, mainly by liver cells, and stored as such in fat depots

FAT METABOLISM

1. Catabolism
   a. hydrolysis of fats to fatty acids and glycerol, primarily in liver cells
   b. glycerol oxidized same as carbohydrates
   c. fatty acids converted to ketone bodies (ketogenesis); occurs mainly in liver; largest proportion of ketones enters blood from liver cells to be transported to tissues for oxidation to carbon dioxide and water via tricaboxylic acid cycle
2. Anabolism—for tissue synthesis and for building various compounds; fats deposited in connective tissue converts it to adipose tissue
3. Fat mobilization—release of fats from adipose tissue cells, followed by their catabolism; occurs when blood contains less glucose than normal or when it contains less insulin than normal; if excessive, leads to ketosis
4. Control—by following major factors
   a. rate of glucose catabolism one of main regulators of fat metabolism; in general, normal or high rates of glucose catabolism accompanied by low rates of fat mobilization and catabolism and high rates of fat deposition; converse also true
   b. insulin helps control fat metabolism by its effects on glucose metabolism; in general, normal amounts of insulin and blood glucose tend to decrease fat mobilization and catabolism and to increase fat deposition; insulin deficiency increases fat mobilization and catabolism; converse also true
   c. growth hormone—decreases fat deposition and increases fat mobilization and utilization, i.e., growth hormone tends to bring about shift from glucose to fat utilization
   d. glucocorticoids help control fat metabolism; in general, when blood glucose lower than normal and in various stress situations, more glucocorticoids secreted and accelerate fat mobilization and gluconeogenesis from them; when blood glucose higher than normal but rate of glucose catabolism low (as in diabetes mellitus), glucocorticoids also increase

fat mobilization, but it is followed by ketogenesis from them; when blood glucose higher than normal, and provided its insulin content adequate, glucocorticoids accelerate fat deposition

PROTEIN METABOLISM

1. Anabolism of proteins of primary importance; their catabolism, secondary, amino acids used to synthesize all kinds of tissue, e.g., for growth and repair; also used to synthesize many other substances such as enzymes, hormones, antibodies, and blood proteins
2. Catabolism
   a. deamination of amino acid molecule to form ammonia and keto acid; mainly in liver cells
   b. ammonia converted to urea (mainly in liver) and excreted via urine
   c. keto acids may be converted to glucose in liver, or to fat, or oxidized in liver or tissue cells via tricarboxylic acid cycle
3. Control
   a. STH and testosterone both have stimulating effect on protein synthesis or anabolism
   b. ACTH and glucocorticoids—protein catabolic hormones; accelerate tissue protein mobilization, i.e., hydrolysis of tissue proteins to amino acids and their release into blood; liver converts amino acids to glucose (gluconeogenesis) or deaminates them
   c. thyroid hormone promotes protein anabolism when nutrition adequate and amount of hormone normal; therefore, adequate amounts necessary for normal growth

METABOLISM OF VITAMINS, MINERAL SALTS, AND WATER

1. Vitamins essential for many physiological processes such as normal metabolism, growth, reproduction, resistance to infection, etc.
2. Mineral salts essential for normal metabolism and for maintenance of favorable internal environment
3. Water essential for all physiological reactions

METABOLIC RATES

Meaning

Amount of heat energy expended in a given time

Ways of expressing

In Calories or as "normal" or as a definite percent above or below normal; e.g., +10% or −10%

Basal metabolic rate

Amount of heat produced (energy expended) in waking state when body at complete rest, twelve to eighteen hours after last meal, in a comfortably warm environment

1. Factors influencing
   a. size—greater surface area, higher BMR (surface area computed from height and weight)
   b. sex—approximately 5% higher in males
   c. age—higher in youth than in age
   d. abnormal functioning of certain endocrines, particularly thyroid gland
   e. fever—each centigrade degree rise in temperature increases BMR approximately 13%
   f. certain drugs, e.g., dinitrophenol, increase BMR
   g. other factors, e.g., pregnancy and emotions, increase BMR
2. How determined
   a. direct calorimetry—too expensive and too time consuming for wide use
   b. indirect calorimetry—measures amount of oxygen inspired in given time; 4.825 Calories of heat produced for each liter of oxygen consumed
3. Total metabolic rate—amount of heat produced by body in average twenty-four hours; equal to basal rate plus number of Calories produced by muscular work, eating and digesting food, and adjusting to cool temperatures; expressed in Calories per twenty-four hours

Energy balance and its relation to body weight

1. Energy balance means that energy input (total Calories in food ingested) equals energy output (i.e., total metabolic rate expressed in Calories)
2. In order for body weight to remain constant (except for variations in water content), energy balance must be maintained—total Calories ingested must equal total metabolic rate
3. Body weight increases when energy input exceeds energy output—when total Calories ingested greater than total metabolic rate
4. Body weight decreases when energy input less than energy output—when total Calories ingested less than total metabolic rate; no diet will reduce weight unless it con-

tains fewer Calories than the total metabolic rate of the individual eating diet

Mechanisms for regulating food intake

1. Thermostat theory holds that moderate decrease in blood temperature acts as stimulant to appetite center so increases appetite; and increase in blood temperature (fever) produces opposite effect
2. Glucostat theory postulates that low blood glucose concentration or low rate of glucose utilization (e.g., diabetes mellitus) acts as stimulant to appetite center so increases appetite; and high blood glucose level produces opposite effect

Homeostasis of body temperature

In order to maintain homeostasis of body temperature heat production must equal heat loss

Heat production

By catabolism of foods in skeletal muscles and liver especially

Heat loss

1. By physical processes of evaporation, radiation, conduction, and convection
2. About 80% of heat loss occurs through skin; rest takes place through mucosa of respiratory, digestive, and urinary tracts

Thermostatic control of heat production and loss

1. Heat-dissipating mechanism—see Fig. 278
2. Heat-gaining mechanism
   a. details not established but mechanism activated by decrease in blood temperature
   b. responses—skin blood vessel constriction, shivering, and voluntary muscle contractions

Skin thermal receptors

Stimulation of skin thermal receptors gives rise to sensations of heat or cold; also initiates voluntary movements to reduce these sensations—e.g., fanning oneself to cool off or exercising to warm up

Review questions

1. Name and describe the coats that compose the walls of the esophagus, stomach, and intestines.
2. Differentiate between the peritoneum, the mesentery, and the omentum.
3. Explain what the tonsils and adenoids are and their locations.
4. Give the names and number of deciduous teeth and of permanent teeth.
5. Discuss the functions of gastric juice.
6. What juices digest proteins? Carbohydrates? Fats?
7. Differentiate between the end products of digestion and the end products of metabolism.
8. Contrast the function or purpose of digestion with the function or purpose of metabolism.
9. Compare anabolism and catabolism as to type of chemical reactions involved and end products.
10. Compare digestion and anabolism as to type of chemical reactions.
11. Discuss the functions of the pancreas in digestion and metabolism.
12. Compare proteins, carbohydrates, and fats as to functions they serve in the body. Mention both similarities and differences.
13. Compare proteins, carbohydrates, and fats as to their metabolic wastes.
14. Differentiate between digestive and metabolic wastes.
15. Differentiate between basal and total metabolic rates.
16. Compare absorption of the three kinds of foods.

Situation: A patient has obstructive jaundice.

17. Which duct, or ducts, might be obstructed to produce the symptom jaundice? Explain.
18. Would this affect this patient's digestion, absorption, or metabolism? Explain.
19. Explain why vitamin K might be given to this patient.

Situation: A patient has advanced liver disease.

20. Discuss possible effects on digestion, absorption, or metabolism.
21. What other functions might be affected?

Situation: Mrs. A., who weighs 160 pounds, is 5 feet, 5 inches tall, and is 50 years of age, has been given a reducing diet by her doctor. She complains to you that she "knows it won't work" because "it isn't what she eats that makes her fat." As proof, she says that both her husband and son "eat twice as much" as she and so does her younger sister.

22. How would you answer Mrs. A?
23. Mrs. A. also tells you that she does not like so much meat and so many eggs and that she would rather do without some of these and have some pie or cake each day. How would you answer her?

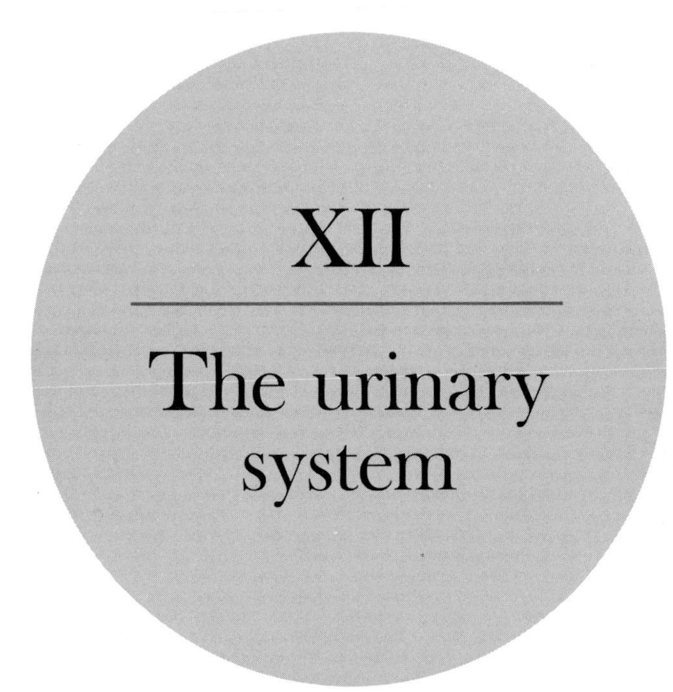

XII

The urinary system

The urinary system consists of those organs that produce urine and eliminate it from the body. They are two kidneys, two ureters, one bladder, and one urethra. The secretion of urine and its elimination from the body are vital functions since together they constitute one of the most important mechanisms for maintaining homeostasis. As one individual has phrased it, "The composition of the blood (and internal environment) is determined not by what the mouth ingests but by what the kidney keeps."[*]

The substances excreted from the kidneys and other excretory organs are listed in Table 54.

*From Smith, H. W.: Lectures on the kidney, Lawrence, Kansas, 1943, University of Kansas, p. 3.

Organs

KIDNEYS

Gross anatomy

Size, shape, and location

The kidneys resemble lima beans in shape. An average-sized kidney measures approximately 4½ inches in length, from 2 to 3 inches in width, and 1 inch in thickness. Usually the left kidney is slightly larger than the right.

The kidneys lie behind the parietal peritoneum, against the posterior abdominal wall, at the level of the last thoracic and first three lumbar vertebrae (or just above the waistline). The liver pushes the right kidney down to a somewhat lower level than the left. A heavy cushion of fat normally keeps the kidneys up in position. Very thin individuals may suffer from pto-

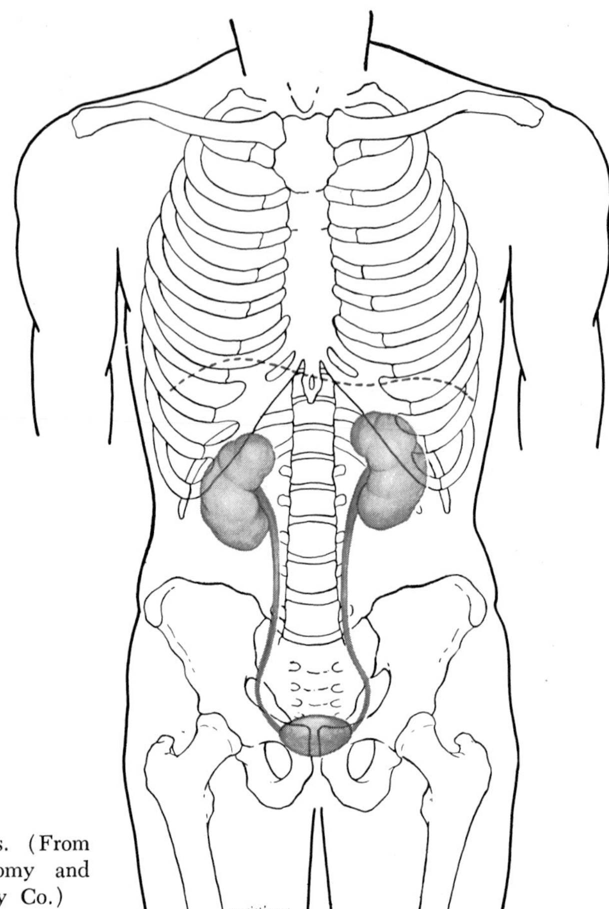

Fig. 279

Normal position of the urinary organs. (From Francis and Farrell: Integrated anatomy and physiology, St. Louis, The C. V. Mosby Co.)

sis (dropping) of one or both of these organs. Connective tissue (renal fasciae) anchors the kidneys to surrounding structures and helps to maintain their normal position.

External structure

The mesial surface of each kidney presents a concave notch called the *hilum.* Structures enter the kidneys through this notch just as they enter the lung through its hilum. A tough white fibrous capsule encases each kidney.

Internal structure

When a coronal section is made through the kidney, two kinds of substances are seen composing its interior: an outer layer, the *cortex,* and an inner portion, the *medulla.* The latter is divided into a dozen or more triangular wedges, the *renal pyramids.* The bases of the pyramids face the cortex, and their apices or *renal papillae* face the center of the kidney. The pyramids have a striated appearance as contrasted with the smooth texture of the cortical substance. The cortex extends inward between each two pyramids, forming the *renal columns.*

Microscopic anatomy

Microscopic examination reveals the kidney to be composed of peculiarly shaped

Table 54. Excretory organs of the body

Excretory organ	*Substance excreted*
Kidneys	Nitrogenous wastes (from protein catabolism) Toxins (e.g., from bacteria) Water (from ingestion and from catabolism) Mineral salts
Skin (sweat glands)	Water Mineral salts Small amounts of nitrogenous wastes
Lungs	Carbon dioxide (from catabolism) Water
Intestine	Wastes from digestion (cellulose, connective tissue, etc.) Some metabolic wastes (e.g., bile pigments; also salts of calcium and other heavy metals)

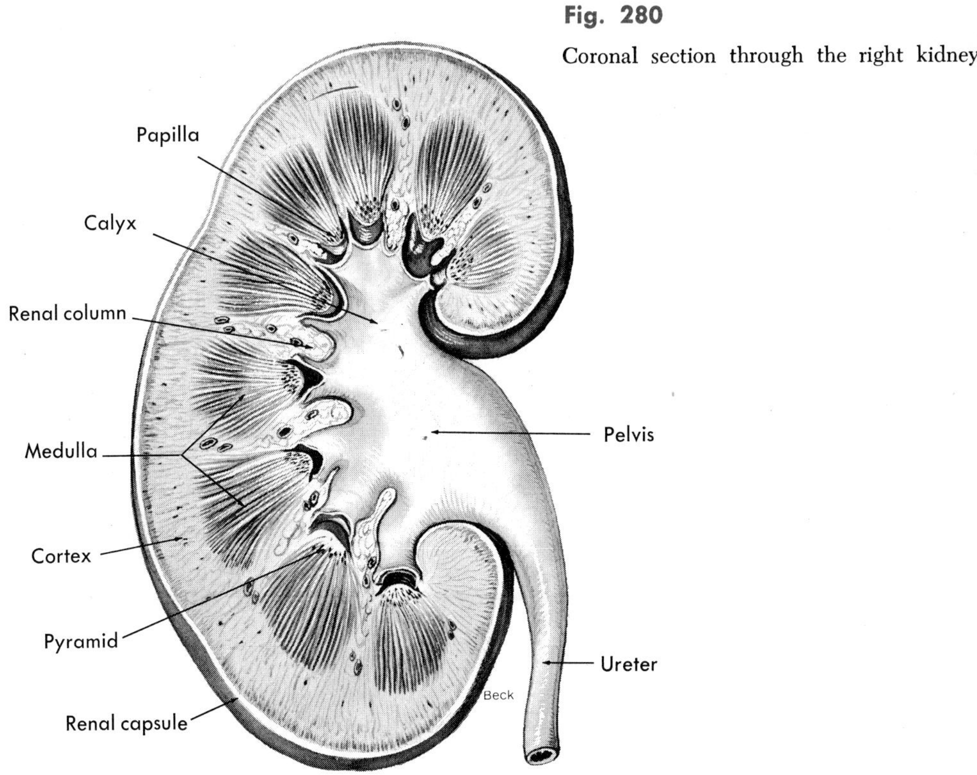

Fig. 280

Coronal section through the right kidney.

structures resembling tiny funnels with proportionately long convoluted stems. The upper portions of these anatomical funnels are called *Bowman's capsules.* They consist of two layers of flat epithelial cells with a space between the layers. Each capsule has invaginated in it a cluster of capillaries designated as a *glomerulus.* A Bowman's capsule and its partially incased glomerulus is named a *renal corpuscle* (or *malpighian* corpuscle).

Blood flows into each glomerulus by way of an afferent arteriole and out of it by way of an efferent arteriole—a unique arrangement. Blood usually flows out of capillaries into what kind of vessels? Extending from

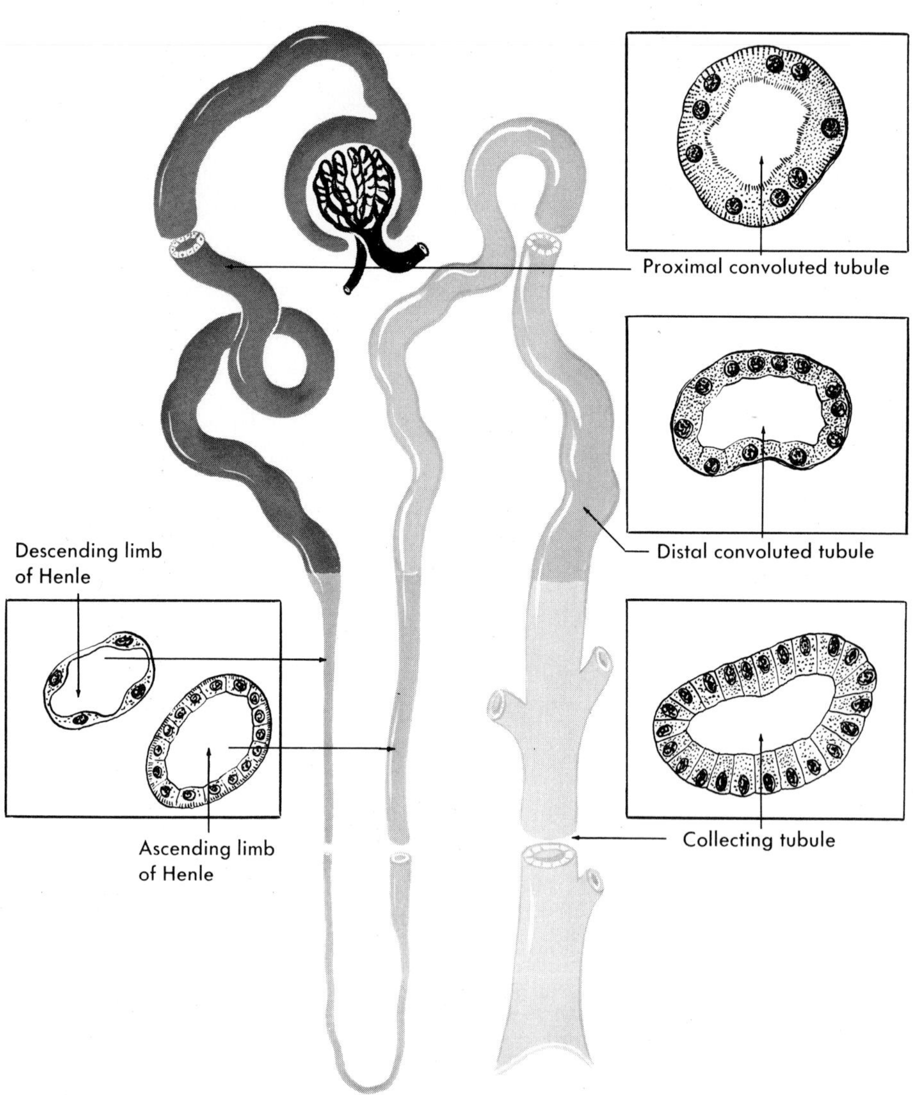

Fig. 281

The nephron unit with sections of the tubule at various levels.

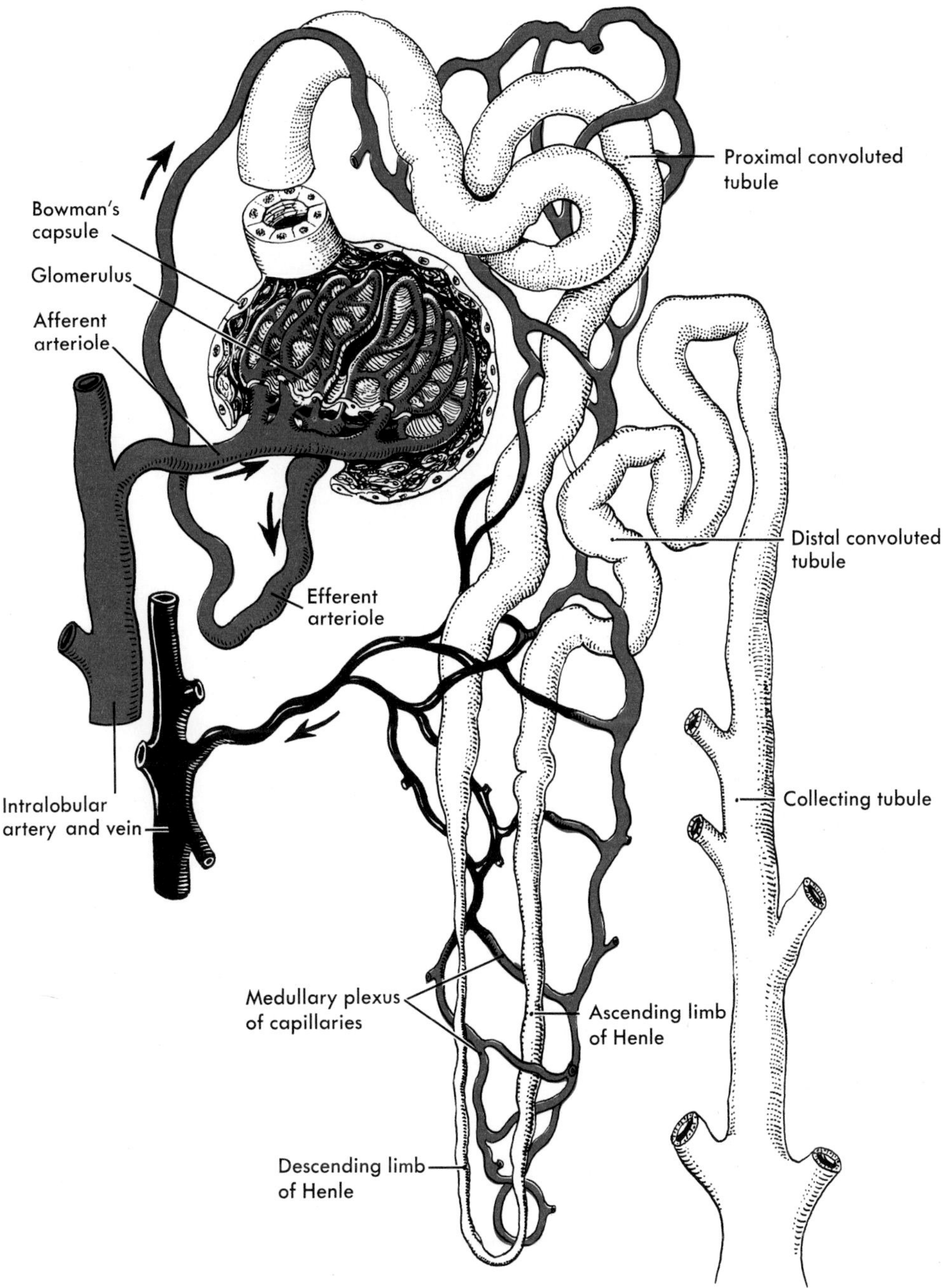

Fig. 282

Blood vessels of the nephron unit. Arrows indicate direction of blood flow from intralobular artery ⟶ afferent arteriole ⟶ glomerulus ⟶ efferent arteriole ⟶ peritubular capillaries (around the tubules) ⟶ venules ⟶ intralobular vein.

each Bowman's capsule is a renal tubule. It consists of several structurally different sections (Fig. 281). The first is known as the *proximal convoluted tubule:* proximal because it is the segment nearest the tubule's origin from the Bowman's capsule and convoluted because it pursues a tortuous rather than a straight course. The proximal tubule becomes the *descending limb* of the *loop of Henle,* which becomes the *ascending limb,* which becomes the *distal convoluted tubule,* which terminates in a straight or *collecting tubule.* Collecting tubules join larger tubules, and all the larger collecting tubules of one renal pyramid converge to form one tube that opens at a renal papilla into one of the small calyces. Bowman's capsules and both convoluted tubules lie in the cortex of the kidney, whereas the loops of Henle and collecting tubules lie in its medulla.

A glomerulus, Bowman's capsule, and its tubule—proximal, convoluted, loop of Henle, and distal convoluted portions—together constitute a *nephron,* the structural and functional unit of the kidney. *Gray's anatomy* says that there are about a million and a quarter nephrons in each kidney.

One of the ways in which the several parts of the nephron differ structurally is in the types of epithelial cells composing them (Fig. 281). And, as you might guess, they also differ functionally. But each part contributes a vital step in the process of urine formation.

Physiology

Functions

The function of the kidneys is to excrete urine, a life-preserving function because homeostasis depends upon it. More than any other organ in the body, the kidneys can adjust the amounts of water and electrolytes leaving the body so that they equal the amounts of these substances entering the body. The vital conditions of fluid and electrolyte balance and acid-base balance, therefore, depend most of all upon adequate kidney functioning. Here are just a few of the blood constituents that cannot be held to their normal concentration ranges if the kidneys fail: sodium, potassium, chloride, and nitrogenous wastes from protein metabolism such as urea. In short, kidney failure means homeostasis failure and, if not relieved, inevitable death.

In addition to excreting urine, the kidneys are now known to influence blood pressure (see Fig. 320, p. 509).

How kidneys excrete urine

Three processes—glomerular filtration, tubular reabsorption, and tubular secretion—together accomplish the kidneys' function of urine excretion.

Glomerular filtration. Filtration, the first step in the formation of urine, takes place from the blood in the glomeruli out into the Bowman's capsules. Water and solutes filter out of the glomeruli even faster than out of ordinary capillaries. At least two structural features make renal corpuscles especially effective filtration membranes. For one thing, glomeruli have many more pores than other capillaries. And the fact that the efferent arteriole is smaller in diameter than the afferent arteriole makes for a higher resistance to blood flow out of glomeruli than out of other capillaries and, therefore, for a higher blood pressure (hydrostatic pressure, that is) in glomeruli than in ordinary capillaries. Glomerular hydrostatic pressure, for instance, averages about 70 mm. Hg, whereas capillary hydrostatic pressure averages only about 30 mm. Hg.

Fluid moves out of the glomeruli into the Bowman's capsules for the same reason that it moves out of other capillaries into interstitial fluid or moves from any area to another—because a pressure gradient exists between the two areas. Normally, glomerular hydrostatic pressure, blood colloidal osmotic pressure, and capsular hydrostatic

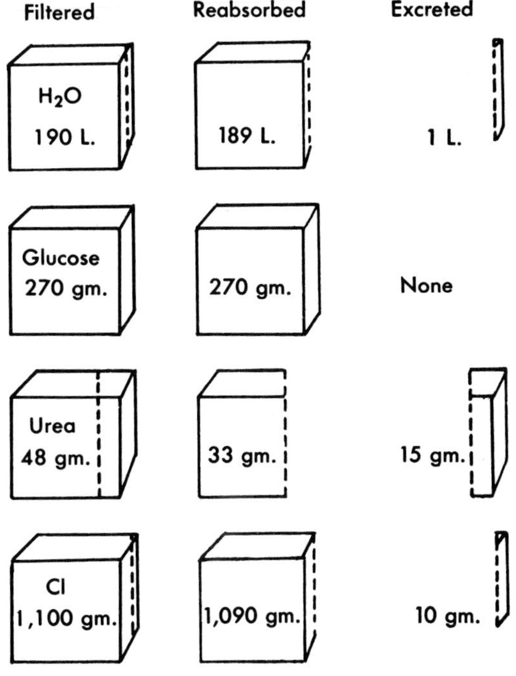

Fig. 283

Left column shows the amount of various substances filtered out of glomeruli into Bowman's capsules in twenty-four hours. Middle column shows the amount reabsorbed back into blood—an index of tubular work. Right column shows amounts finally excreted in the urine.

pressure together determine the pressure gradient (commonly spoken of as the *effective filtration pressure* or EFP) between glomeruli and capsules. And of these three pressures, glomerular hydrostatic pressure is the main driving force, the main determinant of the effective filtration pressure. It tends to move fluid out of the glomeruli. In contrast, the *capsular* hydrostatic pressure and the blood colloidal osmotic pressure both exert force in the opposite direction. (If you do not recall why osmotic pressure is a "water-pulling" rather than a "water-pushing" force, reread p. 25.) Suppose that there is a glomerular hydrostatic pressure of 70 mm. Hg and that it is opposed by a capsular hydrostatic pressure of 20 and a blood colloidal osmotic pressure of 30. There would then be a net or effective filtration pressure of 20 mm. Hg (70 − 20 − 30). In other words, there would be a pressure gradient of 20 mm. Hg, causing fluid to filter out of the glomeruli into the capsules.

Another factor, *capsular* colloidal osmotic pressure, operates when disease has increased glomerular permeability enough to allow blood protein molecules to diffuse out of the blood into the capsular filtrate. Under these circumstances the capsular filtrate exerts an osmotic pressure in opposition to blood osmotic pressure. Capsular osmotic pressure tends to draw water out of the blood and so constitutes another force to be added to glomerular hydrostatic pressure in determining the effective filtration pressure. By using the following formula, you will be able to see how changes in the various pressures cause changes in the glomerular filtration rate.

$$\begin{array}{l}\text{Effective filtration pressure} = \left(\text{Glomerular hydrostatic pressure} + \text{Capsular osmotic pressure}\right) \\ \qquad \text{minus} \left(\text{Glomerular osmotic pressure} + \text{Capsular hydrostatic pressure}\right)\end{array}$$

Glomerular hydrostatic pressure may decrease sharply under stress conditions such as following severe hemorrhage. Table 56 gives pressures which might exist under these circumstances. Using these figures, what do you compute the effective glomerular filtration pressure to be? Do you think it is true, after doing this computation, that glomerular filtration ceases entirely when glomerular hydrostatic pressure falls below a certain critical level?

Kidney disease, as previously noted, sometimes causes a loss of blood proteins in the urine. Since a decrease in blood protein concentration decreases blood colloidal

Table 55. Normal glomerulocapsular pressures

	Hydrostatic pressure	*Colloidal osmotic pressure*
Glomerular blood	70 mm. Hg	30 mm. Hg
Capsular filtrate	20 mm. Hg	——

Table 56. Abnormal glomerulocapsular pressures

	Hydrostatic pressure	*Colloidal osmotic pressure*
Glomerular blood	44 mm. Hg	28 mm. Hg
Capsular filtrate	20 mm. Hg	4 mm. Hg

osmotic pressure, how do you think this changes the glomerular filtration rate?

Glomerular hydrostatic pressure is regulated by mechanisms that change the size of the afferent and efferent arterioles and is also influenced by changes in systemic blood pressure. For example, sympathetic impulses cause constriction of both afferent and efferent arterioles. But with intense sympathetic stimulation, the afferent arteriole becomes much more constricted than the efferent. Consequently, glomerular hydrostatic pressure falls. Sometimes under severe stress conditions, it drops to a level too low to maintain filtration, and the kidneys "shut down" completely. In more technical language, renal suppression occurs (for example, see Table 56). Glomerular hydrostatic pressure and filtration are directly related to systemic blood pressure. By this we mean that an increase in blood pressure tends to produce an increase in glomerular pressure and in the filtration rate. The converse is also true.

Glomerular filtration is inversely related to blood colloidal osmotic pressure and blood protein concentration. For example, a decrease in blood protein concentration causes a decrease in blood osmotic pressure which, in turn, causes an increase in glomerular filtration. Normally the glomerular filtration rate averages about 125 ml. per minute in men and somewhat less in women.

Tubule reabsorption (Fig. 284). The second step in urine formation is reabsorption of substances needed by the body, that is, of most (usually from 97% to 99%) of the water and part of the solutes from the glomerular filtrate back into the blood. Reabsorption is the function of the cells composing the walls of the convoluted tubules and the loop of Henle. In the execution of this function these cells display astonishing powers of selection and discrimination. For example, they absorb most efficiently the substances that the body needs most vitally, such as Na^+, Cl^-, HCO_3^-, H_2O, and glucose.

Reabsorption is not merely a physical matter of diffusion and osmosis but consists also of somewhat obscure active transport mechanisms that require energy release by tubule cells. Because reabsorption is

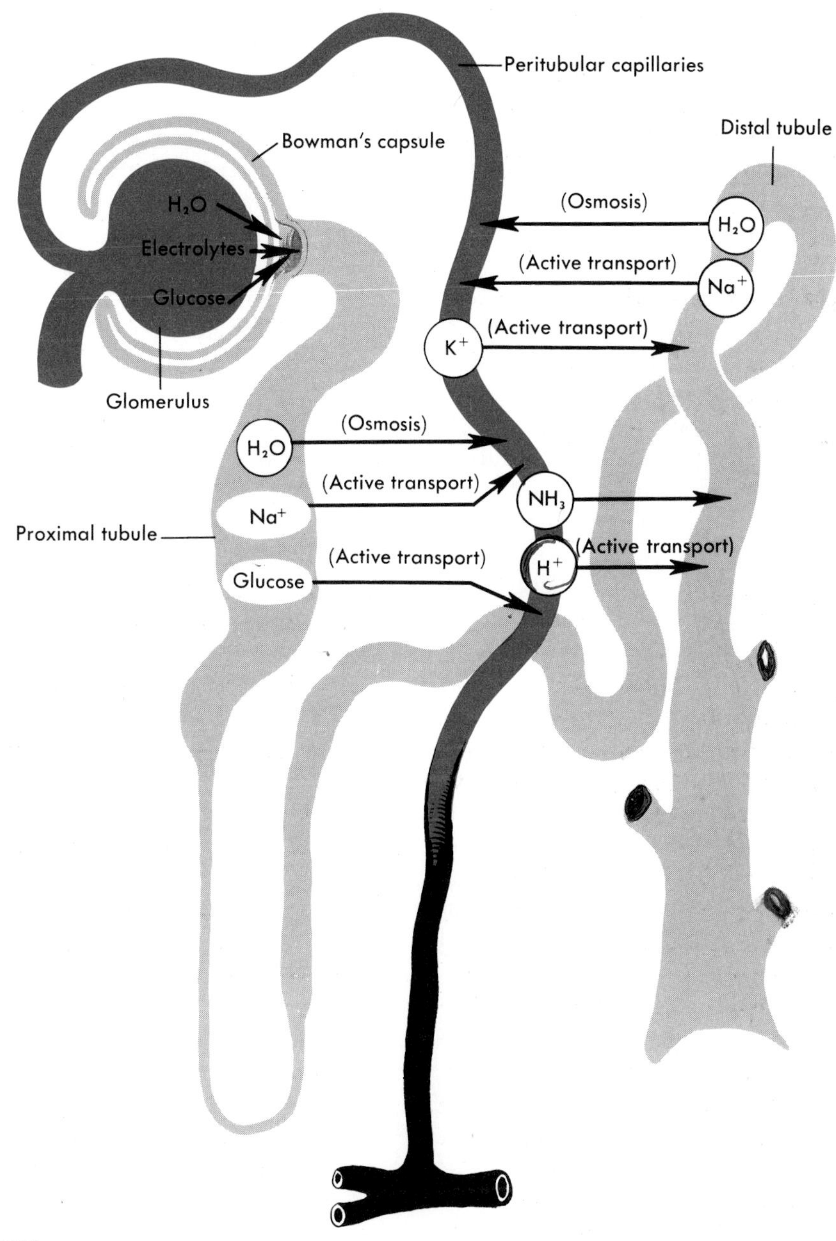

Fig. 284

Diagram showing glomerular filtration, tubular reabsorption, and tubular secretion—the three processes by which the kidneys excrete urine. In the proximal tubule, note that water is reabsorbed from the tubular filtrate into blood by osmosis but sodium and glucose are reabsorbed mainly by active transport mechanisms. Note, too, that water and sodium are also reabsorbed from the distal tubule. But potassium and hydrogen ions and ammonia are secreted into the tubule from the blood.

achieved partly by active transport mechanisms, it is one of the first powers diminished in kidney disease. Practical use is made of this fact in tests that measure the concentration of urine at different times of the day and thereby evaluate the active transport powers of the tubules.

Let us consider first the mechanism for reabsorption of solutes. Active transport mechanisms, whose precise nature is still unknown, absorb glucose, amino acids, and other nutrient substances and at least some electrolytes (salts). Proximal tubule cells transport glucose and other nutrients. So these vitally important materials, after filtering out of the glomeruli, return to the blood from the first part of the renal tubule. The transport mechanisms function so effectively that normally no glucose at all is lost in the urine. If, however, blood glucose exceeds a certain threshold amount (often around 150 mg. per 100 ml. of blood), the glucose transport mechanism cannot reabsorb all of it, and the excess remains in the urine. In other words, this mechanism has a maximum capacity for moving glucose molecules back into the blood. Occasionally this capacity is greatly reduced, in which case glucose appears in the urine (glycosuria or glucosuria), even though the blood sugar may be normal. This condition is known as renal diabetes or renal glycosuria.

Electrolytes are reabsorbed partly by active transport mechanisms and partly by diffusion. Sodium ions, for example, are known to be actively transported from all parts of the tubule. And this has important effects on the reabsorption of certain other ions and on water reabsorption. Sodium ions are positive ions (cations). Therefore, when they diffuse from the tubules into the peritubular blood, the latter momentarily becomes electropositive to the tubular filtrate. This attracts negative ions (notably chloride) and causes an equal number of them to diffuse out of the tubule. Sodium movement out of the tubule also produces a momentary disequilibrium between the tubular filtrate and peritubular blood osmotic pressures. It subtracts sodium ions from the filtrate but adds them to the blood—hence, the osmotic pressure of peritubular blood increases above the level of the filtrate osmotic pressure. Water, obeying the law of osmosis, follows rapidly along to reestablish osmotic equilibrium between the filtrate and blood. In short, the active transport of sodium out of the tubule is the main factor causing osmosis of water out of it. And, therefore, the water reabsorbed from the proximal tubule by this mechanism has been described as "obligatory water reabsorption"—obligatory because demanded by the law of osmosis. The volume of water reabsorbed from more distal parts of the tubule, on the other hand, being more variable than the volume of proximal reabsorption, is referred to as "facultative water reabsorption."

How much water finally moves back into the blood depends upon the presence of a hormone released by the neurohypophysis (posterior pituitary gland). Its name, antidiuretic hormone (ADH), is appropriate because it works against diuresis (large volume of urine). In other words, ADH decreases the amount of urine produced. The dynamics of the ADH mechanism are extremely complex, but the results are clear—increased amounts of water are reabsorbed from both the distal and collecting tubules by osmosis. Therefore, urine volume decreases while its concentration increases. Urine becomes hypertonic to blood under the ADH influence. How important the ADH-tubule mechanism is can be appreciated from the fact that water balance depends upon it and cannot be maintained if it fails (see Fig. 329, p. 534).

Certain adrenal cortex hormones, classified as mineralocorticoids (M-C's), regulate the reabsorption of electrolytes—of ions, that is. Of the natural mineralocorti-

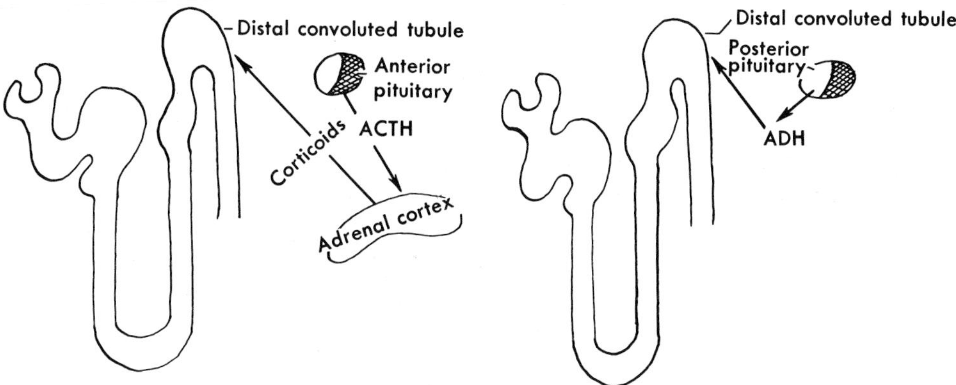

Fig. 285

ADH and corticoid control of distal renal tubule reabsorption. ADH causes increased water reabsorption by distal tubules and, it is now thought, by collecting tubules. Corticoids increase sodium reabsorption and, therefore, water reabsorption.

coids, aldosterone is the most potent. See p. 507 for a discussion of its action.

Tubular secretion. In addition to reabsorption, tubule cells also secrete certain substances. Tubular secretion (or tubular excretion, as it is also called) means the movement of substances out of the blood into the filtrate in the kidney tubules. Tubular reabsorption, you recall, means the movement of substances in the opposite direction, that is, out of the tubule filtrate into the blood. In both reabsorption and secretion, some substances are moved by active transport and some by passive mechanisms (diffusion and osmosis). For example, sodium ions and glucose molecules are reabsorbed and potassium and hydrogen ions are secreted by active transport mechanisms. But water is reabsorbed by osmosis and ammonia is secreted by diffusion, both passive processes. Tubule cells also secrete certain drugs—for example, penicillin and para-aminohippuric acid (PAH), two clinically important substances. For example, by administering a known amount of PAH and then measuring the amount excreted in the urine, tubular secretion can be evaluated. If the tubules are impaired, they, of course, cannot move as much PAH out of the blood, and less appears in the urine within a given time.

The reabsorption and secretion mechanisms are summarized in Table 57. The functions of the different parts of the nephron in forming urine are summarized in Table 58 and Fig. 284.

Mechanisms that control volume of urine secreted

The amount of urine secreted is regulated chiefly by ADH and aldosterone, hormones that influence the amount of water reabsorbed by the distal tubule cells (p. 444). It is thought that only under pathological conditions does the rate of glomerular filtration change enough to alter the volume of urine produced.

The total volume of extracellular fluid is known to influence the volume of urine secreted, presumably by increasing or decreasing ADH secretion. The exact mechanism, however, by which it accomplishes this is still unproved. At any rate, when ECF volume increases, increased urinary output soon follows. Conversely, when ECF volume decreases, decreased urinary output follows. Evidence that the first of these principles operates is the common experi-

Table 57. Reabsorption and secretion mechanisms (for moving substances out of and into renal tubules)

Substance	*Moved out of*	*By mechanism of*	*Into*
Electrolytes, e.g.:			
Sodium ions	Blood in glomeruli	*Filtration*	Bowman's capsules
	Filtrate in tubules (all parts)	*Active transport* (reabsorption)	Blood in peritubular capillaries
Potassium ions	Blood in glomeruli	*Filtration*	Bowman's capsules
	Blood in peritubular capillaries	*Active transport* (secretion)	Filtrate in tubules
Chloride ions	Blood in glomeruli	*Filtration*	Bowman's capsules
	Filtrate in tubules	*Diffusion* (secondary to Na^+-transport)	Blood in peritubular capillaries
Nutrients, e.g.:			
Glucose	Blood in glomeruli	*Filtration*	Bowman's capsules
	Filtrate in proximal tubules	*Active transport* (reabsorption)	Blood in peritubular capillaries
Wastes, e.g.:			
Urea (most abundant solute in urine)	Blood in glomeruli	*Filtration*	Bowman's capsules
	Filtrate in tubules	*Diffusion*	Blood in peritubular capillaries
Water	Blood in glomeruli	*Filtration*	Bowman's capsules
	Filtrate in proximal tubules	*Osmosis* (obligatory water reabsorption)	Blood in peritubular capillaries
	Filtrate in distal and collecting tubules	*Osmosis* (facultative water reabsorption; ADH-controlled)	Blood in peritubular capillaries
Hydrogen ions	Blood in peritubular capillaries	*Active transport* (secretion)	Filtrate in distal tubules
Ammonia	Distal tubule cells	*Diffusion*	Filtrate in distal tubules

ence of increased output following rapid ingestion of a large amount of fluid. Evidence of the second principle is the oliguria or even anuria in dehydrated patients.

Another factor that helps regulate the amount of urine secreted is the total amount of solutes excreted through the kidneys. The more solutes to be excreted, the greater the volume of urine. In diabetes, for example, more solids are excreted than normally due to the excess glucose that "spills over" into the urine, and therefore the volume of urine secreted daily is greater than in the normal individual.

Table 58. Functions of different parts of nephron in urine formation

Part of nephron	*Function*	*Substance moved*
Glomerulus	Filtration	Water All solutes except colloids such as blood proteins
Proximal tubule and loop of Henle	Reabsorption by active transport Reabsorption by diffusion (secondary to active transport) Obligatory water reabsorption by osmosis	Na^+ and probably some other ions; nutrients—glucose and amino acids Cl^-, HCO_3^-, and probably some other ions Water
Distal and collecting tubules	Reabsorption by active transport Facultative water reabsorption by osmosis (ADH-controlled) Reabsorptions by diffusion Secretion by active transport	Na^+, and probably some other ions Water Ammonia K^+, H^+, and some drugs

Influence of kidneys on blood pressure

Clinical observation and animal experiments have established the fact that destruction of a large proportion of total kidney tissue usually results in the development of hypertension. This happens frequently, for example, in patients who have severe renal arteriosclerosis or glomerulonephritis. Many experiments have been performed and various theories devised to explain the mechanism responsible for "renal hypertension." Ischemic kidneys are known to produce a proteolytic enzyme, *renin,* which hydrolyzes one of the blood proteins (a globulin) to produce *angiotonin* (hypertensin), which causes arteriolar constriction and a rise in blood pressure (see Fig. 320, p. 509).

URETERS

Location and structure

The two ureters are tubes from 10 to 12 inches long. At their widest point they measure less than a half inch in diameter. They lie behind the parietal peritoneum and extend from the kidneys to the posterior surface of the bladder. As the upper end of each ureter enters the kidney, it enlarges into a funnel-shaped basin named the *renal pelvis.* The pelvis expands into several branches called *calyces.* Each calyx contains a renal papilla. As urine is secreted, it drops out of the collecting tubules, whose openings are in the papillae, into the calyces, thence into the pelvis, and down the ureters into the bladder.

The walls of the ureters are composed of three coats: a lining coat of mucous membrane, a middle coat of two layers of smooth muscle, and an outer fibrous coat.

Where the ureters empty into the bladder, there is a fold of mucous membrane that serves as a valve preventing the backflow of urine into the ureter when the bladder contracts.

Function

The ureters, together with their expanded upper portions, the pelves and calyces, collect the urine as it forms and drain it into the bladder. Peristaltic waves (about one to five per minute) force the urine down the ureters and into the bladder.

Correlations

Stones known as *renal calculi* sometimes develop within the kidney. Urine may wash them into the ureter where they cause extreme pain if they are large enough to distend its walls.

BLADDER

Structure and location

The bladder is a collapsible bag located directly behind the symphysis pubis. It lies below the parietal peritoneum, which covers only its superior surface. Three layers of smooth muscle (known collectively as the detrusor muscle) fashion its walls, while mucous membrane, arranged in rugae, forms its lining. Because of the rugae and

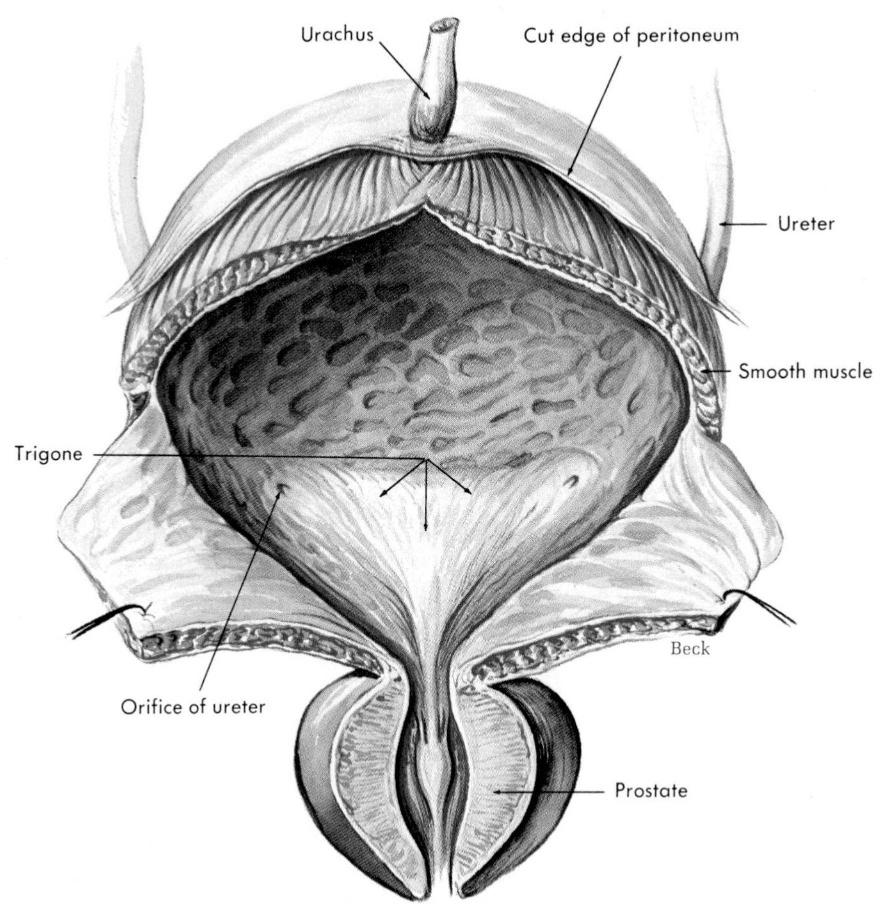

Fig. 286

The male urinary bladder cut to show the interior.

the elasticity of its walls, the bladder is capable of considerable distention, although its capacity varies greatly with individuals. There are three openings in the floor of the bladder—two from the ureters and one into the urethra. The ureter openings lie at the posterior corners of the triangular-shaped floor (the trigone) and the urethral opening at the anterior and lower corner.

Functions

The bladder performs two functions:

1. It serves as a reservoir for urine before it leaves the body.

2. Aided by the urethra, it expels urine from the body. Distention of the bladder with urine stimulates stretch receptors in the bladder wall. This initiates reflex contraction of the bladder wall but simultaneous relaxation of the internal sphincter, followed rapidly by relaxation of the external sphincter and emptying of the bladder. Parasympathetic fibers transmit the impulses that cause contractions of the bladder and relaxation of the internal sphincter. Voluntary contraction of the external sphincter, however, to prevent or terminate micturition is learned. Voluntary control of micturition is possible only if the nerves supplying the bladder and urethra, the projection tracts of the cord and brain, and the motor area of the cerebrum are all intact. Injury to any of these parts of the nervous system, by a cerebral hemorrhage or cord injury, for example, results in involuntary emptying of the bladder at intervals. Involuntary micturition is called *incontinence.* In the average bladder, 250 ml. of urine will cause a moderately distended sensation and therefore the desire to void.

Occasionally an individual is unable to void even though the bladder contains an

Table 59. Physical characteristics of normal urine

Amount (24 hours)	Three pints (1,500 ml.) but varies greatly according to fluid intake, amount of perspiration, and several other factors
Clearness	Transparent or clear; upon standing, becomes cloudy
Color	Amber or straw-colored; varies according to amount voided—less voided, darker the color, usually; diet also may change color; e.g., reddish color from beets
Odor	"Characteristic"; upon standing, develops ammonia odor due to formation of ammonium carbonate
Specific gravity	1.015 to 1.020; highest in morning specimen
Reaction	Acid but may become alkaline if diet is largely vegetables; high-protein diet increases acidity; stale urine has alkaline reaction due to decomposition of urea forming ammonium carbonate; normal range for urine pH 4.8-7.5; average about 6; rarely becomes more acid than 4.5 or more alkaline than 8

excessive amount of urine. This condition is known as *retention*. It often follows pelvic operations and childbirth. Catheterization (introduction of a rubber tube through the urethra into the bladder to remove urine) is used to relieve the discomfort accompanying retention. A more serious complication, which is also characterized by the inability to void, is called *suppression*. In this condition the patient cannot void because the kidneys are not secreting any urine, and therefore the bladder is empty. Catheterization, of course, gives no relief for this condition.

URETHRA

Structure and location

The urethra is a small tube leading from the floor of the bladder to the exterior. In the female it lies directly behind the symphysis pubis and anterior to the vagina. It extends up, in, and back for a distance of about 1 to 1½ inches. The male urethra follows a tortuous course for a distance of approximately 8 inches. Immediately below the bladder, it passes through the center of the prostate gland, then between two sheets of white fibrous tissue connecting the pubic bones, and then through the penis, the external male reproductive organ. These three parts of the urethra are known, respectively, as the prostatic portion, the membranous portion, and the cavernous portion.

The opening of the urethra to the exterior is named the *urinary meatus*.

Mucous membrane lines the urethra as well as the rest of the urinary tract.

Functions

As the terminal portion of the urinary tract, the urethra serves as the passageway for eliminating urine from the body. In addition, the male urethra is the terminal portion of the reproductive tract and serves as the passageway for eliminating the reproductive fluid (semen) from the body. The female urethra serves only the urinary tract.

Urine

Physical characteristics

The physical characteristics of normal urine are listed in Table 59.

Chemical composition

Urine is approximately 95% water, in which are dissolved several kinds of substances, the most important of which are listed as follows:

1. *nitrogenous wastes* from protein metabolism—such as urea (most abundant solute in urine), uric acid, ammonia and creatinine
2. *electrolytes*—mainly the following ions: sodium, potassium, ammonium, chloride, bicarbonate, phosphate, and sulfate; amounts and kinds of minerals vary with diet and other factors
3. *toxins*—during disease, bacterial poisons leave the body in the urine—an important reason for "forcing fluids" on patients suffering with infectious diseases, so as to dilute the toxins that might damage the kidney cells if they were eliminated in a concentrated form
4. *pigments*
5. *hormones*
6. various *abnormal constituents* sometimes found in urine—such as glucose, albumin, blood, casts, calculi, etc.

Definitions

1. *glycosuria*, or *glucosuria*—sugar (glucose) in the urine
2. *hematuria*—blood in the urine
3. *pyuria*—pus in the urine
4. *casts*—substances, such as mucus, that harden and form molds inside the uriniferous tubules and then are washed out into the urine; microscopic in size

5. *dysuria*—painful urination
6. *polyuria*—unusually large amounts of urine
7. *oliguria*—scanty urine
8. *anuria*—absence of urine

Outline summary— The urinary system

Organs

KIDNEYS

Gross anatomy

1. Size, shape, and location
   a. 4½ by 2 by 3 by 1 inch
   b. shaped like lima beans
   c. lie against posterior abdominal wall, behind peritoneum, at level of last thoracic and first three lumbar vertebrae; right kidney slightly lower than left
2. External structure
   a. hilum, concave notch on mesial surface
   b. enveloping capsule of white fibrous tissue
3. Internal structure
   a. outer layer called cortex
   b. inner portion called medulla
   c. renal pyramids triangular wedges of medullary substance, apices of which called papillae
   d. renal columns inward extensions of cortex between pyramids

Microscopic anatomy

1. Cluster of capillaries invaginated in Bowman's capsule called *glomerulus*
2. Bowman's capsule together with glomerulus constitute renal (malpighian) corpuscle
3. Physiological unit of kidney called nephron —consists of renal corpuscle, convoluted tubules, loop of Henle, and straight tubule

Physiology

1. Functions
   a. excrete urine, by which various toxins and metabolic wastes excreted and composition and volume of blood regulated
   b. influence blood pressure
2. How kidneys excrete urine (see Table 57 and Fig. 285)
   a. filtration of substances from blood in glomeruli into Bowman's capsules
   b. reabsorption of most of water and part of solutes from tubular filtrate back into blood
   c. secretion of K^+, H^+, NH_3, and some other substances into tubular filtrate from blood
3. Mechanisms that control volume of urine excreted are factors that change
   a. amount of water reabsorbed from tubular filtrate into blood—most important determinant of amount of urine formed; posterior pituitary ADH increases water reabsorption from distal and collecting tubules; corticoids (especially, aldosterone) increase sodium reabsorption and therefore also increase water reabsorption
   b. rate of filtration from glomeruli—normally quite constant at about 125 ml. per minute; varies directly with changes in glomerular blood pressure, i.e., increased glomerular blood pressure tends to increase glomerular filtration rate and therefore urine volume and vice versa but glomerular blood pressure normally quite constant; decreased blood colloidal osmotic pressure tends to increase glomerular filtration and urine volume and vice versa
   c. total extracellular fluid volume; urine output increases following increase in total ECF and decreases following decrease in ECF
   d. amount of solutes excreted in urine; urine output increases when solutes increase

URETERS

1. Location and structure
   a. lie retroperitoneally
   b. extend from kidneys to posterior part of bladder floor
   c. ureter expands as it enters kidney, becoming renal pelvis, which is subdivided into calyces, each of which contains renal papilla
   d. walls of smooth muscle with mucous lining and fibrous outer coat
2. Function—collect urine and drain it into bladder

BLADDER

1. Structure and location
   a. collapsible bag of smooth muscle lined with mucosa
   b. lies behind symphysis pubis, below parietal peritoneum

   c. three openings—one into urethra and two into ureters
2. Functions
   a. reservoir for urine
   b. expels urine from body by way of urethra, called micturition, urination, or voiding; retention, inability to expel urine from bladder; suppression, failure of kidneys to form urine

URETHRA

1. Structure and location
   a. musculomembranous tube lined with mucosa
   b. lies behind symphysis, in front of vagina in female
   c. extends through prostate gland, fibrous sheet, and penis in male
   d. opening to exterior called urinary meatus
2. Functions
   a. female—passageway for expulsion of urine from body
   b. male—passageway for expulsion of urine and of reproductive fluid (semen)

Urine

1. Physical characteristics—see Table 59
2. Chemical composition—consists of approximately 95% water in which are dissolved
   a. wastes from protein metabolism (urea, uric acid, creatinine, etc.)
   b. mineral salts (sodium chloride main one but various others according to diet)
   c. toxins—from bacteria, e.g.
   d. pigments
   e. sex hormones
   f. abnormal constituents—e.g., glucose in diabetes and numerous others such as albumin, blood, casts, and calculi
3. Definitions
   a. glycosuria—sugar in urine
   b. hematuria—blood in urine
   c. pyuria—pus in urine
   d. casts—microscopic bits of substances that harden and form molds inside tubules
   e. dysuria—painful urination
   f. polyuria—excessive amounts of urine
   g. oliguria—scanty urine
   h. anuria—absence of urine

Review questions

1. What four organs are excretory organs?
2. Which organs eliminate wastes of protein metabolism? Of digestion? Of carbohydrate and fat metabolism?
3. Name, locate, and give main function(s) of each organ of the urinary system.
4. How far and in which direction must a catheter be inserted to reach the bladder in the female? In the male?
5. Describe the microscopic structure of the kidney.
6. Describe the mechanism of urine formation, relating each step to part of the nephron that performs it.

Situation: An artificial kidney consists of a device in which blood flows directly from a patient's body through cellophane tubing immersed in a dialyzing fluid that contains prescribed amounts of various electrolytes and other substances. The two columns below show the composition of one patient's blood and of the dialyzing fluid used for his treatment with the artificial kidney.

	Blood plasma (in coiled tube) mEq./L.	*Dialyzing fluid (around coiled tube) mEq./L.*
Na^+	142	126
K^+	5	5
Ca^{++}	5	0
Mg^{++}	3	0
Cl^-	103	110
HCO_3^-	27	25
$HPO_4^=$	2	0
$SO_4^=$	1	0
	mg./100 ml.	*mg./100 ml.*
Glucose	100	1,750
Urea	26	0
Uric acid	4	0
Creatinine	1	0

7. What body structures do you think the cellophane tube substitutes for?
8. Which, if any, of the above substances diffuse out of the blood into the dialyzing fluid? Give your reasons.
9. Which, if any, of the above substances diffuse into the blood from the dialyzing fluid? Give your reasons.
10. Which, if any, of the above substances do not pass through the cellophane membrane in either direction? Give your reasons.
11. What reasons can you see for having the dialyzing fluid contain the concentration of each substance given above? What does it accomplish?

Situation: Results of a blood urea clearance test indicate that the glomerular filtration rate of a patient who has had a severe hemorrhage is less than 50% of normal.

12. Explain the mechanism responsible for the drop in the glomerular filtration rate.
13. Do you consider this a homeostatic mechanism? Does it serve a useful purpose? If so, what purpose?
14. What is the normal glomerular filtration rate?
15. What would you expect to be true of the volume of urine this patient would excrete—normal, polyuria, oliguria?
16. Define the following terms briefly:

Bowman's capsule	polyuria
calculi	ptosis
calyces	pyelitis
casts	renal capsule
cystitis	renal cortex
dysuria	renal hilum
glomerulus	renal medulla
glycosuria	renal papilla
hematuria	renal pelvis
incontinence	renal pyramids
nephritis	retention
oliguria	suppression

UNIT FIVE

Reproduction of the human being

Meaning and function

Male reproductive organs

- Testes
  - Structure and location
  - Functions
  - Structure of spermatozoa
- Excretory ducts of testes
  - Epididymis
    - Structure and location
    - Functions
  - Seminal duct (vas deferens, ductus deferens)
    - Structure and location
    - Function
    - Correlation
  - Ejaculatory duct
  - Urethra
- Accessory reproductive glands
  - Seminal vesicles
    - Structure and location
    - Function
  - Prostate gland
    - Structure and location
    - Function
  - Bulbourethral glands
    - Structure and location
    - Function
- Supporting structures
  - External—scrotum and penis
  - Scrotum
  - Penis
    - Structure
    - Functions
  - Internal—spermatic cords
- Composition and course of seminal fluid
- Male fertility

Female reproductive organs

- Uterus
  - Structure
  - Location
  - Position
  - Functions
- Uterine tubes—fallopian tubes or oviducts
  - Location
  - Structure
  - Function
- Ovaries—female gonads
  - Location and size
  - Microscopic structure
  - Functions
- Vagina
  - Location
  - Structure
  - Functions
- Vulva
- Perineum
- Breasts
  - Location and size
  - Structure
  - Function
  - Mechanism controlling lactation

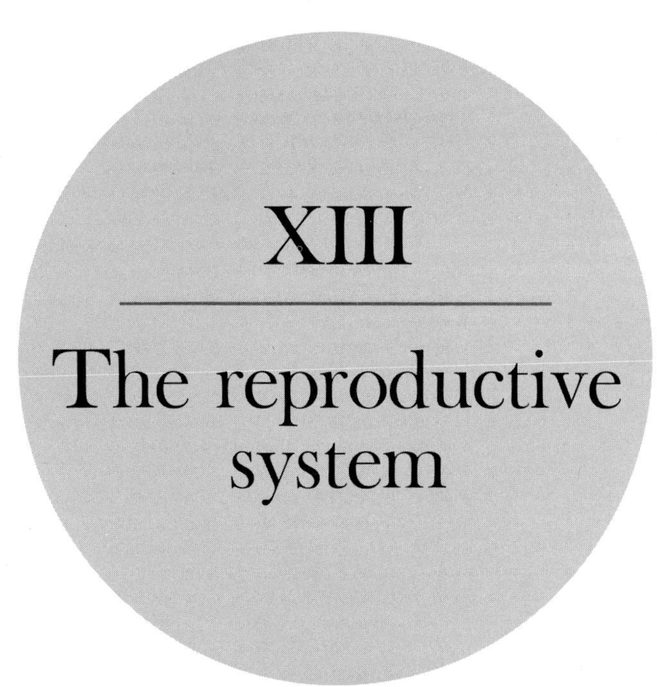

XIII

The reproductive system

Meaning and function

The reproductive system consists of those organs whose function is to produce a new individual, that is, to accomplish reproduction. And some reproductive organs produce hormones. Different forms of life reproduce in different ways, but all living organisms, no matter how simple or how complex, are able to perform this miracle.

Reproduction of cells, of course, must occur in order that reproduction of a multicellular organism may occur. But before pursuing this idea any further, we shall describe the various reproductive organs.

Male reproductive organs

Glands, ducts, and supporting structures compose the male reproductive system. The glands are the testes (paired), seminal vesicles (paired), prostate, and bulbourethral glands (paired). The ducts are the epididymis (paired), seminal ducts (vas deferens, ductus deferens) (paired), ejaculatory ducts (paired), and urethra. And the supporting structures are the scrotum, penis, and spermatic cords (paired). (See Plate XIV of the Trans-Vision® insert.)

TESTES

Structure and location

The testes are small ovoid glands that lie in a pouchlike, skin-covered structure called the *scrotum.* A white fibrous capsule encases each testis and sends partitions through its interior, dividing it into lobules. Each lobule contains a tiny, coiled *seminiferous tubule* (Fig. 289) and numerous interstitial cells (of Leydig). The seminiferous tubules come together to form a plexus from which a few ducts emerge and enter the head of the epididymis.

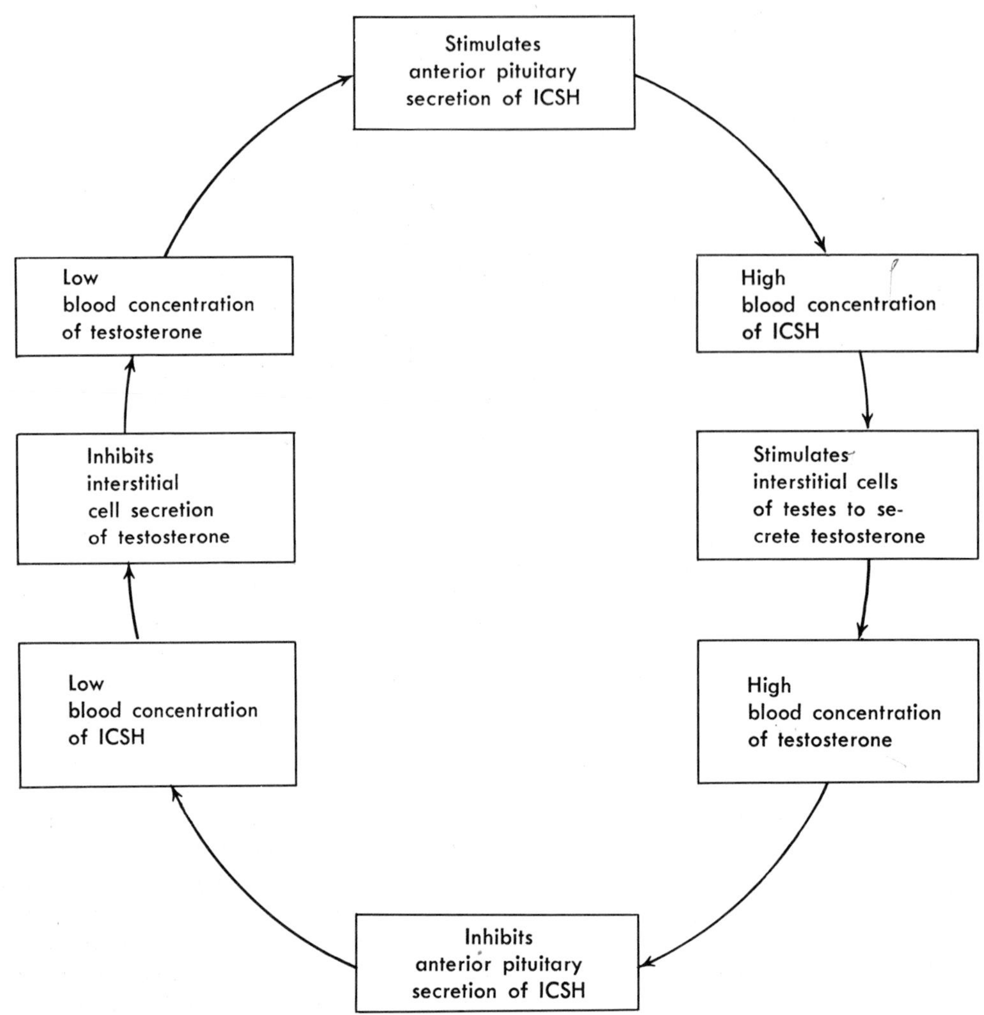

Fig. 287

The negative feedback mechanism that controls anterior pituitary gland secretion of ICSH and interstitial cell secretion of testosterone.

Functions

The testes perform two primary functions:

1. Spermatogenesis, the production of spermatozoa ("sperm"), the male gametes or reproductive cells. The seminiferous tubules produce the sperm.

2. Secretion of hormones, chiefly testosterone (androgen or masculinizing hormone), by interstitial cells (Leydig cells). Testosterone serves the following general functions:

(a) Promotes "maleness," that is, the development and maintenance of male secondary sex characteristics, of male accessory organs such as the prostate, seminal vesicles, etc., and of adult male sexual behavior

(b) Helps regulate metabolism and is sometimes referred to as "the anabolic hormone" because of its marked stimulating effect on protein anabolism. And by stimulating

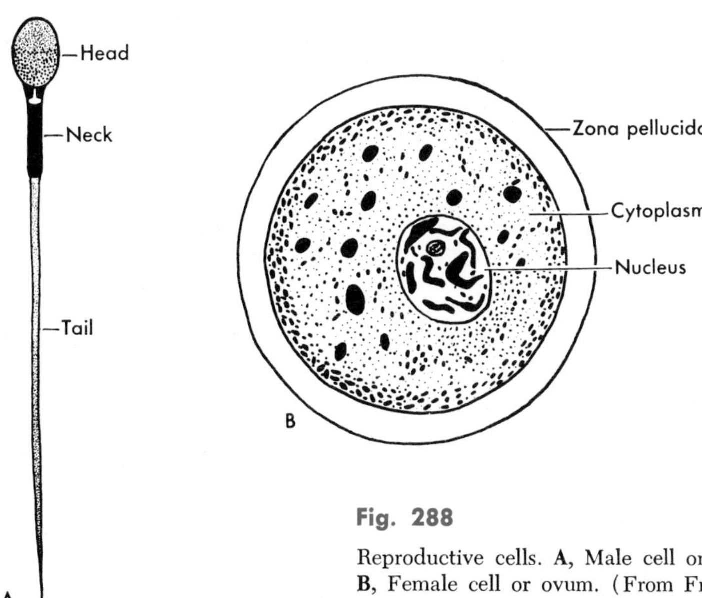

Fig. 288

Reproductive cells. **A**, Male cell or spermatozoon. **B**, Female cell or ovum. (From Francis and Farrell: Integrated anatomy and physiology, St. Louis, The C. V. Mosby Co.)

protein anabolism, testosterone promotes growth of skeletal muscles (responsible for greater muscular development and strength of male) and promotes growth of bone. However, testosterone also promotes closure of the epiphyses so a high blood concentration of this sex hormone tends to limit lengthwise growth of bone

(c) Plays a part in fluid and electrolyte metabolism in that it has a mild stimulating effect on kidney tubule reabsorption of sodium and therefore water; also promotes kidney tubule excretion of potassium

(d) Inhibits anterior pituitary secretion of gonadotrophins, namely, FSH and ICSH (interstitial cell-stimulating hormone; called LH or luteinizing hormone in the female)

The anterior pituitary gland controls the testes by means of its gonadotrophic hormones—specifically, follicle-stimulating hormone (FSH) and ICSH just mentioned. FSH stimulates the seminiferous tubules to produce sperm more rapidly. ICSH stimulates interstitial cells to increase their secretion of testosterone. Soon the blood concentration of testosterone reaches a high level which inhibits anterior pituitary secretion of FSH and ICSH. Thus, a negative feedback mechanism operates between the anterior pituitary gland and the testes. A high blood concentration of gonadotrophins stimulates testosterone secretion. But a high blood concentration of testosterone inhibits (has a negative effect on) gonadotrophin secretion (Fig. 287).

Structure of spermatozoa

Fig. 288, *A*, shows the characteristic parts of a spermatozoon: head, neck, and elongated, lashlike tail.

EXCRETORY DUCTS OF TESTES

Epididymis

Structure and location

Each epididymis consists of a single tightly coiled tube enclosed in a fibrous casing. The tube has a very small diameter (just barely macroscopic) but measures ap-

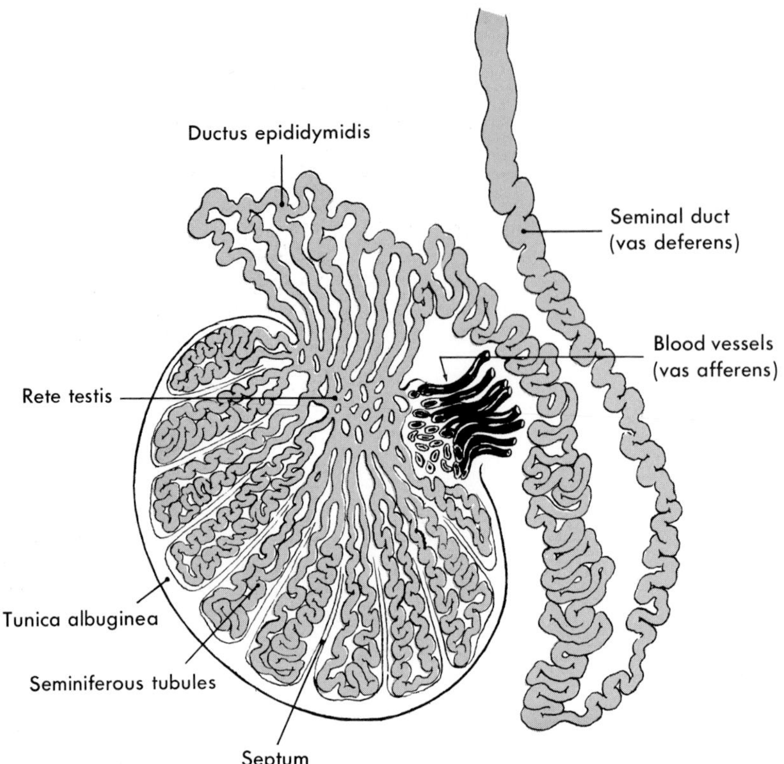

Fig. 289

Diagram showing tubules of the testis and epididymis. The ducts and tubules are exaggerated in size.

proximately 20 feet in length. It lies along the top and side of the testis. As shown in Fig. 289, several small ducts connect the seminiferous tubules of the testis with the epididymis. Also see Fig. 292.

Functions

The epididymis serves the following functions:

1. It serves as one of the ducts through which sperm pass in their journey from the testis to the exterior.
2. It stores a small quantity of sperm prior to ejaculation.
3. It secretes a small part of the seminal fluid (semen).

Seminal duct (vas deferens, ductus deferens)

Structure and location

The seminal duct, like the epididymis, is a tube. In fact, it is an extension of the epididymis. It passes through the inguinal canal, where it is enclosed in a fibrous cylinder, the spermatic cord, into the abdominal cavity. Here it extends over the top and down the posterior surface of the bladder, where it joins the duct from the seminal vesicle to form the ejaculatory duct (Figs. 290 and 291).

Function

The seminal duct serves as one of the excretory ducts for the testis, connecting the epididymis with the ejaculatory duct.

Correlation

Severing of the seminal ducts, usually through incision in the groin, renders the

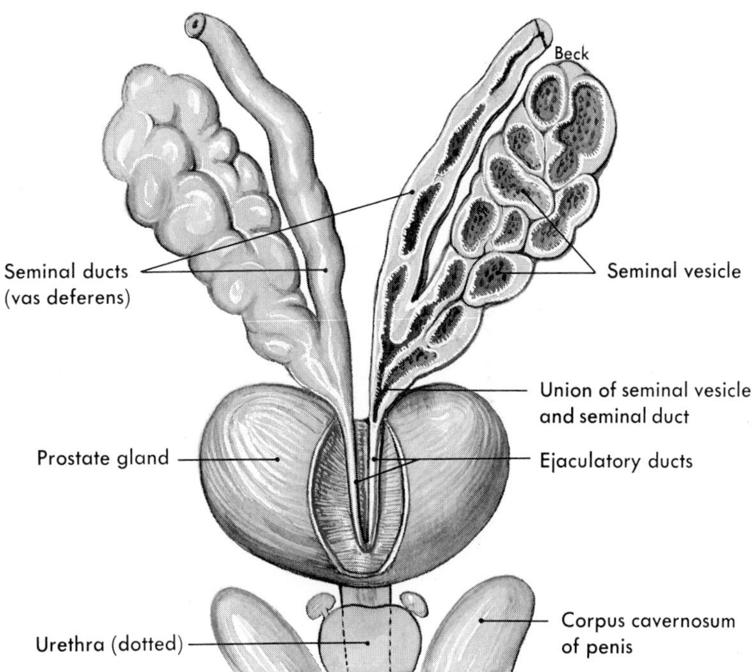

Fig. 290

Formation of the ejaculatory ducts by union of the seminal vesicles with the seminal duct just before entrance into the prostate gland. The ejaculatory ducts open freely into the prostatic portion of the urethra.

patient sterile for the obvious reason that sperm can no longer pass all the way through the epididymis to reach the exterior.

Ejaculatory duct

The two ejaculatory ducts are short tubes that pass through the prostate gland to terminate in the urethra. They are formed by the union of the seminal ducts with the ducts from the seminal vesicles.

Urethra

See p. 450 for a discussion of the urethra.

ACCESSORY REPRODUCTIVE GLANDS

Seminal vesicles

Structure and location

The seminal vesicles are convoluted pouches that lie along the lower part of the posterior surface of the bladder, directly in front of the rectum.

Function

The seminal vesicles secrete the viscous liquid portion of the semen. It contains nutrients that support sperm metabolism. The seminal vesicles, it is now known, do not store sperm.

Prostate gland

Structure and location

The prostate is a compound tubuloalveolar gland that lies just below the bladder and is shaped like a doughnut. The fact that the urethra passes through the small hole in the center of the prostate is a matter of considerable clinical significance. Many older men suffer from enlargement of this gland. As it enlarges, it squeezes the ureth-

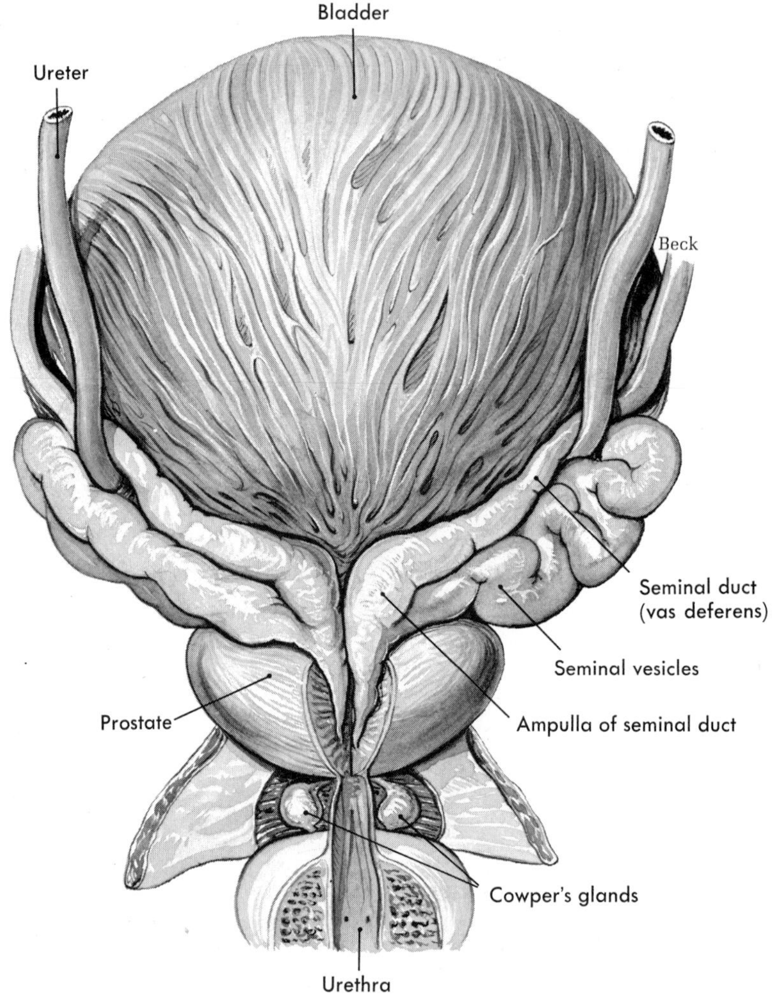

Fig. 291

The urinary bladder and male pelvic reproductive organs viewed from behind.

ra, frequently closing it so completely that urination becomes impossible. Urinary retention results. Surgical removal of the gland (prostatectomy) is resorted to as a cure for this condition when other less radical methods of treatment fail.

Function

The prostate secretes a thin alkaline substance that constitutes the largest part of the seminal fluid. Its alkalinity helps protect the sperm from acid present in the male urethra and female vagina and thereby increases sperm motility. (Acid depresses or, if strong enough, kills sperm. Sperm motility is greatest in neutral or slightly alkaline media.)

Bulbourethral glands

Structure and location

The two bulbourethral or Cowper's glands resemble peas in both size and shape. These compound tubuloalveolar glands lie below the prostate glands. A duct approximately 1 inch long connects them with the membranous portion of the urethra.

Function

Like the prostate, the bulbourethral glands secrete an alkaline fluid important for counteracting the acid present in the male urethra and female vagina.

SUPPORTING STRUCTURES

External—scrotum and penis

Scrotum

The scrotum is a skin-covered pouch suspended from the perineal region. Internally it is divided into two sacs by a septum, each sac containing a testis, epididymis, and lower part of the spermatic cord.

Penis

Structure

Three cylindrical masses of erectile or cavernous tissue, enclosed in separate fibrous coverings and held together by a covering of skin, compose the penis. The two larger and uppermost of these cylinders are named the *corpora cavernosa penis,* whereas the smaller, lower one, which contains the urethra, is called the *corpus cavernosum urethrae.*

Erectile tissue that composes these structures resembles a rubber sponge in structure, consisting, as it does, of many irregular cavernous spaces, the venous sinuses. Under the influence of the sexual emotion, the arteries and arterioles of the penis dilate, flooding and distending the cavernous spaces with blood and thereby causing the organ to become enlarged, rigid, and erect.

At the distal end of the penis there is a slightly bulging structure, the *glans penis,* over which the skin is folded doubly to form a more or less loose-fitting, retractable casing known as the *prepuce* or foreskin. If the foreskin fits too tightly about the glans, a circumcision is usually performed to prevent irritation.

Functions

The penis contains the urethra, the terminal duct for both urinary and reproductive tracts, and it is the copulatory organ by means of which spermatozoa are introduced into the female vagina. The scrotum and penis together constitute the *external genitals* of the male.

Internal—spermatic cords

The *spermatic cords* are cylindrical casings of white fibrous tissue located in the inguinal canals between the scrotum and the abdominal cavity. They enclose the seminal ducts, blood vessels, lymphatics, and nerves.

COMPOSITION AND COURSE OF SEMINAL FLUID

The following structures secrete the substances which, together, make up the seminal fluid or semen:

1. Testes and epididymides—their secretions, according to one estimate, constitute less than 5% of the seminal fluid volume.
2. Seminal vesicles—their secretions are reported to contribute about 30% of the seminal fluid volume.
3. Prostate gland—its secretions constitute the bulk of the seminal fluid volume, reportedly about 60%.
4. Bulbourethral glands—their secretions are said to constitute less than 5% of the seminal fluid volume.

Besides contributing slightly to the fluid part of semen, the testes also add hundreds of millions of sperm. In traversing the distance from their place of origin to the exterior, the sperm must pass from the testis through the epididymis, seminal duct, ejaculatory duct, and urethra. Note that the male gametes originate in an organ located outside the body (that is, not within a

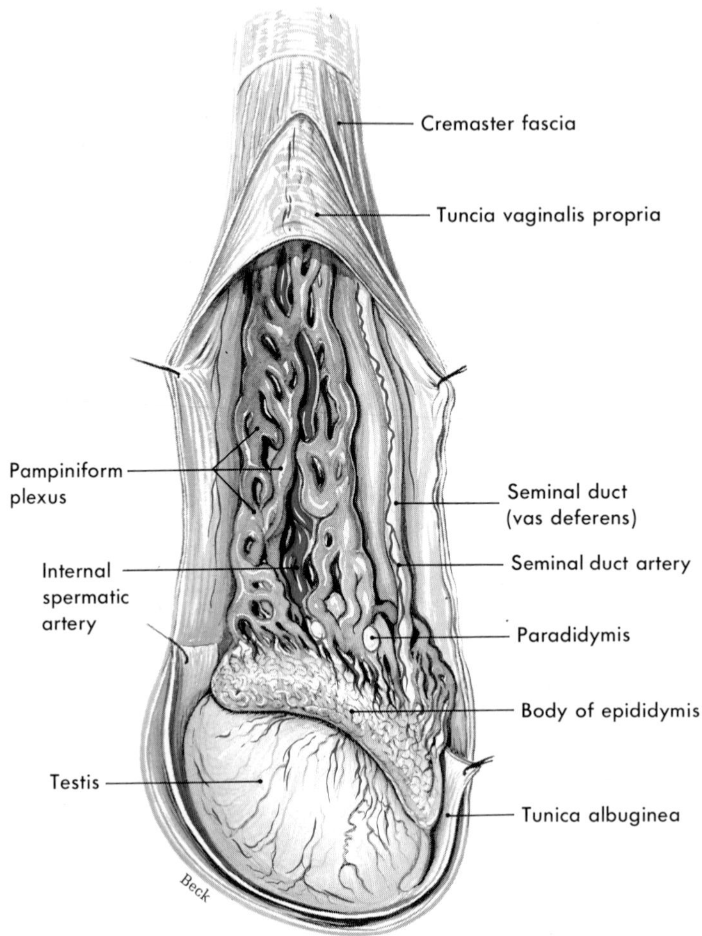

Fig. 292

Lateral view of the *left* spermatic cord and testis.

body cavity), travel inside, and finally are expelled outside.

Early in fetal life the testes are located in the abdominal cavity but normally descend through the spermatic cord into the scrotum some time before birth. Occasionally a baby is born with undescended testes, a condition readily observed by palpation of the scrotum. Because the higher temperature inside the abdominal cavity makes sperm infertile, measures are taken to bring the testes down into the scrotum in order to prevent sterility.

Ejaculation of the seminal fluid occurs at irregular intervals due to arousal of the sexual emotion.

MALE FERTILITY

Male fertility relates to many factors—most of all to the number of sperm ejaculated but also to their size and shape. Fertile sperm have a uniform size and shape. They are highly motile. Although only one sperm fertilizes an ovum, millions of sperm seem to be necessary for fertilization to occur. According to one estimate, when the

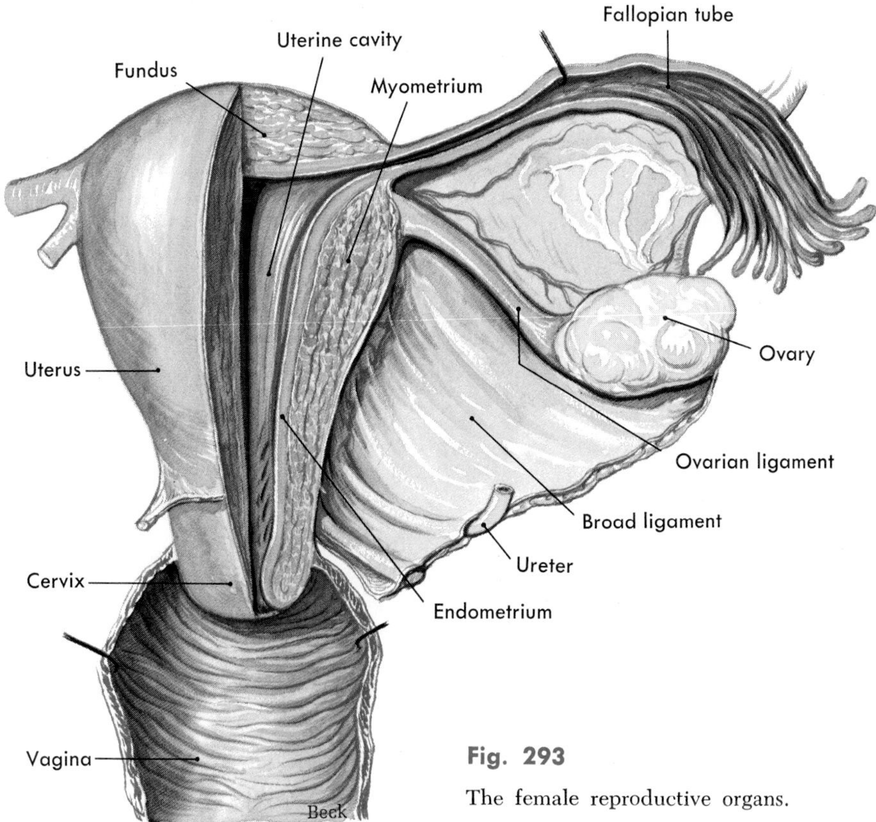

Fig. 293

The female reproductive organs.

sperm count falls below about 50 million per milliliter of semen, sterility results.

One hypothesis suggested to explain this puzzling fact is this: semen that contains an adequate number of sperm also contains enough hyaluronidase to liquefy the intercellular cement between the cells that encase each ovum. Without this, a single sperm cannot penetrate the layers of cells (corona radiata) around the ovum and hence cannot fertilize it.

Female reproductive organs

Examine Figs. 293 and 294 and Plate XIV of the Trans-Vision® insert to identify the following organs of the female reproductive system:

1. *primary sex organs*—the two ovaries (female gonads)
2. *secondary sex organs*—two uterine tubes (fallopian tubes or oviducts), one uterus, one vagina, one vulva (pudendum or external genitalia), and two breasts or mammary glands

UTERUS

Structure

Size, shape, and divisions. The uterus is pear-shaped in its virgin state and measures approximately 3 inches in length, 2 inches in width at its widest part, and 1 inch in thickness. It is composed of two parts: an upper portion, the *body,* and a lower, narrow section, the *cervix.* The body rounds into a bulging prominence above the

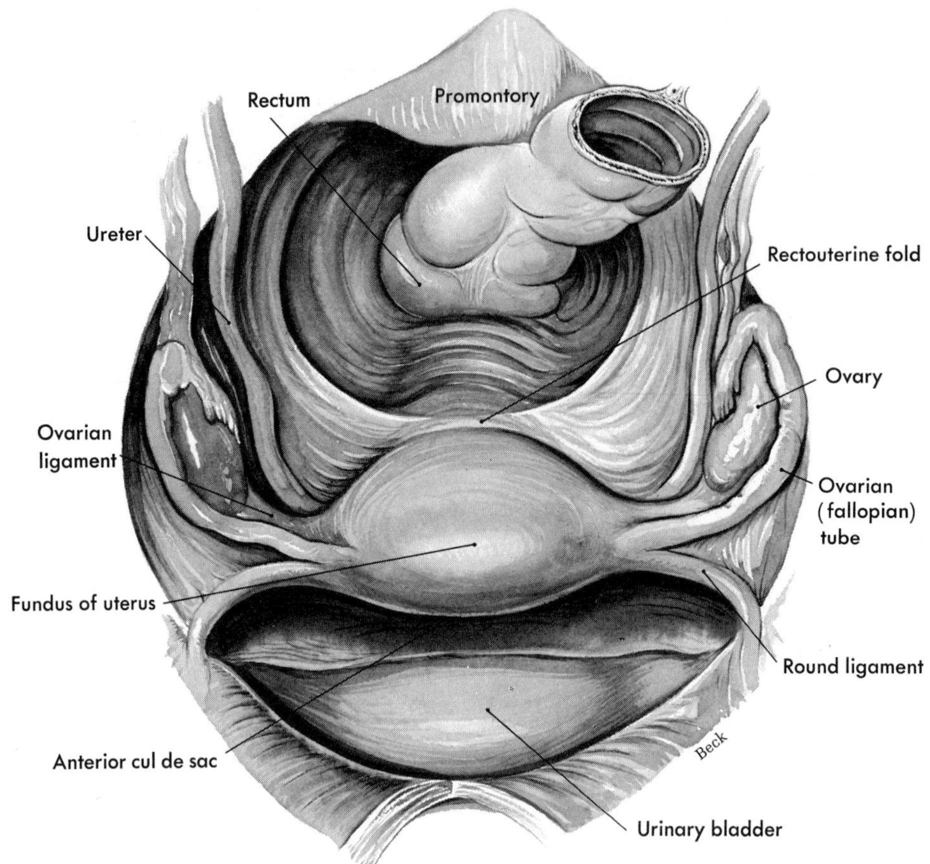

Fig. 294

Female pelvic contents as seen from above and in front.

level at which the uterine tubes enter. This bulging upper surface is called the *fundus.*

Wall. Three coats compose the walls of the uterus: endometrium, myometrium, and parietal peritoneum.

1. A lining of mucous membrane, called the *endometrium,* composed of three layers of tissues: a compact surface layer of columnar epithelium, a spongy middle layer of loose connective tissue, and a basal layer of dense connective tissue that attaches the endometrium to the underlying myometrium. During menstruation and following delivery of a baby, the compact and spongy layers slough off.

2. A thick, middle coat (the *myometrium*) consists of three layers of smooth muscle fibers that extend in all directions, longitudinally, transversely, obliquely, and give the uterus great strength. The myometrium is thickest in the fundus and thinnest in the cervix—a good example of the principle of structural adaptation to function. In order to expel a fetus, that is, move it down and out of the uterus, the fundus must contract more forcibly than the lower part of the uterine wall and the cervix must be stretched or dilated.

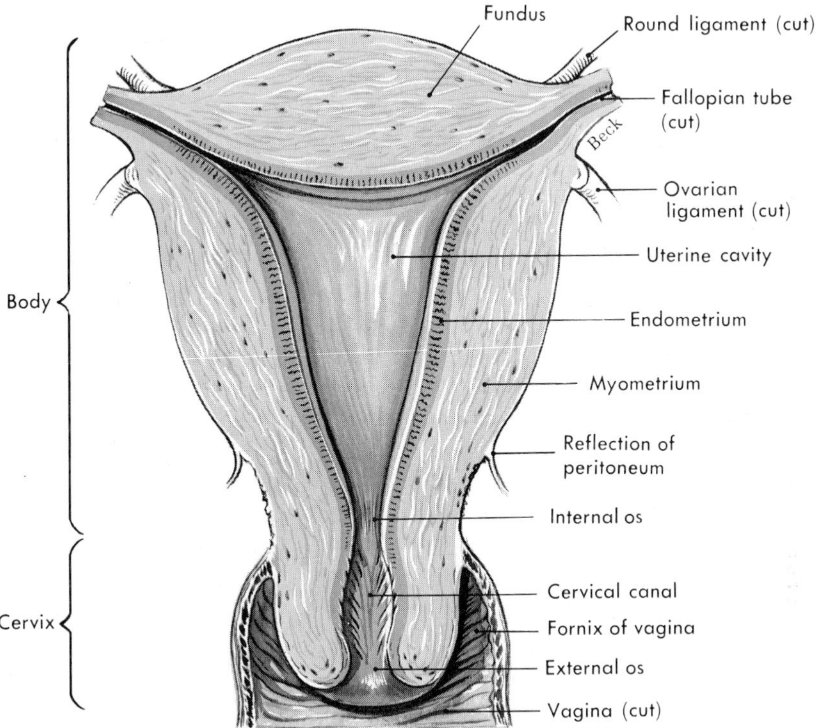

Fig. 295

Sectioned view of the uterus.

3. An external coat of serous membrane, the *parietal peritoneum,* is incomplete since it covers none of the cervix and only part of the body (all except the lower one-fourth of its anterior surface). The fact that the entire uterus is not covered with peritoneum has clinical value because it makes it possible to perform operations on this organ without the risk of infection that attends cutting into the peritoneum.

Cavities. The cavities of the uterus are small due to the thickness of its walls. The body cavity is flat and triangular. Its apex is directed downward and constitutes the *internal os,* which opens into the *cervical canal.* The cervical canal is constricted on its lower end also, forming the *external os,* which opens into the vagina. The uterine tubes open into the body cavity at its upper, outer angles.

Blood supply. The uterus receives a generous supply of blood from uterine arteries, branches of the internal iliac arteries.

Location

The uterus is located in the pelvic cavity between the bladder and the rectum.

Position

1. *Normally* the uterus is flexed between the body and cervix, with the body lying over the superior surface of the bladder, pointing forward and slightly upward. The cervix points downward and backward from the point of flexion, joining the vagina at approximately a right angle. Several ligaments hold the uterus in place but allow its body considerable movement, a characteristic that often leads to malpositions of the organ.

runs from front to back.

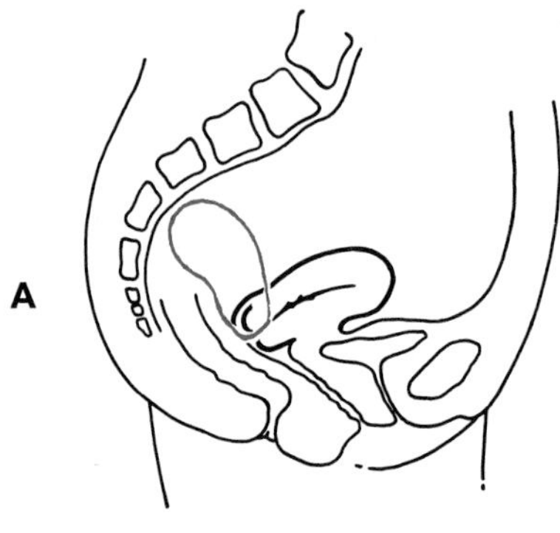

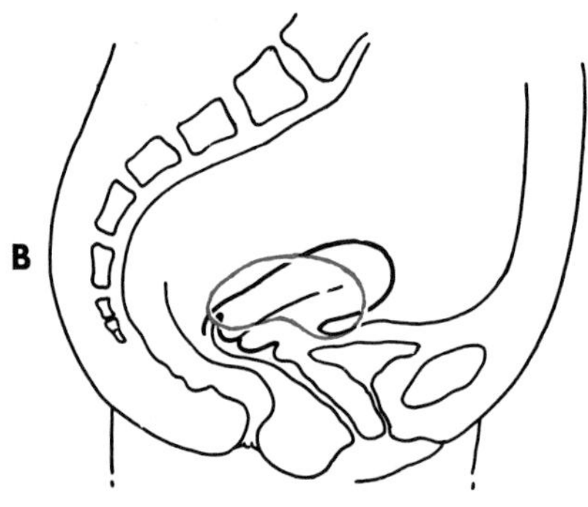

Fig. 296

Normal and abnormal positions of the uterus. Red lines show the abnormal positions. **A,** Retroflexion. **B,** Anteflexion.

2. The uterus may lie in any one of several *abnormal positions.* A common one is retroversion or backward tilting of the entire organ.

3. *Eight ligaments* (three pairs, two single ones) anchor the uterus in the pelvic cavity: broad (paired), uterosacral (paired), posterior (single), anterior (single), and round (paired). Six of these so-called ligaments are actually extensions of the parietal peritoneum in different directions. The other two are fibromuscular cords. (See Figs. 294 and 297.)

(a) The *two broad ligaments* are double folds of parietal peritoneum that form a kind of partition across the pelvic cavity. The uterus is suspended between these two folds.

(b) The *two uterosacral ligaments* are foldlike extensions of the peritoneum from the posterior surface of the uterus to the sacrum, one on each side of the rectum.

(c) The *posterior ligament* is a fold of peritoneum extending from the posterior surface of the uterus to the rectum. This ligament forms a deep pouch known as the *cul-de-sac of Douglas* (or rectouterine pouch) between the uterus and rectum. Since this is the lowest point in the pelvic cavity, pus collects here in pelvic inflammations. To secure drainage, an incision may be made at the top of the posterior wall of the vagina (posterior colpotomy).

(d) The *anterior ligament* is the fold of peritoneum formed by the extension of the peritoneum on the anterior surface of the uterus to the posterior surface of the bladder. This fold also forms a cul-de-sac but one that is less deep than the posterior pouch.

(e) The *two round ligaments* are fibromuscular cords extending from the upper, outer angles of the uterus through the inguinal canals and disappearing in the labia majora.

Functions

The uterus or womb plays a role in the accomplishment of three highly important, though nonvital, functions: menstruation, pregnancy, labor.

1. *Menstruation* is a sloughing away of the compact and spongy layers of the endometrium, attended by bleeding from the torn vessels.

2. In *pregnancy,* the embryo implants itself in the endometrium and there lives as a parasite throughout the fetal period.

3. *Labor* consists of powerful, rhythmic contractions of the muscular uterine wall that result in expulsion of the fetus or birth.

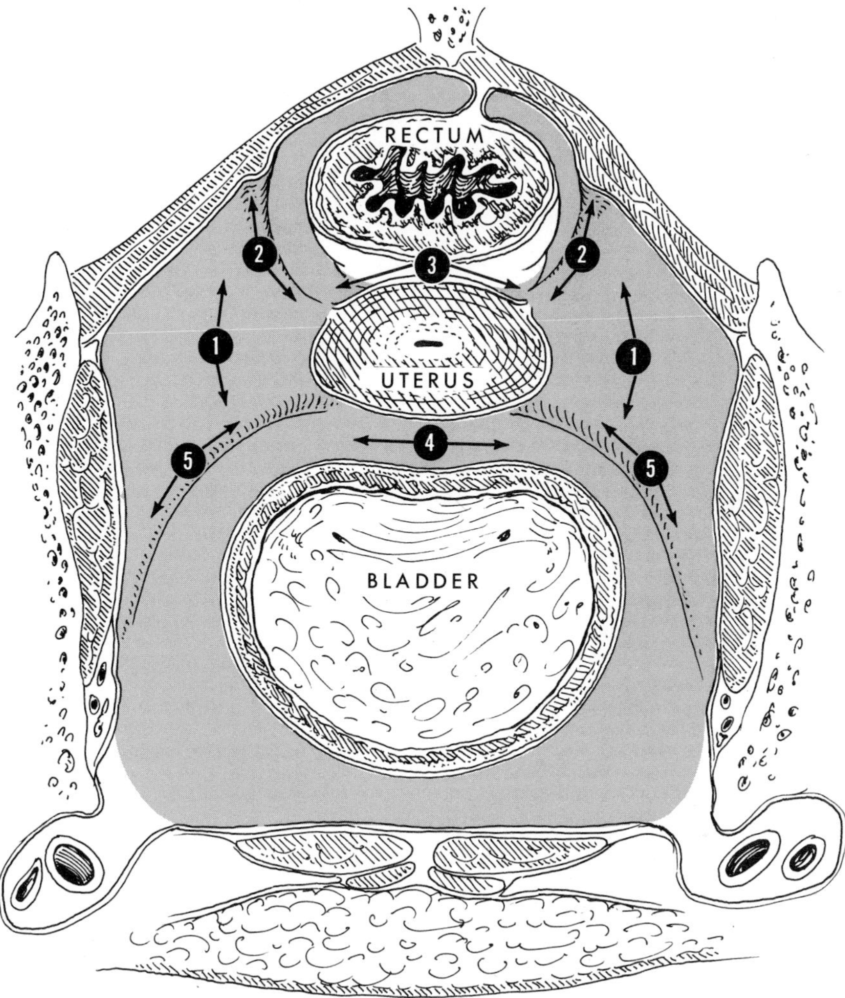

Fig. 297

Eight ligaments that support and anchor the uterus in the pelvic cavity. **1,** Two broad ligaments. **2,** Two uterosacral ligaments. **3,** Posterior ligament. **4,** Anterior ligament. **5,** Two round ligaments. The pink area denotes the peritoneal lining of the pelvis.

UTERINE TUBES—FALLOPIAN TUBES OR OVIDUCTS

Location

The uterine tubes are attached to the uterus at its upper outer angles. They lie between the folds of the broad ligaments and extend upward and outward toward the sides of the pelvis and then curve downward and backward.

Structure

The same three coats (mucous, smooth muscle, serous) of the uterus compose the tubes. The mucosa of the tubes, however, is ciliated. At the distal end, each tube expands into a funnel-like portion called the *infundibulum.* The open outer margin of the infundibulum resembles a fringe in its

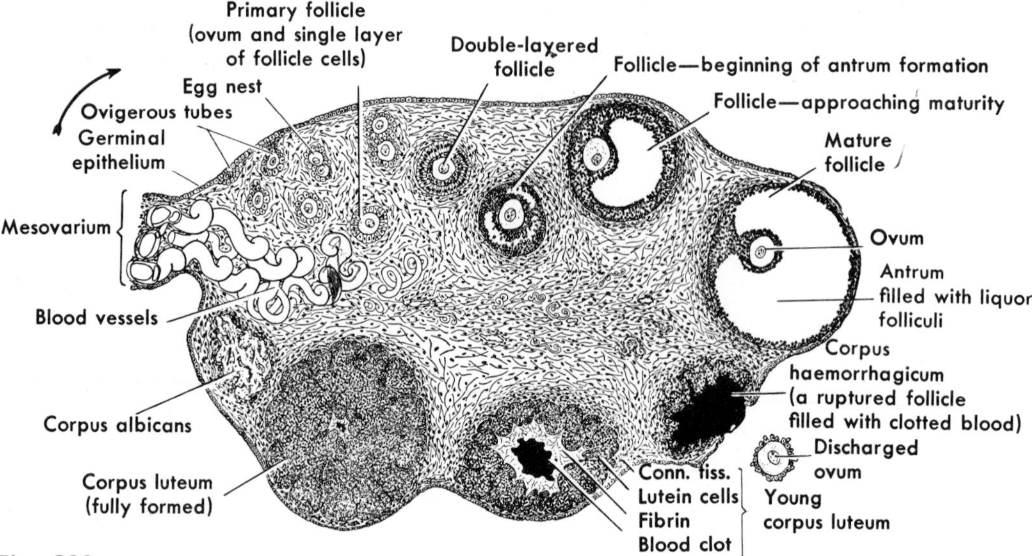

Fig. 298

Diagram of a mammalian ovary showing the life cycle of an ovarian follicle and egg. The successive stages are arranged clockwise starting with the arrow. (From Patten: Embryology of the pig, New York, The Blakiston Co.)

irregular outline. The fringelike projections are known as *fimbriae.* Here the mucous lining of the tubes is directly continuous with the peritoneum—a fact of great clinical significance because the tubal mucosa is continuous with that of the uterus and vagina and, therefore, often becomes infected by gonococci or other organisms introduced into the vagina. And inflammation of the tubes (salpingitis) may readily spread to become inflammation of the peritoneum (peritonitis), a serious condition. In the male there is no such direct route by which microorganisms can reach the peritoneum from the exterior.

Each uterine tube is approximately 4 inches long.

Function

The tubes serve as ducts for the female gametes (ova) even though they are not actually connected to the ovaries, the organs that produce the ova. Fertilization, the union of a spermatozoon with an ovum, normally occurs in the tubes.

OVARIES—FEMALE GONADS

Location and size

The ovaries are glands that resemble large almonds in size and shape and are located one on either side of the uterus, below and behind the uterine tubes. Each ovary lies between the folds of the broad ligament and is attached to its posterior surface by the mesovarian ligament. The ovarian ligament anchors it to the uterus. The distal portion of the tube curves about the ovary in such a way that the fimbriae cup over the ovary but do not actually attach to it. Here, then, is a gland whose duct is detached from it, a fact that makes possible pregnancy in the pelvic cavity instead of in the uterus as is normal.

Microscopic structure

The surface of the ovary consists of a single layer of germinal epithelial cells, whereas its interior is made up of connective tissue in which are embedded thousands of microscopic structures known as *graafian follicles.* After puberty the follicles are present in varying stages of development (Fig. 298). The primordial follicles consist of an *ovum* encased in a nest of epithelial cells. Before puberty, all the follicles are in this stage. Development of the follicles after puberty is discussed on p. 475.

Functions

The ovaries perform two functions: ovulation and secretion. Ova develop and mature in the ovaries and are discharged from them into the pelvic cavity between the folds of the broad ligament. The ovaries also secrete the female hormones—estrogens (chiefly estradiol and estrone) and progesterone. More details about their secretion and their functions appear on pp. 479, 510, and 511.

VAGINA

Location

The vagina is situated between the rectum, which lies posterior to it, and the urethra and bladder, which lie anterior to it. It extends upward and backward from its external orifice.

Structure

The vagina is a collapsible tube, capable of great distention, is composed mainly of smooth muscle, and is lined with mucous membrane arranged in rugae. Its anterior wall, which measures from 2½ to 3 inches in length, is about one inch shorter than the posterior wall because the cervix protrudes into the uppermost portion of the anterior wall. In the virginal state, a fold of mucous membrane, the *hymen,* forms a border around the external opening of the vagina, partially closing the orifice. Occasionally, this structure completely covers the vaginal outlet, a condition referred to as *imperforate hymen.* Perforation has to be done before the menstrual flow can escape.

Functions

The vagina constitutes an essential part of the reproductive tract because of the following:

1. It is the organ that receives the seminal fluid from the male.
2. It serves as the lower part of the birth canal.
3. It acts as the excretory duct for uterine secretions and the menstrual flow.

VULVA

Fig. 299 shows the structures which, together, constitute the female external genitals (reproductive organs) or vulva: mons veneris, labia majora, labia minora, clitoris, urinary meatus, vaginal orifice, and Bartholin's or the greater vestibular glands.

1. The *mons veneris* or mons pubis is a skin-covered pad of fat over the symphysis pubis. Coarse hairs appear on this structure at puberty and persist throughout life.
2. The *labia majora* or "large lips" are covered with pigmented skin and hair on the outer surface and are smooth and free from hair on the inner surface. It is composed mainly of fat and numerous glands.
3. The *labia minora* or "small lips" are located within the labia majora, and are covered with modified skin. These two lips come together anteriorly in the midline. The area between the labia minora is the *vestibule.*
4. The *clitoris* is a small organ composed of erectile tissue, located just behind the junction of the labia minora and homologous to the corpora cavernosa and glans of the penis. The *prepuce* or foreskin covers the clitoris, as it does the glans penis in the male.
5. The *urinary meatus* is the small opening of the urethra, situated between the clitoris and the vaginal orifice.
6. The *vaginal orifice* is an opening which, in the virginal state, is usually only slightly larger than the urinary meatus because of the constricting border formed by

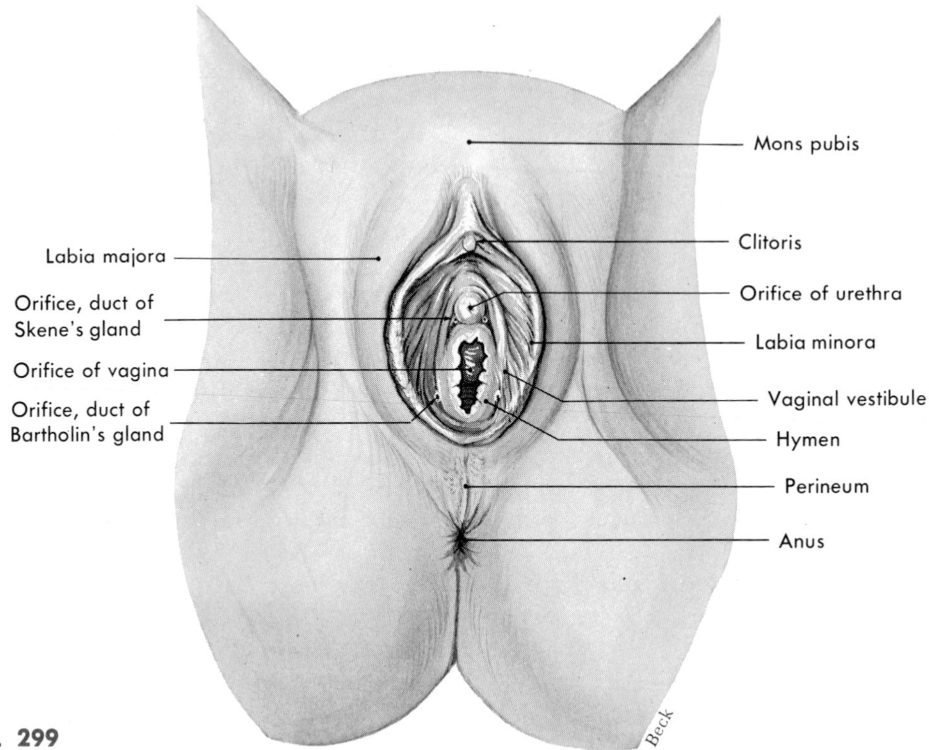

Fig. 299

External female genitalia.

the hymen. In the marital state the vaginal orifice is noticeably larger than the urinary meatus. It is located posterior to the meatus.

7. *Bartholin's* or the *greater vestibular glands* are two bean-shaped glands, one on either side of the vaginal orifice. Each gland opens by means of a single, long duct into the space between the hymen and the labium minus. These glands are of clinical importance because they are frequently infected (bartholinitis or Bartholin's abscess), particularly by the gonococcus. They are homologous to the bulbourethral glands in the male, and they secrete a lubricating fluid. Opening into the vestibule near the urinary meatus by way of two small ducts is a group of tiny mucous glands, the *lesser vestibular* or *Skene's glands.* These have clinical interest because gonococci that lodge there are difficult to eradicate.

PERINEUM

The perineum is the skin-covered muscular region between the vaginal orifice and the anus. This area has great clinical importance because of the danger of its being torn during childbirth. If the tear is deep, it may extend all the way through the perineum and even through the anal sphincter, resulting in involuntary seepage from the rectum until the laceration is repaired. To avoid this possibility, an incision known as an *episiotomy* is usually made in the perineum, particularly at the birth of a first baby.

BREASTS

Location and size

The breasts lie over the pectoral muscles and are attached to them by a layer of connective tissue (fascia). Estrogens and progesterone, two ovarian hormones, control their development during puberty. Estrogens stimulate growth of the ducts of the mammary glands, whereas progesterone stimulates development of the alveoli, the actual secreting cells. Breast size is determined more by the amount of fat around the glandular tissue than by the amount of glandular tissue itself. Hence, the size of the breast does not relate to its functional ability.

Structure

Each breast consists of several lobes separated by septa of connective tissue. Each lobe consists of several lobules, which, in turn, are composed of connective tissue in which are embedded the secreting cells (alveoli) of the gland, arranged in grapelike clusters around minute ducts. The ducts from the various lobules unite, forming a single excretory duct for each lobe, or between fifteen and twenty in each breast. These main ducts converge toward the nipple, like the spokes of a wheel. They enlarge slightly before reaching the nipple into ampullae or small "reservoirs" (Figs. 300 and 301). Each of these main ducts terminates in a tiny opening on the surface of the nipple. Adipose tissue is deposited around the surface of the gland, just under the skin, and between the lobes. The nipples are bordered by a circular pigmented area, the *areola*. It contains numerous sebaceous glands that appear as small nodules under the skin. The areola and nipple change color from delicate pink to brown early in pregnancy, a fact of value in diagnosing a first pregnancy. The color decreases after lactation has ceased but never entirely returns to the virginal hue.

Function

The function of the mammary glands is lactation, that is, the secretion of milk for the nourishment of newborn infants.

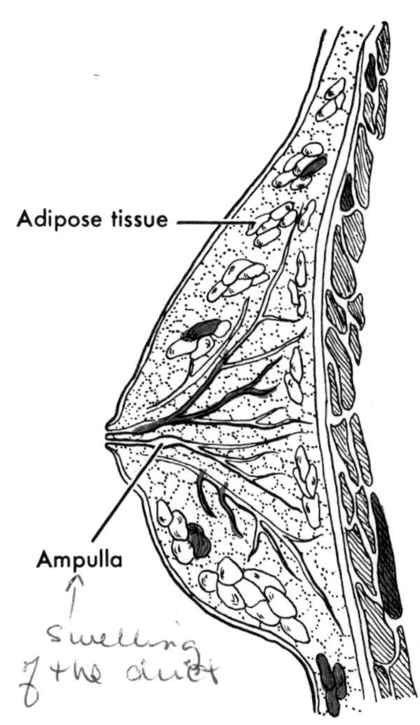

Fig. 300

Structure of the breast. Note the position of the breast superficial to the pectoralis major muscles.

Mechanism controlling lactation

Very briefly, lactation is controlled as follows:

1. The ovarian hormones, estrogens and progesterone, act on the breasts to make them structurally ready to secrete milk. Estrogens promote development of the ducts of the breasts. Progesterone acts on the estrogen-primed breasts, to promote completion of the development of the ducts and development of the alveoli, the secreting cells of the breasts. A high blood concentration of estrogens (for example, during pregnancy) inhibits anterior pituitary secretion of lactogenic hormone.

2. Shedding of the placenta following delivery of the baby cuts off a major source of estrogens. The resulting rapid drop in the blood concentration of estrogens stimulates anterior pituitary secretion of lactogenic hormone. Also, the suckling movements of

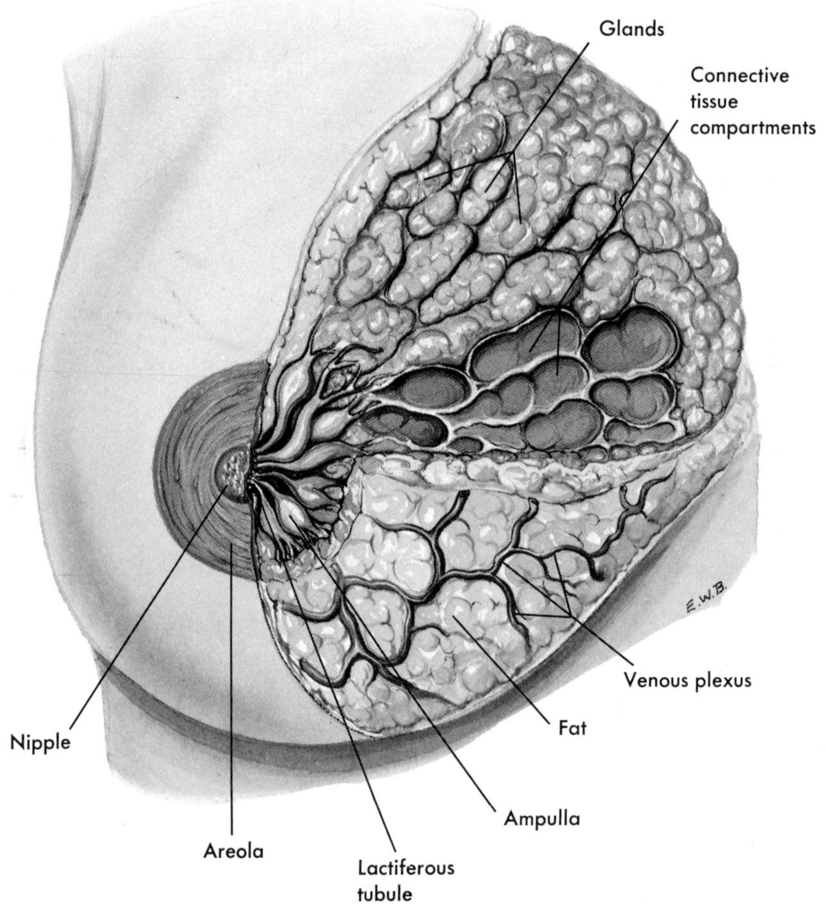

Fig. 301

Anterior view of the breast. The skin has been removed in the lower right quadrant to reveal the plexus overlying the adipose (fatty) tissue. In the upper right quadrant the adipose tissue has been removed to show the alveoli of the glands. The glands have been removed in a small area to reveal the connective tissue compartments that separate the lobules.

a nursing baby act in some way to stimulate both anterior pituitary secretion of lactogenic hormone and posterior pituitary secretion of oxytocin (Fig. 302).

3. Lactogenic hormone stimulates lactation, that is, stimulates alveoli of the mammary glands to secrete milk. Milk secretion starts about the third or fourth day after delivery of a baby, supplanting a thin, yellowish secretion called *colostrum.* With repeated stimulation by the suckling infant, the milk usually continues to form for six to nine months or even longer.

4. Oxytocin stimulates the alveoli of the breasts to eject milk into the ducts, thereby enabling the infant to remove the milk by suckling.

Female sexual cycles

RECURRING CYCLES

Many changes recur periodically in the female during the years between the onset

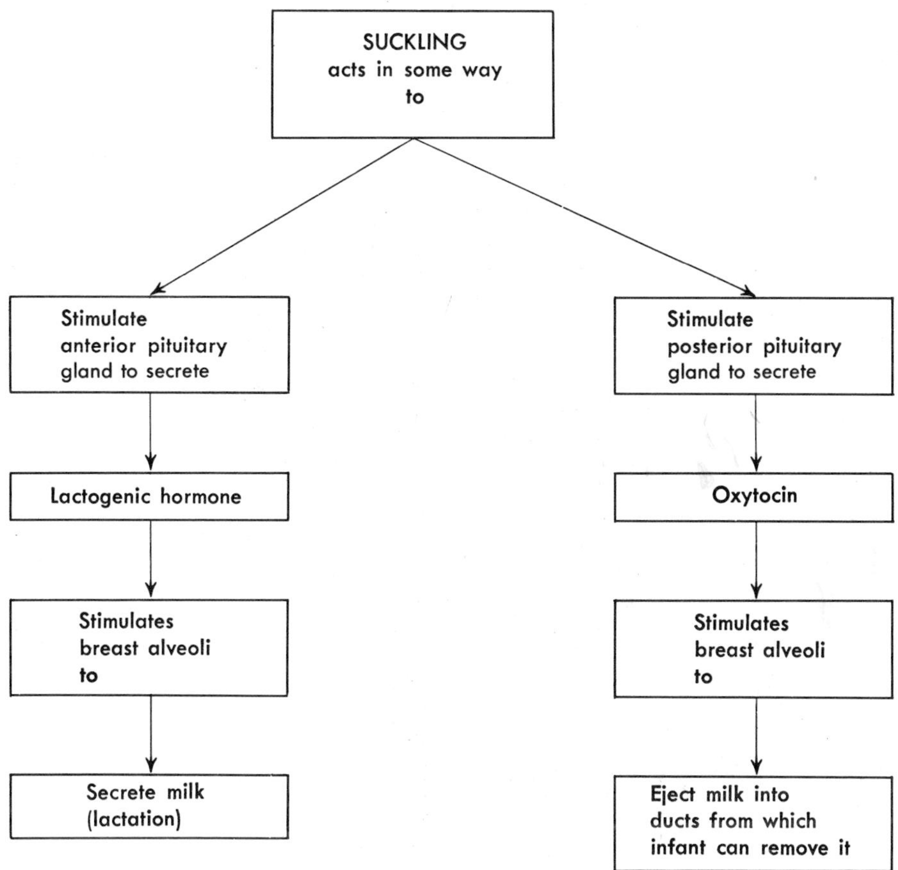

Fig. 302

Mechanism for controlling lactation and milk ejection.

of the menses (menarche) and their cessation (menopause or climacteric). Most obvious, of course, is menstruation—the outward sign of changes in the endometrium. Most women also note periodic changes in the breasts. But these are only two of many changes that occur over and over again at fairly uniform intervals during the thirty some years of female reproductive maturity. Rhythmic changes also take place in the ovaries, the myometrium, the vagina, hormone secretion, body temperature, and even in mood or "emotional tone." We shall investigate some of the details known or postulated about changes in the ovaries, endometrium, myometrium, and hormones and the relations between these changes.

Ovarian cycles

Once each month, on about the first day of menstruation, several primitive graafian follicles and their enclosed ova begin to grow and develop. The follicular cells proliferate and start to secrete estrogens (one kind of female hormone) in increasing amounts for about two weeks. Usually only one follicle matures and migrates to the surface of the ovary. The surface of the follicle degenerates, causing expulsion of the mature ovum into the pelvic cavity (ovulation).

When does ovulation occur? This is a question of great practical importance and one that has been given many answers. Present-day physiologists most frequently answer that ovulation usually occurs fourteen days before the next menstrual period begins. But, they quickly add, there are exceptions to this general rule. Ovulation may even take place nineteen or more days before the onset of the next menses (see last paragraph in next column). A few women experience pain within a few hours after ovulation. This is referred to as *mittelschmerz*—German for middle pain. It has been ascribed to irritation of the peritoneum by hemorrhage from the ruptured follicle.

Shortly before ovulation, the ovum undergoes a special type of mitosis (called meiosis) in which its number of chromosomes is reduced by half. Immediately after ovulation, cells of the ruptured follicle enlarge and, due to the appearance of lipoid substances in them, become transformed into a golden-colored body, the *corpus luteum*. The corpus luteum grows for seven or eight days. During this time it secretes both progesterone and estrogens in increasing amounts. Then, provided that fertilization of the ovum did not occur, the size of the corpus luteum and the amount of its secretions gradually diminish. By the twenty-sixth or twenty-seventh day following onset of the menses, progesterone secretion has ceased entirely and estrogen production has reached a minimum. About two days later another menses starts presumably because of the low blood levels of progesterone and estrogens.

Endometrial or menstrual cycle

During menstruation, necrotic bits of the compact and spongy layers of the endometrium slough off, leaving denuded bleeding areas. Following menstruation, the cells of these layers proliferate, causing the endometrium to reach a thickness of 2 or 3 mm. by the time of ovulation. During this period, endometrial glands and arterioles have lengthened and become more coiled—two factors that also contribute to the thickening of the endometrium. After ovulation, the endometrium grows still thicker (reaching a maximum of about 4 to 6 mm.), but most of this increase is believed due to swelling produced by fluid retention rather than to further proliferation of endometrial cells. The increasingly tortuous endometrial glands start to secrete during the time between ovulation and the next menses. Then, the day before menstruation starts again, the tightly coiled arterioles constrict, producing endometrial ischemia. This leads to necrosis, sloughing, and, once again, menstrual bleeding.

The menstrual cycle is customarily divided into phases, named for major events occurring in them: menses, postmenstrual or preovulatory phase, ovulation, and premenstrual phase.

1. The *menses* or *menstrual period* occurs on cycle days 1 to 5. There is some individual variation, however.

2. The *postmenstrual* or *preovulatory phase* occurs between the end of the menses and ovulation. It usually includes cycle days 6 to 13 or 14 in a 28-day cycle. But the length of this phase varies more than do the others. It lasts longer in long cycles and ends sooner in short ones. This phase is also called the *estrogenic* or *follicular phase* because of the high blood estrogen content due to secretion by the developing follicle. And *proliferative phase* is still another name for it because proliferation of endometrial cells occurs at this time.

3. *Ovulation* (that is, rupture of the nature follicle with expulsion of its ovum into the pelvic cavity) occurs frequently on cycle day 15 in a 28-day cycle. However, it occurs on different days in different length cycles depending on the

length of the preovulatory phase. For example, in a 32-day cycle, the preovulatory phase would probably last until cycle day 18 and ovulation would then occur on cycle day 19 instead of 15. In short, the day of ovulation cannot be predicted with certainty. One cannot know ahead of time precisely how many days the preovulatory phase will last. And this physiological fact probably accounts for most of the unreliability of the rhythm method of contraception.

4. The *premenstrual phase* occurs between ovulation and the onset of the menses. This phase is also called the *luteal phase* because the corpus luteum secretes during this time and *progesterone phase* because this hormone is secreted only during this phase. The length of this premenstrual phase is pretty constant, lasting usually 14 days, that is, cycle days 15 to 28. Differences in length of total menstrual cycle, therefore, exist mainly because of differences in duration of the preovulatory rather than of the premenstrual phase

Myometrial cycle

The myometrium contracts mildly but with increasing frequency during the two weeks preceding ovulation. Contractions decrease or disappear between ovulation and the next menses, thereby lessening the probability of expulsion of an implanted ovum.

Gonadotrophic cycles

The adenohypophysis (anterior pituitary gland) secretes two hormones called gonadotrophins that influence female reproductive cycles. Their names are follicle-stimulating hormone (FSH) and luteinizing hormone (LH). The amount of each gonadotrophin secreted varies with a rhythmic regularity that can be related, as we shall see, to the rhythmic ovarian and uterine changes just described.

CONTROL

Physiologists agree that hormones play the major role in producing the cyclic changes characteristic in the female during the years of reproductive maturity. By correlating the changing blood concentrations of the pituitary gonadotrophins with the monthly ovarian and uterine changes, investigators have arrived at a working hypothesis about the main features of the control mechanisms.

A brief description follows of the mechanisms that produce cyclical changes in the ovaries, uterus, and in the amounts of gonadotrophins secreted.

Cyclical changes in ovaries

Cyclical changes in the ovaries result from cyclical changes in the amounts of gonadotrophins secreted by the anterior pituitary gland. An increasing blood concentration of FSH has two effects: it stimulates one or more primitive graafian follicles and ova to start growing, and it stimulates the follicles to secrete estrogens. The an-

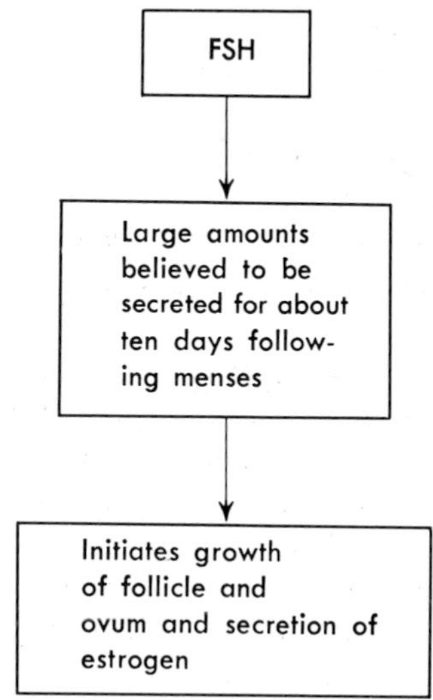

Fig. 303

Ovarian changes produced by the follicle-stimulating hormone (FSH).

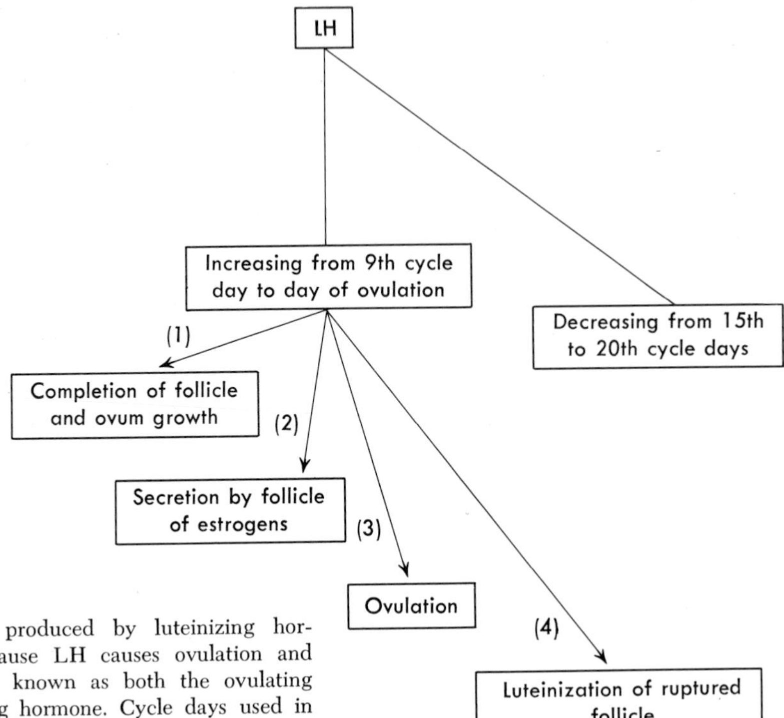

Fig. 304

Ovarian changes produced by luteinizing hormone (LH). Because LH causes ovulation and luteinization, it is known as both the ovulating and the luteinizing hormone. Cycle days used in diagram are approximate.

terior pituitary gland is thought to secrete large amounts of FSH for about ten days after the menses. (Fig. 303 shows ovarian change produced by FSH.)

Several days before ovulation, the anterior pituitary gland starts to release increasing amounts of LH into the blood. LH brings about four ovarian changes:

1. Completion of growth of the follicle and ovum.
2. Increasing secretion of estrogens by the follicle during the preovulatory phase in the menstrual cycle.
3. Rupturing of the mature follicle with expulsion of its ripe ovum (process known as *ovulation*). Because of this function, LH is sometimes called the ovulating hormone.
4. Formation of a golden body, the corpus luteum, in the ruptured follicle (process called *luteinization*). The name luteinizing hormone refers, obviously, to this LH function. Blood LH concentration increases from about the ninth cycle day until ovulation. (Fig. 304 shows ovarian changes produced by LH.)

If pregnancy does not occur, the corpus luteum reaches its maximum development in about 8 days and then starts to regress. Gradually, fibrous tissue (corpus albicans) replaces it. On or about cycle day 25 the corpus luteum stops secreting both progesterone and estrogens. Their blood concentrations drop precipitously. Without stimulation by these hormones, the endometrium degenerates rapidly and starts to bleed. Menstruation, in other words, occurs, and another menstrual cycle has begun.

Cyclical changes in uterus

Cyclical changes in the uterus are brought about by changing blood concentrations of estrogens and progesterone. As blood estrogens increase during the preovulatory phase of the menstrual cycle, they produce the following main changes in the uterus:

1. Proliferation of endometrial cells, producing a thickening of the endometrium
2. Growth of endometrial glands
3. Increase in the water content of the endometrium
4. Increased myometrial contractions

Increasing blood progesterone concentration during the premenstrual phase of the menstrual cycle produces progestational changes in the uterus—that is, changes which are favorable for pregnancy, specifically:

1. Secretion by endometrial glands, thereby preparing the endometrium for implantation of a fertilized ovum
2. Increase in the water content of the endometrium
3. Decreased myometrial contractions

Cyclical changes in amounts of FSH and estrogens secreted

Examine Fig. 305 and note particularly the effect of a high blood concentration of estrogens on anterior pituitary gland secretion and the effect of a low blood concentration of FSH on the development of a graafian follicle and ovum. Establishment of these two facts led eventually to the development of "the pill" for preventing pregnancy. The so-called sequential oral contraceptive pills are designed to imitate as closely as possible the natural sequence of estrogen and progesterone secretion. Therefore, during the menses, that is, on the first through the fourth day of her menstrual cycle, a woman does not take these pills. But on the fifth through the twentieth days she takes a pill containing an estrogen-like preparation each day. And on the twenty-first through the twenty-fifth days she takes a different pill, one containing both a progesterone-like compound and an estrogen-like substance. She then takes no more of the contraceptive pills until after her next menses. Usually the menstrual flow begins two or three days after the last pill has been taken. The first series of pills builds up a high blood concentration of the estrogen-like substance, and this prevents the development of a follicle and its ovum that month. With no mature ovum to be expelled, ovulation does not occur, and therefore pregnancy cannot occur. The next menses, however, does take place—because the progesterone and estrogen dosage is stopped in time to allow their blood levels to decrease as they normally do near the end of the cycle to bring on menstruation.

FUNCTION SERVED BY CYCLES

The major function seems to be to prepare the endometrium each month for a pregnancy. If it does not occur, the thick vascular lining, no longer needed, is shed.

If fertilization of the ovum (pregnancy) occurs, the menstrual cycle is modified as follows:

1. The corpus luteum does not disappear but persists and continues to secrete progesterone and estrogens for six months or more of pregnancy. If it is removed by any means during the early months of pregnancy, spontaneous abortion results.

2. The fertilized ovum, which immediately starts developing into an embryo, travels down the tube and implants itself in the endometrium, so carefully prepared for this event.

MENARCHE AND MENOPAUSE

The menstrual flow first occurs (menarche) at puberty, at about the age of 13 years, although there is wide individual variation according to race, nutrition, health, heredity, etc. Normally, it recurs about every twenty-eight days for some thirty years or so, except during pregnancy, and then ceases (menopause or climacteric) at about the age of 45 years.

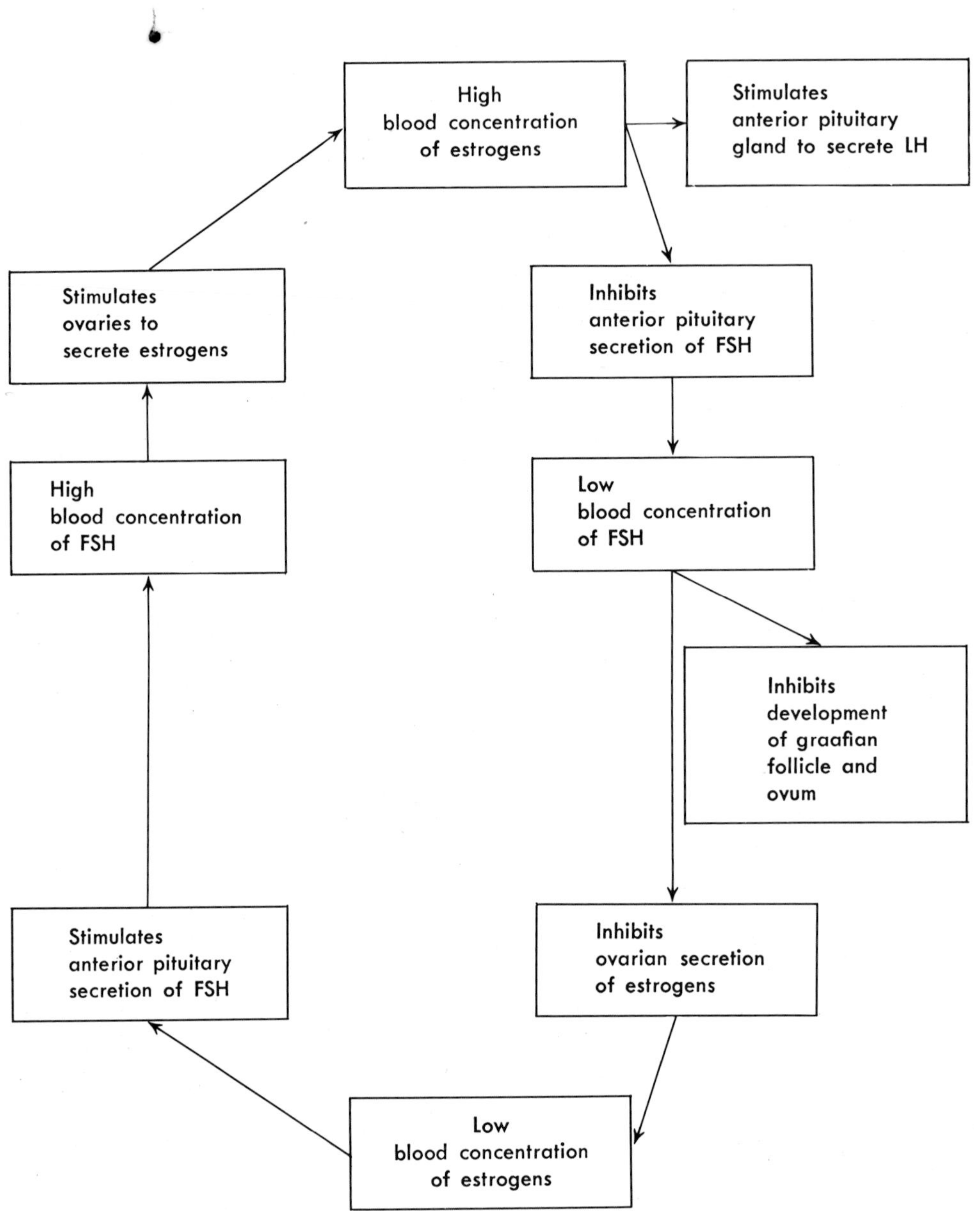

Fig. 305

Feedback mechanism for controlling secretion of follicle-stimulating hormone (FSH) and estrogens. A high blood level of FSH stimulates estrogen secretion, whereas resulting high estrogen level inhibits FSH secretion. How does this compare with interstitial cell–stimulating hormone (ICSH)–testosterone feedback mechanism? (See Fig. 287, p. 458, if you want to check your answer.)

Embryology

MEANING AND SCOPE

Embryology is the science of the development of the individual before birth. It is a story of miracles, describing the means by which a new human life is started and the steps by which a single microscopic cell is transformed into a complex human being. In a work of this kind, it seems feasible to include only a few of the main points in the development of the new individual since the facts amassed by the science of embryology are so many and so intricate that volumes have been written about them.

VALUE OF KNOWLEDGE OF EMBRYOLOGY

The main value to the medical profession of knowing the steps by which a new individual is evolved lies in their explanation of various congenital deformities. For example, one of the most common malformations is harelip (Fig. 306), a condition which results from imperfect fusion of the frontal and maxillary processes during embryonic development.

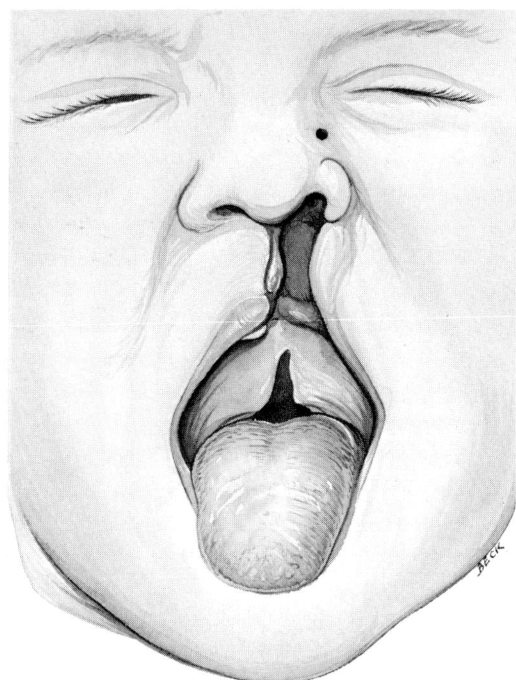

Fig. 306

Harelip and cleft palate, the result of embryological (congenital) malformations. Harelip may be single or on either side of the median line.

STEPS IN DEVELOPMENT OF NEW INDIVIDUAL

Preliminary processes

Production of a new human being starts with the union of a spermatozoon and an ovum to form a single cell. Two preliminary steps, however, are necessary before such a union can take place: maturation of the sex cells (meiosis) and ovulation and insemination.

Maturation of sex cells (meiosis*)—reduction in number of chromosomes to one-half original number. Only when maturation has occurred are the ovum and spermatozoon mature and ready to unite with each other. The necessity for chromosome reduction as a preliminary to union of the sex cells is explained by the fact that the cells of each species of living organisms contain a specific number of chromosomes. Human cells, for example, contain 46 chromosomes. If the male and female cells united without first halving their respective chromosomes, the resulting cell would contain twice as many chromosomes as is specific for human beings. Mature ova and sperm, therefore, contain only 23 chromosomes or one-half as many as other human cells. Of these, one is the sex chromosome and may be either one of two types, known as X or Y. All ova contain an X chromosome. Sperm, on the other hand, have either an X or a Y chromosome. A female child results from the union of an X chromosome-bearing sperm with an ovum and a male child from the union

*For details of the mechanism of meiosis, see suggested supplementary readings for Chapter XIII, reference 3, p. 549.

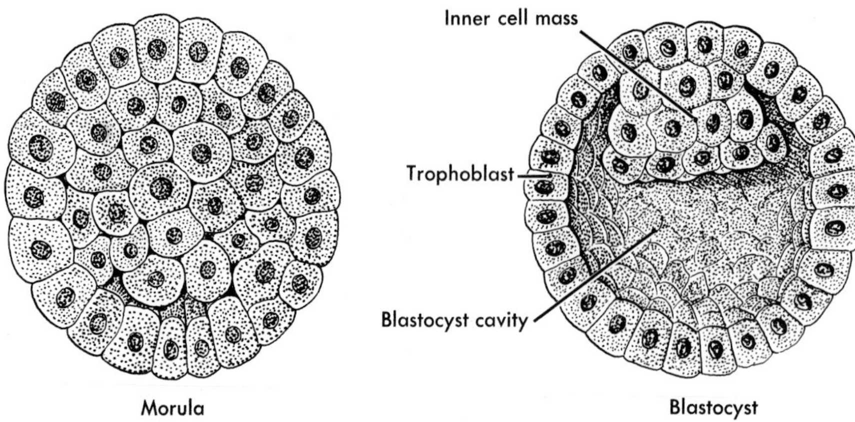

Fig. 307

Stages in the development of the human embryo. The morula consists of an almost solid spherical mass of cells. The embryo reaches this stage about three days after fertilization. The blastocyst (hollowing) stage develops later, after implantation in the uterine lining.

of a Y chromosome-bearing sperm with an ovum.

Ovulation and insemination. The second preliminary step necessary for conception of a new individual consists in bringing the sperm and ovum into proximity with each other so that the union of the two can take place. Two processes are involved in the accomplishment of this step.

1. Ovulation or expulsion of the mature ovum from the graafian follicle into the pelvic cavity, from which it enters one of the uterine tubes.

2. Insemination or expulsion of the seminal fluid from the male urethra into the female vagina. Several million sperm enter the female reproductive tract with each ejaculation of semen. By lashing movements of their flagella-like tails, assisted somewhat by muscular contractions of surrounding structures, the sperm make their way into the external os of the cervix, through the cervical canal and uterine cavity, and into the tubes.

Developmental processes

Fertilization or union of male and female gametes to produce one-celled individual called zygote. The sperm "swim" up the tube toward the ovum. Although numerous sperm surround the ovum, only one penetrates it. As soon as the head and neck of one spermatozoon enter the ovum (the tail drops off), the remaining sperm seem to be repulsed. The sperm head then forms itself into a nucleus that approaches and eventually fuses with the nucleus of the ovum, producing, at that moment, a new single-celled individual or *zygote.* One-half of the 46 chromosomes in the zygote nucleus have come from the sperm and one-half from the ovum. Since chromosomes are composed of *genes* or inheritance determinants, the new being inherits one-half of its characteristics from its father and one-half from its mother.

Normally, fertilization occurs in the uterine tube. Occasionally, however, it takes place in the pelvic cavity, as evidenced by pregnancies that start to develop in the pelvic cavity instead of in the uterus.

Inasmuch as the ovum lives only a short time (probably less than forty-eight hours) after leaving the graafian follicle, fertilization can occur only around the time of ovulation (p. 476). Sperm also have short-lived fertility, probably only about twenty-four hours after entering the female tract.

Cleavage or segmentation. Cleavage consists of repeated mitotic divisions, first of the zygote to form two cells, then of those two cells to form four cells, and so on, resulting, in about three days' time, in the formation of a solid, spherical mass of cells known as a *morula.* About this time the embryo reaches the uterus, where it starts to implant itself in the endometrium. Occasionally, implantation occurs in the tube or pelvic cavity instead of in the uterus. The condition is known as an *ectopic pregnancy.*

As the cells of the morula continue to divide, a hollow ball of cells or *blastocyst,* consisting of an outer layer of cells and an inner cell mass, is formed. Implantation in the uterine lining is now complete. About ten days have elapsed since fertilization. The cells that compose the outer wall of the blastocyst are known as trophoblasts. They eventually become part of the placenta, the structure that anchors the fetus to the uterus.

Differentiation. As the cells composing the inner mass of the blastocyst continue to divide, they arrange themselves into a structure shaped like a figure eight, containing two cavities separated by a double-layered plate of cells known as the *embryonic disc.* The youngest human embryos examined have been at this stage or about two weeks old dated from the time of fertilization. The cells that form the cavity above the embryonic disc eventually become a fluid-filled, shock-absorbing sac (the amnion) in which the fetus floats. The cells of the lower cavity form the yolk sac, a small vesicle attached to the belly of the embryo until about the middle of the second month, when it breaks away. Only the double layer of cells that compose the embryonic disc is destined to form the new individual. The upper layer of cells is called the *ectoderm* and the lower layer the *entoderm.* A third layer of cells, known as the *mesoderm,* develops between the ectoderm and entoderm. Up to this time, all the cells have appeared alike, but now they are differentiated into three distinct types, ectodermal, mesodermal, and entodermal, known as the *primary germ layers,* each of which will give rise to definite structures. For example, the ectoderm cells will form the skin and its appendages and the nervous system; the mesoderm, the muscles, bones, and various other connective tissues; the entoderm, the epithelium of the digestive and respiratory tracts, etc.

Histogenesis and organogenesis. The story of how the primary germ layers develop into many different kinds of tissues (histogenesis) and how those tissues arrange themselves into organs (organogenesis) is long and complicated. Its telling belongs to the science of embryology. Enough for the beginning student of anatomy to appreciate that life begins when two sex cells unite to form a single cell, that the new human body evolves by a series of processes consisting of cell multiplication, cell growth, cell differentiation, and cell rearrangements, all of which take place in definite, orderly sequence. By the end of the second month, a recognizable human form has been formed. At the end of another month the sex is clearly distinguishable, and from then until birth, development is mainly a matter of growth.

Outline summary— The reproductive system

Meaning and function

Consists of organs which, together, produce new individual

Male reproductive organs

1. Glands
   a. testes, gonads (paired)
   b. accessory glands
      1. seminal vesicles (paired)
      2. prostate gland
      3. bulbourethral (Cowper's) glands (paired)

2. Excretory ducts of testes
   a. epididymis (paired)
   b. seminal ducts (vas deferens, ductus deferens) (paired)
   c. ejaculatory ducts (paired)
   d. urethra
3. Supporting structures
   a. external—scrotum and penis
   b. internal—spermatic cords (paired)

TESTES

1. Structure and location
   a. several lobules composed of seminiferous tubules and interstitial cells (of Leydig), separated by septa, encased in fibrous capsule
   b. few ducts emerge from top of organ and enter head of epididymis
   c. located in scrotum, one testis in each of two scrotal compartments
2. Functions
   a. spermatogenesis—formation of mature male gametes (spermatozoa) by seminiferous tubules
   b. secretion of hormone (testosterone) by interstitial cells
3. Structure of spermatozoa—consists of head, neck (middle piece), and whiplike tail

EXCRETORY DUCTS OF TESTES

Epididymis

1. Structure and location
   a. single tightly coiled tube enclosed in fibrous casing
   b. lies along top and side of each testis
2. Functions
   a. duct for seminal fluid
   b. also secretes part of seminal fluid
   c. sperm become capable of motility while they are stored in epididymis

Seminal duct (vas deferens, ductus deferens)

1. Structure and location
   a. tube, extension of epididymis
   b. extends through inguinal canal, into abdominal cavity, over top and down posterior surface of bladder to join duct from seminal vesicle
2. Function
   a. one of excretory ducts for seminal fluid
   b. connects epididymis with ejaculatory duct

Ejaculatory duct

1. Formed by union of seminal duct with duct from seminal vesicle
2. Passes through prostate gland, terminating in urethra

Urethra

See p. 450.

ACCESSORY REPRODUCTIVE GLANDS

Seminal vesicles

1. Structure and location—convoluted pouches on posterior surface of bladder
2. Function—secrete nutrient-rich part of seminal fluid

Prostate gland

1. Structure and location
   a. doughnut-shaped
   b. encircles urethra just below bladder
2. Function—adds alkaline secretion to seminal fluid

Bulbourethral glands

1. Structure and location
   a. small, pea-shaped structures with 1-inch long ducts leading into urethra
   b. lie below prostate gland
2. Function—secrete alkaline fluid that is part of semen

SUPPORTING STRUCTURES

External

1. Scrotum
   a. skin-covered pouch suspended from perineal region
   b. divided into two compartments
   c. contains testis, epididymis, and first part of seminal duct
2. Penis—composed of three cylindrical masses of erectile tissue, one of which contains urethra

Internal

1. Spermatic cords
   a. fibrous cylinders located in inguinal canals
   b. enclose seminal ducts, blood vessels, lymphatics and nerves

COMPOSITION AND COURSE OF SEMINAL FLUID

1. Consists of secretions from testes, epididymides, seminal vesicles, prostate, and bulbourethral glands
2. Each drop contains millions of sperm
3. Passes from testes through epididymis, seminal duct, ejaculatory duct, and urethra

Female reproductive organs

Two ovaries, two uterine tubes, one uterus, one vagina, one set of external genitals (vulva), two breasts

UTERUS

1. Structure
   a. size, shape, and divisions
      1. 3 by 2 by 1 inch in virginal state
      2. pear-shaped
      3. consists of body and cervix; fundus bulging upper surface of body
   b. wall—lining of mucosa called endometrium; thick, middle coat of muscle called myometrium; partial external coat of peritoneum
   c. cavities—body cavity small and triangular in shape with three openings—two from tubes and one (internal os) into cervical canal; external os opening of cervical canal into vagina
   d. blood supply—generous, from uterine arteries
2. Location—in pelvic cavity between bladder and rectum
3. Position
   a. flexed between body and cervix, with body lying over bladder pointing forward and slightly upward
   b. cervix joins vagina at right angles
   c. capable of considerable mobility, therefore, often in abnormal positions, such as retroverted
   d. eight ligaments anchor it—two broad, two uterosacral, one posterior, one anterior, and two round
4. Functions
   a. menstruation
   b. pregnancy
   c. labor and expulsion of fetus

UTERINE TUBES—FALLOPIAN TUBES OR OVIDUCTS

1. Location—attached to uterus at upper, outer angles
2. Structure
   a. same three coats as uterus
   b. distal ends open with fimbriated margins
   c. mucosa and peritoneum in direct contact here
3. Function
   a. serve as ducts for ovaries, providing passageway by which ova can reach uterus
   b. fertilization occurs here normally

OVARIES—FEMALE GONADS

1. Location and size
   a. size and shape of large almonds
   b. lie behind and below uterine tubes
   c. anchored to uterus and broad ligament
2. Microscopic structure
   a. consists of several thousand graafian follicles embedded in connective tissue base
   b. follicles in all stages of development; usually each month one matures, ruptures, and expels its ovum into abdominal cavity
3. Functions
   a. oogenesis—formation of mature female gametes (ova)
   b. secretion of hormones—estrogens and progesterone

VAGINA

1. Location—between rectum and urethra
2. Structure
   a. collapsible, musculomembranous tube, capable of great distention
   b. external outlet protected by fold of mucous membrane, hymen
3. Functions
   a. receive seminal fluid
   b. is lower part of birth canal
   c. is excretory duct for uterine secretions and menstrual flow

VULVA

1. Consists of numerous structures which, together, constitute external genitalia
2. Main structures
   a. mons veneris—skin-covered pad of fat over symphysis pubis
   b. labia majora—hairy, skin-covered lips
   c. labia minora—small lips covered with modified skin
   d. clitoris—small mound of erectile tissue just below junction of two labia minora
   e. urinary meatus—just below clitoris; opens into urethra
   f. vaginal orifice—below urethra
   g. Bartholin's or greater vestibular glands
      1. comparable to bulbourethral glands of male
      2. open by means of long duct in space between hymen and labia minora
      3. ducts from lesser vestibular or Skene's glands open near urinary meatus

PERINEUM

1. Region between vaginal orifice and anus
2. Frequently torn at childbirth

BREASTS

1. Location and size
   a. just under skin, over pectoral muscles

b. size depends on deposits of adipose tissue
2. Structure
a. divided into lobes and lobules; latter composed of racemose glands
b. single excretory duct per lobe opens in nipple
c. circular, pigmented area called areola borders nipple
3. Function—secrete milk for infant
4. Mechanism controlling lactation—see Fig. 302

Female sexual cycles

RECURRING CYCLES

1. Ovarian cycles
   a. each month, follicle and ovum develop
   b. follicle secretes estrogens
   c. ovum matures and follicle ruptures (ovulation)
   d. corpus luteum forms and secretes progesterone and estrogens
   e. if no pregnancy, corpus luteum gradually degenerates and replaced by fibrous tissue; remains if there is pregnancy
2. Endometrial or menstrual cycle
   a. surface of endometrium sloughs off during menses, with bleeding from denuded area
   b. regeneration and proliferation of lining occurs
   c. endometrial glands and arterioles become longer and more tortuous
   d. glands secrete viscous mucus and cycle repeats
3. Myometrial cycle—contractility increases before ovulation and subsides following
4. Gonadotrophic cycles
   a. FSH—a high rate of secretion for about ten days after menses
   b. LH secretion increasing from ninth cycle day to day of ovulation (see Fig. 304)

CONTROL

1. Cyclical changes in ovaries controlled as follows:
   a. increasing blood concentration of FSH (for about ten days after menses) stimulates one or more primitive graafian follicles to start growing and to start secreting estrogens (Fig. 303)
   b. increasing blood concentration of LH (from ninth cycle day to day of ovulation) causes completion of growth of follicle and ovum, stimulates follicle to secrete estrogens, causes ovulation, and causes luteinization (Fig. 304)
2. Cyclical changes in uterus controlled as follows:
   a. increasing blood concentration of estrogens during preovulatory phase causes proliferation of endometrial cells with resultant thickening of endometrium, growth of endometrial glands, increased water content of endometrium, and increased contractions by myometrium
   b. increasing blood concentration of progesterone after ovulation, i.e., during premenstrual phase, causes secretion by endometrial glands and preparation of endometrium for implantation, increased water content of endometrium, and decreased contractions by myometrium
3. Cyclical changes in FSH and estrogen secretion—see Fig. 305

FUNCTIONS SERVED BY CYCLES

1. Preparation of endometrium for pregnancy during preovulatory and premenstrual periods
2. Shedding of progestational endometrium if no pregnancy occurs

MENARCHE AND MENOPAUSE

1. Menarche—onset of menses; about 13 years of age
2. Menopause (climateric)—cessation of menses; about 45 years of age

Embryology

MEANING AND SCOPE

1. Science of development of individual before birth
2. Long and complex study

VALUE OF KNOWLEDGE AND EMBRYOLOGY

Interprets many abnormal formations

STEPS IN DEVELOPMENT OF NEW INDIVIDUAL

1. Preliminary processes
   a. maturation of ovum and sperm or reduction of their chromosomes to one-half original number; i.e., one-half of 46
   b. ovulation and insemination
      1. ovulation once every 28 days, usually about 14 days before beginning of next menstrual period
      2. insemination, indefinite occurrence; sperm introduced into vagina, swim up to meet ovum in tube

2. Developmental processes
   a. fertilization or union of ovum and sperm
      1. normally occurs in tube
      2. only one sperm penetrates ovum
      3. one-celled new individual called zygote formed by union
   b. cleavage or segmentation
      1. multiplication of cells from zygote by repeated mitosis
      2. morula or solid ball of cells formed; becomes hollow with a cluster of cells attached at one point on inner surface of sphere; called blastocyst at this stage; now implanted in endometrium
   c. differentiation of cells into three primary germ layers—ectoderm, mesoderm, and entoderm
   d. histogenesis or formation of various tissues from primary germ layers; organogenesis or formation of various organs by rearrangements of tissues, such as fusions, shiftings, foldings, etc.

Review questions

1. Name the male sex glands. Where are they located?
2. Of what is the seminal fluid composed? Trace its course from its formation in the gonads to the exterior.
3. What and where are the prostate glands?
4. What are where are Cowper's glands?
5. What is the spermatic cord? From what to what does it extend, and what does it contain?
6. Removal of the testes (orchiectomy or castration) results in both sterility and various changes in the secondary sex characteristics. Why?
7. Name the female sex glands. Name all the internal female reproductive organs.
8. What is the perineum? Of what clinical importance is it in the female?
9. Name the three openings to the exterior from the female pelvis. How many openings to the exterior are there in the male?
10. What is a graafian follicle? What does it contain?
11. How many ova mature in a month, usually?
12. When, in the menstrual cycle, is ovulation thought to occur?
13. Discuss the mechanism thought to control menstruation.
14. Name the periods in the menstrual cycle with the approximate length of days in each and the main events.
15. What two organs are necessary for menstruation to occur?
16. Name the divisions of the uterus.
17. What and where are the fallopian tubes? Approximately how long are they? With what are they lined? Their lining is continuous on their distal ends with what? On their proximal ends? Why is an infection of the lower part of the female reproductive tract likely to develop into a very serious condition?
18. What is the cul-de-sac of Douglas?
19. Describe briefly the hormonal control of breast development and lactation.
20. Explain how contraceptive pills act to prevent pregnancy.
21. Where does fertilization normally take place?
22. Which of the following patients will no longer menstruate? Why? (1) One who has had a bilateral salpingectomy (removal of the tubes)? (2) One who has had a panhysterectomy (removal of the entire uterus)? (3) One who has had a bilateral oophorectomy (removal of both ovaries)? (4) One who has had a cervical hysterectomy (body and fundus removed)? (5) One who has had a unilateral oophorectomy?
23. Which of the patients described in Question 22 could no longer become pregnant? Explain.
24. Following menopause, which of the following hormones, estrogens, FSH, progesterone, would you expect to have a high blood concentration? Which a low blood concentration? Explain your reasoning.
25. Define or make an identifying statement about each of the following:

adolescence	meiosis
climacteric	menarche
colostrum	mitosis
corpus luteum	morula
ectopic pregnancy	oophorectomy
embryology	ovum
endometrium	ovulation
fertilization	puberty
fimbriae	salpingitis
gamete	semen
genes	spermatozoon
gonad	vulva
hysterectomy	zygote
maturation	

UNIT
SIX

Integration and control of body functions by hormones

Meaning

Pituitary body (hypophysis cerebri)
- Location and structure

Anterior pituitary gland (adenohypophysis)
- Growth hormone (somatotrophin or somatotrophic hormone)
- Lactogenic hormone
- Trophic hormones
- Melanocyte-stimulating hormone
- Control of secretion

Posterior pituitary gland (neurohypophysis)
- Hormones
- Control of secretion

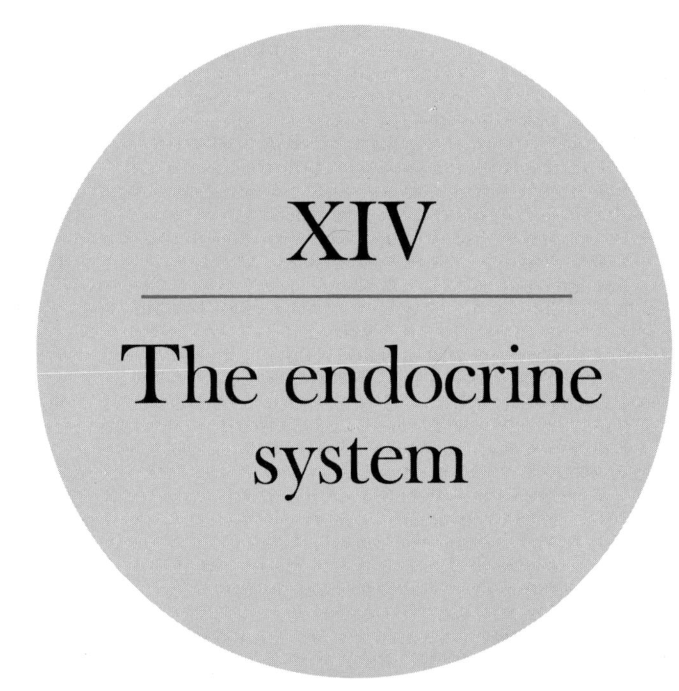

XIV The endocrine system

Meaning

Glands that have no ducts (ductless or endocrine glands) constitute the organs of the endocrine system. Whereas exocrine or duct glands release their secretions into ducts, endocrine glands release theirs into the blood. Endocrine gland secretions, as you undoubtedly know, are called hormones. The names and locations of the main endocrine glands are given in Table 60. You will find an even dozen of them listed if you count the pituitary, adrenal, and the ovary each as two separate glands, which functionally they are.

The endocrine system and the nervous system both perform the same general functions for the body: communication, control, and integration. But they accomplish these general functions through different kinds of mechanisms and with somewhat different types of results. The nervous system's mechanism consists of special cells (neurons) that conduct impulses from one specific structure to another. The endocrine system's mechanism consists of special cells (endocrine gland cells) that secrete special chemicals (hormones) that travel from their place of origin by way of the circulating blood to all parts of the body. Nerve impulses and hormones do not exert exactly the same kind of control, nor do they control precisely the same structures and functions. And this is fortunate. It makes for better timing and more precision of control. For instance, nerve impulses produce rapid, short-lasting responses, whereas hormones produce slower and generally longer-lasting responses. Nerve impulses directly control only two kinds of cells: muscle and gland cells. Some hormones, in contrast, exert control over all kinds of cells.

Exaggerating the importance of endocrine glands is almost impossible. Hor-

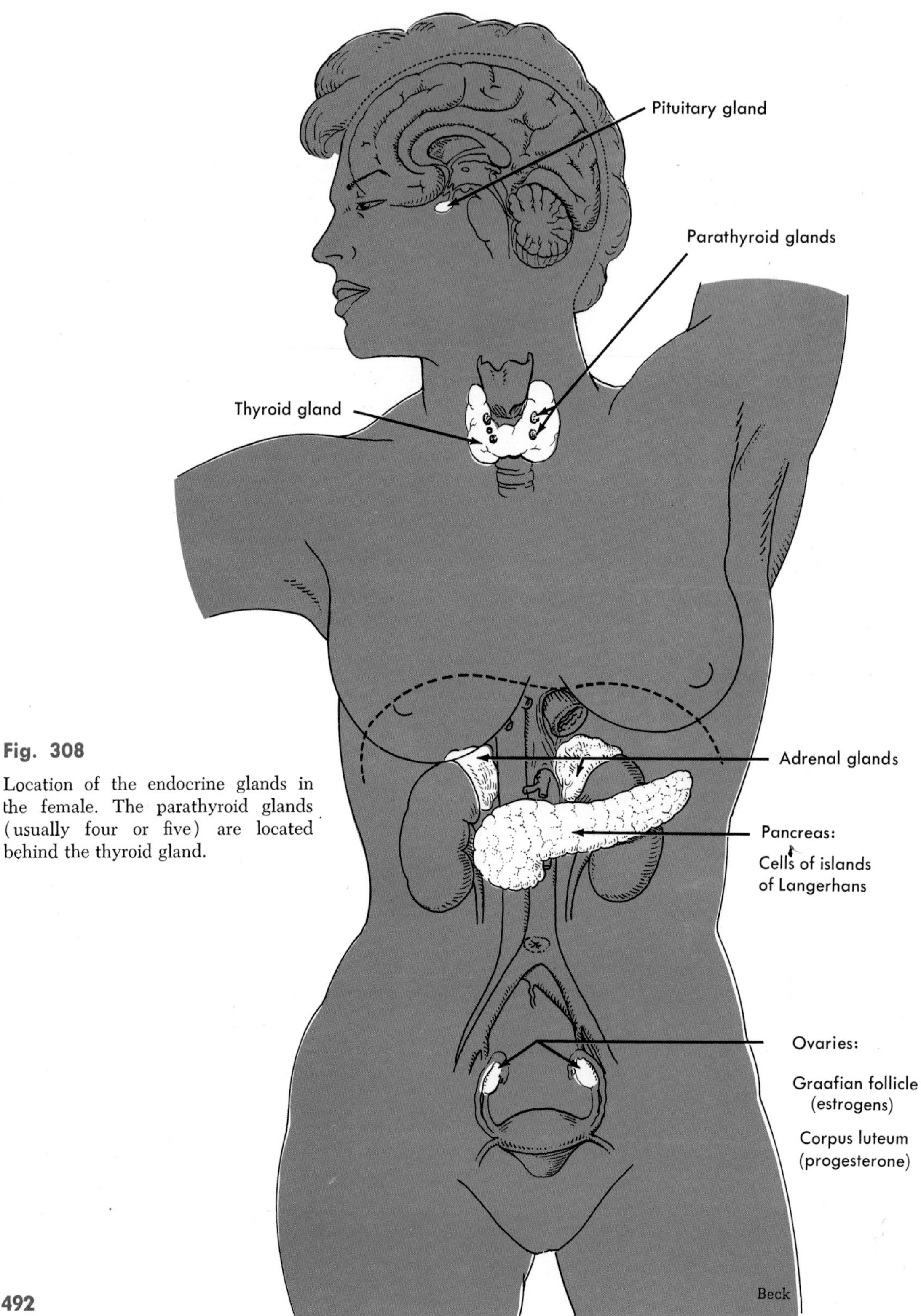

Fig. 308

Location of the endocrine glands in the female. The parathyroid glands (usually four or five) are located behind the thyroid gland.

Table 60. Names and locations of endocrine glands

Name	*Location*
Pituitary gland (hypophysis cerebri)	Cranial cavity
Anterior lobe (adenohypophysis)	
Posterior lobe (neurohypophysis)	
Thyroid gland	Neck
Parathyroid glands	Neck
Adrenal glands	Abdominal cavity (retroperitoneal)
Adrenal cortex	
Adrenal medulla	
Ovaries	Pelvic cavity
Graafian follicle	
Corpus luteum	
Testes (interstitial cells)	Scrotum
Islands of Langerhans	Abdominal cavity (pancreas)
Thymus	Thoracic cavity
Pineal body (pineal gland or epiphysis cerebri)	Cranial cavity

mones are the main regulators of metabolism (and, therefore, of growth and development), of reproduction, and of stress responses. They play roles of the utmost importance in maintaining homeostasis—fluid and electrolyte balance, acid-base balance, and energy balance, for example. Excesses or deficiencies of hormones make the difference between normalcy and all sorts of abnormalities such as idiocy, dwarfism, gigantism, and sterility—and even the difference between life and death in some instances.

We shall start our discussion of the endocrine system with a gland that is truly small but mighty. At its largest diameter, it measures only about ½ inch. By weight it is even less impressive—only about ½ gm., $1/60$ of an ounce! And yet, so crucial are its functions that the "master gland" is a popular name for its anterior lobe. The anatomical name for the entire organ is hypophysis cerebri, but more often it is called simply the pituitary body or gland.

Pituitary body (hypophysis cerebri)

Location and structure

The pituitary body has a protected location. It lies in the sella turcica, which is covered over by an extension of the dura mater known as the pituitary diaphragm. The deepest part of the sella turcica (saddle-shaped depression in the sphenoid bone) is called the pituitary fossa since the pituitary body lies in it. A stemlike portion, the pituitary stalk, juts up through the diaphragm and attaches the gland to the undersurface of the brain. More specifically, the stalk attaches the pituitary body to the hypothalamus. Although the pituitary looks like just one gland, it actually consists of two separate glands—the adenohypophysis or anterior pituitary gland and the neurohypophysis or posterior pituitary gland. These two glands develop from different embryonic structures, have different microscopic structure, and secrete different

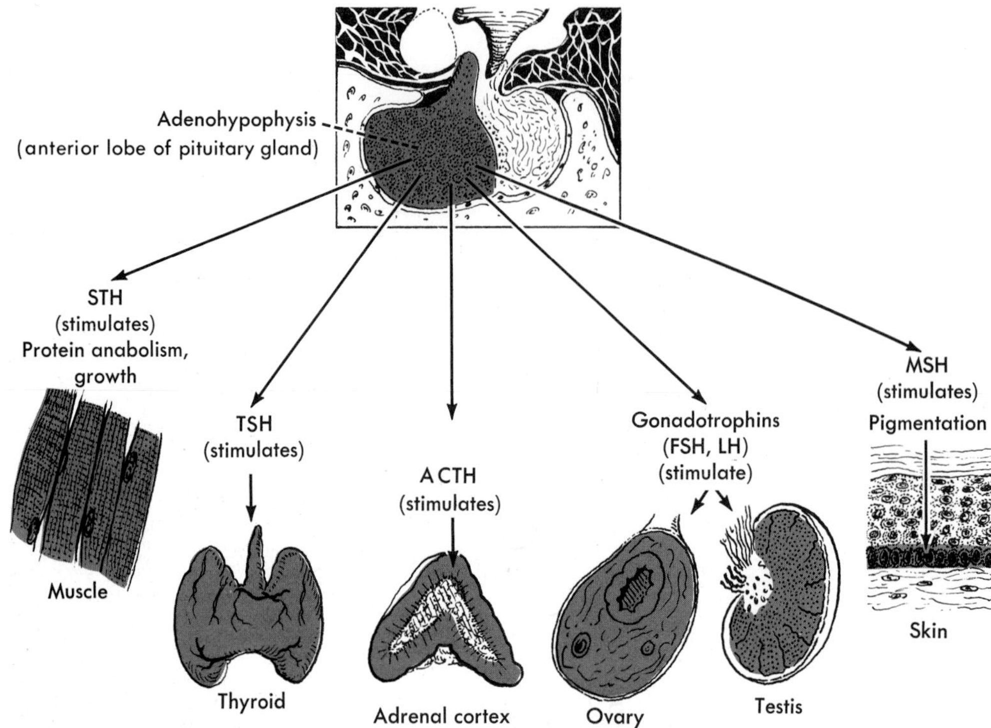

Fig. 309

Hormones of the anterior pituitary gland (adenohypophysis). The latter also secretes lactogenic hormone, not shown in this drawing but discussed in the text.

hormones. The adenohypophysis develops as an upward projection from the embryo's pharynx, whereas the neurohypophysis develops as a downward projection from its brain. Microscopic differences between the two glands are suggested by their names—*adeno* means gland and *neuro* means nervous. In other words, the adenohypophysis has the microscopic structure of an endocrine gland, whereas the neurohypophysis has the structure of nervous tissue. As far as functions are concerned, the two glands are also dissimilar. The anterior lobe secretes seven hormones and the posterior lobe probably secretes only two.

ANTERIOR PITUITARY GLAND (ADENOHYPOPHYSIS)

The anterior pituitary gland consists chiefly of the anterior lobe of the pituitary body. Two main types of epithelial cells compose the anterior lobe: chromophobes (so named because they resist staining) and chromophils (named for their ease of staining). Chromophils, in turn, are subdivided into two main types: acidophils (those that take acid stains) and basophils (those that take basic stains). Chromophobes are said to be precursors or stem cells from which chromophils develop. And chromophils are the cells of the anterior lobe of the pituitary gland that presumably synthesize all seven of its hormones. Acidophils secrete growth hormone (STH) and lactogenic hormone. Basophils secrete the other five hormones of the anterior lobe: thyrotrophin (TH), adrenocorticotrophin (ACTH), two gonado-

Fig. 310

A pituitary giant and dwarf contrasted with normal-sized men. Excessive secretion of the somatotrophic hormone (STH) by the anterior lobe of the pituitary gland during the early years of life produces giants of this type, while deficient secretion of this substance produces well-formed dwarfs. (Courtesy Dr. Edmund E. Beard, Cleveland, Ohio.)

trophins (follicle-stimulating [FSH] and luteinizing hormones [LH]), and melanocyte-stimulating hormone (MSH). Some investigators think it probable that a different type of cell secretes each of these different hormones.

Growth hormone (somatotrophin or somatotrophic hormone)

Growth hormone or somatotrophin (Gr. *soma,* body; *trophe,* nourishment) or somatotrophic hormone (STH) is thought to promote growth indirectly by accelerating amino acid transport into cells—evidence, blood amino acid content decreases within hours after administration of growth hormone to a fasting animal. With the faster entrance of amino acid into cells, anabolism of amino acids to form tissue protein also accelerates. And this, in turn, tends to promote cellular growth. Growth hormone stimulates growth of both bone and soft tissues. If the anterior pituitary gland secretes an excess of growth hormone during the growth years (that is, before closure of the epiphyseal cartilages), bones

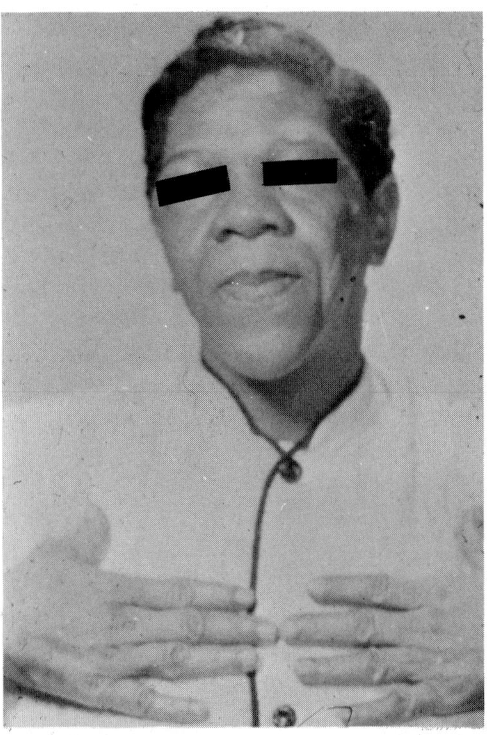

Fig. 311

Acromegaly. (Courtesy Dr. William McKendree Jefferies, Western Reserve University School of Medicine, Cleveland, Ohio.)

grow more rapidly than normal and *gigantism* results. But if oversecretion of growth hormone occurs after the individual is full grown, the condition known as *acromegaly* develops. Characteristic of this disease are enlargement of the bones of the hands, feet, jaws, and cheeks and an increase, too, in their overlying soft tissues (Fig. 311). Undersecretion of the growth hormone produces *dwarfism* when it occurs during the years of skeletal growth and *pituitary cachexia* (Simmonds' disease), a much rarer condition, when the deficiency develops during adult life. Premature aging with marked tissue atrophy characterizes the latter disease.

In addition to its stimulating effect on protein anabolism, growth hormone also influences fat and carbohydrate metabolism. For example, it tends to block fat deposition and to accelerate the mobilization of fats from adipose tissues and to increase their utilization (catabolism) by other tissues. Growth hormone, in other words, causes cells to shift from carbohydrate to fat utilization for energy. Did you notice that the effect of growth hormone on fat metabolism is just the opposite to its effect on protein metabolism? Growth hormone promotes protein *anabolism*. And in contrast, it promotes fat *catabolism*.

The precise actions of growth hormone on carbohydrate metabolism are not known. But that it acts in some way to influence carbohydrate metabolism is known. Growth hormone decreases carbohydrate utilization by cells, while insulin increases it. Hence, growth hormone tends to increase the blood concentration of glucose—it has a hyperglycemic effect. Insulin does the opposite. Because it increases carbohydrate utilization, it tends to decrease the blood concentration of glucose and has a hypoglycemic effect. Whereas adequate amounts of insulin prevent diabetes mellitus, long-continued excess amounts of growth hormone produce diabetes. In short, growth hormone and insulin function as antagonists. Or, as more commonly stated, growth hormone has an anti-insulin effect, a fact of considerable clinical importance. Summarizing very briefly, growth hormone helps regulate metabolism in the following ways:

1. It promotes protein anabolism (synthesis of tissue proteins) so is essential for normal growth.
2. It promotes fat mobilization and catabolism.
3. It acts in some way to oppose insulin. This anti-insulin action decreases glucose utilization and seems to account for the hyperglycemic and diabetogenic effects of growth hormone.

Lactogenic hormone

The anterior pituitary cells called acidophils secrete two hormones: growth hormone and lactogenic hormone. As its name suggests, lactogenic hormone "generates" (that is, initiates) milk secretion. It stimulates the mammary glands to start secreting soon after delivery of a baby. And during pregnancy, it helps promote the breast development that makes possible milk secretion after pregnancy. Other names for lactogenic hormone are *prolactin* and *luteotrophic hormone* (LTH). The latter, however, now seems inappropriate since new evidence suggests that in the human being the lactogenic hormone does not activate the corpus luteum.

Trophic hormones

The anterior pituitary cells known as basophils secrete four trophic hormones—so called because of their "nourishing," that is, stimulating effect on other endocrine glands. Names of the trophic hormones are thyrotrophin, adrenocorticotrophin, and the two gonadotrophins known as follicle-stimulating hormone and luteinizing hormone. They all perform the same general function. Each trophic hormone stimulates one other endocrine gland—stimulates it both to grow and to secrete its hormone at a faster rate. It seems to affect only this one structure as if, like a bullet, it had been aimed at a target. In fact, "target gland" is the name given to the particular gland influenced by a particular hormone.

Individual trophic hormones perform the following functions:

1. *Thyrotrophin* (thyroid-stimulating hormone, TSH) promotes and maintains growth and development of the thyroid gland and stimulates it to secrete thyroxin and tri-iodothyronine, its two hormones (together called thyroid hormone).

2. *Adrenocorticotrophin* (ACTH) promotes and maintains normal growth and development of the adrenal cortex and stimulates it to secrete cortisol and other glucocorticoids.

3. *Follicle-stimulating hormone* (FSH) stimulates primary graafian follicles to start growing and to continue developing to maturity, that is, to the point of ovulation. FSH also stimulates follicle cells to secrete estrogens, one type of female sex hormones. In the male, FSH stimulates development of the seminiferous tubules and maintains spermatogenesis by them.

4. *Luteinizing hormone* (LH). The name of this hormone suggests its second function, that of stimulating formation of the corpus luteum. Prior to this, LH acts with FSH to bring about complete maturation of the follicle and to produce ovulation. And then LH alone stimulates formation of the corpus luteum in the ruptured follicle. Finally, LH in human females stimulates the corpus luteum to secrete progesterone—at least current evidence suggests that this is probably so. The male pituitary gland also secretes LH, but it is called *interstitial cell–stimulating hormone* (ICSH) because it stimulates interstitial cells in the testes to develop and secrete testosterone.

• • •

During childhood, the anterior pituitary gland secretes insignificant amounts of gonadotrophins. Then it steps up their production gradually a few years before puberty. And just before puberty begins, presumably its secretion of these hormones takes a sudden and marked spurt. As a result, the blood concentration of gonadotrophins increases markedly. And this first high blood concentration of gonadotrophins is the stimulus that brings on the first menstrual period and the many other changes that signal the beginning of puberty.

Melanocyte-stimulating hormone

In some species the intermediate part of the adenohypophysis produces the melanocyte-stimulating hormone (MSH). Therefore, MSH was first named *intermedin.* However, in man, it is now thought that the anterior lobe of the pituitary gland produces most of the MSH and that both MSH and another anterior pituitary hormone, namely, ACTH, tend to produce increased pigmentation of the skin. Structurally, also, the two molecules resemble each other. Several of the same amino acids occur in the same sequence in both MSH and ACTH.

Control of secretion

Two types of mechanisms control the secretion of trophic hormones by the anterior lobe of the pituitary gland. One is a homeostatic mechanism that regulates trophic hormone secretion under ordinary circumstances. It is also referred to as a "negative feedback mechanism" (Fig. 312) and as a "hormonal mechanism." Appropriate names for the other kind of mechanism that controls trophic hormone secretion might be "stress mechanism," "neuroendocrine mechanism," or "neurosecretory mechanism." Why these are appropriate designations will become apparent in a later paragraph.

Perhaps we can most clearly explain the type of mechanism that ordinarily regulates the secretion of trophic hormones by the anterior lobe of the pituitary gland if we try to answer a specific question: "How is the anterior lobe's secretion of ACTH controlled under usual conditions, that is, when the body is not in a state of stress?" Very briefly, the answer is that the blood concentration of cortisol "feeds back" to the anterior lobe of the pituitary gland and exerts a negative influence on its secretion of ACTH. By negative influence we mean that a high concentration of cortisol inhibits ACTH secretion and a low concentration of cortisol stimulates ACTH secretion. (ACTH, in contrast, as we have seen, exerts a positive influence on cortisol secretion—a high concentration of ACTH stimulates and a low concentration inhibits cortisol secretion.) Thus, the general principle of the negative feedback type of control is as follows.

A high blood concentration of a target gland hormone inhibits the anterior lobe's secretion of a trophic hormone, whereas a high blood concentration of a trophic hormone stimulates target gland secretion of its hormone. A mechanism of this type operates to regulate the anterior lobe's secretion of thyrotrophin and the thyroid gland's secretion of thyroid hormone. And a similar mechanism controls the anterior lobe's secretion of FSH and the ovary's secretion of estrogens. To see how such a negative feedback mechanism operates to regulate ACTH and cortisol secretion, examine Fig. 312.

Clinical facts furnish interesting evidence about feedback control of hormone secretion by the anterior pituitary gland and its target glands. For instance, if a person has his pituitary gland removed (hypophysectomy) surgically or by radiation, he must be kept on hormone replacement therapy for the rest of his life. If not, he will develop thyroid, adrenocortical, and gonadotrophic deficiencies—deficiencies, that is, of target gland hormones. Another well-known clinical fact is that estrogen deficiency develops in women between 40 and 50 years of age. By then, the ovaries seem to have tired of producing hormones and ovulating each month. Or, at any rate, they no longer respond to FSH stimulation so estrogen deficiency develops, brings about the menopause, and persists after the menopause. What, therefore, would you deduce is true of the blood concentration of FSH after the menopause? What effect does a high concentration of a target gland hormone have on trophic hormone secretion by the anterior pituitary gland?

Neurosecretory control of hormone secretion by the anterior pituitary gland is accomplished via the hypothalamus. Neurons in certain parts of the hypothalamus syn-

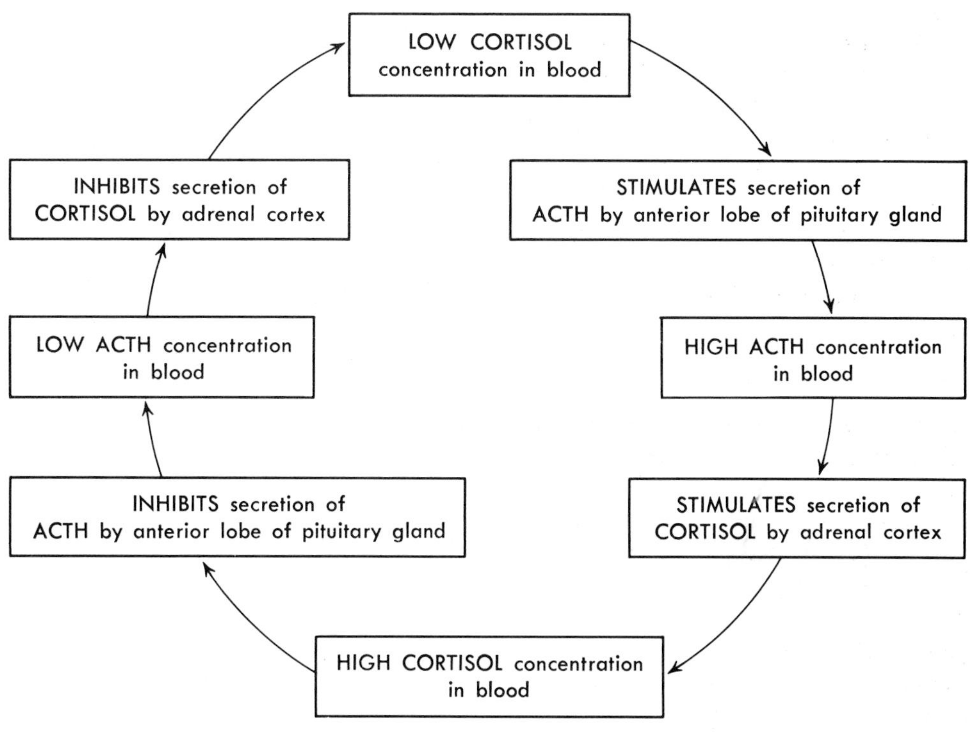

Fig. 312

Scheme to show the negative feedback mechanism that regulates secretion of ACTH by the anterior lobe of the pituitary gland and secretion of cortisol by the adrenal cortex under ordinary conditions. This is a homeostatic mechanism since it tends to keep the blood levels of cortisol (17-hydroxycorticosterone or hydrocortisone) stable within a narrow range.

thesize chemicals called *neurosecretions.* They are released from the axons of these neurons into the blood in a complex of small veins known as the hypophyseal or *pituitary portal system.* Via this portal system, the neurosecretions travel a short distance from the hypothalamus down to the anterior lobe of the pituitary gland. There they stimulate its cells to secrete various hormones. For instance, one neurosecretion from the hypothalamus stimulates the anterior lobe to release ACTH into the blood. It has an appropriate name—corticotrophin-releasing factor (CRF). Almost surely the hypothalamus forms other neurosecretions too—probably substances that control the anterior lobe's secretion of gonadotrophins, thyrotrophin, and lactogenic hormone. At least, considerable and impressive evidence suggests that this may be true.

The hypothalamic-anterior pituitary mechanism described in the preceding paragraph operates as a kind of emergency device—it controls secretion of the anterior lobe in times of stress. It is not yet known definitely but perhaps under these conditions, changes in the blood concentration of various substances and presumably nerve impulses from the cerebral cortex, limbic lobe, and other structures stimulate the hypothalamus to increase its output of neurosecretions into the pituitary portal system. Then, via these vessels, they quickly travel to the anterior lobe, where they stimulate it to increase its secretion of hormones.

In essence, what the hypothalamus does through its neurosecretions is to translate nerve impulses into hormone secretion by endocrine glands.* In other words, the hypothalamus links the nervous system to the endocrine system. It integrates the activities of these two great integrating systems particularly, it seems, in times of stress. When healthy survival is threatened, the hypothalamus, via its neurosecretions into the pituitary portal system, seems to take over the command of the anterior lobe of the pituitary gland. By so doing, it indirectly controls all the endocrine glands influenced by the anterior lobe's trophic hormones—namely, the thyroid gland, the adrenal cortex, and the gonads. And, finally, by means of the hormones these glands secrete, the hypothalamus can dictate the functioning of literally every cell in our bodies. These facts have tremendous implications, especially when coupled with the fact that tracts extend from the cerebral cortex to the hypothalamus. They mean that the cerebral cortex can do more than just receive impulses from all parts of the body and send out impulses to muscles and glands. They mean that the cerebral cortex—and therefore our thoughts and emotions—can, by way of the hypothalamus, influence the functioning of all our billions of cells, not just muscle and gland cells. In short, the brain has two-way contact with every tissue of the body. Not only can all tissues send information to the brain (via sensory conduction paths), but also the brain can send out information to all tissues—not just to muscles and glands as formerly supposed—via neurotransducer mechanisms. And this fact lends support to the now widely held circular theory of mind and body relations, the somatopsychosomatic theory. The state of the body influences mental processes, which, in turn, influence the state of the body. This circular relationship is clearly shown diagrammatically in Fig. 313.

*Recently, the hypothalamus and a few other structures have been referred to as "neuroendocrine transducers." A *neuroendocrine transducer* is defined as a structure that translates the nerve impulses brought to it into endocrine secretions. In short, a neuroendocrine transducer translates impulses into hormones. Known neuroendocrine transducers are the hypothalamus and the adrenal medulla. Very recent evidence seems to indicate that the pineal body may also qualify as one.

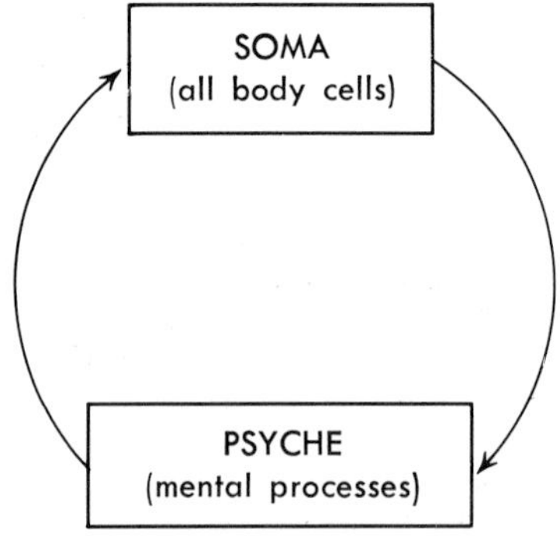

Fig. 313

Scheme to show the somatopsychosomatic theory of a circular relationship between mind and body.

POSTERIOR PITUITARY GLAND (NEUROHYPOPHYSIS)

Hormones

The posterior lobe of the pituitary gland secretes two hormones—one known as the antidiuretic hormone (ADH) and the other called oxytocin. But, strangely enough, cells of the posterior lobe do not themselves make these hormones. Neurons in the hypothalamus (supraoptic and paraventricular nuclei) synthesize them. From the cell bodies of these neurons the hormones pass down along axons (in the hypothalamohypophyseal tract) into the posterior lobe of the pituitary. Later, the posterior lobe secretes them into the blood.

ADH acts on cells of the distal and collecting tubules of the kidney to make them more permeable to water. This causes faster reabsorption of water from tubular urine into blood. And this, in turn, automatically produces antidiuresis (smaller urine volume). Marked diuresis, that is, abnormally large urine volume, occurs if ADH secretion is inadequate, such as occurs in the disease *diabetes insipidus.* A preparation of ADH used to treat this condition is called vasopressin or Pitressin. (The name reflects the fact that ADH tends to constrict blood vessels. However, as far as now known, this action of ADH has no physiological importance.)

Oxytocin has two actions: it stimulates powerful contractions by the pregnant uterus and it causes milk ejection from the lactating breast. Under the influence of this hormone from the posterior lobe of the pituitary gland, alveoli (cells that synthesize milk) release the milk into the ducts of the breast. This is a highly important function of oxytocin because milk cannot be removed by suckling unless it has first been ejected into ducts. However, it was oxytocin's other action—its stimulating effect on contractions of the pregnant uterus—that inspired its name. The term means "swift childbirth" (Gr. *oxys,* swift; *tokos,* childbirth). Whether or not oxytocin takes part in initiating labor is still an unsettled question. Commercial preparations of oxytocin are given to stimulate uterine contractions after delivery of a baby in order to lessen the danger of hemorrhage.

Control of secretion

Details of the mechanism that controls the secretion of ADH by the posterior lobe of the pituitary gland have not been established. However, two factors seem to be involved: the osmotic pressure of the extracellular fluid and its total volume. Without going into a discussion of evidence or details, the general principles of control of ADH secretion are as follows:

1. An increase in the osmotic pressure of extracellular fluid stimulates ADH secretion. This leads to decreased urine output and tends also to increase the volume of extracellular fluid, which, in turn, tends to decrease its osmotic pressure back toward normal (Fig. 329, p. 534). Opposite effects result from a decrease in the osmotic pressure of extracellular fluid.
2. A decrease in the total volume of extracellular fluid acts in some way to stimulate ADH secretion and thereby to decrease urine output and increase extracellular volume back toward normal.
3. Stress acts in some way to stimulate ADH secretion. An interesting clinical application of this principle is the fact that after major surgery patients tend to show signs of water retention.

• • •

About all that is known about the mechanism that controls the secretion of oxytocin by the posterior lobe of the pituitary gland is that stimulation of the nipples by the baby's nursing initiates sensory impulses that eventually reach the supraoptic and paraventricular nuclei of the hypothalamus, stimulating them. They, in turn, stimulate the posterior lobe of the pituitary gland to increase its secretion of oxytocin (see Fig. 302, p. 475).

Thyroid gland

Location and structure

Two fairly large lateral lobes and a connecting portion, the isthmus, constitute the thyroid gland. It is located in the neck just below the larynx. The isthmus lies across the anterior surface of the upper part of the trachea. Thyroid tissue contains numerous small follicles. Colloid, composed largely of an iodine-containing protein known as thyroglobulin, fills these tiny sacs.

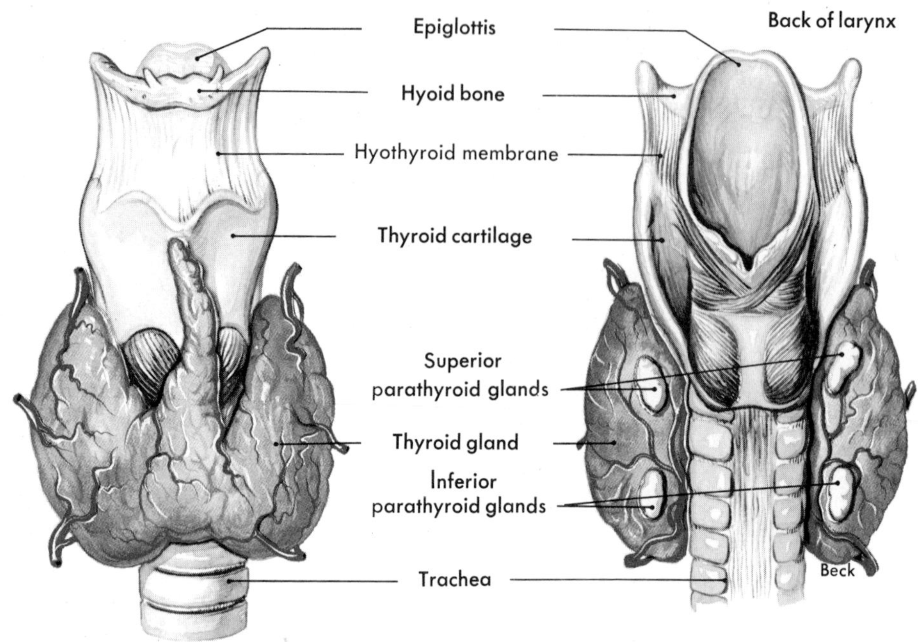

Fig. 314

The thyroid and parathyroid glands and their relations to the larynx (voice box) and trachea.

Functions

The thyroid gland secretes a substance called thyroid hormone. Actually, however, this secretion consists of two hormones. Thyroxine is the name of the main one, and triiodothyronine is the name of the less abundant one. One molecule of thyroxine contains four atoms of iodine, and one molecule of triiodothyronine, as its name suggests, contains three iodine atoms. After synthesizing its hormones, the thyroid gland stores considerable amounts of them before secreting them. (Other endocrine glands do not store up their hormones.) As a preliminary to storage, thyroxin and triiodothyronine combine with a globulin in the thyroid cell to form a compound called thyroglobulin. Then thyroglobulin is stored in the colloid material in the follicles of the gland. Later, the two hormones are released from thyroglobulin and secreted into the blood as thyroxin and triiodothyronine. Almost immediately, however, they combine with a blood protein. They travel in the bloodstream in this protein-bound form. But in the tissue capillaries they are released from the protein and enter tissue cells as thyroxin and triiodothyronine.

The iodine in the thyroxin and triiodothyronine that is bound to protein in the blood is called protein-bound iodine (PBI). The amount of PBI can be measured by a laboratory procedure and, in fact, is widely used as a test of thyroid functioning. (With a normal thyroid gland, the PBI is about 4 to 8 μg per 100 ml. of plasma.)

The main physiological actions of thyroid hormone are to help regulate the metabolic rate and the processes of growth and tissue differentiation. Thyroid hormone increases the metabolic rate, an effect evidenced by increased oxygen consumption

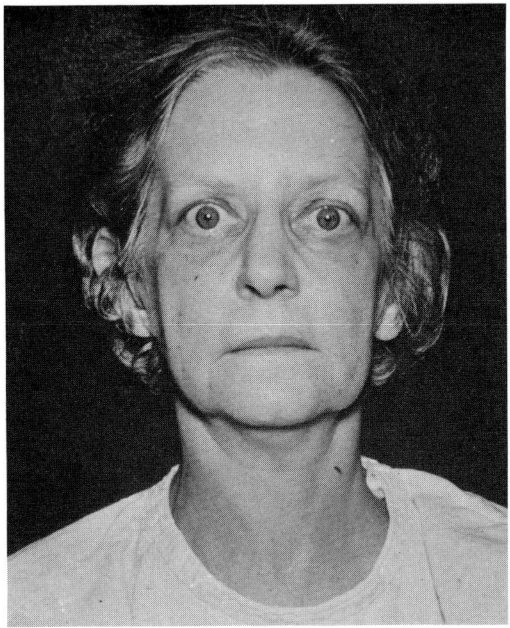

Fig. 315

Graves' disease caused by hypersecretion by the thyroid gland. (Courtesy Dr. William McKendree Jefferies, Western Reserve University of Medicine, Cleveland, Ohio.)

following thyroid administration. Like pituitary somatotrophin, thyroid hormone stimulates growth, but unlike somatotrophin, it also influences tissue differentiation and development. For example, cretins (thyroid deficiency) not only are dwarfed but also are usually mentally retarded because the brain fails to develop normally. Their bones and many other tissues also show an abnormal pattern of development.

Effects of hypersecretion and hyposecretion

Hypersecretion of thyroid hormone produces the disease *exophthalmic goiter* (Graves' disease, Basedow's disease, and several other names), characterized by an elevated PBI, an increased metabolism (+30 or more), an increased appetite, loss of weight, increased nervous irritability, and exophthalmos. Marked edema of the fatty tissue behind the eye, attributed to the high blood titer of thyrotrophic hormone, produces the exophthalmos.

Hyposecretion during the formative years leads to malformed dwarfism or *cretinism,* a condition characterized by retarded mental, physical, and sexual development and lowered metabolic rate. Later in life, deficient thyroid secretion produces the disease *myxedema* (Fig. 316), characterized by decreased metabolic rate, which, in turn, leads to lessened mental and physical vigor and a gain in weight, loss of hair, and a thickening of the skin due to an accumulation of fluid in the subcutaneous tissues. Because of a high mucoprotein content, this fluid is viscous. Therefore, it gives firmness to the skin, and the skin does not pit when pressed, as it does in some other types of edema.

Fig. 316

Myxedema, a condition produced by hyposecretion by the thyroid gland during the adult years. (Courtesy Dr. Edmund E. Beard, Cleveland, Ohio.)

Parathyroid glands

Location and structure

The parathyroid glands are small round bodies attached to the posterior surfaces of the lateral lobes of the thyroid gland. Usually there are four or five, but sometimes there are fewer and sometimes more of these glands.

Functions

The parathyroid glands secrete *parathormone* and, it is now believed, another hormone called *calcitonin.* The chief function of these hormones is to maintain homeostasis of blood calcium concentration. To do this, they act as follows:

1. Parathormone acts on intestine, bones, and kidney tubules to accelerate calcium absorption from them into the blood. Hence, parathormone tends to increase the blood concentration of calcium. Its primary action on bone is to stimulate bone breakdown or resorption. This releases calcium and phosphate, which diffuse into the blood.
2. Parathormone acts on kidney tubules to accelerate their excretion of phosphates from the blood into the urine. Note, therefore, that parathormone has opposite effects on the kidney's handling of calcium and phosphate. It accelerates calcium reabsorption but phosphate excretion by the tubules. Consequently, parathormone tends to increase the blood concentration of calcium and to decrease the blood concentration of phosphate.
3. Calcitonin acts in some way to quickly decrease the blood concentration of calcium when it increases about 20% above the normal level of 5 mEq. per liter. How calcitonin decreases blood calcium is not known, but a logical guess is that it accelerates calcium's movement into bone from blood.

• • •

The maintenance of calcium homeostasis is highly important for healthy survival. Normal neuromuscular irritability, blood clotting, cell membrane permeability, and also normal functioning of certain enzymes all depend upon the blood concentration of calcium being maintained at a normal level. Neuromuscular irritability is inversely related to blood calcium concentration. In other words, neuromuscular irritability increases when the blood concentration of calcium decreases. Suppose, for example, that a parathormone deficiency develops and causes *hypocalcemia* (lower than normal blood concentration of calcium). The hypocalcemia increases neuromuscular irritability—sometimes so much that it produces muscle spasms and convulsions, a condition called tetany.

Parathormone excess produces hypercalcemia or a higher than normal blood concentration of calcium. Sometimes it causes a bone disease with the long name of osteitis fibrosa generalisata. Bone mass decreases (as a result of increased bone destruction followed by fibrous tissue replacement), decalcification occurs, and cystlike cavities appear in the bone.

Adrenal glands

Location and structure

The adrenal glands are located atop the kidneys, fitting like a cap over these organs. The outer portion of the gland is called the *cortex* and the inner substance the *medulla.* Although the adrenal cortex and adrenal medulla are structural parts of one organ, they function as two separate endocrine glands.

ADRENAL CORTEX

Three different zones or layers of cells make up the adrenal cortex. Starting with the zone directly under the outer capsule of the gland, their names are zona glomerulosa, zona fasciculata, and zona reticularis.

According to one theory based on good evidence, the zona glomerulosa secretes hormones called mineralocorticoids. Another type of corticoids, known as glucocorticoids, are secreted chiefly by the middle layer of cells. And the innermost layer secretes small amounts of both glucocorticoids and sex hormones. We shall now discuss briefly the functions of these three kinds of adrenal cortical hormones.

Glucocorticoids

The chief glucocorticoids secreted by the adrenal cortex are cortisol* (also called hydrocortisone and compound F) and corticosterone (also known as compound B). Glucocorticoids affect literally every cell in the body. Their general functions are to promote normal metabolism and to enable the body to resist stress—a good nickname for glucocorticoids might be "metabolic, stress-resisting hormones." Although the precise primary actions of glucocorticoids remain unknown, their most outstanding effects are as follows.

1. Glucocorticoids in adequate amounts promote normal protein metabolism. In excess amounts they produce a "protein cata-

---

*Steroid compounds have the following nucleus:

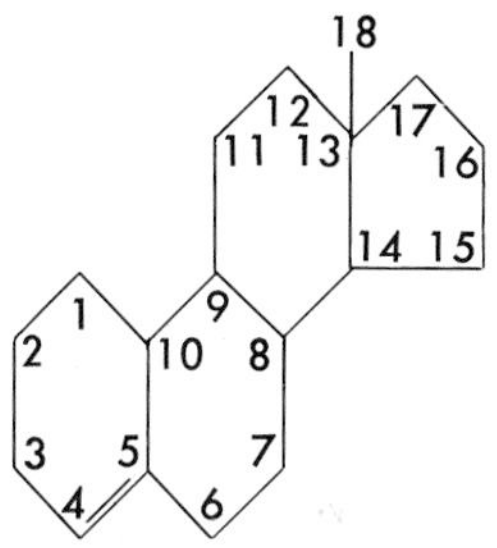

Steroid nucleus

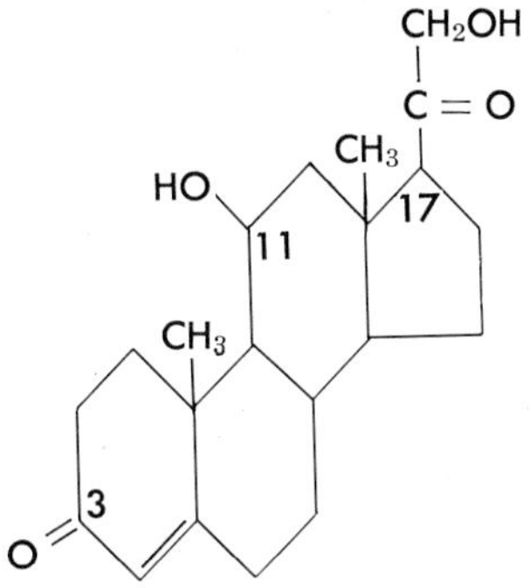

Corticosterone (compound B)

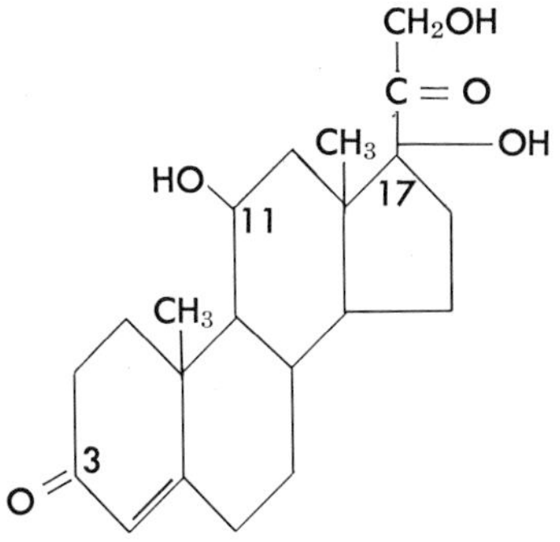

Cortisol (hydrocortisone; compound F)

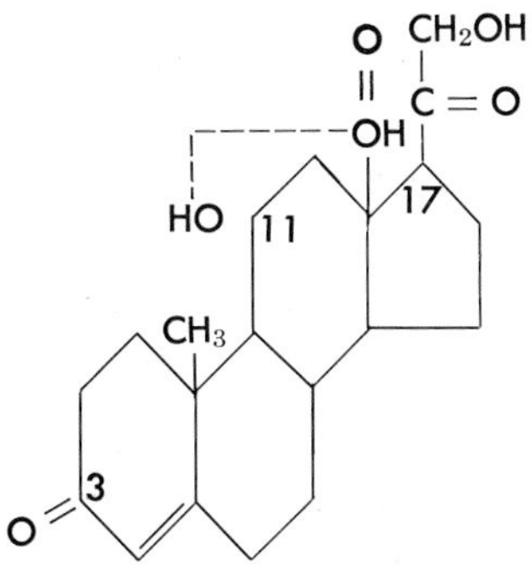

Aldosterone

Corticosterone (compound B) may be the parent substance of other corticoids.

Compound E or cortisone (chemical name, 17-hydroxy-11-dehydrocorticosterone, signifying that the molecule is the same as corticosterone with –OH instead of –H on C-17, and H on C-11).

DOC (11-desoxycorticosterone—corticosterone molecules without any oxygen at C-11).

Relation of molecular structure to function:

1. Oxygen at C-11 produces glucocorticoid effects described on pp. 505 to 507.
2. OH at C-17 (in addition to oxygen at C-11) enhances glucocorticoid effects.
3. Aldehyde group at C-18 (as in aldosterone) produces marked salt-retaining effect.

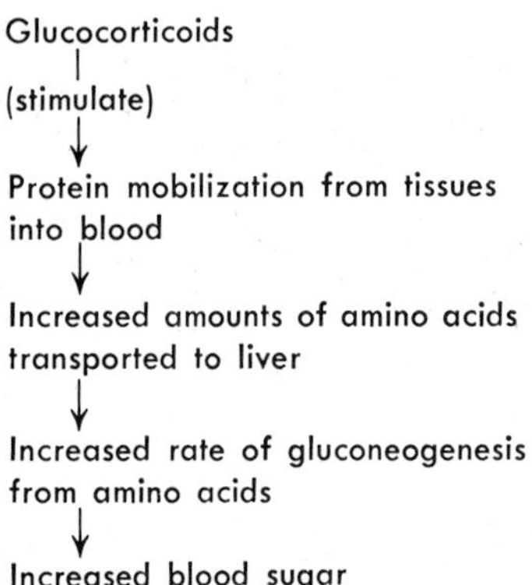

Fig. 317

Scheme showing postulated mechanism by which corticoid control of carbohydrate metabolism may stem from corticoid control of protein metabolism.

bolic effect." That is, a high blood concentration of glucocorticoids accelerates the breakdown of tissue proteins to form amino acids. This increased rate of tissue protein mobilization results in a net loss of tissue proteins—in other words, in a negative nitrogen balance. "Tissue wasting" this is sometimes graphically called. A deficient amount of glucocorticoids produces an opposite effect—it slows tissue protein mobilization.

2. Normal amounts of glucocorticoids promote normal carbohydrate metabolism. Increased glucocorticoids increase liver glyconeogenesis and gluconeogenesis. Presumably, these effects result from the accelerated rate of tissue protein metabolism. As larger amounts of mobilized amino acids reach the liver, its cells synthesize some of them into glycogen and some into glucose. More glucose, therefore, moves out of liver cells into blood and tends to increase the blood glucose level—tends to produce hyperglycemia, that is. Hence, an excess amount of glucocorticoids is said to have gluconeogenic and hyperglycemic or diabetogenic effects. Since this is an opposite effect from that of insulin, it is also referred to as the anti-insulin effect of glucocorticoids. A deficient amount of glucocorticoids, on the other hand, results in slower gluconeogenesis and tends to produce hypoglycemia.

3. Normal amounts of glucocorticoids promote normal fat metabolism. A high blood concentration of glucocorticoids causes faster mobilization of fats from adipose tissue and tends to accelerate fat catabolism. In other words, an increase in glucocorticoids tends to cause a "shift" to fat utilization from the usual carbohydrate utilization by cells for their energy. But, also, the mobilized fats, like mobilized amino acids, may be used for gluconeogenesis. Chronic excess of glucocorticoids, as in Cushing's syndrome (Fig. 318), results in a redistribution of body fat. It apparently accelerates fat mobilization from the extremities but promotes fat deposition in the face ("moon face"), shoulders ("buffalo hump"), trunk, and abdomen.

4. Glucocorticoids sensitize blood vessels to vasopressor substances such as norepinephrine. Therefore, glucocorticoids help maintain the degree of blood vessel constriction necessary for maintaining normal blood pressure.

5. A high blood concentration of glucocorticoids brings about many of the changes that characteristically occur when the body is in a condition of stress. Outstanding among these so-called "stress responses" are as follows.

(a) Lymphocytopenia and eosinopenia—that is, a marked decrease in the number of lymphocytes and eosinophils in the blood (takes place within about two hours after an increase in glucocorticoids occurs)

(b) Involution or decrease in the size of lymphatic tissues, particularly the thymus gland and lymph nodes

(c) Decreased antibody formation, therefore less immunity and decreased hypersensitivity—the so-called anti-immunity and antiallergic effects of glucocorticoids

(d) Decreased proliferation of fibroblasts (connective tissue cells), therefore less inflammation but greater tendency for an infection to spread and also slower wound healing

(e) Increased extracellular fluid volume

(f) Increased resistance to stress

(g) Changes in metabolism noted in items 1, 2, 3 as effects of high glucocorticoid concentration

Mineralocorticoids

Aldosterone and desoxycorticosterone are classified functionally as mineralocorticoids because their main action concerns mineral salt (electrolyte) metabolism. The primary general function of mineralocorticoids seems to be to maintain homeostasis of the blood concentration of sodium. And, in doing this, these hormones also help maintain a normal ratio of blood sodium concentration to potassium concentration and normal volumes of extracellular and intracellular fluids. In short, mineralocorticoids play a crucial part in maintaining electrolyte and fluid balance and therefore in maintaining healthy survival. Aldosterone is some twenty to thirty times more powerful in these respects than desoxycorticosterone, so aldosterone is by far the more important mineralocorticoid.

Aldosterone acts on the distal renal tubule cells, stimulating them to increase their reabsorption of sodium ions from tubule urine back into blood. In exchange for each reabsorbed sodium ion, tubule cells excrete either a potassium or a hydrogen ion. Moreover, as each positive sodium ion is reabsorbed, a negative ion (bicarbonate or chloride—follows along, drawn by the attrac-

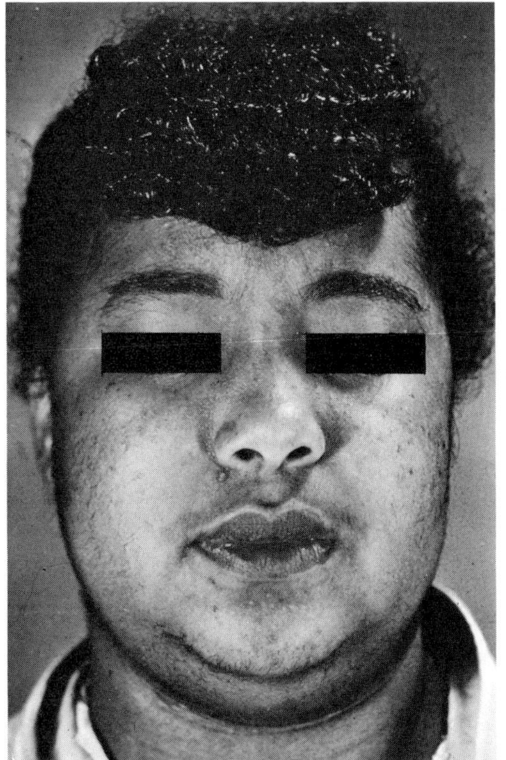

A

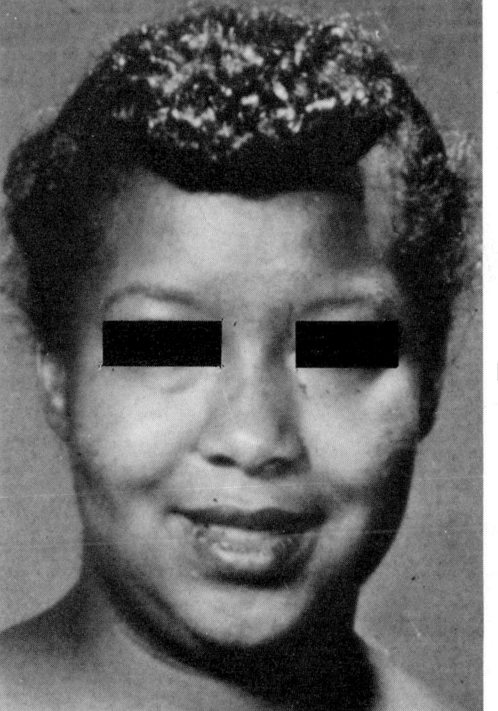

B

Fig. 318

Cushing's syndrome, the result of chronic excess glucocorticoids. **A,** Preoperatively. **B,** Six months postoperatively. (Courtesy Dr. William McKendree Jefferies, Western Reserve University School of Medicine, Cleveland, Ohio.)

tion force between ions that bear opposite electrical charges. Also, the reabsorption of electrolytes causes net diffusion of water back into blood. Briefly, then, because of its primary sodium-reabsorbing effect on kidney tubules, aldosterone tends to produce sodium and water retention but potassium and hydrogen ion loss.

Sex hormones

The adrenal cortex in both sexes secretes small amounts of both male and female hormones, androgens, estrogens, and progesterone, respectively. In the amounts normally secreted, they seem to have no physiological significance. But sometimes tumors of the adrenal cortex secrete excessive amounts of androgens. Because they produce masculinizing effects (for instance, growth of a beard in a woman), they are known as virilizing tumors (Fig. 319).

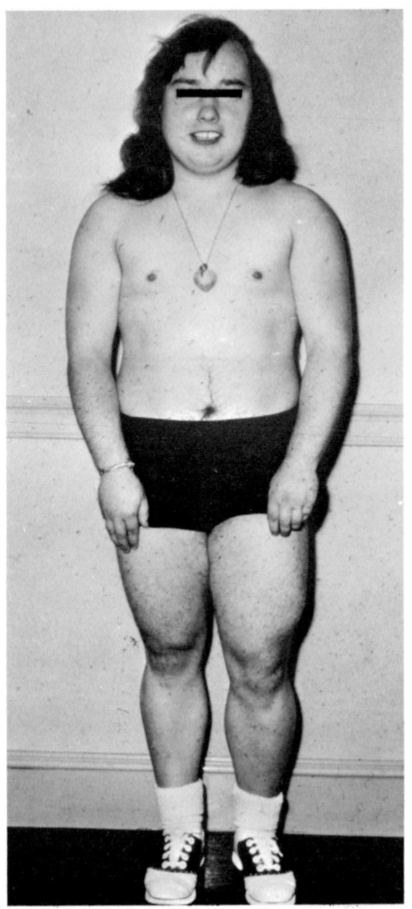

Fig. 319

Virilizing tumor of the adrenal cortex. The tumor secretes excess androgens, thereby producing masculinizing effects. (Courtesy Dr. William McKendree Jefferies, Western Reserve University School of Medicine, Cleveland, Ohio.)

Control of secretion

Glucocorticoids (cortisol, mainly). See pp. 498 and 499 for discussion of mechanisms that control adrenal secretion of these hormones.

Mineralocorticoids (aldosterone, mainly). Many details of the apparently complex mechanism that controls aldosterone output by the adrenal cortex have not yet been established. But these two facts are known about it—that aldosterone secretion quickly increases (1) if the circulating blood volume and arterial blood pressure decrease markedly and (2) if the blood concentration of sodium decreases below a certain point. Probably these factors act in several ways to bring about increased aldosterone secretion. One postulated mechanism that seems to be supported by convincing evidence is shown in Fig. 320 (also see Fig. 321, p. 522).

Two clinical observations seem to illustrate this mechanism in operation—the fact that patients with malignant hypertension generally secrete large amounts of aldosterone and the fact that those with primary aldosteronism (excess aldosterone secretion) usually have hypertension. Excess production of angiotonin II would seem to cause both the malignant hypertension and the high aldosterone output. Interestingly enough, the trade name of a preparation of angiotonin II is Hypertensin.

Recent research* supports the view that

*By Dr. Gordon L. Farrell of Western Reserve University, Cleveland, Ohio, and others.

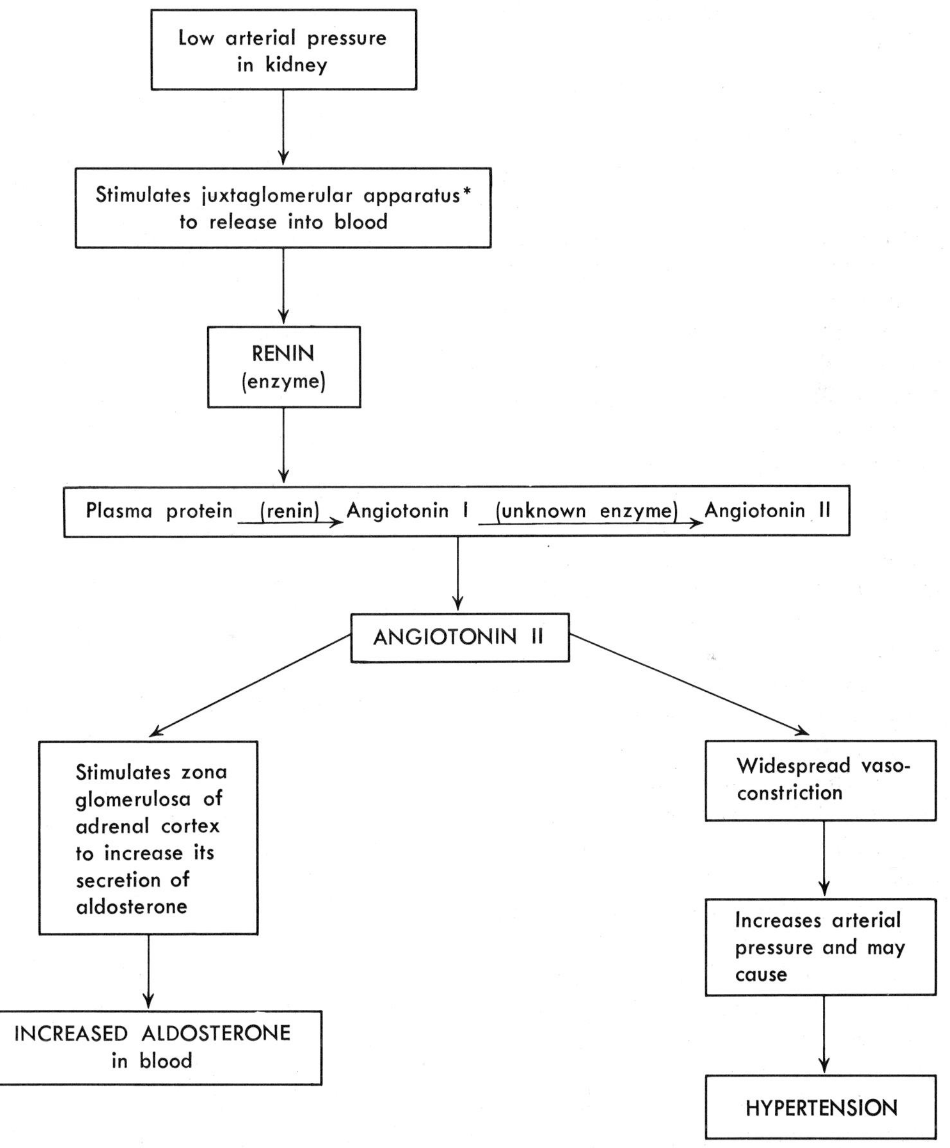

*Juxtaglomerular apparatus (L. juxta, near to)—groups of cells located, as the name suggests, near glomeruli of kidney; lie in afferent arterioles just as they enter glomeruli.

Fig. 320

One mechanism postulated to stimulate aldosterone secretion.

the pineal body secretes a hormone which stimulates the zona glomerulosa of the adrenal cortex to secrete aldosterone and which has therefore been named adrenoglomerulotropin.

ADRENAL MEDULLA

Hormones

The adrenal medulla secretes epinephrine and norepinephrine. Like the adrenal corticoids, these hormones help the body meet stressful situations, but, unlike them, they are not essential for the maintenance of life. Epinephrine affects smooth and cardiac muscles and glands in a way similar to sympathetic stimulation of these structures. It serves to increase and prolong sympathetic effects.

Control of secretion

Increased epinephrine secretion by the adrenal medulla is one of the body's first responses to stress. It is thought to be brought about by impulses from the hypothalamus stimulating sympathetic preganglionic neurons which, in turn, stimulate the adrenal medulla to increase its output of epinephrine. Note that this is another example of the hypothalamus functioning in times of stress. And note, too, that the adrenal medulla is a neuroendocrine transducer, that is, a converter of nerve impulses into increased hormone secretion. We have already mentioned the hypothalamus as a neuroendocrine transducer. It brings about increased anterior pituitary secretion of ACTH (p. 499) and increased ADH secretion by the posterior lobe of the pituitary gland (p. 534) when a state of stress prevails.

Ovaries

The ovaries produce two kinds of steroid female hormones: estrogens (chiefly estradiol and estrone) and progesterone.

Estrogens

Estrogens are secreted mainly by the graafian follicles and during pregnancy by the placenta. They carry on the following functions:

1. Estrogens accelerate proliferation of epithelial cells, particularly in organs of the female reproductive system. For example, during the early phase of each menstrual cycle, by stimulating epithelial cells to reproduce themselves more rapidly, estrogens promote regeneration of the endometrium (which sloughed off during the preceding menses) and cause it to thicken during the preovulatory phase.

Another example of estrogen's accelerating effect on epithelial cell mitosis is the thickening of the vaginal epithelium with cornification that occurs during the early part of each menstrual cycle.

2. Estrogens affect electrolyte and fluid metabolism in a way similar to the adrenal corticoids though to a lesser degree. They promote renal tubule reabsorption of sodium and water so tend to produce salt and water retention, and particularly in the endometrium.

3. Estrogens affect protein metabolism. Specifically, they promote protein anabolism, an action that tends to promote growth. But also, estrogens exert an opposite influence on growth. They promote closure of the epiphyses and thus tend to terminate bone growth. Presumably, a child's height is lessened if she reaches puberty (with its accompanying high rate of estrogen secretion) at an early age. See p. 118 for more about the effects of estrogen on bone.

4. Estrogens promote myometrial contractions.

5. Estrogens help control development and functioning of breasts. During adolescence and pregnancy they especially promote development of ducts in the mammary glands. They inhibit secretion of lactogenic hormone by the anterior lobe of

the pituitary gland. Hence, the high concentration of estrogens maintained during pregnancy inhibits lactation. Shedding of the placenta following delivery cuts off a major source of estrogens. Blood estrogen content drops rapidly and markedly. This decrease in the blood concentration of estrogens stimulates the secretion of lactogenic hormone which, in turn, initiates lactation.

6. A high blood concentration of estrogens inhibits secretion of FSH by the anterior lobe of the pituitary gland—a physiological fact of worldwide importance, for it constitutes the crucial part of the rationale which led to the development of contraceptive pills (p. 479).

7. Estrogens probably contribute to normal sexual desire (libido).

Progesterone

Progesterone is secreted by the corpus luteum and by the placenta. It has the following effects.

1. Progesterone acts on estrogen-primed endometrium, converting it to a secretory type of epithelium. An increasing blood concentration of progesterone causes an increasing secretion by endometrial glands and thereby prepares the uterine lining for implantation of a fertilized ovum. Incidentally, the name progesterone means a hormone that favors gestation, that is, pregnancy.

2. Progesterone acts on estrogen-primed breasts to promote development of the secreting cells to the stage where they can secrete milk when stimulated by lactogenic hormone following delivery of the baby.

3. Progesterone decreases or inhibits contractions of the uterine smooth muscle (myometrium), another progestational effect.

4. Progesterone, like the corticoids, but to a lesser degree, promotes protein catabolism. It also is thought to have a salt- and water-retaining effect, particularly in the endometrium.

Testes

The interstitial cells of the testes secrete testosterone, a steroid hormone classed as an androgen, that is, a substance that promotes "maleness." It promotes development of the secondary sex organs and characteristics, maintains them in the adult state, and contributes to normal sexual behavior (also see p. 458). Urine of both men and women contains androsterone and possibly other androgens of the class of compounds known as 17-ketosteroids. Part of the urinary 17-ketosteroids derive from adrenal cortex secretions and part from testosterone.

Islands of Langerhans

The beta cells of the islands of Langerhans secrete insulin and the alpha cells secrete glucagon. Insulin's primary effects are to accelerate the transport of glucose, amino acids, and fatty acids through cell membranes into the intracellular fluid. Hence, insulin is an anabolic hormone in that it tends to promote glycogenesis, protein synthesis, and lipogenesis (deposition of fat in adipose tissue). But insulin also has a catabolic effect in that it tends to accelerate glucose utilization for energy (see Fig. 264, p. 408). Insulin, of course, tends to decrease blood glucose since it causes it to be transported into cells from the blood at a fast rate.

Glucagon serves as an antagonist to insulin. It accelerates liver glycogenolysis so tends to increase blood glucose. For control of islet secretion of insulin and glucagon, see Figs. 264 and 265, pp. 408 and 409.

Thymus

One of the body's best-kept secrets has been the function of the thymus. During all the years before 1961, there were no significant clues as to its role. Then a young Briton, Dr. Jacques F. A. P. Miller, removed the thymus glands from newborn mice. His findings proved startling and crucial. Almost like a chain reaction, further investigations followed and led at last to an uncovering of the thymus' long-held secret. It now seems clear that this small structure (it weighs at most only about an ounce) plays a critical part in the body's defenses against infections—in its vital immunity mechanism, that is.

In the mouse, and presumably in man as well, the thymus does two things. First, it serves as the original source of lymphocytes before birth. And then soon after birth, it starts secreting a hormone that enables lymphocytes to develop into plasma cells. Plasma cells, you will recall, synthesize antibodies against foreign proteins. Hence, the thymus functions to make possible immunity against microorganisms and other kinds of foreign proteins—for instance, against tissues transplanted from one individual to another. The thymus probably completes its essential work early in childhood. Its size is largest, relative to the rest of the body, when a child is about 2 years old. Its absolute size is largest at puberty. And from then on, it gradually atrophies until in great old age, it may be barely recognizable. The thymus is located in the mediastinal portion of the thoracic cavity and extends up to the lower edge of the thyroid gland in the neck.

Pineal body (pineal gland or epiphysis cerebri)

The pineal body has long been a mystery organ. Even now its function in the human being remains a matter of conjecture. Recent experiments* performed on rats, however, indicate that in these animals the pineal body is a neuroendocrine transducer that serves as a kind of "biological clock." It operates in this way—stimulation of the rat's retina by light initiates impulses in optic nerve fibers. Some of these impulses cross synapses to activate sympathetic neurons in the superior cervical ganglion. These sympathetic fibers then transmit impulses to the pineal gland, inhibiting its secretion of a hormone called melatonin. The resulting low blood concentration of melatonin has a stimulating effect on the rat's ovaries and accelerates its estrus cycle. Darkness initiates an opposite chain of events: increased melatonin synthesis, a resultant inhibition of the rat's ovaries, and a slowing of its estrus cycle. These findings and others have led to interesting speculations—that the pineal body may function in the human being to help regulate sex gland activity and the menstrual cycle and that perhaps it may even play a part in regulating various circadian rhythms such as adrenal cortical secretion. Whether or not these "educated guesses" prove true remains to be shown by further investigations.

The pineal body is also postulated to secrete adrenoglomerulotropin (see p. 510) and serotonin in addition to melatonin. Serotonin plays an essential, but not well understood, part in normal brain functioning.

The pineal body is shaped like a small cone about a centimeter long. It is located in the cranial cavity behind the midbrain and third ventricle and is attached to the roof of the latter. It degenerates at about 7 years of age and in the adult consists of fibrous tissue.

Placenta

The placenta functions as a temporary endocrine gland. During pregnancy, it produces chorionic gonadotrophins—so-called because they are secreted by cells of the chorion, the outermost fetal membrane. In

*See suggested supplementary readings for Chapter XIV, reference 5, p. 550.

addition to gonadotrophins, the placenta also produces estrogens and progesterone. The discovery some fifty years ago by Aschheim and Zondek of the fact that large amounts of gonadotrophic substances are excreted in the urine during pregnancy led to the development of the now well-known pregnancy tests.

Outline summary—The endocrine system

Meaning

1. Composed of glands that pour secretions into blood instead of into ducts
2. General functions and importance
   a. communication, control, integration; hormones main regulators of metabolism, reproduction, and responses to stress
   b. names and locations of endocrine glands —see Table 60, p. 493

Pituitary body (hypophysis cerebri)

Consists of two endocrine glands: anterior lobe of pituitary gland (adenohypophysis) and posterior lobe of pituitary gland (neurohypophysis)

ANTERIOR LOBE OF PITUITARY GLAND (ADENOHYPOPHYSIS)

1. Cells called acidophils secrete growth hormone (STH) and lactogenic hormone
2. Basophils secrete thyrotrophin (TSH), adrenocorticotrophin (ACTH), follicle-stimulating hormone (FSH), luteinizing hormone (LH), and melanocyte-stimulating hormone (MSH)
3. Growth hormone (somatotrophin or somatotrophic hormone)
   a. accelerates protein anabolism so promotes growth
      1. disorders caused by excess growth hormone: gigantism and acromegaly
      2. disorders caused by deficient growth hormone: dwarfism and pituitary cachexia
   b. tends to inhibit fat deposition and to accelerate fat mobilization and catabolism
   c. acts in some way to oppose insulin (anti-insulin, hyperglycemic, diabetogenic effects)
4. Lactogenic hormone—also called prolactin and formerly luteotrophic hormone (LTH)
   a. during pregnancy, promotes breast development
   b. after delivery, initiates milk secretion
5. Trophic hormones
   a. thyrotrophin—thyroid-stimulating hormone (TSH)
      1. promotes growth and development of thyroid gland
      2. stimulates thyroid gland to secrete thyroid hormone
   b. adrenocorticotrophin (ACTH)
      1. promotes growth and development of adrenal cortex
      2. stimulates adrenal cortex to secrete cortisol and other glucocorticoids
   c. follicle-stimulating hormone (FSH)
      1. stimulates primary graafian follicle to start growing and to develop to maturity
      2. stimulates follicle cells to secrete estrogens
      3. in male, stimulates development of seminiferous tubules and maintains spermatogenesis by them
   d. luteinizing hormone (LH)
      1. acts with FSH to cause complete maturation of follicle and ovulation
      2. stimulates formation of corpus luteum (luteinizing effect)
      3. stimulates corpus luteum to secrete progesterone
      4. in male, LH called interstitial cell–stimulating hormone (ICSH); stimulates interstitial cells in testis to develop and secrete testosterone
      5. just before puberty, presumably sudden marked increase in secretion of gonadotrophins (FSH, LH) initiates first menses
6. Melanocyte-stimulating hormone (MSH)—tends to produce increased pigmentation of skin
7. Control of secretion
   a. negative feedback mechanisms operate between target glands and anterior lobe of pituitary gland
      1. high blood concentration of target-gland hormone inhibits secretion of trophic hormone by anterior lobe of pituitary gland
      2. high blood concentration of trophic

hormone stimulates target-gland secretion of its hormone
3. under ordinary conditions, negative feedback mechanisms control anterior pituitary secretion of ACTH, thyroid-stimulating hormone, and FSH and secretion of their respective target hormones

b. neuroendocrine mechanisms dominate control of anterior pituitary secretion under stress conditions
1. hypothalamus releases neurosecretions into pituitary portal system; transported to anterior pituitary, where stimulate it to secrete certain hormones
2. stress acts in some way to stimulate the release of CRF and perhaps other neurosecretions by hypothalamus; e.g., corticotrophin-releasing factor (CRF) from hypothalamus stimulates secretion of ACTH by anterior lobe of pituitary gland

POSTERIOR PITUITARY GLAND (NEUROHYPOPHYSIS)

1. Secretes hormones (antidiuretic hormone [ADH] and oxytocin) synthesized by neurons in hypothalamus
2. ADH (vasopressin or Pitressin) stimulates water reabsorption by distal and collecting tubules and stimulates smooth muscle of blood vessels and intestine
3. Oxytocin stimulates contractions of pregnant uterus and release of milk by lactating breast
4. Control of secretion
   a. ADH secretion—details of mechanism controlling secretion of this hormone not established but general principles follows:
      1. decreased ECF osmotic pressure leads to decreased ADH secretion
      2. decreased ECF volume leads to increased ADH secretion
      3. stress leads to increased ADH secretion
   b. Oxytocin—details of mechanism controlling oxytocin secretion not established but is known that stimulation of nipples by suckling leads to increased oxytocin secretion

Thyroid gland

1. Location and structure
   a. located in neck just below larynx
   b. two lateral lobes connected by isthmus
2. Functions
   a. stores iodine-containing protein, thyroglobulin
   b. secretes two hormones—thyroxin and triiodothyronine—that stimulate rate of oxygen consumption (metabolic rate) of all cells and thereby help regulate physical and mental development, development of sexual maturity, and numerous other processes
3. Effects of hypersecretion and hyposecretion
   a. hypersecretion produces exophthalmic goiter
   b. hyposecretion in early life produces malformed dwarfism or cretinism; in later life, myxedema

Parathyroid glands

1. Location and structure
   a. attached to posterior surfaces of thyroid
   b. small round bodies, usually four or five in number
2. Functions—secrete parathormone and another hormone called calcitonin
   a. parathormone
      1. stimulates bone breakdown or resorption, releasing calcium and phosphate, thereby increasing calcium and phosphate absorption into blood from bone
      2. also accelerates calcium absorption from intestine and kidney tubules
      3. accelerates kidney tubule excretion of phosphates from blood into urine
      4. hypersecretion causes decrease in bone mass with replacement by fibrous tissue
      5. hyposecretion produces hypocalcemia and tetany and death in few hours
   b. calcitonin—acts in some way to decrease blood calcium; perhaps accelerates calcium's movement from blood into bone

Adrenal glands

1. Location and structure
   a. located atop kidneys
   b. outer portion of gland called cortex and inner portion called medulla

ADRENAL CORTEX

1. Zones or layers (from outside in)
   a. zona glomerulosa—secretes mineralocorticoids

   b. zona fasciculata—secretes glucocorticoids
   c. zona reticularis—secretes small amounts of glucocorticoids and sex hormones
2. Glucocorticoids (mainly cortisol, smaller amounts of corticosterone)
   a. promote normal protein metabolism; tend to accelerate tissue protein mobilization with resultant negative nitrogen balance
   b. promote normal carbohydrate metabolism; tend to accelerate liver gluconeogenesis, presumably from mobilized tissue proteins; hence, glucocorticoids tend to produce hyperglycemia
   c. promote normal fat metabolism; tend to accelerate fat mobilization and catabolism; i.e., tend to cause "shift" to fat utilization from usual carbohydrate utilization
   d. sensitize blood vessels to vasopressor substances such as norepinephrine
   e. high blood concentration of glucocorticoids characteristic in stress; brings about many stress responses as follows:
      1. lymphocytopenia and eosinopenia
      2. involution of thymus gland and lymph nodes
      3. decreased antibody formation, decreased immunity, and hypersensitivity
      4. decreased connective tissue proliferation, less inflammation but greater tendency for infection to spread and slower wound healing
      5. increased ECF volume
      6. water diuresis
      7. increased resistance to stress
      8. increased tissue protein mobilization and catabolism, increased fat mobilization and catabolism, and increased liver gluconeogenesis
3. Mineralocorticoids (mainly aldosterone, also desoxycorticosterone)
   a. accelerate renal tubule reabsorption of sodium ions and excretion of potassium ions (or hydrogen ions)
   b. increased renal tubule reabsorption of bicarbonate ions (or chloride ions) and water result from increased sodium reabsorption
4. Sex hormones
   a. small amounts of both male and female hormones secreted in both sexes
   b. amounts normally secreted seem to have no physiological significance
5. Control of secretion
   a. glucocorticoids
      1. under ordinary conditions, negative feedback mechanism operates between anterior pituitary gland and adrenal cortex; high blood concentration of ACTH stimulates glucocorticoid secretion; high blood glucocorticoid concentration inhibits ACTH secretion
      2. under stress conditions increased CRF release by hypothalamus stimulates increased ACTH secretion and therefore increased glucocorticoid secretion
   b. mineralocorticoids
      1. details of mechanism controlling aldosterone secretion not established but known that decreased ECF volume and decreased arterial pressure lead to increased aldosterone secretion (see Figs. 320 and 321, pp. 509 and 522)
      2. pineal body thought to secrete hormone adrenoglomerulotropin, which stimulates aldosterone secretion

ADRENAL MEDULLA

1. Hormones—epinephrine mainly; some norepinephrine
2. Functions of epinephrine—affects visceral effectors (smooth muscle, cardiac muscle, and glands) in same way as does sympathetic stimulation of these structures; epinephrine from adrenal glands intensifies and prolongs sympathetic effects
3. Control of secretion—stress acts in some way to stimulate hypothalamus, which sends impulses to adrenal medulla via sympathetic neurons, stimulating medulla to increase its secretion of epinephrine

Ovaries

1. Hormones secreted—estrogens and progesterone
2. Functions
   a. estrogens
      1. accelerate proliferation of epithelial cells, especially in female reproductive system; e.g., bring about regeneration of endometrium following menses and thickening of it before ovulation
      2. mild stimulation of renal tubule reabsorption of sodium and water
      3. promote protein anabolism and there-

fore growth but also promote epiphyseal closure so tend to terminate bone growth
4. promote myometrial contractions
5. promote development of mammary glands during adolescence and pregnancy; inhibit production of lactogenic hormone by anterior lobe of pituitary gland, thereby inhibiting lactation
6. inhibit production of FSH by anterior lobe of pituitary gland
7. probably contribute to normal sexual desire

b. progesterone
1. converts estrogen-primed endometrium to secretory type epithelium, thereby causing increased secretion by endometrium
2. acts on estrogen-primed breasts, promoting development of secreting cells (to stage where can secrete milk when stimulated by lactogenic hormone)
3. inhibiting effect on myometrial contractions
4. mildly accelerating effect on protein catabolism
5. thought to promote salt and water retention, especially in endometrium

Testes

1. Secrete testosterone, which
- **a.** accelerates protein anabolism so promotes growth, but also promotes epiphyseal closure so tends to terminate bone growth
- **b.** promotes development of secondary sex organs and characteristics and maintains them in adult condition
- **c.** contributes to normal sexual behavior

Islands of Langerhans

1. Hormones
- **a.** beta cells secrete insulin
- **b.** alpha cells secrete glucagon

2. Functions
- **a.** insulin
  1. promotes glucose transport into cells, thereby increasing glucose utilization (catabolism) and glycogenesis and decreasing blood glucose
  2. promotes fatty acid transport into cells and fat anabolism (lipogenesis or fat deposition) in them
  3. promotes amino acid transport into cells and protein anabolism
- **b.** glucagon—accelerates liver glycogenolysis so tends to increase blood glucose; in short, is insulin antagonist

Thymus

1. Postulated functions:
- **a.** before birth, original lymphocytes formed in thymus
- **b.** soon after birth, thymus secretes hormone that enables lymphocytes to develop into plasma cells and synthesize antibodies; hence, thymus plays crucial role in immunity

2. Thymus gradually atrophies after puberty

Pineal body (pineal gland or epiphysis cerebri)

1. Functions not established; recent evidence suggests that it may help regulate rhythmically recurring functions such as menstrual cycle and perhaps even circadian rhythms such as daily variations in amounts of corticoids secreted

2. Postulated to secrete adrenoglomerulotropin, melatonin, and serotonin

Placenta

1. Temporary endocrine glands

2. Secretes estrogens, progesterone, and chorionic gonadotrophin

3. Helps maintain progestational state of endometrium

Review questions

1. Name the endocrine glands and locate each one.
2. Name the hormone or hormones which help control each of the following: (a) blood sugar level, (b) blood calcium level, (c) blood sodium level, and (d) blood potassium level. Explain mechanisms involved.
3. Name the hormone or hormones that help control each of the following: (a) growth, (b) development of secondary male characteristics and female characteristics, (c) fluid and electrolyte balance, (d) resistance to stress, (e) functions of the adrenal cortex, thyroid, and ovaries, and (f) secretion of ACTH, TH, and FSH.
4. What hormone enhances and prolongs sympathetic effects?

5. What hormones help control protein metabolism? Explain.
6. What hormones help control fat metabolism? Explain.
7. What hormones help control carbohydrate metabolism? Explain.
8. What conditions result from a deficiency of thyroid extract early in life? Later in life?
9. What disease results from too much thyroid secretion? From too much pituitary somatotrophic hormone early in life? Too much later in life? Too little early in life?
10. Gigantism results from an oversupply of which endocrine secretion? Cretinism from a deficiency of which one? Acromegaly from an oversupply of which one? Myxedema from a deficiency of which one?
11. Which gland is called the "master gland"? Why?

Situation: A patient goes to his doctor because he feels "so terribly weak and tired all the time and has lost so much weight." After hospital admission and various tests, the doctor tells him he has "something wrong with his adrenal glands." Blood chemistry tests reveal low blood concentrations of sodium and chloride and high potassium.

12. Do you think this patient has a disease of the adrenal medulla or adrenal cortex? State reasons.
13. Is the condition hyperfunctioning or hypofunctioning of the gland? State reasons.
14. How would you explain the patient's chief complaints?
15. Might this patient have any type of water imbalance? If so, what and why? Explain mechanisms involved.
16. Eosinophil counts were done on this patient following injections of epinephrine. Do you think the counts would be normal or not? Explain why. Significance?
17. Blood sugar was measured after a twenty-four-hour fast. Would it be higher or lower than it would be in a normal individual under the same conditions? Why?

Situation: A patient who has a severe form of Cushing's disease is given insulin each day.

18. Should the nurse watch this patient for signs of hypoglycemia or hyperglycemia? Explain.
19. Would this patient be likely to be "insulin sensitive" or "insulin resistant"? Explain.
20. Explain the meaning of the statement "hormone functions are interrelated." Give examples to support or refute this statement.

UNIT
SEVEN

Fluid, electrolyte, and acid-base balance

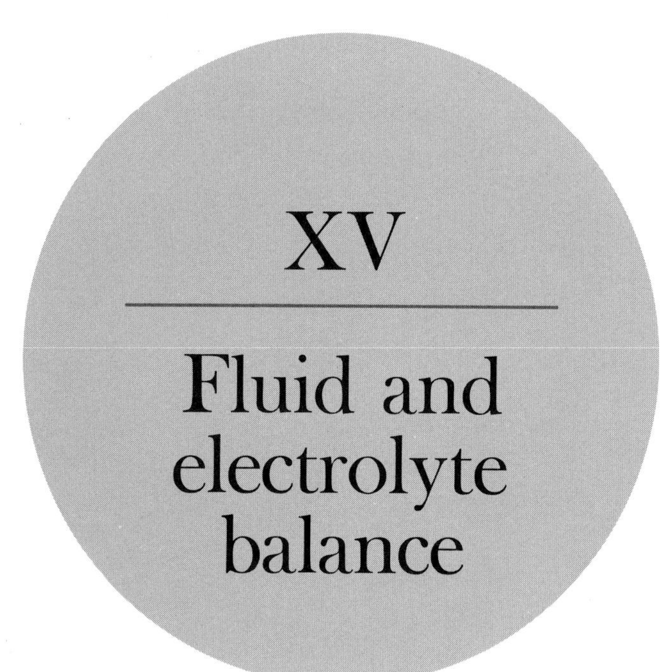

XV

Fluid and electrolyte balance

Introduction

The term fluid balance means several things. It, of course, means the same thing as homeostasis of fluids. To say that the body is in a state of fluid balance is to say that the total amount of water in the body is normal and that it remains relatively constant. But fluid balance also means something more. It also means relative constancy of the distribution of water in the body's three fluid compartments. The volume of water inside the cells, in the interstitial spaces, and in the blood vessels all remains relatively constant when a condition of fluid balance exists. Fluid imbalance, then, means that both the total volume of water in the body and the amount in one or more of its fluid compartments have increased or decreased beyond normal limits.

Fluid balance and electrolyte balance are interdependent. If one deviates from normal, so does the other (Fig. 321). A discussion of one, therefore, necessitates a discussion of the other.

Modern medicine attaches great importance to fluid and electrolyte balance. Today, a large proportion of hospital patients receive some kind of fluid and electrolyte therapy. To help you understand the rationale underlying such treatment, this chapter is included. We shall consider successively some general principles about fluid balance, the avenues by which water enters and leaves the body, the mechanisms that maintain homeostasis of total fluid volume, and the mechanisms that maintain homeostasis of fluid distribution.

Some general principles about fluid balance

1. The cardinal principle about fluid balance is that intake must equal output.

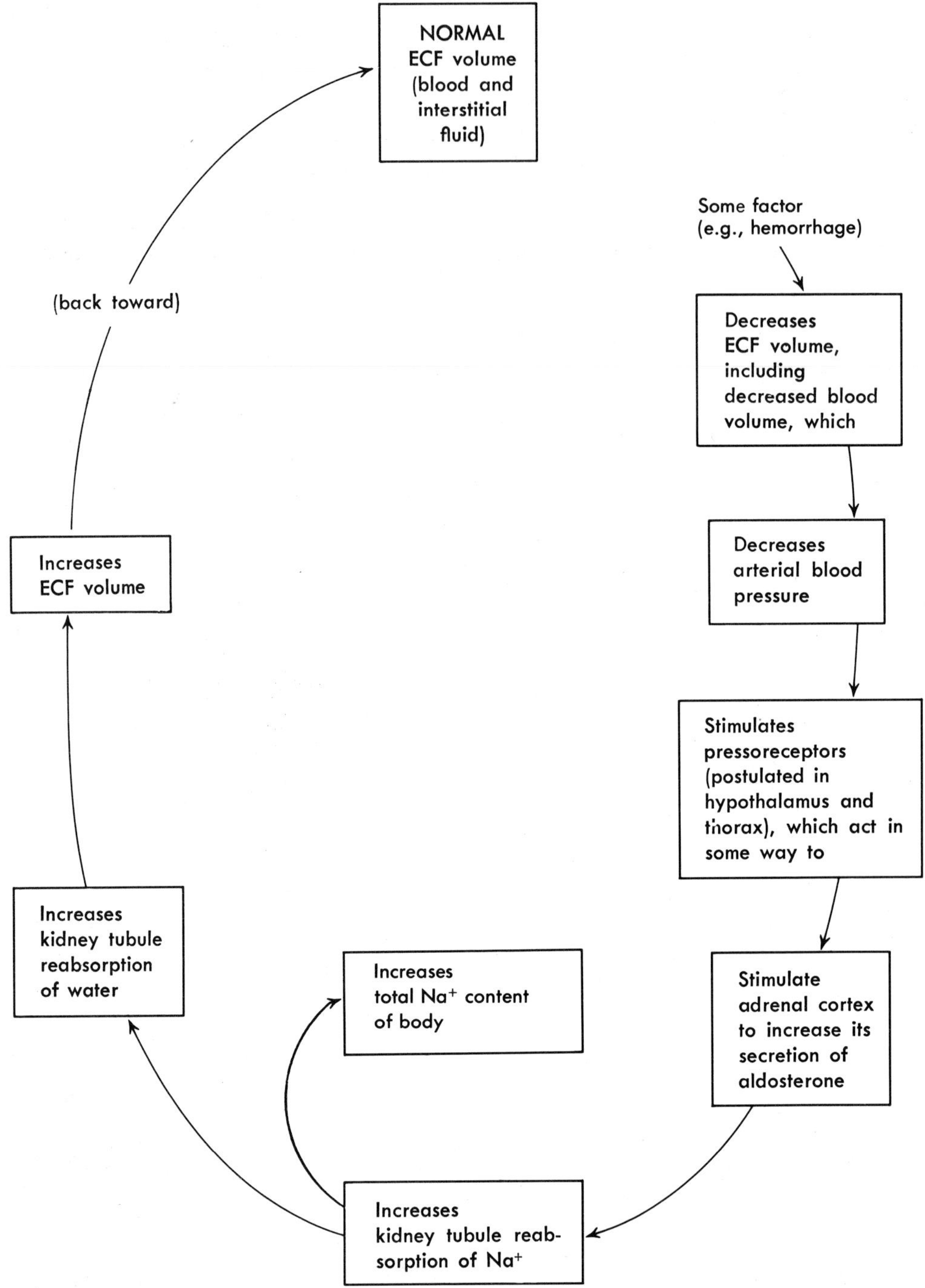

Fig. 321

Aldosterone mechanism that helps restore homeostasis of extracellular fluids (ECF) volume (also, see Fig. 320, p. 509). Excess aldosterone, however, leads to excess extracellular fluid volume—that is, excess blood volume (hypervolemia) and excess interstitial fluid volume (edema)—and also to an excess of the total Na^+ content of the body.

Obviously, if more water or less leaves the body than enters it, fluid balance cannot exist.

2. Devices for varying output so that it equals intake constitute the major mechanism for maintaining fluid balance, but mechanisms for adjusting intake to output also operate.

3. Mechanisms for controlling water movement between the fluid compartments also play a major role in the maintenance of fluid and electrolyte balance.

Avenues by which water enters and leaves body

Water normally enters the body from three sources: from liquids the individual

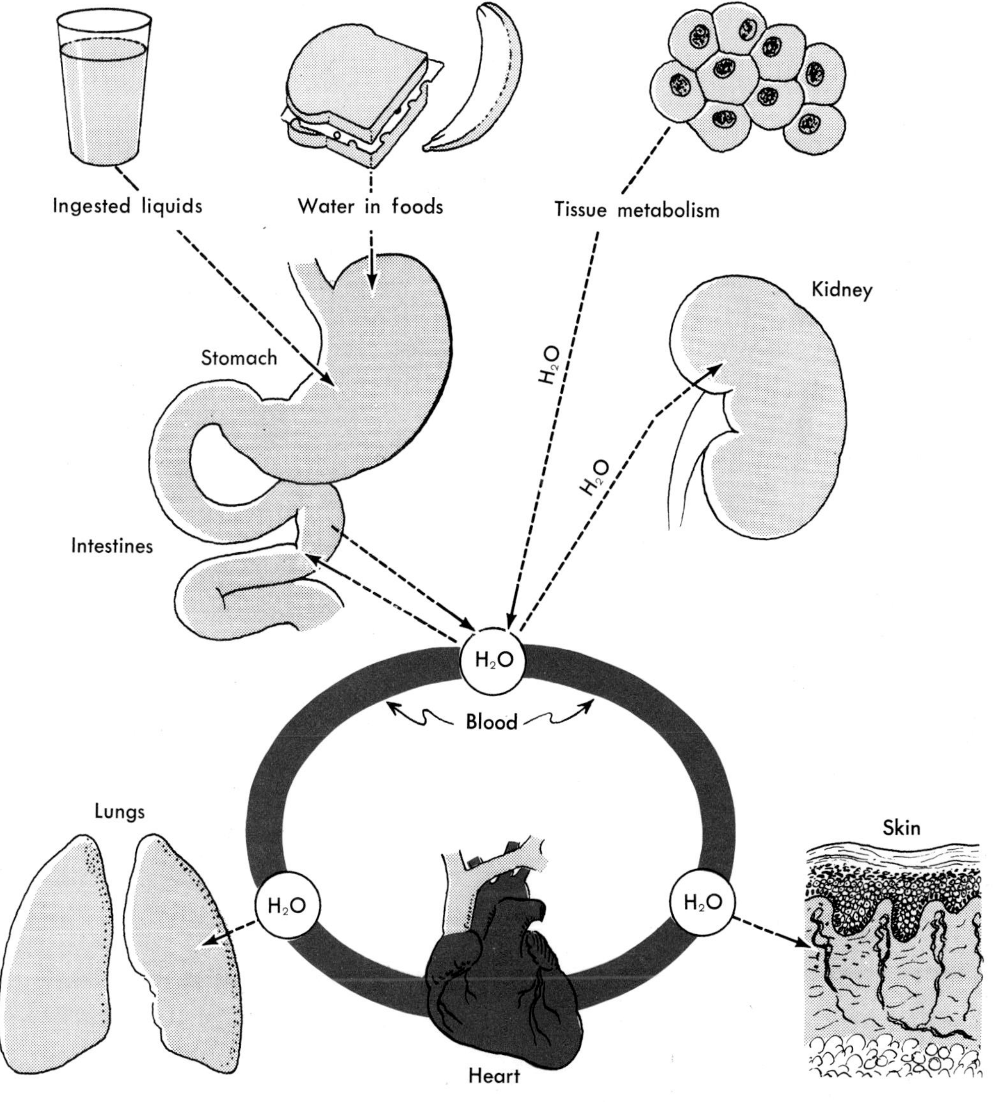

Fig. 322

Diagram showing the three sources of water entry into the body and its four avenues of exit.

Table 61. Typical normal values for each portal of water entry and exit

Intake		*Output*	
Ingested liquids	1,500 ml.	Kidneys (urine)	1,400 ml.
Water in foods	700 ml.	Lungs (water in expired air)	350 ml.
Water formed in metabolism	200 ml.	Skin	
		By diffusion	350 ml.
		By sweat	100 ml.
		Intestines (in feces)	200 ml.
Totals	2,400 ml.		2,400 ml.

drinks, from water in the food he eats, and from water formed when the food he eats is metabolized. Water normally leaves the body by four exits: kidneys (urine), lungs (water in expired air), skin (by diffusion and by sweat), and intestines (feces) (Fig. 322). In accord with the cardinal principle of fluid balance, the total volume of water entering the body normally equals the total volume leaving, or, briefly, intake normally equals output. Table 61 gives normal volumes for each portal of water entry and exit, though, of course, these could vary considerably and still be considered normal.

Mechanisms that maintain homeostasis of total fluid volume

Control of urine volume

Homeostasis of the total volume of water in the body is maintained or restored primarily by devices that adjust output to intake. Most important of these are the mechanisms that control the volume of urine excreted.

Two factors together determine urine volume: the glomerular filtration rate and the renal tubule water reabsorption rate. The glomerular filtration rate, except under abnormal conditions, remains fairly constant, hence does not normally cause urine volume to fluctuate. The rate of tubular reabsorption of water, on the other hand, fluctuates considerably. The rate of tubular reabsorption, therefore, rather than the glomerular filtration rate, normally adjusts urine volume to fluid intake. And the amount of ADH and of aldosterone secreted regulates the amount of water reabsorbed by the kidney tubules (discussed on p. 444; also see Fig. 321, p. 522). In other words, urine volume is regulated chiefly by hormones secreted by the posterior lobe of the pituitary gland (ADH) and the adrenal cortex (aldosterone).

Although changes in the volume of fluid loss via the skin, lungs, and intestines also affect the fluid intake-output ratio, these volumes are not automatically adjusted to intake volume, as is the volume of urine.

Factors that alter fluid loss under abnormal conditions

Both the rate of respiration and the volume of sweat secreted may greatly alter fluid output under certain abnormal conditions. For example, a patient who hyperventilates for an extended time loses an excessive amount of water via the expired air. If, as frequently happens, he also takes in less water by mouth than normal, his fluid output then exceeds his intake and he develops a fluid imbalance, namely, dehydration (that is, a decrease in total body water). Other abnormal conditions such as vomiting, diarrhea, intestinal drainage, etc. also cause fluid and electrolyte output to exceed intake so produce fluid and electrolyte imbalances.

Control of fluid intake

Physiologists disagree about the details of the mechanism for controlling intake so that it increases when output increases and decreases when output decreases. In general, it operates in this way: when dehydration starts to develop, salivary secretion decreases, producing a "dry mouth" feeling and the sensation of thirst. The individual then drinks water, thereby increasing his fluid intake to offset his increased output, and this tends to restore fluid balance (Fig. 323). If, however, an individual takes nothing by mouth for several days, fluid balance cannot be maintained despite every effort of homeostatic mechanisms to compensate for the zero intake. Obviously, under this condition the only way balance could be maintained would be for fluid output to also decrease to zero. This is not possible. Some output is obligatory. For example, as long as respirations continue, some water leaves the body by way of the expired air; as long as life continues, an irreducible minimum of water diffuses through the skin.

Mechanisms that maintain homeostasis of fluid distribution

Comparison of plasma, interstitial fluid, and intracellular fluid

Structurally speaking, body fluids occupy three fluid compartments: blood vessels, tissue spaces, and cells. Thus, we speak of the plasma, interstitial fluid, and intracellular fluid. Functionally, however, these three fluids may be considered as only two fluids:

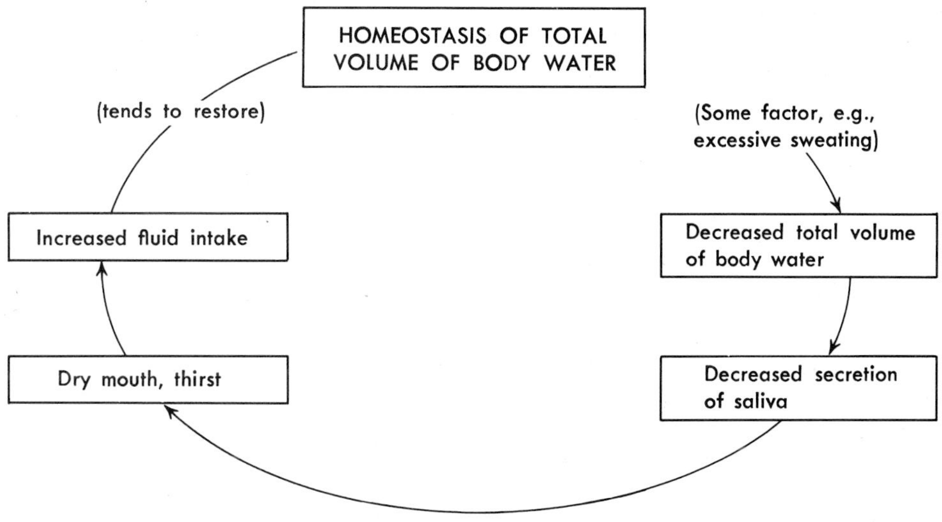

Fig. 323

Diagram illustrating the basic principle of a postulated homeostatic mechanism for adjusting intake to output.

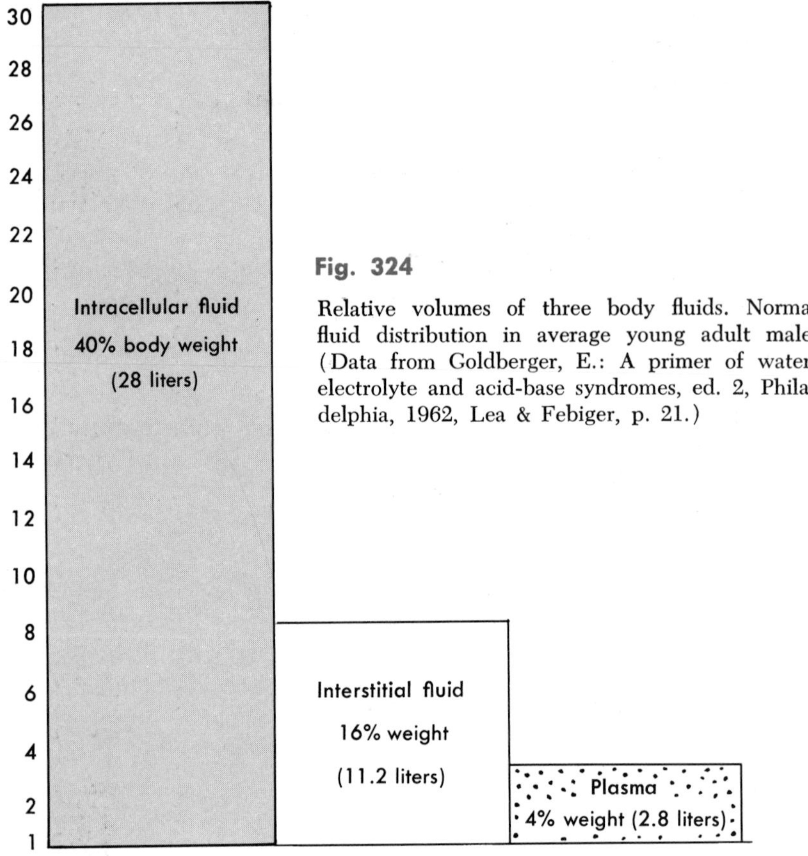

Fig. 324

Relative volumes of three body fluids. Normal fluid distribution in average young adult male. (Data from Goldberger, E.: A primer of water, electrolyte and acid-base syndromes, ed. 2, Philadelphia, 1962, Lea & Febiger, p. 21.)

that which lies outside the cells and that which lies within them. Functionally, then, we speak of the extracellular fluid (ECF), meaning both the plasma and interstitial fluid, and the intracellular fluid (ICF), meaning the water inside all the cells. Extracellular fluid constitutes the internal environment of the body. It, therefore, serves the dual functions of providing the relatively constant environment vital to cells and of transporting substances to and from them. Intracellular fluid, on the other hand, because it is a solvent, functions to facilitate intracellular chemical reactions that maintain life. Compared as to volume, intracellular fluid is the largest, plasma the smallest, and interstitial fluid in between. Fig. 324 gives normal fluid volumes in a typical young adult male. Note that intracellular fluid constitutes 40% of body weight, interstitial fluid 16%, and blood plasma 4%. Or, expressed differently, for every kilogram of its weight the body contains about 400 ml. of intracellular fluid, 160 ml. of interstitial fluid, and 40 ml. of plasma. Fluid volumes, however, vary somewhat—mainly according to the fat content of the body and the sex. Fat people have a lower water content than slender ones, and women have a lower water content than men. Fluid distribution also varies with age. For example, the extracellular fluid volume is proportionately larger in infants and children than in adults. Compared

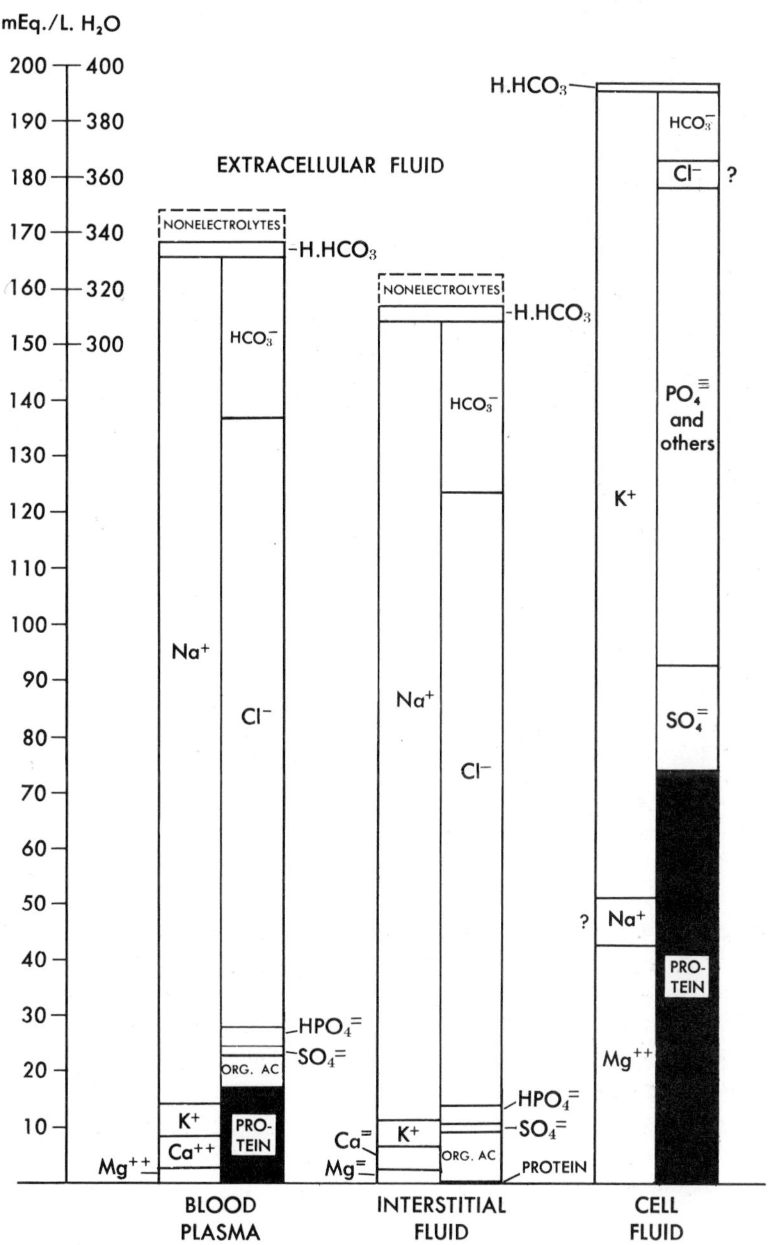

Fig. 325

Diagram showing chief chemical constituents of three fluid compartments. Height of left half of each column indicates total concentration of cations; that of right half, concentrations of anions. Both are expressed in milliequivalents per liter (mEq./L.) of water. Note that chloride and sodium values in cell fluid are questioned. It is probable that at least muscle intracellular fluid contains some sodium but no chloride. (Slightly modified from Bard: Medical physiology, ed. 11, St. Louis, 1961, The C. V. Mosby Co.; after Gamble: Harvey Lect. **42**:247, 1950.)

Table 62. Electrolyte composition of blood plasma*

	Cations	*Anions*
	142 mEq. Na^{+}	102 mEq. Cl^{-}
	4 mEq. K^{+}	26 HCO_3^{-}
	5 mEq. Ca^{++}	17 $protein^{-}$
	2 mEq. Mg^{++}	6 other
		2 $HPO_4^{=}$
Totals	153 mEq./L. plasma	153 mEq./L. plasma

*Data from Ruch, T. C., and Patton, H. D.: Physiology and biophysics, ed. 19, Philadelphia, 1965, W. B. Saunders Co., p. 888

chemically, plasma and interstitial fluid (the two extracellular fluids) are almost identical. Intracellular fluid, on the other hand, shows striking differences from either of the two extracellular fluids. Let us examine first the chemical structure of plasma and interstitial fluid as shown in Fig. 325.

Perhaps the first difference to catch your eye is that blood contains a slightly larger total of electrolytes (ions) than does interstitial fluid. If you compare the two fluids, ion for ion, you will discover the most important difference between blood plasma and interstitial fluid. Look at the anions (negative ions) in these two extracellular fluids. Note that blood contains an appreciable amount of protein anions. Interstitial fluid, in contrast, contains hardly any protein anions. This is the only functionally important difference between blood and interstitial fluid. It exists because the normal capillary membrane is practically impermeable to proteins. Hence, almost all of them remain behind in the blood instead of filtering out into the interstitial fluid. And because proteins remain in the blood, certain other differences also exist between blood and interstitial fluid: notably, blood contains more sodium ions and fewer chloride ions than does interstitial fluid.*

Extracellular fluids and intracellular fluid are more unlike than alike chemically. Chemical difference predominates between the extracellular and intracellular fluids. Chemical similarity predominates between the two extracellular fluids. Study Fig. 325 and make some generalizations about the main chemical differences between the extracellular and intracellular fluids. For example: What is the most abundant cation in the extracellular fluids? In the intracellular fluid? What is the most abundant anion in the extracellular fluids? In the intracellular fluid? What about the relative concentrations of protein anions in extracellular fluid and intracellular fluid?

The only reason we have called attention to the chemical structure of the three body fluids is that here, as elsewhere, structure determines function. In this instance the

*According to the Donnan equilibrium principle, when nondiffusible anions (negative ions) are present on one side of a membrane, there are on that side of the membrane fewer diffusible anions and more diffusible cations (positive ions) than on the other side. Applying this principle to the blood and interstitial fluid: because blood contains nondiffusible protein anions, it contains fewer chloride ions (diffusible anions) and more sodium ions (diffusible cations) than does interstitial fluid.

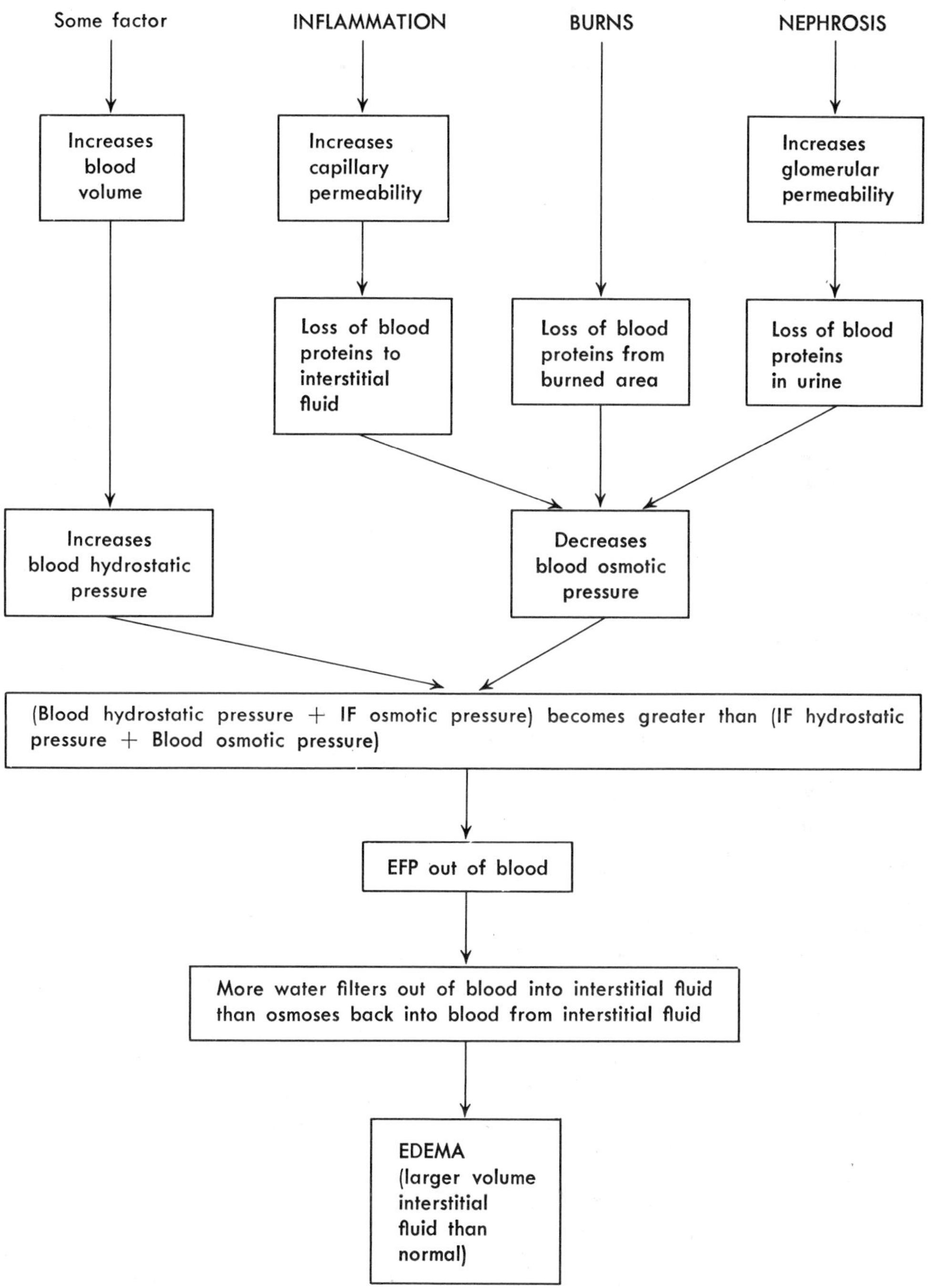

Fig. 326

Scheme to show mechanisms of edema formation in some common conditions (IF, interstitial fluid; EFP, effective filtration pressure). Also see Fig. 327, p. 531.

chemical structure of the three fluids helps control water and electrolyte movement between them. Or, phrased differently, the chemical structure of body fluids, if normal, helps maintain homeostasis of fluid distribution and, if abnormal, results in fluid imbalance. Hypervolemia (excess blood volume) is a case in point. Edema, too, frequently stems from changes in the chemical structure of body fluids (Fig. 326).

We are ready now to try to answer the following question: How does the chemical structure of body fluids control water movement between them and thereby control fluid distribution in the body?

Control of water movement between plasma and interstitial fluid

Over sixty years ago Starling advanced a hypothesis about the nature of the mechanism that controls water movement between plasma and interstitial fluid, that is, across the capillary membrane. This hypothesis has since become one of the major premises of physiology and is often spoken of as Starling's "law of the capillaries." According to this law, the control mechanism for water exchange between plasma and interstitial fluid consists of four pressures: blood hydrostatic and colloid osmotic pressures* on one side of the capillary membrane and interstitial fluid hydrostatic and colloid† osmotic pressures on the other side.

According to the physical laws governing filtration and osmosis (p. 29), blood hydrostatic pressure (HP) tends to force fluid out of capillaries into interstitial fluid (IF), but blood colloid osmotic pressure (OP) tends to draw it back into them. Interstitial fluid hydrostatic pressure, in contrast, tends to force fluid out of the interstitial fluid into the capillaries, and interstitial fluid colloid osmotic pressure tends to draw it back out of capillaries. In short, two of these pressures constitute vectors in one direction and two in the opposite direction. Does this remind you of another mechanism studied earlier? (To check your answer, see p. 441.)

The difference between the two sets of opposing forces obviously represents the net or effective filtration pressure—in other words, the effective force tending to produce the net fluid movement between blood and interstitial fluid. In general terms, Starling's law of the capillaries might be stated, therefore, in this way: the rate and direction of fluid exchange between capillaries and interstitial fluid is determined by the hydrostatic and colloid osmotic pressures of the two fluids. Or, written as a formula:

$$(\text{BHP} + \text{IFOP}) - (\text{IFHP} + \text{BOP}) = \text{EFP}^{*}$$

Note that the factors enclosed in the first set of parentheses tend to move fluid out of capillaries and that those in the second set tend to move fluid into them.

To illustrate operation of Starling's law, let us consider how it controls water exchange at the arterial ends of tissue capillaries. Table 63 gives typical normal pressures. Using these figures in Starling's law of the capillaries:

$(35 + 0) - (2 + 25) = 8$ mm. Hg net pressure (EFP), causing water to filter out of blood at arterial ends of capillaries into interstitial fluid

*Osmotic pressure due to concentrations of protein in blood and interstitial fluid. Since the capillary membrane is permeable to other plasma solutes, they quickly diffuse through the membrane so cause no osmotic pressure to develop against it. Only the proteins, to which the capillary membrane is practically impermeable, cause an actual osmotic pressure against the capillary membrane (explained on pp. 24 and 25).

†A small amount of blood protein passes through the capillary membrane and tends to concentrate around the venous end of capillaries, hence this pressure.

*BHP, Blood hydrostatic pressure. IFOP, Interstitial fluid osmotic pressure. IFHP, Interstitial fluid hydrostatic pressure. BOP, Blood osmotic pressure. EFP, Effective filtration pressure between blood and interstitial fluid.

Table 63. Pressures at arterial end of tissue capillaries

Arterial end of capillary	*Hydrostatic pressure*	*Colloid osmotic pressure*
Blood	35 mm. Hg	25 mm. Hg
Interstitial fluid	2 mm. Hg	0 mm. Hg

Table 64. Pressures at venous end of tissue capillaries

Venous end of capillary	*Hydrostatic pressure*	*Colloid osmotic pressure*
Blood	15 mm. Hg	25 mm. Hg
Interstitial fluid	1 mm. Hg	3 mm. Hg*

*A small amount of blood proteins passes through the capillary membrane and tends to concentrate around the venous ends of capillaries, hence this pressure.

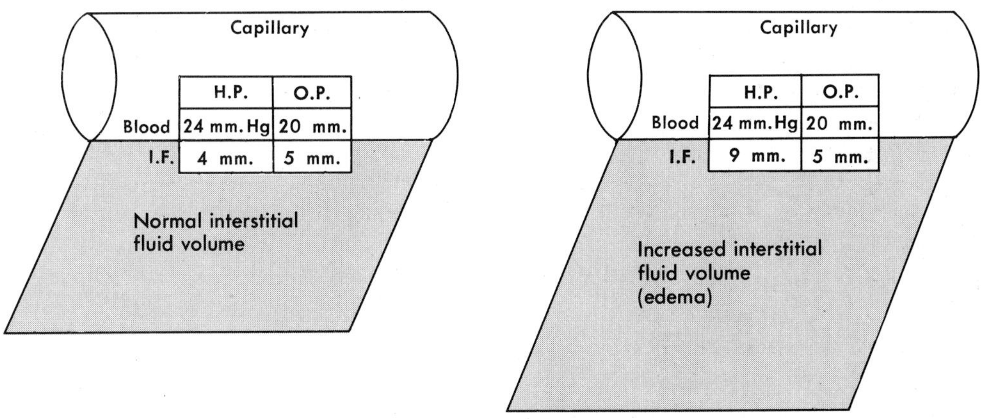

Fig. 327

The mechanism of edema formation whenever blood protein concentration and, therefore, blood osmotic pressure decrease below normal. Left diagram, blood osmotic pressure has just decreased to 20 from the normal 25 mm. Hg. This increases the effective filtration pressure (EFP) to 5 mm. Hg from a normal of 0 (see Starling's formula, p. 530). The EFP of 5 mm. Hg causes fluid shift from blood to interstitial fluid (IF) until the EFP again equals 0, in this case, when interstitial fluid volume has increased enough to raise interstitial fluid hydrostatic pressure to 9 mm. Hg as shown in the digram on the right. At this point a new equilibrium is established and equal amounts of water once more are exchanged between the blood and interstitial fluid. Thus the increased interstitial fluid volume, that is, the edema, becomes stabilized.

The same law operates at the venous end of capillaries (Table 64). Again apply Starling's law of the capillaries. What is the net effective pressure at the venous ends of capillaries? In which direction does it cause water to move? Assuming that the figures given in Table 64 are normal, do you agree that "about the same amount of water returns to the blood at the venous ends of capillaries as left it from the arterial ends"?

On the basis of our discussion thus far, we can formulate some principles about the transfer of water between blood and interstitial fluid:

1. No net transfer of water occurs between blood and interstitial fluid as long as the effective filtration pressure (EFP) equals 0, that is, when

(Blood HP + IFOP) = (IFHP + Blood OP)

2. A net transfer of water, a "fluid shift," occurs between blood and interstitial fluid whenever the EFP does not equal 0, that is, when

(Blood HP + IFOP)
does not equal
(IFHP + Blood OP)

3. Since (Blood HP + IFOP) is a force tending to move water out of capillary blood, a fluid shift from blood to interstitial fluid occurs whenever

(Blood HP + IFOP)
is greater than
(IFHP + Blood OP)

4. Since (IFHP + Blood OP) is a force tending to move water out of interstitial fluid into capillary blood, a fluid shift from interstitial fluid into blood occurs whenever

(IFHP + Blood OP)
is greater than
(Blood HP + IFOP)

or, stated the other way around, whenever

(Blood HP + IFOP)
is less than
(IFHP + Blood OP)

To apply these principles, answer questions 8 to 11 on p. 536 and examine Figs. 326 and 327.

Control of water movement through cell membranes between interstitial and intracellular fluids

The mechanism that regulates water movement through cell membranes is similar to the one that regulates water movement through capillary membranes. In other words, interstitial fluid and intracellular fluid hydrostatic and osmotic pressures regulate water transfer between these two fluids. But because their osmotic pressures vary more than do their hydrostatic pressures, interstitial fluid and intracellular fluid osmotic pressures serve as the chief regulators of water transfer across cell membranes. Their osmotic pressures, in turn, are directly related to their electrolyte concentrations—chiefly, therefore, to interstitial fluid sodium concentration and to intracellular fluid potassium concentration. For example, a decrease in interstitial fluid sodium concentration produces a decrease in the amount of osmotic pressure exerted by interstitial fluid against cell membranes. Interstitial fluid osmotic pressure becomes hypotonic to intracellular fluid osmotic pressure. And this osmotic pressure gradient causes net osmosis out of interstitial fluid into cells (a discussion of osmosis appears on pp. 24 to 29). In short, interstitial fluid and intracellular fluid electrolyte concentrations are the main determinants of their osmotic pressures; their osmotic pressures regulate the amount and direction of water transfer between the two fluids, and this regulates their volumes. Hence, fluid balance depends upon electrolyte balance. And conversely, electrolyte balance depends upon fluid balance. An imbalance in one produces an imbalance in the other (see Fig. 328).

Normal sodium concentration in the in-

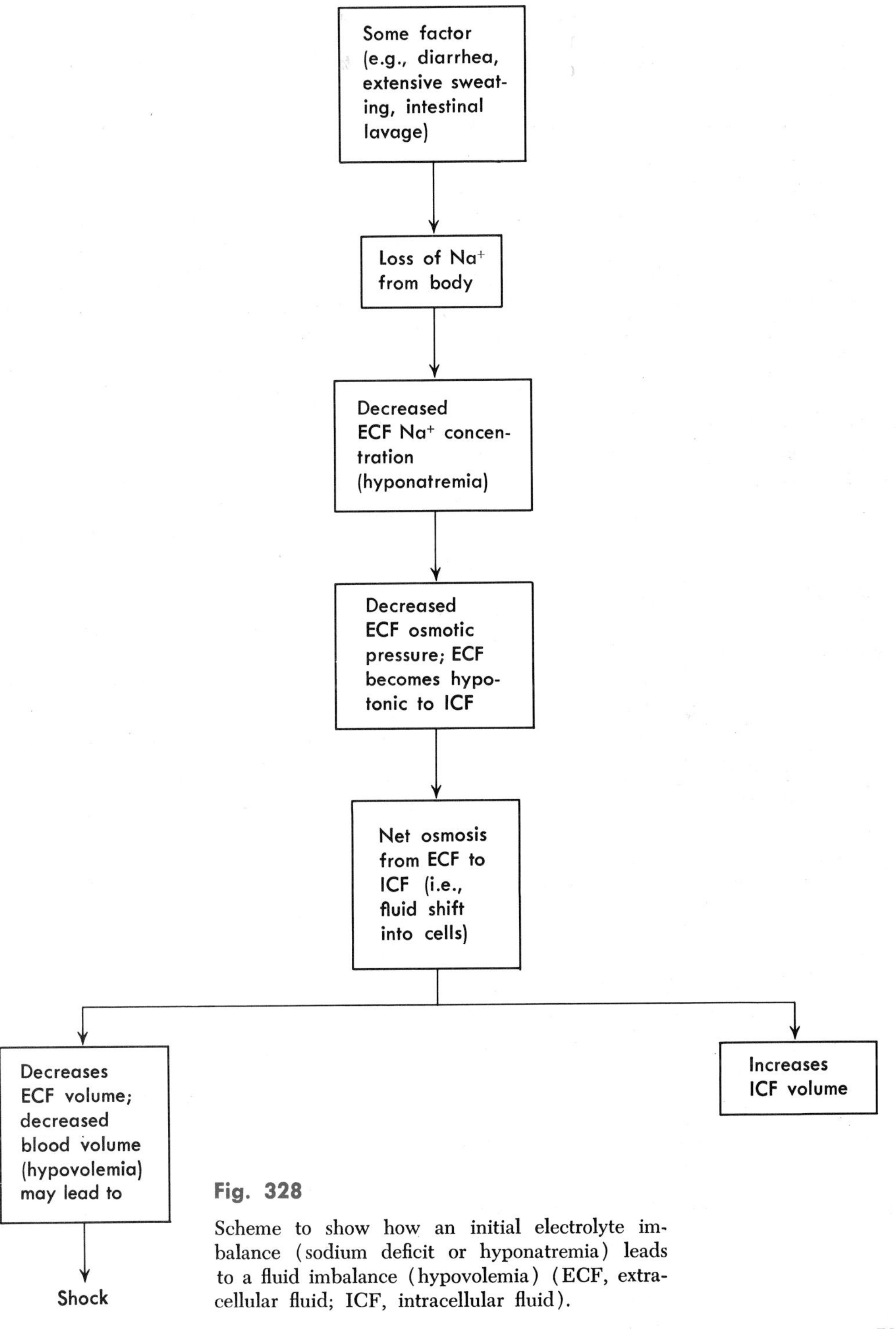

Fig. 328

Scheme to show how an initial electrolyte imbalance (sodium deficit or hyponatremia) leads to a fluid imbalance (hypovolemia) (ECF, extracellular fluid; ICF, intracellular fluid).

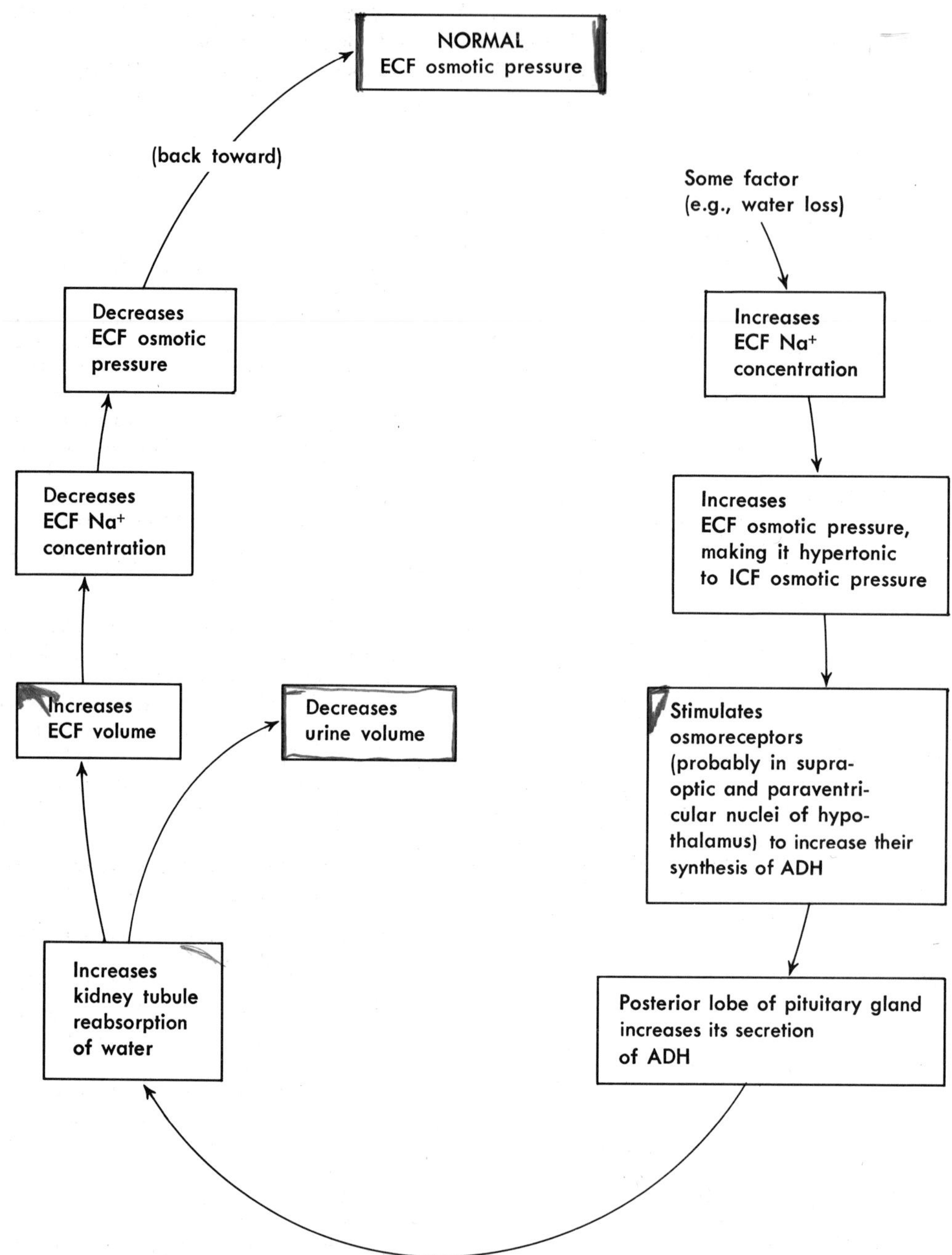

Fig. 329

ADH (antidiuretic hormone) mechanism which helps maintain homeostasis of extracellular fluid (ECF) osmotic pressure by regulating its volume and thereby its electrolyte concentration, that is, mainly ECF Na^+ concentration.

terstitial fluid and potassium concentration in the intracellular fluid depend upon many factors but especially upon the amount of ADH and aldosterone secreted. As shown in Fig. 329, ADH regulates extracellular fluid electrolyte concentration and osmotic pressure by regulating the amount of water reabsorbed into blood by renal tubules. Aldosterone, on the other hand, regulates extracellular fluid volume by regulating the amount of sodium reabsorbed into blood by renal tubules (Fig. 321, p. 522).

Outline summary—Fluid and electrolyte balance

Introduction

1. Meaning of fluid balance
   a. same as homeostasis of fluids, i.e., total volume of water in body normal and remains relatively constant
   b. volume of blood plasma, interstitial fluid, and intracellular fluid all remain relatively constant, i.e., homeostasis of distribution of water as well as of total volume
2. Fluid balance and electrolyte balance interdependent—see Figs. 321 and 329

Some general principles about fluid balance

1. Cardinal principle—intake must equal output
2. Fluid and electrolyte balance maintained primarily by mechanisms that adjust output to intake; secondarily by mechanisms that adjust intake to output
3. Fluid balance also maintained by mechanisms that control movement of water between fluid compartments

Avenues by which water enters and leaves body

1. Water enters body through digestive tract in
   a. liquids
   b. foods
2. Water formed in body by metabolism of foods
3. Water leaves body via kidneys, lungs, skin, and intestines

Mechanisms that maintain homeostasis of total fluid volume

1. Control of urine volume—under normal conditions, by factors that control reabsorption of water by distal and collecting tubules
   a. ECF electrolyte concentration (crystalloid osmotic pressure) controls ADH secretion which controls tubule H_2O reabsorption
   b. ECF volume controls aldosterone secretion which controls tubule Na^+ reabsorption and therefore water reabsorption
2. Factors that alter fluid loss under abnormal conditions—hyperventilation, hypoventilation, vomiting, diarrhea, circulatory failure, etc.
3. Control of fluid intake—see Fig. 323, p. 525
   a. mechanism by which intake adjusted to output not completely known
   b. one controlling factor seems to be degree of moistness of mucosa of mouth—if output exceeds intake, mouth feels dry, sensation of thirst occurs, and individual ingests liquids

Mechanisms that maintain homeostasis of fluid distribution

1. Comparison of plasma, interstitial fluid, and intracellular fluid
   a. Plasma and interstitial fluid constitute extracellular fluid (ECF), internal environment of body or, in other words, environment of cells
   b. intracellular fluid (ICF) volume largest, plasma volume smallest; ICF about 40% of body weight, IF about 16%, and plasma about 4% or ICF volume about ten times that of plasma and IF volume about four times plasma volume
   c. chemically, plasma and IF almost identical except that plasma contains slightly more electrolytes and considerably more proteins than IF; also blood contains somewhat more sodium and fewer chloride ions

   d. chemically, ECF and ICF strikingly different; sodium main cation of ECF, potassium main cation of ICF; chloride main anion of ECF; phosphate main anion of ICF; protein concentration much higher in ICF than in IF
2. Control of water movement between plasma and interstitial fluid
   a. by four pressures—blood hydrostatic and colloid osmotic pressures and interstitial fluid hydrostatic and colloid osmotic pressures
   b. effect of these pressures on water movement between plasma and interstitial fluid expressed in Starling's "law of the capillaries"; only when (blood hydrostatic pressure + IF colloid osmotic pressure) − (blood colloid osmotic pressure + IF hydrostatic pressure) = 0, do equal amounts of water filter out of blood into IF and osmose back into blood from IF; in other words, water balance exists between these two fluids under these conditions
3. Control of water movement through cell membranes between interstitial and intracellular fluids—primarily by relative crystalloid osmotic pressures of ECF and ICF, which depend mainly upon sodium concentration of ECF and potassium concentration of ICF which, in turn, depend upon intake and output of sodium and potassium and upon sodium-potassium transport mechanisms

Review questions

1. Explain in your own words the meaning of the term fluid balance.
2. How is total volume of body fluids kept relatively constant—that is, what other factors must be controlled in order to keep the total volume of water in the body relatively constant?
3. What, if any, are functionally important differences between the chemical composition of plasma and interstitial fluid?
4. What, if any, are functionally important differences between the chemical composition of extracellular and intracellular fluids?
5. Are plasma and interstitial fluid more accurately described as "similar" or "different" as to chemical composition? Volume?
6. Support your answer to question 5 with some specific facts.
7. Are interstitial fluid and intracellular fluid more accurately described as "similar" or "different" as to chemical composition? Volume?
8. Explain Starling's law of the capillaries in your own words. Be as brief and clear as you can. This law describes the mechanism for controlling what?
9. Suppose that in one individual the normal average or mean pressures (in mm. Hg) are capillary blood hydrostatic pressure 24 and osmotic pressure 25; interstitial fluid hydrostatic pressure 4 and osmotic pressure 5. Following a hemorrhage, this patient's blood hydrostatic pressure falls to 18. (a) Assuming that the other pressures momentarily stay the same, what is the EFP now? (b) The new EFP causes a fluid shift in which direction? (c) When will the fluid shift stop and an even exchange of water again go on between blood and interstitial fluids?
10. Formulate a principle by filling in the blanks in the following sentences: Anything that decreases blood hydrostatic pressure in the capillaries tends to cause a fluid shift from __________ into __________. Conversely, anything that increases blood hydrostatic pressure in the capillaries tends to cause a fluid shift out of __________ into __________.
11. Formulate a principle by completing the blanks in the following sentence: A decrease in blood protein concentration tends to decrease blood __________ pressure and therefore tends to cause a fluid shift from __________ to __________.

Situation: A patient has had marked diarrhea for several days.

12. Explain the homeostatic mechanisms that would tend to compensate for this excessive fluid loss.
13. Do you think they could succeed in maintaining fluid balance or would fluid therapy probably be necessary?
14. What, if any, abnormality of fluid distribution do you think would occur in this patient without fluid therapy? Explain your reasoning.
15. Why does dehydration necessarily develop if an individual takes nothing by mouth for several days and receives no fluid therapy? Why cannot homeostatic mechanisms prevent this?

Mechanisms that control pH of body fluids
Meaning of term pH
Types of pH control mechanisms
Effectiveness of pH control mechanisms; range of pH

Buffer mechanism for controlling pH of body fluids
Buffers defined
Buffer pairs present in body fluids
Action of buffers to prevent marked changes in pH of body fluids
Evaluation of role of buffers in pH control

Respiratory mechanism of pH control
Explanation of mechanism
Adjustment of respirations to pH of arterial blood
Some principles relating respirations and pH of body fluids

Urinary mechanism of pH control
General principles about mechanism
Mechanisms that control urine pH

Clinical disturbances in acid-base balance
Acidosis
Alkalosis

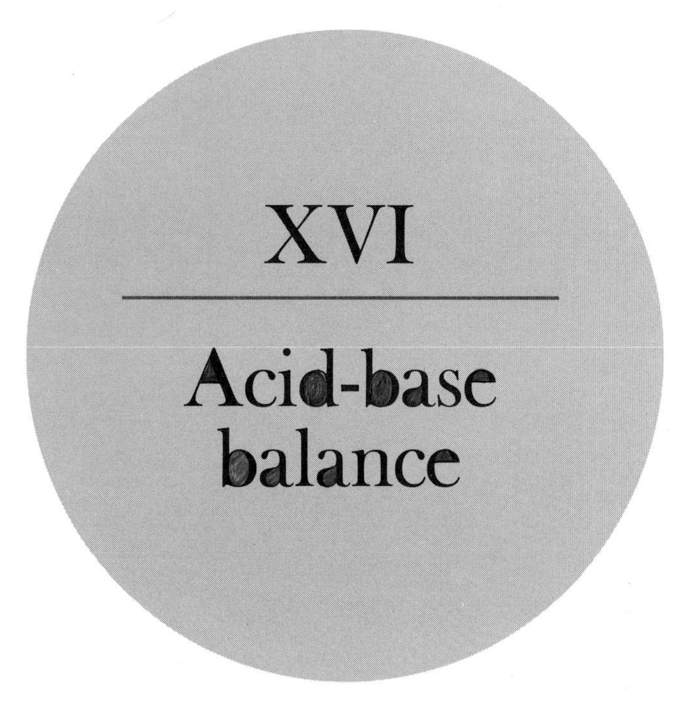

XVI Acid-base balance

Acid-base balance is vitally important. Acid-base balance means maintenance of homeostasis of the hydrogen-ion concentration of body fluids. Even a slight deviation from normal causes pronounced changes in the rate of cellular chemical reactions. This, in turn, threatens survival.

Mechanisms that control pH of body fluids

Meaning of term pH

The term pH is a symbol used to mean the hydrogen-ion concentration of a solution. Actually, pH stands for the negative logarithm of the hydrogen-ion concentration.* pH indicates the degree of acidity and alkalinity of a solution—the latter because as hydrogen-ion concentration increases, OH-ion concentration (alkalinity) necessarily decreases. A pH of 7 indicates neutrality (equal amounts of H^+ and OH^-), a pH of less than 7 indicates acidity

*A pH of 7, for example, means that a solution contains 10^{-7} grams hydrogen ions per liter. Or, translating this logarithm into a number, a pH of 7 means that a solution contains 0.0000001 (that is, 1/10,000,000) gram hydrogen ions per liter. A solution of pH 6 contains 0.000001 (1/1,000,000) gram hydrogen ions per liter and one of pH 8 contains 0.00000001 (1/100,000,000) gram hydrogen ions per liter. Note that a solution with pH 7 contains ten times as many hydrogen ions as a solution with pH 8 and that pH decreases as hydrogen-ion concentration increases.

(more H^+ than OH^-), and one greater than 7 indicates alkalinity (more OH^- than H^+).

Types of pH control mechanisms

Since various acids and bases continually enter the blood from absorbed foods and from metabolism of food, some kind of mechanism for neutralizing or eliminating these substances is necessary if blood pH is to remain constant. Actually, three different devices operate together to maintain constancy of pH. Collectively, these devices—buffers, respirations, and kidney excretion of acids and bases—might be said to constitute the pH homeostatic mechanism.

Effectiveness of pH control mechanisms; range of pH

The most eloquent evidence of the effectiveness of the pH control mechanism is the extremely narrow range of pH, normally 7.35 to 7.45. In terms of hydrogen-ion concentration, this means that normally there is a little more than 1/100,000,000 of a gram of hydrogen ions (pH 8) in a liter of blood but a little less than 1/10,000,000 of a gram (pH 7). Also, the greatest normal amount of hydrogen ions is only about 1/100,000,000 of a gram more than the smallest normal amount. What incredible constancy! Acids continually stream into capillary blood from cell metabolism and yet a liter of venous blood (pH 7.35) contains only about 1/100,000,000 of a gram more hydrogen ions than does a liter of arterial blood (pH 7.45)! The pH homeostatic mechanism does indeed control effectively—astonishingly so.

Buffer mechanism for controlling pH of body fluids

Buffers defined

In terms of action, a buffer is a substance that prevents marked changes in the pH of a solution when an acid or a base is added to it. Let us suppose that a small amount of the strong acid HCl is added to a solution that contains a buffer (to blood, for example) and that its pH decreases from 7.41 to 7.27. But if the same amount of HCl were added to pure water containing no buffers, its pH would decrease much more markedly, from 7 to perhaps 3.4. In both instances, pH decreased upon addition of the acid, but much less so with buffers present than without them.

In terms of chemical composition, buffers consist of two kinds of substances and are, therefore, often referred to as "buffer pairs." Most of the body fluid buffer pairs consist of a weak acid and a salt of that acid, as shown below.

Buffer pairs present in body fluids

The main buffer pairs present in body fluids are as follows:

Bicarbonate pairs $\frac{NaHCO_3}{H_2CO_3}$, $\frac{KHCO_3}{H_2CO_3}$, etc.

Plasma protein pair $\frac{\text{Na·proteinate}}{\text{Proteins (weak acids)}}$

Hemoglobin pairs $\frac{K·Hb}{Hb}$ and $\frac{K·HbO_2}{HbO_2}$

(Hb and HbO_2 are weak acids)

Phosphate buffer pair $\frac{Na_2HPO_4 \text{ (basic phosphate)}}{NaH_2PO_4 \text{ (acid phosphate)}}$

Action of buffers to prevent marked changes in pH of body fluids

Buffers react with a relatively strong acid (or base) to replace it by a relatively weak acid (or base). That is to say, an acid which highly dissociates to yield many H ions is replaced by one which dissociates less highly to yield fewer H ions. Thus, by the buffer reaction, instead of the strong acid remaining in the solution and contributing many H ions to drastically lower the pH of the solution, a weaker acid takes its place, contributes fewer additional H ions to the solution, and thereby lowers its

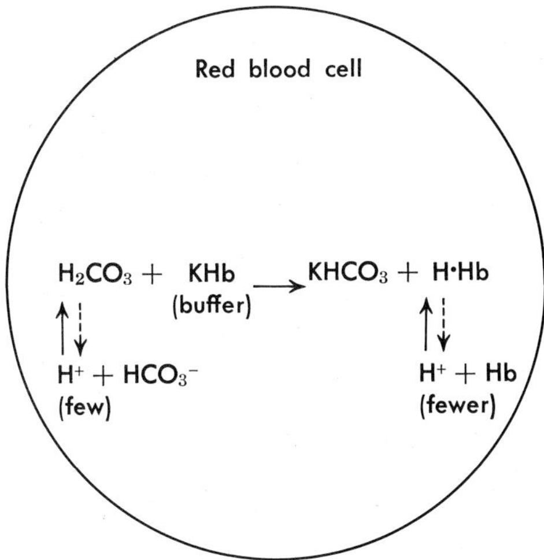

Fig. 330

Buffering of carbonic acid inside red blood cell by potassium salt of hemoglobin. Note that each molecule of carbonic acid is replaced by a molecule of the acid hemoglobin. Since hemoglobin is a weaker acid than carbonic acid, fewer of these hemoglobin molecules dissociate to form hydrogen ions. Hence, fewer hydrogen ions are present in red blood cell intracellular fluid than would have been present without the buffering of carbonic acid by the potassium salt of hemoglobin. Also, since some of the carbonic acid in the red blood cells has come from plasma, fewer hydrogen ions remain in blood than would if there were no buffering of carbonic acid.

pH only slightly. Therefore, because blood contains buffer pairs, its pH fluctuates much less widely than it would without them. In other words, blood buffers constitute one of the devices for preventing marked changes in blood pH. Let us consider some specific examples of buffer action. More carbonic acid is formed in the body than any other acid. It continuously enters tissue capillaries, where it is buffered primarily by the potassium salt of hemoglobin inside the red blood cells as shown in Fig. 330.

Note how this reaction between carbonic acid and the potassium salt of hemoglobin (a buffer) applies the principle of buffering. As a result of the buffering action of KHb, the weaker acid, H·Hb, replaces the stronger acid, H_2CO_3, and, therefore, the hydrogen-ion concentration of blood increases much less than it would if carbonic acid were not buffered.

The potassium salt of oxyhemoglobin, sodium proteinate (sodium salts of blood proteins), and basic sodium phosphate also buffer carbonic acid.

Nonvolatile, or fixed acids, such as lactic acid and ketone bodies, are buffered mainly by the basic member of the bicarbonate buffer pair, mainly by sodium bicarbonate—ordinary baking soda (see the equation given in Fig. 331).

Carbonic acid buffers strong bases as is illustrated by the equation given in Fig. 332.

When blood pH is normal and a state of acid-base balance exists, components of the bicarbonate buffer pair are present in the extracellular fluid in a ratio of 20 parts of base bicarbonate (primarily $NaHCO_3$) to 1 part of carbonic acid. Actually, a liter of plasma normally contains about 27 mEq. of base bicarbonate ($B{\cdot}HCO_3$) and 1.3 mEq. of carbonic acid:

$$\frac{27\ \text{mEq.}{\cdot}B{\cdot}HCO_3}{1.3\ \text{mEq.}\cdot H_2CO_3} = \frac{20}{1} = \text{pH } 7.4$$

An increase in this ratio causes pH to increase (uncompensated alkalosis), and a decrease in it causes pH to decrease (uncompensated acidosis).

Both carbonic acid and nonvolatile acids enter the blood in tissue capillaries and are immediately buffered. If you examine Fig. 331, you can discover how the buffering of nonvolatile acids changes blood's bicarbonate-carbonic acid ratio. Note that this buffering action changes sodium bicarbonate to carbonic acid. So blood leaving the capillaries—venous blood, that is—contains less sodium bicarbonate and more carbonic acid than does arterial blood. And venous blood's base bicarbonate-carbonic acid ratio, therefore, is somewhat lower than arterial

$$\begin{array}{ccc} \text{Lactic acid} + NaHCO_3 & \longrightarrow & \text{Na·lactate} + H_2CO_3 \\ \uparrow\downarrow & & \uparrow\downarrow \\ H^+ + \text{lactate}^- & & H^+ + HCO_3^- \\ \text{(few)} & & \text{(fewer)} \end{array}$$

Fig. 331

Buffering of lactic acid (a fixed or nonvolatile acid) by sodium bicarbonate, the most abundant base bicarbonate in the blood. Carbonic acid (a weaker acid than lactic acid) replaces lactic acid. Result: fewer hydrogen ions are added to blood than would be if lactic acid were not buffered. Ketone bodies (for example, acetoacetic acid) from fat catabolism are also buffered by base bicarbonate.

$$\begin{array}{ccc} NaOH + H_2CO_3 & \longrightarrow & NaHCO_3 + HOH \\ \downarrow\uparrow & & \uparrow\downarrow \\ Na^+ + OH^- & & H^+ + OH^- \\ \text{(many)} & & \text{(very few)} \end{array}$$

Fig. 332

Buffering of base NaOH by carbonic acid.

blood's. And this necessarily means that venous blood's pH is also lower than arterial blood's pH.

Evaluation of role of buffers in pH control

Buffering alone cannot maintain homeostasis of pH. As we have seen, extra hydrogen ions continually enter capillary blood despite buffering. If even a few more hydrogen ions were added to blood every time it circulated and no way were provided for eliminating them, blood hydrogen-ion concentration would gradually but continually increase and pH continually decrease. The additional respiratory and urinary devices must, therefore, function concurrently with the buffers in order to expel excess hydrogen ions from the body and maintain constancy of pH.

Respiratory mechanism of pH control

Explanation of mechanism

Respirations play a vital part in controlling pH. With every expiration, carbon dioxide and water leave the body in the expired air. The carbon dioxide has come from the venous blood—has diffused out of it as it moves through the lung capillaries. Therefore, less carbon dioxide remains in the arterial blood leaving the lung capillaries and fewer hydrogen ions can be formed in it by the following reactions:

$$CO_2 + H_2O \xrightarrow{\text{(carbonic anhydrase)}} H_2CO_3$$
$$H_2CO_3 \longrightarrow H^+ + HCO_3^-$$

So arterial blood has a lower hydrogen-ion concentration and a higher pH than venous blood. A typical average pH for venous blood is 7.36, and 7.41 is a typical average pH for arterial blood.

Adjustment of respirations to pH of arterial blood

Obviously, in order for respirations to serve as a mechanism of pH control, there must be some arrangement so respirations can vary as needed to maintain or restore normal pH. Suppose that blood pH has decreased (that is, hydrogen-ion concentration has increased). Respirations then need to increase in order to eliminate more carbon dioxide from the body, thereby leaving less carbonic acid and fewer hydrogen ions in the blood.

The mechanism for adjusting respirations to arterial blood carbon dioxide content or pH operates in this way. Neurons of the respiratory center are sensitive to changes in arterial blood carbon dioxide content and to changes in its pH. If the amount of carbon dioxide in arterial blood increases beyond a certain level, or if arterial blood pH decreases below about 7.38, the respiratory center is stimulated and respirations accordingly increase in rate and depth. This, in turn, eliminates more carbon dioxide, reduces carbonic acid and hydrogen ions, and increases pH back toward the normal level (Fig. 333). The carotid chemoreflexes (p. 368) are also devices by which respirations adjust to blood pH and, in turn, adjust pH.

Some principles relating respirations and pH of body fluids

1. A decrease in blood pH below normal (that is, acidosis) tends to cause increased respirations (hyperventilation) which tends to increase pH back toward normal. In other words, acidosis causes hyperventilation which, in turn, acts as a compensating mechanism for the acidosis.
2. Prolonged hyperventilation may increase blood pH enough to produce alkalosis.
3. An increase in blood pH above normal (or alkalosis) causes hypoventilation, which serves as a compensating mechanism for the alkalosis by decreasing blood pH back toward normal.

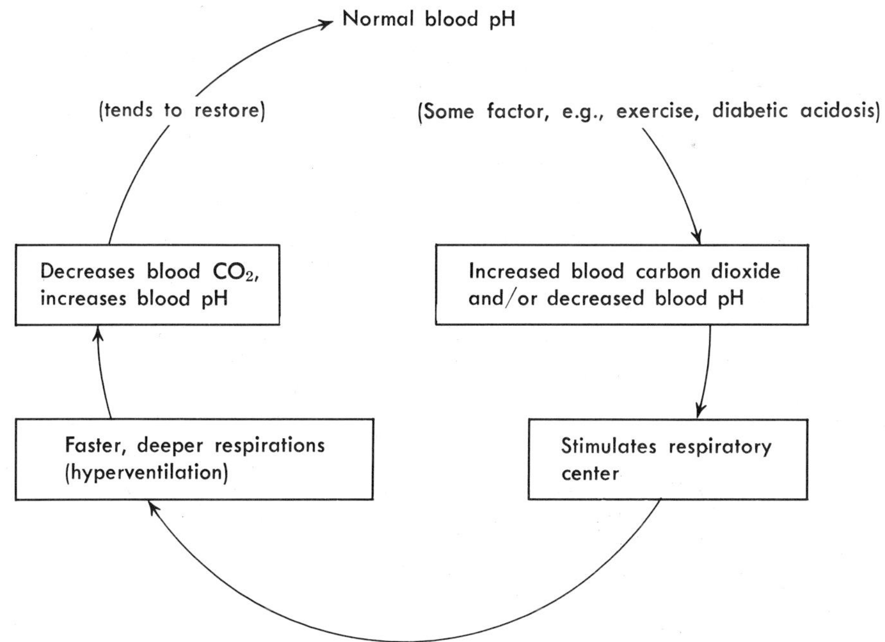

Fig. 333

Respiratory mechanism of pH control. A rise in arterial blood CO_2 content or a drop in its pH (below about 7.38) stimulates respiratory center neurons. Hyperventilation results. Less CO_2 and therefore less carbonic acid and fewer hydrogen ions remain in blood so that blood pH increases, often reaching the normal level.

4. Prolonged hypoventilation may decrease blood pH enough to produce acidosis.

Urinary mechanism of pH control

General principles about mechanism

Because the kidneys can excrete varying amounts of acid and base, they, like the lungs, play a vital role in pH control. Kidney tubules, by excreting many or few hydrogen ions, in exchange for reabsorbing many or few sodium ions, control urine pH and thereby help control blood pH. If, for example, blood pH decreases below normal, kidney tubules remove more hydrogen ions from the blood to the urine and reabsorb more sodium ions from the urine back into the blood. This, of course, decreases urine pH. But simultaneously—and of far more importance—it increases blood pH back toward normal. This urinary mechanism of pH control is a device for excreting varying amounts of hydrogen ions from the body to match the amounts entering the blood. It constitutes a much more effective device for adjusting hydrogen output to hydrogen input than does the body's only other mechanism for expelling hydrogen ions—namely, the respiratory mechanism previously described. But abnormalities of any one of the three pH control mechanisms soon throws the body into a state of acid-base imbalance. Only when all three parts of this complex mechanism—buffering, respirations, and urine secretion—function adequately can acid-base balance be maintained.

Let us turn our attention now to the mechanisms that adjust urine pH to counteract changes in blood pH.

Mechanisms that control urine pH

A decrease in blood pH accelerates the renal tubule ion-exchange mechanisms that tend to increase the blood pH back to normal by acidifying urine. The following paragraphs describe these mechanisms.

1. Distal and collecting tubules secrete hydrogen ions into the urine in exchange for basic ions, which they reabsorb. Fig. 334 illustrates the mechanism by which they do this. Carbon dioxide diffuses from tubule capillaries into distal tubule cells where the enzyme carbonic anhydrase accelerates the combining of carbon dioxide with water to form carbonic acid. The latter dissociates into hydrogen ions and bicarbonate ions. The hydrogen ions then diffuse into the tubular urine, where they displace basic ions (most often sodium) from a basic salt of a weak acid and thereby change the basic salt to an acid salt or to a weak acid that is eliminated in the urine. While this is happening, the displaced sodium or other basic ion diffuses into a tubule cell. Here it combines with the bicarbonate ion left over from the carbonic acid dissociation to form sodium bicarbonate. The sodium bicarbonate then diffuses, is reabsorbed, that is, into the blood. Note the various results of this mechanism. Sodium bicarbonate (or other base bicarbonate) is conserved for the body. Instead of all the basic salts that filter out of glomerular blood being eliminated in the urine, considerable amounts are recovered into peritubular capillary blood. In addition, extra hydrogen ions are added to the urine and thereby eliminated from the body. Both the reabsorption of base bicarbonate into blood and the excretion of hydrogen ions into urine tend to increase the ratio of the bicarbonate buffer pair, $\frac{B \cdot HCO_3}{H \cdot HCO_3}$, present in blood and this increases blood pH. In short, kidney tubule base bicarbonate reabsorption and hydrogen-ion excretion both tend to alkalinize blood by acidifying urine.

Renal tubules can excrete either hydrogen or potassium in exchange for the sodium they reabsorb. Therefore, in general,

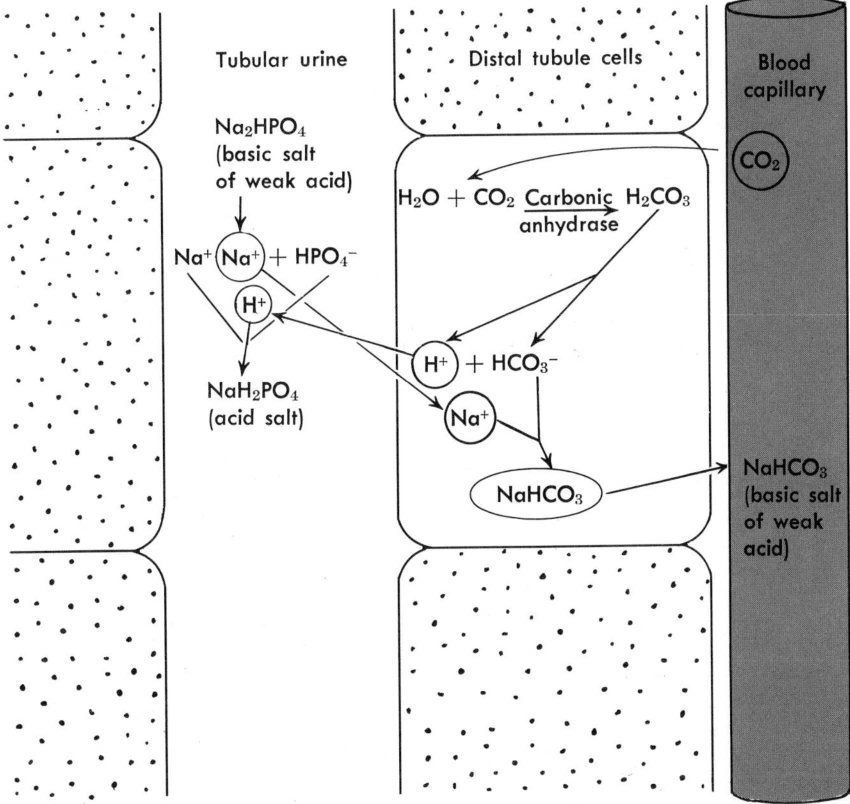

Fig. 334

Acidification of urine and conservation of base by distal renal tubule excretion of H ions (discussed on 542).

the more hydrogen ions they excrete, the fewer the potassium ions they can excrete. For example, in acidosis, tubule excretion of hydrogen ions increases markedly and potassium ion excretion decreases—an important fact because it may lead to *hyperkalemia* (excessive blood potassium), a dangerous condition because it can cause heart block and death.

2. Distal and collecting tubule cells excrete ammonia into the tubular urine. The ammonia combines with hydrogen to form an ammonium ion (Fig. 335). The ammonium ion displaces sodium or some other basic ion from a salt of a fixed (nonvolatile) acid to form an ammonium salt. The basic ion then diffuses back into a tubule cell and combines with bicarbonate ion to form a basic salt which, in turn, diffuses into tubular blood. Thus, like the renal tubules' excretion of hydrogen ions, their excretion of ammonia and its combining with hydrogen to form ammonium ions also tends to increase the blood bicarbonate buffer pair ratio and, therefore, tends to increase blood pH. Quantitatively, however, ammonium ion excretion is more important than hydrogen-ion excretion.

Renal tubule excretion of hydrogen and ammonia is controlled at least in part by the blood pH level. As indicated in Fig. 336, a decrease in blood pH accelerates tubule excretion of both hydrogen and ammonia. An increase in blood pH produces the opposite effects.

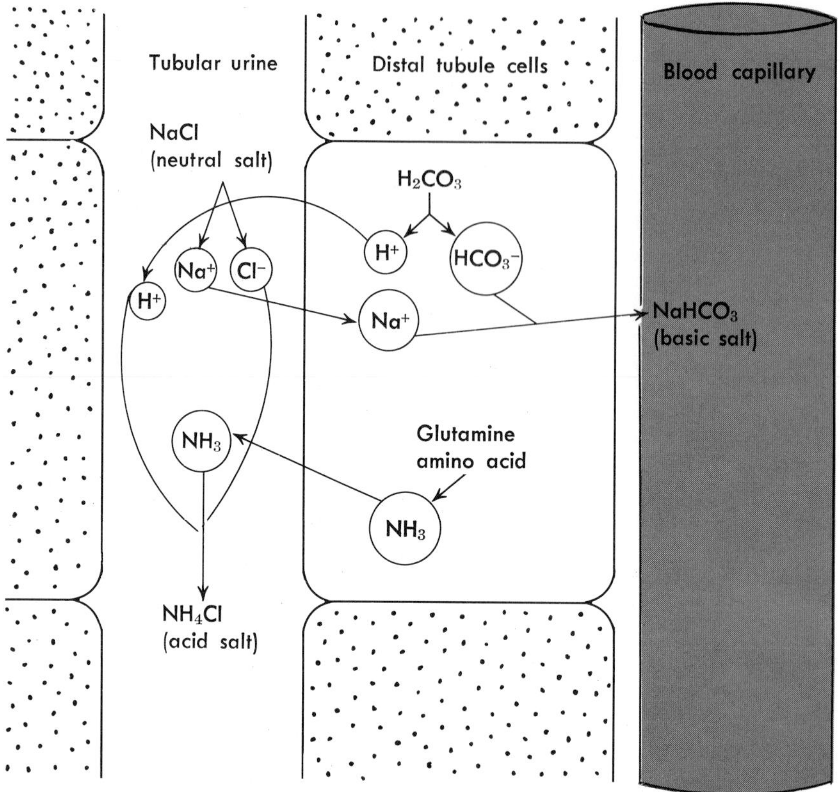

Fig. 335

Acidification of urine by tubule excretion of ammonia (NH_3). An acid (glutamine) leaves blood, enters a tubule cell, and is deaminized to form ammonia which is excreted into urine. In exchange, the tubule cell reabsorbs a basic salt (mainly $NaHCO_3$) into blood from urine.

Acid-base imbalances

Acidosis

During the course of certain diseases, such as diabetic ketosis or starvation, for instance, abnormally large amounts of nonvolatile acids enter the blood. All three types of pH control mechanisms—buffers, respiratory, and urinary—are enlisted in an all-out effort to compensate for the excess acid and to maintain acid-base balance. Basic bicarbonate buffers immediately react with the acids (Fig. 331). This decreases the ratio of base bicarbonate-carbonic acid of blood and therefore decreases blood pH. The decreased blood pH stimulates the respiratory centers. Respirations become faster and deeper (hyperventilation) so more carbon dioxide leaves the blood and less carbonic acid remains in it. This increases the ratio, $\frac{B{\cdot}HCO_3}{H{\cdot}HCO_3}$, and thereby increases blood pH back up toward normal. The kidney tubules increase their excretion of H^+ and NH_3 in exchange for reabsorbed Na^+ (Figs. 334 and 335). And these actions also tend to increase the preceding ratio and blood pH.

If hyperventilation and urine acidification together succeed in preventing a decrease in the base bicarbonate–carbonic acid ratio, blood pH remains normal and a state of *compensated acidosis* exists. But

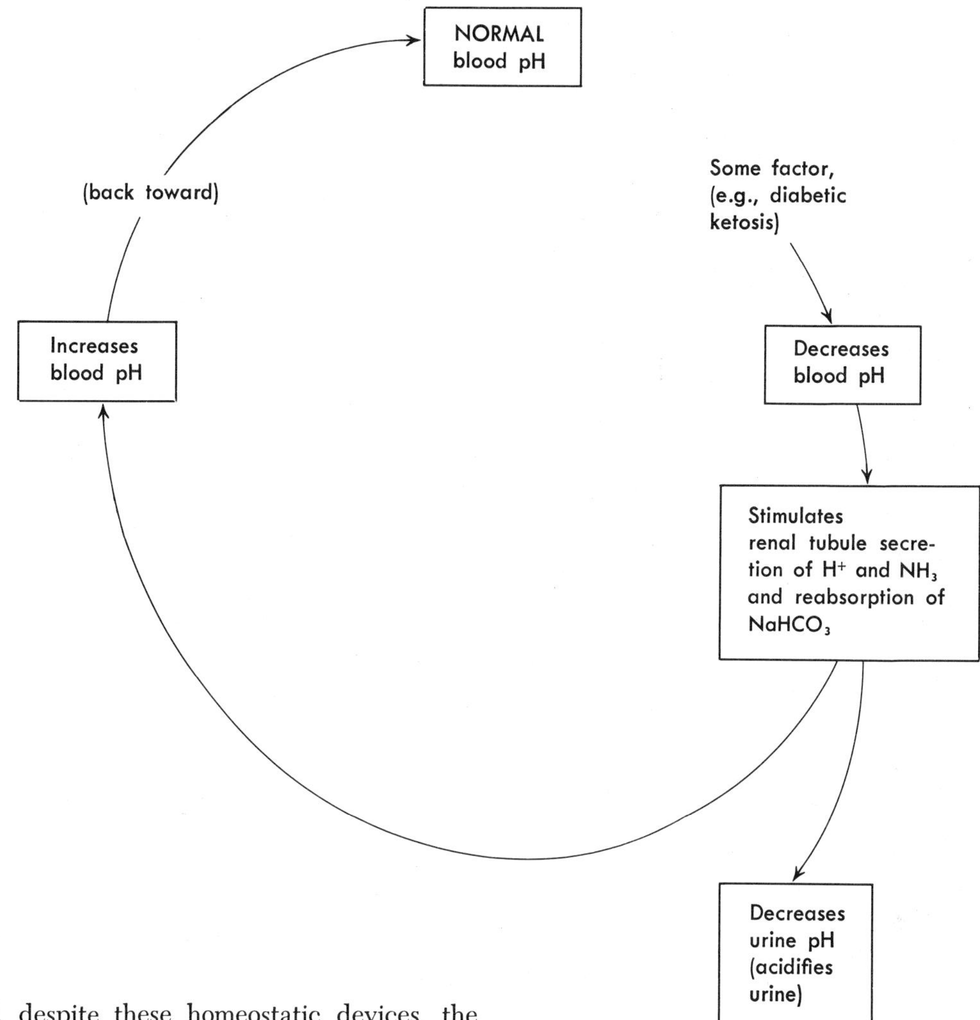

Fig. 336

Scheme to show main parts of urinary mechanism for maintaining homeostasis of blood pH.

if, despite these homeostatic devices, the ratio and pH decrease, *uncompensated acidosis* develops.

Increased blood hydrogen-ion concentration (i.e., decreased blood pH), as we have noted, stimulates the respiratory center. For this reason, hyperventilation is an outstanding clinical sign of acidosis. Increases in hydrogen-ion concentration above a certain level depress the central nervous system and, therefore, produce such symptoms as disorientation and coma.

Alkalosis

Alkalosis develops less often than acidosis. Some circumstances, however, such as ingestion of an excessive amount of an alkaline drug, or hyperventilation, or excessive vomiting can produce alkalosis. Base bicarbonate increases above normal in alkalosis. In compensated alkalosis, carbonic acid also increases—enough to maintain a normal base bicarbonate–carbonic acid ratio and pH. In uncompensated alkalosis, the ratio and, therefore, the pH increase.

Outline summary— Acid-base balance

Mechanisms that control pH of body fluids

1. Meaning of term pH—negative logarithm of H ion concentration of solution
2. Types of pH control mechanisms
   a. buffers
   b. respirations
   c. secretion of urine of varying pH
3. Effectiveness of pH control mechanisms; range of pH—extremely effective, normally maintain pH within very narrow range of 7.35 to 7.45

Buffer mechanism for controlling pH of body fluids

1. Buffers defined
   a. substances that prevent marked change in pH of solution when acid or base added to it
   b. consist of weak acid (or its acid salt) and basic salt of that acid
2. Buffer pairs present in body fluids—mainly carbonic acid, proteins, hemoglobin, acid phosphate, and sodium and potassium salts of these weak acids
3. Action of buffers to prevent marked changes in pH of body fluids
   a. volatile acids, chiefly carbonic acid, buffered mainly by potassium salts of hemoglobin and oxyhemoglobin
   b. nonvolatile acids, such as lactic acid and ketone bodies, buffered mainly by sodium bicarbonate
   c. bases buffered mainly by carbonic acid

   (Ratio $\frac{B \cdot HCO_3}{H_2CO_3} = \frac{20}{1}$ when homeostasis of pH at 7.4 exists)
4. Evaluation of role of buffers in pH control —cannot maintain normal pH without adequate functioning of respiratory and urinary pH control mechanisms

Respiratory mechanism of pH control

1. Explanation of mechanism
   a. amount of blood carbon dioxide directly related to amount of carbonic acid and, therefore, to concentration of H ions
   b. with increased respirations, less carbon dioxide remains in blood, hence less carbonic acid and fewer H ions; with decreased respirations, more carbon dioxide remains in blood, hence more carbonic acid and more H ions
2. Adjustment of respirations to pH of arterial blood—see Fig. 333, p. 541
3. Some principles relating respirations and pH of body fluids
   a. acidosis ⟶ hyperventilation

      ↓

      increases elimination of CO_2

      ↓

      decreases blood CO_2

      ↓

      decreases blood H_2CO_3

      ↓

      decreases blood H ions, i.e., increases blood pH

      ↓

      tends to correct acidosis, i.e., to restore normal pH
   b. prolonged hyperventilation, by decreasing blood H ions excessively, may produce alkalosis
   c. alkalosis causes hypoventilation, which tends to correct alkalosis by increasing blood CO_2 and, therefore, blood H_2CO_3 and H ions
   d. prolonged hypoventilation, by eliminating too little CO_2, causes increase in blood H_2CO_3 and, consequently, in blood H ions, thereby may produce acidosis

Urinary mechanism of pH control

1. General principles about mechanism—plays vital role in acid-base balance because kidneys can eliminate more H ions from body while reabsorbing more base when pH tends toward acid side and eliminate fewer H ions while reabsorbing less base when pH tends toward alkaline side
2. Mechanisms that control urine pH
   a. secretion of H ions into urine—when blood CO_2, H_2CO_3, and H ions increase above normal, distal tubules secrete more H ions into urine to displace basic ion (mainly sodium) from a urine salt and then reabsorb sodium into blood in exchange for the H ions excreted
   b. secretion of NH_3—when blood hydrogen-ion concentration increases, distal tubules secrete more NH_3, which combines with H ion of urine to form NH_4 ion, which displaces basic ion (mainly sodium) from a salt; basic ion then reabsorbed back into blood in exchange for ammonium ion excreted

Clinical disturbances in acid-base balance

1. Acidosis
   a. compensated metabolic acidosis—decreased alkaline reserve (mainly $NaHCO_3$), but ratio $\frac{BHCO_3}{H_2CO_3}$ maintained at normal $\frac{20}{1}$ by proportionately decreasing blood carbonic acid by hyperventilation
   b. uncompensated acidosis—alkaline reserve, $\frac{BHCO_3}{H_2CO_3}$ ratio, and blood pH all decrease below normal
2. Alkalosis
   a. compensated alkalosis—opposite to compensated acidosis
   b. uncompensated alkalosis—opposite to uncompensated acidosis

Review questions

1. Explain, in your own words, what the term pH means.
2. What is the normal range for pH of body fluids?
3. Explain what a buffer is in terms of its chemical composition and in terms of its function. Cite specific equations to illustrate your explanation.
4. What is the numerical value of the ratio of $B{\cdot}HCO_3/H_2CO_3$ when blood pH is 7.4 and the body is in a state of acid-base balance?
5. Is the ratio $B{\cdot}HCO_3/H_2CO_3$ necessarily abnormal when an acid-base disturbance is present? Give reasons to support your answer.
6. Is blood pH always abnormal when an acid-base disturbance is present? Give reasons for your answer.
7. Explain how the "respiratory mechanism of pH control" operates.
8. Why is hyperventilation a characteristic clinical sign in acidosis?

Situation: A patient has suffered a severe head injury. Respirations are markedly depressed.

9. Which, if either, do you think is a potential danger—acidosis or alkalosis? State your reasons.
10. Describe the homeostatic mechanisms that would operate to try to maintain acid-base balance in this patient.

Situation: A mother brings her baby to the hospital and reports that he has seemed very sick for the past twenty-four hours and that he has not eaten during that time and has passed no urine.

11. Do you think acidosis or alkalosis may be present in this baby?
12. Why?

Suggested supplementary readings

Chapter I

1. Cannon, Walter B.: The wisdom of the body, ed. 2, New York, 1963, W. W. Norton & Co., Inc.

Chapter II

1. Allfrey, V. G., and Mirsky, A. E.: How cells make molecules, Sci. Amer. **205**:74 (Sept.), 1961.
2. Baserga, R., and Kisieleski, W. E.: Autobiographies of cells, Sci. Amer. **209**:103 (Aug.), 1963.
3. Bearn, A. G., and German, J. L., III: Chromosomes and disease, Sci. Amer. **205**:66 (Nov.), 1961.
4. Beermann, Wolfgang, and Clever, Ulrich: Chromosome puffs, Sci. Amer. **210**:50 (April), 1964.
5. Benzer, S.: The fine structure of the gene, Sci. Amer. **206**:70 (Jan.), 1962.
6. Brachet, J.: The living cell, Sci. Amer. **205**:50 (Sept.), 1961.
7. Crick, F. H. C.: The genetic code, Sci. Amer. **207**:66 (Oct.), 1962.
8. de Duve, Christian: The lysosome, Sci. Amer. **208**:64 (May), 1963.
9. Fraenkel-Conrat, Heintz: The genetic code of a virus, Sci. Amer. **211**:47 (Oct.), 1964.
10. Green, David E.: The mitochondrion, Sci. Amer. **210**:67 (Jan.), 1964.
11. Ham, Arthur W., and Leeson, Thomas S.: Histology, ed. 5, Philadelphia, 1965, J. B. Lippincott Co.
12. Hayashi, T.: How cells move, Sci. Amer. **205**:184 (Sept.), 1961.
13. Hokin, Mabel, and Hokin, Lowell: The chemistry of cell membranes, Sci. Amer. **213**:78 (Oct.), 1965.
14. Holter, H.: How things get into cells, Sci. Amer. **205**:167 (Sept.), 1961.
15. Hurwitz, J., and Furth, J. J.: Messenger RNA, Sci. Amer. **206**:41 (Feb.), 1962.
16. Lehninger, A. L.: How cells tranform energy, Sci. Amer. **205**:62 (Sept.), 1961.
17. Nirenberg, Marshall W.: The genetic code II, Sci. Amer. **208**:80 (March), 1963.
18. Rich, Alexander: Polyribosomes, Sci. Amer. **209**:44 (Dec.), 1963.
19. Solomon, Arthur K.: Pumps in the living cell, Sci. Amer. **207**:100 (Aug.), 1962.

Chapter III

1. Bevelander, G.: Essentials of histology, ed. 5, St. Louis, 1965, The C. V. Mosby Co.

2. Ham, Arthur W., and Leeson, Thomas S.: Histology, ed. 5, Philadelphia, 1965, J. B. Lippincott Co.

Chapter VI

1. Morehouse, Laurence E., and Miller, Augustus T., Jr.: Physiology of exercise, ed. 4, St. Louis, 1963, The C. V. Mosby Co.
2. Wells, K. S.: Kinesiology, ed. 3, Philadelphia, 1960, W. B. Saunders Co.
3. Chapman, C. B., and Mitchell, J. H.: The physiology of exercise, Sci. Amer. **212**:88 (May), 1965.
4. Huxley, H. E.: The mechanism of muscular contraction, Sci. Amer. **213**:18 (Dec.), 1965.
5. Porter, Keith R., and Franzine-Armstrong, Clara: The sarcoplasmic reticulum, Sci. Amer. **212**:72 (March), 1965.

Chapter VII

1. Crosby, Elizabeth C., Hymphrey, Tryphena, and Lauer, Edward W.: Correlative anatomy of the nervous system, New York, 1962, The Macmillan Co.
2. Eccles, Sir John: The synapse, Sci. Amer. **212**:56 (Jan.), 1965.
3. Gardner, Ernest: Fundamentals of neurology, ed. 4, Philadelphia, 1964, W. B. Saunders Co.
4. Hyden, H.: Satellite cells in the nervous system, Sci. Amer. **205**:62 (Dec.), 1961.
5. Penfield, W., and Rasmussen, T.: The cerebral cortex of man, New York, 1957, The Macmillan Co.
6. Robertson, J. David: The membrane of the living cell, Sci. Amer. **206**:65 (April), 1962.
7. Ruch, Theodore C., and Patton, Harry D.: Physiology and biophysics, ed. 19, Philadelphia, 1965, W. B. Saunders Co., pp. 3-25.
8. Wilson, Victor J.: Inhibition in the central nervous system, Sci. Amer. **214**:102 (May), 1966.

Chapter VIII

1. Botelho, Stella Y.: Tears and the lacrimal gland, Sci. Amer. **211**:78 (Oct.), 1964.
2. Rosenzweig, M. R.: Auditory localization, Sci. Amer. **205**:132 (Oct.), 1961.

Chapter IX

1. Mayerson, H. S.: The lymphatic system, Sci. Amer. **208**:80 (June), 1963.
2. Ruch, T. C., and Patton, H. D.: Physiology and biophysics, ed. 19, Philadelphia, 1965, W. B. Saunders Co., pp. 543-549 and 617-678.

Chapter X

1. Comroe, Julius H., Jr.: The lung, Sci. Amer. **214**:56 (Feb.), 1966.
2. Ruch, T. C., and Patton, H. D.: Physiology and biophysics, ed. 19, Philadelphia, 1965, W. B. Saunders Co., pp. 733-738, 762-769, and 788-796.

Chapter XI

1. Benzinger, T. H.: The human thermostat, Sci. Amer. **204**:134 (Jan.), 1961.
2. Hickey, Mary Catherine: Hypothermia, Amer. J. Nurs. **65**:116 (Jan.), 1965.
3. Martin, Marguerite M.: Diabetes mellitus: current concepts, Amer. J. Nurs. **66**:510 (March), 1966.
4. Morehouse, Laurence E., and Miller, Augustus T., Jr.: Physiology of exercise, ed. 4, St. Louis, 1963, The C. V. Mosby Co.
5. Programmed instruction: potassium imbalance, Amer. J. Nurs. **67**:343 (Feb.), 1967.
6. Rich, Alexander: Polyribosomes, Sci. Amer. **209**:44 (Dec.), 1963.

Chapter XII

1. Grollman, Arthur: Diuretics, Amer. J. Nurs. **65**:84 (Jan.), 1965.
2. Trusk, Carol Williams: Hemodialysis for acute renal failure, Amer. J. Nurs. **65**:80 (Feb.), 1965.

Chapter XIII

1. Behrman, S. J.: Management of infertility, Amer. J. Nurs. **66**:552 (March), 1966.
2. Eichner, Eduard: Progestins, Amer. J. Nurs. **65**:78 (Sept.), 1965.
3. Kormondy, E. J.: Introduction to genetics, New York, 1964, McGraw-Hill Book Co., pp. 23-45.

Chapter XIV

1. Ham, Arthur W.: Histology, ed. 5, Philadelphia, 1965, J. B. Lippincott Co., pp. 814-876 and 890-899 (ovary and hormones).
2. Hawken, Patty: Hypophysectomy with yttrium 90, Amer. J. Nurs. **65**:122 (Oct.), 1965.
3. Selye, Hans: The stress syndrome, Amer. J. Nurs. **65**:97 (March), 1965.

4. Shea, Kathleen M., and others: What and how to teach a patient with adrenal insufficiency, Amer. J. Nurs. **65**:80 (Dec.), 1965.
5. Wurtman, Richard J., and Axelrod, Julius: The pineal gland, Sci. Amer. **213**:50 (July), 1965.

Chapter XV

1. Anthony, Catherine P.: Fluid imbalances—formidable foes to survival, Amer. J. Nurs. **63**:75 (Dec.), 1963.
2. Bard, P.: Medical physiology, ed. 11, St. Louis, 1961, The C. V. Mosby Co., pp. 301-359.
3. Best, Charles H., and Taylor, M. B.: The physiological basis of medical practice, ed. 8, Baltimore, 1966, Williams & Wilkins Co.
4. Burgess, Richard E.: Fluids and electrolytes, Amer. J. Nurs. **65**:90 (Oct.), 1965.
5. Gamble, J. L.: Chemical anatomy, physiology, and pathology of extracellular fluid, ed. 6, Cambridge, Mass., 1958, Harvard University Press.

Chapter XVI

1. Bard, P.: Medical physiology, ed. 11, St. Louis, 1961, The C. V. Mosby Co., pp. 359-361.
2. Best, Charles H., and Taylor, M. B.: The physiological basis of medical practice, ed. 8, Baltimore, 1966, Williams & Wilkins Co.

Additional references

Biochemistry

Kleiner, and Arten, J. M.: Biochemistry, ed. 7, St. Louis, 1966, The C. V. Mosby Co.

Gross anatomy, atlases

Sobotta, J., and Figge, F. H. J.: Atlas of human anatomy, 3 vols., ed. 8, New York, 1963, Hafner Publishing Co., Inc.
Spalteholz-Spanner: Atlas of human anatomy, ed. 16, New York, 1967, F. A. Davis Co.

Gross anatomy, textbooks

Gray, Henry: Anatomy of the human body, ed. 27 (edited by Charles Mayo Goss), Philadelphia, 1959, Lea & Febiger.
Hamilton, W. J., editor: Textbook of human anatomy, New York, 1957, The Macmillan Co.

Microscopic anatomy

Ham, Arthur W., and Leeson, Thomas S.: Histology, ed. 5, Philadelphia, 1965, J. B. Lippincott Co.
Bloom, William, and Fawcett, Don W.: A textbook of histology, ed. 8, Philadelphia, 1962, W. B. Saunders Co.

Developmental anatomy

Arey, Leslie Brainerd: Developmental anatomy—a textbook and laboratory manual of embryology, ed. 7, Philadelphia, 1965, W. B. Saunders Co.

Physiology

Best, Charles Herbert, and Taylor, Norman Burke: The physiological basis of medical practice, ed. 8, Baltimore, 1966, Williams & Wilkins Co.
Cannon, W. B.: The wisdom of the body, rev. ed., New York, 1963, W. W. Norton & Co., Inc.
Elkinton, J. Russell, and Danowski, T. S.: The body fluids: basic physiology and practical therapeutics, Baltimore, 1955, Williams & Wilkins Co.
Guyton, Arthur C.: Textbook of medical physiology, ed. 3, Philadelphia, 1966, W. B. Saunders Co.
Ruch, Theodore C., and Patton, Harry D.: Physiology and biophysics, ed. 19, Philadelphia, 1965, W. B. Saunders Co.
Steen, E. B.: Medical abbreviations, Philadelphia, 1960, F. A. Davis Co.
Steen, E. B., and Montagu, A.: Anatomy and physiology (college outline series), vols. 1 and 2, New York, 1959, Barnes & Noble, Inc.
Tuttle, W. W., and Schottelius, Byron A.: Textbook of physiology, ed. 15, St. Louis, 1965, The C. V. Mosby Co.

Periodicals

American Journal of Medical Sciences
American Journal of Nursing
American Journal of Physiology
Annual Review of Physiology
Harvey Lectures
Journal of Anatomy
Journal of Neurophysiology
Journal of the American Medical Association
Science Newsletter
Scientific American

Commonly used abbreviations and prefixes

Abbreviations

A Angstrom unit
ACTH adrenocorticotrophic hormone
ADP adenosine diphosphate
ATP adenosine triphosphate
BMR basal metabolic rate
BNA Basle Nomina Anatomica (see Glossary)
C. centigrade
Cal. large calorie
cm. centimeter
CNS central nervous system
CP creatine phosphate
CRF corticotrophin-releasing factor
CVA cardiovascular accident
DNA deoxyribonucleic acid
DPN diphosphopyridine nucleotide
ECF extracellular fluid
EFP effective filtration pressure
EPSP excitatory postsynaptic potential
F. Fahrenheit
FSH follicle-stimulating hormone
GH growth hormone
Hb hemoglobin
HbO_2 oxyhemoglobin
HP hydrostatic pressure
ICF intracellular fluid
ICSH interstitial cell–stimulating hormone
IF interstitial or intercellular fluid
IPSP inhibitory postsynaptic potential
Kcal. kilocalorie
kg. kilogram
LH luteinizing hormone
mEq. milliequivalents
mg. milligram
μ micron
ml. milliliter
mm. millimeter
mm. Hg pres. millimeter mercury pressure
MSH melanocyte-stimulating hormone
mv. millivolt
MW molecular weight
OP osmotic pressure
PAH para-aminohippuric acid
PBI protein-bound iodine
Pco_2 partial pressure of carbon dioxide
pH hydrogen-ion concentration; negative logarithm of hydrogen-ion concentration
Po_2 partial pressure of oxygen
PNS peripheral nervous system
RBC, rbc red blood cells
RNA ribonucleic acid
SD systolic discharge
SDA specific dynamic action
STH somatotrophic hormone
SV stroke volume

Commonly used abbreviations and prefixes

TH thyrotrophic hormone
TMR total metabolic rate
TSH thyroid-stimulating hormone
WBC, wbc white blood cells

Prefixes

ab- away from
ad- to, toward
adeno- glandular
amphi- on both sides
ante- before, forward
anti- against
bi- two, double, twice
circum- around, about
contra- opposite, against
de- away from, from
dys- difficult
ecto- outside
endo- in, within
ento- inside, within
epi- on, upon
eu- well
ex- from out of, from
extra- outside, beyond, in addition
hemi- half
hyper- over, excessive, above
hypo- under, deficient
infra- underneath, below
inter- between, among
intra- within, on the side
para- beside, to side of
peri- round about, beyond
post- after, behind
pre- before, in front of
pro- before, in front of
retro- backward, back
semi- half
sub- under, beneath
super- above, over
supra- above, on upper side
syn- with, together
trans- across, beyond

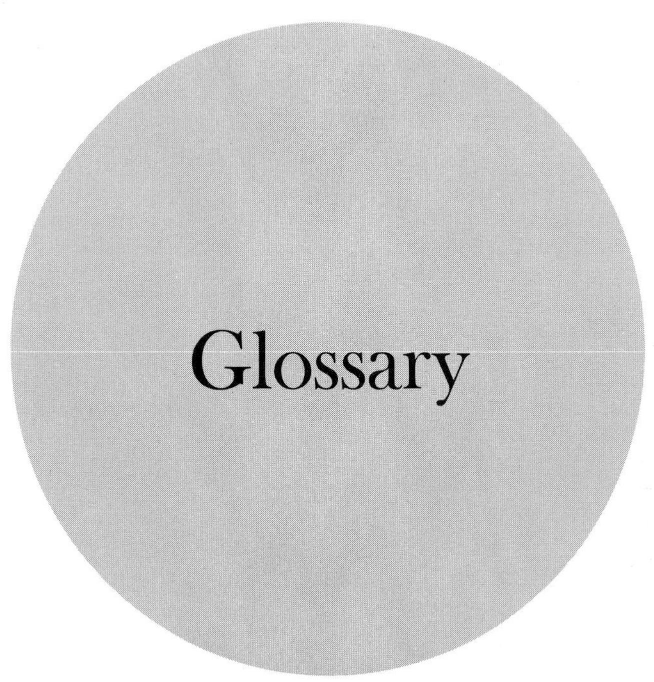

Glossary

abdomen body area between the diaphragm and pelvis.

abduct to move away from the midline; opposite of adduct.

absorption passage of a substance through a membrane (e.g., skin or mucosa) into blood.

acapnia marked decrease in blood carbon dioxide content.

acetabulum socket in the hip bone (os coxae or innominate bone) into which the head of the femur fits.

acetone bodies ketone bodies, acids formed during the first part of fat catabolism; namely—acetoacetic acid, beta-hydroxybutyric acid, and acetone.

Achilles tendon tendon inserted on calcaneus; so-called because of the Greek myth that Achilles' mother held him by the heels when she dipped him in the river Styx, thereby making him invulnerable except in this area.

acidosis condition in which there is an excessive proportion of acid in the blood.

acromion bony projection of the scapula; forms point of the shoulder.

adduct to move toward the midline; opposite of abduct.

adenohypophysis anterior pituitary gland.

adenoids glandlike; adenoids or pharyngeal tonsils are paired lymphoid structures in the nasopharynx.

adolescence period between puberty and adulthood.

adrenergic fibers axons whose terminals release norepinephrine and epinephrine.

adventitia, externa outer coat of a tube-shaped structure such as blood vessels.

aerobic requiring free oxygen; opposite of anaerobic.

afferent neuron transmitting impulses to the central nervous system.

albuminuria albumin in the urine.

aldosterone a hormone secreted by adrenal cortex.

alkali reserve bicarbonate salts present in body fluids; mainly sodium bicarbonate.

alkalosis condition in which there is an excessive proportion of alkali in the blood; opposite of acidosis.

alveolus literally a small cavity; alveoli of lungs are microscopic saclike dilatations of terminal bronchioles.

ameboid movement movement characteristic of amebae; (i.e., by projections of protoplasm (pseudopodia) toward which the rest of the cell's protoplasm flows.

amenorrhea absence of the menses.

Glossary

amino acid organic compound having an NH_3 and a COOH group in its molecule; has both acid and basic properties; amino acids are the structural units from which proteins are built.

amphiarthrosis slightly movable joint.

ampulla saclike dilatation of a tube or duct.

anabolism synthesis by cells of complex compounds (e.g., protoplasm, hormones) from simpler compounds (amino acids, simple sugars, fats, minerals); opposite of catabolism, the other phase of metabolism.

anaerobic not requiring free oxygen; opposite of aerobic.

anastomosis connection between vessels; the circle of Willis, e.g., is an anastomosis of certain cerebral arteries.

anemia deficient number of red blood cells or deficient hemoglobin.

anesthesia loss of sensation.

aneurysm blood-filled saclike dilatation of the wall of an artery.

angina any disease characterized by spasmodic suffocative attacks; e.g., angina pectoris, paroxysmal thoracic pain with feeling of suffocation.

Ångstrom unit 1/10 millimicron or 1/10 millionth meter or about 1/250 millionth inch.

anorexia loss of appetite.

anoxemia deficient blood oxygen content.

anoxia deficient oxygen supply to tissues.

antagonistic muscles those having opposing action; e.g., muscles that flex the upper arm are antagonistic to muscles that extend it.

anterior front or ventral; opposite of posterior or dorsal.

antibody, immune body substance produced by the body that destroys or inactivates a specific substance (antigen) that has entered the body; e.g., diphtheria antitoxin is the antibody against diphtheria toxin.

antigen substance which, when introduced into the body, causes formation of antibodies against it.

antrum cavity; e.g., the antrum of Highmore, the space in each maxillary bone, or the maxillary sinus.

anus distal end or outlet of the rectum.

apex pointed end of a conical structure

aphasia loss of a language faculty such as the ability to use words or to understand them.

apnea temporary cessation of breathing.

aponeurosis flat sheet of white fibrous tissue that serves as a muscle attachment.

aqueduct tube for conduction of liquid; e.g., the cerebral aqueduct conducts cerebrospinal fluid from the third to the fourth ventricle.

arachnoid delicate, weblike middle membrane of the meninges.

areola small space; the pigmented ring around the nipple.

arteriole small branch of an artery.

artery vessel carrying blood away from the heart.

arthrosis joint or articulation.

articular referring to a joint.

articulation joint.

arytenoid ladle-shaped; two small cartilages of the larynx.

ascites accumulation of serous fluid in the abdominal cavity.

asphyxia loss of consciousness due to deficient oxygen supply.

aspirate to remove by suction.

asthenia bodily weakness.

ataxia loss of power of muscle coordination.

atrium chamber or cavity; e.g., atrium of each side of the heart.

astrocytes star-shaped neuroglia, connective tissue cells in brain and cord.

atrophy wasting away of tissue; decrease in size of a part.

auricle part of the ear attached to the side of the head; earlike appendage of each atrium of heart.

autonomic self-governing, independent.

axilla armpit.

axon nerve cell process that transmits impulses away from the cell body.

baroreceptor receptor stimulated by change in pressure.

Bartholin seventeenth century Danish anatomist.

basophil white blood cell that stains readily, with basic dyes.

biceps two headed.

bilirubin red pigment in the bile.

biliverdin green pigment in the bile.

B. N. A. (Basle Nomina Anatomica) anatomic terminology accepted at Basle by the Anatomical Society in 1895.

Bowman nineteenth century English physician.

brachial pertaining to the arm.

bronchiectasis dilatation of the bronchi.

bronchiole small branch of a bronchus.

bronchus one of the two branches of the trachea.

buccal pertaining to the cheek.

buffer compound that combines with an acid or with a base to form a weaker acid or base, thereby lessening the change in hydrogen-ion concentration that would occur without the buffer.

bursa fluid-containing sac or pouch lined with synovial membrane.
buttock prominence over the gluteal muscles.

calcitonin a hormone secreted by the parathyroid glands.
calculus stone formed in various parts of the body; may consist of different substances.
calorie heat unit; a large Calorie is the amount of heat needed to raise the temperature of 1 kg. of water 1° C.
calyx cup-shaped division of the renal pelvis.
canaliculus little canal.
capillary microscopic blood vessel; capillaries connect arterioles with venules; also, microscopic lymphatic vessels.
carbhemoglobin, carbaminohemoglobin compound formed by union of carbon dioxide with hemoglobin.
carbohydrate organic compounds containing carbon, hydrogen, and oxygen in certain specific proportions; e.g., sugars, starches, cellulose.
carboxyhemoglobin compound formed by union of carbon monoxide with hemoglobin.
carcinoma cancer, a malignant tumor.
caries decay of teeth or of bone.
carotid from Greek word meaning to plunge into deep sleep; carotid arteries of the neck so called because pressure on them may produce unconsciousness.
carpal pertaining to the wrist.
casein protein in milk.
cast mold; e.g., formed in renal tubules.
castration removal of testes or ovaries.
catabolism breakdown of food compounds or of protoplasm into simpler compounds; opposite of anabolism, the other phase of metabolism.
catalyst substance that alters the speed of a chemical reaction.
cataract opacity of the lens of the eye.
catecholamines norepinephrine and epinephrine.
caudal pertaining to the tail of an animal; opposite of cephalic.
cecum blind pouch; the pouch at the proximal end of the large intestine.
celiac pertaining to the abdomen.
cellulose polysaccharide, the main plant carbohydrate.
centimeter 1/100 of a meter, about ⅖ of an inch.
centrioles two dots seen (with light microscope) in centrosphere; active during mitosis.
centromere structure that joins each pair of chromatids produced by chromosome duplication.
centrosphere, centrosome spherical area or body near center of cell.
cephalic pertaining to the head; opposite of caudal.
cerumen earwax.
cervix neck; any necklike structure.
chemoreceptor distal end of sensory dendrites especially adapted for chemical stimulation.
chiasm crossing; specifically, a crossing of the optic nerves.
cholecystectomy removal of the gallbladder.
cholesterol organic alcohol present in bile, blood, and various tissues.
cholinergic fibers axons whose terminals release acetylcholine.
cholinesterase enzyme; catalyzes breakdown of acetylcholine.
choroid, chorioid skinlike.
chromatids newly formed chromosomes.
chromatin deep-staining substance in the nucleus of cells; divides into chromosomes during mitosis.
chromosomes deep-staining, rod-shaped bodies in cell nucleus; composed of genes.
chyle milky fluid; the fat-containing lymph in the lymphatics of the intestine.
chyme partially digested food mixture leaving the stomach.
cilia hairlike projections of protoplasm.
circadian daily.
cochlea snail shell or structure of similar shape.
coenzyme nonprotein substance which activates an enzyme.
collagen principle organic constituent of connective tissue.
colloid solute particles with diameters of 1 to 100 millimicrons.
colostrum first milk secreted after childbirth.
commissure bundle of nerve fibers passing from one side to the other of the brain or cord.
concha shell-shaped structure; e.g., bony projections into the nasal cavity.
condyle rounded projection at the end of a bone.
congenital present at birth.
contralateral on the opposite side.
coracoid like a raven's beak in form.
corium true skin or derma.
coronal of or like a crown.
coronary encircling; in the form of a crown.
corpus body.
corpuscles very small body or particle.
cortex outer part of an internal organ; e.g., of the cerebrum and of the kidneys.

costal pertaining to the ribs.
crenation, plasmolysis shriveling of a cell due to water withdrawal.
cretinism dwarfism due to hypofunction of the thyroid gland.
cribriform sievelike.
cricoid ring shaped; a cartilage of this shape in the larynx.
cruciate cross shaped.
crystalloid solute particle less than 1 millimicron in diameter.
cubital pertaining to the forearm.
cutaneous pertaining to the skin.
cyanosis bluish appearance of the skin due to deficient oxygenation of blood.
cytokinesis dividing of cytoplasm to form two cells.
cytology study of cells.
cytoplasm the protoplasm of a cell exclusive of the nucleus.

deamination chemical reaction by which the amino group NH_3 is split from an amino acid.
deciduous temporary; shedding at a certain stage of growth; e.g., deciduous teeth.
decussation crossing over like an X.
defecation elimination of waste matter from the intestines.
deferens carrying away.
deglutition swallowing.
deltoid triangular; e.g., deltoid muscle.
dendrite, dendron branching or treelike; a nerve cell process that transmits impulses toward the cell body.
dens tooth.
dentate having toothlike projections.
dentine main part of a tooth, under the enamel.
dentition teething; also, number, shape, and arrangement of the teeth.
dermatome area of skin supplied by sensory fibers of a single dorsal root.
dermis, corium true skin.
dextrose glucose, a monosaccharide, the principal blood sugar.
dialysis separation; the separation of crystalloids from colloids by the faster diffusion of the former through a membrane.
diapedesis passage of blood cells through intact blood vessel walls.
diaphragm membrane or partition that separates one thing from another; the muscular partition between the thorax and abdomen; the midriff.
diaphysis shaft of a long bone.
diarthrosis freely movable joint.
diastole relaxation of the heart interposed between its contractions; opposite of systole.
diencephalon "tween" brain; parts of the brain between the cerebral hemispheres and the mesencephalon or midbrain.
diffusion spreading; e.g., scattering of solute particles.
digestion conversion of food into assimilable compounds.
diplopia double vision; seeing one object as two.
disaccharide sugar formed by the union of two monosaccharides; contains twelve carbon atoms.
distal toward the end of a structure; opposite of proximal.
diverticulum outpocketing from a tubular organ such as the intestine.
dorsal, posterior pertaining to the back; opposite of ventral.
Douglas Scottish anatomist of the late seventeenth and early eighteenth centuries.
dropsy accumulation of serous fluid in a body cavity, in tissues; edema.
duct canal or passage.
dura mater literally strong or hard mother; outermost layer of the meninges.
dyspnea difficult or labored breathing.
dystrophy faulty nutrition.

ectopic displaced; not in the normal place; e.g., extrauterine pregnancy.
edema excessive fluid in tissues; dropsy.
effector responding organ; e.g., voluntary and involuntary muscle, the heart, and glands.
efferent carrying from, as neurons that transmit impulses from the central nervous system to the periphery; opposite of afferent.
electrocardiogram graphic record of heart's action potentials.
electroencephalogram graphic record of brain's action potentials.
electrolyte substance that ionizes in solution, rendering the solution capable of conducting an electric current.
electron minute, negatively charged particle.
elimination expulsion of wastes from the body.
embolism obstruction of a blood vessel by foreign matter carried in the bloodstream.
embryo animal in early stages of intrauterine development; the human fetus the first three months after conception.
emesis vomiting.
emphysema dilatation of pulmonary alveoli.
empyema pus in a cavity; e.g., in the chest cavity.

encephalon brain.
endocrine secreting into the blood or tissue fluid rather than into a duct; opposite of exocrine.
endoplasm cytoplasm located toward center of cell, as distinguished from ectoplasm located nearer periphery of cell.
endoplasmic reticulum network of tubules and vesicles in cytoplasm.
energy power or ability to do work; *kinetic or active,* due to moving particles (e.g., mechanical energy, heat); *potential or stored,* due to attraction between particles (e.g., chemical energy).
enteron intestine.
enzyme catalytic agent formed in living cells.
eosinophil, acidophil white blood cell readily stained by eosin.
epidermis "false" skin; outermost layer of the skin.
epinephrine secretion of the adrenal medulla.
epiphyses ends of a long bone.
erythrocyte red blood cell.
ethmoid sievelike.
eupnea normal respiration.
Eustachio Italian anatomist of the sixteenth century.
exocrine secreting into a duct; opposite of endocrine.
exophthalmos abnormal protrusion of the eyes.
extrinsic coming from the outside; opposite of intrinsic.

facilitation decrease in a neuron's resting potential to a point above its threshold of stimulation.
Fallopius sixteenth century Italian antomist.
fascia sheet of connective tissue.
fasciculus little bundle.
fetus unborn young, especially in the later stages; in human beings, from third month of intrauterine period until birth.
fiber threadlike structure.
fibrin insoluble protein in clotted blood.
fibinogen soluble blood protein that is converted to insoluble fibrin during clotting.
filtration passage of water and solutes through a membrane due to hydrostatic pressure gradient.
fimbria fringe.
fissure groove.
flaccid soft, limp.
follicle small sac or gland.
fontanel "soft spots" of the infant's head; unossified areas in the infant's skull.
foramen small opening.
fossa cavity or hollow.
fovea small pit or depression.
fundus base of a hollow organ; e.g., the part farthest from its outlet.

ganglion cluster of nerve cell bodies outside the central nervous system.
gasserian named for Gasser, a sixteenth century Austrian surgeon.
gastric pertaining to the stomach.
gene part of the chromosome that transmits a given hereditary trait.
genitalia reproductive organs.
gestation pregnancy.
gland secreting structure.
gomerulus compact cluster; e.g., of capillaries in the kidneys.
glossal of the tongue.
glucagon hormone secreted by alpha cells of the islands of Langerhans.
glucocorticoids hormones that influence food metabolism; secreted by adrenal cortex.
glucokinase enzyme; catalyzes conversion of glucose to glucose-6-phosphate.
gluconeogenesis formation of glucose from protein or fat compounds.
glucose monosaccharide or simple sugar; the principal blood sugar.
gluteal of or near the buttocks.
glycerin, glycerol product of fat digestion.
glycogen "animal starch"; main polysaccharide stored in animal cells.
glycogenesis formation of glycogen from glucose or from other monosaccharides, fructose or galactose.
glycogenolysis hydrolysis of glycogen to glucose-6-phosphate or to glucose.
glyconeogenesis the formation of glycogen from protein or fat compounds.
gonad sex gland in which reproductive cells are formed.
graafian named for Graaf, a seventeenth century Dutch anatomist.
gradient a slope or difference between two levels, e.g., concentration gradient; a difference between the concentrations of two substances.
gustatory pertaining to taste.
gyrus convoluted ridge.

haversian named for Havers, English anatomist of the late seventeenth century.
helix spiral; coil.
hemiplegia paralysis of one side of the body.
hemoglobin iron-containing protein in red blood cells.
hemolysis destruction of red blood cells with

escape of hemoglobin from them into surrounding medium.
hemopoiesis blood cell formation.
hemorrhage bleeding.
hepar liver.
heparin substance obtained from the liver that inhibits blood clotting.
heredity transmission of characteristics from a parent to a child.
hernia, "rupture" protrusion of a loop of an organ through an abnormal opening.
hilus, hilum depression where vessels enter an organ.
His German anatomist of the late nineteenth century.
histology science of minute structure of tissues.
homeostasis relative uniformity of the normal body's internal environment.
hormone substance secreted by an endocrine gland.
hyaline glasslike.
hydrocortisone a hormone secreted by the adrenal cortex; compound F.
hydrolysis literally "split by water"; chemical reaction in which a compound reacts with water.
hymen Greek for skin; mucous membrane that may partially or entirely occlude the vaginal outlet.
hyoid shaped like the letter U; bone of this shape at the base of the tongue.
hyperemia increase blood in a heart.
hyperkalemia higher than normal concentration of potassium in the blood.
hypernatremia higher than normal concentration of sodium in the blood.
hyperopia farsightedness.
hyperplasia increase in the size of a part due to an increase in the number of its cells.
hyperpnea abnormally rapid breathing; panting.
hypertension abnormally high blood pressure.
hyperthermia fever; body temperature above 37° C.
hypertrophy increased size of a part due to an increase in the size of its cells.
hypervolemia larger volume of blood than normal.
hypokalemia lower than normal concentration of potassium in the blood.
hyponatremia lower than normal concentration of sodium in the blood.
hypophysis Greek for undergrowth; hence the pituitary gland, which grows out from the undersurface of the brain.
hypothalamus part of the diencephalon; gray matter in the floor and walls of the third ventricle.
hypothermia subnormal body temperature; below 37° C.
hypovolemia subnormal volume blood.
hypoxia oxygen deficiency.

inclusions any foreign or heterogenous substance contained in a cell or in any tissue or organ that was not introduced as a result of trauma.
incus anvil; the middle ear bone that is shaped like an anvil.
inferior lower; opposite of superior.
inguinal of the groin.
inhalation inspiration or breathing in; opposite of exhalation or expiration.
inhibition an increase in a neuron's resting potential above its usual level.
innominate not named, anonymous; e.g., ossa coxae (hip bones) formerly known as innominate bones.
insulin hormone secreted by beta cells of the islands of Langerhans in the pancreas.
intercellular between cells; interstitial.
interneurons (internuncial or ***intercalated neurons)*** conduct impulses from sensory to motor neurons; lie entirely within the central nervous system.
interstitial of or forming small spaces between things; intercellular.
intima innermost.
intrinsic not dependent upon externals; located within something; opposite of extrinsic.
involuntary not willed; opposite of voluntary.
involution return of an organ to its normal size after enlargement; also retrograde or degenerative change.
ion electrically charged atom or group of atoms.
ipsilateral on the same side; opposite of contralateral.
irritability excitability; ability to react to a stimulus.
ischemia local anemia; temporary lack of blood supply to an area.
isotonic of the same tension or pressure.

keratin protein compound present in the human body, chiefly in hair and nails.
ketones acids (acetoacetic, beta-hydroxybutyric, and acetone) produced during fat catabolism.
ketosis excess amount of ketone bodies in the blood.
kilogram 1,000 gm., approximately 2.2 lb.

kinesthesia "muscle sense"; i.e., sense of position and movement of body parts.

labia lips.
lacrimal pertaining to tears.
lactation secretion of milk.
lactose milk sugar, a disaccharide
lacuna space of cavity; e.g., lacunae in bone contain bone cells.
lamella thin layer, as of bone.
lateral of or toward the side; opposite of medial.
lemniscus, medial a flat band of sensory fibers extending up from the medulla, through the pons and midbrain to the thalamus.
leukocyte white blood cell.
ligament bond or band connecting two objects; in anatomy, a band of white fibrous tissue connecting bones.
limbic lobe or ***system*** cerebral cortex on the medial surface of the brain that forms a border around the corpus callosum; older name rhinencephalon.
lipid fats and fatlike compounds.
loin part of the back between the ribs and hip bones.
lumbar of or near the loins.
lumen passageway or space within a tubular structure.
luteum golden yellow.
lymph watery fluid in the lymphatic vessels.
lymphocyte one type of white blood cells.
lysis the destruction of cells and other antigens by a specific lysin antibody.
lysosomes membranous organelles containing various enzymes that can dissolve most cellular compounds; hence called "digestive bags" or "suicide bags" of cells.

malleolus small hammer; projections at the distal ends of the tibia and fibula.
malleus hammer; the tiny middle ear bone that is shaped like a hammer.
Malpighii seventeenth century Italian anatomist.
maltose disaccharide or "double" sugar.
mammary pertaining to the breast.
mammillary like a nipple.
manometer instrument used for measuring the pressure of fluids.
manubrium handle; upper part of the sternum.
mastication chewing.
matrix ground substance in which cells are embedded.
meatus passageway.
medial of or toward the middle; opposite of lateral.
mediastinum middle section of the thorax; i.e., between the two lungs.
medulla Latin for marrow; hence, the inner portion of an organ in contrast to the outer portion or cortex.
meiosis nuclear division in which the number of chromosomes are reduced to half their original number before the cell divides in two.
membrane thin layer or sheet.
menstruation monthly discharge of blood from the uterus.
mesencephalon midbrain.
mesentery fold of peritoneum that attaches the intestine to the posterior abdominal wall.
mesial situated in the middle; median.
metabolism complex process by which food is utilized by a living organism.
metabolite any substance produced by metabolism.
metacarpus "after" the wrist; hence the part of the hand between the wrist and fingers.
metatarsus "after" the instep; hence the part of the foot between the tarsal bones and toes.
meter about 39.5 inches.
microglia one type of connective tissue cell found in the brain and cord.
micron 1/1,000 mm.; about 1/25,000 inch.
micturition urination, voiding.
milliequivalent a unit of chemical equivalence computed by the following formula:

$$\frac{\text{mg.}}{\text{atomic weight}} \times \text{Valence} = \text{mEq.}$$

$$\text{e.g., } \frac{3{,}266 \text{ mg. Na}^+}{23 \text{ (At. wt. Na)}} \times 1 = 142 \text{ mEq. Na}^+$$

millimeter 1/1,000 meter; about 1/25 inch.
mineralocorticoids hormones that influence mineral salt metabolism; secreted by adrenal cortex.
mitochondria threadlike structures.
mitosis indirect cell division involving complex changes in the nucleus.
mitral shaped like a miter.
molar concentration number of grams solute per liter of solution divided by the solute's molecular weight.
mole molecular weight of a compound in grams; also called gram molecular weight.
monosaccharide simple sugar.
Monro eighteenth century English surgeon.
motoneurons ***(motor*** or ***efferent neurons)***

transmit nerve impulses away from the brain or spinal cord.
myelin lipoid substance found in the myelin sheath around some nerve fibers.
myocardium muscle of the heart.
myopia nearsightedness.

nares nostrils.
neurilemma nerve sheath.
neurohypophysis posterior pituitary gland.
neuron nerve cell, including its processes.
neurovesicles microscopic sacs in axon terminals; contain transmitter substance.
neutrophil white blood cell that stains readily with neutral dyes.
nuchal pertaining to the nape of the neck.
nucleotide component of DNA and RNA; a nucleotide is composed of a sugar (deoxyribose or ribose), a nitrogenous base (adenine, thymine, cytosine, or guanine), and a phosphate group.
nucleus spherical structure within a cell; a group of neuron cell bodies in the brain or cord.

occiput back of the head.
olecranon elbow.
olfactory pertaining to the sense of smell.
oligodendroglia a type of connective tissue cell found in the brain and cord.
ophthalmic pertaining to the eyes.
organelle cell organ; one of the specialized parts of a single-celled organism (protozoon), serving for the performance of some individual function.
os Latin for mouth and for bone.
osmosis movement of a fluid through a semipermeable membrane.
ossicle little bone.
oxidation loss of hydrogen or electrons from a compound or element.
oxyhemoglobin a compound formed by union of oxygen with hemoglobin.

palate roof of the mouth.
palpebrae eyelids.
papilla small nipple-shaped elevation.
paralysis loss of the power of motion or sensation, especially voluntary motion.
parenchyma the distinguishing, functional cells of an organ.
parietal of the walls of an organ or cavity.
parotid located near the ear.
parturition act of giving birth to an infant.
patella small, shallow pan; the kneecap.
Pavlov Russian physiologist of the late nineteenth and early twentieth centuries.
pectineal pertaining to the pubic bone.
pectoral pertaining to the chest or breast.
pelvis basin or funnel-shaped structure.
Peyer Swiss anatomist of the late seventeenth and early eighteenth centuries.
peripheral pertaining to an outside surface.
peroneus, peroneal of or near the fibula.
petrous rocklike.
pH hydrogen ion concentration; the negative logarithm of hydrogen ion concentration.
phagocytosis process by which a segment of cell membrane forms a small pocket around a bit of solid outside the cell, breaks off from rest of the membrane, and moves into the cell; briefly, ingestion and digestion of particles by a cell.
phalanges finger or toe bones.
phrenic pertaining to the diaphragm.
pia mater gentle mother; the vascular innermost covering (meninges) of the brain and cord.
pilomotor mover of a hair.
pineal shaped like a pine cone.
pinocytosis a process by which a segment of cell membrane forms a small pocket around a bit of fluid outside the cell, breaks off from rest of membrane, and moves into the cell.
piriformis pear shaped.
pisiform pea shaped.
plantar pertaining to the sole of the foot.
plasma liquid part of the blood.
plasmolysis shrinking of a cell due to water loss by osmosis.
plexus network.
plica fold.
polymorphonuclear having many-shaped nuclei.
polyribosomes a group of ribosomes working together to synthesize proteins.
polysaccharide a carbohydrate containing a large number of saccharide groups, $(C_6H_{10}O_5)$; e.g., starch, glycogen.
pons bridge.
popliteal behind the knee.
posterior following after; hence, located behind; opposite of anterior.
potential, action difference in electrical charges on inner and outer surfaces of the cell membrane during impulse conduction; outer surface negative to inner.
potential or ***potential difference*** difference in electrical charges; e.g., on outer and inner surfaces of cell membrane.
potential, resting difference in electrical charges on inner and outer surfaces of the

cell membrane when it is not conducting impulses; outer surface positive to inner.
Poupart seventeenth century French anatomist.
presbyopia "oldsightedness"; farsightedness of old age.
pressoreceptors receptors stimulated by a change in pressure; baroreceptors.
pronate to turn palm downward.
proprioreceptors receptors located in the muscles, tendons, and joints.
protoplasm living substance.
proximal next or nearest; located nearest the center of the body or the point of attachment of a structure.
psoas pertaining to the loin, the part of the back between the ribs and hip bones.
psychosomatic pertaining to the influence of the mind (notably the emotions) on body functions.
pterygoid wing shaped.
puberty age at which the reproductive organs become functional.

racemose like a cluster of grapes.
ramus branch.
Ranvier French pathologist of the late nineteenth and early twentieth centuries.
receptor peripheral ending of a sensory neuron.
reflex involuntary action.
refraction bending of a ray of light as it passes from a medium of one density to one of a different density.
refractory resisting stimulation.
renal pertaining to the kidney.
reticular netlike.
reticulum a network.
rhinencephalon *see* limbic lobe.
ribosomes organelles in cytoplasm of cells; synthesize proteins, so nicknamed "protein factories."
rugae wrinkles or folds.

sagittal like an arrow; longitudinal.
salpinx tube; oviduct.
sartorius tailor; hence, the thigh muscle used to sit cross-legged like a tailor.
sciatic pertaining to the ischium.
sclera from Greek for hard.
scrotum bag.
sebum Latin for tallow; secretion of sebaceous glands.
sella turcica Turkish saddle; saddle-shaped depression in the sphenoid bone.
semen Latin for seed; male reproductive fluid.
semilunar half-moon shaped.
senescence old age.
serratus saw toothed.
serum any watery animal fluid; clear, yellowish liquid that separates from a clot of blood.
sesamoid shaped like a sesame seed.
sigmoid S shaped.
sinus cavity.
soleus pertaining to a sole; a muscle in the leg shaped like the sole of a shoe.
somatic of the body framework or walls, as distinguished from the viscera or internal organs.
sphenoid wedged shaped.
sphincter ring-shaped muscle.
splanchnic visceral.
squamous scalelike.
stapes stirrup; tiny stirrup-shaped bone in the middle ear.
Starling English physiologist of the late nineteenth and early twentieth centuries.
stereognosis awareness of the shape of an object by means of touch.
stimulus agent that causes a change in the activity of a structure.
stratum layer.
stress, physiological according to Selye, a condition in the body produced by all kinds of injurious factors that he calls "stressors" and manifested by a syndrome.
stressor any injurious factor that produces biological stress; e.g., emotional trauma, infections, severe exercise, etc.
striated marked with parallel lines.
stroma Greek for mattress or bed; hence, the framework or matrix of a structure.
sudoriferous secreting sweat.
sulcus furrow or groove.
superior higher; opposite of inferior.
supinate to turn the palm of the hand upward; opposite of pronate.
Sylvius seventeenth century anatomist.
symphysis Greek for a growing together.
synapse joining; point of contact between adjacent neurons.
synovia literally "with egg"; secretion of the synovial membrane resembles egg white.
synthesis putting together of parts to form a more complex whole.
systole contraction of the heart muscle.

talus ankle; one of the bones of the ankle.
tarsus instep.
Tawara Japanese physiologist (1873-).
tegmentum part of the brainstem that covers the posterior surface of the cerebral peduncles and the pons.

tendon band or cord of fibrous connective tissue that attaches a muscle to a bone or other structure.
thorax chest.
thrombosis formation of a clot in a blood vessel.
tibia Latin for shin bone.
tonus continued, partial contraction of muscle.
tract bundle of axons located within the central nervous system.
trauma injury.
trochlear pertaining to a pulley.
trophic having to do with nutrition.
tropic having to do with a turning or a change.
tunica covering.
turbinate shaped like a cone or like a scroll or spiral.
tympanum drum.

umbilicus navel.
utricle little sac.
uvula Latin for a little grape; a projection hanging from the soft palate.

vagina sheath.
vagus Latin for wandering.
valve structure that permits flow of a fluid in one direction only.
vas vessel or duct.
vastus wide, of great size.
Vater German anatomist of the late seventeenth and early eighteenth centuries.
vein vessel carrying blood to the heart.
ventral of or near the belly; in man, front or anterior; opposite of dorsal or posterior.
ventricle small cavity.
vermiform worm shaped.
villus hairlike projection.
viscera internal organs.
volar pertaining to the palm of the hand or the sole of the foot; palmar; plantar.
vomer ploughshare.

Willis seventeenth century English anatomist.

xiphoid sword shaped.

zygoma yoke.

Index

A

Index

C

Index

F

G

Index

Index

N

O

Q

R

S

T

W

X

Y

Z